TEACHER'S EDITION

Volume 2   Chapters 7–12

PRENTICE HALL

COURSE 1

MATHEMATICS

Randall I. Charles

Judith C. Branch-Boyd

Mark Illingworth

Darwin Mills

Andy Reeves

PEARSON

Prentice
Hall

Needham, Massachusetts
Upper Saddle River, New Jersey

Teacher's Edition package (Volumes 1 and 2): ISBN 0-13-063137-X
Volume 1: ISBN 0-13-180756-0
Volume 2: ISBN 0-13-180757-9

4 5 6 7 8 9 10   07 06 05 04

Teacher's Edition Contents
Volume 2

Teacher Handbook

Student Edition With Teacher Notes

Authors

Series Author

Randall I. Charles, Ph.D., is Professor Emeritus in the Department of Mathematics and Computer Science at San Jose State University, San Jose, California. He began his career as a high school mathematics teacher, and he was a mathematics supervisor for five years. Dr. Charles has been a member of several NCTM committees and is the former Vice President of the National Council of Supervisors of Mathematics. Much of his writing and research has been in the area of problem solving. He has authored more than 75 mathematics textbooks for kindergarten through college. *Scott Foresman-Prentice Hall Mathematics Series Author Kindergarten through Algebra 2*

Program Authors

Judith C. Branch-Boyd, Ph.D., is the Area 24 Mathematics Coordinator for the Chicago Public School District. She works with high school teachers to provide quality instruction to students who are mandated to take Algebra, Geometry, and Advanced Algebra-Trigonometry. She also works with middle school and high school teachers to help students transition to Algebra 1. Dr. Branch-Boyd is active in several professional mathematics organizations at the state and national levels, including the National Council of Teachers of Mathematics. She believes,"All children can learn to love mathematics if it is taught with energy!"

PEARSON
Prentice
Hall

ISBN 0-13-063136-1

3 4 5 6 7 8 9 10   07 06 05 04 03

Mark Illingworth has taught fifth-graders and enrichment programs for fifteen years. During this time, he received the Christa McAullife sabbatical to develop problem-solving materials and projects for middle-grades math students, and he was granted the Presidential Award for Excellence in Mathematics Teaching. In addition to serving as the district math task force coordinator for the last six years, he has written two of his own books and has contributed to both math and science textbooks at Prentice Hall. Mr. Illingworth has recently shifted from teaching fifth-graders to teaching math to high school students.

Darwin Mills is a mathematics lead teacher for the public schools in Newport News, Virginia, and a mathematics adjunct professor at Thomas Nelson Community College in Hampton, Virginia. He has received various teaching awards, including teacher of the year for the 1999–2000 school year and an Excellence in Teaching Award from the College of Wooster, Ohio, in 2002. He is a frequent presenter for staff development, especially in the area of graphing calculator usage in the classroom. He believes that all students can learn mathematics if given the proper instruction.

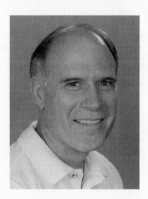

Andy Reeves, Ph.D., teaches at the University of South Florida in St. Petersburg. His career in education spans 30 years and includes seven years as a middle grades teacher. He subsequently served as Florida's K–12 mathematics supervisor and more recently he supervised the publication of the *Mathematics Teacher*, *Mathematics Teaching in the Middle School*, and *Teaching Children Mathematics* for NCTM. Prior to entering education, he worked as an engineer for Douglas Aircraft.

Contributing Author

Denisse R. Thompson, Ph.D., is Associate Professor of Mathematics Education at the University of South Florida. She has particular interests in the connections between literature and mathematics and in the teaching and learning of mathematics in the middle grades. Dr. Thompson contributed to the Reading Math lessons and features.

Reviewers

Course 1 Reviewers

Donna Anderson
Math Supervisor 7–12
West Hartford Public Schools
West Hartford, Connecticut

Nancy L. Borchers
West Clermont Local Schools
Cincinnati, Ohio

Kathleen Chandler
Walnut Creek Middle School
Erie, Pennsylvania

Jane E. Damaske
Lakeshore Public Schools
Stevensville, Michigan

Frank Greco
Parkway South Middle School
Manchester, Missouri

Rebecca L. Jones
Odyssey Middle School
Orlando, Florida

Marylee R. Liebowitz
H. C. Crittenden Middle School
Armonk, New York

Kathy Litz
K. O. Knudson Middle School
Las Vegas, Nevada

Don McGurrin
Wake County Public School
System
Raleigh, North Carolina

Ron Mezzadri
K–12 Mathematics Supervisor
Fair Lawn School District
Fair Lawn, New Jersey

Sylvia O. Reeder-Tucker
Prince George's County Math
Department
Upper Marlboro, Maryland

Julie A. White
Allison Traditional Magnet
Middle School
Wichita, Kansas

Charles Yochim
Bronxville Middle School
Bronxville, New York

Course 2 Reviewers

Cami Craig
Prince William County Public
Schools
Marsteller Middle School
Bristow, Virginia

Donald O. Cram
Lincoln Middle School
Rio Rancho, New Mexico

Pat A. Davidson
Jacksonville Junior High School
Jacksonville, Arkansas

Yvette Drew
DeKalb County School System
Open Campus High School
Atlanta, Georgia

Robert S. Fair
K–12 District Mathematics
Coordinator
Cherry Creek School District
Greenwood Village, Colorado

Michael A. Landry
Glastonbury Public Schools
Glastonbury, Connecticut

Nancy Ochoa
Weeden Middle School
Florence, Alabama

Charlotte J. Phillips
Wichita USD 259
Wichita, Kansas

Mary Lynn Raith
Mathematics Curriculum
Specialist
Pittsburgh Public Schools
Pittsburgh, Pennsylvania

Tammy Rush
Consultant, Middle School
Mathematics
Hillsborough County Schools
Tampa, Florida

Judith R. Russ
Prince George's County
Public Schools
Capitol Heights, Maryland

Tim Tate
Math/Science Supervisor
Lafayette Parish School
System
Lafayette, Louisiana

Dondi J. Thompson
Alcott Middle School
Norman, Oklahoma

Candace Yamagata
Hyde Park Middle School
Las Vegas, Nevada

Course 3 Reviewers

Linda E. Addington
Andrew Lewis Middle School
Salem, Virginia

Jeanne Arnold
Mead Junior High School
Schaumburg, Illinois

Sheila S. Brookshire
A. C. Reynolds Middle School
Asheville, North Carolina

Jennifer Clark
Mayfield Middle School
Putnam City Public Schools
Oklahoma City, Oklahoma

Nicole Dial
Chase Middle School
Topeka, Kansas

Christine Ferrell
Lorin Andrews Middle School
Massillon, Ohio

Virginia G. Harrell
Education Consultant
Hillsborough County, Florida

Jonita P. Howard
Mathematics Curriculum Specialist
Lauderdale Lakes Middle School
Lauderdale Lakes, Florida

Patricia Lemons
Rio Rancho Middle School
Rio Rancho, New Mexico

Susan Noce
Robert Frost Junior High School
Schaumburg, Illinois

Carla A. Siler
South Bend Community School
  Corp.
South Bend, Indiana

Kathryn E. Smith-Lance
West Genesee Middle School
Camillus, New York

Kathleen D. Tuffy
South Middle School
Braintree, Massachusetts

Patricia R. Wilson
Central Middle School
Murfreesboro, Tennessee

Patricia Young
Northwood Middle School
Pulaski County Special School
  District
North Little Rock, Arkansas

Content Consultants

Courtney Lewis
Mathematics
Prentice Hall Senior National Consultant
Baltimore, Maryland

Deana Cerroni
Mathematics
Prentice Hall National Consultant
Las Vegas, Nevada

Kimberly Margel
Mathematics
Prentice Hall National Consultant
Scottsdale, Arizona

Sandra Mosteller
Mathematics
Prentice Hall National Consultant
Anderson, South Carolina

Rita Corbett
Mathematics
Prentice Hall Consultant
Elgin, Illinois

Cathy Davies
Mathematics
Prentice Hall Consultant
Laguna Niguel, California

Sally Marsh
Mathematics
Prentice Hall Consultant
Baltimore, Maryland

Addie Martin
Mathematics
Prentice Hall Consultant
Upper Marlboro, Maryland

Rose Primiani
Mathematics
Prentice Hall Consultant
Brick, New Jersey

Loretta Rector
Mathematics
Prentice Hall Consultant
Foresthill, California

Charlotte Samuels
Mathematics
Prentice Hall Consultant
Lafayette Hill, Pennsylvania

Margaret Thomas
Mathematics
Prentice Hall Consultant
Indianapolis, Indiana

Contents in Brief

Decimals

Student Support

Contents   **vii**

Chapter 2

Patterns and Variables

Number Theory and Fractions

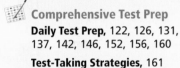

Adding and Subtracting Fractions

Multiplying and Dividing Fractions

Chapter 6

Ratios, Proportions, and Percents

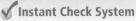

Data and Graphs

Tools of Geometry

Geometry and Measurement

Chapter

10

Integers

Exploring Probability

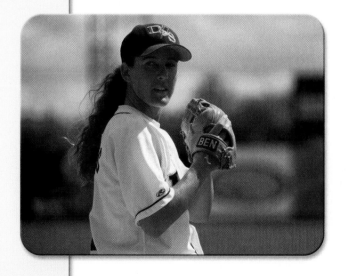

Equations and Inequalities

Pacing Options for Course 1

Pacing Guide

This chart is provided merely as a guide to help you customize your course. To accommodate flexible scheduling, most lessons are subdivided into objectives. Within the lessons of the Student Edition, these objectives are indicated in red by the symbol ▼. The Assignment Guide for each lesson indicates which exercises in the Student Edition correspond to each objective of the lesson.

Detailed Chapter Pacing Options precede each chapter and give you lesson-by-lesson pacing suggestions for that specific chapter.

CHAPTER	Traditional (45-minute class periods)	Block (90-minute class periods)
1	15 days	7 days
2	15 days	7 days
3	14 days	7 days
4	14 days	7 days
5	13 days	7 days
6	15 days	7 days
7	13 days	7 days
8	13 days	7 days
9	14 days	7 days
10	15 days	7 days
11	11 days	6 days
12	8 days	4 days
Total	160 days	80 days

Differentiated Scope of Course

B = Basic Course   C = Core Course   A = Advanced Course

Chapter 1 Decimals	B	C	A
1-1: Understanding Whole Numbers	✓	✓	
• Investigation: Exploring Decimal Models	✓	✓	
1-2: Reading and Writing Decimals	✓	✓	
1-3: Comparing and Ordering Decimals	✓	✓	✓
1-4: Estimating With Decimals	✓	✓	✓
• Investigation: Using Models	✓	✓	
1-5: Adding and Subtracting Decimals	✓	✓	✓
1-6: Using a Problem-Solving Plan	✓	✓	✓
• Investigation: Modeling Multiplication of Decimals	✓	✓	
1-7: Multiplying Decimals	✓	✓	✓
1-8: Multiplying and Dividing Decimals by 10, 100, and 1,000	✓	✓	✓
1-9: Dividing Decimals	✓	✓	✓
1-10: Order of Operations	✓	✓	✓
• Technology: Exploring Order of Operations	✓	✓	✓

Chapter 2 Patterns and Variables	B	C	A
2-1: Describing a Pattern	✓	✓	✓
2-2: Variables and Expressions	✓	✓	✓
2-3: Writing Algebraic Expressions	✓	✓	✓
• Technology: Using Formulas	✓	✓	✓
2-4: Make a Table and Look for a Pattern	✓	✓	✓
2-5: Using Number Sense to Solve One-Step Equations	✓	✓	✓
• Investigation: Using Models to Solve Equations	✓	✓	✓
2-6: Solving Addition and Subtraction Equations	✓	✓	✓
2-7: Solving Multiplication and Division Equations	✓	✓	✓
2-8: Exponents	✓	✓	✓
• Extension: Scientific Notation		✓	✓
2-9: The Distributive Property	✓	✓	✓

Chapter 3 Number Theory and Fractions	B	C	A
3-1: Divisibility and Mental Math	✓	✓	✓
3-2: Prime Numbers and Prime Factorization	✓	✓	✓
• Extension: The Sieve of Eratosthenes		✓	✓
3-3: Greatest Common Factor	✓	✓	✓
• Investigation: Modeling Fractions		✓	✓
3-4: Equivalent Fractions	✓	✓	✓

	B	C	A
• Technology: Simplifying Fractions	✓	✓	✓
3-5: Mixed Numbers and Improper Fractions	✓	✓	✓
3-6: Least Common Multiple	✓	✓	✓
3-7: Comparing and Ordering Fractions	✓	✓	✓
3-8: Fractions and Decimals	✓	✓	✓
3-9: Try, Check, and Revise	✓	✓	✓

Chapter 4 Adding and Subtracting Fractions	B	C	A
4-1: Estimating Sums and Differences	✓	✓	✓
4-2: Fractions With Like Denominators	✓	✓	✓
• Investigation: Modeling Unlike Denominators	✓	✓	✓
4-3: Fractions With Unlike Denominators	✓	✓	✓
4-4: Adding Mixed Numbers	✓	✓	✓
4-5: Subtracting Mixed Numbers	✓	✓	✓
4-6: Equations With Fractions	✓	✓	✓
• Technology: Computing With a Fraction Calculator	✓	✓	✓
4-7: Measuring Elapsed Time	✓	✓	✓
4-8: Draw a Diagram	✓	✓	✓

Chapter 5 Multiplying and Dividing Fractions	B	C	A
5-1: Multiplying Fractions	✓	✓	✓
5-2: Multiplying Mixed Numbers	✓	✓	✓
• Investigation: Fraction Division	✓	✓	✓
5-3: Dividing Fractions	✓	✓	✓
5-4: Dividing Mixed Numbers	✓	✓	✓
• Technology: Using a Calculator for Fractions	✓	✓	✓
5-5: Solving Fraction Equations by Multiplying	✓	✓	✓
5-6: Solve a Simpler Problem	✓	✓	✓
5-7: The Customary System	✓	✓	✓
5-8: Changing Units in the Customary System	✓		✓

Chapter 6 Ratios, Proportions, and Percents	B	C	A
6-1: Ratios	✓	✓	✓
6-2: Unit Rates	✓	✓	✓
6-3: Understanding Proportions	✓	✓	✓
6-4: Using Cross Products	✓	✓	✓
6-5: Scale Drawings	✓	✓	✓
• Investigation: Modeling Percents	✓	✓	
6-6: Percents, Fractions, and Decimals	✓	✓	✓
6-7: Finding a Percent of a Number	✓	✓	✓

Scope and Sequence for Prentice Hall Mathematics

This scope and sequence of content is organized around the major strands and specific objectives in the **National Assessment of Educational Progress (NAEP) 2005 Assessment Specifications**. These NAEP skills are an important benchmark for No Child Left Behind. Also included here are the process skills referenced in the **NCTM Principles and Standards for School Mathematics 2000**.

Since **Prentice Hall Mathematics** is a complete Grades 6–12 program, a detailed scope and sequence chart for the entire program—middle school through high school—is available at PHSchool.com/math. Also available is a Grades Pre-K–8 scope and sequence chart that shows the careful articulation between **Prentice Hall Mathematics Courses 1–3** and **Scott Foresman-Addison Wesley Mathematics Grades Pre-K–5**, which together provide a complete mathematics curriculum for Grades Pre-K–8.

Course	1	2	3
Number Properties and Operations			
Number Sense			
● **Use place value to model numbers**			
— whole numbers	Introduce	Introduce	Maintain & Apply
— decimals	Develop	Develop	Maintain & Apply
● **Model rational numbers or numerical relationships**			
— number line models	Develop	Develop	Develop
— other models	Develop	Develop	Develop
● **Write or rename rational numbers**			
— read and write decimals	Develop	Develop	Maintain & Apply
— read and write integers	Develop	Introduce	Maintain & Apply
— read and write rational numbers	Develop	Introduce	Maintain & Apply
— irrational numbers		Introduce	Develop
— real numbers			Develop
● **Express multiple representations of rational numbers and translate between them**			
— equivalent decimals	Develop	Introduce	Maintain & Apply
— equivalent fractions	Develop	Introduce	Maintain & Apply
— simplest form	Develop	Introduce	Maintain & Apply
— mixed numbers and improper fractions		Introduce	Maintain & Apply
— convert between fractions and decimals	Develop	Develop	Maintain & Apply
● **Use scientific notation**			
— scientific notation	Introduce	Develop	Develop
● **Find or model absolute value**			
— absolute value	Introduce	Develop	Maintain & Apply
● **Compare and order rational numbers**			
— whole numbers	Introduce	Introduce	Develop
— decimals	Develop	Introduce	Maintain & Apply

Course	1	2	3
— fractions	Develop	Develop	Maintain & Apply
— integers	Introduce	Introduce	Maintain & Apply
— rational numbers		Introduce	Develop
— irrationals numbers			Develop
Estimation			
● **Establish benchmarks**			
— fractions	Develop	Develop	Maintain & Apply
● **Make appropriate estimates**			
— rounding	Develop	Develop	Maintain & Apply
— operations	Develop	Develop	Maintain & Apply
— clustering	Develop	Develop	Maintain & Apply
— compatible numbers	Introduce	Develop	Maintain & Apply
— front-end	Introduce	Develop	Maintain & Apply
● **Determine reasonableness of results**			
— determine reasonableness of answers	Develop	Develop	Develop
● **Estimate square and cube roots**			
— squares and square roots	Introduce	Develop	Develop
Number Operations			
● **Perform computation with rational numbers**			
— add, subtract, multiply, and divide whole numbers	Introduce	Introduce	Maintain & Apply
— add and subtract decimals	Develop	Develop	Maintain & Apply
— multiply and divide decimals	Develop	Develop	Maintain & Apply
— add and subtract fractions, like denominators	Develop	Introduce	Maintain & Apply
— add and subtract fractions, unlike denominators	Develop	Develop	Maintain & Apply
— add and subtract mixed numbers	Develop	Develop	Maintain & Apply
— multiply and divide fractions	Develop	Develop	Maintain & Apply
— multiply and divide mixed numbers	Develop	Develop	Maintain & Apply
— add and subtract integers	Develop	Develop	Maintain & Apply

Legend: ▰ **INTRODUCE**   ▱ **DEVELOP**   ▰ **MAINTAIN & APPLY**

Course	1	2	3
— multiply and divide integers	→	→	→
— use mental math	→	→	→
— choose a computation method	→	→	→
● Describe the effect of operations			
— check for reasonableness	→	→	→
● Interpret rational number operations			
— add and subtract	→	→	→
— multiply and divide	→	→	→
● Solve application problems			
— solve problems using rational numbers	→	→	→

Ratios and Proportional Reasoning

Course	1	2	3
● Use ratios to describe problem situations			
— read and write	→	→	→
— equal ratios	→	→	→
● Use fractions to represent ratios and proportions			
— equivalent forms for ratios	→	→	→
● Use proportional reasoning			
— solve proportions	→	→	→
— estimate solutions to proportions	→	→	→
— reasoning with proportions	→	→	→
— unit rate	→	→	→
— unit price	→	→	→
— distance, rate, time problems	→	→	→
● Solve problems involving percent			
— use percent models	→	→	→
— write as ratio and decimal	→	→	→
— greater than 100%	→	→	→
— less than 1%	→	→	→
— estimate	→	→	→
— find using a proportion	→	→	→
— find using an equation	→	→	→
— find percent of a number	→	→	→
— find percent one number is of another		→	→
— find number when percent is known		→	→
— percent change		→	→

Properties of Number and Operations

Course	1	2	3
● Describe odd and even integers			
— integers	→	→	→

Course	1	2	3
● Use factors, multiples, or prime factorization			
— factors	→	→	→
— prime factorization	→	→	→
— greatest common factor	→	→	→
— multiples	→	→	→
— least common multiple	→	→	→
● Use prime and composite numbers			
— prime and composite numbers	→	→	→
● Use divisibility or remainders			
— divisibility rules	→	→	→
● Apply basic properties of operations			
— order of operations	→	→	→
— positive exponents	→	→	→
— negative exponents	→	→	
● Explain a mathematical concept or relationship			
— verbalize and define concepts	→	→	→

Measurement

Measuring Physical Attributes

Course	1	2	3
● Compare objects by attribute (length, area, volume, angle, weight, mass)			
— use customary units of length, area, volume, weight, capacity	→	→	→
— use metric units of length, area, volume, weight, capacity	→	→	→
● Estimate size by attribute			
— estimate length	→	→	→
— estimate area of irregular figures	→	→	→
— estimate volume	→	→	→
— estimate time	→	→	→
● Use appropriate measurement instruments			
— compasses	→	→	→
— graph paper	→	→	→
— protractors	→	→	→
— rulers (metric and customary)	→	→	→
● Solve measurement problems			
— area of squares and rectangles	→	→	→
— area of parallelograms	→	→	→
— area of triangles	→	→	→
— area of trapezoids	→	→	→
— area of circles	→	→	→

Course	1	2	3
— area of composite figures	Introduce	Develop	Maintain & Apply
— surface area of prism	Introduce	Develop	Maintain & Apply
— surface area of cylinders	Introduce	Develop	Maintain & Apply
— volume of prisms	Develop	Develop	Maintain & Apply
— volume of cylinders	Introduce	Develop	Maintain & Apply
— volume of cones and pyramids			Introduce
— volume of spheres			Develop
— dimension analysis		Introduce	Develop

Systems of Measurement

• Select appropriate type of unit for a particular attribute

Course	1	2	3
— use length, area, or volume	Develop	Develop	Develop

• Use conversion to solve problems

Course	1	2	3
— convert within customary system	Develop	Develop	Maintain & Apply
— convert within metric system	Develop	Develop	Maintain & Apply
— convert units of time	Develop	Maintain & Apply	Maintain & Apply

• Estimate measurement from one system to another

Course	1	2	3
— use conversion factors		Introduce	Develop

• Determine appropriate size of measurement units

Course	1	2	3
— choose appropriate units	Develop	Develop	Maintain & Apply

• Determine accuracy of measurement

Course	1	2	3
— precision		Introduce	Develop
— significant digits			Develop

• Solve problems using scale drawings

Course	1	2	3
— scale drawing	Introduce	Develop	Develop

Geometry

Dimension and Shape

• Describe/draw shortest length between points

Course	1	2	3
— line	Develop	Develop	Maintain & Apply
— line segment	Develop	Develop	Maintain & Apply
— points on a line	Develop	Develop	Maintain & Apply

• Identify geometric object by description of its properties

Course	1	2	3
— identify polygons	Develop	Develop	Maintain & Apply
— classify quadrilaterals	Develop	Develop	Maintain & Apply
— classify triangles	Develop	Develop	Maintain & Apply
— congruent angles	Develop	Develop	Develop

Course	1	2	3
• Identify geometric objects in plane and space by visual representation			
— spatial visualization	Introduce	Develop	Develop
• Draw figures from written description			
— polygons	Develop	Develop	Develop
— circles, semicircles	Develop	Develop	Develop
— similar triangles	Introduce	Develop	Develop
• Represent 3-dimensional figures in 2-dimensional space			
— use nets	Develop	Develop	Develop
• Demonstrate understanding of 2- and 3-dimension shapes in the real world			
— different viewpoints	Develop	Develop	Maintain & Apply
— spatial visualization	Develop	Develop	Maintain & Apply

Transformation of Shapes and Preservation of Properties

Course	1	2	3
• Identify lines of symmetry and classify types of symmetry			
— symmetry	Develop	Develop	Develop
• Recognize effect of transformations on 2-dimensional shapes			
— reflections across lines of symmetry	Introduce	Develop	Develop
— rotations	Introduce	Develop	Develop
— translations	Introduce	Develop	Develop
— enlargements			Introduce
— reductions			Introduce
— dilations			Introduce
• Predict results of combining, subdividing, and changing shapes			
— plane figures	Introduce	Develop	Develop
• Justify and apply relationships of congruence and similarity			
— congruence	Introduce	Develop	Develop
— congruent polygons		Develop	Develop
— similarity	Introduce	Develop	Develop
— similar polygons	Introduce	Develop	Develop
• Use relationships of proportionality and conservation of angle			
— congruent angles	Introduce	Develop	Maintain & Apply
— proportions in similar figures	Introduce	Develop	Develop

Relationships Between Geometric Figures

Course	1	2	3
• Use properties and relationships to solve problems			
— draw a diagram	Develop	Develop	Develop
— use a proportion	Develop	Develop	Develop
— congruent angles	Introduce	Develop	Develop

Legend: ▬ INTRODUCE   ▬ DEVELOP   ▬ MAINTAIN & APPLY

Course	1	2	3
— *similar triangles*	▶	▶	▶
— *trigonometric ratios (sine, cosine, tangent)*			▶
● **Use geometric models to solve problems**			
— *make a model*	▶	▶	▶
● **Use Pythagorean theorem to solve problems**			
— *Pythagorean theorem*	▶	▶	▶
— *trigonometric ratios*			▶
● **Describe properties and relationships among polygonal plane figures**			
— *angles*	▶	▶	▶
— *congruence*	▶	▶	▶
— *similarity*	▶	▶	▶
— *ratio of sides and areas*		▶	▶
— *ratio of sides and volume*		▶	▶
● **Describe properties and relationships of parallel or intersecting lines**			
— *parallel lines*	▶	▶	▶
— *perpendicular lines*	▶	▶	▶

Position and Direction

	1	2	3
● **Describe relative positions of points and lines**			
— *coordinate geometry*	▶	▶	▶
● **Describe intersection of two or more figures in a plane**			
— *coordinate geometry*			▶
● **Represent figures in the coordinate plane**			
— *coordinate geometry*	▶	▶	▶

Mathematical Reasoning

	1	2	3
● **Make and test a conjecture about regular polygons**			
— *make and test conjectures*	▶	▶	▶

Data Analysis and Probability

Data Representation

	1	2	3
● **Read and interpret data**			
— *analyze and interpret data*	▶	▶	▶
● **Represent data set graphically and then solve a problem**			
— *decide how to present data*	▶	▶	▶
— *tables and charts*	▶	▶	▶
— *frequency tables*	▶	▶	▶
— *line plots*	▶	▶	▶

Course	1	2	3
— *histograms*	▶	▶	▶
— *bar graphs*	▶	▶	▶
— *double bar graphs*	▶	▶	▶
— *stacked bar graphs*			▶
— *sliding bar graphs*			▶
— *line graphs*	▶	▶	▶
— *multiple line graphs*	▶	▶	▶
— *circle graphs*	▶	▶	▶
— *scatter plots*		▶	▶
— *stem-and-leaf plots*	▶	▶	▶
— *back-to-back stem-and-leaf plots*			▶
— *box-and-whisker plots*	▶	▶	▶
— *draw and compare different representations*	▶	▶	▶
● **Use estimation and computation to solve problems from data sets**			
— *interpolation and extrapolation*	▶	▶	▶
— *determine trends from data*	▶	▶	▶
● **Determine appropriateness and effectiveness of data representations**			
— *choose an appropriate graph or statistic*	▶	▶	▶
● **Compare and contrast different representations of same data**			
— *draw and compare different representations*	▶	▶	▶

Characteristics of Data Sets

	1	2	3
● **Calculate, use, interpret mean, median, mode, range**			
— *mean, median, mode*	▶	▶	▶
— *range*	▶	▶	▶
— *quartiles*	▶	▶	▶
— *analyze data*	▶	▶	▶
● **Identify outliers and determine their effect**			
— *outlier*	▶	▶	▶
● **Compare two or more data sets using appropriate statistical measures**			
— *identify misleading graphs and statistics*	▶	▶	▶
— *choose an appropriate graph or statistic*	▶	▶	▶
● **Select "best fit" line and use it to make predictions**			
— *trend lines*		▶	▶
— *make predictions from graphs*		▶	▶

Experiments and Samples

	1	2	3
● **Identify sources of bias in sampling**			
— *analyze bias in surveys*		▶	▶

Scope and Sequence

Legend: ▬ INTRODUCE   ▭ DEVELOP   ■ MAINTAIN & APPLY

Course	1	2	3
● Distinguish between random and non-random samples			
— *analyze sampling techniques*		Develop	Develop
● Evaluate design of an experiment			
— *plan and analyze surveys*		Develop	Develop
Probability			
● Analyze probability of independent events			
— *theoretical probability*	Develop	Develop	Maintain & Apply
— *experimental probability*	Develop	Develop	Maintain & Apply
— *probability of complements*	Introduce	Develop	Develop
— *odds*	Introduce	Develop	Develop
● Determine theoretical probability of simple and compound events			
— *counting principle*	Introduce	Develop	Develop
● Estimate probability of simple and compound events			
— *estimate probability*	Introduce	Develop	Develop
— *simulations*	Introduce	Develop	Develop
● Distinguish between experimental and theoretical probability			
— *analyze probability*	Introduce	Develop	Maintain & Apply
● Determine sample space for a given situation			
— *tree diagrams/sample space*	Develop	Develop	Develop
● Use sample space to determine probability of possible outcomes			
— *simple probability*	Introduce	Develop	Develop
— *compound probability*	Introduce	Develop	Develop
● Represent probability using fractions, decimals, percents			
— *find and write probability*	Develop	Develop	Develop
— *permutations*	Introduce	Develop	Develop
— *combinations*		Introduce	Develop
● Determine probability of dependent and independent events			
— *independent events*	Introduce	Develop	Develop
— *dependent events*		Introduce	Develop
● Interpret probability within a given context			
— *conduct experiments and simulations*	Develop	Develop	Develop

Algebra

Patterns, Relations, and Functions

Course	1	2	3
● Use, describe, extend numerical and geometric patterns			
— *numerical patterns*	Develop	Develop	Develop
— *geometric patterns*	Introduce	Develop	Develop

Course	1	2	3
● Generalize pattern in a number sequence, table or graph			
— *look for and describe a pattern*	Develop	Develop	Develop
● Analyze or create patterns, sequences, functions			
— *write a rule*	Introduce	Develop	Develop
— *input-output tables*	Develop	Develop	Develop
— *sequences*	Introduce	Develop	Develop
— *Fibonacci sequence*	Introduce	Develop	Develop
● Identify linear and nonlinear functions			
— *functions*	Introduce	Develop	Develop
— *linear*	Introduce	Develop	Develop
— *quadratic*		Introduce	Develop
— *other nonlinear*		Introduce	Develop
● Interpret meaning of slope or intercepts in linear functions			
— *using slope*		Introduce	Develop
— *graphing and using intercepts*			Introduce
Algebraic Representations			
● Translate between different linear expressions			
— *evaluate*	Develop	Develop	Develop
● Analyze or interpret linear relationships			
— *use linear relationships*	Introduce	Develop	Develop
● Graph or interpret points represented by ordered pairs			
— *ordered pairs*	Develop	Develop	Maintain & Apply
● Solve problems in the coordinate system			
— *graphing equations*	Introduce	Develop	Develop
— *graphing inequalities*		Introduce	Develop
● Make conclusions and generalizations about linear relationships			
— *make generalizations*	Introduce	Develop	Develop
● Represent functional relationships			
— *linear functions*	Introduce	Develop	Develop
— *quadratic functions*		Introduce	Develop
Variables, Expressions, and Operations			
● Write algebraic expressions, equations, inequalities			
— *write from word phrases*	Develop	Develop	Maintain & Apply
— *write from word sentences*	Develop	Develop	Maintain & Apply
— *write inequalities*	Introduce	Develop	Develop
● Perform basic operations on linear algebraic expressions			
— *evaluate*	Develop	Develop	Develop
— *simplify*	Develop	Develop	Develop

Course	1	2	3
— commutative property	▸	▸	▸
— associative property	▸	▸	▸
— distributive property	▸	▸	▸

Equations and Inequalities

	1	2	3
● **Solve linear equations or inequalities**			
— solve one-step equations	▸	▸	▸
— solve two-step equations	▸	▸	▸
— solve systems of linear equations			▸
— solve one-step inequalities	▸	▸	▸
— solve two-step inequalities			▸
● **Understand the concept of equivalence**			
— properties of equations	▸	▸	▸
— properties of inequalities	▸	▸	▸
● **Solve problems using equations and inequalities with coefficients**			
— write from word sentences	▸	▸	▸
— solve equations with integer solutions	▸	▸	▸
— solve inequalities	▸	▸	▸
● **Relate linear expressions and graphs of lines using slope, intercept**			
— write and graph equations		▸	▸
● **Use and evaluate common formulas**			
— formulas	▸	▸	▸

Mathematical Processes

Problem Solving

	1	2	3
● **Problem-solving skills**			
— use a problem-solving plan	▸	▸	▸
— too much or too little information	▸	▸	▸
— check for reasonableness	▸	▸	▸
— use a proportion	▸	▸	▸
— use a calculator	▸	▸	▸
— use a computer	▸	▸	▸
— use estimation	▸	▸	▸
— use formulas	▸	▸	▸
— use graphs	▸	▸	▸
● **Problem-solving strategies**			
— choosing a strategy	▸	▸	▸
— draw a diagram	▸	▸	▸
— look for a pattern	▸	▸	▸

Course	1	2	3
— make a graph	▸	▸	▸
— make an organized list	▸	▸	▸
— make a table	▸	▸	▸
— simulate a problem	▸	▸	▸
— solve a simpler problem	▸	▸	▸
— try, check, and revise	▸	▸	▸
— use logical reasoning	▸	▸	▸
— use multiple strategies	▸	▸	▸
— work backward	▸	▸	▸
— write an equation	▸	▸	▸

Reasoning and Proof

	1	2	3
— justify answers	▸	▸	▸
— make and test conjectures	▸	▸	▸
— make generalizations	▸	▸	▸
— reason from graphs	▸	▸	▸
— reason with proportions	▸	▸	▸
— recognize patterns	▸	▸	▸
— use logical reasoning	▸	▸	▸
— evaluate mathematical arguments	▸	▸	▸
— use or construct Venn diagrams	▸	▸	▸

Communication

	1	2	3
— interpret mathematical ideas through discussing, writing, reading	▸	▸	▸
— make convincing arguments using mathematical ideas	▸	▸	▸
— relate mathematical language to everyday language	▸	▸	▸
— analyze and evaluate mathematical thinking of others	▸	▸	▸

Connections

	1	2	3
— use connections among mathematical ideas	▸	▸	▸
— apply mathematics in contexts outside of mathematics	▸	▸	▸
— use technology	▸	▸	▸

Representation

	1	2	3
— use representations to develop mathematical ideas	▸	▸	▸
— use tables, graphs, words, and symbols interchangeably	▸	▸	▸
— solve problems using pictures/diagrams	▸	▸	▸
— algebra tiles	▸	▸	▸
— decimal models	▸	▸	▸
— fraction models	▸	▸	▸
— number line models	▸	▸	▸
— two-color chips	▸	▸	▸

CHAPTER 7 — Data and Graphs

Chapter at a Glance

7-1 Mean, Median, and Mode
pp. 322–325

Objectives
1. Finding the Mean
2. Finding the Median and the Mode

New Vocabulary
mean, outlier, median, mode

NCTM Standards
1, 5, 6, 7, 8, 9, 10

Local Standards

7-2 Organizing and Displaying Data
pp. 326–330

Objectives
1. Making a Frequency Table
2. Making a Line Plot and Finding the Range

New Vocabulary
frequency table, line plot, range

NCTM Standards
1, 5, 6, 7, 8, 9, 10

Local Standards

7-3 Problem Solving — Make an Organized List
pp. 332–334

Objectives
1. Solving Problems by Making an Organized List

NCTM Standards
1, 5, 6, 7, 8, 9, 10

Local Standards

✓ Checkpoint Quiz 1

7-4 Bar Graphs and Line Graphs
pp. 335–339

Objectives
1. Making Bar Graphs
2. Making Line Graphs

New Vocabulary
bar graph, histogram, line graph

Optional Materials
straight edge or ruler, graph paper

NCTM Standards
1, 5, 6, 7, 8, 9, 10

Local Standards

7-5 Circle Graphs
pp. 341–345

Objectives
1. Reading and Making Circle Graphs

New Vocabulary
circle graph

Optional Materials
compass, metric ruler, scissors

NCTM Standards
1, 3, 4, 5, 6, 7, 8, 9, 10

Local Standards

7-6 Using Spreadsheets to Organize Data
pp. 347–350

Objectives
1. Reading Data in a Spreadsheet
2. Writing Formulas for a Spreadsheet

New Vocabulary
spreadsheet, cell

NCTM Standards
1, 2, 3, 6, 7, 8, 9, 10

Local Standards

✓ Checkpoint Quiz 2

7-7 Stem-and-Leaf Plots
pp. 352–355

Objectives
1. Using a Stem-and Leaf Plot

New Vocabulary
stem-and-leaf plot

NCTM Standards
1, 5, 6, 7, 8, 9, 10

Local Standards

7-8 Misleading Graphs and Statistics
pp. 358–362

Objectives
1. Identifying Misleading Graphs
2. Identifying Misleading Statistics

NCTM Standards
1, 5, 6, 7, 8, 9, 10

Local Standards

Reaching All Students

Additional Instructional Options in Chapter 7

Reading and Math Literacy

📖 Reading Math

Reading Graphs, p. 331

Reading Math hints, pp. 322, 342, 348

Reading Comprehension, p. 367

Understanding Vocabulary, p. 364

✏️ Writing in Math

Writing to Persuade, p. 346

Daily Writing Practice, pp. 324, 328, 333, 338, 344, 349, 354, 361, 366

Above Level

ⓒ Challenge exercises

pp. 325, 330, 333, 338, 345, 349, 355, 361

⬤ Extension

Double Bar and Line Graphs, p. 340

Box-and-Whisker Plots, pp. 356–357

Hands-On and Technology

🔍 Investigations

Exploring the Mean, p. 321

Graphing and Reporting Survey Results, p. 337

Exploring Circle Graphs, p. 341

💻 Technology

Making a Graph From a Spreadsheet, p. 351

Activities and Projects

📖 Real-World Snapshots

Using Data and Graphs, pp. 368–469

📁 Chapter Project

On Your Own Time, p. 639

Test Prep

📝 Daily Test Prep

pp. 325, 330, 334, 339, 345, 350, 355, 362

📝 Test-Taking Strategies

Answering the Question Asked, p. 363

📝 Test Prep

Reading Comprehension, p. 367

Chapter Assessment

✔️ Checkpoint Quiz

pp. 334, 350

⬤ Chapter Review

pp. 364–365

⬤ Chapter Test

p. 366

Pacing Options

This chart suggests pacing only for the core lessons and their parts. It is provided as a possible guide. It will help you determine how much time you have in your schedule to cover the additional features and assessment, as described at the left.

Day	Traditional 45-minute class periods	Block 90-minute class periods
1	7-1 ▽	7-1 ▽ ▽
2	7-1 ▽	7-2 ▽ ▽
3	7-2 ▽	7-3 ▽ 7-4 ▽
4	7-2 ▽	7-4 ▽ 7-5 ▽
5	7-3 ▽	7-5 ▽ 7-6 ▽
6	7-4 ▽	7-6 ▽ 7-7 ▽
7	7-4 ▽	7-8 ▽ ▽
8	7-5 ▽	
9	7-6 ▽	
10	7-6 ▽	
11	7-7 ▽	
12	7-8 ▽	
13	7-8 ▽	

NCTM STANDARDS 2000

1 Number and Operations	6 Problem Solving
2 Algebra	7 Reasoning and Proof
3 Geometry	8 Communication
4 Measurement	9 Connections
5 Data Analysis and Probability	10 Representation

Math Background

Skills Trace

BEFORE Chapter 7
Grade 5 presented graphical displays of data.

DURING Chapter 7
Course 1 reviews and extends the graphical display of data to stem-and-leaf plots and misleading graphs.

AFTER Chapter 7
Throughout this course students make and interpret graphical displays of data.

7-1 Mean, Median, and Mode

Math Understandings
- There are different statistics for describing the "center" of a numerical data set.
- The mean, median, and mode are common measures for the central tendency of a data set.

The **mean** of a set of data is the sum of the data divided by the number of data items. The **median** is the middle number of a set of ordered data. When there is an even number of data items, you can find the median by adding the two middle numbers and dividing by 2. The **mode** is the data item that appears most often. There may be no mode, or one or more modes. If all data items occur the same number of times, there is no mode. An **outlier** is a data item that is far apart from the rest of the data. If a data set has an outlier, then the mean may not describe the data set very well.

Example: For the data set 9, 27, 8, 11, 17, 14, 12, 17, 16, 11 the median is 13.   8, 9, 11, 11, (12, 14,) 16, 17, 17, 27

The mean is $\frac{142}{10}$, or 14.2. The two modes are 11 and 17. The data set appears to have an outlier of 27.

7-2 Organizing and Displaying Data

Math Understandings
- A frequency table shows how often each data value occurs.
- A line plot visually represents a frequency table on a number line.

A **frequency table** is a table that lists each item in a data set with the number of times the item occurs. A **line plot** is a graph that shows the shape of a data set by stacking X's above each data value on a number line. The **range** of a data set is the difference between the least and greatest values.

DVDs Rental by Each Customer		
Number	Tally	Frequency
One	IIII I	5
Two	IIII I	6
Three	IIII	4
Four	IIII	5
Five	II	2
Six	I	1

DVDs Rented by Each Customer

7-3 Make an Organized List

Using an organized list makes easier to find patterns in data.

7-4 Bar Graphs and Line Graphs

Math Understandings
- You can display numerical information with a bar graph, a histogram, or a line graph.
- A bar graph shows comparisons.
- A histogram shows the frequency of each data item.
- A line graph shows trends over time.

A **bar graph** uses vertical or horizontal bars to display numerical information. A **histogram** is a bar graph that shows the frequency of each data item with equal-sized intervals and no spaces between the bars. A **line graph** uses a series of line segments to show changes of one variable compared to another.

**Histogram
Germination Rates**

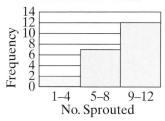

**Bar Graph
One Month Grain Heights**

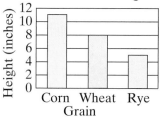

Germination Rates	
No. Sprouted	Frequency
1–4	2
5–8	7
9–12	12

One Month Grain Heights	
Grain	Height
Corn	11 in.
Wheat	8 in.
Rye	5 in.

7-5 Circle Graphs

Math Understandings
• You can use a circle graph when the data is in the various categories total to 100%.

A **circle graph** is a graph of data where the entire circle represents the whole. Each wedge in the circle represents part of the whole.

7-6 Using Spreadsheets to Organize Data

Math Understandings
• A computer spreadsheet is an electronic workspace that you can use to organize information in cells so that you can use that information in calculations and graphs.
• You can use spreadsheet software and formulas to make repeated calculations that reflect changing data.

A **spreadsheet** is a table made up of rows and columns used to organize data. A **cell** is a box in a spreadsheet where a particular row and column meet.

7-7 Stem-and-Leaf Plots

Math Understandings
• A stem-and-leaf plot shows the distribution of a data set.
• Each stem-and-leaf plot must include a key that shows what the stems and leaves represent for a particular plot.

A **stem-and-leaf** plot is a graph that uses the digits of each number to show the shape of the data. Each data value is broken into a "stem" (digit or digits on the left) and a "leaf" (digit or digits on the right).

**Times to Get Ready
for School (minutes)**

```
2 | 3 3 5 7 8 8
3 | 3 4 5 7 7 7 9
4 | 0 0 2 3 3 5
5 | 8
```
Key: 2 | 3 means 23 min

7-8 Misleading Graphs and Statistics

Math Understandings
• Choices made about the labels, scale intervals, and style of a graph can create a misleading impression.

When you read a graph, make sure the axis scales start at zero and use equal intervals. Otherwise, the graph may be misleading. Statistics such as a mean can also be misleading if the data set contains extreme values, or outliers, that distort the mean.

Additional Professional Development Opportunities

Chapter 3 Math Background notes:
pp. 323, 327, 332, 336, 342, 348, 353, 359

Additional resources available from SkyLight Professional Development:

On-site courses, workshops, summer institutes. Online courses and chat rooms. Videocassettes and books. Visit www.skylightedu.com.

Ongoing Assessment and Intervention

The *Prentice Hall Mathematics* program provides many options for assessment in the Student Edition, Teacher's Edition, and teaching resources. From these options you may choose instructional materials that are appropriate for your students and that support your district's curriculum requirements.

Daily Assessment

✓ Instant Check System™ in Chapter 7

Allows students to check their own learning before, during, and after each lesson.

Diagnosing Readiness before the chapter (p. 320)

Check Skills You'll Need exercises in each lesson (pp. 322, 326, 332, 335, 341, 347, 352, 358)

Check Understanding questions with each Example (pp. 322, 323, 326, 327, 332, 335, 336, 342, 347, 348, 352, 353, 358, 359)

Checkpoint Quiz (pp. 334, 350)

Formal Assessment

Assessment in the Student Text and in Additional Resources

Assess student progress throughout the Course 1 textbook and with blackline masters and CD-ROM.

Student Edition
- Chapter 7 Review, with Vocabulary, Skills, and Concepts Review, pp. 364–365
- Chapter 7 Test, p. 366

Assessment Resources
- Checkpoint Quizzes 1 & 2
- Chapter Test, forms A & B
- Chapter Alternative Assessment

Spanish versions available.

Computer Test Generator CD-ROM
- Instant Chapter Tests™—pre-made tests with items that vary every time you print.
- Online Testing allows you to give tests online and receive progress reports.
- Prepare students by making tests based on standardized test objectives.

Algebra Readiness Tests
- Includes Basic Skills Tests and Concept-Readiness Tests.
- Assess understanding of skills and concepts needed for success in algebra.

Intervention

Skills Intervention Kit

Online Intervention

Integrated within the iText, this online intervention system includes diagnostic tests and prescribed remediation, plus reports to track student mastery.

A *complete* system for the student who is struggling with course-level work

Eight intervention units cover core skills and allow you to:
- **Diagnose** students' gaps in basic skills
- **Prescribe** an individualized course of study
- **Monitor** student progress

Includes print workbooks, tutorial CD-ROM, teacher editions, progress folders, and more. *Available in Spanish.*

Standardized Test Preparation

The *Prentice Hall Mathematics* program integrates preparation for high-stakes standardized tests in every lesson of the Student Edition and continues this support in the Prentice Hall Assessment System.

Test Prep

In Student Text, Chapter 7

Teaches students strategies and gives them practice with all the test item formats they will encounter on high-stakes tests.

Test Prep exercises in each lesson (pp. 325, 330, 334, 339, 345, 350, 355, 362)

Test-Taking Strategies Answering the Question Asked, p. 363

Test Prep Reading Comprehension, p. 367

A three-step approach to preparing students for high stakes, national, and state exams.

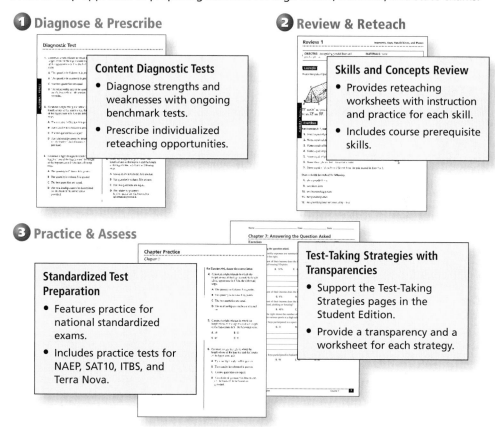

1 Diagnose & Prescribe

Content Diagnostic Tests
- Diagnose strengths and weaknesses with ongoing benchmark tests.
- Prescribe individualized reteaching opportunities.

2 Review & Reteach

Skills and Concepts Review
- Provides reteaching worksheets with instruction and practice for each skill.
- Includes course prerequisite skills.

3 Practice & Assess

Standardized Test Preparation
- Features practice for national standardized exams.
- Includes practice tests for NAEP, SAT10, ITBS, and Terra Nova.

Test-Taking Strategies with Transparencies
- Support the Test-Taking Strategies pages in the Student Edition.
- Provide a transparency and a worksheet for each strategy.

Correlation to Standardized Tests

Lesson		NAEP	Terra Nova				Local Test
			CAT6	CTBS	ITBS	SAT10	
7-1	Mean, Median, and Mode	D2a–D2c		■	■	■	
7-2	Organizing and Displaying Data	D1b	■		■	■	
7-3	Problem Solving: Make an Organized List						
7-4	Bar Graphs and Line Graphs	D1b	■		■	■	
7-5	Circle Graphs	D1b				■	
7-6	Using Spreadsheets to Organize Data	D1c					
7-7	Stem-and-Leaf Plots	D1b					
7-8	Misleading Graphs and Statistics	D1d					

NAEP National Assessment of Educational Progress
CAT6/Terra Nova California Achievement Test, 6th Ed.

CTBS/Terra Nova Comprehensive Test of Basic Skills
ITBS Iowa Test of Basic Skills, Form M.

SAT10 Stanford Achievement Test, 10th Ed.

Program Resources

	Resources in Grab & Go™ Files				Resources for Reaching All Students				Spanish Resources			Transparencies					Presentation Assistant Plus!
	Practice	Reteach	Enrich	Checkpt Quiz	Reading & Math Literacy	Technology Activities	Hands-On Activities	Guided Problem Solving	Practice	Reading & Math Literacy	Checkpt Quiz	Skills Check	Problem of the Day	Additional Examples	Answers to Exercises	Lesson Quiz	Prentice Hall Presentation Pro CD-ROM
7-1	■	■	■		■			■	■			■	■	■	■	■	■
7-2	■	■	■			■		■	■			■	■	■	■	■	■
7-3	■	■	■	■	■			■	■	■	■	■	■	■	■	■	■
7-4	■	■	■			■		■	■			■	■	■	■	■	■
7-5	■	■	■			■	■	■	■			■	■	■	■	■	■
7-6	■	■	■	■				■	■		■	■	■	■	■	■	■
7-7	■	■	■				■					■	■	■	■	■	■
7-8	■	■	■					■	■			■	■	■	■	■	■
For the Chapter	Chapter Projects, Chapter Tests, Alternative Assessment, Cumulative Review, Cumulative Assessment				**On web site only:** Home Activities, Interdisciplinary Activities, Algebra Readiness Puzzles				Spanish Chapter Tests, Alternative Assessment, Cumulative Review, Cumulative Assessment			Classroom Aid Transparencies					

Also available for use with the chapter:

 PRENTICE HALL ASSESSMENT SYSTEM *See page 318F.*

- Practice Workbook
- Solution Key
- MathNotes folder

- For teacher support and access to student Web materials, use the Web Code aak-5500.
- For additional online and technology resources, *see below*.

 ## Technology

iTEXT Online and on CD-ROM

Complete Interactive Student Text online and on CD-ROM—with instant feedback assessment, tutorial help, dynamic activities, instructional and real-world videos, audio, and additional practice.

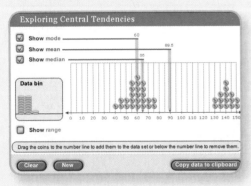

www.PHSchool.com For Students

Use Web codes for easy access to online activities, chapter projects, self-grading lesson quizzes, chapter tests, vocabulary quizzes, updated data sources, graphing calculator procedures, and more.

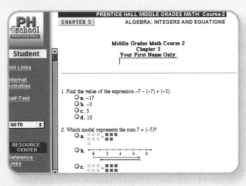

PH SuccessNet For Teachers

Online lesson planning with built-in state correlations, all the teaching resources, complete reference library, your own calendar and Teacher Web page, professional development, and more.

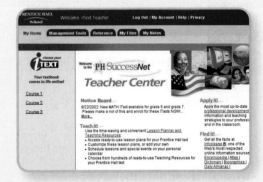

Presentation Assistant Plus!

The *Prentice Hall Presentation Assistant Plus!* provides you with the material you need to teach a lesson from beginning to end. Two easy-to-use formats—Transparencies and PowerPoint®—allow you to present a lesson the way you are most comfortable.

Transparencies

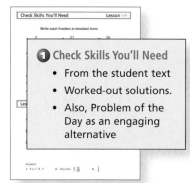
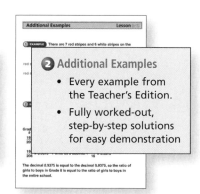

1 Check Skills You'll Need
- From the student text
- Worked-out solutions.
- Also, Problem of the Day as an engaging alternative

2 Additional Examples
- Every example from the Teacher's Edition.
- Fully worked-out, step-by-step solutions for easy demonstration

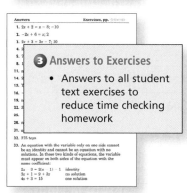
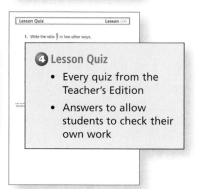

3 Answers to Exercises
- Answers to all student text exercises to reduce time checking homework

4 Lesson Quiz
- Every quiz from the Teacher's Edition
- Answers to allow students to check their own work

 Throughout the Teacher's Edition, this symbol indicates material that is available in the Presentation Assistant Plus!

PowerPoint Prentice Hall Presentation Pro CD-ROM

- Includes all Transparencies.
- Conveniently organized by lesson so you can easily **1** Introduce, **2** Teach, **3** Check Homework, and **4** Assess each lesson.
- Animated examples allow step-by-step instruction at your own pace.
- Easy to edit so you can create custom presentations.

Teaching Chapter 7 Using Presentation Assistant Plus!

	1 Introduce	**2 Teach**	**3 Check Homework**	**4 Assess**
	Check Skills You'll Need	Additional Examples	Student Edition Answers	Lesson Quiz
7-1	p. 56	p. 90	✔	p. 56
7-2	p. 57	p. 91	✔	p. 58
7-3	p. 59	p. 92	✔	p. 59
7-4	p. 60	pp. 93–95	✔	p. 61
7-5	p. 62	pp. 96–97	✔	p. 62
7-6	p. 63	p. 98	✔	p. 63
7-7	p. 64	pp. 99–100	✔	p. 64
7-8	p. 65	p. 101	✔	p. 65

Prentice Hall Presentation Pro

CD-ROM with dynamic PowerPoint® presentations for every lesson. Helps you introduce and develop concepts, check homework, and assess progress. Part of Presentation Assistant Plus! *(See above.)*

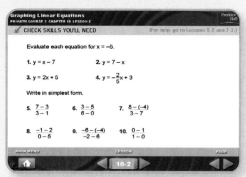

Computer Test Generator

CD-ROM to create practice sheets and tests for course objectives and standardized tests. Includes Instant Chapter Tests™, online testing, and student reports. Part of the PH Assessment System. *(See page 318F.)*

Resource Pro® with Planning Express®

CD-ROM with a lesson planning tool that allows you to import state and local objectives. Includes electronic versions of all the teaching resources.

Chapter Resources

Reading and Math Support

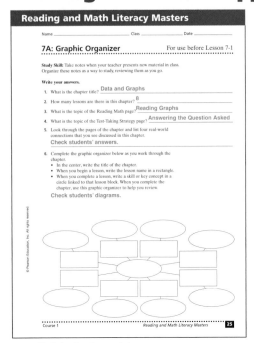

7A: Graphic Organizer   For use before Lesson 7-1

Study Skill: Take notes when your teacher presents new material in class. Organize these notes as a way to study, reviewing them as you go.

Write your answers.

1. What is the chapter title? Data and Graphs
2. How many lessons are there in this chapter? 8
3. What is the topic of the Reading Math page? Reading Graphs
4. What is the topic of the Test-Taking Strategy page? Answering the Question Asked
5. Look through the pages of the chapter and list four real-world connections that you see discussed in this chapter.
   Check students' answers.
6. Complete the graphic organizer below as you work through the chapter.
   • In the center, write the title of the chapter.
   • When you begin a lesson, write the lesson name in a rectangle.
   • When you complete a lesson, write a skill or key concept in a circle linked to that lesson block. When you complete the chapter, use this graphic organizer to help you review.
   Check students' diagrams.

Available in Spanish

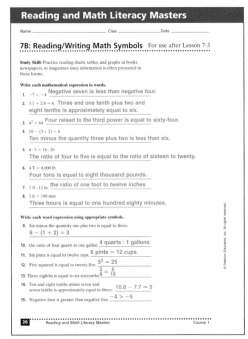

7B: Reading/Writing Math Symbols   For use after Lesson 7-3

Study Skill: Practice reading charts, tables, and graphs in books, newspapers, or magazines since information is often presented in these forms.

Write each mathematical expression in words.

1. $-7 < -4$ Negative seven is less than negative four.
2. $3.1 + 2.8 \approx 6$ Three and one tenth plus two and eight tenths is approximately equal to six.
3. $4^3 = 64$ Four raised to the third power is equal to sixty-four.
4. $10 - (3 + 2) < 6$ Ten minus the quantity three plus two is less than six.
5. $4 : 5 = 16 : 20$ The ratio of four to five is equal to the ratio of sixteen to twenty.
6. $4\ T = 8,000\ lb$ Four tons is equal to eight thousand pounds.
7. $1\ ft : 12\ in.$ the ratio of one foot to twelve inches
8. $3\ h = 180\ min$ Three hours is equal to one hundred eighty minutes.

Write each word expression using appropriate symbols.

9. Six minus the quantity one plus two is equal to three. $6 - (1 + 2) = 3$
10. the ratio of four quarts to one gallon   4 quarts : 1 gallons
11. Six pints is equal to twelve cups.   6 pints = 12 cups
12. Five squared is equal to twenty-five. $5^2 = 25$
13. Three eighths is equal to six sixteenths $\frac{3}{8} = \frac{6}{16}$
14. Ten and eight tenths minus seven and seven tenths is approximately equal to three. $10.8 - 7.7 \approx 3$
15. Negative four is greater than negative five. $-4 > -5$

Available in Spanish

7C: Reading Comprehension   For use after Lesson 7-6

Study Skill: Use tables and charts when you need to organize complex information.

Food coloring comes in red, blue, green, and yellow colors. By mixing these standard colors, you can make many different colors.

Use the chart below to answer the questions.

Number of Drops Required

Blended Shades	RED	YELLOW	BLUE	GREEN
Turquoise	0	0	4	1
Brown	7	4	0	2
Grape	5	0	1	0
Lime	0	3	0	1
Pistachio	0	1	0	4
Orange	2	3	0	0
Peach	1	2	0	0
Salmon	3	2	0	0

1. What information is contained in the chart? the number of drops of each color needed to make various blended shades of color
2. What colors are needed to make salmon? red and yellow
3. If you use 6 drops of yellow to make lime, how many drops of green will you need? 2 drops
4. To make brown, how many colors will you need to mix together? 3 colors
5. Of the eight blended shades listed, which one requires the greatest number of drops (total)? brown
6. Which shade requires the least number of drops? peach
7. Which shades do not require any red? turquoise, lime, pistachio
8. What is the ratio of blue drops to red drops required to make grape? 1 drop blue : 5 drops red
9. How many total drops are needed to make brown if 8 yellow drops are used? 26
10. If you were to make each blended shade in the chart, which standard color of dye would have had the most drops used? red

Available in Spanish

Problem Solving

7D: Vocabulary   For use with the Chapter Review

Study Skill: Pay attention in class. Some concepts are very difficult to grasp unless you devote your full attention to learning them.

Circle the word that best completes the sentence.

1. The (median, *mean*) is the sum of the data values divided by the number of data items.
2. You can use a (circle, *bar*) graph to show trends.
3. A (*solution*, statement) is a value for a variable that makes an equation true.
4. Two numbers are (*reciprocals*, opposites) if their product is equal to one.
5. The (numerator, *denominator*) is the bottom number in a fraction.
6. A (*circle*, line) graph compares parts to a whole.
7. A(n) (*ratio*, integer) compares two quantities using division.
8. Two equal ratios can be written as a (percent, *proportion*).
9. On a map, the (*scale*, ratio) would tell you that 1 inch = 50 miles.
10. The time between the occurrence of two events is called (benchmark, *elapsed time*).
11. The (*median*, mode) is the middle number in a set of ordered data.
12. A (prime, *composite*) number is a whole number greater than one that has more than two factors.
13. You can use the (*commutative*, associative) property to change the order in an addition or multiplication expression.
14. (Simplest, *Equivalent*) fractions represent the same amount.
15. A (whole, *mixed*) number represents the sum of a whole number and a fraction.
16. A (*multiple*, factor) of a number is the product of that number and a non-zero whole number.

Available in Spanish

7-1 • Guided Problem Solving

GPS Student Page 324, Exercise 20:

Number Sense The median of four numbers is 48. If three of the numbers are 42, 51, and 52, what is the other number?

Read and Understand

1. What are you being asked to do?
   Find the fourth number.
2. What is the median?
   The median is the middle number in a set of ordered data.
3. How do you find the median when there is an even number of data items?
   You add the two middle numbers and divide by 2.

Plan and Solve

4. Order the three numbers. 42, 51, 52
5. Between which two numbers does the missing number belong?
   42 and 51 since 48 > 42 and 48 < 51.
6. 48 is the number between the missing number and which other number? 51
7. What is the difference between the answer to Step 6 and 48? 3
8. What is the difference between the missing number and 48? Why?
   3; 48 is halfway between 42 and 51.
9. What is the missing number? 48 − 3 or 45

Look Back and Check

10. Explain how to check your answer.
    (45 + 51) ÷ 2 = 96 ÷ 2 = 48

Solve Another Problem

11. The median of six numbers is 36. If five of the numbers are 29, 38, 34, 38, and 40, what is the other number?
    29, 34, 38, 38, 40; (34 + 38) ÷ 2 = 72 ÷ 2 = 36; 30

7-2 • Guided Problem Solving

GPS Student Page 329, Exercise 14:

Speed Limits On a highway, the minimum speed allowed is 40 miles per hour and the maximum speed is 65 miles per hour. What is the range of speeds allowed on the highway?

Read and Understand

1. Underline the words that indicate which numbers you are to use to answer this question.
2. What is the range?
   The range is the difference between the least and the greatest values.

Plan and Solve

3. What is the least possible highway speed?
   40 mi/h
4. What is the greatest possible highway speed?
   65 mi/h
5. Write a subtraction expression to answer the question.
   65 − 40 = 25
6. What is the range?
   25 mi/h

Look Back and Check

7. How can you check your answer? Does your answer check?
   Find the sum of 25 and 40 and see it equals 65; yes.

Solve Another Problem

8. You have to be at least 36 inches tall to ride the rides at Kiddie Land, but you cannot be any taller than 48 inches. What is the range of heights for these rides?
   48 − 36 = 12; 12 inches

Name _____ Class _____ Date _____

7-3 • Guided Problem Solving

GPS Student Page 332, Exercise 4:

How many triangles are in the figure at the right?

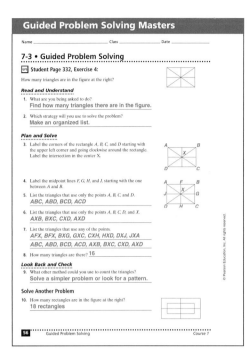

Read and Understand

1. What are you being asked to do?
   Find how many triangles there are in the figure.

2. Which strategy will you use to solve the problem?
   Make an organized list.

Plan and Solve

3. Label the corners of the rectangle A, B, C, and D starting with the upper left corner and going clockwise around the rectangle. Label the intersection in the center X.

4. Label the midpoint lines F, G, H, and J, starting with the one between A and B.

5. List the triangles that use only the points A, B, C, and D.
   ABC, ABD, BCD, ACD

6. List the triangles that use only the points A, B, C, D, and X.
   AXB, BXC, CXD, AXD

7. List the triangles that use any of the points.
   AFX, BFX, BXG, GXC, CXH, HXD, DXJ, JXA
   ABC, ABD, BCD, ACD, AXB, BXC, CXD, AXD

8. How many triangles are there? 16

Look Back and Check

9. What other method could you use to count the triangles?
   Solve a simpler problem or look for a pattern.

Solve Another Problem

10. How many rectangles are in the figure at the right?
    18 rectangles

Name _____ Class _____ Date _____

7-4 • Guided Problem Solving

GPS Student Page 338, Exercise 6:

Prime Ministers Make a bar graph to show how many years each prime minister was in office.

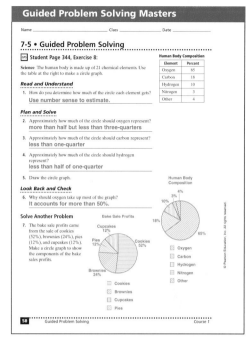

Gro Harlem Brundtland
Norway 13 years

Read and Understand

1. What is a bar graph?
   A bar graph uses vertical or horizontal bars to display numerical information.

Plan and Solve

2. If the bars are to be vertical, what should go along the horizontal axis?
   the names of the prime ministers

3. What should go along the vertical axis? the number of years

4. What is the maximum number of years? What scale should you use? 18; one mark = 2 years

5. Draw the bar graph. Sample answer:

Indira Gandhi
India 18 years

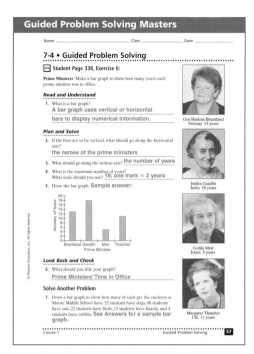

Look Back and Check

6. What should you title your graph?
   Prime Ministers' Time in Office

Solve Another Problem

7. Draw a bar graph to show how many of each pet the students at Moore Middle School have. 52 students have cats, 22 students have dogs, 68 students have birds, 15 students have lizards, and 4 students have rabbits. See Answers for a sample bar graph.

Golda Meir
Israel 5 years

Margaret Thatcher
UK 11 years

Name _____ Class _____ Date _____

7-5 • Guided Problem Solving

GPS Student Page 344, Exercise 8:

Human Body Composition	
Element	Percent
Oxygen	65
Carbon	18
Hydrogen	10
Nitrogen	3
Other	4

Science The human body is made up of 21 chemical elements. Use the table at the right to make a circle graph.

Read and Understand

1. How do you determine how much of the circle each element gets?
   Use number sense to estimate.

Plan and Solve

2. Approximately how much of the circle should oxygen represent?
   more than half but less than three-quarters

3. Approximately how much of the circle should carbon represent?
   less than one-quarter

4. Approximately how much of the circle should hydrogen represent?
   less than half of one-quarter

5. Draw the circle graph.

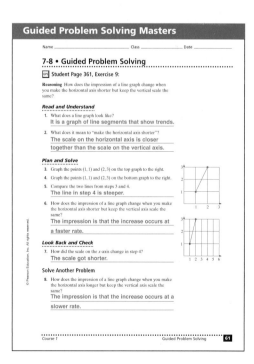

Human Body Composition

Look Back and Check

6. Why should oxygen take up most of the graph?
   It accounts for more than 50%.

Solve Another Problem

7. The bake sale profits came from the sale of cookies (52%), brownies (24%), pies (12%), and cupcakes (12%). Make a circle graph to show the components of the bake sales profits.

Bake Sale Profits

- ☒ Oxygen
- ☐ Carbon
- ▥ Hydrogen
- ☒ Nitrogen
- ☒ Other

- ☐ Cookies
- ☒ Brownies
- ▥ Cupcakes
- ☒ Pies

Name _____ Class _____ Date _____

7-6 • Guided Problem Solving

GPS Student Page 349, Exercise 11:

Wages Suppose your cousin works at a part-time job and earns $7 per hour. The spreadsheet shows a typical schedule for a week.

Write a formula for cell D2 and calculate the value in cell D2.

	A	B	C	D	E
1	Day	Time In (P.M.)	Time Out (P.M.)	Hours Worked	Amount Earned
2	9/15	3	8	?	?
3	9/17	4	8	?	?
4	9/19	3	6	?	?
5			Total:	?	?

Read and Understand

1. What are you being asked to do?
   Write a formula for a spreadsheet cell and calculate its value.

2. What does column D represent? the number of hours worked

3. What does row 2 represent?
   the date (9/15), the time in (3 P.M.), and the time out (8 P.M.).

Plan and Solve

4. What operation do you use to figure the number of hours worked? subtraction

5. What cells do you need for the formula? B2 and C2

6. Write the formula for D2. D2 = C2 − B2

7. Calculate the value of D2. 8 − 3 = 5; 5 hours

Look Back and Check

8. Explain how you can check your answer.
   Add 5 and 3 or subtract 5 from 8.

Solve Another Problem

9. Your cousin's friend worked from 12 noon to 9 P.M. on 9/15. Create a row like your cousin's row 2 for his friend.

A	B	C	D	E
9/15	12	9	9	$63

Name _____ Class _____ Date _____

7-7 • Guided Problem Solving

GPS Student Page 354, Exercise 10a:

Heights The heights of nine people are given below.

5 ft 10 in.   4 ft 11 in.   5 ft 4 in.
5 ft 6 in.   6 ft 7 in.   6 ft 8 in.
6 ft 10 in.   5 ft 8 in.   5 ft 7 in.

a. Make a stem-and-leaf plot.

Read and Understand

1. Looking at the data, which numbers, the feet or the inches, should be the stems? Explain.
   feet, because those numbers are read first

2. Looking at the data, which numbers, the feet or the inches, should be the leaves? Explain.
   inches, because those numbers are read second

Plan and Solve

3. Order the heights from least to greatest.
   4 ft 11 in., 5 ft 1 in., 5 ft 4 in., 5 ft 6 in., 5 ft 7 in.,
   5 ft 8 in., 5 ft 10 in., 6 ft 7 in., 6 ft 10 in.

4. Write the stems in order. Draw a vertical line next to the stems.

4	
5	
6	

5. Write the leaves in order for each stem.

4	11
5	1 4 6 7 8 10
6	7 10

6. Include a key to explain what the stems and leaves represent. Key: 4|11 means 4 ft 11 in.

Look Back and Check

7. How can you check to make sure you used all the data values?
   Count them; there are 9 values.

Solve Another Problem

8. Eight friends were in a race. Their times are given below.
   1 min 48 s; 1 min 54 s; 2 min 20 s; 1 min 58 s; 3 min 2 s; 2 min 45 s; 2 min 30 s; 2 min 3 s
   Make a stem-and-leaf plot for the data. See Answers.

Name _____ Class _____ Date _____

7-8 • Guided Problem Solving

GPS Student Page 361, Exercise 9:

Reasoning How does the impression of a line graph change when you make the horizontal axis shorter but keep the vertical scale the same?

Read and Understand

1. What does a line graph look like?
   It is a graph of line segments that show trends.

2. What does it mean to "make the horizontal axis shorter"?
   The scale on the horizontal axis is closer together than the scale on the vertical axis.

Plan and Solve

3. Graph the points (1, 1) and (2, 3) on the top graph to the right.

4. Graph the points (1, 1) and (2, 3) on the bottom graph to the right.

5. Compare the two lines from steps 3 and 4.
   The line in step 4 is steeper.

6. How does the impression of a line graph change when you make the horizontal axis shorter but keep the vertical axis scale the same?
   The impression is that the increase occurs at a faster rate.

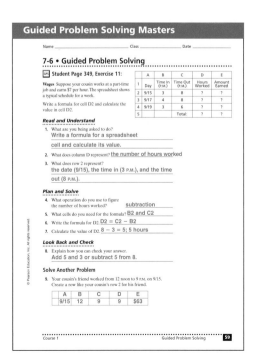

Look Back and Check

7. How did the scale on the x-axis change in step 4?
   The scale got shorter.

Solve Another Problem

8. How does the impression of a line graph change when you make the horizontal axis longer but keep the vertical axis scale the same?
   The impression is that the increase occurs at a slower rate.

Activities and Projects

Hands-On Activities

Name _____ Class _____ Date _____

Activity 24: Circle Graphs

Materials needed: protractor, compass

The data below represents the results of a survey in which 20 students were asked to name as many state capitals as possible. Each number represents the number of correctly named capitals from a student.

9	20	15	4	48	30	10	12	8	5
22	28	34	16	13	41	29	11	33	19

1. Arrange the data in a table like the one shown below. Set interval ranges for the number of correct responses, for instance 1 to 5 correct responses, 6 to 10 correct responses, etc., and enter the intervals in the first column of your table. Make sure your intervals are equal.

Number of Correct Responses	Tally of Students	Tally Totals	%	Central Angle

2. Count the tallies for each interval range. Record the totals in your table.

3. Calculate the percent of students within each interval range. For example, in an interval of 1 to 5 correct responses, you would divide the number of students (2) by the total (20) and multiply by 100 to get $\frac{2}{20} \times 100 = 10\%$.

4. To calculate the central angle for each interval, multiply the percent by 360°. For example, $10\% \times 360° = 0.10 \times 360° = 36°$. Record your calculations.

5. Construct a circle graph to display the results. Use a compass to draw a circle like the one at the right. Then, use a protractor to construct each of the central angles you found. Be sure to label each sector of the circle graph with the correct percentage and the corresponding interval.

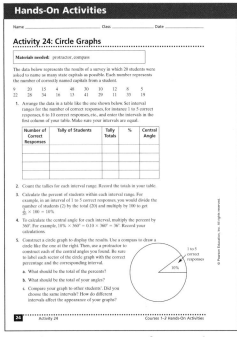

a. What should be the total of the percents?

b. What should be the total of your angles?

c. Compare your graph to other students'. Did you choose the same intervals? How do different intervals affect the appearance of your graphs?

Hands-On Activities

Name _____ Class _____ Date _____

Activity 26: Plotting Height

Materials needed: ruler, graph paper

Work in small groups of 3–4 students, or do as a whole-class activity.

1. a. Measure each class member's or group member's height to the nearest inch.

   b. On a separate sheet of paper, write the measurements in order from smallest to largest. Include a measurement for each member of your class or group; you may need to write some heights more than once.

2. What is the range of your data?

3. a. Draw a line on a separate piece of paper, and write the range of numbers below the line.

   b. Measure with a ruler to evenly space the numbers along the line.

   c. Write each number only once; don't leave out any numbers in the range.

4. a. Place an X for each member's height above the correct number on the line plot.

   b. Stack the X's if you need to write more than one X per height.

5. Use the line plot to find the mean, median, and mode.

6. Using the data you've collected, plan and draw a stem-and-leaf plot on a separate piece of paper.

7. Using the same data, plan and draw a box-and-whisker plot on the same paper with the stem-and-leaf plot.

8. Compare the three different kinds of plots. Which one shows the data "best"? Explain.

Hands-On Activities

Name _____ Class _____ Date _____

Activity 40: Graphing Negative Numbers

Materials needed: graph paper, ruler

Work with a partner.

North Shore Ski Resort   Daylight Temperatures for 1/29

8 A.M.	9 A.M.	10 A.M.	11 A.M.	12 noon	1 P.M.	2 P.M.	3 P.M.	4 P.M.
−18°	−6°	0°	4°	10°	15°	6°	−3°	−10°

1. The table gives daylight temperatures for a day at a ski resort. Use the information in the table to draw a line graph on axes like those below showing the range of temperatures.

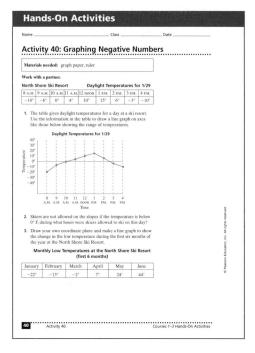

2. Skiers are not allowed on the slopes if the temperature is below 0° F. during what hours were skiers allowed to ski on this day?

3. Draw your own coordinate plane and make a line graph to show the change in the low temperature during the first six months of the year at the North Shore Ski Resort.

Monthly Low Temperatures at the North Shore Ski Resort (first 6 months)

January	February	March	April	May	June
−22°	−13°	−2°	7°	24°	44°

Sample pages; see p. G for complete list.

Technology Activities

Name _____ Class _____ Date _____

Circle Graphs   Activity 13

Use your graphing calculator to do this activity.

Example: In an experiment, some classmates watched a busy highway for an hour and counted the vehicles that they saw. Their results are shown in the table below. What percent of the total vehicles counted were cars, trucks, and busses? Display the data in a circle graph.

Vehicle Type	Number
Cars	238
Trucks	71
Busses	9

① Press **LIST** and clear any data already in the list.

② In the L1 column, enter the vehicle types. To enter text, press **2nd** [TEXT], use the arrow keys to select the symbol or letter, then press **ENTER**. Begin and end each vehicle type with quotation marks. For example, enter "CARS". When you finish entering each vehicle type, select **Done** and press **ENTER**. To put the word in the list, press **ENTER** again. In the L2 column, enter each number. For example, in L2(1) enter 238 for 238 cars.

③ Press **2nd** [PLOT] **4: Plots Off ENTER** to turn off all plots. Press **Y=** and clear any equations on that screen. Now you are ready to press **2nd** [PLOT] **1: Plot1** to set up your circle graph. On the Plot1 screen, highlight **On** and press **ENTER**. Highlight the circle graph and press **ENTER**. Make sure **CategList** says L1 and **Data List** says L2. On the bottom row of the screen, highlight **Percent** and press **ENTER**.

④ Press **GRAPH**. Your circle graph appears on the screen. The areas of the graph are labeled 1, 2, and 3. The key shows the percentages for each area.

⑤ Press **TRACE**. At the bottom of the screen you see **L1: CARS** and **L2: 238**. The highlighted number 1 in the graph tells you that the area labeled 1 goes with Cars and, as you can see, there are 238 cars. The key says that area 1 is 74.843% of the graph, so cars account for about 75% of the vehicles the classmates counted. Press the right or left arrow keys to see which vehicles correspond to the other areas of the graph.

Exercise

Use your calculator to draw a graph and fill in the table below. Round to the nearest whole percent.

Player	Points Scored	Percent of Total
Jen	12	
Lisa	8	
Maria	22	

Chapter Project

Name _____ Class _____ Date _____

Chapter 7 Project: On Your Own Time
Conduct a Survey

Beginning the Chapter Project

RING!!! The last bell of the day has rung. You and your classmates will soon head in different directions. Some of your classmates are on the same team or in the same club as you. Some of them are not. Do you know how much time your classmates spend on their favorite activities? You could guess the answers to the last question, but a more accurate method of finding the answers would be to collect real data.

For this chapter project, you will survey 25 of your friends and classmates. You can choose the survey subject, such as how much time your classmates spend on sports. You will organize and graph the data. Then you will present your findings to your class.

Activities

Activity 1: Collecting Check students' work.

Choose a survey topic. Identify seven or eight responses for students to choose. Decide how to organize the responses of your 25 friends or classmates. Collect and record the data in a table or chart.

Activity 2: Analyzing

Order the responses of your classmates by popularity. Find the mean, median, and mode of the data. Determine which measure is the more typical of the responses. Explain why.

Activity 3: Displaying

Display the data from your survey in three different ways.

• Consider different graphs as well as some type of table or chart.

• Which method do you think expresses the information the best? Why?

Chapter Project

Name _____ Class _____ Date _____

Chapter 7 Project: On Your Own Time (continued)

Finishing the Project

Make a presentation to the class that displays the information neatly and accurately. Explain which of the three methods of displaying the data you feel is best and why you feel that way. Make sure your display includes your chosen topic, the choices, and the data you collected, as well as the mean, median, and mode of your data.

Reflect and Revise

Review your project with a friend or someone at home. Are your graphs complete and accurate? Would a different type of graph be more appropriate? Are any of your graphs misleading? How might the information you collected and graphed be used? If necessary, make changes to improve your project.

Extending the Project

One common activity many students enjoy is listening to music. Conduct a survey to find what type of music is most popular. Display your findings in a graph. Then research the origin and elements of the most popular type of music found in your survey. Include the research with your display.

Take It to the NET Visit www.PHschool.com for information and links you might find helpful as you complete your project.

Chapter Project

Name _____ **Class** _____ **Date** _____

Chapter Project Manager

Chapter 7: On Your Own Time

Getting Started

Read about the project. As you work on it, you will need several sheets of paper. If available, a spreadsheet program also can be used. Keep all your work for the project in a folder, along with this Project Manager.

Checklist **Suggestions**

❑ Activity 1: collecting   ❑ Frequency tables are a good method for collecting data.

❑ Activity 2: analyzing   ❑ Use the frequency table to order the data and find the mean, median, and mode.

❑ Activity 3: displaying   ❑ Use a pie chart, bar graph, or table on a poster board to display the results.

Scoring Rubric

3 You correctly use three different display methods to show the data you collected. Your displays are attractive and self-explanatory. You identified both the best display method and the best averaging method. You gave reasons to support your choices.

2 You created three displays of your data and calculated the mean, median, and mode. Either your displays or your explanations are not as complete as they could be.

1 Your survey data is complete, but you only completed two displays of the data. Either your displays are not self-explanatory, or you neglected to compare display methods or averaging techniques.

0 Either your survey was not thorough or complete, or you left out important parts of your presentation.

Your Evaluation of the Project Evaluate your work based on the Scoring Rubric.

Teacher's Evaluation of the Project

Chapter Project

Name _____ **Class** _____ **Date** _____

Chapter Project Teacher Notes

Chapter 7: On Your Own Time

About the Project

The Chapter Project will give students an opportunity to gather and analyze data and display the information in a graph. The Project Link questions will help students understand and complete the process.

Introducing the Project

Encourage students to keep all project-related materials in a separate folder or notebook. Ask students:

- *Do you know what a market survey is?*
- *How can a market survey help a company make or improve their products?*

Activity 1: Collecting

Survey topics might include favorite sports, hobbies, musical groups, foods, or pets.

Activity 2: Analyzing

Have students rephrase the questions using the terms from this lesson.

Activity 3: Displaying

Help students recall the different reasons for using each type of graph.

Finishing the Project

You may wish to plan a project day in which students share their completed projects. Encourage students to explain their processes as well as their products.

Have students review their methods for gathering data, making graphs, and analyzing data for the projects.

Take It to the NET Visit **www.PHSchool.com** for information, student links, and teacher support for this project.

Transparencies

Problem of the Day

Problem of the Day	**Lesson 7-1**

Express each fraction as a decimal and then find their sum.

$$\frac{1}{2}, \frac{1}{4}, \frac{1}{8}, \frac{1}{8}$$

Answer

0.5 + 0.25 + 0.125 + 0.125 = 1

Problem of the Day	**Lesson 7-2**

Evaluate each of the following expressions for $n = 6$.

a. Multiply n by 4 and add 6.

b. Multiply n by 9 and add 12.

Answers

a. 30   b. 66

Problem of the Day	**Lesson 7-3**

Lucy and Shay are both batting under 3.00. Lucy's average is 0.298. Shay's is one one-thousandth of a point higher than Lucy's. What is Shay's batting average?

Answer

0.299

Problem of the Day

Problem of the Day	**Lesson 7-4**

Maria can package 14 seashells in a box. If she has 300 seashells, how many full boxes will she have? How many shells will be left over after all the boxes have been filled?

Answer

21; 6

Problem of the Day	**Lesson 7-5**

What fraction of 2 dollars is represented by the total of these coins: 3 quarters, 2 dimes, and 2 nickels?

Answer

$\frac{21}{40}$

Problem of the Day	**Lesson 7-6**

Coach Brown bought six T-shirts for her volleyball players for $47.88. What was the price per shirt?

Answer

$7.98

Problem of the Day

Problem of the Day	**Lesson 7-7**

What combination of two bills and three coins can be used to make $15.45?

Answer

one $10 bill, one $5 bill, one quarter, and two dimes

Problem of the Day	**Lesson 7-8**

Find three numbers between 400 and 410 that are divisible by 3.

Answer

402, 405, 408

Check Skills You'll Need

Check Skills You'll Need	**Lesson 7-1**

Find each quotient. Round to the nearest hundredth if necessary.

1. 330 ÷ 12   2. 255.5 ÷ 6   3. 237.4 ÷ 4

4. $\frac{29.5}{5}$ 5. $\frac{68.4}{8}$ 6. $\frac{9.261}{3}$

Solutions

```
        27.5              42.583            59.35
1. 12)330.0       2. 6)255.500      3. 4)237.40
      -24                 -24               -20
       90                  15                37
      -84                 -12               -36
       60                  35                14
      -60                 -30               -12
        0                  50                20
                          -48               -20
                           20                 0
```

330 ÷ 12 = 27.5   255.5 ÷ 6 ≈ 42.58   237.4 ÷ 4 = 59.35

4. $\frac{29.5}{5}$ = 5.9   5. $\frac{68.4}{8}$ = 8.55   6. $\frac{9.261}{3}$ = 3.087 ≈ 3.09

Lesson Quiz	**Lesson 7-1**

Find the mean, median, and mode of each data set.

1. 65, 47, 93, 100, 65   2. 115, 200, 95, 200, 45

3. 90, 48, 120, 48, 72, 90   4. 126, 210, 54, 108, 126, 162

Answers

1. mean: 74; median: 65; mode: 65   2. mean: 131; median: 115; mode: 200
3. mean: 78; median: 81; mode: 48 and 90
4. mean: 131; median: 126; mode: 126

Sample page; see p. H for complete list.

318L

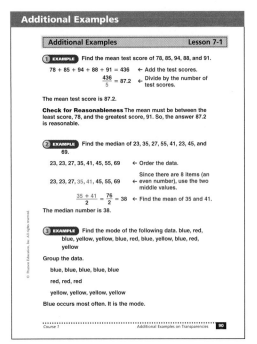

Sample page; see p. H for complete list.

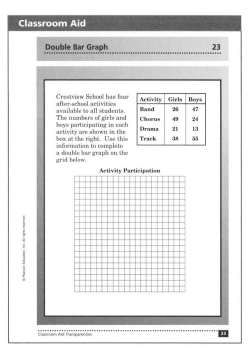

Sample page.

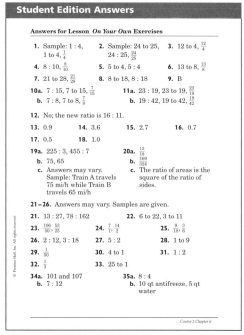

Sample page; see p. H for complete list.

Assessment

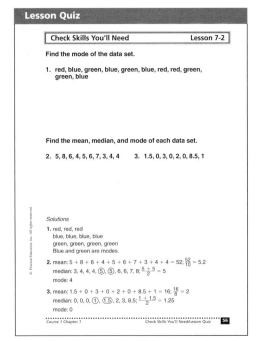

Sample page; see p. H for complete list.

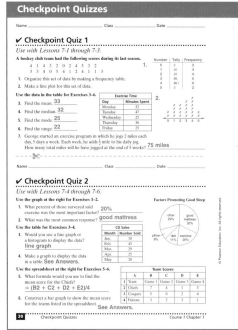

Available in Spanish

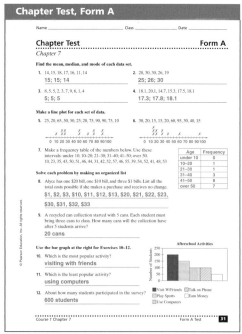

Available in Spanish

Chapter Test (continued) — Form A
Chapter 7

Name _____ Class _____ Date _____

Use the circle graph at the right for Exercises 13–15.

13. Where does the government collect the most amount of money from? **individual income tax**

14. About what percent of the income is generated from individual income tax? **about 45%**

15. Why do you think there is a portion labeled "Other"? **Sample answer: To group other sources of tax income that are too small to show by themselves.**

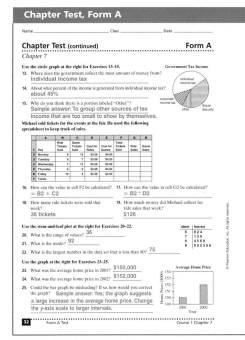

Government Tax Income

Michael sold tickets for the events at the fair. He used the following spreadsheet to keep track of sales.

	A	B	C	D	E	F	G	H
1	Day	Ride Tickets Sold	Game Tickets Sold	Cost for Rides	Cost for Games	Total Tickets Sold	Ride Sales	Game Sales
2	Monday	8	15	$3.50	$4.50			
3	Tuesday	5	7	$3.50	$4.50			
4	Wednesday	7	12	$3.50	$4.50			
5	Thursday	6	9	$3.50	$4.50			
6	Friday	10	5	$3.50	$4.50			
7	Totals							

16. How can the value in cell F2 be calculated? **= B2 + C2**

17. How can the value in cell G2 be calculated? **= B2 * D2**

18. How many ride tickets were sold that week? **36 tickets**

19. How much money did Michael collect for rides that week? **$126**

Use the stem-and-leaf plot at the right for Exercises 20–22.

20. What is the range of values? **36**

21. What is the mode? **92**

22. What is the largest number in the data set that is less than 80? **75**

stem	leaves
6	0 2 4
7	1 3 5
8	4 5 6 9
9	0 2 2 3 5 6

Use the graph at the right for Exercises 23–25.

23. What was the average home price in 2001? **$150,000**

24. What was the average home price in 2002? **$152,000**

25. Could the bar graph be misleading? If so, how would you correct the graph? **Sample answer: Yes; the graph suggests a large increase in the average home price. Change the y-axis scale to larger intervals.**

Average Home Price

Available in Spanish

Chapter Test — Form B
Chapter 7

Name _____ Class _____ Date _____

Find the mean, median, and mode of each data set.

1. 19, 20, 23, 22, 21, 16, 19
   20; 20; 19

2. 25, 35, 35, 31, 24
   30; 31; 35

3. 7, 4, 4, 3, 2, 6, 8, 5, 0, 1
   4; 4; 4

4. 18.6, 20.6, 15.2, 15.8, 18.0, 18.6
   17.8; 18.3; 18.6

Make a line plot for each set of data.

5. 40, 35, 60, 60, 40, 35, 10, 85, 20, 20, 85

6. 10, 40, 25, 25, 50, 70, 85, 40, 50, 25

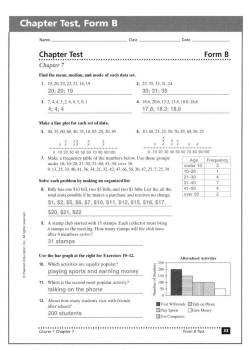

7. Make a frequency table of the numbers below. Use these groups: under 10; 10–20; 21–30; 31–40; 41–50; over 50.
   9, 13, 25, 33, 40, 41, 36, 34, 21, 32, 42, 47, 66, 56, 36, 47, 25, 7, 25, 39

Age	Frequency
under 10	2
10–20	1
21–30	4
31–40	7
41–50	4
over 50	2

Solve each problem by making an organized list.

8. Billy has one $10 bill, two $5 bills, and two $1 bills. List all the total costs possible if he makes a purchase and receives no change.
   $1, $2, $5, $6, $7, $10, $11, $12, $15, $16, $17, $20, $21, $22

9. A stamp club started with 15 stamps. Each collector must bring 4 stamps to the meeting. How many stamps will the club have after 4 members arrive? **31 stamps**

Use the bar graph at the right for Exercises 10–12.

10. Which activities are equally popular? **playing sports and earning money**

11. Which is the second most popular activity? **talking on the phone**

12. About how many students visit with friends after school? **200 students**

Afterschool Activities

■ Visit W/Friends ▨ Talk on Phone
▨ Play Sports ▢ Earn Money
▨ Use Computers

Available in Spanish

Chapter Test (continued) — Form B
Chapter 7

Name _____ Class _____ Date _____

Use the circle graph at the right for Exercises 13–15.

13. Where does the government collect the least amount of money from? **other tax**

14. About what percent of the income is generated from Social Security? **about 35%**

15. What would be an appropriate title for this graph? **Sample answer: Government Tax Income Sources**

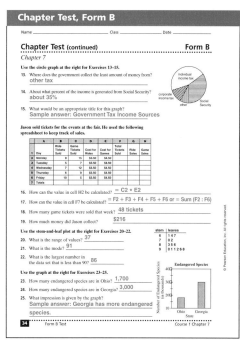

Jason sold tickets for the events at the fair. He used the following spreadsheet to keep track of sales.

	A	B	C	D	E	F	G	H
1	Day	Ride Tickets Sold	Game Tickets Sold	Cost for Rides	Cost for Games	Total Tickets Sold	Ride Sales	Game Sales
2	Monday	8	15	$3.50	$4.50			
3	Tuesday	5	7	$3.50	$4.50			
4	Wednesday	7	12	$3.50	$4.50			
5	Thursday	6	9	$3.50	$4.50			
6	Friday	10	5	$3.50	$4.50			
7	Totals							

16. How can the value in cell H2 be calculated? **= C2 * E2**

17. How can the value in cell F7 be calculated? **= F2 + F3 + F4 + F5 + F6 or = Sum (F2 : F6)**

18. How many game tickets were sold that week? **48 tickets**

19. How much money did Jason collect? **$216**

Use the stem-and-leaf plot at the right for Exercises 20–22.

20. What is the range of values? **37**

21. What is the mode? **91**

22. What is the largest number in the data set that is less than 90? **86**

stem	leaves
6	1 4 7
7	0 2
8	3 5 6
9	0 1 1 2 6 8

Use the graph at the right for Exercises 23–25.

23. How many endangered species are in Ohio? **1,700**

24. How many endangered species are in Georgia? **3,000**

25. What impression is given by the graph? **Sample answer: Georgia has more endangered species.**

Endangered Species

Available in Spanish

Alternative Assessment — Form C
Chapter 7

Name _____ Class _____ Date _____

FUND-RAISING

Each year in December, the sixth grade at Wayside Middle School raises money. The money goes to a Toys-for-Children program that buys holiday toys for needy children. Most of the money that the sixth graders raise is change that they collect at lunchtime every day for a week.

Each year's sixth graders try to raise more money than the previous year's sixth graders. Last year the class raised $111.28. This year's group hopes to do better.

Emilio and Tamlyn are in charge of making a graph that shows how much money has been raised this year. First they thought of making a circle graph like the one below, but they decided against it.

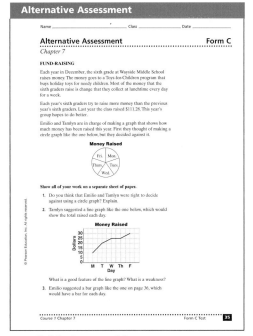

Money Raised

Show all of your work on a separate sheet of paper.

1. Do you think that Emilio and Tamlyn were right to decide against using a circle graph? Explain.

2. Tamlyn suggested a line graph like the one below, which would show the total raised each day.

Money Raised

What is a good feature of the line graph? What is a weakness?

3. Emilio suggested a bar graph like the one on page 36, which would have a bar for each day.

Available in Spanish

Alternative Assessment (continued) — Form C
Chapter 7

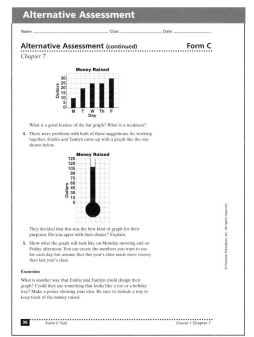

Money Raised

What is a good feature of the bar graph? What is a weakness?

4. There were problems with both of these suggestions. So, working together, Emilio and Tamlyn came up with a graph like the one shown below.

Money Raised

They decided that this was the best kind of graph for their purposes. Do you agree with their choice? Explain.

5. Show what the graph will look like on Monday morning and on Friday afternoon. You can create the numbers you want to use for each day, but assume that this year's class made more money than last year's class.

Excursion

What is another way that Emilio and Tamlyn could design their graph? Could they use something that looks like a toy or a holiday tree? Make a poster showing your idea. Be sure to include a way to keep track of the money raised.

Available in Spanish

Alternative Assessment (continued) — Form C
Chapter 7

Name _____ Class _____ Date _____

Scoring Rubric

Exercise	Points	Explanation
1.	1	Good explanation of why circle graph is inappropriate
	0	No response OR other response
2.	2	Strength: shows daily amounts; weakness: no total
	1	Strength OR weakness correctly given
	0	No response OR other response
3.	2	Strength: shows daily amounts; weakness: no total
	1	Strength OR weakness correctly given
	0	No response OR other response
4.	1	Either a yes or no answer; justification given
	0	No response OR a yes or no answer without justification
5.	4	Correct graph for both Monday and Friday; clear labels
	3	Correct graph for either Monday or Friday with clear labels but incomplete or incorrect graph for the other day OR correct graphs for both days but labels missing
	2	Graphs for both days incomplete but some correct elements
	1	Graphs for both days are so incomplete that they lack correct elements
	0	No response OR response does not contain graphs
Excursion	5	Creative and interesting way to track money raised
	4	Correct way to track money but lacking creativity OR creative method that does not show money being tracked
	3	Incomplete presentation of an adequate design
	2	Method is incorrect
	1	Response does not contain a visual element but is somewhat related to task OR response contains a visual element but is not related to task
	0	No response OR other response

Available in Spanish

Cumulative Review

Name _____ Class _____ Date _____

Cumulative Review
Chapters 1–7

Multiple Choice. Choose the letter of the best answer.

Use the circle graph for Questions 1–2.

Preferred Preparation of Eggs

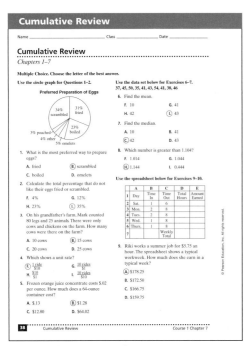

- 31% scrambled
- 34% fried
- 23% boiled
- 5% omelets
- 4% other
- 3% poached

1. What is the most preferred way to prepare eggs?
- A. fried
- B. scrambled
- C. boiled
- D. omelets

2. Calculate the total percentage that do not like their eggs fried or scrambled.
- F. 4%
- G. 12%
- H. 23%
- L. 35%

3. On his grandfather's farm, Mark counted 80 legs and 25 animals. There were only cows and chickens on the farm. How many cows were there on the farm?
- A. 10 cows
- B. 15 cows
- C. 20 cows
- D. 25 cows

4. Which shows a unit rate?
- F. $\frac{1 \text{ ride}}{\$10}$
- G. $\frac{10 \text{ rides}}{\$1}$
- H. $\frac{\$10}{\$1}$
- I. $\frac{10 \text{ rides}}{\$10}$

5. Frozen orange juice concentrate costs $0.02 per ounce. How much does a 64-ounce container cost?
- A. $.13
- B. $1.28
- C. $12.80
- D. $64.02

Use the data set below for Exercises 6–7.
37, 45, 50, 35, 41, 43, 54, 41, 38, 46

6. Find the mean.
- F. 10
- G. 41
- H. 42
- I. 43

7. Find the median.
- A. 10
- B. 41
- C. 42
- D. 43

8. Which number is greater than 1.104?
- F. 1.014
- G. 1.044
- H. 1.144
- I. 0.444

Use the spreadsheet below for Exercises 9–10.

	A	B	C	D	E
1	Day	Time In	Time Out	Total Hours	Amount Earned
2	Sat.	1	6		
3	Mon.	2	8		
4	Tues.	2	8		
5	Wed.	1	8		
6	Thurs.	1	8		
7				Weekly Total	

9. Riki works a summer job for $5.75 an hour. The spreadsheet shows a typical workweek. How much does she earn in a typical week?
- A. $178.25
- B. $172.50
- C. $166.75
- D. $159.75

Available in Spanish

Cumulative Review

Name _____ Class _____ Date _____

Cumulative Review (continued)
Chapters 1–7

10. What formula should *not* be used to calculate the value of cell E7?
- F. =E2+E3+E4+E5+E6
- G. =5.75*D7
- H. =(D2+D3+D4+D5+D6)*5.75
- I. =(E2+E3+E4+E5+E6)*5.75

11. Which comparison is correct?
- A. $\frac{3}{4} > \frac{4}{5}$
- B. $\frac{6}{7} < \frac{5}{6}$
- C. $\frac{6}{9} < \frac{2}{3}$
- D. $\frac{3}{7} > \frac{2}{9}$

12. An office supply store sells packages of 6 folders each and 9 labels each. Which is the least number of packages of folders you should buy if you want to buy the same number of folders and labels?
- F. 2
- G. 3
- H. 18
- I. 36

13. Which expression can be used to find the product 6×498?
- A. $(6 \times 500) + (6 \times 2)$
- B. $(6 \times 500) - 2$
- C. $(6 \times 500) - (6 \times 2)$
- D. $500 - 2 \times 6$

14. Bryce has $\frac{2}{3}$ yard of ribbon. He uses $\frac{1}{2}$ yard to wrap a gift. How much ribbon does he have left?
- F. $\frac{1}{6}$ yd
- G. $\frac{2}{5}$ yd
- H. $\frac{4}{3}$ yd
- I. $1\frac{1}{6}$ yd

15. Which of the following is the best estimate of $5\frac{3}{8} - 2\frac{7}{9}$?
- A. 2
- B. 3
- C. 4
- D. 7

16. Which question could NOT be answered by using the line plot below?

Ages of Students Who Volunteer at the Library

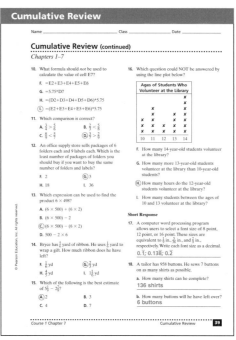

				x
	x		x	x
	x		x	x
x	x	x	x	x
x	x	x	x	x
10	11	12	13	14

- F. How many 14-year-old students volunteer at the library?
- G. How many more 13-year-old students volunteer at the library than 10-year-old students?
- H. How many hours do the 12-year-old students volunteer at the library?
- I. How many students between the ages of 10 and 13 volunteer at the library?

Short Response

17. A computer word processing program allows users to select a font size of 8 point, 12 point, or 16 point. These sizes are equivalent to $\frac{1}{9}$ in., $\frac{2}{12}$ in., and $\frac{2}{9}$ in., respectively. Write each font size as a decimal.

$0.\overline{1}$; $0.13\overline{8}$; $0.\overline{2}$

18. A tailor has 958 buttons. He sews 7 buttons on as many shirts as possible.
- a. How many shirts can he complete?

136 shirts

- b. How many buttons will he have left over?

6 buttons

Available in Spanish

Benchmark Test

Name _____ Class _____ Date _____

Benchmark Test 1

1. What is the value of the digit 2 in the number 4.0725?
- A. 2 tenths
- B. 2 hundredths
- C. 2 thousandths
- D. 2 ten-thousandths

2. How is the decimal 2.016 expressed in words?
- A. two and sixteen thousandths
- B. two and sixteen hundredths
- C. two and sixteen tenths
- D. two and sixteenths

3. Quincy ran a lap in seventy-five and thirteen hundredths seconds. How is this time-written in standard form?
- A. 75.013 seconds
- B. 75.03 seconds
- C. 75.103 seconds
- D. 75.13 seconds

4. Which set of decimals is ordered from least to greatest?
- A. 2.67, 2.71, 2.99, 2.02
- B. 2.99, 2.67, 2.71, 2.02
- C. 2.02, 2.67, 2.71, 2.99
- D. 2.71, 2.02, 2.99, 2.67

5. Which of the following statements is true?
- A. 1.971 > 1.97
- B. 2.53 < 2.3
- C. 4.825 > 4.85
- D. 6.74 < 6.740

6. The table below shows the surface ocean temperature for five days. On which day was the daily ocean temperature coolest?

Daily Ocean Temperature

Day	Temperature (°F)
Monday	80.07
Tuesday	81.03
Wednesday	80.90
Thursday	81.50
Friday	81.20

- A. Monday
- B. Tuesday
- C. Wednesday
- D. Friday

7. Which addition problem is modeled below?

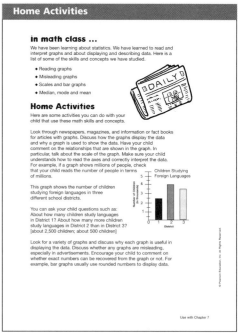

- A. $8 + 3 = 11$
- B. $0.8 + 3 = 3.8$
- C. $0.8 + 0.3 = 1.1$
- D. $0.08 + 0.3 = 0.38$

On PH Website

Test-Taking Strategies transparency

Test-Taking Strategies: Answering the Question Asked

Incorrect choices may answer related questions.

> **Example** Midori owes $20 on a restaurant bill, and wants to tip the server 15%. How much should Midori pay altogether?
>
> A. $3   B. $15   C. $20   D. $23
>
> Calculate the tip: $0.15 \times 20 = \$3$
>
> Choice A is $3, but this is how much Midori should leave for a tip, not how much to pay altogether.
>
> Calculate the total bill: $20 + 3 = 23$
>
> The answer is $23, or choice D.

Answer the question asked. Explain your reasoning.

1. Clarisse earns $10 per hour and works about 25 hours per week. How much could she earn in a year?
- A. $250
- B. $1,000
- C. $3,000
- D. $13,000

2. Find the area of the triangle.

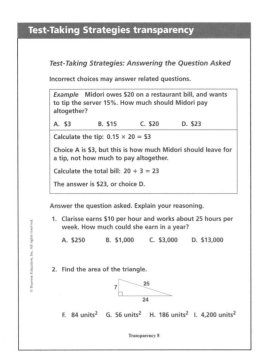

7, 25, 24

- F. 84 units²
- G. 56 units²
- H. 186 units²
- I. 4,200 units²

Transparency 8

Test-Taking Strategies worksheet

Name _____ Class _____ Date _____

Chapter 7: Answering the Question Asked
Exercises

Solve by answering the question asked.

1. A family's monthly expenses are summarized in the circle graph at the right.

Monthly Expenses
- Food 16%
- Housing 32%
- Other 14%
- Entertainment 10%
- Transportation 9%
- Clothing 8%
- Utilities 6%
- Savings 5%

- a. What percent of their income does the family spend on food *and* housing? Explain.
  - A. 16%
  - B. 32%
  - C. 48%
  - D. 50%

The question asks for the percent spent on food *and* housing. Add the two percents for these categories. The total is 16% + 32% = 48%, so the answer is C.

- b. What percent of their income does the family save?
  - F. 5%
  - G. 6%
  - H. 8%
  - I. 9%

- c. What percent of their income does the family *not* spend on food, clothing or housing?
  - A. 16%
  - B. 48%
  - C. 54%
  - D. 46%

2. The table at the right shows the number of boys participating in various sports at a high school.

Sport	Boys Participating
Baseball	21
Basketball	34
Football	62
Track	16
Wrestling	14

- a. How many boys participated in a sport other than football? Explain.
  - F. 62
  - G. 21
  - H. 34
  - I. 85

The question asks for the number of boys who participated in a sport other than football. Add the number of boys who participated in all the other sports. The total is 21 + 34 + 16 + 14 = 85 boys, so the answer is I.

- b. How many boys participated in basketball or football?
  - A. 34
  - B. 96
  - C. 62
  - D. 86

Home Activities

in math class …

We have been learning about statistics. We have learned to read and interpret graphs and about displaying and describing data. Here is a list of some of the skills and concepts we have studied.

- ◆ Reading graphs
- ◆ Misleading graphs
- ◆ Scales and bar graphs
- ◆ Median, mode and mean

Home Activities

Here are some activities you can do with your child that use these math skills and concepts.

Look through newspapers, magazines, and information or fact books for articles with graphs. Discuss how the graphs display the data and why a graph is used to show the data. Have your child comment on the relationships that are shown in the graph. In particular, talk about the scale of the graph. Make sure your child understands how to read the axes and correctly interpret the data. For example, if a graph shows millions of people, check that your child reads the number of people in terms of millions.

This graph shows the number of children studying foreign languages in three different school districts.

Children Studying Foreign Languages

You can ask your child questions such as: About how many children study languages in District 1? About how many more children study languages in District 2 than in District 3? [about 2,500 children; about 500 children]

Look for a variety of graphs and discuss why each graph is useful in displaying the data. Discuss whether any graphs are misleading, especially in advertisements. Encourage your child to comment on whether exact numbers can be recovered from the graph or not. For example, bar graphs usually use rounded numbers to display data.

Use with Chapter 7

*Available in Spanish;
Web Code: aak-5500*

Name _____   *Math and Science/Technology*

Marine Monsters

Read and interpret graphs.

Imagine that you are deep-sea fishing for bluefish. You and your friends are happily hauling in one bluefish after another. Each fish is about 3 feet long and weighs about 10 pounds. Then, suddenly, someone in your group shouts, "Look! Over there! I think it's a whale shark!" Everyone turns their attention in the direction of a huge fish that has just broken the water's surface. It is enormous! You estimate its length at around 40 feet, about the size of a school bus. In seconds the shark is gone. You go back to fishing with a new appreciation for the size of animals that live in the sea.

Often, the largest and most frightening ocean animals are the ones that humans rarely, if ever, see. Here are a few of the most impressive ones:

Whale shark: This animal got its name from the fact that it is as big as some whales. It is so big that it has earned the title of the largest fish in the sea. The whale shark weighs around 40,000 pounds. In spite of its size, it is not a threat to people because it has very tiny teeth. It feeds on small fish and even smaller living things that float in the sea.

Giant squid: Weighing more than 4000 pounds, the giant squid is the biggest of the squids and lives in the depths of all the oceans.

Arctic lion's mane jellyfish: This creature, which lives in northern ocean waters, is the largest jellyfish in the world. About 1200 tentacles, 120 feet in length, hang from its bell-shaped body, which can be more than 7 feet in diameter. Each tentacle has poisonous stinging cells.

Giant spider crab: Found in the waters around Japan, the giant spider crab's legs are about 5 feet long. Each leg is tipped with five-inch pincers that are used for catching prey, fighting, and digging.

Blue whale: Found in all the oceans, this mammal is the heaviest known animal ever to have lived on Earth. Weighing more than 6000 pounds at birth, the blue whale can weigh an amazing 500,000 pounds as an adult.

It is often not the weight of the animal that amazes us. It is the creature's incredible length. Study the following graph. It allows you to compare the lengths of the animals mentioned above.

Called a whale shark, this animal is not a mammal like the whale, but a fish.

Use with Chapter 7

Web Code: aak-5500

Name _____   *Math and Science/Technology*

1. When the Arctic lion's mane jellyfish spreads out its long tentacles, it covers an area of more than 45,000 square feet. How does this ability help the jellyfish satisfy its need for large amounts of food?

_____

_____

_____

_____

_____

2. Rank the giant sea creatures from the shortest to longest.

_____

_____

_____

3. About how many times as long is the blue whale than the giant squid?

_____

_____

4. A bluefish is about 3 feet long. How many times longer are the other animals in the graph than the bluefish?

_____

_____

_____

_____

_____

5. It's sometimes hard to appreciate the size of objects from numbers alone. You can get a more realistic idea of the sizes of the sea creatures described on page one by drawing pictures of them to actual size. Do research to find pictures of the animals and use chalk to draw them in a large open area on your school grounds. As an alternative, you could use string to outline them on an athletic field. How many times longer is each animal than you?

_____

_____

_____

_____

_____

6. As big as it is, the blue whale feeds on very tiny creatures. These tiny creatures feed on even tinier green living things. As these green things live, they give off oxygen into the air, which all animals including humans breathe. Identify the living things in the blue whale's food chain and tell what you think might happen if the world's blue whales became extinct.

_____

_____

_____

_____

_____

Use with Chapter 7

Web Code: aak-5500

Name _____ Class _____ Date _____

Missing Values   Puzzle 7

Data and Graphs

Solve the following problems. Use the numbers in the solutions to fill in the puzzle blocks at the bottom of the page. Each solution is used only once.

1. The average of Brandon's chapter test scores is 86%. Listed below are his grades.

Chapter	1	2	3	4
Grade	90%	75%	?%	88%

What was his Chapter 3 test grade?

2. Allison had the following test scores: 78%, 80%, 93%, 94%, 94%. What is her median test score?

_____

3. Christy's average dropped three points after the last test. Use the chart to determine Christy's average test score *before* and *after* the last test, her last test score, and the range of her test scores.

Chapter	1	2	3	4	5
Grade	81%	89%	94%	88%	?%

Christy's test average
before the last test: _____%

Christy's Chapter 5 test score: _____%

Christy's test average
after the last test: _____%

Range of scores: _____

4. To achieve the final grade, Mrs. Peters drops the lowest score, finds the average, and rounds the grade to the nearest whole number. What is the sum of Christy, Brandon, and Allison's final grades?

Algebra Readiness Puzzles   7

Web Code: aak-5500

Data and Graphs

Chapter 7 Overview

In this chapter students work with statistics and graphs as they organize, interpret, analyze, display, and evaluate data. They interpret and make bar graphs, line graphs, circle graphs, and stem-and-leaf plots. They conclude the chapter by examining misleading graphs and statistics.

 Reading Math
- Reading Graphs, p. 331
- **Vocabulary:** A complete list, plus exercises, in the Chapter Review, p. 364
- **Illustrated Glossary:** Examples for each vocabulary term, plus definitions in English and Spanish, on p. 669

Writing in Math
Writing to Persuade, p. 346

Test-Taking Strategies
Answering the Question Asked, p. 363

Real-World Problem Solving
- **Strategies:** Make an Organized List, pp. 332–334
- **Real-World Snapshots:** A Peak Experience, pp. 368–369
- **Chapter Project:** On Your Own Time, p. 639

 www.PHSchool.com
Internet support includes:
- Self-grading Vocabulary and Chapter 7 Tests
- Activity Masters
- Chapter Project support
- Chapter Planner
- Ch. 7 Resources

Plus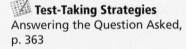

Data and Graphs

Lessons

Key Vocabulary

- bar graph (p. 335)
- cell (p. 347)
- circle graph (p. 342)
- frequency table (p. 326)
- histogram (p. 336)
- line graph (p. 336)
- line plot (p. 327)
- mean (p. 322)
- median (p. 323)
- mode (p. 323)
- outlier (p. 322)
- range (p. 327)
- spreadsheet (p. 347)
- stem-and-leaf plot (p. 352)

Data and Graphs

Teaching Notes

Activating Prior Knowledge

In this chapter students build on and extend their knowledge of statistics and graphing. They also draw upon their understanding of decimal computations as they find and interpret measures of central tendency. Ask questions such as:

• *What is the sum of 0.4, 12.5, and 0.08?* 12.98

• *What is (5 + 24 + 12 + 7) ÷ 4?* 12

• *What is the order of the following decimals from least to greatest? 3.25, 3.2, 4.5, 5.4, 3.15, 3, 2.75* 2.75, 3, 3.15, 3.2, 3.25, 4.5, 5.4

 Real-World Snapshots

The data here will be used throughout the chapter. Have a volunteer read the opening sentences and the title of the chart, which contains information about the heights of the highest peaks on each of the continents. Focus students on the data in the chart and ask:

• *Which peaks round to 6,000 m when rounded to the nearest 1,000 meters?* Kilimanjaro, Elbrus, McKinley

• *What fraction shows how many of the peaks are between 16,000 and 20,000 feet high?* $\frac{3}{7}$

Real-World Snapshots

What is it like to climb Mount Everest, the highest mountain on Earth, $5\frac{1}{2}$ miles above sea level? At the top, there is not enough oxygen to fill your lungs and the air is dangerously cold. Sunlight reflected off the snow is so bright, it can be blinding.

Data File Highest Peak on Each Continent

Land Mass	Highest Peak	Height (feet)	Height (meters)
Africa	Kilimanjaro	19,340	5,895
Asia	Everest	29,035	8,850
Australia	Kosciusko	7,310	2,228
Antarctica	Vinson Massif	16,066	4,897
Europe	Elbrus	18,510	5,642
North America	McKinley	20,320	6,194
South America	Aconcagua	22,834	6,960

SOURCE: *Time Almanac 2003*

You will use the data above in this chapter:

• p. 324   Lesson 7-1
• p. 329   Lesson 7-2

Real-World Snapshots On pages 368 and 369, you will solve problems involving mountain peaks.

Reading and Math Literacy

7A: Graphic Organizer   For use before Lesson 7-1

Study Skill: Take notes when your teacher presents new material in class. Organize these notes as a way to study, reviewing them as you go.

Write your answers.

1. What is the chapter title?
   Data and Graphs

2. How many lessons are there in this chapter?
   8

3. What is the topic of the Reading Math page?
   Reading Graphs

4. What is the topic of the Test-Taking Strategy page?
   Answering the Question Asked

5. Look through the chapter and list four real-world connections that are discussed.
   Answers will vary.

6. Complete the graphic organizer below as you work through the chapter.
   • In the center, write the title of the chapter.
   • When you begin a lesson, write the lesson name in a rectangle.
   • When you complete a lesson, write a skill or key concept in a circle linked to that lesson block.
   • When you complete the chapter, use this graphic organizer to help you review.

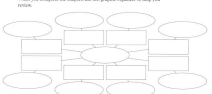

Available in Spanish

Chapter 7: Data and Graphs

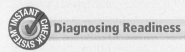

Diagnosing Readiness

Students will find answers to these exercises in the back of their textbooks.

Prescribing Intervention
For intervention, direct students to:

Ordering Decimals
Lesson 1-3: Example 4. Extra Practice, p. 642.

Adding Decimals
Lesson 1-5: Example 1. Extra Practice, p. 642.

Subtracting Decimals
Lesson 1-5: Examples 3–4. Extra Practice, p. 642.

Dividing Decimals
Lesson 1-8: Example 4. Extra Practice, p. 642.

Where You've Been

- In Chapter 1, you learned to order decimals. You also learned to add, subtract, multiply, and divide decimals.

- In Chapter 6, you learned to use ratios, proportions, and percents.

Where You're Going

- In Chapter 7, you will find the mean, median, mode, and range of a set of data. You will also organize, display, and graph data.

- Applying what you learn, you will use a graph to keep track of the number of DVDs rented at a movie rental store.

Businesses use graphs to organize and display product sale figures.

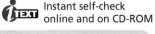
Instant self-check online and on CD-ROM

Diagnosing Readiness

? **For help, go to the lesson in green.**

Ordering Decimals (Lesson 1-3)

Order from least to greatest.

1. 0.12, 0.13, 0.45, 0.35, 0.21 See above right.

1. 0.12, 0.13, 0.21, 0.35, 0.45

2. 45.1, 44, 46.01, 45.01
44, 45.01, 45.1, 46.01

3. 102, 133, 124.32, 99.9, 100.80
99.9, 100.80, 102, 124.32, 133

4. 0.99, 2.5, 7.04, 4.9, 0.22
0.22, 0.99, 2.5, 4.9, 7.04

Adding Decimals (Lesson 1-5)

Find each sum.

5. 13.2 + 23.6 + 26.3 **63.1**

6. 152.3 + 143.6 + 128 **423.9**

7. 49.0 + 22.2 + 11.22 + 23.4 **105.82**

8. 6.09 + 1.5 + 4.68 + 13.6 **25.87**

Subtracting Decimals (Lesson 1-5)

Find each difference.

9. 109.55 − 89.34 **20.21**

10. 10.42 − 9.36 **1.06**

11. 75 − 73.2 **1.8**

Dividing Decimals (Lesson 1-9)

Find each quotient.

12. 142.03 ÷ 10 **14.203**

13. 361.6 ÷ 16 **22.6**

14. 100.75 ÷ 25 **4.03**

Exploring the Mean

Work Together Activity   1–6. Check students' work.

1. Write the full first name of each student in your class on strips of grid paper. Use one box for each letter.

2. Arrange the strips in order, based on the lengths of the names. Then use the data to make a lineplot.

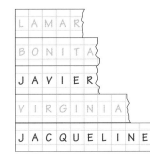

Length of First Names

```
              X
   X    X         X         X
   5    6    7    8    9   10
         Number of Letters
```

3. **a.** What is the number of letters in the shortest name?
   b. How many letters are in the longest name?

4. **Writing in Math** What is a typical length of a name of a classmate? Explain how you determined your choice(s).

5. Suppose you were to make a new name for each classmate. You must use as many letters from the strips as possible. Each name must be the same length. Here is a way to find out how many letters will be in each name:
   a. Find the total number of letters in the names of your classmates.
   b. Divide this sum by the number of names. If necessary, round to the nearest whole number.

6. The number you found in Question 5 is the average, or *mean*, length of a name of a classmate.
   a. How does the mean compare to the lengths of the shortest and longest names?
   b. How does the mean compare to the typical length you found in Question 4?

Exploring the Mean

In Lesson 7-1 that follows, students will learn about three measures of central tendency: mean, median, and mode. This feature introduces them to the mean, the measure they are most likely to think of as the "average" of a set of numbers.

Optional Materials

- paper strips of grid paper
- snap cubes or centimeter cubes
- Classroom Aid 2

Teaching Notes

Tell students that in this investigation they will learn about ways to show averages of sets of numbers. Draw upon their prior knowledge of this subject; many students will have an informed or intuitive understanding of the concept of *mean.* Have students suggest reasons for why the mean is a useful measure. Ask them to cite instances of its use in the real-world.

Work Together
Work through the steps of the activity with the whole class. For the line plot shown in Step 2, ask: *Why are there no X's above the 7 and 9?* Sample: No names had 7 or 9 letters.

Tactile Learners
For a hands-on approach to investigating mean, distribute snap cubes or colored centimeter cubes to groups of students. Have them make rows (trains) of these, corresponding to the length of each name. They compute the mean by adding or removing cubes to form rows that are of the same length.

Teaching Tip
Guide students to summarize what they have learned about *mean* from this activity.

321

Lesson Preview

 Check Skills You'll Need PowerPoint

Dividing by a Whole Number
Lesson 1-9: Example 1. Extra
Practice, p. 642.

Lesson Resources

 Teaching Resources
Practice, Reteaching, Enrichment

 Reaching All Students
Practice Workbook 7-1
Spanish Practice Workbook 7-1
Guided Problem Solving 7-1

 Presentation Assistant Plus!
Transparencies
• Check Skills You'll Need 7-1
• Problem of the Day 7-1
• Additional Examples 7-1
• Student Edition Answers 7-1
• Lesson Quiz 7-1
PH Presentation Pro CD-ROM 7-1

PRENTICE HALL
ASSESSMENT SYSTEM

Computer Test Generator CD

 Technology
Resource Pro® CD-ROM
Computer Test Generator CD
PH Presentation Pro CD-ROM

 www.PHSchool.com
Student Site
• Teacher Web Code: aak-5500
• Algebra Readiness Puzzles 7
• Self-grading Lesson Quiz

PH SuccessNet Teacher Center
• Lesson Planner
• Resources

Plus **i TEXT**

What You'll Learn

OBJECTIVE 1 To find the mean

OBJECTIVE 2 To find the median and the mode

. . . And Why

To find a mean test score, as in Example 1

 Check Skills You'll Need   For help, go to Lesson 1-9.

Find each quotient. Round to the nearest hundredth if necessary.

1. $330 \div 12$ **27.5**
2. $255.5 \div 6$ **42.58**
3. $237.4 \div 4$ **59.35**
4. $\frac{29.5}{5}$ **5.9**
5. $\frac{68.4}{8}$ **8.55**
6. $\frac{9.261}{3}$ **3.09**

New Vocabulary   • mean   • outlier   • median   • mode

 i TEXT Interactive lesson includes instant self-check, tutorials, and activities.

 **Finding the Mean**

One way to describe a set of numbers is to find the mean. The **mean** of a set of data is the sum of the data divided by the number of data items.

1 EXAMPLE   **Finding the Mean**   🌎 Real World

Reading Math
Another word for mean is *average*.

Grades Alena took four science tests. She scored 81, 77, 92, and 89. Find her mean test score.

$$81 + 77 + 92 + 89 = 339 \quad \leftarrow \text{Add the test scores.}$$

$$\frac{339}{4} = 84.75 \quad \leftarrow \text{Divide by the number of test scores.}$$

Alena's mean test score is 84.75.

Check for Reasonableness The mean must be between the least score, 77, and the greatest score, 92. So, the answer 84.75 is reasonable.

✓ **Check Understanding** ① Find the mean of each data set.

a. 3, 2, 8, 4, 2, 3, 1, 5   **3.5**
b. 12, 23, 19, 32, 26   **22.4**
c. 4, 16, 20, 40   **20**
d. 5, 15, 75, 105, 85   **57**
e. **Reasoning** Using the data set from part (d), find the mean of the numbers without the value 105. What do you notice?
45; the new mean is much less.

An **outlier** is a data item that is much greater or less than the rest of the data items. If a data set has an outlier, then the mean may not describe the data very well. For example, the mean of 1, 2, 6, and 47 is 14. This is much greater than the mean of 1, 2, and 6, which is 3.

 Ongoing Assessment and Intervention

Before the Lesson	During the Lesson	After the Lesson
Diagnose prerequisite skills using:	Monitor progress using:	Assess knowledge using:
• Check Skills You'll Need	• Check Understanding	• Lesson Quiz
	• Additional Examples	• Computer Test Generator CD
	• Test Prep	

The **median** is the middle number in a set of ordered data.

$$4 \quad 7 \quad \underset{\underset{\text{median}}{\uparrow}}{9} \quad 13 \quad 25$$

When there is an even number of data items, you can find the median by adding the two middle numbers and dividing by 2.

2 **EXAMPLE** Real-World  Problem Solving

Biology A biologist studying the ecology of a river makes a weekly fish count. The results are 19, 18, 22, 23, 20, 24, 23, 20, 34, and 19. Find the median number of fish.

18, 19, 19, 20, 20, 22, 23, 23, 24, 34   ← Order the data.

18, 19, 19, 20, 20, 22, 23, 23, 24, 34   ← Since there are 10 items (an even number), use the two middle values.

$\dfrac{20 + 22}{2} = \dfrac{42}{2} = 21$ ← Find the mean of 20 and 22.

○ The median number of fish is 21.

Real-World  Connection

Careers A biologist studies the origins, structures, and activities of living organisms.

✔ **Check Understanding** **2** Find the median of each data set.
a. 86, 90, 88, 84, 102, 95, 7 **88**   **b.** 8, 42, 13, 7, 50, 91 **27.5**

You can also describe data by the mode. The **mode** is the data item(s) that appears most often. *If all data items occur the same number of times, there is no mode.* The mode is especially useful when the data are not numerical.

3 **EXAMPLE** **Finding the Mode**

The list shows the favorite lunches of 15 students. What is the mode?

Group the data.

pizza, pizza, pizza, pizza, pizza

hamburger, hamburger, hamburger

taco, taco, taco, taco

spaghetti, spaghetti, spaghetti

○ Pizza occurs most often. It is the mode.

> **Favorite Lunch**
>
> hamburger, pizza, taco, pizza, spaghetti, taco, spaghetti, hamburger, hamburger, pizza, taco, pizza, pizza, spaghetti, taco

✔ **Check Understanding** **3** Find the mode of the following data. **apple**
orange, banana, apple, orange, apple, apple, orange, apple

2. Teach

Professional Development

Math Background

The mean, median, and mode are each single statistics that describe the central tendency of a set of data. The *mean* of a set of data is the sum of the data values divided by the number of data items. The *median* is especially useful when the data set includes very high or low values that distort the mean. The *mode*, or most often occurring data value, is especially useful when the data are not numerical.

Teaching Notes

1 EXAMPLE Inclusion

After reviewing the Example, ask:
• *What would happen to the mean if the lowest score is dropped?* The mean score would increase.
• *If there was one more test, what score would raise the mean?* any score greater than 84.75

Technology Tip
For students who use calculators to find the mean, have them first find the sum before dividing. Otherwise, students should use parentheses to group the sum of the data items.

3 EXAMPLE Visual Learners

Ask: *Which measure: mean, median, or mode, is always an actual data value?* the mode

PowerPoint
Additional Examples

1 Find the mean test score of 78, 85, 94, 88, and 91. **87.2**

2 Find the median of 23, 35, 27, 55, 41, 23, 45, and 69. **38**

3 Find the mode of the following data. blue, red, blue, yellow, yellow, blue, red, blue, yellow, blue, red, yellow **blue**

Closure

How do you find the median of a set of data? Write the data values in order and find the middle item in the set of data, or find the mean of the two middle items.

323

👥 Reaching All Students

| **Below Level** Students use graph paper to write an evenly-spaced ordered list of the data values in Example 2. They then fold the paper in half to find the middle quartile, and in half again to find the other four quartiles. | **Advanced Learners** Ask: *Can a mode be both greater than and less than the median? Explain.* Yes, a bimodal data set contains two modes; one can be greater than the median and one can be less. | **Inclusion** See note on page 323. **Visual Learners** See note on page 323. |

3. Practice

Assignment Guide

1 Objective 1
A B Core 1–5, 15, 19
C Extension 22

2 Objective 2
A B Core 6–14, 16–18, 20–21
C Extension 23

Test Prep 24–26
Mixed Review 27–34

Error Prevention!

Exercises 6–9 Students must rewrite the data in numerical order.

For more practice, see *Extra Practice*.

EXERCISES

A Practice by Example

Example 1 (page 322)

Find the mean of each data set. Exercise 1 has been started for you.

1. $12, 9, 11, 8, 9, 12, 9$; $\dfrac{12 + 9 + 11 + 8 + 9 + 12 + 9}{7} = \blacksquare$ **10**

2. $14, 16, 28, 17, 20$ **19**

3. $3, 2, 0, 2, 2, 3, 3, 1$ **2**

4. $121, 95, 115, 92, 113, 108, 99, 97$ **105**

5. $2.4, 1.8, 3.5, 2.3, 6.5$ **3.3**

Example 2 (page 323)

Find the median of each data set.

6. $500, 450, 475, 450, 500$ **475**

7. $0, 1, 1, 1, 0, 1, 1, 0, 0, 0$ **0.5**

8. $\dfrac{3}{4}, \dfrac{1}{2}, \dfrac{5}{8}, \dfrac{3}{8}, \dfrac{1}{16}$ **$\dfrac{1}{2}$**

9. $14.1, 20.7, 24.3, 16.0, 20.8$ **20.7**

 10. Temperatures The daily high temperatures (°F) for one week are $86, 78, 92, 79, 87, 77$, and 91. Find the median high temperature. **86**

Example 3 (page 323)

Find the mode of each data set.

11. $8, 7, 8, 9, 8, 7$ **8**

12. $15, 12, 17, 13, 20, 19$ **none**

13. $95, 80, 91, 92, 94, 94, 98$ **94**

14. $23, 24, 27, 25, 26, 23, 21$ **23**

B Apply Your Skills

 15. Milk Prices The prices for a gallon of milk at four locations are $\$1.99, \$2.29, \$2.19$, and $\$1.88$. What is the mean price for a gallon of milk? Round your answer to the nearest cent. **$2.09**

16a. mean ≈ 19,059 ft, median = 19,340 ft.

b. Everest, Aconcagua, Kilimanjaro, McKinley

c. Everest, McKinley, Aconcagua

16. Data File, p. 319 Use the data for the highest peaks on each continent.
   a. Find the mean and median heights in feet of the highest peaks.
   b. Which peaks are taller than the mean?
   c. Which peaks are taller than the median? 16a–c. See left.

19. Increase; decrease; stay the same. Explanations may vary. Sample: If a new value is added to a data set, and if the value is greater than/less than/equal to the mean of the original data set, the new mean will increase/decrease/ stay the same.

Find the mean, median, and mode of each data set.

17. $12\dfrac{1}{2}, 15, 13\dfrac{1}{2}, 11, 13$

18. $8, 7\dfrac{8}{10}, 7\dfrac{1}{10}, 9, 8\dfrac{3}{10}, 7\dfrac{8}{10}$

13; 13; no mode

8; $7\dfrac{9}{10}$; $7\dfrac{8}{10}$

19. **Writing in Math** The mean gas mileage (miles per gallon) for the family car is 23.5. How will the mean change if the next gas mileage reading is 27.3? 18.9? 23.5? Explain. See left.

20. **Number Sense** The median of four numbers is 48. If three of the GPS numbers are 42, 51, and 52, what is the other number? **45**

21. **Books** The page lengths of five books are 198, 240, 153, 410, and 374. What is the median? **240**

GPS Use the Guided Problem Solving worksheet with Exercise 20.

Practice 7-1   Mean, Median, and Mode

Find the mean, median, and mode of each data set.

1. 85, 91, 76, 85, 93   86, 85, 85

2. 72, 76, 73, 74, 75   74, 74, no mode

3. $\frac{1}{2}, \frac{5}{8}, \frac{1}{16}, \frac{5}{8}, \frac{3}{8}, \frac{3}{8}$ $\frac{7}{16}, \frac{7}{16}, \frac{3}{8}$

4. $\frac{2}{3}, \frac{8}{9}, \frac{1}{3}, \frac{5}{18}, \frac{2}{9}, \frac{7}{9}, \frac{1}{3}, \frac{1}{6}$ $\frac{25}{54}, \frac{1}{3}$, and $\frac{2}{3}$

5. 86.4, 87.2, 95.7, 96.4, 88.1, 94.9, 98.5, 94.8   92.75, 94.85, no mode

Use the tables for Exercises 6–11.

Active Volcanoes	
Name	Height Above Sea Level (ft)
Camaroon Mt.	13,354
Mount Erebus	12,450
Asama	8,300
Gerde	9,705
Sarychev	5,115
Ometepe	5,106
Fogo	9,300
Mt. Hood	11,245
Lascar	19,652

6. What is the mean height of the active volcanoes listed to the nearest foot?
10,470 ft

7. What is the median height of the active volcanoes listed?
9,705 ft

8. What is the mode of the heights of the active volcanoes listed?
no mode

Hourly Wages of Production Workers 1991 (includes benefits)	
Country	Wage
Austria	$17.47
Brazil	$2.55
Finland	$20.57
France	$15.26
Hong Kong	$3.58
Japan	$14.41
Mexico	$2.17
Spain	$12.65
United States	$15.45

9. What is the mean of the wages listed?
$11.57

10. What is the median of the wages listed?
$14.41

11. What is the mode of the wages listed?
no mode

Each student in a class has taken five tests. The teacher allows the students to pick the mean, median, or mode of each set of scores to be their average. Which average should each student pick in order to have the highest average?

12. 100, 87, 81, 23, 19   median
13. 90, 80, 74, 74, 72   mean
14. 80, 80, 70, 67, 68   mode
15. 75, 78, 77, 70, 70   median
16. 100, 47, 45, 32, 31   mean
17. 86, 86, 77, 14, 12   mode
18. 79, 78, 77, 76, 85   mean
19. 86, 80, 79, 70, 70   median

Reteaching 7-1   Mean, Median, and Mode

• The *mean* of a set of data is the sum of the values divided by the number of data items.
74 + 77 + 80 + 81 + 85 + 87 + 94 + 94 = 672
672 ÷ 8 = 84
The mean math test grade is 84.

Math Test Grades	
Sharon	81
Rashid	94
Durrin	77
Nicole	80
Terry	74
Mei-lin	94
Kevin	87
Carlos	85

• The *median* of a data set is the middle value when the data are arranged in numerical order. When the grades are arranged in order from least to greatest, there are two middle numbers.
74, 77, 80, 81, 85, 87, 94, 94
To find the median, add the two middle numbers and divide the total by 2.
81 + 85 = 166
166 ÷ 2 = 83
The median grade is 83.

• The *mode* of a data set is the item in the data set that appears most often. For this data, 94 is the mode.

Find the mean of each data set.

1. 8, 6, 5, 9, 7, 13   8
2. 12, 10, 16, 14, 8, 24   14
3. 9, 12, 14, 6, 8, 5   9
4. 104, 126, 128, 100, 97   111
5. 86, 68, 70, 48, 66, 76   69
6. 65, 50, 95, 35, 75, 100   70

Find the median of each data set.

7. 5, 4, 7, 9, 8   7
8. 12, 16, 19, 14, 14, 18   15
9. 9, 19, 21, 13   16
10. 46, 38, 22, 48, 61   46
11. 60, 57, 53, 78, 44, 51   55
12. 8, 6, 6, 5, 8, 9   7

Find the mode of each data set.

13. 3, 4, 5, 5, 3, 5, 4, 2   5
14. 1, 2, 1, 1, 2, 2, 3, 1   1
15. 6, 8, 3, 8, 3, 9, 3   3
16. 33, 35, 34, 33, 35, 33   33
17. 98, 97, 98, 98, 97   98
18. 110, 121, 121, 110, 115, 117, 119   110, 121

324

C Challenge

22. **Algebra** The mean of 22, 19, 25, and *x* is 23. Find *x*. 26

23. **Stretch Your Thinking** Three purple and three white beads are arranged on a circle of string. How many different patterns are possible?
   3 patterns

Test Prep

Reading Comprehension   Read the passage below and answer the questions that follow.

The Hawaiian Rain Forest

Tropical wet climates are found near the equator. With year-round heat and heavy rainfall, vegetation grows lush and green. Dense rain forests grow in these rainy climates.

   In the United States, only Hawaii has a tropical wet climate. In some parts of Hawaii, rainfall is very heavy—over 400 inches per year on the windward side of the Hawaiian island of Kauai.

   The table shows the monthly rainfall for one year at a reporting station in Hawaii.

Rainfall in Hilo, Hawaii

Month	Rainfall (in.)
January	5
February	1
March	15
April	43
May	9
June	9
July	11
August	11
September	14
October	12
November	36
December	6

SOURCE: *The Weather Almanac*

25. Answers may vary. Sample: There are two modes, 9 and 11; 11 describes the data better because it's also the median.

24. Find the mean and the median of the rainfall data in the table.
   $14\frac{1}{3}$, 11

25. Find the mode. Does it represent the data well? Explain. **See above.**

Take It to the NET
Online lesson quiz at
www.PHSchool.com
Web Code: aaa-0701

26. One year earlier, the total rainfall for April was 11 inches. Find the mean and the median using 11 inches, instead of 43 inches, for April.
   $11.\overline{6}$, 11

Mixed Review

Lesson 6-6   **Write each fraction as a decimal and as a percent.**

27. $\frac{11}{20}$ 0.55; 55%   28. $\frac{13}{25}$ 0.52; 52%   29. $\frac{1}{50}$ 0.02; 2%   30. $\frac{1}{80}$
   0.0125; 1.25%

Lesson 5-5   **Algebra** **Solve each equation. Check the solution.**

31. $\frac{a}{8} = 20$ 160   32. $\frac{3}{4}b = 1$ $\frac{4}{3}$ 33. $\frac{c}{10} = 3$ 30   34. $\frac{6}{7}d = 6$ 7

---

4. Assess

PowerPoint Lesson Quiz 7-1

Find the mean, median, and mode of each data set.

1. 65, 47, 93, 100, 65 mean: 74; median: 65; mode: 65

2. 115, 200, 95, 200, 45 mean: 131; median: 115; mode: 200

3. 90, 48, 120, 48, 72, 90 mean: 78; median: 81; mode: 48 and 90

4. 126, 210, 54, 108, 126, 162 mean: 131; median: 126; mode: 126

Alternative Assessment

Each student in a pair writes five different data sets, each with 4 to 8 numbers. Partners exchange papers and find the mean, median, and mode for each data set. If necessary, students should round the mean and the median to the nearest tenth.

Test Prep

Resources
For additional practice with a variety of test item formats:
• Test Prep, p. 367
• Test-Taking Strategies, p. 363
• Test-Taking Strategies With Transparencies

Enrichment 7-1   Mean, Median, and Mode
Critical Thinking

The box below shows some prices students paid for mountain and ten-speed bikes. Organize this information and use it to answer the questions below.

Bicycle Prices
$180, $275, $675, $420, $385,
$450, $610, $295, $450, $145,
$395, $265, $515, $495, $235

1. What is the *mean* price for a bicycle? How do you know?
   $386, because the sum of the data, $5,790, divided by the number of items, 15, is $386.

2. What is the *median* price for a bicycle? How do you know?
   $395, because it is the middle number.

3. What is the *mode* price for a bicycle? How do you know?
   $450, because it occurs most often.

4. Would you use the mean, median, or mode price as your savings goal if you wanted to buy a bicycle? Explain.
   Sample answer: Use the median because half of the bicycles are priced above it and half are priced below it.

5. Suppose you add bicycles that cost $435 and $565 to the data set. Will the mean, median, and mode change? If so, what are the new values?
   New median: $420; new mean: $399.41; same mode: $450

6. Would the addition of the new data affect your decision in Exercise 4? Why or why not?
   Sample answer: Yes; the median increases from $395 to $420, so I need to save $25 more.

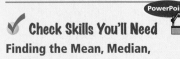

1. Plan

Lesson Preview

✓ **Check Skills You'll Need**

Finding the Mean, Median, and Mode
Lesson 7-1: Examples 1–3. Extra Practice, p. 648.

Lesson Resources

📁 **Teaching Resources**
Practice, Reteaching, Enrichment

👥 **Reaching All Students**
Practice Workbook 7-2
Spanish Practice Workbook 7-2
Guided Problem Solving 7-2
Hands-On Activities 25, 40

🕐 **Presentation Assistant Plus!**
Transparencies
• Check Skills You'll Need 7-2
• Problem of the Day 7-2
• Additional Examples 7-2
• Student Edition Answers 7-2
• Lesson Quiz 7-2
• Classroom Aid 2, 7
PH Presentation Pro CD-ROM 7-2

PRENTICE HALL ASSESSMENT SYSTEM

Computer Test Generator CD

💻 **Technology**
Resource Pro® CD-ROM
Computer Test Generator CD
PH Presentation Pro CD-ROM

💻 **www.PHSchool.com**
Student Site
• Teacher Web Code: aak-5500
• Self-grading Lesson Quiz

PH SuccessNet Teacher Center
• Lesson Planner
• Resources

Plus 🄸TEXT

7-2 Organizing and Displaying Data

What You'll Learn

OBJECTIVE 1 To organize data by making a frequency table

OBJECTIVE 2 To make a line plot and find the range

. . . And Why

To organize data about DVDs, as in Example 2

✓ **Check Skills You'll Need** ❓ For help, go to Lesson 7-1.

Find the mode of the data set.

1. red, blue, green, blue, green, blue, red, red, green, green, blue blue and green

Find the mean, median, and mode of each data set.

2. 5, 8, 6, 4, 5, 6, 7, 3, 4, 4 **5.2; 5; 4**

3. 1.5, 0, 3, 0, 2, 0, 8.5, 1 **2; 1.25; 0**

New Vocabulary • frequency table • line plot • range

OBJECTIVE 1 **Making a Frequency Table**

🄸TEXT Interactive lesson includes instant self-check, tutorials, and activities.

A **frequency table** is a table that lists each item in a data set with the number of times the item occurs.

1 EXAMPLE **Making a Frequency Table**

A student made the list at the left to show her classmates' favorite colors. Organize the data by making a frequency table. What is the mode?

Favorite Colors

Blue	Blue
Purple	Red
Red	Orange
Blue	Yellow
Blue	Green
Yellow	Blue
Green	Yellow
Purple	Blue

Favorite Color

Color	Tally	Frequency
Blue	卌 I	6
Green	II	2
Orange	I	1
Purple	II	2
Red	II	2
Yellow	III	3

Make a tally mark for each color chosen.

The number of tally marks in each row is the frequency.

Since most students selected blue as their favorite color, the mode is blue.

✓ **Check Understanding** ① The first initial of the names of 15 students are listed below.

1a. See back of book.

A J B K L C K D L S T D V P L

a. Organize the data by making a frequency table. What is the mode?

b. **Reasoning** Explain why you cannot find the mean of the data in part (a). The data items are letters, not numbers.

326 Chapter 7 Data and Graphs

 Ongoing Assessment and Intervention

Before the Lesson	During the Lesson	After the Lesson
Diagnose prerequisite skills using:	Monitor progress using:	Assess knowledge using:
• Check Skills You'll Need	• Check Understanding	• Lesson Quiz
	• Additional Examples	• Computer Test Generator CD
	• Test Prep	

A **line plot** is a graph that shows the shape of a data set by stacking *X*'s above each data value on a number line.

 EXAMPLE **Making a Line Plot**  Real World

Business Suppose your cousin works at Uptown Movie Rental. His manager asks him to keep track of the number of DVDs rented by each customer. Make a line plot to display the data shown below.

3 5 1 2 2 1 4 1 4 2 3
3 4 1 5 2 6 2 2 4 3 1 4

DVDs Rented by Each Customer

```
                    X
X   X           X              ← Each X represents
X   X   X   X                     one customer.
X   X   X   X
X   X   X   X   X
X   X   X   X   X   X
1   2   3   4   5   6          ← The data range
    Number of DVDs                from 1 to 6.
```

✔ **Check Understanding** ② Make a line plot of the number of phone calls made by employees in one day: 2, 3, 0, 7, 1, 1, 9, 8, 2, 8, 1, 2, 8, 7, 1, 8, 6, 1. **See left.**

2. **Number of Phone Calls**

```
X
X                   X
X   X               X
X   X           X   X
X X X X     X X X X
0 1 2 3 4 5 6 7 8 9
    Phone Calls
```

The **range** of a data set is the difference between the least and greatest values.

③ **EXAMPLE** **Finding the Range** Real World

Geography In 1849 and 1850, six different surveyors made the following measurements of the height of Mount Everest.

28,990 ft; 28,992 ft; 28,999 ft; 29,002 ft; 29,005 ft; 29,026 ft

What is the range of the measurements?

$29{,}026 - 28{,}990 = 36$ ← **Subtract the least from the greatest value.**

The range of measurements is 36 feet.

Real-World 🌐 **Connection**

Mount Everest is nearly 5.5 miles above sea level.

✔ **Check Understanding** ③ Find the range for each data set.
a. 36, 21, 9, 34, 36, 10, 4, 35, 5, 30, 28, 27, 5, 10 **32**
b. 0.12, 0.11, 0.16, 0.15, 0.20, 0.18, 0.24, 0.7 **0.59**
c. Reasoning If two sets of data have the same range do they also have the same median? Explain your reasoning.
No. Explanations may vary. Sample: Add 10 to all data in the first set. The range stays the same, but the median increases by 10.

7-2 Organizing and Displaying Data **327**

👥 **Reaching All Students**

Below Level Explain that each tally mark indicates one time that the data value appears. The fifth tally mark is made diagonally through the other 4 marks. This makes it easy to see groups of 5 tally marks.	**Advanced Learners** Compare frequency tables and line plots. Sample: Both show how often each data value occurs. A frequency table is easier to write but does not give as clear a shape of the data.	**Inclusion** See note on page 327. **Diversity** See note on page 329.

---

2. Teach

Professional Development

Math Background

A *frequency table* lists each item in a data set with the number of times it occurs. A *line plot* shows the frequency distribution of a data set by stacking Xs on a number line to represent each data item. The *range* of a data set is the difference between the least and greatest values.

Teaching Notes

③ **EXAMPLE** Inclusion

Help students recognize that range only makes sense for numerical data. Ask: *Can you find the range of favorite colors in Example 1?* **no**

PowerPoint

Additional Examples

① The favorite lunch for ten students is: pizza, pizza, chicken, hamburger, chicken, pizza, chicken, pizza, pizza, pizza. Organize the data by making a frequency table. What is the mode? **pizza**

Lunch	Tally	Freq
hamburger	I	1
pizza	ЖⅢ I	6
chicken	III	3

② Make a line plot to display the dinner hour for 7 families.
5 7 6 6 8 7 6

Dinner Hours
```
        X
    X   X
X   X   X   X
5   6   7   8
```

③ Find the range for the dinner hour of 7 families. **3 hours**
5 7 6 6 8 7 6

Closure

• *What is a frequency table?* a table that lists each item in a data set with the number of times the data item occurs

• *What is a line plot?* a graph that shows the shape of the data set by stacking Xs above each data value on a number line

327

Assignment Guide

 Objective 1
- Ⓐ Ⓑ Core 1–2, 9, 18
- Ⓒ Extension 21–22

 Objective 2
- Ⓐ Ⓑ Core 3–8, 10–17, 19–20
- Ⓒ Extension 23

Test Prep 24–26
Mixed Review 27–34

Error Prevention!

Exercises 3–4 Help students make reasonable scales for each plot.

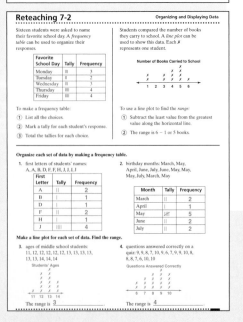

Ⓐ **Practice by Example**

Organize each set of data by making a frequency table. See below left.

Example 1
(page 326)

1. days in each month:

31 28 31 30 31 30 31 31 30 31 30 31

2. vehicles in a parking lot: See margin.

pick-up	compact	compact	mid-size
compact	SUV	mid-size	SUV
mid-size	compact	station wagon	pick-up
compact	compact	mid-size	pick-up
compact	mid-size	SUV	compact
compact	compact	mid-size	station wagon

1.

Number of Days	Tally	Frequency
28	|	1
30	||||	4
31	卌 ||	7

Example 2
(page 327)

Make a line plot for each set of data.

3. lengths of baseball bats (inches): See margin.

30 29 31 28 29 29 30 32 30 29 28 30 30

4. Word Lengths in a Sentence

```
X X          X X
X X X        X X X X X
1 2 3 4 5 6 7 8 9 10
```
Word Lengths (letters)

4. lengths of words in a sentence (letters): See left.

7 2 6 1 7 6 9 1 8 4 2 3 10

Example 3
(page 327)

Find the range for each data set.

5. land areas of the seven midwestern states: shown in the table at the right
43,612 square miles

6. ages of the first ten U.S. Presidents when they took office: 57, 61, 57, 57, 58, 57, 61, 54, 68, 51 **17 years**

7. heights of trees (meters): 2.3, 1.8, 3.4, 2.5, 2.9, 3.1, 3.2, 3.5, 2.8, 2.7, 2.6, 2.7, 2.2 **1.7 m**

8. prices of new CD players: $145, $219, $359, $270, $162, $349 **$214**

Land Areas of Midwestern States (square miles)	
Illinois	55,646
Indiana	35,936
Iowa	55,965
Michigan	56,959
Minnesota	79,548
Ohio	41,004
Wisconsin	54,424

Ⓑ **Apply Your Skills**

9. Social Studies A town in Wales, Great Britain, is named **9a.** See margin.
Llanfairpwllgwyngyllgogerychwyrndrobwllllantysiliogogogoch.

9b. Use the mode, L; the data are not numbers, therefore the mode is the best way to represent the data.

a. Make a frequency table for the letters that make up the name of the Welsh town.

b. **Writing in Math** Use the mean, median, or mode to describe the data recorded in your frequency table. Explain your choice.

10. Concert Tickets The prices of tickets for a concert are $45, $36, $30, $41, $25, $20, $44, $38, and $34. Find the range. **$25**

GPS Use the Guided Problem Solving worksheet with Exercise 14.

2.

Type of Car	Tally	Frequency
compact	卌 卌	10
mid-size	卌 |	6
SUV	|||	3
wagon	||	2
pick-up	|||	3

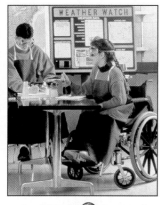

Real-World Connection
Science grades often include students' lab work.

Use the line plot at the right for Exercises 11–13.

Semester Science Grades

		X	
		X	
X	X	X	
X	X	X	X
X	X	X	X
A	B	C	D

Letter Grades

11. What information is displayed?
frequency of letter grades in Science

12. How many grades are recorded?
13 grades

13. How many students received a grade of C or better? **11 students**

14. Speed Limits On a highway, the minimum speed allowed is 40 miles per hour and the maximum speed is 65 miles per hour. What is the range of speeds allowed on the highway? **25 mi/h**

Draw a line plot for each frequency table. 15–16. See left.

15.

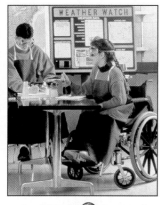
(line plot 15)
X
X X X
X X X
X X X X X X   X
1 2 3 4 5 6 7 8 9 10

15.

Number	Tally	Frequency
1	IIII	4
2	I	1
3	III	3
4	IIII	3
5	I	1
6	I	1
7	I	1
10	I	1

16.

Number	Tally	Frequency
15	I	1
17	I	1
18	I	1
19	II	2
20	IIII	4
21	II	2
22	II	2
24	I	1

16.
(line plot 16)
X
X
X X X X
X X X X X X   X
15 16 17 18 19 20 21 22 23 24

17. Siblings The line plot at the right shows the number of siblings (brothers and sisters) that each student has.

X
X
X X
X X X
X X X
X X X X
X X X X X
0 1 2 3 4

   a. Find the median and mode. **1, 1**

   b. Reasoning Would it make sense to use the mean to describe these data? Why or why not? **See left.**

   c. How many siblings do the 19 students have? **27 siblings**

17b. Answers may vary. Sample: No; the mean is not a whole number.

Correct Answers on Quiz

Number Correct	Tally	Frequency
20	II	2
19	II	2
18	HTT	5
17	HTT I	6
16	II	2
15	II	2
14	III	3

18. The frequency table at the left shows the number of correct answers for each student on a 20-question quiz.
   a. What is the mean number of correct answers? **17**
   b. What score is the median? **17**
   c. What score is the mode? **17**
   d. What is the range of the number of correct answers? **6**

19. Data File, p. 319 What is the range in meters of the highest peaks on each continent? **6,622 meters**

20. Open-Ended Make two sets of data with the same range but different means.
Answers may vary. Sample: 98, 99, 100; range 2, mean 99. 97, 98, 99; range 2, mean 98.

9a.

Letter	Tally	Frequency
a	III	3
b	I	1
c	II	2
d	I	1
e	I	1
f	I	1
g	HTT II	7
h	II	2
i	III	3
l	HTT HTT I	11
n	IIII	4
o	HTT	6
p	I	1
r	IIII	4
s	I	1
t	I	1
w	IIII	4
y	HTT	5

3. Baseball Bat Lengths (in.)

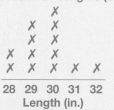
X
X X
X X
X X X
X X X X X
28 29 30 31 32
Length (in.)

Exercises 5–8 Remind students that their answers must include units. The range is a statistic that retains the units of the data values.

Visual Learners
Exercises 11–13 Make sure students understand that each data value is indicated by an X and that all data values are shown in the line plot.

Diversity
Exercise 14 Some students may be unfamiliar with the abbreviation of mph as "miles per hour." For students familiar with metric measurements, explain that 40 mph is about 65 km/h and that 65 mph is about 105 km/h.

4. Assess

Lesson Quiz 7-2

The heights of several middle school students are: 61, 63, 65, 60, 61, 61, and 62 in.

1. Organize the data by making a frequency table.

Height	60	61	62	63	64	65
Tally	I	III	I	I		I
Freq.	1	3	1	1	0	1

2. Make a line plot for the data.

Heights of Students

```
        X
        X
 X   X  X   X       X
 60  61 62  63  64  65
```
Height in Inches

3. Find the range of the data.
5 in.

Test Prep

Resources

For additional practice with a variety of test item formats:
- Test Prep, p. 367
- Test-Taking Strategies, p. 363
- Test-Taking Strategies With Transparencies

330

C **Challenge**   Use the frequency table for Exercises 21 and 22.

Pets Owned

Pet	Tally	Frequency
Bird	卌 II	7
Cat	卌 卌 卌	15
Dog	卌 卌 卌 III	18
Fish	卌 IIII	9
Hamster	III	3
Other	卌	5

21. What percent of the pets are dogs? Round to the nearest percent
about 32%

22. Half of the pet owners surveyed had one pet and the other half had two pets. How many pet owners are represented in this survey?
38 pet owners

23. **Stretch Your Thinking** Henry, Curtis, and Leon were trying to guess the number of buttons in a jar. Henry guessed 113, Curtis guessed 119, and Leon guessed 120. One of the guesses was correct, one missed by 6, and one missed by 1. Who guessed the correct number of buttons? **Curtis**

Test Prep

Use the quiz results at the right.

Quiz Scores		
8	5	9
7	8	6
10	10	8
8	7	10

Multiple Choice

24. What is the range of the quiz scores? **C**
A. 10   **B.** 9   **C.** 5   **D.** 4

Take It to the NET
Online lesson quiz at
www.PHSchool.com
Web Code: aaa-0702

25. What is the mean? Median? Mode? **H**
F. 7; 8; 10   **G.** 5; 6; 9
H. 8; 8; 8   **I.** 8; 8; 10

Short Response

26. a. Make a line plot of the quiz scores.   **See margin.**
b. How many grades are greater than 7?

Mixed Review

Lesson 6-5   Use a map scale of 1 cm : 100 km to find the actual distance for each map distance given below.

27. 5 cm   **500 km**   **28.** 1.8 cm   **180 km** **29.** 8.3 cm   **830 km** **30.** 0.9 cm   **90 km**

Lesson 5-1   Find each product.

31. $\frac{3}{5} \times \frac{1}{2}$ $\frac{3}{10}$ **32.** $\frac{5}{8} \times \frac{3}{10}$ $\frac{3}{16}$ **33.** $\frac{1}{4} \times \frac{8}{9}$ $\frac{2}{9}$ **34.** $\frac{3}{16} \times \frac{32}{33}$ $\frac{2}{11}$

330   Chapter 7   Data and Graphs

Alternative Assessment

Each student in a pair writes a numerical data set. Partners exchange data sets and make a frequency table and a line plot of the data. Partners also report the range of the data.

26.[2] a.   **Quiz Scores**
```
          X
       X  X
    X  X  X
 X  X  X  X  X  X
 5  6  7  8  9 10
       Score
```
b. **8 grades**

[1] line plot is incomplete or missing OR line plot is complete but part (b) is incorrect

7-3

Make an Organized List

7-3

1. Plan

Lesson Preview

✓ **Check Skills You'll Need** PowerPoint

Finding Number Patterns
Lesson 2-1: Example 1. Extra
Practice, p. 643.

Lesson Resources

Teaching Support includes:
Practice, Reteaching, Enrichment
Assessment, Reading & Literacy,
Activities, Transparencies,
Technology, CD-ROMs, Spanish,
and More

*See pp 318G–318H for a complete
list of resources for this lesson.*

💻 **www.PHSchool.com**
• Teacher Web Code: aak-5500

Plus

2. Teach

Math Background

Professional Development

Make an organized list helps you
organize the given information,
and often makes it easier to
identify patterns in the data.

PowerPoint
Additional Examples

① How many ways can you make
18¢. Solve by making an
organized list. **6 ways**

Dimes	1	1	0	0	0	0
Nickels	0	1	3	2	1	0
Pennies	8	3	3	8	13	18

What You'll Learn

 OBJECTIVE 1 To solve a problem
by making an
organized list

... And Why

To keep track of exercise
data, as in Example 1

✓ **Check Skills You'll Need** ❓ For help, go to Lesson 2-1.

Write the next three terms in each number pattern.

1. $7, 14, 21, 28, \ldots$ **35, 42, 49**

2. $1, 4, 7, 10, \ldots$ **13, 16, 19**

3. $88, 79, 70, 61, \ldots$ **52, 43, 34**

4. $4, 12, 36, 108, \ldots$ **324, 972, 2,916**

OBJECTIVE 1

 Solving Problems By Making an Organized List

 iTEXT Interactive lesson includes instant self-check, tutorials, and activities.

When to Use This Strategy An organized list can help you analyze data.

① **EXAMPLE** Using an Organized List   Real World

Running Tara wants to walk in a charity event. In her first week of training,
she walks three miles each day. Each week after that she adds $\frac{3}{4}$ mile to her
daily distance. In which week of training does Tara walk six miles per day?

Read and Understand During the first week of training, Tara walks three
miles each day. Each week, she walks an additional $\frac{3}{4}$ mile every day. You
need to find the week when her daily walk will be six miles.

Plan and Solve Make an organized list that
shows week and distance. Stop when the distance
reaches six miles.

Tara walks six miles per day during her fifth
week of training.

Look Back and Check You can check by
working backward. In five weeks there were
4 increases of $\frac{3}{4}$ mile. $4 \times \frac{3}{4} = 3$. So, the total
increase was 3 miles. The 3-mile increase plus the
original 3 miles per day = 6 miles.

Week	Distance (miles/day)
1	3
2	$3 + \frac{3}{4} = 3\frac{3}{4}$
3	$3\frac{3}{4} + \frac{3}{4} = 4\frac{1}{2}$
4	$4\frac{1}{2} + \frac{3}{4} = 5\frac{1}{4}$
5	$5\frac{1}{4} + \frac{3}{4} = 6$

✓ **Check Understanding** ① Suppose you plan to read a novel. Every day, you want to read two more
pages than you did the day before. If you read just one page on the first day,
on what day will you reach page 64? **day 8**

  **Ongoing Assessment and Intervention**

Before the Lesson
Diagnose prerequisite skills using:
• Check Skills You'll Need

During the Lesson
Monitor progress using:
• Check Understanding
• Additional Examples
• Test Prep

After the Lesson
Assess knowledge using:
• Lesson Quiz
• Computer Test Generator CD
• Chapter Checkpoint 1 (p. 334)

① **EXAMPLE** Error Prevention

Review the addition of fractions
with like and unlike denominators.

Closure

*How does making an organized
list help you solve a problem?*
**Sample: You can better see
patterns and work logically.**

331

Assignment Guide

1 Objective 1
- Ⓐ Ⓑ Core 1–6
- Ⓒ Extension 7–8

Test Prep 9–12
Mixed Review 13–19

4. Assess

 Lesson Quiz 7-3

1. Vern has seven ties and four dress shirts. How many different combinations of shirt and tie can he wear?
28 combinations

✓ **Chapter Checkpoint**

To check understanding of Lessons 7-1 to 7-3:

Checkpoint Quiz 1 (p. 334)

📁 **Teaching Resources**
Checkpoint Quiz 1 (also in Prentice Hall Assessment System)

👐 **Reaching All Students**
Reading and Math Literacy 7B

Spanish versions available

Alternative Assessment

Each student in a pair writes a problem that can be solved by making an organized list. Partners exchange problems and solve.

Test Prep

Resources
For additional practice with a variety of test item formats:
- Test Prep, p. 367
- Test-Taking Strategies, p. 363
- Test-Taking Strategies With Transparencies

 Use the Guided Problem Solving worksheet with Exercise 4.

EXERCISES

❓ For more practice, see *Extra Practice*.

Ⓐ **Practice by Example**

Example 1
(page 331)

Solve each problem by making an organized list.

🌐 1. **Making Change** How many ways can you make 25 cents using pennies, nickels, and dimes? **12 ways**

2. A baseball team has six pitchers (players A, B, C, D, E, and F) and three catchers (players G, H, and I). How many pitcher-catcher pairs can the coach choose from? An organized list has been started for you. **18 pairs**

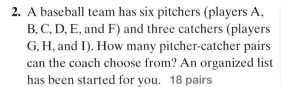

Pitcher – Catcher
A – G
A – H
A – I

3. Find the smallest number that meets all of these conditions. **43**
- When you divide the number by 7, the remainder is 1.
- When you divide the number by 9, the remainder is 7.
- When you divide the number by 11, the remainder is 10.

❓ Need Help?
- Reread the problem.
- Identify the key facts and details.
- Tell the problem in your own words.
- Try a different strategy.
- Check your work.

Ⓑ **Apply Your Skills**

Choose a strategy to solve each problem.

GPS 4. How many triangles are in the figure at the right?
16 triangles

🌐 5. **Saving** Your plan is to save $1 the first week, $2 the second week, $4 the third week, $8 the fourth week, $16 the fifth week, and so on.
a. List the total amount you will have saved after each of the first 6 weeks. **$1, $3, $7, $15, $31, $63**
b. **Writing in Math** How can you use the amount saved in a given week to predict the total saved by that week? **Answers may vary. Sample: The total saved will be $1 less than twice the amount saved that week.**

6. **Patterns** The numbers 1, 3, 6, 10, . . . are called *triangular numbers* because of the following pattern.

```
  1        3         6          10
  •        •         •          •
          • •       • •        • •
                   • • •      • • •
                             • • • •
```

a. What number can you add to 10 to get the next triangular number? **5**
b. What are the next two triangular numbers after 10? **15, 21**

Strategies

- Draw a Diagram
- Make a Graph
- Make an Organized List
- Make a Table and Look for a Pattern
- Simulate a Problem
- Solve a Simpler Problem
- Try, Check, and Revise
- Use Logical Reasoning
- Work Backward
- Write an Equation

Ⓒ **Challenge**

🌐 7. **Clocks** A clock chimes once at 1:00, twice at 2:00, and so on. The clock also chimes once at 1:30, 2:30, and so on. How many times will the clock chime from 3 P.M. Monday through 2:59 P.M. Tuesday? **180 times**

8. **Stretch Your Thinking** You open a book to two facing pages. The product of the two page numbers is 600. Find the page numbers.
24 and 25

👐 **Reaching All Students**

Below Level In Check Understanding 1, students may incorrectly divide 64 by 2 to obtain 32 days. Remind them to make an organized list. Then help them recognize that the number of pages read each day increases by 2 pages.	**Advanced Learners** Have students write an equation to solve Example 1. $3 + \frac{3}{4}(w - 1) = 6$ or $2\frac{1}{4} + \frac{3}{4}w = 6$	**Error Prevention** See note on page 332.

Multiple Choice

9. A bank account is opened with d dollars. Each month, $3 is deposited. How much money was deposited to the account in one year? **D**

   A. $3d$ **B.** $d + 3$ **C.** $d + 12$ **D.** $d + 36$

Take It to the NET
Online lesson quiz at
www.PHSchool.com
Web Code: aaa-0703

10. Which of the following is NOT equivalent to the other three? **H**

   F. 3^4 **G.** 27×3 **H.** $6 \cdot 13$ **I.** 9^2

11. Which equation has the solution $m = 2$? **B**

   A. $10m = 5$ **B.** $2 - m = 0$ **C.** $m + 1 = 1$ **D.** $3m = 5$

Short Response

12. Suppose you have 1 nickel, 1 dime, and 1 quarter. Explain how you would find the different amounts of money that can be made using one or more coins by using an organized list. **See margin.**

Mixed Review

Lesson 5-8   **Choose the heavier weight.**

13. 14 oz or 1 lb   **1 lb**   **14.** 34 oz or 3 lb   **3 lb**   **15.** $\frac{1}{4}$ lb or 8 oz   **8 oz**

Lesson 5-3   **(Algebra)** Find each quotient for $x = \frac{3}{4}$. Write the answer in simplest form.

16. $15 \div x$ **20**   **17.** $x \div 12$ $\frac{1}{16}$ **18.** $\frac{9}{16} \div x$ $\frac{3}{4}$ **19.** $x \div \frac{15}{16}$ $\frac{4}{5}$

✓ Checkpoint Quiz 1   Lessons 7-1 through 7-3

iTEXT Instant self-check quiz online and on CD-ROM

1. Find the mean, median, mode, and range of the following data.
                                                   30; 30; 30; 26

      40   30   42   31   16   30   33   18   30

Grams of Fat	Tally	Frequency
0	ⅣⅡ Ⅲ	8
1	ⅣⅡ ⅢⅢ	9
2	ⅣⅡ	5
3	ⅢⅢ	3

Use the line plot for Exercises 2 and 3.

2. Find the median.   **21**

3. Find the mode.   **21**

High Temperatures

```
                          X
                          X   X
                          X   X       X
          X   X   X   X   X   X       X       X
         17  18  19  20  21  22  23  24  25  26
                  Temperature (°C)
```

4. Nutrition The grams of fat per serving for 25 breakfast cereals are 0, 1, 1, 3, 1, 1, 2, 2, 0, 3, 1, 3, 2, 0, 1, 0, 2, 1, 1, 0, 0, 0, 2, 1, and 0. Make a frequency table of the data. **See above left.**

5. How many ways can you make $.50 with nickels, dimes, and/or quarters?
10 ways

12. **[2] a. Answers may vary. Sample:** List successively greater amounts possible, starting with 5¢. Count the total number of amounts in the list.

[1] explanation is not shown OR incorrect work is shown

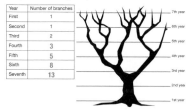

Reading Graphs

Teaching students strategies for reading mathematics must include strategies for reading and interpreting graphs. Since graphs contain a wealth of information and their own unique elements not found in running text, they present special reading challenges for students. This feature guides students to pay attention to the type of graph they are reading, the title, the labels, and the scale.

Teaching Notes

Teaching Tip
Review and compare the uses of the three kinds of graphs named and described. Ask students to suggest data that would be displayed most effectively in a bar graph, in a line graph, and in a circle graph.

EXAMPLE Visual Learners

Guide students to notice the clear and concise title and labels, and the reasonable scale used for each axis. Discuss that a bar graph is ideal for showing a comparison of quantities, like these. To make sure students are reading the graph correctly, ask:
- *How many students in 2001 are in the band?* **20 students**
- *How many more students in 2003 than in 2002 are in the band?* **10 students**

Exercises
Assign the exercises for independent work. Then discuss them as a whole class.

6. **Siblings Students Have**

```
        X
        X
      X X
      X X
      X X   X
    X X X X       X
    X X X X       X   X
    X X X X   X X   X
    0 1 2 3 4 5 6 7 8
    Number of Siblings
```

334

When you read a graph, pay attention to the following.

- **Type of Graph** *Bar graphs* show comparisons. *Line graphs* show trends over time. *Circle graphs* describe the parts that make up the whole.
- **Title** This tells the information you will find in the graph.
- **Labels on the Axes** These tell what the data on each axis represent. Use the numbers on an axis to determine the scale of the graph.

EXAMPLE

Identify the parts on the graph at the right. What can you learn from the data?

- Type of graph: The graph is a bar graph and shows comparisons.
- Title: The title is "Students Enrolled in Band."
- Labels on the axes: The horizontal axis gives the year. The vertical axis gives the number of students. The scale counts by 5.
- Summary: The graph shows that each year more students were enrolled in band.

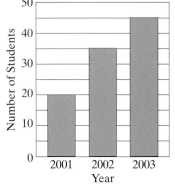

Students Enrolled in Band

EXERCISES

Use the graph at the right for Exercises 1–4.

1. What type of graph is shown? **line graph**

2. What is the title of the graph? **Money Collected for Community Project**

3. **a.** Describe the axes. **See margin.**
   b. What interval is used on the vertical axis? **$50**

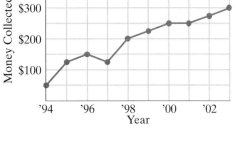

Money Collected for Community Project

4. What can you learn from the graph?
   Answers may vary. Sample: Over time, the amount of money collected has increased.

5. Which of the following could be represented by the graph at the right? **A**
   A. the number of brothers and sisters students have
   B. the ages of students in the class
   C. the number of days absent from school in one week

6. Based on your answer to Exercise 5, write a label for the axis and a title for the graph. **See margin for graph.**
   Answers may vary. Sample: Title, Siblings Students Have; Axis label, Number of Siblings

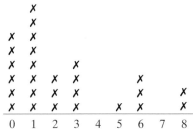

```
        X
        X
      X X
      X X
      X X   X
    X X X X       X
    X X X X       X   X
    X X X X   X X   X
    0 1 2 3 4 5 6 7 8
```

3a. The horizontal axis gives the year and the vertical axis gives the amount of money collected.

7-4 Bar Graphs and Line Graphs

What You'll Learn

OBJECTIVE 1 To make bar graphs

OBJECTIVE 2 To make line graphs

. . . And Why

To display nutrition data in a graph, as in Example 1

 Check Skills You'll Need For help, go to Lesson 7-2.

Make a line plot for each set of data. 1–3. See back of book.

1. 5, 6, 7, 8, 6, 5, 8, 7, 10, 9, 8, 8, 7, 5, 12

2. 1.3, 1.2, 1.0, 1.0, 1.1, 1.4, 1.3, 1.0, 1.2, 1.2, 1.3, 1.0

3. 13, 17, 10, 21, 17, 15, 15

New Vocabulary
• bar graph • histogram • line graph

Lesson Preview

 PowerPoint

 Check Skills You'll Need

Making a Line Plot
Lesson 7-2: Example 2. Extra Practice, p. 648.

Lesson Resources

Optional Materials
• graph paper
• straight edge or ruler

Teaching Resources
Practice, Reteaching, Enrichment

Reaching All Students
Practice Workbook 7-4
Spanish Practice Workbook 7-4
Guided Problem Solving 7-4
Hands-On Activities 25, 40

Presentation Assistant Plus!
Transparencies
• Check Skills You'll Need 7-4
• Problem of the Day 7-4
• Additional Examples 7-4
• Student Edition Answers 7-4
• Lesson Quiz 7-4
• Classroom Aid 2, 11, 23, 24, 25, 26
PH Presentation Pro CD-ROM 7-4

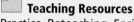
PRENTICE HALL
ASSESSMENT SYSTEM

Computer Test Generator CD

Technology
Resource Pro® CD-ROM
Computer Test Generator CD
PH Presentation Pro CD-ROM

www.PHSchool.com
Student Site
• Teacher Web Code: aak-5500
• Self-grading Lesson Quiz

PH SuccessNet Teacher Center
• Lesson Planner
• Resources

Plus

OBJECTIVE 1
Making Bar Graphs

 Interactive lesson includes instant self-check, tutorials, and activities.

A **bar graph** uses vertical or horizontal bars to display numerical information. You can use a bar graph to compare amounts.

1 EXAMPLE **Making a Bar Graph** **Real World**

Nutrition Make a bar graph to display the data at the left.

Calcium Content

Food Item (1 cup)	Calcium (mg)
Milk	300
Yogurt	250
Cottage Cheese	150
Ice Cream	200
Broccoli	80
Dried Beans	90

SOURCE: Carnegie Mellon University Health Services

Draw and label the horizontal and vertical axes.

Choose an appropriate title.

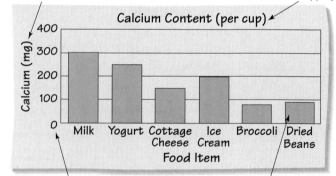

Choose a scale. The data go from 80 to 300. Mark 0 to 400 in intervals of 100.

Draw bars of equal widths. The heights will vary.

 Check Understanding 1 Make a bar graph to display the data below. See back of book.

Allowance Each Week					
Amount of Money ($)	3	4	5	6	7
Number of Students	10	21	34	12	6

Ongoing Assessment and Intervention

Before the Lesson
Diagnose prerequisite skills using:
• Check Skills You'll Need

During the Lesson
Monitor progress using:
• Check Understanding
• Additional Examples
• Test Prep

After the Lesson
Assess knowledge using:
• Lesson Quiz
• Computer Test Generator CD

Math Background

Graphs visually communicate information. A *bar graph* uses the length of bars to compare numerical amounts.

A *histogram* is a bar graph that uses equal-sized intervals to illustrate the frequency distribution of a data set. Unlike a bar graph, no spaces are used between consecutive bars.

Line graphs illustrate trends by showing how two quantities relate to one another. There are only three possible changes between points on a line (or bars in bar graphs and histograms): an increase, a decrease, or no change.

Teaching Notes

① EXAMPLE Inclusion

For Check Understanding 1, ask: *Which item would you place along the horizontal axis? Why?* Sample: Amount of money because the number of students is the variable that depends on the amount of money.

③ EXAMPLE Visual Learners

Point out that both temperature and time of day are continuous. So, connecting the data points gives the approximate temperature for times between each point. As a contrast, have students examine the bar graph in Example 1. Ask: *Can the Food Items on the horizontal axis be listed in a different order? Why?* Sample: Yes; the food items are categories that do not have a logical sequence like time.

Teaching Tip

Elicit the fact that there are only three possible changes shown in a graph: increase, decrease, or no change. Ask: *What does a horizontal line represent?* no change

Investigation (Optional)

Consider approving each student's question to ensure that they are not biased toward certain responses. Have students record their data in an organized manner.

336

A **histogram** is a bar graph that shows the frequency of each data item. Histograms often combine data into equal-sized intervals.

② EXAMPLE Making a Histogram   Real World

Batteries Make a histogram to display the data at the left.

Intervals	Hours of Battery Life
8–11	11, 9, 8
12–15	12, 14, 15, 15
16–19	19, 17
20–23	22, 23, 21

Step 1 Make a frequency table.

Hours	Tally	Frequency
8–11	III	3
12–15	IIII	4
16–19	II	2
20–23	III	3

Step 2 Make a histogram.

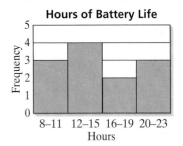

✔ **Check Understanding** ② In Example 2, which interval contains the median? **12–15 hours**

OBJECTIVE

2 Making Line Graphs

A **line graph** uses a series of line segments to show changes in data. Usually, a line graph shows changes over time.

③ EXAMPLE Making a Line Graph   Real World

Temperatures Throughout the Day	
Time	Temperature
8 A.M.	62°F
10 A.M.	70°F
12 P.M.	78°F
2 P.M.	81°F
4 P.M.	76°F
6 P.M.	74°F

Temperature Use the data at the left to make a line graph.

Choose an appropriate title.

Temperatures Throughout the Day

Choose a scale. The data range from 62 to 81. Mark 60 to 85 in units of 5.

Draw and label the axes.

Plot a point for each data item. Then connect the points with straight line segments.

The break symbol means that the values between 0 and 60 are not shown.

✔ **Check Understanding** ③ Use the table at the right to make a line graph. **See back of book.**

Ticket Sales				
Week	1	2	3	4
Tickets Sold	22	35	33	46

👥 Reaching All Students

Below Level Review simple bar graphs and line graphs. Help students find the value for the height of each bar on the vertical axis; and help students find vertical axis values for specific horizontal axis values in a line graph.

Advanced Learners Have students find real-world examples of pictographs. Then have them construct their own pictograph using a symbol of their own design.

Inclusion
See note on page 336.

Visual Learners
See note on page 336.

Investigation: Graphing and Reporting Survey Results

1–4. Check students' work.

1. Write a survey question such as one of the following.
   - What is your favorite type of music?
   - How many hours do you spend watching television each week?
   - How many pets do you have?

2. Have each classmate answer your survey question.

3. Organize your data into a graph of your choice.

4. Write a paragraph to summarize the data you collected. Describe the mean, median, mode, and range, if possible.

EXERCISES

? For more practice, see *Extra Practice*.

(A) Practice by Example

Example 1 (page 335)

Budgets Use the table at the right.

1–2. See margin.

1. Make a bar graph to display the planned budgets.

2. Make a bar graph to display the actual budgets.

Monthly Budget

Cost Item	Planned	Actual
Dining Out	$40	$28
Clothes	$35	$42
Concerts	$18	$6
Movies	$22	$22

Example 2 (page 336)

Make a histogram of the data from each table.

3. See margin.   4. See left.

3. Time Spent on Homework

Intervals	Minutes
0–59	30, 25, 45
60–119	107, 78, 65, 90
120–179	135
180–239	185

4. Plant Height

Intervals	Inches
0–24	7, 8, 19, 3, 4, 5
25–49	43, 29, 26
50–74	61
75–99	78, 84

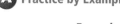

4.
Plant Height

Example 3 (page 336)

 5. Hot Lunches Make a line graph of the data below. See back of book.

Students Buying Hot Lunch

Day	Mon.	Tue.	Wed.	Thur.	Fri.
Number of Students	125	143	165	48	183

Additional Examples

① Make a bar graph of the data.

Students With Employer Jobs

Age	Percent
14	33%
15	60%
16	74%

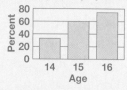

Students With Employer Jobs

② Make a histogram to display the speeds of ticketed drivers.

Speed (mi/h)	Frequency
36-40	5
41-45	8
46-50	12
51-55	6
56-60	3

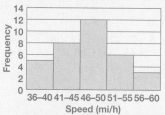

Speeds of Ticketed Drivers

③ Make a line graph of the data.

Running Shoes Sales

Month	Pairs Sold
Feb	54
March	86
April	121
May	115

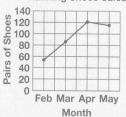

Running Shoes Sales

Closure

How do you make a bar graph?
Draw and label each axis.
Choose scales and draw bars to their proper heights. Write a title.

337

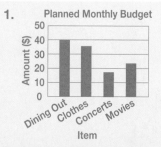

1. Planned Monthly Budget

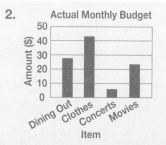

2. Actual Monthly Budget

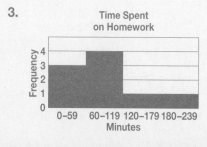

3. Time Spent on Homework

3. Practice

Assignment Guide

▼ 1 Objective 1
- Ⓐ Ⓑ Core 1–4, 6, 9
- Ⓒ Extension 11

▼ 2 Objective 2
- Ⓐ Ⓑ Core 5, 7–8
- Ⓒ Extension 10

Test Prep 12–15
Mixed Review 16–23

Error Prevention!

Exercises 1–2 Remind students that each bar width must be the same thickness.

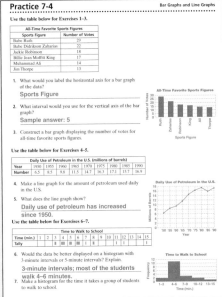

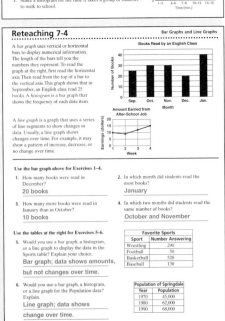

Ⓑ **Apply Your Skills**   🌐 **6. Prime Ministers** Make a bar graph to show how many years each prime GPS minister was in office. **See below left.**

| Golda Meir Israel 5 years | Indira Gandhi India 18 years | Margaret Thatcher UK 11 years | Gro Harlem Bruntland Norway 13 years |

6.

Prime Ministers' Years in Office

(bar graph: Years vs Prime Minister — Meir, Gandhi, Thatcher, Bruntland)

7a.

Daily Number of Customers

(line graph: Number vs Day of Week — Mon. through Sat.)

7b. The daily number of customers increases, starting on Wednesday.

Ⓒ **Challenge**   🌐 **10. a. Airports** Which would you use to display the data at the right, a bar graph or a line graph? Explain your answer.
   b. Draw the graph.

🌐 **7. Business** A store tracks the number of customers it has each day.
   a. Make a line graph of the data. Monday: 134, Tuesday: 94, Wednesday: 113, Thursday: 146, Friday: 181, Saturday: 234
   b. What trend does your line graph show? **7a–b. See below left.**

8. Data Collection Make a line graph showing the amount of time you spent on homework for each day of one week. **Check students' work.**

9. a. Make a histogram using each set of data below. **9a–b. See back of book.**
   b. <u>Writing in Math</u> Compare the histograms. Do you think the data is better represented using 3 or 4 intervals? Explain your reasoning.

Age of Contestants

Intervals	Years
20–34	21, 28, 25
35–49	39, 36
50–64	57, 55

Age of Contestants

Intervals	Years
20–29	21, 28, 25
30–39	39, 36
40–49	
50–59	57, 55

10a–b. See back of book.

11. Stretch Your Thinking How many four-digit whole numbers can you make using the digits 1, 4, 6, and 9 if you use each digit only once in each number? **24 numbers**

World's Busiest Airports

Airport	Passengers (millions)
Atlanta	76
Chicago O'Hare	67
Los Angeles	62
London	61
Tokyo	59
Dallas-Ft. Worth	55

SOURCE: Airports Council International

338   **Chapter 7** Data and Graphs

GPS   Use the Guided Problem Solving worksheet with Exercise 6.

Gridded Response

For Exercises 12–15, use the graph showing electoral votes.

12. How many votes do these five states have in all? **167**

13. What is the range? **31**

14. How many more votes does Texas have than Florida? **7**

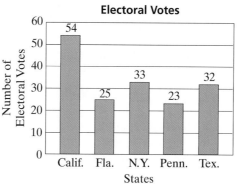

Electoral Votes

15. To be elected President, a candidate needs 270 electoral votes. Suppose a candidate wins the five states above. How many more electoral votes would the candidate need to be elected? **103**

Take It to the NET
Online lesson quiz at
www.PHSchool.com
Web Code: aaa-0704

Mixed Review

Lesson 6-8

Estimate the sale price of each item. 16–19. Answers may vary. Samples given.

16. sandals on sale for 30% of $18
$6

17. boots on sale for 80% of $62
$48

18. stereo on sale for 60% of $210
$120

19. hair clip on sale for 40% of $9.95
$4

Lesson 6-1

Write three ratios equal to each given ratio. 20–23. Answers may vary. Samples given.

20. 3:5
6:10, 9:15,
15:25

21. 5 to 9
10 to 18,
20 to 36,
25 to 45

22. $\frac{48}{80}$
$\frac{3}{5}, \frac{6}{10}, \frac{96}{160}$

23. 12:15
4:5, 8:10,
16:20

Practice Game

······· Bar Graph Race

What You'll Need
• two number cubes
• graph labeled as shown at the right

Sample Gameboard

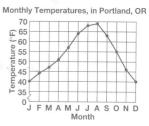

Player A ■ Player B ☐
(7 or 8)   (5 or 6)

How to Play
• Player A chooses a number from 2 to 12. Player B then chooses two of the remaining numbers. Player A then chooses one of the remaining numbers.
• Roll the two number cubes. If the sum is a player's number, that player fills in one unit on the graph above that number.
• Roll the two number cubes again until one player's bar reaches a frequency of six. That player wins.

7-4 Bar Graphs and Line Graphs **339**

Test Prep

Resources
A sheet of blank grids is available in the *Test-Taking Strategies With Transparencies* booklet. Give copies of this sheet to students so they can practice filling in grids.

For additional practice with a variety of test item formats:
• Test Prep, p. 367
• Test-Taking Strategies, p. 363
• Test-Taking Strategies With Transparencies

PowerPoint Lesson Quiz 7-4

1. The final math grades for all 6th graders were A: 125, B: 200, C: 350, D: 95, and F: 25. Make a bar graph to display this data.

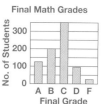

Final Math Grades

2. The normal monthly temperatures (in °F) in Portland, OR, from January through December, respectively, are 40, 44, 47, 51, 57, 64, 68, 69, 63, 55, 46, and 40. Use this data to make a line graph.

Monthly Temperatures, in Portland, OR

Alternative Assessment

Pairs of students find two sets of real-world data and work together to make a bar graph and a line graph.

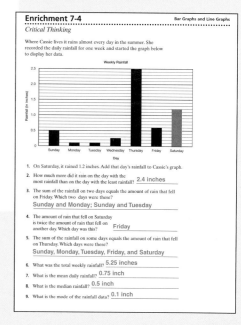

Extension

Double Bar and Line Graphs

For Use With Lesson 7-4

Students plot two sets of data on the same graph to make visual comparisons of the data sets.

Optional Materials

- graph paper
- ruler
- Classroom Aid 2, 23–26

Teaching Notes

Use plain language to review the uses of bar graphs and of line graphs. For instance, bar graphs compare amounts in categories and line graphs show trends of one quantity compared to another. A double bar or double line graph visually compares two related sets of data.

EXAMPLE Visual Learners

Have students examine the double bar graph and ask:

- *Why is it important to use a different color for each data set in the double bar graph?* Sample: The different colors help you quickly distinguish which set of data each bar belongs to, making comparisons easier.

- *What significance does the legend have?* Sample: The legend identifies what each color in the graph represents.

Inclusion

Remind students that there are only three possible changes between bars or points on a line: an increase, a decrease, or no change.

Exercises

Exercises 1–2 Have students work independently to answer these questions. Make sure students can correctly answer these questions before proceeding to make graphs.

Exercises 3–4 Have students work in pairs to make a double bar graph and a double line graph.

340

You can plot two data sets on the same graph to compare them more easily.

EXAMPLE **Graphing Two Sets of Data**

Sales A bookstore tracks sales of cooking and travel books. Make a double bar graph and a double line graph of the data at the right.

Use a different color for each data set in the double bar graph and double line graph.

Books Sold Each Month

Month	Jan.	Feb.	Mar.	Apr.
Cooking	86	98	112	110
Travel	100	106	88	102

Use a key to show which bar or line represents each data set.

EXERCISES

Use the example above for Exercises 1 and 2.

1. Which graph shows most clearly how book sales increased from January to February? **double line graph**

2. Which graph shows most clearly the differences in sales between the two types of books? **double bar graph**

Use the table at the right for Exercises 3 and 4. 3–4. See margin.

3. Make a double bar graph to show the differences between the numbers of endangered plants and animals.

4. Make a double line graph to show how the numbers of endangered plants and animals change over time.

Number of Endangered Species in the U.S.

Year	1980	1985	1990	1995	2000
Plants	50	93	179	432	592
Animals	174	207	263	324	379

Source: U.S. Fish and Wildlife Service.
Go to **www.PHSchool.com** for a data update.
Web Code: aag-2041

3.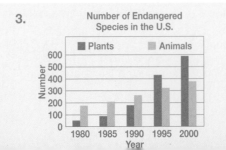

4.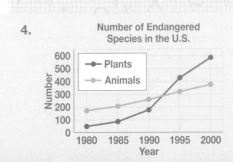

Circle Graphs

What You'll Learn

OBJECTIVE 1 To read and make circle graphs

...And Why

To compare parts of a whole, as in Example 2

 Check Skills You'll Need

? For help, go to Lesson 6-7.

Find each percent.

1. 35% of 280 **98**
2. 52% of 200 **104**
3. 25% of 384 **96**
4. 11% of 800 **88**
5. 75% of 820 **615**
6. 85% of 160 **136**

New Vocabulary
• circle graph

OBJECTIVE 1

ⓘTEXT Interactive lesson includes instant self-check, tutorials, and activities.

Reading and Making Circle Graphs

 Investigation: Exploring Circle Graphs

You can make a circle graph to display the data below about children's sources of income. **1–4. Check students' work.**

Allowance	Doing Chores	Earned Outside the Home	Gifts
54%	20%	10%	16%

1. Cut a strip of paper slightly more than 100 mm (10 cm) long with a tab at the end as shown.

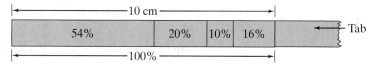

Each millimeter represents 1% of the strip. To represent 54%, mark a line 54 mm (5.4 cm) from the end of the strip. Mark the strip with lines that represent the percents in the table.

2. Form a ring with the strip. Line up the beginning of the strip with the 100% line and tape the ends. This is your "percent ring."

3. Use a compass. Draw a circle slightly larger than your percent ring. Place a dot in the center of the circle.

4. Use your percent ring to mark the percents around the edge of the circle. Use a ruler to connect the marks to the center of the circle.

Ongoing Assessment and Intervention

Before the Lesson
Diagnose prerequisite skills using:
• Check Skills You'll Need

During the Lesson
Monitor progress using:
• Check Understanding
• Additional Examples
• Test Prep

After the Lesson
Assess knowledge using:
• Lesson Quiz
• Computer Test Generator CD

---

1. Plan

Lesson Preview

PowerPoint

 Check Skills You'll Need

Finding a Percent of a Number
Lesson 6-7: Examples 1–3. Extra Practice, p. 647.

Lesson Resources

Optional Materials
• compass
• metric ruler
• scissors

📁 Teaching Resources
Practice, Reteaching, Enrichment

👫 Reaching All Students
Practice Workbook 7-5
Spanish Practice Workbook 7-5
Guided Problem Solving 7-5
Technology Activities 13
Hands-On Activities 24

🕐 Presentation Assistant Plus!
Transparencies
• Check Skills You'll Need 7-5
• Problem of the Day 7-5
• Additional Examples 7-5
• Student Edition Answers 7-5
• Lesson Quiz 7-5
• Classroom Aid 2, 27, 28
PH Presentation Pro CD-ROM 7-5

ASSESSMENT SYSTEM

Computer Test Generator CD

💻 Technology
Resource Pro® CD-ROM
Computer Test Generator CD
PH Presentation Pro CD-ROM

💻 www.PHSchool.com
Student Site
• Teacher Web Code: aak-5500
• Self-grading Lesson Quiz

PH SuccessNet Teacher Center
• Lesson Planner
• Resources

Plus

Math Background

Circle graphs visually compare parts of a whole. The entire circle represents the whole and each wedge in the circle represents part of that whole. Circle graphs generally use percents and are most dramatic when they use a limited number of wedges. If a circle is divided into too many wedges, it becomes difficult to compare among the many wedges. Bar graphs are more appropriate when a large number of categories are desired.

Teaching Notes

Investigation (Optional)

To avoid errors in measuring percents, have students work in small groups. Group members can help those who may have difficulty using a compass to draw circles.

① EXAMPLE Visual Learners

Have students examine the "Where Do All the Apples Go?" circle graph. Ask:
- *Are the actual numbers of apples given in the graph?* no
- *Do circle graphs always give exact data values?* Sample: No; circle graphs give percents which may be calculated.
- *If you were given the total number of apples, how could you find the number for each wedge?* Multiply the percent of each wedge times the total number of apples.

② EXAMPLE Error Prevention

Encourage students to check that their percents add to 100%. For Example 2, 32% + 22% + 20% + 26% = 100%. Note that rounding may give results slightly more or less than 100%.

Tactile Learners

For Check Understanding 2, have students work in small groups to make a poster-sized circle graph. Ask: *Since 50 students were surveyed, how can you quickly find the percent for each category?* Multiply each category of students by 2 and insert %.

342

A **circle graph** is a graph of data where the entire circle represents the whole. Each wedge in the circle represents part of the whole.

Reading Math

A circle graph is often called a pie chart. Each wedge of a circle graph is like a "piece of the pie."

① EXAMPLE Reading a Circle Graph Real World

Apples Use the circle graph.

a. For what purpose are 48% of apples used?

48% are eaten fresh.

b. What percent of apples are exported?

13% are exported.

Where Do All the Apples Go?

Eaten fresh — Processed — 48% 39% — 13% — Exported

✓ **Check Understanding** ① a. According to the graph, how are 39% of apples used? **39% are processed.**
b. What percent of apples are not exported? **87%**

② EXAMPLE Making a Circle Graph Real World

Sports In 2001, the Seattle Mariners baseball team stole a total of 174 bases. Make a circle graph of the data.

First, use a calculator to change the data to percents of the total. Round to the nearest percent.

$$\frac{56}{174} \approx 32\% \qquad \frac{39}{174} \approx 22\%$$

$$\frac{34}{174} \approx 20\% \qquad \frac{45}{174} \approx 26\%$$

Use number sense to divide the circle.

$32\% \approx \frac{1}{3}$ 22% is slightly less than $\frac{1}{4}$ of the circle.

$26\% \approx \frac{1}{4}$ 20% is what is left over.

Stolen Bases by Seattle Mariners

Player	Total
Ichiro Suzuki	56
Mark McLemore	39
Mike Cameron	34
Other players combined	45
Total number of stolen bases	174

Stolen Bases by Seattle Mariners

20% 26% 32% 22%

☐ Ichiro Suzuki
☐ Mark McLemore
☐ Mike Cameron
☐ Other players

Label the divided circle with each percent. You can also use a different color for each player. Add a title.

2. Lunches of 50 Students

Hot — Sandwiches — Packed — Salad Bar

✓ **Check Understanding** ② Of 50 students surveyed, 13 preferred hot lunch, 9 packed lunch, 6 ate at the salad bar, and 22 bought sandwiches. Make a circle graph of the data. See above left.

👥 Reaching All Students

Below Level Ask: *How can you tell which part of the circle graph represents the greatest amount?* the widest wedge *the least amount?* the narrowest wedge	**Advanced Learners** Ask: *What happens if a circle graph has a large number of wedges?* Sample: It becomes difficult to see differences between the many smaller wedges.	**Visual Learners** See note on page 342. **Tactile Learners** See note on page 342.

More Than One Way

Four NASA space shuttles flew 19 missions from 1999 through 2002. Draw a graph for the following data: *Atlantis*, 6 missions; *Columbia*, 2 missions; *Discovery*, 5 missions; *Endeavour*, 6 missions.

Zack's Method

I can make a bar graph to display the data.

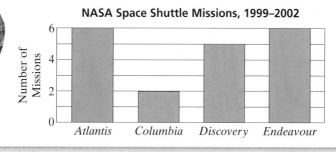

NASA Space Shuttle Missions, 1999–2002

Jessica's Method

I can make a circle graph to display the data.

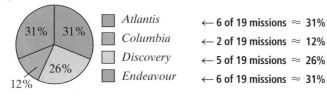

Space Shuttle Missions, 1999–2002

- Atlantis ← 6 of 19 missions ≈ 31%
- Columbia ← 2 of 19 missions ≈ 12%
- Discovery ← 5 of 19 missions ≈ 26%
- Endeavour ← 6 of 19 missions ≈ 31%

Check students' graph. Sample:

How Students Get to School

Choose a Method

Of 25 students, 6 ride to school in a car, 14 ride a bus, 1 rides a bike, and 4 walk. Draw a graph to display the data. Explain your choice of graph. **See left.**

Explanations may vary. Sample:
I chose a circle graph because it shows how each type of transportation relates to all types of transportation.

EXERCISES

🔍 For more practice, see *Extra Practice*.

Ⓐ Practice by Example

Example 1 (page 342)

Use the graph at the right for Exercises 1–3.

Favorite Sport

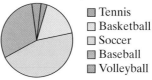

- ☐ Tennis
- ☐ Basketball
- ☐ Soccer
- ☐ Baseball
- ☐ Volleyball

1. Which sport is the least popular?
   tennis
2. Which is more popular, basketball or volleyball? **basketball**
3. List the sports from least to most popular.
   tennis, volleyball, basketball, baseball, soccer

7-5 Circle Graphs **343**

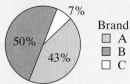

343

3. Practice

Assignment Guide

1 Objective 1
- Ⓐ Ⓑ Core 1–17
- Ⓒ Extension 18–19

Test Prep 20–22
Mixed Review 23–30

Error Prevention!

Exercises 11–13 Help students compare fractions to common fractions they know, or convert them to percents.

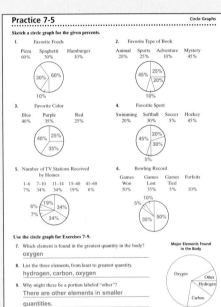

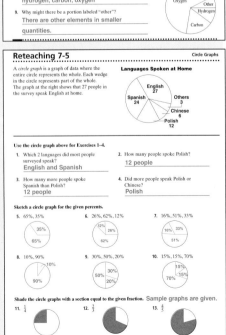

Example 2
(page 342)

Sketch a circle graph for the given percents. 4–7. See margin.

4. 10%, 40%, 50%

5. 5%, 14%, 33%, 48%

6. 12%, 26%, 62%

7. 12%, 34%, 21%, 33%

Ⓑ **Apply Your Skills**

Real-World 🌐 **Connection**

Bone is made up of calcium, phosphorus, oxygen, hydrogen, and many other elements.

8. Science The human body is made up of 21 chemical elements. Use the table at the right to make a circle graph.
See back of book.

9. Data Collection List the things you do on a Saturday. Estimate the hours you spend on each activity. Write each time as a percent of a 24-hour day. Make a circle graph. **Check students' graphs.**

Human Body Composition

Element	Percent
Oxygen	65
Carbon	18
Hydrogen	10
Nitrogen	3
Other	4

10. Taxes The table below shows that taxes make up a large part of the price of gasoline. Make two circle graphs to compare gasoline taxes to the price of gasoline in the United States and the United Kingdom.
See back of book.

Taxes on One Gallon of Gasoline

Country	Price (including tax)	Tax
United States	$1.64	$.38
United Kingdom	$4.57	$3.48

Sketch a circle graph for each set of fractions.
11. See margin.
12–13. See back of book

11. $\frac{1}{2}, \frac{1}{3}, \frac{1}{6}$

12. $\frac{3}{4}, \frac{1}{10}, \frac{1}{10}, \frac{1}{20}$

13. $\frac{3}{8}, \frac{1}{8}, \frac{4}{10}, \frac{1}{10}$

14. Surveys A group of 100 students were asked how they like to spend their free time. Of those surveyed, 53% said they like to go to the mall, 80% said they like to watch TV, 72% said they like to play outside, and 34% said they like to search the Internet.

14a. Answers may vary. Sample: The sum of the percents is greater than 100.

a. Writing in Math Explain why you cannot use a circle graph to display the data. **See left.**

b. What kind of graph could you use to display these data? **bar graph**

15. Customers A video arcade recorded the ages of customers for a 1-hour period. The results are shown in the line plot.

a. Draw a circle graph.

b. What percent of the customers are older than 15?

c. Reasoning Can you find the percent of customers who are 11 years old? Explain.

15a–c. See back of book.

Customer Ages at Video Arcade

```
                          X
            X             X
            X             X
            X             X
            X             X                     X
    X       X       X     X     X
    X       X       X     X     X
  ─────────────────────────────────→
  Under 11  11–15  16–20  21–25  Over 25
                    Years
```

GPS Use the Guided Problem Solving worksheet with Exercise 8.

4.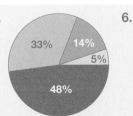

5.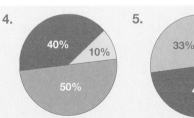

6.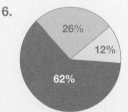

Use the graph at the right for Exercises 16 and 17.

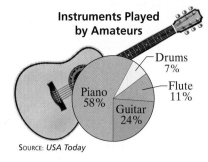

Instruments Played by Amateurs

Drums 7%
Flute 11%
Piano 58%
Guitar 24%

Source: *USA Today*

16. What instrument do more amateur musicians play than any other? **piano**

17. What percent play the guitar? **24%**

C **Challenge** **18. Fundraising** A class collected 700 coins to donate to charity.
 a. How many quarters were donated? **84**
 b. How many more nickels were donated than quarters? **112**
 c. How much money was donated? **$57.05**

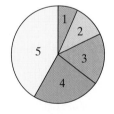

Coins Donated

Quarters 12%
Pennies 25%
Dimes 35%
28%
Nickels

19. Stretch Your Thinking Eve sells candles. Each day, she sells 3 more candles than the day before. If she sold 24 candles on the sixth day, how many candles did she sell on the first day? **9 candles**

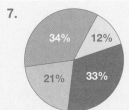

Test Prep

Multiple Choice Use the circle graph.

20. How many teachers do the greatest number of students have? **D**
 A. 1   **B.** 2   **C.** 4   **D.** 5

Take It to the NET
Online lesson quiz at
www.PHSchool.com
Web Code: aaa-0705

21. How many teachers do about 25% of students have? **H**
 F. 2   **G.** 3   **H.** 4   **I.** 5

Number of Teachers for Middle Grade Students

1 2 3 4 5

Short Response

22. Do more than half of the students have 5 teachers? Explain your reasoning.
See back of book.

Mixed Review

Lesson 6-7 **Find each percent.**

23. 15% of 80
12
24. 25% of 120
30
25. 82% of 200
164
26. 1% of 125
1.25

Lesson 5-2 **Algebra** Evaluate each expression for $x = 3\frac{3}{4}$.

27. $8x$ **30**
28. $\frac{2}{5}x$ **$1\frac{1}{2}$**
29. $\frac{4}{3}x$ **5**
30. $x \times 2\frac{1}{2}$ **$9\frac{3}{8}$**

7-5   Circle Graphs   **345**

7.
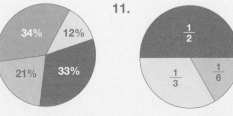
34% 12%
21% 33%

11.
$\frac{1}{2}$
$\frac{1}{3}$ $\frac{1}{6}$

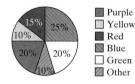
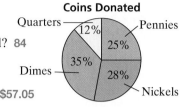

Alternative Assessment

Each student in a pair finds real-world data that can be displayed in a circle graph. Partners exchange data and make circle graphs to display each other's data.

345

Writing to Persuade

Students need to be able to write coherently when formulating and sharing their mathematical thoughts and methods. In this feature, they are introduced to the skill of writing persuasively, which includes using mathematical language and tools to get across a point of view.

Teaching Notes

Teaching Tip
Discuss real-world examples of persuasive writing (editorials, advertisements, political speeches, cartoons, brochures, and so on). Invite students to share their prior knowledge of the features of persuasive writing by asking questions like these:
- *What are features and techniques common to all effective persuasive writing?*
- *What must writers consider in order to make their arguments as effectively as they can?*
Accept all reasonable answers.

Emphasize the importance of being able to communicate mathematical ideas clearly, succinctly, and persuasively. Elicit from students the value of backing up arguments with examples and visual displays, and of knowing their audience well. Ask: *Why is it important to know your audience when you write to persuade?* to determine the level of complexity, the language to use, and the examples and support to include

Exercises
Have students work independently on the exercises. Then have them share their efforts with classmates. Guide listeners to look for a clear understanding of audience and purpose, a logical and focused argument, support by way of an appropriate and effective graph, and a strong conclusion.

Writing in Math

Writing to Persuade

For Use With Lesson 7-5

To persuade others to see things in a certain way, you should
- Identify your audience and your goal.
- Collect data.
- Decide how to display your information.

EXAMPLE

You think the school mascot should be changed and you know many students agree with you.

Identify the Audience and Goal You want to persuade the school administration that students want the school mascot to be changed.

Collect Data You survey the 394 students in your school.

Should the School Change Its Mascot?

Category	Strongly disagree	Disagree	No opinion	Agree	Strongly agree
Number of Students	79	63	51	159	42

Display the Information You decide to make a table and a circle graph of the data. You combine *agree* and *strongly agree* to emphasize the numbers of students that want to change the mascot.

Agree + Strongly Agree: $\frac{159 + 42}{394} \approx 51\%$

Should the School Change Its Mascot?

Category	Disagree or strongly disagree	No opinion	Agree or strongly agree
Number of Students	142	51	201
Percent of Students	36%	13%	51%

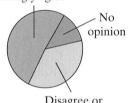

Change the School Mascot?

Agree or strongly agree

No opinion

Disagree or strongly disagree

EXERCISE

1a. Answers may vary. Sample: director of the school cafeteria.

1. You would like macaroni and cheese on the school lunch menu more often. You collect the data at the right.
   a. Identify your audience.
   b. Make a display of your information. **Check students' work.**

Should the School Cafeteria Offer Macaroni and Cheese Twice a Week?

Category	Strongly disagree	Disagree	No opinion	Agree	Strongly agree
Number of Students	20	35	125	195	125

Using Spreadsheets to Organize Data

What You'll Learn

OBJECTIVE 1 To read data in a spreadsheet

OBJECTIVE 2 To write formulas for a spreadsheet

. . . And Why

To find the recording time of CDs, as in Example 1

✔ Check Skills You'll Need

❓ For help, go to Lesson 2-3.

Write an expression for each word phrase.

1. 5 times x $5x$
2. 7 less than b $b - 7$
3. 52 decreased by x $52 - x$
4. a divided by 9 $\frac{a}{9}$
5. the product of x and y xy
6. the quotient of a and b $\frac{a}{b}$

New Vocabulary • spreadsheet • cell

Lesson Preview

✔ Check Skills You'll Need PowerPoint

Writing Algebraic Expressions
Lesson 2-3: Example 1. Extra Practice, p. 643.

Lesson Resources

📁 **Teaching Resources**
Practice, Reteaching, Enrichment
Checkpoint Quiz 2

👥 **Reaching All Students**
Practice Workbook 7-6
Spanish Practice Workbook 7-6
Reading and Math Literacy 7C
Spanish Reading and Math Literacy 7C
Spanish Checkpoint Quiz 2
Guided Problem Solving 7-6

⏱ **Presentation Assistant Plus!**
Transparencies
• Check Skills You'll Need 7-6
• Problem of the Day 7-6
• Additional Examples 7-6
• Student Edition Answers 7-6
• Lesson Quiz 7-6
• Classroom Aid 4, 11
PH Presentation Pro CD-ROM 7-6

PRENTICE HALL ASSESSMENT SYSTEM

Checkpoint Quiz 2
Computer Test Generator CD

💻 **Technology**
Resource Pro® CD-ROM
Computer Test Generator CD
PH Presentation Pro CD-ROM

💻 **www.PHSchool.com**
Student Site
• Teacher Web Code: aak-5500
• Self-grading Lesson Quiz

PH SuccessNet Teacher Center
• Lesson Planner
• Resources

Plus 📘**TEXT**

OBJECTIVE 1

Reading Data in a Spreadsheet

📘TEXT Interactive lesson includes instant self-check, tutorials, and activities.

A **spreadsheet** is a table made up of rows and columns used to organize data. A **cell** is a box in a spreadsheet where a particular row and column meet. A computer spreadsheet is an electronic table that is especially useful when you need to repeat calculations.

1 EXAMPLE Using a Spreadsheet 🌎 Real World

Music The spreadsheet shows the lengths of 15 CDs from five different categories. Identify the value in cell B5 and tell what this number represents.

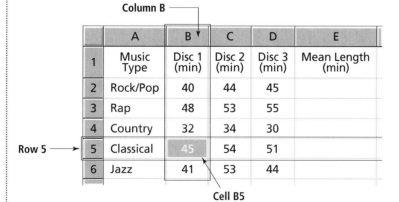

Column B

	A	B	C	D	E
1	Music Type	Disc 1 (min)	Disc 2 (min)	Disc 3 (min)	Mean Length (min)
2	Rock/Pop	40	44	45	
3	Rap	48	53	55	
4	Country	32	34	30	
5	Classical	45	54	51	
6	Jazz	41	53	44	

Row 5 →

Cell B5

1a. 30; the third country CD is 30 min long.

b. A2, B2, C2, D2; the length (in minutes) of each of the three rock/pop CDs.

The value in cell B5 is 45. This means the first classical CD is 45 minutes long.

✔ Check Understanding ①
a. What is the value in cell D4? What does this number represent?
b. What cells are in row 2? What do the numbers in these cells represent?
  1a–b. See above left.

Ongoing Assessment and Intervention

Before the Lesson
Diagnose prerequisite skills using:
• Check Skills You'll Need

During the Lesson
Monitor progress using:
• Check Srunderstanding
• Additional Examples
• Test Prep

After the Lesson
Assess knowledge using:
• Lesson Quiz
• Computer Test Generator CD
• Chapter Checkpoint 2 (p. 350)

Math Background

A computer *spreadsheet* is an electronic table that organizes data and formulas into columns and rows. The intersection of each column and row identifies a *cell* in a spreadsheet. For example, cell A1 identifies the intersection of column A and row 1.

Teaching Notes

1 EXAMPLE Tactile Learners

Have students use index fingers to trace down column B and across row 5 at the same time.

English Learners

Use plain language to explain that *cells* are named by the column letter and row number. Emphasize that columns are vertical and are listed first in a cell name.

Error Prevention!

Some students may confuse *columns* and *rows*.

PowerPoint

Additional Examples

1 Use the spreadsheet below.

	A	B	C
1	Date	Phone	Utilities
2	10/15	$68	$118
3	11/15	$55	$143
4	12/15	$72	$159

a. What is the value in cell C3? **$143**

b. Identify the cell(s) that indicate the category *Phone*. **B1, B2, B3, B4**

2 Use the spreadsheet in Question 1. Write a formula for cell D3 that will calculate the total for 11/15. **=B3+C3**

Closure

- *What is a spreadsheet?* an electronic table that organizes data using columns and rows
- *What is a spreadsheet formula?* a statement of a mathematical relationship that begins with =

348

Need Help?

These operation symbols are used in spreadsheets:
+ addition
− subtraction
* multiplication
/ division

A computer automatically enters a value in a cell of a spreadsheet when you assign a formula to that cell. A formula is a statement of a mathematical relationship. An "=" sign tells the computer that an expression is a formula.

2 EXAMPLE Formulas in a Spreadsheet

The spreadsheet below gives the numbers of cans three classrooms collected during two weeks of a food drive. Write a formula for cell D2 that will calculate the total number of cans collected by Room 105.

	A	B	C	D
1	Room Number	Week 1 (cans)	Week 2 (cans)	Total (cans)
2	105	389	416	
3	106	592	462	▣
4	107	481	493	▣
5		▣	▣	▣

← Add the entries in cells B2 and C2.

The formula that should go in cell D2 is = B2 + C2.

Check Understanding 2 a. Write a formula for cell B5 that will calculate the total number of cans collected in Week 1. **=B2+B3+B4**

b. For cell D5, write a formula that will calculate the total number of cans collected by all three classrooms. **=D2+D3+D4**

EXERCISES

For more practice, see *Extra Practice*.

A Practice by Example

Use the spreadsheet below for Exercises 1–10.

Four groups of students made videos and received scores for originality, effort, and quality.

	A	B	C	D	E	F
1	Group	Originality	Effort	Quality	Total	Mean Score
2	Red	90	85	80	▪	▪
3	Orange	90	90	60	▪	▪
4	Yellow	95	100	75	▪	▪
5	Green	65	80	80	▪	▪

👥 Reaching All Students

Below Level Use a map to introduce the letter and number grid organization of a spreadsheet. Students use the index to identify the location of the school. They then find its location on the map.	**Advanced Learners** Ask: *How might more than 26 columns be named in a spread sheet?* **Sample: Use double letters: AA, AB, and so on.**	**English Learners** See note on page 348. **Tactile Learners** See note on page 348.

Example 1
(page 347)

Identify the cell(s) that indicate each category.

1. Effort
C2, C3, C4, C5

2. Mean Score
F2, F3, F4, F5

3. Green
B5, C5, D5, E5, F5

4. Total
E2, E3, E4, E5

Write the value for the given cell.

5. C4 100

6. C5 80

7. B4 95

8. B2 90

Example 2
(page 348)

Write a formula to find each quantity.

9. the total in cell E4 =B4+C4+D4

10. the mean score in cell F4 =E4/3 or =(B4+C4+D4)/3

B Apply Your Skills

 Wages Suppose your cousin works at a part-time job and earns
$7 per hour. The spreadsheet shows a typical schedule for a week.

	A	B	C	D	E
1	Day	Time In (P.M.)	Time Out (P.M.)	Hours Worked	Amount Earned
2	9/15	3	8	▦	▦
3	9/17	4	8	▦	▦
4	9/19	3	6	▦	▦
5			Total:	▦	▦

GPS

11. Write a formula for cell D2 and calculate the value in cell D2.
=C2−B2; 5

12. Write a formula for cell E2 and calculate the value in cell E2.
=D2*7; 35

13. Write a formula for cell E5.
=D5*7 or =E2+E3+E4

14. Answers may vary. Sample: Copy the formula =C2−B2 into cell D2. The "fill down" function will apply that formula to the entire column D.

14. Writing in Math Spreadsheets have a "fill down" function that copies formulas into the cell(s) below and automatically updates the cell references to the corresponding row. How could you use the "fill down" function in the spreadsheet above? **See left.**

C Challenge

15. Number Sense In Example 2, what will happen to the value in cell D4 if each of the following occurs?
a. The value in cell C4 increases. It will increase.
b. The value in cell B4 decreases. It will decrease.

16. Stretch Your Thinking A palindrome, such as 54,345, reads the same forward and backward. A certain palindrome has three digits. Its first digit is twice its middle digit. The sum of its digits is 10. What is the palindrome? 424

GPS Use the Guided Problem Solving worksheet with Exercise 11.

Assignment Guide

1 Objective 1
Ⓐ Ⓑ Core 1–8
Ⓒ Extension 15

2 Objective 2
Ⓐ Ⓑ Core 9–14
Ⓒ Extension 16

Test Prep 17–19
Mixed Review 20–23

Auditory Learners
Exercises 5–8 Have students read the cell names aloud to themselves as they locate the cell value.

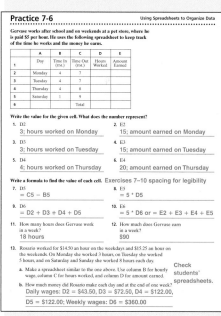

Practice 7-6 Using Spreadsheets to Organize Data

Gervase works after school and on weekends at a pet store, where he is paid $5 per hour. He uses the following spreadsheet to keep track of the time he works and the money he earns.

	A	B	C	D	E
1	Day	Time In (P.M.)	Time Out (P.M.)	Hours Worked	Amount Earned
2	Monday	4	7		
3	Tuesday	4	7		
4	Thursday	4	8		
5	Saturday	1	9		
6			Total		

Write the value for the given cell. What does the number represent?

1. D2
3; hours worked on Monday

2. E2
15; amount earned on Monday

3. D3
3; hours worked on Tuesday

4. E3
15; amount earned on Tuesday

5. D4
4; hours worked on Thursday

6. E4
20; amount earned on Thursday

Write a formula to find the value of each cell. Exercises 7–10 spacing for legibility

7. D5
= C5 − B5

8. E5
= 5 * D5

9. D6
= D2 + D3 + D4 + D5

10. E6
= 5 * D6 or = E2 + E3 + E4 + E5

11. How many hours does Gervase work in a week?
18 hours

12. How much does Gervase earn in a week?
$90

13. Rosario worked for $14.50 an hour on the weekdays and $15.25 an hour on the weekends. On Monday she worked 3 hours, on Tuesday she worked 5 hours, and on Saturday and Sunday she worked 8 hours each day.
  a. Make a spreadsheet similar to the one above. Use column B for hourly wage, column C for hours worked, and column D for amount earned. Check students' spreadsheets.
  b. How much money did Rosario make each day and at the end of one week?
  Daily wages: D2 = $43.50, D3 = $72.50, D4 = $122.00, D5 = $122.00; Weekly wages: D6 = $360.00

Reteaching 7-6 Using Spreadsheets to Organize Data

Party Pals has party equipment for rent. The company uses a *spreadsheet* to keep track of the number of hours its equipment is rented.

	A	B	C	D	E	F
1	Machine	Fri.	Sat.	Sun.	Total	Mean Rental Time
2	Party Popcorner	4	8	6		
3	Juice Fountain	0	3	3		
4	Soft Ice Cream Machine	8	9	4		
5	Pretzel Oven	1	6	5		

- A *cell* is a box in a spreadsheet where a particular row and column meet. In column C, you find the cells C1, C2, C3, and so on. C2 shows 8. Its value is 8 hours.
- Missing values can be found by telling the spreadsheet what calculation to do. The value for cell E3 can be found by using the formula = B3 + C3 + D3.

Use the spreadsheet above for Exercises 1–13. Identify the cell(s) that indicate each category.

1. machines rented
A2−A5

2. rental times for Saturday
C2−C5

3. total rental hours for the Popcorner
E2

4. mean rental time for the pretzel oven
F5

Write the value for the given cell.

5. B5
1 hour

6. C4
9 hours

7. D3
3 hours

8. B3
0 hours

9. D5
5 hours

Write a formula to find each quantity.

10. the total in cell E4
= B4 + C4 + D4

11. the total in cell E5
= B5 + C5 + D5

12. the total in cell E2
= B2 + C2 + D2

13. the mean score in cell F5
= E5/3 or = (B5 + C5 + D5)/3

Lesson Quiz 7-6

Use the spreadsheet to answer the questions.

	A	B	C
1	Name	1st Term	2nd Term
2	Eve	85	95
3	Sam	90	96
4	Carl	92	86

1. What are the values of cell C4 and B3? **C4 is 86; B3 is 90**

2. What formula could you write in cell D2 to find Eve's average? **=(B2+C2)/2**

 Chapter Checkpoint

To check understanding of Lessons 7-4 to 7-6:

Checkpoint Quiz 2 (p. 350)

📁 **Teaching Resources**
Checkpoint Quiz 2 (also in Prentice Hall Assessment System)

Reaching All Students
Reading and Math Literacy 7C

Spanish versions available

 Test Prep

Multiple Choice

Use the spreadsheet at the right.

	A	B	C	D
1	Type of Seat	Tickets Sold	Ticket Price	Total
2	Balcony	36	$13.00	▪
3	Mezzanine	105	$18.50	▪
4	Front row	10	$26.50	▪
5			TOTAL:	▪

17. What formula can you use in cell D2? **C**
   A. = B2 + C2
   B. = B2 – C2
   C. = B2 * C2
   D. = B2/C2

 Take It to the NET
Online lesson quiz at
www.PHSchool.com
Web Code: aaa-0706

18. What is the value in cell D3? **I**
   F. $86.50
   G. $58.00
   H. $123.50
   I. $1,942.50

Short Response

19. What is the value in cell D5? Explain your answer. **$2,675.50; See back of book for rubric.**

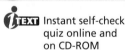 **Mixed Review**

Lesson 6-7   **Find each percent.**

20. 11% of 200 **22**   21. 3% of 150 **4.5**   22. 20% of 50 **10**

Lesson 6-9   23. You need $1\frac{1}{2}$ cups of water and milk for a recipe. You have $\frac{2}{3}$ cup of milk. How much water do you need? Solve by writing and solving an equation. $\frac{5}{6}$ **c; Equations may vary. Sample:** $\frac{2}{3} + w = 1\frac{1}{2}$

✓ **Checkpoint Quiz 2**   **Lessons 7-4 through 7-6**

TEXT Instant self-check quiz online and on CD-ROM

Use the spreadsheet below for Exercises 1–4.

1. Write a formula for cell B6.
   =B2+B3+B4+B5
2. How much money was collected from the fundraisers? **$800**

	A	B
1	Fundraiser	Collected ($)
2	Book sale	200
3	Car wash	125
4	Food stand	325
5	Paper drive	150
6	TOTAL:	▪

3. Draw a bar graph of the data. **See back of book.**
4. Draw a circle graph of the data. **See back of book.**

5.

Bank Balance

(line graph: Balance ($) vs Month — Jan. ~37, Feb. ~40, Mar. ~55, Apr. ~15)

5. Suppose your bank account balance is $37 in January, $40 in February, $55 in March, and $15 in April. Draw a line graph of the data. **See left.**

Alternative Assessment

Each student in a pair makes a spreadsheet similar to Example 1. They write several questions that can be answered using their spreadsheets. Partners exchange spreadsheets and questions. Then they answer each other's questions.

Test Prep

Resources
For additional practice with a variety of test item formats:
• Test Prep, p. 367
• Test-Taking Strategies, p. 363
• Test-Taking Strategies With Transparencies

Making a Graph From a Spreadsheet

For Use With Lesson 7-6

You can use spreadsheet programs to make circle, line, and bar graphs. Enter and highlight the data you want to graph. Use the menu to choose the type of graph and labels. Finally, insert the labels.

EXAMPLE

Sierra makes a table showing how she spends her time on weekdays. She enters the data in the spreadsheet below. Sierra then chooses a circle graph because it shows the portion of her weekday spent on each activity.

	A	B
	Activity	Number of Hours
1	School	7
2	Homework	2
3	Recreation	4
4	Eating	3
5	Sleeping	8

How Sierra Spends Her Time on Weekdays

- Homework 8%
- Recreation 17%
- Eating 13%
- School 29%
- Sleeping 33%

EXERCISES

Enter the data below in a spreadsheet. Then use the program to make a graph of the data. Explain why you chose to make each type of graph. 1–3. See margin for graphs.

1.

Ages of Customers at Freddy's Restaurant

Age	Under 12	12–18	19–30	31–50	Over 50
Number of People	80	120	60	30	70

2.

How Theo Spends His Weekly Allowance

Category	Food	School	Fun	Savings	Other
Amount Spent	$4	$5	$6	$2	$1

3.

How Often People Need to Search for Keys

Category	Never	Once a year	Once a month	Once a week	Once a day
Number of Responses	31	15	23	9	2

3. Explanations may vary. Sample: A bar graph makes it easy to compare the number of responses in each category.

1. Explanations may vary. Sample: A circle graph shows which percentage of customers at Freddy's restaurant are from each age group.

2. Explanations may vary. Sample: A circle graph shows what part of Theo's allowance he spends on each category.

3. See margin.

1–3. Graphs may vary. Samples are given.

1. Ages of Customers at Freddy's Restaurant

- 12–18
- 19–30
- Under 12
- Over 50
- 31–50

2. See back of book.

 **Check Skills You'll Need**

Finding the Median
Lesson 7-1: Example 2. Extra
Practice, p. 648.

Lesson Resources

📁 **Teaching Resources**
Practice, Reteaching, Enrichment

👥 **Reaching All Students**
Practice Workbook 7-7
Spanish Practice Workbook 7-7
Guided Problem Solving 7-7
Hands-On Activities 26

⏱ **Presentation Assistant Plus!**
Transparencies
• Check Skills You'll Need 7-7
• Problem of the Day 7-7
• Additional Examples 7-7
• Student Edition Answers 7-7
• Lesson Quiz 7-7
• Classroom Aid 29, 30, 31, 32, 33
PH Presentation Pro CD-ROM 7-7

PRENTICE HALL
ASSESSMENT SYSTEM

Computer Test Generator CD

💻 **Technology**
Resource Pro® CD-ROM
Computer Test Generator CD
PH Presentation Pro CD-ROM

💻 **www.PHSchool.com**
Student Site
• Teacher Web Code: aak-5500
• Self-grading Lesson Quiz

PH SuccessNet Teacher Center
• Lesson Planner
• Resources

Plus iTEXT

7-7 Stem-and-Leaf Plots

What You'll Learn

OBJECTIVE 1 To use a stem-and-leaf plot

. . . And Why

To describe wage data, as in Example 2

✓ **Check Skills You'll Need**   ❓ For help, go to Lesson 7-1.

Find the median of each data set.

1. 23, 32, 32, 15, 26, 52, 38, 44 **32**

2. 15, 10, 15, 21, 32, 48, 10, 15 **15**

3. 125, 213, 325, 100, 212, 125, 216 **212**

4. 6.7, 5.8, 8.9, 3.5, 4.6, 5.8, 3.8, 2.5 **5.2**

New Vocabulary   • stem-and-leaf plot

OBJECTIVE
1   **Using a Stem-and-Leaf Plot**

📱 Interactive lesson includes instant self-check, tutorials, and activities.

A **stem-and-leaf plot** is a graph that uses the digits of each number to show the shape of the data. Each data value is broken into a "stem" on the left and a single-digit "leaf" on the right. To read the data, combine the stem with each leaf in the same row.

$$\text{stem} \rightarrow 5\,|\,8 \leftarrow \text{leaf}$$

1 EXAMPLE   **Reading a Stem-and-Leaf Plot**

The stem-and-leaf plot below shows the number of minutes students take to get ready for school. How many students take less than 30 minutes to get ready for school? How many take more than 40 minutes?

**Times to Get Ready
for School (minutes)**

2	3 3 5 7 8 8
3	3 4 5 7 7 7 9
4	0 0 2 3 3 5
5	8

Key: 2 | 3 means 23 minutes

6 students take less than 30 minutes.
Their times are 23, 23, 25, 27, 28, and 28.

5 students take more than 40 minutes.
Their times are 42, 43, 43, 45, and 58.

Six students take less than 30 minutes to get ready for school. Five students take more than 40 minutes.

✓ **Check Understanding** **1** **a.** How many students take 37 minutes? **3**

b. What is the range of the data? **35**

c. **Reasoning** What advantage does a stem-and-leaf plot have compared to an ordered list of values? **Answers may vary. Sample: A stem-and-leaf plot groups the data so that it is easier to find the median and mode.**

Ongoing Assessment and Intervention

Before the Lesson	**During the Lesson**	**After the Lesson**
Diagnose prerequisite skills using:	Monitor progress using:	Assess knowledge using:
• Check Skills You'll Need	• Check Understanding • Additional Examples • Test Prep	• Lesson Quiz • Computer Test Generator CD

Hourly Wages The data at the left shows hourly wages for a group of people. Make a stem-and-leaf plot of the data.

Hourly Wages	
$8.20	$7.00
$7.30	$8.90
$7.20	$8.30
$8.00	$7.00
$7.70	$7.60
$8.10	$8.70
$8.10	$7.30
$7.20	$10.50
$7.60	$8.50
$6.50	$6.80

Step 1 Write the stems in order. Use the whole number part. Draw a vertical line to the right of the stems.

stems →
```
 6 |
 7 |
 8 |
 9 |
10 |
```

Step 2 Write the leaves in order. Use the values in the tenths place because there is no nonzero digit in the hundredths place.

```
 6 | 5 8            ← leaves
 7 | 0 0 2 2 3 3 6 6 7
 8 | 0 1 1 2 3 5 7 9
 9 |
10 | 5
```

Step 3 Choose a title and include a key to explain what your stems and leaves represent.

Hourly Wages ($)
```
 6 | 5 8
 7 | 0 0 2 2 3 3 6 6 7
 8 | 0 1 1 2 3 5 7 9
 9 |
10 | 5
```
Key: 6 | 5 means $6.50   ← key

2.
```
12 | 1 3 4 5 5 6 7
13 | 0 2 3 6 7 8 8
14 | 0 1 4 5
15 | 0 5
16 |
17 |
18 | 1
```
Key: 12|3 means 123

✓ **Check Understanding** 2 Make a stem-and-leaf plot of the data: 137, 125, 145, 123, 181, 132, 155, 141, 140, 133, 138, 127, 150, 126, 124, 130, 125, 138, 144, 121, and 136. (*Hint:* Use the one's digit for the leaves.) See above left.

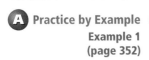

EXERCISES

? For more practice, see *Extra Practice*.

A **Practice by Example**
Example 1
(page 352)

Use the stem-and-leaf plot at the right.

Number of Seconds Customers on Hold	

1. What does "0 | 8" represent? **8 seconds**

2. How many entries have a value of 15?
3 entries

```
0 | 7 8 8 8 9 9
1 | 0 2 2 3 4 5 5 5 6 7 7
```
Key: 0 | 7 means 7 seconds

3. How many customers were on hold for 11 seconds? **none**

4. How many customers waited less than 9 seconds? **4 customers**

---

2. Teach

Professional Development

Math Background

A *stem-and-leaf plot* uses the digits of the data values to display the shape of a data set. A stem-and-leaf plot separates the digits in each data value into a *stem* and a *leaf*. The stem is recorded once, forming an interval. The leaf lists each data value as often as it appears in the data set.

Teaching Notes

1 EXAMPLE **Error Prevention**

Make sure students understand that every data value is listed even if it is a repeated value such as 23.

2 EXAMPLE **Inclusion**

For Check Understanding 2, it may help students to write all of the stems before plotting the leaves.

PowerPoint
Additional Examples

1 Use the stem-and-leaf plot.

Wait Times for Haircuts
```
0 | 1 1 3 4 5 6 9
1 | 0 0 1 3 4 4 9
2 | 1 2 4 6
3 | 0 2
```
Key: 0 | 5 means 5 min

a. How many customers waited more than 10 min?
11 customers

b. How long was the longest wait? **32 min**

2 Make a stem-and-leaf plot of the following bowling scores.
130 90 141 128 133 142
123 148 105 93 108 130
133 100 124 146 97 108

Bowling Scores
```
 9 | 0 3 7
10 | 0 5 8 8
11 |
12 | 3 4 8
13 | 0 0 3 3    Key:
14 | 1 2 6 8    9 | 0 means 90
```

Closure

What is a stem-and-leaf plot?
a graph that uses the digits of each number to show the shape of the data

---

🌱 Reaching All Students

Below Level Ask: *How is a stem-and-leaf plot similar to a line plot?* Both plots show the shape of the data. Both plots also represent each data value.	**Advanced Learners** Ask: *How are stem-and-leaf plots different from line plots?* Sample: The line plot is organized by each value and the stem-and-leaf plot is organized by stems into intervals.	**English Learners** See note on page 354. **Inclusion** See note on page 353.

Assignment Guide

1 Objective 1
  Ⓐ Ⓑ Core 1–12
  Ⓒ Extension 13–14

Test Prep 15–18
Mixed Review 19–26

English Learners
Exercise 2 Elicit that *entries* are data values in the stem-and-leaf plot.

Error Prevention!

Exercises 5–10 Make sure students include a title and key in their plots.

Practice 7-7   Stem-and-Leaf Plots

Use the stem-and-leaf plot for Exercises 1–7.

Ages of Grandparents
stem	leaf
6	7 8 8
7	0 1 2 3 4 9 9
8	1 3 3 3 4 7
9	0 2 5

1. What is the age of the youngest grandparent? **67**
2. What is the age of the oldest grandparent? **95**
3. How many grandparents are 79 years old? **2**
4. How many grandparents are older than 74? **11**
5. What is the range of the data? **28**
6. What is the median? **79**
7. What is the mode? **83**

Make a stem-and-leaf plot for each set of data.

8. scores on a history test

84, 93, 72, 87, 86, 97, 68, 74, 86, 91, 64, 83, 79, 80, 72, 83, 76, 90, 77
stem	leaf
6	4 8
7	2 2 4 6 7 9
8	0 3 3 4 6 6 7
9	0 1 3 7

9. number of badges earned by local scouts

7, 12, 9, 2, 17, 24, 0, 3, 10, 20, 12, 3, 6, 4, 9, 15
stem	leaf
0	0 2 3 3 4 6 7 9 9
1	0 2 2 5 7
2	0 4

10. minutes to travel to a friend's house

12, 31, 5, 10, 23, 17, 21, 12, 8, 33, 3, 11, 10, 25, 9, 16
stem	leaf
0	3 5 8 9
1	0 0 1 2 2 6 7
2	1 3 5
3	1 3

Reteaching 7-7   Stem-and-Leaf Plots

A stem-and-leaf plot is a graph that uses the digits of each number to show the shape of the data. Each data value is broken into a "stem" on the left and a "leaf" on the right. A vertical segment separates the stems from the leaves. To read the data, combine the stem with each leaf in the same row.

Example: Make a stem-and-leaf diagram of the data showing minutes spent eating lunch.

Minutes Spent Eating Lunch
46, 35, 12, 37, 28, 10, 22, 54, 19, 13, 46, 51

① Decide what the stem of the diagram will represent. Since these data are two-digit numbers, the stem will be the tens digits and the leaves will be the ones digits.

② Write the tens digits in order in the lefthand column of the diagram. Then write each leaf at the right of its stem as they occur in the problem.

③ Complete the second stem-and-leaf diagram, with the leaves in order from least to greatest.

②
Stem	Leaf
1	2 0 9 3
2	8 2
3	5 7
4	6 6
5	4 1

③
Stem	Leaf
1	0 2 3 9
2	2 8
3	5 7
4	6 6
5	1 4

For Exercises 1–4, use the stem-and-leaf plot at the right.

Ages of People Attending a Poetry Reading
Stem	Leaf
0	5 8 8 9
1	8 8 9 9
2	3 5 5 6 8 8 9
3	2 2 7
4	0 1 3
5	2 8
6	4 4 6 7 8

Key 0 | 8 means 8 years old

1. What does 1 | 8 represent?
   18 years old
2. How many entries have a value of 25?
   2 entries
3. How many people were older than 40?
   9 people
4. How many people were at the poetry reading?
   28 people
5. Make a stem-and-leaf plot for the data showing the monthly attendance at the teen club.

Attendance at Teen Club
489, 527, 479, 519, 514, 480, 493, 523, 508, 504
Stem	Leaf
47	9
48	0 9
49	3
50	4 8
51	4 9
52	3 7

354

Example 2
(page 353)

6. Test Scores (percent)
6	4 8
7	6
8	1 4 4 5 5 6 9
9	1 3 5 7

Key: 6|4 means 64%

Ⓑ Apply Your Skills

10a. Heights of People
4	1 1
5	1 4 6 7 8 10
6	7 10

Key: 4|11 means 4 ft 11 in.

11c. Line plot. Explanations may vary. Sample: The column with the most X's is the mode.

d. Stem-and-leaf plot. Explanations may vary. Sample: The data with a stem of 1 and a leaf of 3 or more represent the teenagers.

Make a stem-and-leaf plot for each set of data.

5. heights of tomato plants (inches): **See margin.**

   27 40 31 33 35 33 26 36 41 29 30 36

6. test scores (percents): **See left.**

   93 76 85 85 68 81 84 89 84 91 97 95 86 64

7. number of jelly beans in a scoop: **See margin.**

   47 28 38 47 58 34 76 35 32 45 53 43 35 27

 8. **Population** The table at the right shows the populations of nine states.
   a. Make a stem-and-leaf plot.
   b. **Reasoning** Would it be easier to make a stem-and-leaf plot if the state populations were written out (for example: 5,456,453 for Arizona)? Explain your answer. **8a–b.**
      See margin.

9. **Writing in Math** Explain how you can find the median and mode of the data in a stem-and-leaf plot. **See margin.**

10. **Heights** The heights of nine people are given below.

   5 ft 10 in.   4 ft 11 in.   5 ft 4 in.
   5 ft 6 in.   6 ft 7 in.   5 ft 7 in.
   6 ft 10 in.   5 ft 8 in.   5 ft 1 in.

   GPS a. Make a stem-and-leaf plot. **See left.**
   b. Find the median. **5 ft 7 in.**
   c. Find the mode. **none**
   d. Are there any outliers? If so, what are they?
      Yes; 6 ft 7 in. and 6 ft 10 in.

11. The ages of 18 people are shown below. **11a–b. See back of book.**

   21 12 15 13 35 24 16 23 40   **11c–d. See left.**
    9 19 12 15 13 12 20 11 12

   a. Make a stem-and-leaf plot.
   b. Make a line plot.
   c. **Reasoning** Which plot shows the mode most clearly? Explain.
   d. **Reasoning** Which plot shows the number of people in their teens most clearly? Explain your answer.

12. a. **Data Collection** Choose a paragraph from a book and record the number of letters in each word.
   b. Make a stem-and-leaf plot.
   c. Use the plot to find the median length word in the paragraph.
   12a–c. Check students' work.

State	Population (millions)
Arizona	5.5
Colorado	4.5
Indiana	6.2
Kentucky	4.1
Maryland	5.5
Minnesota	5.0
Oregon	3.5
Tennessee	5.8
Wisconsin	5.4

SOURCE: U.S. Census Bureau.
Go to **www.PHSchool.com** for a data update. Web Code: aag-2041

354   Chapter 7   Data and Graphs

GPS Use the Guided Problem Solving worksheet with Exercise 10a.

5. Height of Tomato Plants (inches)
2	6 7 9
3	0 1 3 3 5 6 6
4	0 1

Key: 2|6 means 26 in.

7. Number of Jelly Beans in a Scoop
2	7 8
3	2 4 5 5 8
4	3 5 7 7
5	3 8
6	
7	6

Key: 2|7 means 27 jelly beans

Challenge

13. A data set has a least value of 17.26 and a greatest value of 17.89.

   a. What is the range of the data? **0.63**

   b. Explain how you would display the data using a stem-and-leaf plot.
     See left.

13b. Use stems ranging from 172 to 178, and the key 172|6 means 17.26.

14. Stretch Your Thinking Draw the figure at the right without lifting your pencil from the paper and without retracing any line. **See back of book.**

Test Prep

Multiple Choice

Use the stem-and-leaf plot below.

15. What is the mode? **C**

  A. 7   **B.** 54

  C. 67   **D.** 68

4	0 9
5	2 4 4 5 9
6	3 7 7 7 8 8 9
7	2 4 6

Key: 4 | 0 means 40

16. How many data items are greater than 67? **G**

  F. 3   **G.** 6

  H. 10   **I.** 17

17. What is the median of the data? **C**

  A. 17   **B.** 54   **C.** 67   **D.** 77

Short Response

18. Which measure would be easiest to find from a stem-and-leaf plot, mean, median, or range? Justify your answer. **See back of book.**

Mixed Review

Lesson 6-9   **Algebra** Solve each problem by writing an equation.

19. On the first Wednesday of every month, a department store offers a 10% discount on any item in the store. How much is the regular price if the sale price of a jacket is $54? **$60**

20. Before tax, your restaurant dinner plus a 15% tip totals $13.80. What was the cost of the meal alone? **$12.00**

Lesson 6-3   Determine whether each pair of ratios forms a proportion.

21. $\frac{45}{100}, \frac{4}{10}$ **no**   **22.** $\frac{24}{56}, \frac{3}{7}$ **yes**   **23.** $\frac{105}{49}, \frac{36}{16}$ **no**

Lesson 6-4   Solve each proportion.

24. $\frac{9}{5} = \frac{c}{11}$ **25.** $\frac{8}{m} = \frac{3}{20}$ **26.** $\frac{7}{10} = \frac{5}{x}$

   19.8   **53$\frac{1}{3}$ or 53.$\overline{3}$**   **7$\frac{1}{7}$ or 7.$\overline{142857}$**

7-7 Stem-and-Leaf Plots   **355**

 **Lesson Quiz 7-7**

The Eagles scored the following points in the basketball games they played this season: 67, 59, 75, 49, 68, 72, 84, 59, 71, 69, 81, 55, 68, 83, and 77.

1. Make a stem-and-leaf plot for the data.

Points Scored in a Game

4	9
5	5 9 9
6	7 8 8 9
7	1 2 5 7 **Key:**
8	1 3 4 8	4 means 84

Alternative Assessment

Students work in pairs to find real-world data. Partners make a stem-and-leaf plot of the data and then write questions that involve interpreting their plot. Pairs exchange their plots and questions with other pairs and answer the questions.

Test Prep

Resources
For additional practice with a variety of test item formats:
• Test Prep, p. 367
• Test-Taking Strategies, p. 363
• Test-Taking Strategies With Transparencies

Enrichment 7-7   Stem-and-Leaf Plots

Decision Making

Make a stem-and-leaf plot for the data set below.

The ten fastest fish in the world (in miles per hour) include the following: sailfish, 68; blue shark, 43; swordfish, 40; marlin, 50; bluefin tuna, 46; wahoo, 41; tarpon, 35; bonefish, 40; yellowfin tuna, 44; tiger shark, 33.

1. Write the stems from least to greatest. Then write each leaf to the right of its stem as it occurs in the problem.

Stem	Leaf
3	5 3
4	3 0 6 1 0 4
5	0
6	8

2. Redraw the stem-and-leaf diagram, with the leaves in order from least to greatest.

Stem	Leaf
3	3 5
4	0 0 1 3 4 6
5	0
6	8

3. Which digits are the "stems" and which digits are the "leaves"? **stems: 3, 4, 5, 6; leaves: 3, 5, 0, 1, 3, 4, 6, 8**

4. What other ways could you display the data? **Sample answers: bar graph or line plot**

5. Make a stem-and-leaf diagram to organize the data. The average lengths (in feet) of some of the fastest fish in the world are: sailfish, 8; swordfish, 11; marlin, 35; bluefin tuna, 14; wahoo, 3; tarpon, 8; bonefish, 2; yellowfin tuna, 11. (*Hint:* Use zero as one of the stems.)

Stem	Leaf
0	8 3 8 2
1	1 4 1
2	
3	5

Stem	Leaf
0	2 3 8 8
1	1 1 4
2	
3	5

6. Why is a stem-and-leaf plot helpful when trying to organize a large set of data? **A stem-and-leaf plot can display a large amount of data in a small space.**

8a. State Populations in Millions

3	5
4	1 5
5	0 4 5 5 8
6	2

Key: 3|5 means 3.5 million

b. No; explanations may vary. Sample: The stem and the leaf would have too many digits to read easily.

9. Answers may vary. Sample: The median is the data item that corresponds with the middle leaf. The mode is the data item that corresponds with the leaf that occurs most often.

Box-and-Whisker Plots

Students learn how to find quartiles and make a box-and-whisker plot to show the distribution of a data set.

Optional Materials

- ruler
- Classroom Aid 31–33

Teaching Notes

Explain that a *box-and-whisker plot* is a visual summary of a data set that shows five key values on a number line: the least value, the greatest value, and three quartiles. To make a box-and-whisker plot you first need to find the quartiles, or numbers that divide the data set into four equal parts.

English Learners

Help students relate quartile to "quarter" to remember its meaning. Ask: *How many quarters make a dollar?* **four**

1 EXAMPLE Inclusion

Help students understand that *three* quartiles, or numbers, divide the data set into *four* equal parts. Ask:
- *If you want to fold a piece of paper into two equal-sized parts, how many folds would you make?* **one**
- *If you want to fold a piece of paper into four equal-sized parts, how many folds would you make?* **three**

Error Prevention!

Exercise 1 Emphasize that the first step in finding the median of a data set is to list the data in numerical order.

A *box-and-whisker plot* is a graph that describes a data set along a number line. It shows the greatest value, the least value, and quartiles.

Quartiles divide the data into four equal parts. The *middle quartile* is the median of the data. The *lower quartile* is the median of the lower half of the data. The *upper quartile* is the median of the upper half of the data.

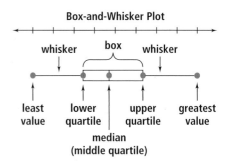

Box-and-Whisker Plot

whisker · box · whisker
least value · lower quartile · upper quartile · greatest value
median (middle quartile)

1 EXAMPLE Finding Quartiles

Find the middle, lower, and upper quartiles for the data below.

Home Runs Hit by Barry Bonds

Year	1993	1994	1995	1996	1997	1998	1999	2000	2001	2002
Home Runs	46	37	33	42	40	37	34	49	73	46

SOURCE: Major League Baseball Players Association

Step 1 Find the median of the data.

33 34 37 37 40 42 46 46 49 73 ← Order the data.

$$\frac{40 + 42}{2} = 41 \quad \leftarrow \text{Find the median.}$$

The median of the data is 41, so the middle quartile is 41.

Step 2 Find the median of the lower half of the data and the upper half of the data.

33 34 37 37 40 ← List the lower half of the data.

The median of the lower half of the data is 37, so the lower quartile is 37.

42 46 46 49 73 ← List the upper half of the data.

The median of the upper half of the data is 46, so the upper quartile is 46.

EXERCISES

Find the middle, lower, and upper quartiles for the data below.

1. 6 8 7 6 5 8 5 6 4 8 7 5 4 7 6 8 6 7 6; 5; 7

2. 12 24 18 35 30 45 42 21 17 25 24.5; 18; 35

② EXAMPLE Making a Box-and-Whisker Plot

Make a box-and-whisker plot for the data in Example 1.

Step 1 Find the least value and greatest value.

33   34   37   37   40   42   46   46   49   73   ← **Order the data.**

The least value is 33 and the greatest value is 73.

Step 2 Draw a number line that shows the range of the data. Below the number line, plot the least value, greatest value, and quartiles found in Example 1.

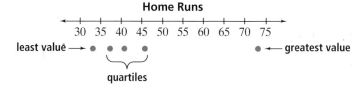

Step 3 Draw a box through each quartile as shown.

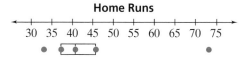

Step 4 Connect the least and the greatest values to the box to make the whiskers.

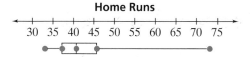

EXERCISES (continued)

Make a box-and-whisker plot for each data set.

3. The heights of eight students in a class are listed below in inches.

58   67   63   60   61   60   64   66

Heights of Eight Students (inches)

4. The birth weights of 12 kittens are listed below in grams.

114   112   110   113   121   115   117   106   115   108   116   114

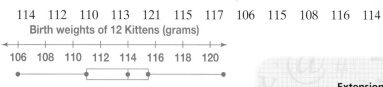

② EXAMPLE **Visual Learners**

Help students see that the upper and lower quartiles form a "box" and the least and greatest data values each form "whiskers" that connect to the "box." Ask:
- *What does the box represent?* Sample: the middle 50% of the data values, or data values between the lower and upper quartiles
- *What do the whiskers represent?* Sample: the top 25% and the bottom 25% of the data values

Inclusion

Have students examine the box-and-whisker plot in Step 4 of Example 2. Ask:
- *How many numbers are needed to make a box-and-whisker plot?* five
- *What do the numbers represent?* least value, greatest value, median (or middle quartile), lower quartile, and upper quartile
- *From the plot, can you find the range of the data set? If so, what is it?* Yes, it is 40.

Teaching Tip

Help students understand that box-and-whisker plots do not retain all of the data values like a stem-and-leaf plot or a line plot.

Error Prevention!

Exercises 1–2 Watch for students who do not recognize that the upper and lower quartiles require finding a mean of the two middle values (of the respective upper and lower halves of the data set).

Lesson Preview

✓ **Check Skills You'll Need**   PowerPoint

Finding the Mean
Lesson 7-1: Example 1. Extra Practice, p. 648.

Lesson Resources

📁 **Teaching Resources**
Practice, Reteaching, Enrichment

👥 **Reaching All Students**
Practice Workbook 7-8
Spanish Practice Workbook 7-8
Guided Problem Solving 7-8

⏰ **Presentation Assistant Plus!**
Transparencies
• Check Skills You'll Need 7-8
• Problem of the Day 7-8
• Additional Examples 7-8
• Student Edition Answers 7-8
• Lesson Quiz 7-8
• Classroom Aid 2
PH Presentation Pro CD-ROM 7-8

PRENTICE HALL
ASSESSMENT SYSTEM

Computer Test Generator CD

💻 **Technology**
Resource Pro® CD-ROM
Computer Test Generator CD
PH Presentation Pro CD-ROM

💻 **www.PHSchool.com**
Student Site
• Teacher Web Code: aak-5500
• Self-grading Lesson Quiz

PH SuccessNet Teacher Center
• Lesson Planner
• Resources

 Plus **TEXT**

What You'll Learn

OBJECTIVE 1 To identify misleading graphs

OBJECTIVE 2 To identify misleading statistics

. . . And Why

To look at graphs critically, as in Example 1

✓ **Check Skills You'll Need** 🔍 For help, go to Lesson 7-1.

Find the mean for each set of data. Round to the nearest tenth.

1. 21, 25, 52, 58, 64, 71, 71, 82 **55.5**   **2.** 8, 9, 11, 12, 13, 13, 18, 24 **13.5**

3. 111, 121, 131, 141, 151 **131**   **4.** 3, 10, 85, 87, 98, 99 **63.7**

5. Without finding each median, in which of the sets of data above do you expect the greatest difference between the mean and the median? Explain. **The data set in Exercise 4, which has outliers.**

OBJECTIVE 1   Interactive lesson includes instant self-check, tutorials, and activities.

Identifying Misleading Graphs

Data is often presented to influence you. As you look at data displays, consider these questions: Is the information shown accurately? Is the presentation trying to influence you?

1 EXAMPLE **Misleading Line Graphs**   Real World

Politics Each month residents of a town were asked, "Do you think the mayor is doing a good job?" The results are shown below.

1.
Mayor's Performance
(graph: Percent Who Approve vs. Month Jan. Feb. Mar. Apr.)

a. What impression is given by the mayor's graph?

The graph suggests only a slight drop in support for the mayor.

b. Why is the graph misleading?

The vertical scale uses unequal intervals. So, the drop from 70% to 40% does not look so large.

Mayor's Performance

✓ **Check Understanding** ① Redraw the graph so that it is not misleading. **See above left.**

Bar graphs and histograms create a misleading impression if the vertical scale does not start at 0.

Ongoing Assessment and Intervention

Before the Lesson	During the Lesson	After the Lesson
Diagnose prerequisite skills using:	**Monitor progress using:**	**Assess knowledge using:**
• Check Skills You'll Need	• Check Understanding • Additional Examples • Test Prep	• Lesson Quiz • Computer Test Generator CD

2 EXAMPLE Misleading Bar Graphs **Real World**

Advertising An auto dealer made the graph at the right.

a. What impression is given by the graph?

It looks like there was a dramatic increase in sales.

b. Why is the graph misleading?

The vertical scale does not begin at 0. So, you are looking just at the top of the graph.

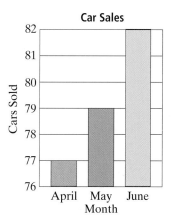

Car Sales

✔ **Check Understanding** 2 Use the graph in Example 2.
  a. How many times as tall is the bar for June compared to the bar for May? **two times taller**
  b. How many more cars were sold in June than in May? **3 cars**
  c. Redraw the graph so that it is not misleading. **See below left.**

OBJECTIVE

2 Identifying Misleading Statistics

The mean is a statistic that can be misleading. This is because the mean can be distorted by outliers.

2c.

3 EXAMPLE Real-World  **Problem Solving**

Sports Five players on a professional basketball team have a mean salary of $2.2 million. Their five salaries are shown at the right. Why might the mean salary be misleading?

Only one person makes more than the mean of $2.2 million. The $7.2 million salary is an outlier and greatly increases the mean.

Players' Salaries
$7,200,000
$1,200,000
$1,000,000
$800,000
$800,000

✔ **Check Understanding** 3 **a.** Find the players' mean salary in Example 3 without the outlier. **$950,000**
  b. Reasoning In Example 3, which would better describe the basketball player's salaries, the median or the mode? Explain. **Median; the mode is the least data value. It occurs only twice, so its value is really too low to give a good idea of what a typical data value is.**

The median is often used to describe data sets that have outliers. Salaries and home prices are typical examples.

7-8 Misleading Graphs and Statistics **359**

Reaching All Students

Below Level Review with students the key terms *scale*, *axis*, and *intervals*. For Example 1, have students find the interval for the scale of the vertical axis, 5, and count by 5's to find where the interval changes.

Advanced Learners Ask: *Can a data set have two outliers but still have a mean that is not distorted?* **Sample: Yes, the outliers can compensate for one another and therefore not distort the mean.**

Diversity
See note on page 360.
Error Prevention
See note on page 359.

---

2. Teach

Professional Development

Math Background

Graphs can be misleading if the scale used is unequal or if it does not start at zero. Statistics can also be misleading when they do not accurately reflect the data.

Teaching Notes

1 EXAMPLE Error Prevention

Have students look for differences between successive intervals.

PowerPoint

Additional Examples

1 Admission Price
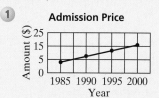

a. What impression is given by the graph? **Sample: The admission price is gradually increasing.**

b. Why is the graph misleading? **The vertical scale has unequal increments.**

2 College Enrollment
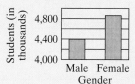

a. What impression is given by the graph? **Sample: The number of females enrolled is more than twice the number of males enrolled.**

b. Why is the graph misleading? **The vertical scale does not start at 0.**

3 Five hourly wages are $5, $8, $7.50, $35, and $7. Why might the mean wage be misleading? **Sample: The mean wage of $12.50 is greater than all wages except the outlier.**

Closure

How can graphs be misleading? **The scale might have unequal intervals or not start at zero.**

359

For more practice, see *Extra Practice*.

EXERCISES

Assignment Guide

1 Objective 1
Ⓐ Ⓑ Core 1–4, 8–12
Ⓒ Extension 15

2 Objective 2
Ⓐ Ⓑ Core 5–7, 13
Ⓒ Extension 14, 16

Test Prep 17–20
Mixed Review 21–25

Diversity
Exercise 5 Have a volunteer who bowls explain how the game is played and scored.

Ⓐ **Practice by Example**

Examples 1, 2
(pages 358, 359)

Decide whether each graph is misleading. If a graph is misleading, answer the following. 1–4. See margin.

a. What impression is given by the graph?
b. Why is the graph misleading?
c. Redraw the graph so that it is not misleading.

1. Plant Growth
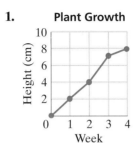

2. Phone Sales

3. Dogs in Animal Shelter

4. Number of Complaints to City Hall
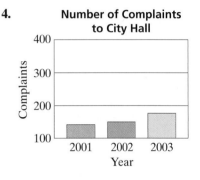

5a–b. See margin.

Example 3
(page 359)

5. Bowling Jill and Allen bowl a match of three games. Their scores are shown at the right.
a. Jill claims she won the match. How can she support her claim?
b. Allen claims he won the match. How can he support his claim?

Bowling Scores

Game	Jill	Allen
1	96	75
2	60	81
3	75	75

6. Cameras A salesman wants to convince you to buy a digital camera. The prices of cameras available are

$138 $138 $138 $179 $189 $198 $219 $249 $449.

Would the salesman use the mean, median, or mode to encourage you to look at the cameras? Explain your answer. See margin.

7. Tests Bill scored 100%, 100%, 90%, 70%, and 60% on five quizzes.
a. Which makes his grades look the highest, the mean, the median, or the mode? mode
b. Which measure should his teacher use to convince Bill to study harder for the exam? mean

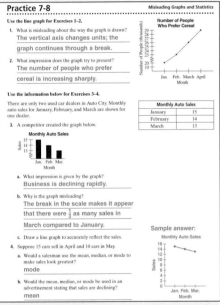

360 Chapter 7 Data and Graphs

GPS Use the Guided Problem Solving worksheet with Exercise 9.

1. The graph does not seem misleading.

2a. It looks like there was a dramatic decrease in phone sales.

b. The vertical scale does not begin at 0. So, you are looking at just the top of the graph.

c. Phone Sales
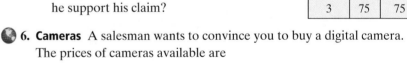

B Apply Your Skills

8. Candidate A: graph I, Candidate B: graph II; the candidate would present a graph where they look more favorable.

9. The rises and falls of the values represented on the vertical axis are more pronounced, which give the impression of greater increases and decreases.

8. Election Results Two graphs of the same election results are shown. Which graph might be presented by Candidate A? Which might be presented by Candidate B? Explain. **See left.**

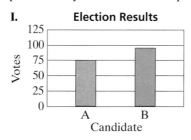
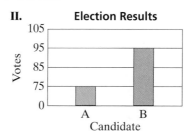

9. Reasoning How does the impression of a line graph change when you [GPS] make the horizontal axis shorter but keep the vertical scale the same? **See left.**

Money Pledged to a Public Radio Station

Year	Amount Pledged
1997	$34,096
1998	$39,021
1999	$41,132
2000	$42,209
2001	$44,172
2002	$45,071
2003	$45,759

13c. Answers may vary. Sample: Both are misleading because the vertical scales were tampered with to create a specific type of impression.

C Challenge

Fundraising Use the table at the left. **10–11. See back of book.**

10. Draw a bar graph showing that the money pledged appeared to increase greatly from 1997 to 2003.

11. Draw a bar graph showing that the money pledged appeared to increase slowly from 1997 to 2003.

12. Writing in Math Explain how you drew the graphs in Exercises 10 and 11 to get the desired results. **See margin.**

13. Track and Field In successive track meets, Andre jumps the following distances. **13a–b. See back of book.**

11 ft 5 in.   11 ft 8 in.   12 ft 1 in.   11 ft 10 in.   12 ft 1 in.

a. Draw a line graph that shows Andre's jumps increasing sharply.
b. Draw a line graph that shows Andre's jumps increasing slightly.
c. Explain whether these graphs are misleading. **See left.**
14a–b. See back of book.

14. Use the data at the right.
a. Make a bar graph using a scale that makes it seem as if there is not much difference in the number of votes for apple juice and orange juice.
b. Make a bar graph using a scale that makes it seem as if there is a significant difference in the number of votes for apple juice and orange juice.

Favorite Juice

Juice	Number of Votes
Orange	30
Grapefruit	6
Apple	21
Grape	15
Cherry	10
Tropical mix	5
Mixed berry	18

Careers
Exercises 10–12 Fundraisers make grant applications and organize social events to solicit donations for non-profit institutions.

3a. The number of dogs in the animal shelter has increased at a steady rate from January to April.

b. The intervals on the vertical axis are unequal.

c.

4a. The graph gives the impression that there are very few complaints.

b. The vertical scale does not start with 0.

c.

5. Answers may vary. Samples are given.

a. She might point out that she had a high score that was much better than Allen's.

b. He might point out that their median and mean scores were the same and that all his scores were higher than Jill's low score of 60.

6. If he is less than fair, he might use the mode, since it has the lowest value and might be most attractive to price-conscious customers.

12. In Exercise 10, I used a vertical scale that had the part between 0 and 34 removed. In Exercise 11, I chose a vertical scale that made the heights of the bars vary only a little.

PowerPoint Lesson Quiz 7-8

1. Is the graph misleading? Explain.

Video Sales

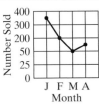

Yes, the scale does not have equal intervals so the drop in sales from January to March does not look as severe as it really is.

2. Five costs for a car wash were $18, $6, $58, $12, and $6. Which measure, the mean, the median, or the mode best represents the costs? **Sample: The median of $12 is most representative of the data.**

Test Prep

Resources

For additional practice with a variety of test item formats:
• Test Prep, p. 367
• Test-Taking Strategies, p. 363
• Test-Taking Strategies With Transparencies

Enrichment 7-8   Misleading Graphs and Statistics
Decision Making

Make a bar graph of the topic of your choice. You might want to find data such as climate in your social studies book, or the amount of calcium in food in your health book. You can use the questions below to help you organize your work. **Check students' work.**

1. Write the data about your topic in these spaces.

2. Write a number sentence to show the range of your data.

3. What interval will you use on your scale? How did you decide which interval to use?

4. Use the information in Exercises 1, 2, and 3 to construct your bar graph.

5. What are the advantages to using a bar graph to analyze the data? Explain.
Sample answer: A bar graph allows you to compare the data visually and make generalizations.

15. Which number could you remove from this list so that the mean and the median are equal? **14**

$$2 \quad 7 \quad 12 \quad 14 \quad 17$$

16. Stretch Your Thinking A number is as much greater than 36 as it is less than 94. What is the number? **65**

Test Prep

Multiple Choice   Use the graph below for Exercises 17–20.

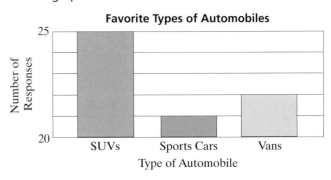

Favorite Types of Automobiles

Take It to the NET
Online lesson quiz at
www.PHSchool.com
Web Code: aaa-0708

17. How many people like sports cars? **A**
   A. 21   **B.** 22   **C.** 23   **D.** 24

18. How many people selected a favorite type of automobile? **I**
   F. 25   **G.** 65   **H.** 67   **I.** 68

19. About what percent of people prefer an automobile other than an SUV? **B**
   A. 67%   **B.** 63%   **C.** 50%   **D.** 43%

Short Response   **20.** Is the bar graph misleading? Explain. **See margin.**

Mixed Review

Lesson 7-1   **Find the mean, median, and mode of each data set.**

21. 5, 6, 8, 9, 10, 4, 6 $6\frac{6}{7}$; 6; 6

22. 600, 550, 475, 520, 500
   529; 520; no mode

23. 15, 14, 15, 12, 11, 13
   $13\frac{1}{3}$; 13.5; 15

24. 4.5, 4, 4.5, 5.5, 6, 6.5
   $5\frac{1}{6}$; 5; 4.5

Lesson 5-6   **25.** Tara wants to tile the floor of a 13-foot by 12-foot room with 8-inch by 8-inch tiles.
   a. How many tiles will she need?   **351 tiles**
   b. Explain how you solved part (a).   **Answers may vary. Sample: The floor has an area of 13 ft by 12 ft, or 156 ft². Each tile has an area of $\frac{2}{3}$ ft by $\frac{2}{3}$ ft, or $\frac{4}{9}$ ft². Tara needs 156 ÷ $\frac{4}{9}$, or 351 tiles.**

362   Chapter 7   Data and Graphs

Alternative Assessment

Each student makes an accurate line graph or bar graph. Then the student redraws the graph to make it misleading.

20. [2] The vertical axis does not start at 0, and the bars have different widths.

[1] Only one misleading feature given.

Answering the Question Asked

When answering a question, be sure to answer the question that is asked. Read the question carefully and identify the answer that you are asked to find. Somze answer choices are answers to related questions, so you have to be careful.

 **1** **EXAMPLE**

In Mrs. Sanchez's class, students received the scores shown in the line plot. How many students took the test?

A. 9 **B.** 19 **C.** 20 **D.** 28

The question asks for the number of students who took the test. The total number of scores is $4 + 4 + 4 + 1 + 6 + 9 = 28$. The answer is D.

The number of students who scored 20 points is 9. The mode is 20. The median is 19. But none of these are what is asked for.

Student Scores

```
                          ✗
                          ✗
                          ✗
                    ✗    ✗
                    ✗    ✗
 ✗   ✗   ✗          ✗    ✗
 ✗   ✗   ✗          ✗    ✗
 ✗   ✗   ✗          ✗    ✗
 ✗   ✗   ✗    ✗    ✗    ✗
 15  16  17  18   19   20
              Score
```

2 **EXAMPLE**

The stem-and-leaf plot shows the heights of 11 students in inches. What is the median height?

A. 60 in. **B.** 62 in. **C.** 63 in. **D.** 64 in.

The question asks for the median height. For eleven data items, the sixth is the median. The sixth height is 62 in. The correct answer is B.

The mode is 60 in. The mean is 63 in. Answer D is the average of 57 in. and 71 in., or 64 in. But none of these are what is asked for.

Heights of Students

```
5 | 7 8
6 | 0 0 1 2 3 4 7
7 | 0 1
```

Key: 5 | 8 means 58 inches

EXERCISES

1. In Example 1, what is the mean? **C**
   A. 17 **B.** 17.5 **C.** 18 **D.** 19

2. In Example 2, how tall is the tallest student who is less than 70 in. tall? **G**
   F. 60 in. **G.** 67 in. **H.** 70 in. **I.** 71 in.

3. In Example 2, what is the range of the data? **A**
   A. 14 in. **B.** 57 in. **C.** 64 in. **D.** 71 in.

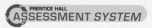
Answering the Question Asked

This feature alerts students to the importance of reading test questions carefully to make sure that they are answering the question asked.

Resources

PRENTICE HALL
ASSESSMENT SYSTEM

Test-Taking Strategies With Transparencies
• Transparency 8
• Practice master, p. 7

Teaching Notes

Inclusion
Review the distinction between these statistics: range, mean, median, and mode. Review the features of stem-and-leaf plots and line plots.

Teaching Tip
Discuss with students that test questions are written to include answer choices that are correct given a *misreading* of the question asked. Emphasize the importance of reading the question very carefully in order to avoid this trap.

Test-Taking Strategies With Transparencies

Chapter 7: Answering the Question Asked

Exercises

Solve by answering the question asked.

Monthly Expenses
Food 16%
Housing 32%
Other 14%
Transportation 10%
Utilities 9%
Entertainment 8%
Clothing 6%
Savings 4%

1. A family's monthly expenses are summarized in the circle graph at the right.
   a. What percent of their income does the family spend on food *and* housing? Explain.
      A. 16%   B. 32%   C. 48%   D. 50%
      The question asks for the percent spent on food *and* housing. Add the two percents for these categories. The total is 16% + 32% = 48%, so the answer is C.

   b. What percent of their income does the family save?
      F. 5%   G. 6%   H. 8%   I. 9%

   c. What percent of their income does the family *not* spend on food, clothing or housing?
      A. 16%   B. 48%   C. 54%   D. 46%

2. The table at the right shows the number of boys participating in various sports at a high school.

Sport	Boys Participating
Baseball	21
Basketball	34
Football	62
Track	16
Wrestling	14

   a. How many boys participated in a sport other than football? Explain.
      F. 62   G. 21   H. 34   I. 85
      The question asks for the number of boys who participated in a sport other than football. Add the number of boys who participated in all the other sports. The total is 21 + 34 + 16 + 14 = 85 boys, so the answer is I.

   b. How many boys participated in basketball *or* football?
      A. 34   B. 96   C. 62   D. 86

Chapter Review

Resources

Student Edition
Extra Practice, Ch. 7, p. 648
English/Spanish Glossary, p. 669
Table of Symbols, p. 666

 Reaching All Students
Reading and Math Literacy 7D
Spanish Reading and Math
Literacy 7D

PRENTICE HALL
ASSESSMENT SYSTEM

Test Preparation
• Chapter 7 practice in test
  formats

 www.PHSchool.com

Student Site
• Self-grading vocabulary test

Teacher Center
• Resources

Plus *iTEXT*

Vocabulary

bar graph (p. 335)	**line graph** (p. 336)	**outlier** (p. 322)
cell (p. 347)	**line plot** (p. 327)	**range** (p. 327)
circle graph (p. 342)	**mean** (p. 322)	**spreadsheet** (p. 347)
frequency table (p. 326)	**median** (p. 323)	**stem-and-leaf plot** (p. 352)
histogram (p. 336)	**mode** (p. 323)	

 Reading Math:
Understanding
Vocabulary

Take It to the NET
Online vocabulary quiz
at **www.PHSchool.com**
Web Code: aaj-0751

Choose the correct vocabulary term to complete each sentence. Not all choices will be used.

1. A(n) __?__ is a way to organize data by listing each item in a data set with the number of times it occurs. **C**

2. To calculate the __?__ of a set of data, divide the sum of the values by the number of values in the set. **A**

3. A(n) __?__ of a data set is much greater or much less than the other data values. **G**

4. On the computer, you can use a(n) __?__ to organize data in a table made up of rows and columns. **F**

5. A(n) __?__ typically shows changes over time. **E**

A. mean
B. mode
C. frequency table
D. median
E. line graph
F. spreadsheet
G. outlier

Skills and Concepts

7-1 Objectives
▼ To find the mean
▼ To find the median and the mode

The **mean** of a set of data is the sum of the values divided by the number of data items. The **median** is the middle value when data are arranged in numerical order. The **mode** is the value or item that appears most often.

Find the mean, median, and mode of each data set.

6. 34, 49, 63, 43, 50, 50, 26 **45, 49, 50**   7. 3, 7, 1, 9, 9, 5, 8 **6, 7, 9**

7-2 Objectives
▼ To organize data by making a frequency table
▼ To make a line plot and find the range

A **frequency table** lists each item in a data set with the number of times the item occurs. A **line plot** displays a data set by stacking X's above each data value on a number line.

8. Make a frequency table showing the number of times each vowel occurs in the paragraph above. Consider *y* a vowel. **See margin.**

9. Make a line plot showing the number of time the words *the, and, a,* and *of* appear in the paragraph above. **See margin.**

8.

Number of Times Vowels Occur		
Vowels	Tally	Frequency
A	⊬⊬ ⊬⊬ ⊬⊬ III	18
E	⊬⊬ ⊬⊬ ⊬⊬ III	18
I	⊬⊬ ⊬⊬	10
O	⊬⊬	5
U	⊬⊬	5
Y	III	3

9.
Number of Times Listed
Words Appear

```
                  X
                  X
                  X
                  X
      X           X
      X     X     X     X
    ─────────────────────
     the   and   a     of
            Words
```

7-3 Objective
▼ To solve problems by making an organized list

You can make a list to organize possible solutions to a problem.

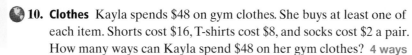 **10. Clothes** Kayla spends $48 on gym clothes. She buys at least one of each item. Shorts cost $16, T-shirts cost $8, and socks cost $2 a pair. How many ways can Kayla spend $48 on her gym clothes? **4 ways**

7-4 and 7-5 Objectives
▼ To make bar graphs
▼ To make line graphs
▼ To read and make circle graphs

A **bar graph** is used to compare amounts. A key identifies data that are compared. A **line graph** shows how an amount changes over time. A **circle graph** compares parts to a whole. **11–13. See margin.**

11. Tickets Make a line graph to display the cost of tickets shown in the table at the right.

12. Make a bar graph to display the data in the table at the right.

13. Books Use the data in the table below to make a circle graph.

Ticket Prices

Year	Price
1970	$10
1975	$15
1980	$20
1985	$25
1990	$30

Favorite Types of Books

Mysteries	Biographies	Fiction	Humor
22%	13%	55%	10%

7-6 Objectives
▼ To read data in a spreadsheet
▼ To write formulas for a spreadsheet

16.
```
3 | 01 41 67 79 88 99
4 | 65 79 79 83
5 | 07 12 43 48
```
Key: 4|65 means 465

You can use a **spreadsheet** to organize and analyze data. A **cell** is the spreadsheet box where a row and column meet. A formula is a set of mathematical instructions.

	A	B	C	D	E
1	Date	Kite Sales ($)	String Sales ($)	Book Sales ($)	Total Sales ($)
2	9/9/03	50	8	145	▦
3	9/10/03	75	6	125	▦

14. Which cells indicate kite sales? **B2, B3**   **15.** Write the formula for cell E2. **=B2+C2+D2**

7-7 and 7-8 Objectives
▼ To use a stem-and-leaf plot
▼ To identify misleading graphs
▼ To identify misleading statistics

A **stem-and-leaf plot** orders data and lets you see the values and frequencies.

16. Make a stem-and-leaf plot of the data: 507, 301, 479, 367, 543, 388, 512, 479, 483, 379, 548, 341, 399, and 465. **See above left.**

Which measure best describes the data—the mean, median, or mode?

17. 72, 67, 62, 77, 82
mean or median since they are the same

18. 1, 1.5, 4.5, 8, 5, 12
median

11.

12.
Ticket Costs

13. Favorite Types of Books
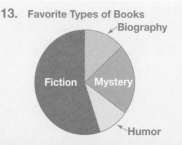

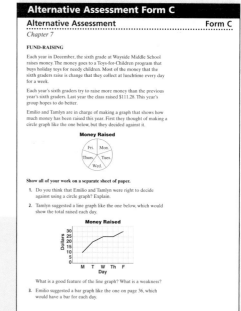

Resources

Teaching Resources
Ch. 7 Test, Forms A & B
Ch. 7 Alternative Assessment,
Form C

Reaching All Students
Spanish Ch. 7 Test, Forms A & B
Spanish Ch. 7 Alternative
Assessment, Form C

 PRENTICE HALL
ASSESSMENT SYSTEM

Assessment Resources
• Ch. 7 Test, Forms A & B
• Ch. 7 Alternative Assessment,
Form C

Computer Test Generator CD
• Ch. 7 Instant Chapter Test™
• Make your own Ch. 7 test

www.PHSchool.com
Student Site
• Self-grading Ch. 7 test

PH SuccessNet Teacher Center
• Resources

Plus **iTEXT**

Take It to the NET
Online chapter test at
www.PHSchool.com
Web Code: aaa-0752

Chapter 7 Chapter Test

1. Find the mean, median, mode, and range of the data set: 31, 20, 31, 51, and 27. **32, 31, 31, 31**

2. Use the circle graph.
   a. How do *most* students get to school? **bus**
   b. What method do students use *least*? **bicycle**
   c. **Writing in Math** Why might a circle graph be better for displaying these data than a bar graph? **See margin.**

How Students Get to School

3. The following spreadsheet shows three quiz scores for two students. Write the formulas for cells E2 and E3. **=(B2+C2+D2)/3; =(B3+C3+D3)/3**

	A	B	C	D	E
1	Student	Q 1	Q 2	Q 3	Mean
2	Yori	81	95	88	▦
3	Sarah	78	81	87	▦

4. Make a stem-and-leaf plot for these state fair pumpkin weights (pounds): 288, 207, 210, 212, 226, 233, 212, 218, 247, 262, 269, 203, and 271. **See back of book.**

5. **Enrollment** Use the bar graph below. Which grade level has the least number of students enrolled? **Preschool**

Public School Enrollment

SOURCE: U.S. Department of Education
Go to **www.PHSchool.com** for a data update. Web Code: aag-2041

6a–b. See margin.
6. The numbers of children in 15 families are 1, 3, 2, 1, 3, 1, 2, 6, 2, 3, 3, 4, 3, 4, and 5.
   a. Make a frequency table.
   b. Make a line plot.

7. **Coins** How many ways can you have $1.05 with only dimes, nickels, and quarters? **31 ways**

8. **Reading** Use the data to make a circle graph.

Amount of Time Adults Think They Spend Reading for Pleasure	
Too much	7%
Too little	73%
About right	16%
Don't know	4%

SOURCE: Gallup Organization

See margin.

9. **Profits** A business has weekly profits of $5,000, $3,000, $2,000, $2,500, and $5,000. Why is using the mode to describe this data set misleading? **See margin.**

10. **Hot Lunches** Use the line graph below. What is the median number of students buying hot lunch? **150**

Students Buying Hot Lunch

Use the stem-and-leaf plot for Exercises 11 and 12.

11. Find the range. **3.1**

12. Find the median. **6.65**

```
5 | 0 2 6
6 | 1 3 6 7
7 | 4 8 9
8 | 0 1
Key: 5 | 0 means 5.0
```

2c. Showing the relation of parts to the whole is helpful.

6a.

Children in Families		
Number of Children	Tally	Frequency
1					3
2					3
3						5
4				2
5			1
6			1

b.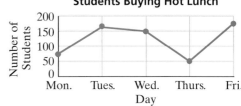

1 2 3 4 5 6
Number of Children

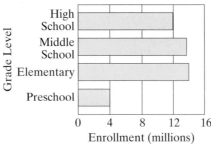

Chapter Test – Form B

Chapter Test – Form A

Chapter Test Form B
Chapter 7

Find the mean, median, and mode of each data set.
1. 19, 20, 23, 22, 21, 16, 19   2. 25, 35, 35, 31, 24
   20; 20; 19   30; 31; 35
3. 7, 4, 4, 3, 2, 6, 8, 5, 0, 1   4. 18.6, 20.6, 15.2, 15.8, 18.0, 18.6
   4; 4; 4   17.8; 18.3; 18.6

Make a line plot for each set of data.
5. 40, 35, 60, 60, 40, 35, 10, 85, 20, 20, 85   6. 10, 40, 25, 25, 50, 70, 85, 40, 50, 25

7. Make a frequency table of the numbers below. Use these groups: under 10; 10–20; 21–30; 31–40; 41–50; over 50.
9, 13, 25, 33, 40, 41, 36, 34, 21, 32, 42, 47, 66, 56, 36, 47, 25, 7, 25, 39

Age	Frequency
under 10	2
10–20	1
21–30	4
31–40	7
41–50	4
over 50	2

Solve each problem by making an organized list.
8. Billy has one $10 bill, two $5 bills, and two $1 bills. List the all the total costs possible if he makes a purchase and receives no change.
$1, $2, $5, $6, $7, $10, $11, $12, $15, $16, $17, $20, $21, $22

9. A stamp club started with 15 stamps. Each collector must bring 4 stamps to the meeting. How many stamps will the club have after 4 members arrive?
31 stamps

Use the bar graph at the right for Exercises 10–12.
10. Which activities are equally popular?
playing sports and earning money
11. Which is the second most popular activity?
talking on the phone
12. About how many students visit with friends after school?
200 students

366

Test Prep

Test Prep

Students must be able to extract information from reading passages, answer multiple-choice questions, and construct responses in order to be successful in current state and national assessments.

Resources

📁 **Teaching Resources**
Cumulative Review

👥 **Reaching All Students**
Spanish Cumulative Review

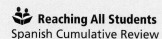
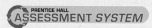

Test Preparation
• Ch. 7 standardized test prep

Assessment Resources
• Cumulative Review

Computer Test Generator CD
• Standardized test prep

💻 **www.PHSchool.com**
• Standardized test prep
• Resources

Plus 📘**TEXT**

Reading Comprehension Read each passage and answer the questions that follow.

> **Age of Leadership** In 1787 twelve of the original thirteen states sent delegates to Philadelphia to work on forming a government for our new country. In all, 55 delegates attended. You probably know some of their names: James Madison (36 years old), Alexander Hamilton (32), George Washington (55), and Benjamin Franklin (the oldest delegate, at 81).

1. What is the mean age of the delegates mentioned in the passage? **C**
   A. 32   B. 45   C. 51   D. 55

2. What is the median age of the delegates mentioned? **G**
   F. 32   G. 45.5   H. 51   I. 55

3. The mean age of all of the delegates was 42. What was the sum of the ages of all 55 delegates? **B**
   A. 2,106 years   B. 2,310 years
   C. 2,501 years   D. 2,525 years

4. Franklin was in poor health and did not attend many of the meetings. Suppose a 60-year-old delegate replaced him. How would that affect the mean and the median ages of the four delegates mentioned in the passage? **F**
   F. The mean would be lower.
   G. The median would be lower.
   H. The mean and the median would both be lower.
   I. Neither the mean nor the median would change.

> **Math in Space** The first American astronaut to circle Earth was John Glenn. In 1962, Glenn made three orbits at an average speed of 17,544 miles per hour. He traveled a total distance of 75,679 miles. This was only a short trip into space. Soon astronauts would be looking beyond Earth orbit to the moon, about 240,000 miles away.

5. Based on the passage, about how far did Glenn travel in one orbit around Earth? **C**
   A. 25 miles   B. 17,544 miles
   C. 25,000 miles   D. 52,632 miles

6. About how long did an average orbit take? **F**
   F. 1.4 hours   G. 4.3 hours
   H. 10 hours   I. 13 hours

7. At Glenn's rate of travel, about how long would it take to reach the moon? **B**
   A. 10 hours   B. 14 hours
   C. 24 hours   D. 38 hours

8. *Apollo 11* took about 3 days to go from Earth orbit to moon orbit. About how fast was *Apollo 11*'s average speed? **I**
   F. 80,000 mi/h   G. 17,544 mi/h
   H. 10,000 mi/h   I. 3,333 mi/h

8.
Amount of Time Adults Think They Spend Reading for Pleasure

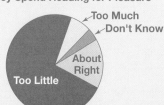

Too Much
Don't Know
About Right
Too Little

9. It occurs only twice and is greater than all the other values by a significant amount.

Cumulative Review

Cumulative Review
Chapters 1–7

Multiple Choice. Choose the letter of the best answer.

Use the circle graph for Questions 1–2.

Preferred Preparation of Eggs

34% scrambled
31% fried
3% poached
4% other
23% boiled
5% omelets

1. What is the most preferred way to prepare eggs?
   A. fried   B. scrambled
   C. boiled   D. omelets

2. Calculate the total percentage that do not like their eggs fried or scrambled.
   F. 4%   G. 12%
   H. 23%   I. 35%

3. On his grandfather's farm, Mark counted 80 legs and 25 animals. There were only cows and chickens on the farm. How many cows were there on the farm?
   A. 10 cows   B. 15 cows
   C. 20 cows   D. 25 cows

4. Which shows a unit rate?
   F. 1 ride / $10   G. 10 rides / $1
   H. $10 / $1   I. 10 rides / $10

5. Frozen orange juice concentrate costs $.02 per ounce. How much does a 64-ounce container cost?
   A. $.13   B. $1.28
   C. $12.80   D. $64.02

Use the data set below for Exercises 6–7.
37, 45, 50, 35, 41, 43, 54, 41, 38, 46

6. Find the mean.
   F. 10   G. 41
   H. 42   I. 43

7. Find the median.
   A. 10   B. 41
   C. 42   D. 43

8. Which number is greater than 1.104?
   F. 1.014   G. 1.044
   H. 1.144   I. 0.444

Use the spreadsheet below for Exercises 9–10.

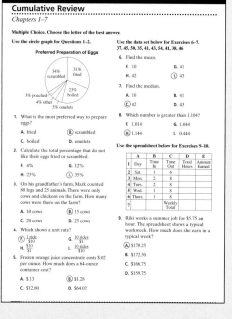

	A	B	C	D	E
1	Day	Time In	Time Out	Total Hours	Amount Earned
2	Sat.	1	6		
3	Mon.	2	8		
4	Tues.	2	8		
5	Wed.	1	8		
6	Thurs.	1	8		
7				Weekly Total	

9. Riki works a summer job for $5.75 an hour. The spreadsheet shows a typical workweek. How much does she earn in a typical week?
   A. $178.25
   B. $172.50
   C. $166.75
   D. $159.75

A Peak Experience

Students will use data from these two pages and from the Chapter Opener on p. 319 to answer the questions posed here in Put It All Together.

Activating Prior Knowledge

Have students who have hiked into state or national parks and those who have rock climbed share their experiences with the class. Elicit information about special clothing and equipment that are needed for such activities.

Teaching Notes

Have a volunteer read the introductory paragraph. Ask: *Where is Mt. Everest?* Asia Have students turn back to p. 319 in their text to review the data on the page. Have volunteers read the data and information.

Science Connection

Ask:
• *What is the average air pressure at sea level?* about 1,000 mb (one thousand millibars)
• *What is the air pressure at the top of Mt. Everest?* about 300 mb

History Connection

Have interested students research the ascent of Sir Edmund Hillary and Sherpa Tenzing Norgay to the summit of Mt. Everest in 1953.

Social Studies Connection

A *Sherpa* is a member of a Tibetan people living on the high southern slopes of the Himalayas. Sherpas are skilled in mountain climbing.

Diversity

Have students who have lived in or visited a country mentioned in this feature share their experiences with the class.

368

A Peak Experience

Applying Data Analysis Earth's highest natural features, its great mountains, dwarf even the tallest structures made by humans. The air at the top of Mt. Everest, in the Himalayan mountains, is three times thinner than the air at sea level. Because of the thin air, numbing cold, and unpredictable weather, it takes even the most experienced climbers many weeks to reach the top of Mt. Everest.

Mt. Aconcagua is the highest peak in South America at 6,960 meters.

Mt. Elbrus is Europe's highest peak at 5,642 meters.

Mt. Everest towers over volcanoes like Mt. Kilimanjaro, Fujiyama, and Mt. Vesuvius.

Mt. Kilimanjaro, in Tanzania, rises to 5,895 meters.

Fujiyama is Japan's highest peak at 3,776 meters.

Mt. Vesuvius, in Italy, is 1,277 meters high.

It's All Relative

Although Kilimanjaro is 2,955 meters shorter than Everest, it is still 40 times as tall as the Great Pyramid in Egypt.

Volcanic Storm

Mount St. Helens, a volcano in Washington state, erupted on May 18, 1980, throwing huge clouds of ash into the sky. Before the eruption, the summit was 2,950 meters high. Afterward, it was about 400 meters lower.

Mt. Cook is New Zealand's highest peak at 3,754 meters.

Mt. St. Helens: 2,550 meters

Put It All Together

Data File Use the information on these two pages and on page 319 to answer these questions.

1. **a.** Write the names of the mountain peaks in the table on page 319 in order from highest to lowest elevation.
   b. Graph the data (in meters) on a number line. Label each point with the name of the mountain.
   c. Insert data points and labels for New Zealand's highest mountain, Mt. Cook, and the Matterhorn, in the European Alps.
2. How tall is Hawaii's Mauna Kea?

1a. Everest
Aconcagua
McKinley
Kilimanjaro
Elbrus
Vinson Massif
Kosciusko

b. Answers may vary. Sample:

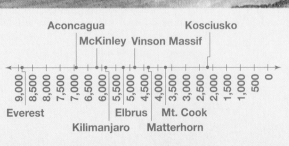

Mt. Everest: 8,850 meters

Yaks can live at elevations as high as 6,000 meters.

Edmund Hillary and Sherpa Tenzing Norgay, the first people to climb Mt. Everest, pitched their base camp at 5,486 meters.

Mauna Kea   Mt. Everest

Mauna Kea is a volcano in Hawaii. Measured from its base on the ocean floor, Mauna Kea is 1,352 meters taller than Mt. Everest.

Mt. McKinley is the highest peak in North America at 6,194 meters.

Vinson Massif, Antarctica: 4,897 meters

The Matterhorn, in the European Alps, is 4,478 meters above sea level.

Mont Blanc, in the European Alps: 4,810 meters

Straight to the Top
Sherpas are people who live on the Himalayas. Many Sherpas act as guides on Mt. Everest.

3. What did the height of Mount St. Helens become after its eruption in 1980?

4. A mountain climber scaled both Mont Blanc and the Matterhorn. How many meters did she climb?

5. a. **Estimation** About how tall is the Great Pyramid of Egypt?
   b. About how many times taller than the Great Pyramid is Mt. Everest?

6. **Number Sense** Suppose a Sherpa has guided climbers 12 times from a base camp at 5,486 meters to the peak of Mt. Everest. How many kilometers of vertical elevation has he traveled as a guide?

Take It to the NET For more information about mountains, go to **www.PHSchool.com**.
Web Code: aae-0753

369

Put It All Together

Have students work in pairs to make the graphs and answer the questions.

English Learners
Students might benefit from working in small groups in which at least one member is a proficient reader who can assist other team members.

Exercise 1b Have students graph the data using meter as the unit of measure. Have students agree on a range and a scale for the number line, for example, segments of 1,000 m, ranging from 0 through 10,000 m. Elicit the fact that the tics on the number line would be at 0, 1, 2, 3, . . . , 10.

Exercise 6 Ask questions such as:
• *What operation do you need to use to solve this problem?* **multiplication**
• *What factors do you multiply?* **12 · 5,486**
• *How many meters are there in one kilometer?* **1,000 m**
• *How do you change meters into kilometers?* **Divide the number of meters by 1,000.**

2. 10,202 m

3. about 2,550 m

4. about 9,288 m

5a. Answers may vary. Accept all reasonable estimates. Sample: about 147 m

b. about 60

6. about 80.736 km

Chapter at a Glance

8-1

Points, Lines, Segments, and Rays
pp. 373–377

Objectives
1. Points, Lines, Segments, and Rays
2. Parallel, Intersecting, and Skew Lines

New Vocabulary
point, line, segment, ray, collinear, plane, intersecting lines, parallel lines, skew lines

NCTM Standards
3, 6, 7, 8, 9, 10

Local Standards

8-2

Angles
pp. 379–383

Objectives
1. Measuring and Classifying Angles

New Vocabulary
angle, vertex, degree, acute angle, right angle, obtuse angle, straight angle, perpendicular lines

Optional Materials
protractor

NCTM Standards
3, 4, 6, 7, 8, 9, 10

Local Standards

8-3

Special Pairs of Angles
pp. 386–390

Objectives
1. Complement and Supplement of an Angle
2. Special Pairs of Angles

New Vocabulary
angles: complementary, supplementary, vertical, congruent, interior, exterior and transversal

Optional Materials
protractor

NCTM Standards
1, 2, 3, 4, 6, 7, 8, 9, 10

Local Standards

✓ **Checkpoint Quiz 1**

8-4

Classifying Triangles
pp. 392–396

Objectives
1. Classifying Triangles by Angles
2. Classifying Triangles by Sides

New Vocabulary
acute triangle, obtuse triangle, right triangle, congruent segments, equilateral triangle, isosceles triangle, scalene triangle

NCTM Standards
1, 2, 3, 4, 6, 7, 8, 9, 10

Local Standards

8-5

Exploring and Classifying Polygons
pp. 397–400

Objectives
1. Identifying Polygons
2. Classifying Quadrilaterals

New Vocabulary
polygon, quadrilateral, trapezoid, parallelogram, rectangle, rhombus, square

NCTM Standards
1, 2, 3, 4, 6, 7, 8, 9, 10

Local Standards

8-6 Problem Solving

Using Logical Reasoning
pp. 401–404

Objectives
1. Solving Problems Using Logical Reasoning

NCTM Standards
1, 3, 6, 7, 8, 9, 10

Local Standards

8-7

Congruent and Similar Figures
pp. 405–409

Objectives
1. Identifying Congruent Figures
2. Identifying Similar Figures

New Vocabulary
congruent figures, similar figures

Optional Materials
dot paper

NCTM Standards
1, 2, 3, 6, 7, 8, 9, 10

Local Standards

8-8

Line Symmetry
pp. 410–414

Objectives
1. Finding Lines of Symmetry

New Vocabulary
line symmetry, line of symmetry

Optional Materials
scissors

NCTM Standards
3, 6, 7, 8, 9, 10

Local Standards

✓ **Checkpoint Quiz 2**

8-9

Transformations
pp. 415–419

Objectives
1. Translations and Reflections
2. Rotations

New Vocabulary
image, translation, reflection, line of reflection, rotation, center of rotation

Optional Materials
graph paper

NCTM Standards
3, 4, 5, 6, 7, 8, 9, 10

Local Standards

Reaching All Students
Additional Instructional Options in Chapter 8

Reading and Math Literacy

Reading Math

Common Words and Prefixes, p. 378

Reading Math hints, pp. 374, 379, 398

Understanding Vocabulary, p. 422

Writing in Math

Daily Writing Practice, pp. 376, 382, 385, 389, 395, 399, 403, 408, 413, 418, 424, 427

Above Level

C Challenge exercises

pp. 376, 382, 389, 396, 399, 404, 409, 413, 419

Extension

Basic Constructions, pp. 384-385

Tessellations, p. 420

Hands-On and Technology

Investigations

Angle Measures, p. 387

Comparing Triangles, p. 406

Symmetry, p. 410

Technology

Investigating Angles in a Triangle, p. 391

Activities and Projects

Real-World Snapshots

Applying Geometry, pp. 426–427

Chapter Project

Puzzling Pictures, p. 639

Test Prep

Daily Test Prep

pp. 377, 383, 390, 396, 400, 404, 409, 414, 419

Test-Taking Strategies

Drawing a Diagram, p. 421

Test Prep

Cumulative Review (Chapters 1–8), p. 425

Chapter Assessment

Checkpoint Quiz

pp. 390, 414

Chapter Review

pp. 422–423

Chapter Test

p. 424

Pacing Options

This chart suggests pacing only for the core lessons and their parts. It is provided as a possible guide. It will help you determine how much time you have in your schedule to cover the additional features and assessment, as described at the left.

Day	Traditional 45-minute class periods	Block 90-minute class periods
1	8-1	8-1 / 8-2
2	8-2	8-3
3	8-3	8-4
4	8-3	8-5
5	8-4	8-6
6	8-4	8-7 / 8-8
7	8-5	8-9
8	8-5	
9	8-6	
10	8-7	
11	8-8	
12	8-9	
13	8-9	

NCTM STANDARDS 2000

1	Number and Operations	6	Problem Solving
2	Algebra	7	Reasoning and Proof
3	Geometry	8	Communication
4	Measurement	9	Connections
5	Data Analysis and Probability	10	Representation

Math Background

Skills Trace

BEFORE Chapter 8

Grade 5 presented the basic geometric figures such as triangles, squares and circles.

DURING Chapter 8

Course 1 reviews and extends geometry with special angles, congruent and similar figures, line symmetry, and transformations.

AFTER Chapter 8

Throughout this course students apply geometric skills, concepts, and vocabulary.

8-1 Points, Lines, Segments, and Rays

Math Understandings

• Points, lines, and planes are ideas that do not physically exist.

A **point** is a location in space, named with a capital letter. A **line** is a series of points that extends in two opposite directions without end, named by any two points on the line. A **ray** consists of one endpoint and all the points of a line on one side of the endpoint, named first by the endpoint, and then by any other point on the ray. A **segment** is part of a line with two endpoints, named by its endpoints. Points on the same line are **collinear**.

Example: *A*, *B*, and *C* are points. $\overleftrightarrow{CA}$ is a line. $\overrightarrow{AC}$ is a ray. $\overline{AB}$ is a segment.

A **plane** is a flat surface that extends indefinitely in all directions. **Intersecting lines** have exactly one point in common. **Parallel lines** have no points in common. **Skew lines** are lines that lie in different planes, and they are not parallel and do not intersect.

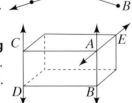

$\overleftrightarrow{AB}$ is parallel to $\overleftrightarrow{DC}$.
$\overleftrightarrow{AE}$ and $\overleftrightarrow{CD}$ are skew.

8-2 Angles

Math Understandings

• The measure of an angle describes the opening between the two sides, or rays, that form the angle. It does not depend on the lengths of the sides.

Every **angle** has two sides and a vertex. The sides are rays, and the vertex is their common endpoint. Angles are measured in units called **degrees**. Lines that intersect to form right angles are called **perpendicular lines**. You can use measures to classify angles.

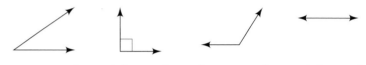

| **Acute Angle** | **Right Angle** | **Obtuse Angle** | **Straight Angle** |
| $> 0°$ and $< 90°$ | $90°$ | $> 90°$ and $< 180°$ | $180°$ |

8-3 Special Pairs of Angles

Math Understandings

• Pairs of angles with certain relationships have special names.
• A pair of angles need not be adjacent to be either complementary or supplementary.

If the sum of the measures of two angles is $90°$, the angles are **complementary angles**. If the sum of the measures of two angles is $180°$, the angles are **supplementary angles**. **Vertical angles** are formed by two intersecting lines. Vertical angles have equal measures. Angles with equal measures are **congruent angles**. A **transversal** crosses two or more lines at different points. **Interior angles** are on either side of a transversal between a pair of lines. **Exterior angles** are on either side of a transversal outside of a pair of lines.

8-4, 8-5 Classifying Triangles / Exploring and Classifying Polygons

Math Understandings

• You can name a polygon by counting the number of sides.
• You can classify polygons by the relationships among the sides and angles.

Triangles can be classified by their angle measures and the number of congruent sides as summarized below.

Name	Angles	Name	Congruent Sides
acute	3 acute	scalene	0
obtuse	1 obtuse	isosceles	2 or 3
right	1 right	equilateral	3

A **polygon** is a closed figure that has three or more line segments that do not cross. Any polygon with four sides is called a **quadrilateral**. A **trapezoid** has one pair of parallel lines. A **parallelogram** has two pairs of parallel lines. There are three special types of parallelograms: a **rectangle** (four right angles), a **rhombus** (four congruent sides), a **square** (four right angles and four congruent sides).

| **Parallelogram** | **Rhombus** | **Rectangle** | **Square** |

8-6 Using Logical Reasoning

You can *use logical reasoning* when you are given a series of clues or when you are playing a game.

8-7 Congruent and Similar Figures

Math Understandings
- Congruent figures have congruent corresponding sides and congruent corresponding angles.
- When two figures are congruent, you can fit one exactly on top of the other, although one may have to be turned or flipped.

Congruent figures have the same size and shape. **Similar figures** have the same shape, but not necessarily the same size. Corresponding angles of similar figures are congruent and the corresponding sides of similar figures are proportional.

8-8 Line Symmetry

Math Understandings
- A figure may have no line of symmetry, one line of symmetry, or more than one line of symmetry.
- If you fold a figure on its line of symmetry, the two parts match.

A figure has **line symmetry** if a line can be drawn through the figure so that each part is a mirror image of the other. This line is a **line of symmetry**.

8-9 Transformations

Math Understandings
- To translate a figure, you need to know the distance and the direction of the translation.
- To reflect a figure, you need to know the line of reflection.
- To rotate a figure, you need to know the center of rotation and the angle of rotation.

Translating, rotating, and reflecting change only the position of a figure, and not its shape or size. The new figure is the **image** of the original. A **translation**, or *slide,* moves every point of a figure the same distance and in the same direction. A **reflection**, or flip, flips a figure over a line. This line is the **line of reflection**. A **rotation**, or turn, turns a figure about a point. This point stays fixed and is called the **center of rotation**.

Additional Professional Development Opportunities

Chapter 8 Math Background notes: pp. 374, 380, 387, 393, 398, 402, 406, 411, 416

Additional resources available from SkyLight Professional Development:

On-site courses, workshops, summer institutes. Online courses and chat rooms. Videocassettes and books. Visit www.skylightedu.com.

Ongoing Assessment and Intervention

The *Prentice Hall Mathematics* program provides many options for assessment in the Student Edition, Teacher's Edition, and teaching resources. From these options you may choose instructional materials that are appropriate for your students and that support your district's curriculum requirements.

Daily Assessment

✓ Instant Check System™ in Chapter 8

Allows students to check their own learning before, during, and after each lesson.

Diagnosing Readiness before the chapter (p. 372)

Check Skills You'll Need exercises in each lesson (pp. 373, 379, 386, 392, 397, 401, 405, 410, 415)

Check Understanding questions with each Example (pp. 374, 475, 379, 380, 386, 387, 388, 392, 393, 394, 397, 398, 401, 402, 405, 406, 407, 411, 415, 416, 417)

Checkpoint Quiz (pp. 390, 414)

Intervention

Skills Intervention Kit

Formal Assessment

Assessment in the Student Text and in Additional Resources

Assess student progress throughout the Course 1 textbook and with blackline masters and CD-ROM.

Student Edition
- Chapter 8 Review, with Vocabulary, Skills, and Concepts Review, pp. 422–423
- Chapter 8 Test, p. 424

Assessment Resources
- Checkpoint Quizzes 1 & 2
- Chapter Test, forms A & B
- Chapter Alternative Assessment

Spanish versions available.

 **Computer Test Generator CD-ROM**
- Instant Chapter Tests™—pre-made tests with items that vary every time you print.
- Online Testing allows you to give tests online and receive progress reports.
- Prepare students by making tests based on standardized test objectives.

Algebra Readiness Tests
- Includes Basic Skills Tests and Concept-Readiness Tests.
- Assess understanding of skills and concepts needed for success in algebra.

Online Intervention
Integrated within the iText, this online intervention system includes diagnostic tests and prescribed remediation, plus reports to track student mastery.

A *complete* system for the student who is struggling with course-level work

Eight intervention units cover core skills and allow you to:
- **Diagnose** students' gaps in basic skills
- **Prescribe** an individualized course of study
- **Monitor** student progress

Includes print workbooks, tutorial CD-ROM, teacher editions, progress folders, and more. *Available in Spanish.*

How to Use with Chapter 8

8-1	Geometry, Skills 1, 2, 13
8-2	Geometry, Skills 1, 2
8-3	Geometry, Skills 1, 2
8-4	Geometry, Skills 6, 7
8-5	Geometry, Skills 4, 9
8-7	Geometry, Skill 10
8-8	Geometry, Skill 12
8-9	Geometry, Skill 11

Standardized Test Preparation

The *Prentice Hall Mathematics* program integrates preparation for high-stakes standardized tests in every lesson of the Student Edition and continues this support in the Prentice Hall Assessment System.

Test Prep

In Student Text, Chapter 8

Teaches students strategies and gives them practice with all the test item formats they will encounter on high-stakes tests.

Test Prep exercises in each lesson (pp. 377, 383, 390, 396, 400, 404, 409, 414, 419)

Test-Taking Strategies Drawing a Diagram, p. 421

Test Prep Cumulative Review (Chapters 1–8), p. 425

A three-step approach to preparing students for high stakes, national, and state exams.

1 Diagnose & Prescribe

Content Diagnostic Tests
- Diagnose strengths and weaknesses with ongoing benchmark tests.
- Prescribe individualized reteaching opportunities.

2 Review & Reteach

Skills and Concepts Review
- Provides reteaching worksheets with instruction and practice for each skill.
- Includes course prerequisite skills.

3 Practice & Assess

Standardized Test Preparation
- Features practice for national standardized exams.
- Includes practice tests for NAEP, SAT10, ITBS, and Terra Nova.

Test-Taking Strategies with Transparencies
- Support the Test-Taking Strategies pages in the Student Edition.
- Provide a transparency and a worksheet for each strategy.

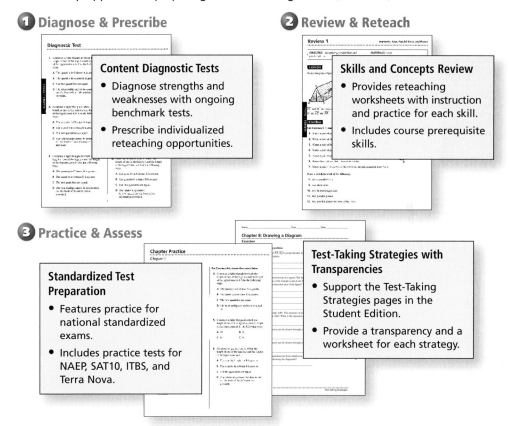

Correlation to Standardized Tests

Lesson		NAEP	Terra Nova		ITBS	SAT10	Local Test
			CAT6	CTBS			
8-1	Points, Lines, Segments, and Rays	G3g	■	■		■	
8-2	Angles	G1c		■		■	
8-3	Special Pairs of Angles	G1c, G3b		■			
8-4	Classifying Triangles	G1f, G3f		■		■	
8-5	Exploring and Classifying Polygons	G1c-G1f, G3f		■	■		
8-6	Problem Solving: Use Logical Reasoning		■	■			
8-7	Congruent and Similar Figures	G2e		■			
8-8	Line Symmetry	G2c	■	■		■	
8-9	Transformations	G2c	■	■		■	

NAEP National Assessment of Educational Progress
CAT6/Terra Nova California Achievement Test, 6th Ed.
CTBS/Terra Nova Comprehensive Test of Basic Skills
ITBS Iowa Test of Basic Skills, Form M.
SAT10 Stanford Achievement Test, 10th Ed.

Program Resources

	Resources in Grab & Go™ Files				Resources for Reaching All Students				Spanish Resources			Transparencies (Presentation Assistant Plus!)					Prentice Hall Presentation Pro CD-ROM
	Practice	Reteach	Enrich	Checkpt Quiz	Reading & Math Literacy	Technology Activities	Hands-On Activities	Guided Problem Solving	Practice	Reading & Math Literacy	Checkpt Quiz	Skills Check	Problem of the Day	Additional Examples	Answers to Exercises	Lesson Quiz	
8-1	■	■	■		■		■	■	■	■		■	■	■	■	■	■
8-2	■	■	■				■	■	■	■		■	■	■	■	■	■
8-3	■	■	■	■	■		■	■	■	■	■	■	■	■	■	■	■
8-4	■	■	■			■	■	■	■	■		■	■	■	■	■	■
8-5	■	■	■				■	■	■	■		■	■	■	■	■	■
8-6	■	■	■				■	■	■	■		■	■	■	■	■	■
8-7	■	■	■				■	■	■	■		■	■	■		■	■
8-8	■	■	■	■	■		■	■	■	■	■	■	■	■	■	■	■
8-9	■	■	■				■	■	■	■		■	■	■	■	■	■
For the Chapter	Chapter Projects, Chapter Tests, Alternative Assessment, Cumulative Review, Cumulative Assessment				**On web site only:** Home Activities, Interdisciplinary Activities, Algebra Readiness Puzzles				Spanish Chapter Tests, Alternative Assessment, Cumulative Review, Cumulative Assessment			Classroom Aid Transparencies					

Also available for use with the chapter:

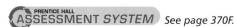 *See page 370F.*

- Practice Workbook
- Solution Key
- MathNotes folder

- For teacher support and access to student Web materials, use the Web Code aak-5500.
- For additional online and technology resources, see *below.*

Technology

 iTEXT **Online and on CD-ROM**

Complete Interactive Student Text online and on CD-ROM—with instant feedback assessment, tutorial help, dynamic activities, instructional and real-world videos, audio, and additional practice.

www.PHSchool.com For Students

Use Web codes for easy access to online activities, chapter projects, self-grading lesson quizzes, chapter tests, vocabulary quizzes, updated data sources, graphing calculator procedures, and more.

PH SuccessNet **For Teachers**

Online lesson planning with built-in state correlations, all the teaching resources, complete reference library, your own calendar and Teacher Web page, professional development, and more.

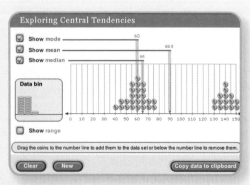

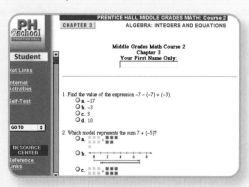

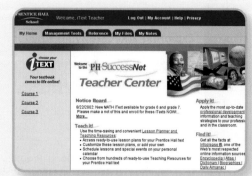

Presentation Assistant Plus!

The *Prentice Hall Presentation Assistant Plus!* provides you with the material you need to teach a lesson from beginning to end. Two easy-to-use formats—Transparencies and PowerPoint®—allow you to present a lesson the way you are most comfortable.

Transparencies

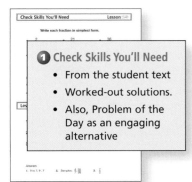
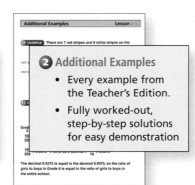

1 Check Skills You'll Need
- From the student text
- Worked-out solutions.
- Also, Problem of the Day as an engaging alternative

2 Additional Examples
- Every example from the Teacher's Edition.
- Fully worked-out, step-by-step solutions for easy demonstration

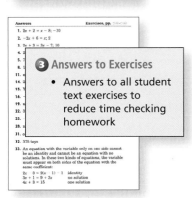
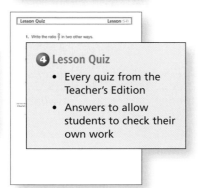

3 Answers to Exercises
- Answers to all student text exercises to reduce time checking homework

4 Lesson Quiz
- Every quiz from the Teacher's Edition
- Answers to allow students to check their own work

 PowerPoint Throughout the Teacher's Edition, this symbol indicates material that is available in the Presentation Assistant Plus!

PowerPoint Prentice Hall Presentation Pro CD-ROM

- Includes all Transparencies.
- Conveniently organized by lesson so you can easily **1** Introduce, **2** Teach, **3** Check Homework, and **4** Assess each lesson.
- Animated examples allow step-by-step instruction at your own pace.
- Easy to edit so you can create custom presentations.

Teaching Chapter 8 Using Presentation Assistant Plus!

	1 Introduce Check Skills You'll Need	**2 Teach** Additional Examples	**3 Check Homework** Student Edition Answers	**4 Assess** Lesson Quiz
8-1	p. 66	pp. 102–103	✔	p. 66
8-2	p. 67	p. 104	✔	p. 67
8-3	p. 68	pp. 105–106	✔	p. 68
8-4	p. 69	pp. 107–108	✔	p. 69
8-5	p. 70	p. 109	✔	p. 70
8-6	p. 71	pp. 110–111	✔	p. 71
8-7	p. 72	pp. 112–113	✔	p. 72
8-8	p. 73	p. 114	✔	p. 73
8-9	p. 74	pp. 115–116	✔	p. 74

Prentice Hall Presentation Pro

CD-ROM with dynamic PowerPoint® presentations for every lesson. Helps you introduce and develop concepts, check homework, and assess progress. Part of Presentation Assistant Plus! *(See above.)*

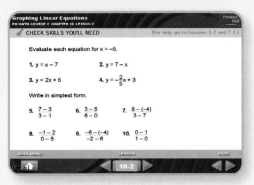

Computer Test Generator

CD-ROM to create practice sheets and tests for course objectives and standardized tests. Includes Instant Chapter Tests™, online testing, and student reports. Part of the PH Assessment System. *(See page 370F.)*

Resource Pro® with Planning Express®

CD-ROM with a lesson planning tool that allows you to import state and local objectives. Includes electronic versions of all the teaching resources.

Chapter Resources

Reading and Math Support

Reading and Math Literacy Masters

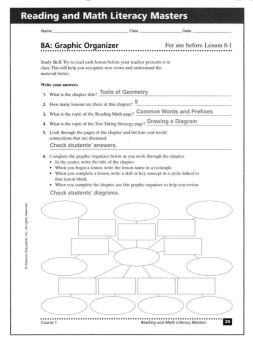

Reading and Math Literacy Masters

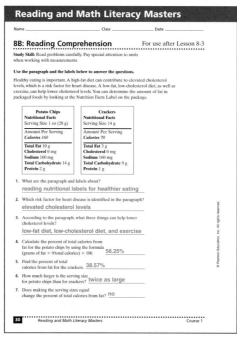

Reading and Math Literacy Masters

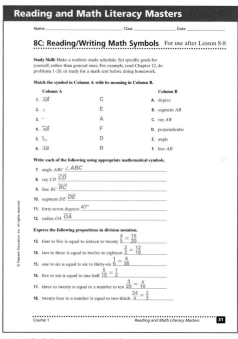

Problem Solving

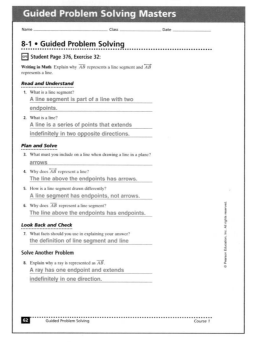

Name _____ Class _____ Date _____

8-3 • Guided Problem Solving

GPS Student Page 389, Exercise 21:

Architecture Before renovations, the Leaning Tower of Pisa stood at an angle of about 5° with a vertical line. What is the measure of the acute angle that the tower made with the ground? What is the measure of the obtuse angle?

Read and Understand

1. What is the first thing you are being asked to do?
   Find the measure of the acute angle that the
   tower made with the ground.

2. What is the second thing you are being asked to do?
   Find the measure of the obtuse angle that
   the tower made with the ground.

Plan and Solve

3. If the tower did not lean, what angle would the tower form with the ground?
   90°

4. By what angle measure from the vertical line was the tower leaning before the renovations?
   5°

5. Write a subtraction expression that you can use to find the acute angle.
   90 − 5 = 85

6. What was the acute angle the tower made with the ground?
   85°

7. What was the obtuse angle the other side of the tower made with the ground?
   180 − 85 = 95; 95°

Look Back and Check

8. How can you check your answer?
   Add the two angle measures to see if they
   equal 180°.

Solve Another Problem

9. A stop sign stands at an angle of 90° with the ground. During a snow storm, a car slid off the road and hit the sign so that it now forms a 62° angle with the ground. What is the obtuse angle formed on the other side of the sign?
   180 − 62 = 118; the obtuse angle formed is 118°.

Name _____ Class _____ Date _____

8-4 • Guided Problem Solving

GPS Student Page 395, Exercise 20:

Sailing A triangular sail allows a boat to sail in any direction, even into the wind. Judging by its appearance, give all names possible for the triangle in the photo.

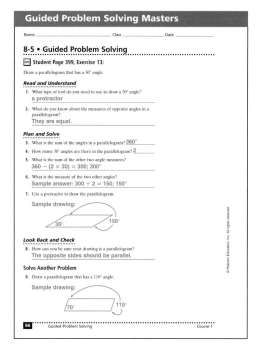

Read and Understand

1. Name the three ways you can classify a triangle by its angle measures.
   acute, obtuse, right

2. Name the three ways you can classify a triangle by the number of congruent segments or sides.
   equilateral, isosceles, scalene

Plan and Solve

3. Can a triangle be classified in more than one way? yes

4. Look at the picture of the sailboat. What appears to be true about the angle measures of the sail?
   The angles appear to be the same measure.

5. What appears to be true about the measures of the side lengths of the sail?
   The lengths appear to be congruent.

6. Classify the sail by the measures of its angles. acute triangle

7. Classify the sail by the number of congruent sides.
   equilateral or isosceles triangle

8. Give all possible names for the triangular sail.
   acute equilateral; acute isosceles

Look Back and Check

9. Did you classify the triangular sail correctly?
   yes

Solve Another Problem

10. A sailboat has a sail shaped as shown. Judging by *its appearance*, give all names possible for the triangle in the diagram.
    right scalene

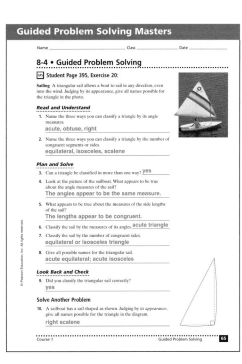

Name _____ Class _____ Date _____

8-5 • Guided Problem Solving

GPS Student Page 399, Exercise 13:

Draw a parallelogram that has a 30° angle.

Read and Understand

1. What type of tool do you need to use to draw a 30° angle?
   a protractor

2. What do you know about the measures of opposite angles in a parallelogram?
   They are equal.

Plan and Solve

3. What is the sum of the angles in a parallelogram? 360°

4. How many 30° angles are there in the parallelogram? 2

5. What is the sum of the other two angle measures?
   360 − (2 × 30) = 300; 300°

6. What is the measure of the two other angles?
   Sample answer: 300 ÷ 2 = 150; 150°

7. Use a protractor to draw the parallelogram.

   Sample drawing:

   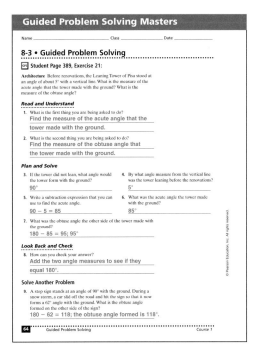
   30°   150°

Look Back and Check

8. How can you be sure your drawing is a parallelogram?
   The opposite sides should be parallel.

Solve Another Problem

9. Draw a parallelogram that has a 110° angle.

   Sample drawing:

   70°   110°

Name _____ Class _____ Date _____

8-6 • Guided Problem Solving

GPS Student Page 403, Exercise 7:

Collections Your friend decides to sort his collection of baseball cards. When he tries to put the cards in equal piles of two, he has one card left over. He also has one left over when he sorts the cards in piles of three or piles of four. But when he puts them in piles of seven, he has none left over. What is the least possible number of cards in your friend's collection?

Read and Understand

1. What does it mean that when he puts the cards in piles of seven, he has none left over?
   It means that 7 divides evenly into the
   number of cards that he has.

2. What does it mean that when he puts the cards in piles of 2, 3, or 4, he has cards left over?
   It means the number of cards he has is not
   divisible by 2, 3, or 4.

Plan and Solve

3. List the first 10 numbers divisible by 7, starting with 7.
   7, 14, 21, 28, 35, 42, 49, 56, 63, 70

4. Delete the even numbers. Which numbers remain?
   7, 21, 35, 49, 63

5. Delete the numbers divisible by 3. Which numbers remain?
   7, 35, 49

6. Divide these numbers by 2, 3, and 4. Which number only gives a remainder of 1?
   49

Look Back and Check

7. Explain another way to do this problem.
   Divide the multiples of 7 by 2, 3, and 4 to see
   which quotients have a remainder of one card.

Solve Another Problem

8. A teacher puts her students into groups. When she pairs the students, she has 1 student left over. When she groups them in 3s, she has 2 students left over. When she groups them in 4s, she has 3 students left over. Finally, when she groups them in 5s, she has none left over. If the school allows no more than 40 students in a class, how many students does the teacher have?
   35 students

Name _____ Class _____ Date _____

8-7 • Guided Problem Solving

GPS Student Page 408, Exercise 18a:

Triangles *MNO* and *PQR* are similar.

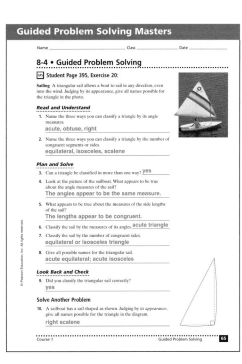

a. List the pairs of congruent angles.

Read and Understand

1. What does it mean to be *congruent*?
   to be the same

2. How do you know if the angles in triangles MNO and PQR are right angles?
   There is a square drawn at the vertex of the
   angle.

Plan and Solve

3. Name the right angle in each triangle.
   ∠NMO; ∠QPR

4. Name the angle opposite the shortest side in each triangle.
   ∠NOM; ∠QRP

5. Name the angle opposite the second longest side in each triangle.
   ∠MNO; ∠RQP

Look Back and Check

6. How do you know if you paired the correct angles together?
   They are opposite their corresponding sides.

Solve Another Problem

7. List the pairs of corresponding sides in the figure above.
   MN, PQ; MO, PR; ON, RQ

Name _____ Class _____ Date _____

8-8 • Guided Problem Solving

GPS Student Page 413, Exercise 19:

Reasoning How many lines of symmetry does a square have? Draw a diagram to support your answer.

Read and Understand

1. What is a line of symmetry?
   If you fold a drawing on its line of symmetry,
   the two sides match.

2. What could you create that might help you to answer this question?
   Create a square out of paper and fold it.

Plan and Solve

3. Draw a square and a line making a diagonal.

4. In the same square, draw a line making another diagonal.

5. In the same square, draw a line joining the midpoints of the opposite sides of the square.

6. In the same square, draw another line joining the midpoints of the opposite sides of the square.

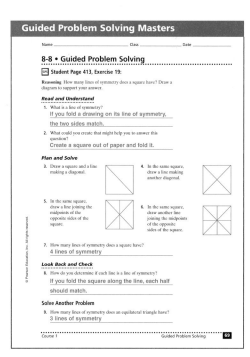

7. How many lines of symmetry does a square have?
   4 lines of symmetry

Look Back and Check

8. How do you determine if each line is a line of symmetry?
   If you fold the square along the line, each half
   should match.

Solve Another Problem

9. How many lines of symmetry does an equilateral triangle have?
   3 lines of symmetry

370J

Activities and Projects

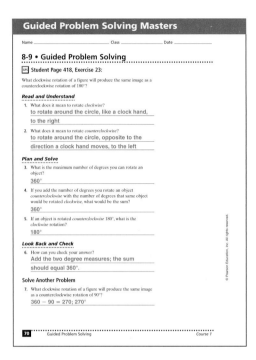

Guided Problem Solving Masters

Name _____ Class _____ Date _____

8-9 • Guided Problem Solving

GPS Student Page 418, Exercise 23:

What clockwise rotation of a figure will produce the same image as a counterclockwise rotation of 180°?

Read and Understand

1. What does it mean to rotate *clockwise*?

   to rotate around the circle, like a clock hand, to the right

2. What does it mean to rotate *counterclockwise*?

   to rotate around the circle, opposite to the direction a clock hand moves, to the left

Plan and Solve

3. What is the maximum number of degrees you can rotate an object?

   360°

4. If you add the number of degrees you rotate an object *counterclockwise* with the number of degrees that same object would be rotated *clockwise*, what would be the sum?

   360°

5. If an object is rotated *counterclockwise* 180°, what is the *clockwise* rotation?

   180°

Look Back and Check

6. How can you check your answer?

   Add the two degree measures; the sum should equal 360°.

Solve Another Problem

7. What clockwise rotation of a figure will produce the same image as a counterclockwise rotation of 90°?

   360 − 90 = 270; 270°

70   Guided Problem Solving   Course 1

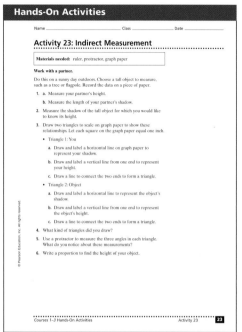

Hands-On Activities

Name _____ Class _____ Date _____

Activity 23: Indirect Measurement

Materials needed: ruler, protractor, graph paper

Work with a partner.

Do this on a sunny day outdoors. Choose a tall object to measure, such as a tree or flagpole. Record the data on a piece of paper.

1. a. Measure your partner's height.

   b. Measure the length of your partner's shadow.

2. Measure the shadow of the tall object for which you would like to know its height.

3. Draw two triangles to scale on graph paper to show these relationships. Let each square on the graph paper equal one inch.

   • Triangle 1: You

     a. Draw and label a horizontal line on graph paper to represent your shadow.

     b. Draw and label a vertical line from one end to represent your height.

     c. Draw a line to connect the two ends to form a triangle.

   • Triangle 2: Object

     a. Draw and label a horizontal line to represent the object's shadow.

     b. Draw and label a vertical line from one end to represent the object's height.

     c. Draw a line to connect the two ends to form a triangle.

4. What kind of triangles did you draw?

5. Use a protractor to measure the three angles in each triangle. What do you notice about these measurements?

6. Write a proportion to find the height of your object.

Courses 1–3 Hands-On Activities   Activity 23   23

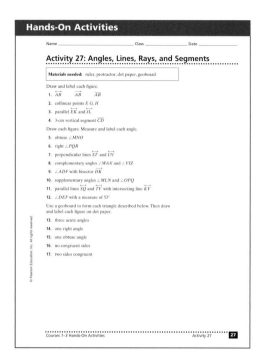

Hands-On Activities

Name _____ Class _____ Date _____

Activity 27: Angles, Lines, Rays, and Segments

Materials needed: ruler, protractor, dot paper, geoboard

Draw and label each figure.

1. $\overleftrightarrow{AB}$ $\overrightarrow{AB}$ $\overline{AB}$

2. collinear points F, G, H

3. parallel $\overrightarrow{EK}$ and $\overrightarrow{JL}$

4. 3-cm vertical segment $\overline{CD}$

Draw each figure. Measure and label each angle.

5. obtuse $\angle MNO$

6. right $\angle PQR$

7. perpendicular lines $\overleftrightarrow{ST}$ and $\overleftrightarrow{UV}$

8. complementary angles $\angle WAX$ and $\angle YIZ$

9. $\angle ADF$ with bisector $\overrightarrow{DK}$

10. supplementary angles $\angle MLN$ and $\angle OPQ$

11. parallel lines $\overleftrightarrow{SQ}$ and $\overleftrightarrow{TV}$ with intersecting line $\overleftrightarrow{KY}$

12. $\angle DEF$ with a measure of 53°

Use a geoboard to form each triangle described below. Then draw and label each figure on dot paper.

13. three acute angles

14. one right angle

15. one obtuse angle

16. no congruent sides

17. two sides congruent

Courses 1–3 Hands-On Activities   Activity 27   27

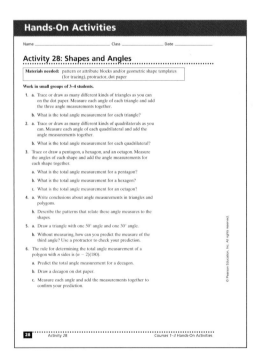

Hands-On Activities

Name _____ Class _____ Date _____

Activity 28: Shapes and Angles

Materials needed: pattern or attribute blocks and/or geometric shape templates (for tracing), protractor, dot paper

Work in small groups of 3–4 students.

1. a. Trace or draw as many different kinds of triangles as you can on the dot paper. Measure each angle of each triangle and add the three angle measurements together.

   b. What is the total angle measurement for each triangle?

2. a. Trace or draw as many different kinds of quadrilaterals as you can. Measure each angle of each quadrilateral and add the angle measurements together.

   b. What is the total angle measurement for each quadrilateral?

3. Trace or draw a pentagon, a hexagon, and an octagon. Measure the angles of each shape and add the angle measurements for each shape together.

   a. What is the total angle measurement for a pentagon?

   b. What is the total angle measurement for a hexagon?

   c. What is the total angle measurement for an octagon?

4. a. Write conclusions about angle measurements in triangles and polygons.

   b. Describe the patterns that relate these angle measures to the shapes.

5. a. Draw a triangle with one 50° angle and one 30° angle.

   b. Without measuring, how can you predict the measure of the third angle? Use a protractor to check your prediction.

6. The rule for determining the total angle measurement of a polygon with n sides is $(n − 2)(180)$.

   a. Predict the total angle measurement for a decagon.

   b. Draw a decagon on dot paper.

   c. Measure each angle and add the measurements together to confirm your prediction.

28   Activity 28   Courses 1–3 Hands-On Activities

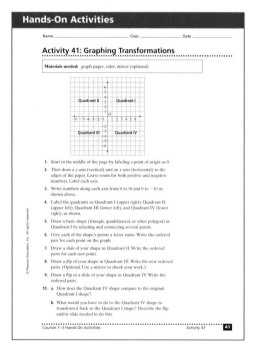

Hands-On Activities

Name _____ Class _____ Date _____

Activity 41: Graphing Transformations

Materials needed: graph paper, ruler, mirror (optional)

1. Start in the middle of the page by labeling a point of origin as 0.

2. Then draw a y-axis (vertical) and an x-axis (horizontal) to the edges of the paper. Leave room for both positive and negative numbers. Label each axis.

3. Write numbers along each axis from 0 to 10 and 0 to −10 as shown above.

4. Label the quadrants as Quadrant I (upper right), Quadrant II (upper left), Quadrant III (lower left), and Quadrant IV (lower right), as shown.

5. Draw a basic shape (triangle, quadrilateral, or other polygon) in Quadrant I by selecting and connecting several points.

6. Give each of the shape's points a letter name. Write the ordered pair for each point on the graph.

7. Draw a *slide* of your shape in Quadrant II. Write the ordered pairs for each new point.

8. Draw a *flip* of your shape in Quadrant III. Write the new ordered pairs. (Optional: Use a mirror to check your work.)

9. Draw a flip or a slide of your shape in Quadrant IV. Write the ordered pairs.

10. a. How does the Quadrant IV shape compare to the original Quadrant I shape?

    b. What would you have to do to the Quadrant IV shape to transform it back to the Quadrant I shape? Describe the flip and/or slide needed to do this.

Courses 1–3 Hands-On Activities   Activity 41   41

Technology Activities

Name _____ Class _____ Date _____

Classifying Triangles   Activity 14

Use your geometry software to do this activity.

Example: Triangle ABC has vertices $A(−3, 1)$, $B(0, 7)$ and $C(3, 1)$. Classify $\triangle ABC$ by its angles and sides.

① Pull down the **Graph** menu and select **Show Grid**.

② Graph and label these points: $A(−3, 1)$, $B(0, 7)$ and $C(3, 1)$. To graph points, pull down the **Graph** menu and select **Plot Points**. Then enter the x- and y-coordinates of each point. When you are finished, click **Done**. Label the points in order by selecting the **Text Tool** and clicking on the point.

③ Highlight only points A, B, and C. Pull down the **Construct** menu and select **Segments**. You now have constructed $\triangle ABC$.

④ Highlight only $\overline{AB}$. Pull down the **Measure** menu and select **Length**. The length of $\overline{AB}$ is now displayed on the screen. Repeat this procedure for $\overline{BC}$ and $\overline{AC}$.

⑤ Highlight only points B, A, and C, *in that order*. Pull down the **Measure** menu and select **Angle**. The measure of $\angle BAC$ is now displayed on the screen. Repeat this procedure to display the measures of $\angle ABC$ and $\angle BCA$.

⑥ Look at the angle measurements. The triangle has three acute angles, so it is an acute triangle.

⑦ Next look at the segment length measurements. Two of the sides of the triangle are congruent, so the triangle is isosceles.

Classifying by angles and sides, you can say that $\triangle ABC$ is an acute, isosceles triangle.

Exercises

Classify each triangle by its angles and sides.

1. Triangle XYZ has vertices $X(1, 1)$, $Y(4, 3)$ and $Z(7, 1)$.

2. Triangle TUV has vertices $T(2, 3)$, $U(5, 3)$ and $V(5, 8)$.

3. Triangle JKL has vertices $J(−1, 1)$, $K(6, 4)$ and $L(9, 1)$.

4. Triangle MNO has vertices $M(−6, 1)$, $N(−5, 2.74)$ and $O(−4, 1)$.

14   Activity 14   Technology Activities

Sample pages; see p. G for complete list.

Name _____ Class _____ Date _____

Chapter 8 Project: Puzzling Pictures
Create a Puzzle

Beginning the Chapter Project.

Do you remember putting together simple puzzles when you were younger? Puzzles designed for young children are often made of wood and have large pieces. The pieces have straight sides so that the child can put the puzzle together easily.

Think about one of your favorite pictures. How would it look as a puzzle? Your project is to make an attractive but challenging puzzle for your classmates. Include as many geometric shapes as you can.

Activities

Activity 1: Identifying Check students' answers.

The diagram shows a puzzle known as a tangram. Identify the geometric shapes used to form the large square.

5 triangles, 1 square, 1 parallelogram

Activity 2: Drawing

Your puzzle must include at least one of each of the following triangles: right, equilateral, isosceles, scalene. Try drawing a rectangular puzzle on a piece of paper.

Activity 3: Planning

Your puzzle must also include at least one of each of the following polygons: quadrilateral, pentagon, hexagon, rhombus, trapezoid, and parallelogram. Draw a new puzzle that includes these shapes as well as the four triangle types.

Activity 4: Designing

Prepare the plan for your puzzle. Make sure it includes two triangles that are congruent and two triangles that are similar, but not congruent.

Name _____ Class _____ Date _____

Chapter 8 Project: Puzzling Pictures (continued)

Finishing the Project

Imagine you are a toy salesman trying to convince your boss that you have a great new puzzle to sell. Hand out the puzzle for your classmates to try and solve.

Be sure your work is neat and clear. Write all explanations you think are necessary.

Reflect and Revise

Make a checklist of the requirements for your puzzle. Use the checklist to see if your tangram satisfies all the requirements. How few pieces can you have and still satisfy all the requirements?

Exchange puzzles with a classmate and put them together as quickly as possible. Have your classmate write a list of what he/she liked about your puzzle. Then have him/her give you a list of suggestions for how to improve your puzzle.

Review the information from your classmate and determine if you want to change your puzzle. If so, write an explanation of why you decided to implement your classmate's suggestions.

Extending the Project

Research the various types of puzzle games you find in the newspaper and on the Internet. Create a list of the types of puzzles that use mathematics. Identify the mathematical concept used in each type of puzzle. For instance, a decoding type puzzle might use the problem solving strategy of logical reasoning.

Create a poster displaying the various types of puzzles that use mathematical concepts. Place the puzzles underneath one of the following headings.

Number Theory	Algebra
Geometry	Data Statistics
Patterns	Problem Solving Strategies

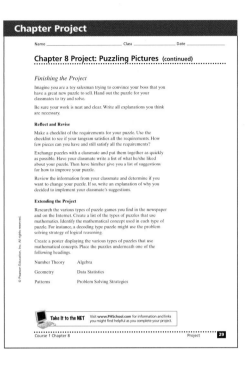

Take It to the NET Visit www.PHSchool.com for information and links you might find helpful as you complete your project.

Name _____ Class _____ Date _____

Chapter Project Manager
Chapter 8: Puzzling Pictures

Getting Started

Read about the project. As you work on it, you will need several sheets of paper. If available, a spreadsheet program also can be used. Keep all your work for the project in a folder, along with this Project Manager.

Checklist	Suggestions
☐ Activity 1: identifying	☐ Make flashcards of the different types of polygons and triangles in this project.
☐ Activity 2: drawing	☐ Practice drawing different types of triangles. Practice drawing them inside one another.
☐ Activity 3: planning	☐ Add polygons to your practice pictures.
☐ Activity 4: designing	☐ Review the definitions of similar and congruent triangles.
☐ Recommendations	☐ Create a puzzle with thick poster board paper.

Scoring Rubric

3 Your puzzle includes the ten required shapes as well as the necessary congruent and similar triangles. Your puzzle is carefully made and includes a list of the triangles and polygons you used.

2 Your puzzle meets at least nine of the twelve requirements listed in the project links. Your list of the triangles and polygons in your puzzle is adequate, and your puzzle is attractive.

1 You leave out more than three of the required shapes in your puzzle, you incorrectly identify shapes in your list, or you pay little attention to the appearance of your finished puzzle.

0 You do not complete a puzzle, or you leave out most of the required triangles and polygons.

Your Evaluation of Project Evaluate your work based on the Scoring Rubric.

Teacher's Evaluation of Project

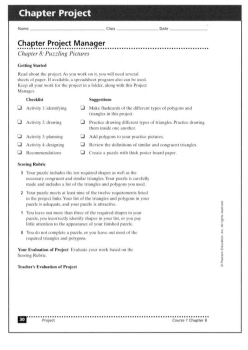

Transparencies

Name _____ Class _____ Date _____

Chapter Project Teacher Notes
Chapter 8: Puzzling Pictures

About the Project The Chapter Project allows students to use their knowledge of geometric shapes to make a challenging puzzle.

Introducing the Project

Ask students:
- *Have you ever solved a jigsaw puzzle? How do you determine which pieces fit together?*
- *Have you ever seen a tangram puzzle? How is it similar and how is it different from a jigsaw puzzle?*

Activity 1: Identifying

Inform students that the tangram puzzle originated in China. Suggest they review the names of the geometric shapes.

Activity 2: Drawing

To construct the puzzle, students can start by drawing a rectangle into triangles. Challenge them to make as many different types of triangles as they can.

Activity 3: Planning

Students may need to draw this new puzzle on a larger rectangle. They may want to use stencils as patterns for some of their pieces. When they have drawn their new puzzle, suggest they cut out the pieces and try to reassemble it.

Activity 4: Designing

Students may need to adjust the sizes and shapes of previous puzzle pieces to accommodate the new shapes. Students can prepare plans by sketching with pencil and tracing paper.

Finishing the Project

You may wish to plan a project day on which students share their completed projects. Encourage students to explain their processes as well as their projects.

Ask students to review their project work and bring their notebooks up to date.

Take It to the NET Visit www.PHSchool.com for information, student links, and teacher support for this project.

Problem of the Day — Lesson 8-1

Leah's scores on her math tests were 84, 64, 72, 86, 69, 85, and 87. Her teacher says that Leah's average score on the tests is about 78. Leah calculated an 84 average. What did each person mean? Whose interpretation of the data describes it most accurately? Why?

Answer

Her teacher gave the mean; Leah gave the median. The teacher's interpretation was more accurate because the scores dropped quite far below the median.

Problem of the Day — Lesson 8-2

What is the result if you divide 50 by $\frac{1}{2}$ and then subtract 25?

Answer

75

Problem of the Day — Lesson 8-3

Describe the pattern:

18, 15.25, 12.5, 9.75, . . .

Answer

Start with 18 and subtract 2.75 repeatedly.

Problem of the Day — Lesson 8-4

What is the greatest multiple of 8 less than 1,000? Less than 10,000? Less than 100,000?

Answer

992; 9,992; 99,992

Problem of the Day — Lesson 8-5

A video store has two membership plans. Plan A costs $15 to join and $2.50 per video. Plan B costs $20 to join and $1.75 per video. How many videos must a customer rent before plan B is the better deal?

Answer

7 videos

Problem of the Day — Lesson 8-6

Find the value of each expression.

a. $1.6 - 0.3 \times 0.4 + 2.6$ b. $4.5 - 0.024 + 1.8 - 0.36$

Answers

a. 4.08   b. 5.916

Problem of the Day — Lesson 8-7

Can two acute angles be supplementary? Explain your answer.

Answer

No; the measure of each angle must be less than 90°, so the sum of their measures must be less than 180°. To be supplementary the sum must equal 180°.

Problem of the Day — Lesson 8-8

Draw a quadrilateral that is not a parallelogram and that has exactly two pairs of congruent sides.

Answer

Check students' drawings. Quadrilaterals will be kite-shaped.

Problem of the Day — Lesson 8-9

Find two even integers whose sum is 20 and whose product is 96.

Answer

8 and 12

Check Skills You'll Need — Lesson 8-1

Find the length of each segment. Measure to the nearest $\frac{1}{16}$ inch.

1. _____

2. _____

3. _____

Solutions

1. $2\frac{13}{16}$ in.   2. 2 in.   3. $3\frac{6}{16}$ in. = $3\frac{3}{8}$ in.

Lesson Quiz — Lesson 8-1

Name each figure.

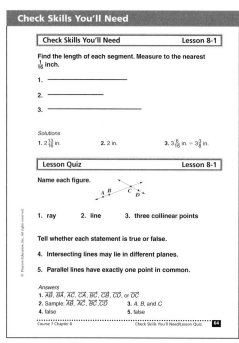

1. ray   2. line   3. three collinear points

Tell whether each statement is true or false.

4. Intersecting lines may lie in different planes.

5. Parallel lines have exactly one point in common.

Answers

1. $\overline{AB}$, $\overline{BA}$, $\overline{AC}$, $\overline{CA}$, $\overline{BC}$, $\overline{CB}$, $\overline{CD}$, or $\overline{DC}$
2. Sample: $\overline{AB}$, $\overline{AC}$, $\overline{BC}$, $\overline{CD}$ 3. A, B, and C
4. false   5. false

Sample page; see p. H for complete list.

Additional Examples — Lesson 8-1

1 EXAMPLE Name each segment, ray, or line.

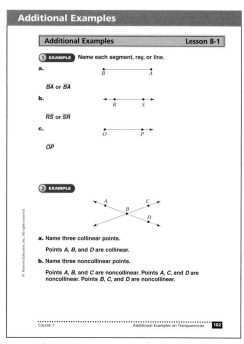

a.
$\overline{BA}$ or $\overline{BA}$

b.
$\overleftrightarrow{RS}$ or $\overleftrightarrow{SR}$

c.
$\overrightarrow{OP}$

2 EXAMPLE

a. Name three collinear points.

Points A, B, and D are collinear.

b. Name three noncollinear points.

Points A, B, and C are noncollinear. Points A, C, and D are noncollinear. Points B, C, and D are noncollinear.

Sample page; see p. H for complete list.

Protractor   5

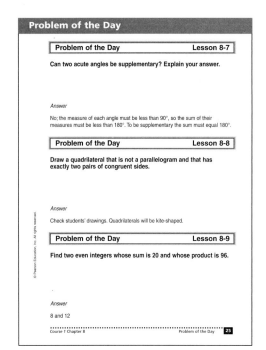

Sample pages.

Venn Diagram   22

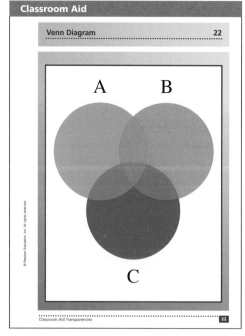

Answers for Lesson *On Your Own* Exercises

1. Sample: 1 : 4, 1 to 4, $\frac{1}{4}$
2. Sample: 24 to 25, 24 : 25, $\frac{24}{25}$
3. 12 to 4, $\frac{12}{4}$
4. 8 : 10, $\frac{8}{10}$
5. 5 to 4, 5 : 4
6. 13 to 8, $\frac{13}{8}$
7. 21 to 28, $\frac{21}{28}$
8. 8 to 18, 8 : 18
9. B
10a. 7 : 15, 7 to 15, $\frac{7}{15}$
  b. 7 : 8, 7 to 8, $\frac{7}{8}$
11a. 23 : 19, 23 to 19, $\frac{23}{19}$
  b. 19 : 42, 19 to 42, $\frac{19}{42}$
12. No; the new ratio is 16 : 11.
13. 0.9   14. 3.6   15. 2.7   16. 0.7
17. 0.5   18. 1.0
19a. 225 : 3, 455 : 7
  b. 75, 65
  c. Answers may vary. Sample: Train A travels 75 mi/h while Train B travels 65 mi/h
20a. $\frac{13}{18}$
  b. $\frac{169}{324}$
  c. The ratio of areas is the square of the ratio of sides.
21–26. Answers may vary. Samples are given.
21. 13 : 27, 78 : 162   22. 6 to 22, 3 to 11
23. $\frac{106}{50}$, $\frac{53}{25}$ 24. $\frac{7}{1}$, $\frac{14}{2}$ 25. $\frac{9}{18}$, $\frac{3}{6}$
26. 2 : 12, 3 : 18   27. 5 : 2   28. 1 to 9
29. $\frac{1}{50}$ 30. 4 to 1   31. 1 : 2
32. $\frac{1}{3}$ 33. 25 to 1
34a. 101 and 107   35a. 8 : 4
  b. 7 : 12   b. 10 qt antifreeze, 5 qt water

Sample page; see p. H for complete list.

Assessment

Lesson Quiz

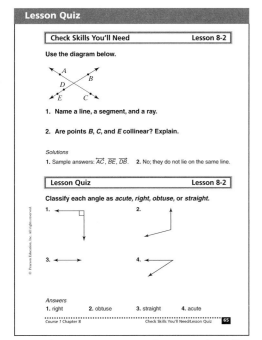

Check Skills You'll Need — Lesson 8-2

Use the diagram below.

1. Name a line, a segment, and a ray.

2. Are points *B*, *C*, and *E* collinear? Explain.

Solutions

1. Sample answers: $\overrightarrow{AC}$, $\overline{BE}$, $\overrightarrow{DB}$. 2. No; they do not lie on the same line.

Lesson Quiz — Lesson 8-2

Classify each angle as *acute, right, obtuse,* or *straight.*

1.   2.

3.   4.

Answers

1. right   2. obtuse   3. straight   4. acute

Course 1 Chapter 8   Check Skills You'll Need/Lesson Quiz   65

Sample page; see p. H for complete list.

Checkpoint Quizzes

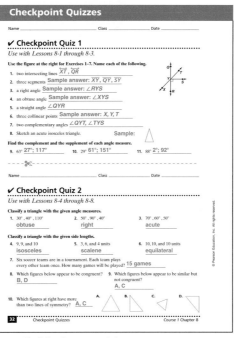

Name _____ Class _____ Date _____

✔ **Checkpoint Quiz 1**
Use with Lessons 8-1 through 8-3.

Use the figure at the right for Exercises 1–7. Name each of the following.

1. two intersecting lines $\overleftrightarrow{XT}$, $\overleftrightarrow{QR}$
2. three segments Sample answer: $\overline{XY}$, $\overline{QY}$, $\overline{SY}$
3. a right angle Sample answer: $\angle RYS$
4. an obtuse angle Sample answer: $\angle XYS$
5. a straight angle $\angle QYR$
6. three collinear points Sample answer: X, Y, T
7. two complementary angles $\angle QYT$, $\angle TYS$
8. Sketch an acute isosceles triangle.   Sample:

Find the complement and the supplement of each angle measure.

9. 63° 27°; 117°   10. 29° 61°; 151°   11. 88° 2°; 92°

Name _____ Class _____ Date _____

✔ **Checkpoint Quiz 2**
Use with Lessons 8-4 through 8-8.

Classify a triangle with the given angle measures.

1. 30°, 40°, 110° obtuse   2. 50°, 90°, 40° right   3. 70°, 60°, 50° acute

Classify a triangle with the given side lengths.

4. 9, 9, and 10 isosceles   5. 3, 6, and 4 units scalene   6. 10, 10, and 10 units equilateral

7. Six soccer teams are in a tournament. Each team plays every other team once. How many games will be played? 15 games

8. Which figures below appear to be congruent? B, D   9. Which figures below appear to be similar but not congruent? A, C

10. Which figures at right have more than two lines of symmetry? A, C

32   Checkpoint Quizzes   Course 1 Chapter 8

Available in Spanish

Chapter Test, Form A

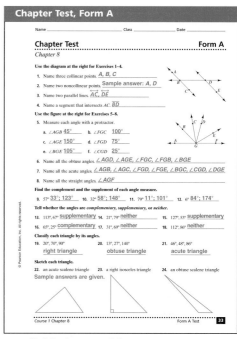

Name _____ Class _____ Date _____

Chapter Test — Form A
Chapter 8

Use the diagram at the right for Exercises 1–4.

1. Name three collinear points A, B, C
2. Name two noncollinear points Sample answer: A, D
3. Name two parallel lines $\overleftrightarrow{AC}$, $\overleftrightarrow{DE}$
4. Name a segment that intersects AC $\overline{BD}$

Use the figure at the right for Exercises 5–8.

5. Measure each angle with a protractor.
   a. $\angle AGB$ 45°   b. $\angle FGC$ 100°
   c. $\angle AGE$ 150°   d. $\angle FGD$ 75°
   e. $\angle BGE$ 105°   f. $\angle CGD$ 25°

6. Name all the obtuse angles $\angle AGD$, $\angle AGE$, $\angle FGC$, $\angle FGB$, $\angle BGE$
7. Name all the acute angles $\angle AGB$, $\angle AGC$, $\angle FGD$, $\angle FGE$, $\angle BGC$, $\angle CGD$, $\angle DGE$
8. Name all the straight angles $\angle AGF$

Find the complement and the supplement of each angle measure.

9. 57° 33°; 123°   10. 32° 58°; 148°   11. 79° 11°; 101°   12. 6° 84°; 174°

Tell whether the angles are *complementary, supplementary,* or *neither.*

13. 113°, 67° supplementary   14. 21°, 79° neither   15. 127°, 53° supplementary
16. 65°, 25° complementary   17. 31°, 69° neither   18. 112°, 86° neither

Classify each triangle by its angles.

19. 20°, 70°, 90° right triangle   20. 13°, 27°, 140° obtuse triangle   21. 46°, 48°, 86° acute triangle

Sketch each triangle.

22. an acute scalene triangle   23. a right isosceles triangle   24. an obtuse scalene triangle
Sample answers are given.

Course 1 Chapter 8   Form A Test   33

Available in Spanish

Chapter Test, Form A

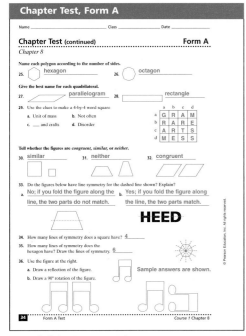

Name _____ Class _____ Date _____

Chapter Test (continued) — Form A
Chapter 8

Name each polygon according to the number of sides.

25. hexagon   26. octagon

Give the best name for each quadrilateral.

27. parallelogram   28. rectangle

29. Use the clues to make a 4-by-4 word square
   a. Unit of mass   b. Not often
   c. ... and crafts   d. Disorder

	a	b	c	d
a	G	R	A	M
b	R	A	R	E
c	A	R	T	S
d	M	E	S	S

Tell whether the figures are *congruent, similar,* or *neither.*

30. similar   31. neither   32. congruent

33. Do the figures below have line symmetry for the dashed line shown? Explain?
   a. No; if you fold the figure along the line, the two parts do not match.   b. Yes; if you fold the figure along the line, the two parts match.

HEED

34. How many lines of symmetry does a square have? 4
35. How many lines of symmetry does the hexagon have? Draw the lines of symmetry. 6
36. Use the figure at the right.
   a. Draw a reflection of the figure.
   b. Draw a 90° rotation of the figure.   Sample answers are shown.

34   Form A Test   Course 1 Chapter 8

Available in Spanish

Chapter Test, Form B

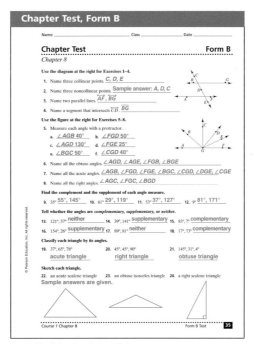

Name _____ Class _____ Date _____

Chapter Test — Form B
Chapter 8

Use the diagram at the right for Exercises 1–4.

1. Name three collinear points C, D, E
2. Name three noncollinear points Sample answer: A, D, C
3. Name two parallel lines $\overleftrightarrow{AF}$, $\overleftrightarrow{BG}$
4. Name a segment that intersects CD $\overline{BG}$

Use the figure at the right for Exercises 5–8.

5. Measure each angle with a protractor.
   a. $\angle AGB$ 40°   b. $\angle FGD$ 50°
   c. $\angle AGD$ 130°   d. $\angle FGE$ 25°
   e. $\angle BGC$ 50°   f. $\angle CGD$ 40°

6. Name all the obtuse angles $\angle AGD$, $\angle AGE$, $\angle FGB$, $\angle BGE$
7. Name all the acute angles $\angle AGB$, $\angle FGD$, $\angle FGE$, $\angle BGC$, $\angle CGD$, $\angle DGE$, $\angle CGE$
8. Name all the right angles $\angle AGC$, $\angle FGC$, $\angle BGD$

Find the complement and the supplement of each angle measure.

9. 35° 55°; 145°   10. 61° 29°; 119°   11. 53° 37°; 127°   12. 9° 81°; 171°

Tell whether the angles are *complementary, supplementary,* or *neither.*

13. 121°, 57° neither   14. 39°, 141° supplementary   15. 83°, 7° complementary
16. 154°, 26° supplementary   17. 89°, 81° neither   18. 17°, 73° complementary

Classify each triangle by its angles.

19. 37°, 65°, 78° acute triangle   20. 45°, 45°, 90° right triangle   21. 145°, 31°, 4° obtuse triangle

Sketch each triangle.

22. an acute scalene triangle   23. an obtuse isosceles triangle   24. a right scalene triangle
Sample answers are given.

Course 1 Chapter 8   Form B Test   35

Available in Spanish

Chapter Test, Form B

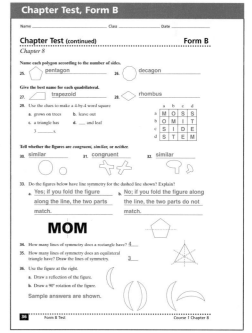

Name _____ Class _____ Date _____

Chapter Test (continued) — Form B
Chapter 8

Name each polygon according to the number of sides.

25. pentagon   26. decagon

Give the best name for each quadrilateral.

27. trapezoid   28. rhombus

29. Use the clues to make a 4-by-4 word square
   a. grows on trees   b. leave out
   c. a triangle has   d. ... and leaf
   3. ... s

	a	b	c	d
a	M	O	S	S
b	O	M	I	T
c	S	I	D	E
d	S	T	E	M

Tell whether the figures are *congruent, similar,* or *neither.*

30. similar   31. congruent   32. similar

33. Do the figures below have line symmetry for the dashed line shown? Explain?
   a. Yes; if you fold the figure along the line, the two parts match.   b. No; if you fold the figure along the line, the two parts do not match.

MOM

34. How many lines of symmetry does a rectangle have? 4
35. How many lines of symmetry does an equilateral triangle have? Draw the lines of symmetry. 3
36. Use the figure at the right.
   a. Draw a reflection of the figure.
   b. Draw a 90° rotation of the figure.
   Sample answers are shown.

36   Form B Test   Course 1 Chapter 8

Available in Spanish

Name _____ Class _____ Date _____

Alternative Assessment   Form C
Chapter 8

TRIANGLES EVERYWHERE

Look at the two triangles below. Notice how you can put them together to form a rectangle.

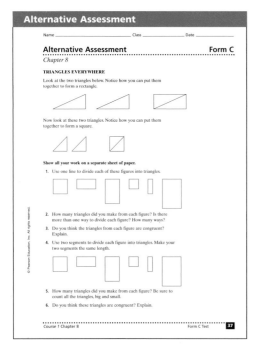

Now look at these two triangles below. Notice how you can put them together to form a square.

Show all your work on a separate sheet of paper.

1. Use one line to divide each of these figures into triangles.

2. How many triangles did you make from each figure? Is there more than one way to divide each figure? How many ways?

3. Do you think the triangles from each figure are congruent? Explain.

4. Use two segments to divide each figure into triangles. Make your two segments the same length.

5. How many triangles did you make from each figure? Be sure to count all the triangles, big and small.

6. Do you think these triangles are congruent? Explain.

Available in Spanish

Name _____ Class _____ Date _____

Alternative Assessment (continued)   Form C
Chapter 8

7. Use three line segments to divide this square into triangles.

8. Now use a different color to add one more line to the square. How many triangles did you add with this fourth line?

9. Now add one more line to the square. Count the total number of triangles in the square. Be sure to include all the triangles, big and small. How many triangles are there? Explain how you kept track as you counted.

10. Do you think you could continue adding more lines to make more triangles? Explain.

Excursion

Below is a fun and easy puzzle. To solve it, you must count all the triangles you can find within the square.

Now make up your own puzzle like the one above. The outside shape of your puzzle can be a square or any other shape you choose. The inside should contain many triangles of different sizes and shapes. Make the puzzle as hard as you can. Then give the answer to your puzzle. Your answer should tell how many triangles and the different kinds of triangles you made in your puzzle.

Available in Spanish

Name _____ Class _____ Date _____

Alternative Assessment (continued)   Form C
Chapter 8

Scoring Rubric

Exercise	Points	Explanation
1.	1	Figures correctly divided into triangles
	0	No response OR other response
2.	1	Two triangles; yes, two ways to do it
	0	No response OR other response
3.	1	Triangles considered congruent and justification given
	0	No response OR other response
4.	1	Figures correctly divided into triangles
	0	No response OR other response
5.	1	Response of eight triangles (not all the same size) for triangles formed by diagonals; judge other responses on their merits
	0	No response OR other response that lacks merit
6.	1	Same sizes: yes; different sizes: no; justification given
	0	No response OR other response
7.	1	Figure divided into triangles, using three lines
	0	No response OR other response
8.	1	Responses should be accurate in terms of drawing
	0	No response OR other response
9.	1	Responses will vary; explanation of the method given
	0	No response OR other response
10.	1	Explanation of how lines can be added indefinitely
	0	No response OR other response
Excursion	5	Complex puzzle with good explanation of answer
	4	Complex puzzle with adequate explanation OR less complex puzzle with good explanation
	3	Less complex puzzle with adequate explanation OR complex puzzle with weak explanation
	2	Less complex puzzle with weak explanation
	1	Puzzle with no explanation
	0	No response

Available in Spanish

Name _____ Class _____ Date _____

Cumulative Review
Chapters 1–8

Multiple Choice. Choose the letter of the best answer.

1. What is the LCM (least common multiple) of 5 and 6?

   A. 11   **B.** 30
   C. 60   D. 90

2. Which list shows the fractions $\frac{1}{3}, \frac{3}{5}, \frac{3}{4}, \frac{4}{9}$ from least to greatest?

   F. $\frac{3}{4}, \frac{3}{5}, \frac{4}{9}, \frac{1}{3}$ G. $\frac{3}{5}, \frac{3}{4}, \frac{1}{3}, \frac{4}{9}$
   H. $\frac{4}{9}, \frac{3}{4}, \frac{1}{3}, \frac{3}{5}$ **I.** $\frac{1}{3}, \frac{4}{9}, \frac{3}{5}, \frac{3}{4}$

Use the table for Exercises 3 and 4.

Number on Number Cube	Tally
1	...
2	...
3	...
4	...
5	...
6	...

3. How many times was the number cube rolled?

   A. 10   **B.** 50
   C. 21   D. 30

4. What was the greatest number of times any one number was rolled?

   F. 6   G. 20
   H. 10   I. 4

5. Use mental math to find 14% of 200.

   A. 14   **B.** 28
   C. 56   D. 70

6. Which two fractions are equivalent to $\frac{2}{9}$?

   F. $\frac{3}{1}, \frac{4}{12}$ G. $\frac{4}{12}, \frac{8}{18}$
   H. $\frac{6}{18}, \frac{12}{24}$ I. $\frac{6}{18}, \frac{12}{24}$

Use the figure below to answer Exercises 7–10.

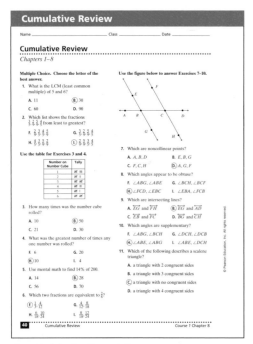

7. Which are noncollinear points?

   A. A, B, D B. E, B, G
   C. F, C, H **D.** A, G, F

8. Which angles appear to be obtuse?

   F. $\angle ABG, \angle ABE$ G. $\angle BCH, \angle BCF$
   H. $\angle FCD, \angle EBC$ I. $\angle EBA, \angle FCB$

9. Which are intersecting lines?

   A. $\overline{EG}$ and $\overline{FH}$ **B.** $\overline{EG}$ and $\overline{AD}$
   C. $\overline{EB}$ and $\overline{FC}$ D. $\overline{BG}$ and $\overline{CH}$

10. Which angles are supplementary?

   F. $\angle ABG, \angle BCH$ G. $\angle DCH, \angle DCB$
   H. $\angle ABE, \angle ABG$ I. $\angle ABE, \angle DCH$

11. Which of the following describes a scalene triangle?

   A. a triangle with 2 congruent sides
   B. a triangle with 3 congruent sides
   C. a triangle with no congruent sides
   D. a triangle with 4 congruent sides

Available in Spanish

Name _____ Class _____ Date _____

Cumulative Review (continued)
Chapters 1–8

12. Suppose $\frac{2}{5}$ of the area of a garden is flowers. Zinnias cover $\frac{1}{3}$ of the flower area. What fraction of the garden is zinnias?

   F. $\frac{8}{15}$
   G. $\frac{15}{45}$
   H. $\frac{20}{24}$
   I. $\frac{20}{15}$

13. Find the difference.

$$\frac{11}{12} - \frac{9}{12}$$

   A. $\frac{5}{6}$ B. $\frac{1}{3}$
   C. $\frac{5}{12}$ **D.** $\frac{1}{6}$

14. A cookie recipe calls for $2\frac{1}{4}$ cups of flour. Hedi plans to triple the recipe. How much flour will she need? Write the answer as a mixed number in simplest form.

   F. $4\frac{1}{4}$ c
   G. $6\frac{1}{4}$ c
   H. $6\frac{3}{4}$ c
   I. 9c

15. 24 cups is how many quarts?

   A. 2 qt   B. 4 qt
   C. 6 qt   D. 12 qt

16. Which ratio compares 10 girls to 12 boys?

   F. 5 to 6   G. 5 to 11
   H. $\frac{6}{5}$ I. 10:22

17. What pair shows $\frac{3}{5}$ as a percent and as a decimal?

   A. 35%, 0.35
   B. 30%, 0.3
   C. 53%, 0.53
   D. 60%, 0.6

18. Write $\frac{1}{125}$ as a decimal and as a percent.

   F. 8%; .08
   G. 1.8%; .018
   H. 0.8%; .008
   I. 0.18%; .0018

19. Find 221.7% of 49.

   A. 4.5
   B. 45.2
   C. 108.6
   D. 186

20. The length of a road on a map is 6 inches. The actual length of the road is 36 miles. What is the scale of the map?

   F. 1 in. : 6 mi
   G. 1 in. : 12 mi
   H. 1 in. : 18 mi
   I. 1 in. : 36 mi

Short Response

21. Six students plan to work in pairs on their science projects, but they cannot decide on a partner. Their teacher told Tim, Susan, Anna, Maria, Matt, and Jake to figure out all the different pairs they could make. How many different pairs did they find?

   15 pairs

Available in Spanish

Name _____ Class _____ Date _____

Benchmark Test 1

1. What is the value of the digit 2 in the number 4.0725?

   A 2 tenths
   B 2 hundredths
   C 2 thousandths
   D 2 ten-thousandths

2. How is the decimal 2.016 expressed in words?

   A two and sixteen thousandths
   B two and sixteen hundredths
   C two and sixteen tenths
   D two and sixteenths

3. Quincy ran a lap in seventy-five and thirteen hundredths seconds. How is this time written in standard form?

   A 75.013 seconds
   B 75.03 seconds
   C 75.103 seconds
   D 75.13 seconds

4. Which set of decimals is ordered from least to greatest?

   A 2.67, 2.71, 2.99, 2.02
   B 2.99, 2.67, 2.71, 2.02
   C 2.02, 2.67, 2.71, 2.99
   D 2.71, 2.02, 2.99, 2.67

5. Which of the following statements is true?

   A 1.971 > 1.97
   B 2.53 < 2.3
   C 4.825 > 4.85
   D 6.74 < 6.740

6. The table below shows the surface ocean temperature for five days. On which day was the daily ocean temperature coolest?

Daily Ocean Temperature

Day	Temperature (°F)
Monday	80.07
Tuesday	81.03
Wednesday	80.90
Thursday	81.50
Friday	81.20

   A Monday
   B Tuesday
   C Wednesday
   D Friday

7. Which addition problem is modeled below?

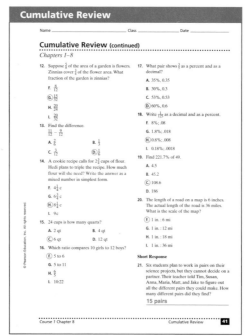

   A 8 + 3 = 11
   B 0.8 + 3 = 3.8
   C 0.8 + 0.3 = 1.1
   D 0.08 + 0.3 = 0.38

On PH Website

Test-Taking Strategies transparency

Test-Taking Strategies: Drawing a Diagram

A diagram can help you see how to solve a problem.

> **Example** A square quilt has 6 in. by 6 in. fabric squares. The outside perimeter is 144 in. How many squares are on the quilt perimeter?
>
> A. 144   B. 36   C. 24   D. 20
>
> Each side must be 144 ÷ 4 = 36 in.
>
> Let one unit on graph paper represent 6 in.
>
> There must be 36 ÷ 6 = 6 squares on each side.
>
> Draw a diagram, and count the perimeter squares.
>
> The answer is 20, or choice D.

Use a diagram to find the answer. Explain your reasoning.

1. Tess wants to fence in her garden, which is 5 ft long and 4 ft wide. She will put a post at each corner and at every foot. How many fence posts will she need?

   A. 14   B. 20   C. 18   D. 19

2. What is the area of the shaded square in the figure?

   F. 50 cm²
   G. 100 cm²
   H. 200 cm²
   I. 400 cm²

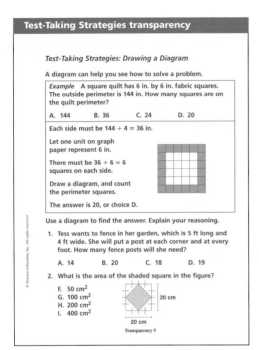

Transparency 9

Test-Taking Strategies worksheet

Name _____ Class _____ Date _____

Chapter 8: Drawing a Diagram

Exercises

Draw a diagram to solve each problem. Check students' diagrams.

1. Point Q is the midpoint of $\overline{PR}$. $\overline{SQ}$ is perpendicular to $\overline{PR}$. Name two right angles. Explain.

   ∠SQR is a right angle. The angle may also
   be written as ∠RQS. ∠SQP is a right angle.
   The angle may also be written as ∠PQS.

2. An isosceles triangle is placed on top of a square. The base of the square is 6 cm and the base of the triangle is also 6 cm. The height of the triangle is 5 cm. What is the total area of the figure? Explain.

   Area of the square = 6 × 6 = 36 cm²;
   Area of the triangle = ½ (6)(5) = 15 cm²;
   The total area of the figure is
   36 + 15 = 51 cm².

3. Point B is the vertex of angle ABC. The measure of angle ABC is 64°. Ray BD bisects angle ABC. What is the measure of angle ABD?
   32°

4. How many lines of symmetry can be drawn through an equilateral triangle?
   3

5. How many lines of symmetry can be drawn through an isosceles triangle?
   1

6. What are the only two quadrilaterals from which you can form 4 congruent triangles by drawing the diagonals?
   a square and a rhombus

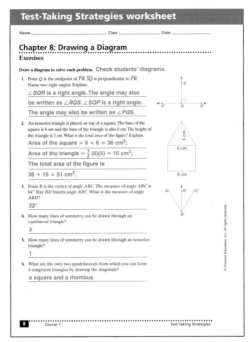

8   Course 1   Test-Taking Strategies

Home Activities

in math class ...

We have been learning about the geometry of polygons. Here is a list of some of the skills and concepts we have studied.

- Classifying lines
- Classifying angles
- Measuring angles
- Exploring angles and sides in a triangle
- Polygons
- Flips and line symmetry
- Slides and tessellations

Home Activities

Here are some activities you can do with your child that use these math skills and concepts.

Divide a sheet of paper into nine equal sections. You can do this by dividing the paper into thirds using vertical lines or folds and then thirds using horizontal lines or folds. Have your child fill one of the squares with a polygon. Use slides, flips, or turns of the polygon to make a design on the paper. Discuss what geometric shapes are in the design and how they are related to each other. Encourage your child to include some kind of pattern in the design. Your child may want to color the design to make it more appealing. Discuss how color affects the design.

One possible slide, flip, and turn for a "T":

Extend the activity by having your child make several different designs. You may want to vary the number of sections and the number of polygons in the design.

Use with Chapter 8

Available in Spanish;
Web Code: aak-5500

Interdisciplinary Activities

Name _____   *Math and Social Studies*

Secrets of the Pyramids

Identify polygons to distinguish the parts of pyramids.

A pyramid is a solid figure made up of a base and planes whose edges meet at a single point above the base called the vertex. There is something mysterious and appealing about the pyramid. Throughout history, ancient civilizations have used this geometrical shape to build great monuments.

Egyptian pyramids were constructed from about 2700 B.C. to about 1700 B.C. They were used as gigantic tombs for royalty. Inside the pyramids a maze of stairs and passageways led to several rooms containing the royal person's body as well as many valuable treasures. The largest Egyptian pyramid, called the Great Pyramid at Giza, was built around 2600 B.C. It was considered one of the Seven Wonders of the World. It was originally 147 meters tall. It is made of five polygons and is comprised of four sides and a base. Each side of its base measures

230 meters. The Great Pyramid is made of huge limestone blocks and covers 13 acres of land.

People once assumed that the Egyptians influenced the building of pyramids in the Americas, which came later. However, a close look at the New World pyramids shows that they aren't copies of the Egyptian model. In fact they aren't really pyramids.

Take the Pyramid of the Sun at Teotihuacán, in Mexico, as an example. It has four sides that do not meet at the top at a single point. Thus, it has no vertex. The Pyramid of the Sun looks like a pyramid with the top chopped off. This is called a *truncated pyramid*. Unlike the Egyptian pyramids, the New World versions were never used to bury royalty. Their truncated tops formed bases for religious temples.

The sides of Egyptian pyramids, such as the Great Pyramid at Giza, Egypt, come to a single point at the top.

Use with Chapter 8

Available in Spanish;
Web Code: aak-5500

Interdisciplinary Activities

Name _____   *Math and Social Studies*

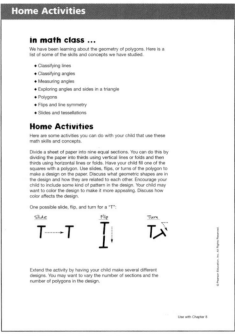

The sides of New World pyramids, such as the Pyramid of the Sun at Teotihuacán, Mexico, have truncated, or flat, tops.

1. What kind of quadrilateral is the base of the Great Pyramid?

2. Look at the sides of the pyramid. What kind of polygons do they form?

3. The sides of the Great Pyramid are identical in shape. Are they isosceles or scalene triangles?

4. What kinds of polygon form the sides of the Pyramid of the Sun?

5. Suppose you extended the lines of the Pyramid of the Sun until they met at a vertex. What kinds of polygons would the sides change into?

6. How were people able to move huge blocks of stone to build ancient pyramids? Do some research on the subject and write a short report on what you find.

Use with Chapter 8

Available in Spanish;
Web Code: aak-5500

Algebra Readiness Puzzles

Name _____   Class _____   Date _____

Geometry in Art   Puzzle 8

Tools of Geometry

1. How many specific polygons can you find?

Polygon type	triangle	rectangle	square	octagon	trapezoid
number of occurrences					

2. How many circles are in the picture? _____

3. Are there more than 60 right angles in the picture? _____

4. Are there more or less than 12 obtuse angles are in the picture? _____

5. Are there more or less than 5 acute angles in the picture? _____

6. What type of shape is formed by the light given off by the headlight? _____

7. Describe a pair of vertical angles.

8. Describe a pair of supplementary angles.

8   Algebra Readiness Puzzles   © Pearson Education, Inc.

Web Code: aak-5500

CHAPTER 8

Tools of Geometry

Chapter 8 Overview

In this chapter students study geometric concepts and terms to get the tools they need to classify geometric figures. First, they examine the difference between lines, line segments, and rays. Next they learn about angles and special kinds of angles. They then explore and classify different kinds of polygons. Finally, they investigate congruence, similarity, symmetry, and transformations.

 Reading Math
• Common Words and Prefixes, p. 378
• **Vocabulary:** A complete list, plus exercises, in the Chapter Review, p. 422
• **Illustrated Glossary:** Examples for each vocabulary term, plus definitions in English and Spanish, on p. 669

 **Test-Taking Strategies**
Drawing a Diagram, p. 421

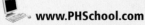 **Real-World Problem Solving**
• **Strategies:** Use Logical Reasoning, pp. 401–404
• **Real-World Snapshots:** Building Outside the Box, pp. 426–427
• **Chapter Project:** Puzzling Pictures, p. 639

 www.PHSchool.com
Internet support includes:
• Self-grading Vocabulary and Chapter 8 Tests
• Activity Masters
• Chapter Project support
• Chapter Planner
• Ch. 8 Resources

Plus **i TEXT**

CHAPTER 8

Key Vocabulary

• angle (p. 379)
• collinear (p. 374)
• congruent angles (p. 387)
• line (p. 373)
• line symmetry (p. 410)
• parallel lines (p. 374)
• point (p. 373)
• polygon (p. 397)
• quadrilateral (p. 398)
• ray (p. 373)
• reflection (p. 416)
• rotation (p. 416)
• segment (p. 373)
• similar figures (p. 406)
• translation (p. 415)

Tools of Geometry

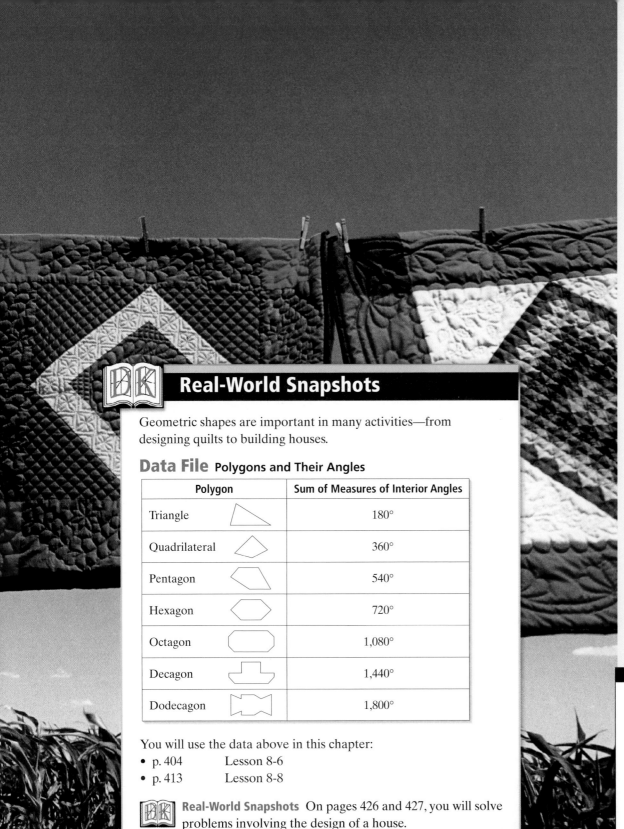

Real-World Snapshots

Geometric shapes are important in many activities—from designing quilts to building houses.

Data File Polygons and Their Angles

Polygon		Sum of Measures of Interior Angles
Triangle		180°
Quadrilateral		360°
Pentagon		540°
Hexagon		720°
Octagon		1,080°
Decagon		1,440°
Dodecagon		1,800°

You will use the data above in this chapter:

- p. 404   Lesson 8-6
- p. 413   Lesson 8-8

Real-World Snapshots On pages 426 and 427, you will solve problems involving the design of a house.

Teaching Notes

Activating Prior Knowledge
In this chapter students build on and extend their knowledge of geometry concepts. They also draw upon their understanding of ratio and proportion as they work with congruent and similar figures. Ask questions such as:
- *What is n in $\frac{n}{12} = \frac{1}{6}$?* **n = 2**
- *What is the perimeter of a rectangle with length of 4 ft and width of 2.5 ft?* **13 ft**
- *The length of a rectangle is 6 in. Its perimeter is 21 in. What is the width of the rectangle?* **4.5 in.**

Real-World Snapshots
The data here about polygons and their angles will be used throughout the chapter. Focus students on the data in the chart and ask:
- *What is the sum of the measures of the angles of a pentagon?* **540°**
- *What is the difference between the interior angle measures for a triangle and a quadrilateral?* **180°**
- *How many sides does a decagon appear to have?* **10**

Reading and Math Literacy

8A: Graphic Organizer   For use before Lesson 8-1

Study Skill: Try to read each lesson before your teacher presents it in class. This will help you recognize new terms and understand the material better.

Write your answers.

1. What is the chapter title?
   Tools of Geometry

2. How many lessons are there in this chapter?
   9

3. What is the topic of the Reading Math page?
   Common Word and Prefixes

4. What is the topic of the Test-Taking Strategy page?
   Drawing a Diagram

5. Look through the chapter and list four real-world connections that are discussed.
   Answers will vary.

6. Complete the graphic organizer below as you work through the chapter.
   - In the center, write the title of the chapter.
   - When you begin a lesson, write the lesson name in a rectangle.
   - When you complete a lesson, write a skill or key concept in a circle linked to that lesson block.
   - When you complete the chapter, use this graphic organizer to help you review.

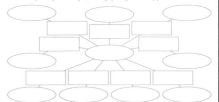

Available in Spanish

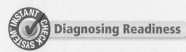

Students will find answers to these exercises in the back of their textbooks.

Prescribing Intervention
For intervention, direct students to:

Using Number Sense to Solve One-Step Equations
Lesson 2-5: Example 2. Extra Practice, p. 643.

Solving Equations by Subtracting
Lesson 2-6: Example 1. Extra Practice, p. 643.

Solving Equations by Adding
Lesson 2-6: Example 3. Extra Practice, p. 643.

Recognizing Proportions
Lesson 6-3: Example 1. Extra Practice, p. 647.

Chapter 8 Preview

Where You've Been

- In Chapter 2, you solved one-step equations by using number sense, subtracting, and adding.

- In Chapter 6, you learned to recognize and solve proportions.

Where You're Going

- In Chapter 8, you will learn how to identify points, lines, and planes.

- You will also find the measurements of angles and sides of figures. You will identify and classify figures and learn about congruency, similarity, and symmetry.

- You will identify geometric figures in real-world situations, such as garden mazes.

Geometric shapes are used in this garden maze in Versailles, France.

 Instant self-check online and on CD-ROM

Diagnosing Readiness   ❓ **For help, go to the lesson in green.**

Using Number Sense to Solve One-Step Equations (Lesson 2-5)

Use mental math to solve each equation.

1. $a + 9 = 18$ 9   **2.** $y \div 3 = 3$ 9   **3.** $11k = 44$ 4   **4.** $c - 5 = 5$ 10

Solving Equations by Subtracting (Lesson 2-6)

Solve each equation. Then, check the solution.

5. $0.23 + x = 1.5$ 1.27   **6.** $p + 120.5 = 180$ 59.5   **7.** $62.9 + b = 90$ 27.1

Solving Equations by Adding (Lesson 2-6)

Solve each equation. Then, check the solution.

8. $d - 13 = 4.5$ 17.5   **9.** $g - 22 = 11.3$ 33.3   **10.** $c - 0.45 = 11.62$ 12.07

Recognizing Proportions (Lesson 6-3)

Do the ratios in each pair form a proportion?

11. $\frac{3}{4}, \frac{18}{24}$ Yes   **12.** $\frac{11}{12}, \frac{121}{144}$ No   **13.** $\frac{16}{20}, \frac{64}{100}$ No

14. $\frac{12}{15}, \frac{24}{30}$ Yes   **15.** $\frac{5}{8}, \frac{15}{20}$ No   **16.** $\frac{4}{9}, \frac{16}{36}$ Yes

Points, Lines, Segments, and Rays

What You'll Learn

OBJECTIVE 1 To name points, lines, segments, and rays

OBJECTIVE 2 To identify parallel, intersecting, and skew lines

...And Why

To identify parallel streets on a map, as in Example 3

 Check Skills You'll Need   For help, go to Lesson 3-4.

Find the length of each segment. Measure to the nearest $\frac{1}{16}$ inch.

1. _____ $2\frac{13}{16}$ in.

2. _____ 2 in.

3. _____ $3\frac{3}{8}$ in. or $3\frac{6}{16}$ in.

New Vocabulary
• point • line • segment • ray • collinear
• plane • intersecting lines • parallel lines • skew lines

Lesson Preview

 Check Skills You'll Need

Fractions on a Ruler
Lesson 3-4 Investigation: Example 2. Extra Practice, p. 644.

Lesson Resources

Teaching Resources
Practice, Reteaching, Enrichment

Reaching All Students
Practice Workbook 8-1
Spanish Practice Workbook 8-1
Guided Problem Solving 8-1
Hands-On Activities 27

Presentation Assistant Plus!
Transparencies
• Check Skills You'll Need 8-1
• Problem of the Day 8-1
• Additional Examples 8-1
• Student Edition Answers 8-1
• Lesson Quiz 8-1
PH Presentation Pro CD-ROM 8-1

ASSESSMENT SYSTEM
Computer Test Generator CD

Technology
Resource Pro® CD-ROM
Computer Test Generator CD
PH Presentation Pro CD-ROM

www.PHSchool.com
Student Site
• Teacher Web Code: aak-5500
• Self-grading Lesson Quiz

PH SuccessNet Teacher Center
• Lesson Planner
• Resources

Plus **iTEXT**

OBJECTIVE 1

Naming Points, Lines, Segments, and Rays

iTEXT Interactive lesson includes instant self-check, tutorials, and activities.

You can locate a star in the sky if you can find the group, or constellation, to which it belongs. The stars in such constellations are like points that can be connected to form a picture.

To find the constellation Orion, the Hunter, look for the three stars in a row that form the belt.

Points A, B, and C

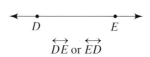

$\overleftrightarrow{DE}$ or $\overleftrightarrow{ED}$

A **point** is a location in space. It has no size. You name a point with a capital letter.

A **line** is a series of points that extends in two opposite directions without end. It has no thickness. Use any two points on a line to name it. Read $\overleftrightarrow{DE}$ as "line DE."

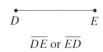

$\overline{DE}$ or $\overline{ED}$

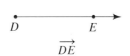

$\overrightarrow{DE}$

A **segment** has two endpoints and all the points of the line between the endpoints. You name a segment by its endpoints. Read $\overline{DE}$ as "segment DE."

A **ray** consists of one endpoint and all the points of a line on one side of the endpoint. To name a ray, use its endpoint first and then any other point on the ray. Read $\overrightarrow{DE}$ as "ray DE."

 Ongoing Assessment and Intervention

Before the Lesson	During the Lesson	After the Lesson
Diagnose prerequisite skills using:	**Monitor progress using:**	**Assess knowledge using:**
• Check Skills You'll Need	• Check Understanding	• Lesson Quiz
	• Additional Examples	• Computer Test Generator CD
	• Test Prep	

Math Background

A *point* is an exact location in space that has no size. A *line* is a series of points that extends in opposite directions without end. A line has no thickness. A *ray* is part of a line with one endpoint and extends forever in one direction. A *line segment* is a part of a line with two endpoints.

A *plane* is a flat surface that extends indefinitely in all directions. When two lines lie in a plane they are either *parallel*—having no points in common—or *intersecting*—having one point in common. *Skew lines* are neither parallel nor intersecting and they lie in different planes.

Teaching Notes

English Learners
Point out that the term *line* is often used in daily life to describe a line segment. Clarify that in mathematics the term *line* is used more precisely for a series of points that extends without end.

1 EXAMPLE Error Prevention
Ask: *Explain why you cannot name ray KJ as ray JK.* The name of a ray always begins with its endpoint.

Geometry Connection
Collinear points always lie in the same plane. However, three *noncollinear* points define a plane. Three noncollinear points also determine three intersecting lines that form a triangle.

Visual Learners
Emphasize that a plane does not physically exist because it has no thickness and extends indefinitely in all directions. Ask:
• *What are some physical objects that can represent a plane?* Sample: ceiling, chalk board, sheet of paper, desk, and so on.
• *What aspect of these objects allows them to represent a plane?* Sample: They are flat. Note that some students may incorrectly assume that only rectangular shapes can represent a plane.

374

---

1 EXAMPLE Naming Lines, Segments, and Rays

Name the line, the segment, and the ray.

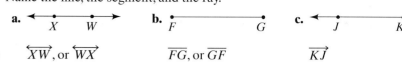

a. $\overleftrightarrow{XW}$, or $\overleftrightarrow{WX}$ b. $\overline{FG}$, or $\overline{GF}$ c. $\overrightarrow{KJ}$

✔ Check Understanding

1a. Answers may vary.
Sample: $\overleftrightarrow{VP}$, $\overleftrightarrow{MV}$

1 Use the figure at the right.
a. Give two names for the line. **See left.**
b. Name three segments. $\overline{VM}$, $\overline{VP}$, $\overline{MP}$
c. **Reasoning** How is $\overrightarrow{VM}$ different from $\overrightarrow{MV}$? **See margin.**

Points on the same line are **collinear.** If you cannot draw one line through all the points, the points are *noncollinear.*

Reading Math
Co means "together with." So *collinear* means "together with points on the same line."

Collinear points   Noncollinear points

2 EXAMPLE Collinear and Noncollinear Points

Name three collinear points.

Points L, Q, and T are collinear.

Answers may vary. Samples are given.

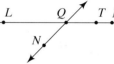

✔ Check Understanding

2 a. Name a different set of three collinear points. Q, T, and M
b. Name three noncollinear points. N, Q, and M.

OBJECTIVE

2 Identifying Parallel, Intersecting, and Skew Lines

A **plane** is a flat surface with no thickness that extends without end in all directions on the surface.

Two lines that lie in the same plane are either intersecting or parallel. **Intersecting lines** have exactly one point in common. **Parallel lines** have no points in common. Parallel segments lie in parallel lines.

Skew lines are lines that are not parallel and do not intersect. Skew lines lie in different planes. Skew segments lie in skew lines.

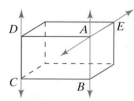

Plane $ABCD$

$\overleftrightarrow{AB}$ is parallel to $\overleftrightarrow{DC}$.
$\overleftrightarrow{AE}$ intersects $\overleftrightarrow{AB}$.
$\overleftrightarrow{AE}$ and $\overleftrightarrow{DC}$ are skew.

👥 Reaching All Students

| **Below Level** Have students model the intersecting lines in Example 2 using two straws for the lines and clay for the five points. Review *collinear* points and *noncollinear* points using their models. | **Advanced Learners** Ask: *If two line segments are in the same plane and do not intersect, are the segments parallel? Explain.* Not necessarily; the segments might intersect if they extended into lines. | **English Learners** See note on page 374. **Inclusion** See note on page 375. |

③ EXAMPLE Real-World 🌐 Problem Solving

Maps Are the indicated lines on the map parallel or intersecting?

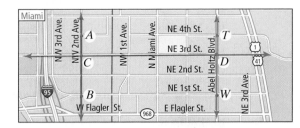

a. $\overleftrightarrow{AB}$ and $\overleftrightarrow{CD}$

$\overleftrightarrow{AB}$ and $\overleftrightarrow{CD}$ are intersecting.

b. $\overleftrightarrow{AB}$ and $\overleftrightarrow{TW}$

$\overleftrightarrow{AB}$ and $\overleftrightarrow{TW}$ are parallel.

✔ **Check Understanding** ③

Answers may vary. Samples are given.
a. Name two other streets on the map that are parallel. 3a–b. See left.
b. Name two other streets on the map that intersect.
c. Reasoning Can streets on this map represent skew lines? Explain.
No; all lines on the map represent streets in the same plane.

3a. NE 3rd St. and NE 2nd St.

3b. NE 4th St. and N Miami Ave.

EXERCISES

❓ For more practice, see *Extra Practice*.

(A) **Practice by Example**

Example 1
(page 374)

Match each figure with its name.

1.  E F B

2. E F A

3. E F D

4. E F C

A. $\overrightarrow{EF}$ **B.** $\overline{EF}$ **C.** $\overleftrightarrow{EF}$ **D.** $\overrightarrow{FE}$

Name each segment, ray, or line.

5. H J $\overline{HJ}$

6. Q P $\overrightarrow{QP}$

7. X Y $\overleftrightarrow{XY}$

8. D W $\overrightarrow{DW}$

9. C R $\overrightarrow{RC}$

10. K E $\overleftrightarrow{KE}$

11. M N $\overline{MN}$

12. R T $\overrightarrow{RT}$

1c. Answers may vary. Samples are given. $\overrightarrow{VM}$ **is a ray that has vertex V and contains M.** $\overrightarrow{MV}$ **is a ray that has vertex M and contains V.**

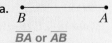

🖥 Additional Examples

① Name each segment, ray, or line.
a. B A
$\overline{BA}$ or $\overline{AB}$

b. R S
$\overleftrightarrow{RS}$ or $\overleftrightarrow{SR}$

c. O P
$\overrightarrow{OP}$

②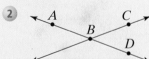
a. Name three collinear points. *A, B, and D*
b. Name three noncollinear points. *A, B, and C; A, C, and D; or B, C, and D*

③ Name each of the following.
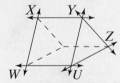
a. two parallel lines $\overleftrightarrow{XY}$ and $\overleftrightarrow{WU}$ or $\overleftrightarrow{XW}$ and $\overleftrightarrow{YU}$

b. two intersecting lines 9 possibilities exist; Sample: $\overleftrightarrow{WU}$ and $\overleftrightarrow{UY}$, or $\overleftrightarrow{WX}$ and $\overleftrightarrow{XY}$, or $\overleftrightarrow{XY}$ and $\overleftrightarrow{YZ}$

c. two skew lines $\overleftrightarrow{WX}$ and $\overleftrightarrow{ZU}$, $\overleftrightarrow{WX}$ and $\overleftrightarrow{ZY}$, $\overleftrightarrow{YZ}$ and $\overleftrightarrow{WU}$, or $\overleftrightarrow{ZU}$ and $\overleftrightarrow{XY}$

Closure

- *What is a point, a line, a line segment, and a ray?* **A point is a location in space. A line is a series of points that extends in two opposite directions without end. A line segment is part of a line with two endpoints. A ray is part of a line with one endpoint.**

- *What are parallel lines and skew lines?* **Parallel lines are lines that lie in the same plane but have no points in common. Skew lines are neither parallel nor intersecting; they lie in different planes.**

Assignment Guide

1 Objective 1
Ⓐ Ⓑ Core 1–17, 22–25, 30, 32

2 Objective 2
Ⓐ Ⓑ Core 18–21, 26–29, 31
Ⓒ Extension 33–34

Test Prep 35–39
Mixed Review 40–49

Error Prevention!

Exercises 13–15 Elicit the fact that collinear points can be connected with a single line.

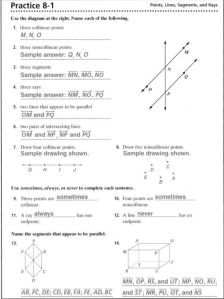

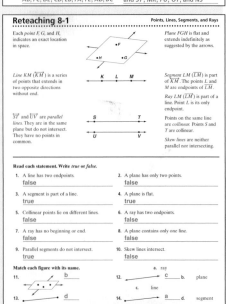

Example 2
(page 374)

Use the diagram at the right for Exercises 13–17.

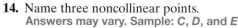

13. Name three collinear points.
A, B, and *C*

14. Name three noncollinear points.
Answers may vary. Sample: C, D, and *E*

15. Name four noncollinear points.
Answers may vary. Sample: A, B, C, and *E*

Complete each sentence with *collinear* or *noncollinear*.

16. Points *B* and *D* are __?__.
collinear

17. Points *B, D,* and *E* are __?__.
noncollinear

Example 3
(page 375)

Use the diagram below. Name each of the following.
18–21. Answers may vary. Samples are given.

18. a line parallel to $\overleftrightarrow{PQ}$ $\overleftrightarrow{SR}$

19. two skew lines $\overleftrightarrow{RV}$ and $\overleftrightarrow{PS}$

20. a line parallel to $\overleftrightarrow{SW}$ and $\overleftrightarrow{RV}$ $\overleftrightarrow{QU}$

21. a segment that intersects $\overline{SW}$
and $\overleftrightarrow{RV}$ $\overline{WV}$

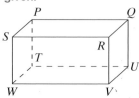

Ⓑ **Apply Your Skills**

Use *sometimes, always,* or *never* to complete each sentence.

22. Four points are __?__ collinear.
sometimes

23. A ray __?__ has two endpoints.
never

24. A segment __?__ has two endpoints.
always

25. A line __?__ has two endpoints.
never

26. Skew lines __?__ intersect.
never

27. Parallel lines __?__ intersect.
never

Use the diagram at the left. Name each of the following.

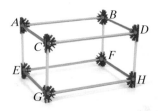

28. the segments that intersect $\overline{GH}$
$\overline{GC}, \overline{GE}, \overline{DH},$ and $\overleftrightarrow{HF}$

29. a line parallel to $\overleftrightarrow{AB}$
Answers may vary. Sample: $\overleftrightarrow{GH}$

30. the point where $\overleftrightarrow{EF}$ and
$\overleftrightarrow{AE}$ intersect *E*

31. a segment skew to $\overleftrightarrow{AC}$
Answers may vary. Sample: $\overline{DH}$

32. **Writing in Math** Explain why $\overline{AB}$ represents a line segment and $\overleftrightarrow{AB}$
GPS represents a line. **See margin.**

Ⓒ **Challenge**

33. a. Given two points on a line, *A* and *B*, describe the points that $\overrightarrow{AB}$ and
$\overrightarrow{BA}$ have in common. $\overline{AB}$

b. Where would point *C* need to be placed if $\overrightarrow{AB}$ contains *C*, but $\overrightarrow{CA}$
does not contain *B*? **between *A* and *B***

34. Stretch Your Thinking Find a four-digit number where the first digit is one third the second, the first and second digits add up to the third, and the last digit is three times the second. **1,349**

GPS Use the Guided Problem Solving worksheet with Exercise 32.

32. The arrows in the symbol for a line indicate that the line continues infinitely in both directions. The lack of arrows in the symbol for a line segment indicate that a segment has two endpoints.

Practice 8-1 — Points, Lines, Segments, and Rays

Use the diagram at the right. Name each of the following.

1. three collinear points
   M, N, O
2. three noncollinear points
   Sample answer: *Q, N, O*
3. three segments
   Sample answer: $\overline{MN}, \overline{MO}, \overline{NO}$
4. three rays
   Sample answer: $\overrightarrow{NM}, \overrightarrow{NO}, \overrightarrow{PQ}$
5. two lines that appear to be parallel
   $\overleftrightarrow{OM}$ and $\overleftrightarrow{PQ}$
6. two pairs of intersecting lines
   $\overleftrightarrow{OM}$ and $\overleftrightarrow{NP}, \overleftrightarrow{NP}$ and $\overleftrightarrow{PQ}$
7. Draw four collinear points.
   Sample drawing shown.
8. Draw five noncollinear points.
   Sample drawing shown.

Use *sometimes, always,* or *never* to complete each sentence.

9. Three points are **sometimes** collinear.
10. Four points are **sometimes** noncollinear.
11. A ray **always** has one endpoint.
12. A line **never** has an endpoint.

Name the segments that appear to be parallel.

13. $\overline{AB}, \overline{FC}, \overline{DE}; \overline{CD}, \overline{EB}, \overline{FA}; \overline{FE}, \overline{AD}, \overline{BC}$

14. $\overline{MN}, \overline{OP}, \overline{RS},$ and $\overline{UT}; \overline{MP}, \overline{NO}, \overline{RU},$ and $\overline{ST}; \overline{MR}, \overline{PU}, \overline{OT},$ and $\overline{NS}$

Reteaching 8-1 — Points, Lines, Segments, and Rays

Each *point F, G,* and *H,* indicates an exact location in space.

Plane *FGH* is flat and extends indefinitely as suggested by the arrows.

Line *KM* ($\overleftrightarrow{KM}$) is a series of points that extends in two opposite directions without end.

Segment *LM* ($\overline{LM}$) is part of $\overleftrightarrow{KM}$. The points *L* and *M* are endpoints of $\overline{LM}$.

Ray *LM* ($\overrightarrow{LM}$) is part of a line. Point *L* is its only endpoint.

$\overrightarrow{ST}$ and $\overrightarrow{UV}$ are *parallel lines.* They are in the same plane but do not intersect. They have no points in common.

Points on the same line are *collinear.* Points *S* and *T* are collinear.

Skew lines are neither parallel nor intersecting.

Read each statement. Write *true* or *false.*

1. A line has two endpoints. **false**
2. A plane has only two points. **false**
3. A segment is part of a line. **true**
4. A plane is flat. **true**
5. Collinear points lie on different lines. **false**
6. A ray has two endpoints. **false**
7. A ray has no beginning or end. **false**
8. A plane contains only one line. **false**
9. Parallel segments do not intersect. **true**
10. Skew lines intersect. **false**

Match each figure with its name.

11. — b
12. — c
13. — d
14. — a

a. ray
b. plane
c. line
d. segment

Reading Comprehension

Read the passage and answer the questions below.

Eclipses

Earth is about 248,550 miles from the moon and 93,000,000 miles from the sun. The diameter of Earth is about 7,910 miles. The moon's diameter is about 2,220 miles. The diameter of the sun is about 865,000 miles. A solar eclipse occurs when the moon comes between the sun and Earth. A lunar eclipse occurs when Earth comes between the moon and the sun.

35. Using geometric terms, describe the position of the centers of the moon, Earth, and sun during a solar eclipse.   **They are collinear.**

36. How much greater is the diameter of Earth than the diameter of the moon?   **about 5,690 miles**

Multiple Choice

Use the diagram at the right.

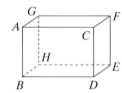

37. Which segment is skew to $\overline{AB}$?   **C**
   A. $\overline{AC}$ **B.** $\overline{DC}$
   C. $\overline{CF}$ **D.** $\overline{BD}$

38. Which segment intersects $\overline{AG}$?   **I**
   F. $\overline{CF}$ **G.** $\overline{DE}$ **H.** $\overline{BD}$ **I.** $\overline{AC}$

39. Which segment is parallel to $\overline{CF}$ and skew to $\overline{AB}$?   **B**
   A. $\overline{GF}$ **B.** $\overline{DE}$ **C.** $\overline{BD}$ **D.** $\overline{DC}$

Take It to the NET
Online lesson quiz at
www.PHSchool.com
Web Code: aaa-0801

Mixed Review

Lesson 7-1   **Find the median of each data set.**

40. 5, 6, 8, 9, 10, 4, 7   **7**   **41.** 600, 550, 475, 520, 500   **520**

42. 22, 23, 25, 26, 28, 21   **24**   **43.** 130, 145, 156, 150, 129   **145**

Lesson 6-6   **Write each percent as a fraction in simplest form.**

44. 70% $\frac{7}{10}$ **45.** 55% $\frac{11}{20}$ **46.** 12% $\frac{3}{25}$

47. 5% $\frac{1}{20}$ **48.** 125% $\frac{5}{4}$ **49.** 1% $\frac{1}{100}$

---

4. Assess

Name each figure.

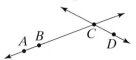

1. ray $\overrightarrow{AB}$, $\overrightarrow{BA}$, $\overrightarrow{AC}$, $\overrightarrow{CA}$, $\overrightarrow{BC}$, $\overrightarrow{CB}$, $\overrightarrow{CD}$, or $\overrightarrow{DC}$

2. line   Sample: $\overleftrightarrow{AB}$, $\overleftrightarrow{AC}$, $\overleftrightarrow{BC}$, $\overleftrightarrow{CD}$

3. three collinear points *A*, *B*, and *C*

Tell whether each statement is true or false.

4. Intersecting lines may lie in different planes. **false**

5. Parallel lines have exactly one point in common. **false**

Alternative Assessment

Each student in a pair takes a turn naming a figure discussed in the lesson while the partner draws and labels the figure.

Test Prep

Resources
For additional practice with a variety of test item formats:
• Test Prep, p. 425
• Test-Taking Strategies, p. 421
• Test-Taking Strategies With Transparencies

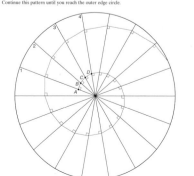

Enrichment 8-1   Points, Lines, Segments, and Rays
Patterns in Geometry

You can use a corner or a ruler to draw perpendicular lines.

1. Draw a line perpendicular to radius 1 at point *A*. Label its intersection with radius 2, *B*.

2. Draw a line perpendicular to radius 2 at point *B*. Label its intersection with radius 3, *C*.

3. Draw a line perpendicular to radius 3 at point *C*. Label its intersection with radius 4, *D*.

4. Describe the pattern in the drawing.
Sample answer: Connect each point to an adjacent radius by drawing a perpendicular line.

5. Continue this pattern until you reach the outer edge circle.

Common Words and Prefixes

This feature presents strategies students can use to help them learn new words with mathematical meanings. Students can apply these strategies to learning new words they come across in any content area.

Teaching Notes

Discuss that sometimes knowing the ordinary meaning of a word can help students uncover its mathematical meaning. In addition to the two words presented, suggest others. For example, ask:

• *What do you call the line that goes straight down the middle of a road?* median

• *What is the mathematical meaning of median?* the middle-most number in a set of numbers

Keep in mind, however, that while some words have the same meaning in ordinary use and in mathematical use, others have a specialized meaning in math (*similar* for example). Still others have different meaning in math than in ordinary usage (*difference*, for example).

Teaching Tip

Knowing and using prefixes and word roots is another dependable strategy for unlocking the meaning of math terms. Help students understand the difference between a prefix, like *bi*, and a word root, like *okto*. Then have them suggest other prefixes and roots they can use to figure out the meanings of new math terms.

Exercises

Assign the exercises for independent work. Challenge early finishers to come up with additional ordinary words they can use to understand mathematical words as in Exercises 1–2.

Here are two strategies to help you learn new vocabulary words.

Make Connections to Common English Words

Common meanings of words can help you understand their meanings in mathematics.

> • You watch a *segment*, or part, of a television show. In mathematics, a segment is part of a line.
>
> • Two roads meet at an *intersection* and share a piece of the road. Intersecting lines meet and share a common point.

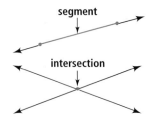

Know Important Prefixes and Root Words

Many mathematics terms are based on Greek or Latin words. Prefixes and root words can help you understand the meaning of a new term.

> • *Para* means "alongside." So, *parallel* lines are lines alongside each other.
>
> • *Poly* means "many" and *gon* means "angle." So, a *polygon* means a figure with many angles.
>
> • *Bi* means "two" and *sectus* means "to cut." *Bisect* means to cut something into two equal parts.

Dictionaries often include the root words and prefixes of terms.

EXERCISES

Use the common meaning of each word to help you write the mathematics meaning. Check your meaning with the definition in the Glossary.

1. reflection
   See margin.

2. rotation
   See margin.

Use the root words and prefixes of each word to help you write the mathematics meaning. Check your meaning for each word with the definition in the Glossary.

3. hexagon (*Hex* means "six" and *gon* means "angle.")
   a figure with 6 angles

4. quadrilateral (*Quadri* means "four" and *latus* means "side.")
   a figure with 4 sides

1. a transformation that flips a figure across a line

2. a transformation that rotates a figure around a fixed point

8-2 Angles

What You'll Learn

OBJECTIVE 1
To measure and classify angles

...And Why

To measure angles related to sports, as in Example 1

✔ Check Skills You'll Need

? For help, go to Lesson 8-1.

Use the diagram at the right.

1. Name a line, a segment, and a ray.
   See margin.
2. Are points *B*, *C*, and *E* collinear? Explain.
   No; they do not lie on the same line.

New Vocabulary
- angle • vertex • degree • acute angle
- right angle • obtuse angle • straight angle • perpendicular lines

---

OBJECTIVE 1

Measuring and Classifying Angles

iTEXT Interactive lesson includes instant self-check, tutorials, and activities.

> **Reading Math**
> The plural of *vertex* is *vertices*.

An **angle** has two sides and a vertex. The sides are rays, and the **vertex** is their common endpoint. The angle at the right may be called ∠*Y*, ∠*XYZ*, ∠*ZYX*, or ∠1.

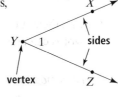

Angles are measured in units called **degrees**. Use the symbol ° for degrees. You can use a *protractor* to find the measure of an angle.

1 EXAMPLE Real-World 🌎 Problem Solving

Ice Hockey Measure the angle the hockey stick forms with the ground.

③ Read the scale where the other side of the angle crosses the protractor.

② Make sure that one side of the angle passes through zero on the protractor scale. Start measuring from zero.

① Place the hole of the protractor on the vertex of the angle.

● The angle measure is 45°.

✔ Check Understanding 1

a. Use a protractor to measure the angle at the right. **125°**

b. Reasoning Will an angle that measures 100° be greater than or less than the angle formed by a corner of a piece of paper?
greater

⟳ Ongoing Assessment and Intervention

Before the Lesson
Diagnose prerequisite skills using:
- Check Skills You'll Need

During the Lesson
Monitor progress using:
- Check Understanding
- Additional Examples
- Test Prep

After the Lesson
Assess knowledge using:
- Lesson Quiz
- Computer Test Generator CD

Lesson Preview

PowerPoint

✔ Check Skills You'll Need 🖳

Naming and Lines, Segments, Points, Rays
Lesson 8-1: Examples 1–2. Extra Practice, p. 649.

Lesson Resources

Optional Materials
- protractors

📁 **Teaching Resources**
Practice, Reteaching, Enrichment

👥 **Reaching All Students**
Practice Workbook 8-2
Spanish Practice Workbook 8-2
Guided Problem Solving 8-2
Hands-On Activities 27

🕐 **Presentation Assistant Plus!**
Transparencies
- Check Skills You'll Need 8-2
- Problem of the Day 8-2
- Additional Examples 8-2
- Student Edition Answers 8-2
- Lesson Quiz 8-2
- Classroom Aid 5
PH Presentation Pro CD-ROM 8-2

PRENTICE HALL
ASSESSMENT SYSTEM

Computer Test Generator CD

💻 **Technology**
Resource Pro® CD-ROM
Computer Test Generator CD
PH Presentation Pro CD-ROM

💻 **www.PHSchool.com**
Student Site
- Teacher Web Code: aak-5500
- Self-grading Lesson Quiz

PH SuccessNet Teacher Center
- Lesson Planner
- Resources

Plus **iTEXT**

1. Answers may vary. Samples are given.
   $\overleftrightarrow{AC}$, $\overline{BE}$, $\overrightarrow{DB}$

379

2. Teach

Professional Development

Math Background

An *angle* has two sides and a vertex. The sides are rays that share a common endpoint, called the *vertex*. The angle formed by two rays can be named in a variety of ways. For example, the angle formed by $\overrightarrow{XY}$ and $\overrightarrow{XZ}$ can be named $\angle YXZ$, $\angle ZXY$, or $\angle X$ for short. Notice that X must be the middle letter in both three letter names because it is the vertex.

You can use a protractor to measure angles. The unit of measure is degrees. Angles can be classified by their measures as acute, right, obtuse, and straight.

Teaching Notes

① EXAMPLE Error Prevention

For Check Understanding 1, some students may read the wrong scale because the angle measure is greater than 90°. Have students trace the angle on their own paper. Students must extend each ray to intersect the protractor's scale. Emphasize that extending the sides of an angle does not change the angle's measure. Then help students use the correct scale by counting ten degree increments, starting at 0° and passing through 90°.

Inclusion

Some students may confuse angle degrees with temperature degrees. Make sure they understand that the two are unrelated. Encourage them to use the context of the situation to understand which degrees are being discussed.

Teaching Tip

Before presenting Example 2, ask:
• *In the diagram above Example 2, name the angle that includes the right angle symbol.* ∠AED or ∠DEA
• *What two rays form this right angle?* $\overrightarrow{EA}$ and $\overrightarrow{ED}$
• *Are the other angles formed by the perpendicular lines also right angles?* Yes, all four angles are right angles.

380

You can use measures to classify angles.

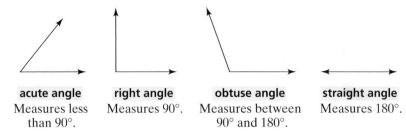

acute angle	**right angle**	**obtuse angle**	**straight angle**
Measures less than 90°.	Measures 90°.	Measures between 90° and 180°.	Measures 180°.

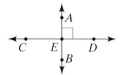

Test-Prep Tip
When you see a right-angle symbol, remember that the angle measures 90°.

Lines that intersect to form right angles are called **perpendicular lines.** The symbol ⌐ on the diagram shows that $\angle AED$ is a right angle and that $\overleftrightarrow{AB}$ is perpendicular to $\overleftrightarrow{CD}$.

② EXAMPLE Classifying Angles

Classify each angle as *acute*, *right*, *obtuse*, or *straight*.

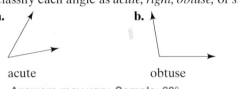

a. acute   b. obtuse   c. right

✓ **Check Understanding ②**
Answers may vary. Sample: 60°
a. **Estimation** Estimate the measure of the angle.
b. Classify the angle as *acute, right, obtuse,* or *straight*. **acute**

More Than One Way

Use a protractor to measure the angle.

Elena's Method

I place the center point of the protractor on the vertex of the angle. Then I turn the protractor so that 0° lines up with the inside scale for one side of the angle. The second side crosses the inside scale at 50°.

The angle measures 50°.

380 Chapter 8 Tools of Geometry

👥 Reaching All Students

Below Level Have students use magazines and newspapers to find pictures that illustrate acute, obtuse, right, and straight angles.

Advanced Learners *What angle measure do two right angles make?* **180°** *What angle measure is half of a right angle?* **45°** *What angle measure is a right angle plus a straight angle?* **270°**

English Learners See note on page 381.
Inclusion See note on page 380.

Zack's Method

I place the center hole of the protractor on the vertex of the angle. I read the scale where each side intersects the protractor. Then I find the difference between the two scale readings.

Since $120 - 70 = 50$, the angle measures $50°$.

Choose a Method

Measure the angle. Describe your method.
70°; check students' work.

EXERCISES

🔴 **For more practice, see** *Extra Practice.*

A Practice by Example

Measurement **Use a protractor to measure each angle.**

Example 1
(page 379)

1. 120°

2. 60°

3. 90°

4. 160°

5. 40°

6. 100°

Example 2
(page 380)

Classify each angle as *acute, right, obtuse,* or *straight.*

7. acute

8. right

9. acute

8-2 Angles **381**

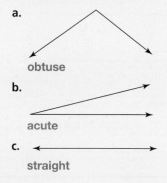
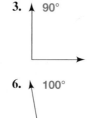
381

Assignment Guide

1 Objective 1
  Ⓐ Ⓑ Core 1–27
  Ⓒ Extension 28–33

Test Prep 34–38
Mixed Review 39–44

Exercises 10–15 Remind students that the length of each side has no effect on the angle measure.

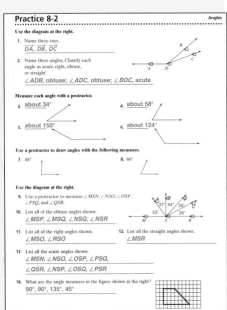

Ⓑ Apply Your Skills

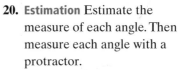

Real-World 🌐 Connection

Careers Professional photographers use a variety of lenses to achieve the images they want.

20a. 20°
 b. 70°
 c. 160°
 d. 120°
 e. 140°
 f. 90°

Use a protractor to draw angles with the following measures.
10–15. See margin.
10. 30°   **11.** 135°   **12.** 90°
13. 45°   **14.** 120°   **15.** 75°

🌐 **16. Photography** A 35-mm camera lens has a 45° viewing angle. What kind
GPS of angle is this? acute

17. Reasoning Does increasing the lengths of the sides of an angle change the measurement of the angle? Explain. No; the measure of an angle is not related to the length of the rays that form the angle.

18. Open-Ended Describe examples of perpendicular lines in your classroom.
See margin.

19. Writing in Math Explain how to fold a piece of paper so that the crease lines form four right angles. Fold the piece of paper lengthwise. Without unfolding, fold it widthwise.

Use the figure at the right for Exercises 20–24.

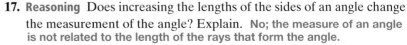

20. Estimation Estimate the measure of each angle. Then measure each angle with a protractor.
  a. ∠AGB   **b.** ∠BGD
  c. ∠BGF   **d.** ∠EGB
  e. ∠AGE   **f.** ∠DGF   20a–f. See left.

21. Name all the obtuse angles.
  AGE, BGE, BGF, CGF
22. Name all the right angles.
  AGD, DGF, CGE
23. Name all the straight angles.
  AGF
24. Name all the acute angles.
  AGB, AGC, BGC, BGD, CGD, DGE, EGF

Without using your protractor, sketch angles with the following measures. Then use your protractor to see how close you are.

25. 30°   **26.** 60°   **27.** 120°
25–27. Check students' work.

Ⓒ Challenge 🌐 **Clocks** Find and classify the angle formed by the minute and hour hands of a clock at each of the following times.

28. 1:00   **29.** 5:00   **30.** 6:00   **31.** 9:00
  30°; acute   150°; obtuse   180°; straight   90°; right

🌐 **32. Navigation** You are facing north. If you turn 270° counterclockwise, which direction will you face? east

33. Stretch Your Thinking Find the missing numbers if each number after the first two is the sum of the two preceding numbers. 5.5; 13.5; 21.5; 35
  ■, 8, ■, ■, ■, 56.5

GPS Use the Guided Problem Solving worksheet with Exercise 16.

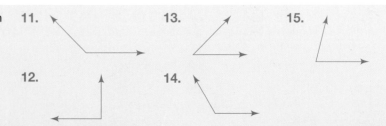

10.

11.

12.

13.

14.

15.

Multiple Choice

Use the diagram at the right for Exercises 34–35.

34. Which measure is NOT a measure of one of the angles shown at the right? **A**
  A. 60°   B. 95°
  C. 120°   D. 145°

35. How many pairs of angles appear to have the same measure? **H**
  F. 1   G. 2   H. 3   I. 4

36. Which angle in the figure at the right has the greatest measure? **D**
  A. ∠ABC   B. ∠CBD
  C. ∠ABD   D. ∠ABE

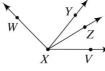

37. Which of the following is NOT correct? **F**
  F. A 43° angle is obtuse.
  G. An 89° angle is acute.
  H. A 90° angle is right.
  I. A 180° angle is straight.

Take It to the NET
Online lesson quiz at
www.PHSchool.com
Web Code: aaa-0802

Short Response

38. a. How many angles with vertex *X* are in the figure at the right?
   b. List each angle.
   [2] a. 6
       b. *WXY*; *WXZ*; *WXV*;
           YXZ; *YXV*; *ZXV*
   [1] at least 4
       angles are
       correctly identified

Mixed Review

Lesson 7-3

39. You want to buy a sweatshirt. Color choices are red, black, white, or green. Each color comes in crew neck or V-neck. How many choices do you have? Make an organized list to find the solution. **See margin.**

Lesson 5-7

Choose an appropriate unit for each measurement.

40. length of a soccer field **yards**

41. width of this page **inches**

42. distance from Miami, Florida to Austin, Texas **miles**

43. width of your hand **inches**

Lesson 5-3

44. You have a gallon of fruit punch and paper cups that hold a serving of $\frac{3}{4}$ cup of liquid. Do you have enough punch for 25 servings? Explain why or why not. (*Hint:* 1 gallon = 16 cups) **No; you would need more than 18 cups.**

8-2 Angles **383**

---

18. Answers may vary.
Sample: In a rectangular window the side molding meets the sill at a 90° angle so they are perpendicular.

39. 8; red, crew; red, v-neck; black, crew; black, v-neck; white, crew; white, v-neck; green, crew; green, v-neck

---

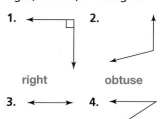
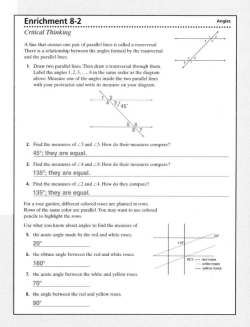

Basic Constructions

This feature introduces students to using a compass and a straightedge to construct a perpendicular bisector and an angle bisector.

Materials

- compass
- straightedge

Teaching Notes

Error Prevention!

Emphasize that in both constructions, students must keep their compass opening *unchanged*.

Inclusion

Review, as needed, the correct way to draw and label lines, line segments, rays, and angles.

English Learners

Spend the time needed to make sure students fully understand the vocabulary that appears throughout the lesson: *perpendicular, bisector, compass, intersect, point, ray, line, line segment, width, acute, obtuse,* and so on.

A *perpendicular bisector* is a line that is perpendicular to a segment and passes through that segment's *midpoint*. You can use a compass and straightedge to construct a perpendicular bisector.

1 EXAMPLE

Use a compass and straightedge to construct the perpendicular bisector of $\overline{AB}$.

Step 1 Open the compass to more than half the length of $\overline{AB}$. Put the tip of the compass point at A. Draw a part of a circle, or *arc*, that intersects $\overline{AB}$.

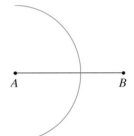

Step 2 Keep the compass open to the same width. Put the tip of the compass at B. Draw another arc that intersects $\overline{AB}$. Label the points of intersection of the two arcs C and D.

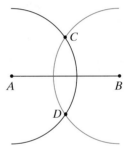

Step 3 Draw $\overleftrightarrow{CD}$. Label the intersection of $\overleftrightarrow{CD}$ and $\overline{AB}$ point M.

$\overleftrightarrow{CD}$ intersects $\overline{AB}$ at its midpoint M.

$\overleftrightarrow{CD}$ is the perpendicular bisector of $\overline{AB}$.

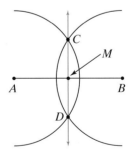

An *angle bisector* is a ray that divides an angle into two angles with equal measures.

Use a compass and straightedge to construct the angle bisector of ∠E.

Step 1 Put the tip of the compass at E. Draw an arc that intersects both sides of ∠E. Label the points of intersection F and G.

Step 2 Place the tip of the compass at F. Draw a large arc.

Step 3 Keep the compass open to the same width, and place the tip at G. Draw another large arc. Label the point of intersection of the two large arcs H.

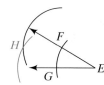

Step 4 Draw $\overrightarrow{EH}$.

$\overrightarrow{EH}$ divides ∠FEG into two angles with equal measures, ∠FEH and ∠HEG.

$\overrightarrow{EH}$ is the angle bisector of ∠FEG.

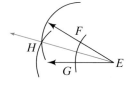

EXERCISES

1. Draw $\overline{JK}$ two inches long. Then construct its perpendicular bisector. **1–3. See margin.**

2. Draw an acute angle and construct its bisector.

3. Draw an obtuse angle and construct its bisector.

4. **Writing in Math** Explain how you can use what you know about perpendicular bisectors and angle bisectors to construct a 90° angle and a 45° angle. **See margin.**

1.
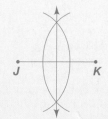

2.
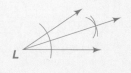

3.
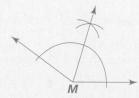

② EXAMPLE
Before working Example 2, ask: *What do you think an angle bisector does?* Sample: An angle bisector divides an angle into two congruent angles.

Teaching Tip
To check students' understanding, ask: *What are the roles of the compass and straightedge in making these constructions?* Sample: The compass ensures identical measures, while the straightedge is for making straight lines.

Exercises
Students may struggle with these constructions. Pair weaker students with stronger ones. Then be prepared to spend time circulating, to observe students working at their seats and to offer pointers, as needed.

4. Four right angles are formed at the intersection of a segment and its perpendicular bisector. The bisector of a 90° angle divides it into two 45° angles.

385

Special Pairs of Angles

Lesson Preview

 Check Skills You'll Need

Measuring Angles
Lesson 8-2: Example 1. Extra
Practice, p. 649.

Lesson Resources

Optional Materials
• protractors

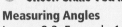 **Teaching Resources**
Practice, Reteaching, Enrichment
Checkpoint Quiz 1

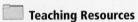 **Reaching All Students**
Practice Workbook 8-3
Spanish Practice Workbook 8-3
Reading and Math Literacy 8B
Spanish Reading and Math
 Literacy 8B
Spanish Checkpoint Quiz 1
Guided Problem Solving 8-3
Hands-On Activities 27

 **Presentation Assistant Plus!**
Transparencies
• Check Skills You'll Need 8-3
• Problem of the Day 8-3
• Additional Examples 8-3
• Student Edition Answers 8-3
• Lesson Quiz 8-3
• Classroom Aid 5
PH Presentation Pro CD-ROM 8-3

 PRENTICE HALL ASSESSMENT SYSTEM

Checkpoint Quiz 1
Computer Test Generator CD

 Technology
Resource Pro® CD-ROM
Computer Test Generator CD
PH Presentation Pro CD-ROM

 www.PHSchool.com
Student Site
• Teacher Web Code: aak-5500
• Self-grading Lesson Quiz

PH SuccessNet Teacher Center
• Lesson Planner
• Resources

Plus **iTEXT**
386

What You'll Learn

OBJECTIVE 1 To find complements and supplements

OBJECTIVE 2 To identify special pairs of angles

. . . And Why
To use angles in carpentry, as in Example 3

✓ **Check Skills You'll Need**   ? For help, go to Lesson 8-2.

Use a protractor to draw each angle.   **1–4. Check students' work.**

1. 30°   **2.** 60°   **3.** 45°   **4.** 120°

New Vocabulary
• complementary angles   • supplementary angles
• vertical angles   • congruent angles   • transversal
• interior angles   • exterior angles

OBJECTIVE 1

iTEXT Interactive lesson includes instant self-check, tutorials, and activities.

Finding the Complement and Supplement of an Angle

If the sum of the measures of two angles is 90°, the angles are **complementary angles.** If the sum of the measures of two angles is 180°, the angles are **supplementary angles.**

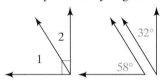

Complementary angles

Two angles, the sum of whose measures is 90°

Supplementary angles

Two angles, the sum of whose measures is 180°

1 EXAMPLE   **Finding the Complement of an Angle**

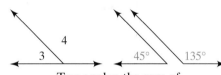

Algebra Find the value of x.

Let x = the measure of the angle's complement.

$$x + 60° = 90° \quad \leftarrow \text{The angles are complementary.}$$
$$x + 60° - 60° = 90° - 60° \quad \leftarrow \text{Subtract 60° from each side.}$$
$$x = 30° \quad \leftarrow \text{Simplify.}$$

✓ **Check Understanding 1** Find the value of x.

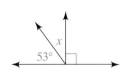

Ongoing Assessment and Intervention

Before the Lesson
Diagnose prerequisite skills using:
• Check Skills You'll Need

During the Lesson
Monitor progress using:
• Check Understanding
• Additional Examples
• Test Prep

After the Lesson
Assess knowledge using:
• Lesson Quiz
• Computer Test Generator CD
• Chapter Checkpoint 1 (p. 390)

 **EXAMPLE** Using Diagrams

Algebra Find the value of x.

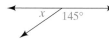

$x + 60° = 180°$ ← The angles are supplementary.

$x + 60° - 60° = 180° - 60°$ ← Subtract 60° from each side.

$x = 120°$ ← Simplify.

✔ **Check Understanding** ② Find the value of x.
35°

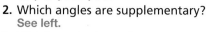

OBJECTIVE

2 **Identifying Special Pairs of Angles**

Investigation: Angle Measures

2. ∠1 and ∠3; ∠1 and ∠4;
∠2 and ∠3; ∠2 and ∠4.

1. Measure each numbered angle in the figure at the right.
40°, 40°, 140°, 140°

2. Which angles are supplementary?
See left.

3. Which angles have the same measure? ∠1 and ∠2; ∠3 and ∠4

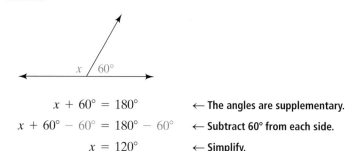

Real-World 🌐 **Connection**

The ladder's horizontal brace forms a transversal with the sides of the ladder.

Vertical angles are formed by two intersecting lines. In the drawing at the right, angles 1 and 2 are vertical angles. So are angles 3 and 4. Vertical angles have equal measures. Angles with equal measures are **congruent angles.**

A **transversal** crosses two or more lines at different points. **Interior angles** are on either side of a transversal between a pair of lines. Angles 1, 2, 7, and 8 are interior angles. **Exterior angles** are on either side of a transversal outside of a pair of lines. Angles 3, 4, 5, and 6 are exterior angles.

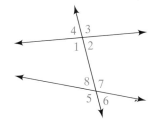

👥 **Reaching All Students**

Below Level *What is the angle measure of a right angle?* 90° *What is the angle measure of a straight angle?* 180° Then explain that complementary angles form a right angle and supplementary angles form a straight angle.	**Advanced Learners** *If two lines are cut by a transversal, what is the sum of the measures of the interior angles?* 360° *What is the sum of the measures of the exterior angles?* 360°	**English Learners** See note on page 388. **Inclusion** See note on page 388.

Professional Development

Math Background

Two angles are *complementary angles* if their sum is 90°. Two angles are *supplementary angles* if their sum is 180°. When two lines intersect, four angles are formed giving two pairs of *vertical angles*. Vertical angles are opposite from one another and congruent.

A *transversal* is a line that crosses two (or more) lines at two (or more) different points. The angles formed between the two lines are called *interior angles* and the angles outside the two lines are called *exterior angles*.

Teaching Notes

① EXAMPLE Auditory Learners

Some students may confuse the terms *supplementary* and *complementary*. Suggest this mnemonic device: *c* is before *s* in the alphabet, so complementary angles are smaller than supplementary angles.

Error Prevention!

Clarify for students that complementary and supplementary angles need not be adjacent angles—that is next to one another. Their definitions only require that the sum of their measures is 90° and 180°, respectively.

Investigation (Optional)

Have students trace the two lines and extend them to measure each angle with a protractor. Make sure students correctly transfer the numerical labels to their figures.

PowerPoint
Additional Examples

① Find the complement and supplement of a 66° angle.
complement: 24°;
supplement: 114°

② Find the value of x.
   a. 55°   **b.** 50°

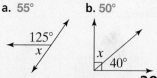

388

---

3 EXAMPLE Real-World Problem Solving

Carpentry The boards that hold this door together are two parallel lines and a transversal. Identify the angles described below.

a. a pair of acute vertical angles   ∠2 and ∠4

b. two supplementary interior angles   ∠3 and ∠5

✓ **Check Understanding** 3 Use the diagram above to identify each of the following.

a. a pair of obtuse vertical angles   b. a pair of supplementary angles
          ∠3 and ∠6   Answers may vary.
                                                         Sample: ∠6 and ∠5

EXERCISES   ? For more practice, see *Extra Practice*.

A Practice by Example

Examples 1 and 2
(pages 386, 387)

Find the complement and the supplement of each angle measure.

1. 12°   **2.** 45°   **3.** 83°   **4.** 68°   **5.** 4°
   78°; 168°   45°; 135°   7°; 97°   22°; 112°   86°; 176°

Find the value of x in each figure.

6. 62°   **7.** 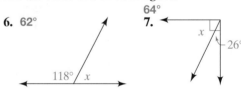   **8.**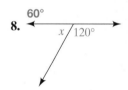

Example 3
(page 388)

Use the diagram at the right to identify each of the following.

9. a transversal $\overleftrightarrow{CE}$

10. two exterior angles
     ∠AHE; ∠CDG

11. two interior angles   10–12. Answers may vary. Samples are given.
     ∠BHD; ∠EDF

12. a pair of obtuse vertical angles   ∠AHE and ∠CHB

B **Apply Your Skills**

Complete each sentence with *sometimes*, *always*, or *never*.

13. Two acute angles are __?__ complementary. **sometimes**

14. Two obtuse angles are __?__ complementary. **never**

15. Two obtuse angles are __?__ supplementary. **never**

16. Two right angles are __?__ supplementary. **always**

(Algebra) **Find the value of *x* in each figure.**

17. 50°

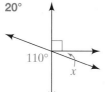

18. 45°

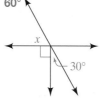

19. 20°

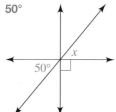

20. 60°

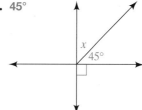

21. Architecture Before renovations, the Leaning Tower of Pisa
stood at an angle of about 5° with a vertical line. What is the
measure of the acute angle that the tower made with the
ground? What is the measure of the obtuse angle? **85°; 95°**

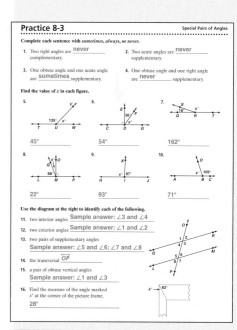

22. Writing in Math Explain how to draw a pair of supplementary
angles without a protractor. **See margin.**

23. Reasoning An angle measures 115°. Explain why you cannot
find both a complement and a supplement of the angle.
An obtuse angle does not have a complement.

C **Challenge**
24. Stretch Your Thinking A number has four digits. The sum
of the first and last digits is twice the second digit.
The second digit is 2 less than the third digit.
The last digit is twice the first digit. Some of
the digits are alike. What is the number? **4,688**

25. Food The pizza is cut into unequal slices.
One slice forms an angle whose measure
is 65°. Find the measure of the angles
formed by the other two slices. **115° and 180°**

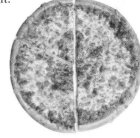

22. Draw a line and a ray
with its vertex on the line.
The two angles are
supplementary.

GPS Use the Guided Problem
Solving worksheet with
Exercise 21.

Assignment Guide

1 **Objective 1**
 A **B** Core 1–8, 13–16,
 21–23
 C Extension 24

2 **Objective 2**
 A **B** Core 9–12, 17–20
 C Extension 25

Test Prep 26–29
Mixed Review 30–34

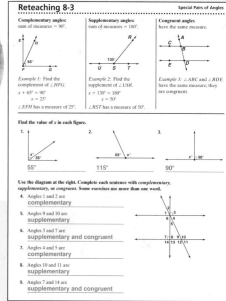

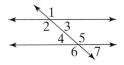

Lesson Quiz 8-3

1. Find the complement and supplement of 32°. 58°; 148°

Use the diagram to identify each of the following.

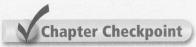

2. interior angles 2, 3, 4, and 5

3. supplementary exterior angles 6 and 7

✔ Chapter Checkpoint

To check understanding of Lessons 8-1 to 8-3:

Checkpoint Quiz 1 (p. 390)

📁 Teaching Resources
Checkpoint Quiz 1 (also in Prentice Hall Assessment System)

👥 Reaching All Students
Reading and Math Literacy 8B

Spanish versions available

Enrichment 8-3
Critical Thinking   Special Pairs of Angles

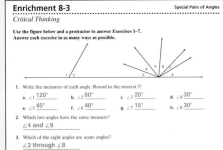

Use the figure below and a protractor to answer Exercises 1–7.
Answer each exercise in as many ways as possible.

1. Write the measures of each angle. Round to the nearest 5°.
   a. ∠1 120°   b. ∠2 60°   c. ∠3 20°   d. ∠4 30°
   e. ∠5 45°   f. ∠6 40°   g. ∠7 15°   h. ∠8 30°

2. Which two angles have the same measure?
   ∠4 and ∠8

3. Which of the eight angles are acute angles?
   ∠2 through ∠8

4. Which of the eight angles are obtuse angles?
   ∠1

5. Which two angles can be joined to form a right angle?
   ∠2 and ∠4; ∠2 and ∠8

6. Which three angles can be joined to form a right angle?
   ∠3, ∠4, and ∠6; ∠5, ∠7, and ∠8; ∠3, ∠6, and ∠8; ∠4, ∠5, and ∠7

7. Which three angles can be joined to form a straight angle?
   ∠1, ∠3, and ∠6; ∠1, ∠4, and ∠8; ∠1, ∠5, and ∠7

8. Choose an angle from the figure above. Use a protractor to draw two angles with the same measure as the chosen angle. Then use from four to six other angle measures from the diagram above to make a circle. Label each angle measure. Remember that a circle measures 360°.
   Sample answer:

Multiple Choice   Use the diagram at the right.

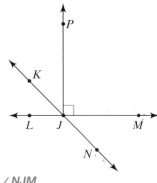

26. Which angle appears to be obtuse? **B**
    A. ∠URS   B. ∠PRS
    C. ∠TUR   D. ∠WUV

27. Which pair of angles is supplementary? **I**
    F. ∠TUW, ∠PRS   G. ∠WUR, ∠PRS
    H. ∠TUW, ∠QRU   I. ∠WUV, ∠TUW

💻 Take It to the NET
Online lesson quiz at
www.PHSchool.com
Web Code: aaa-0803

28. Which lines appear to be parallel? **D**
    A. $\overleftrightarrow{QS}$, $\overleftrightarrow{PW}$ B. $\overleftrightarrow{TV}$, $\overleftrightarrow{PW}$ C. $\overleftrightarrow{QS}$, $\overleftrightarrow{RW}$ D. $\overleftrightarrow{TV}$, $\overleftrightarrow{QS}$

29. Which points are noncollinear? **G**
    F. Q, R, S   G. Q, R, U   H. T, U, V   I. R, U, W

🔵 Mixed Review

Lesson 7-4

30. Draw a bar graph to display the data at the right.
    See margin.

City	Annual Precipitation
Los Angeles, CA	about 15 in.
Atlanta, GA	about 50 in.
Miami, FL	about 55 in.
Phoenix, AZ	about 8 in.
Duluth, MN	about 30 in.

Source: *World Almanac 2000*

Lesson 6-7   **Find each answer.**

31. 5% of 100
    5

32. 30% of 50
    15

33. 12% of 80
    9.6

34. 75% of 42
    31.5

✔ Checkpoint Quiz 1   Lessons 8-1 through 8-3

📱 TEXT Instant self-check quiz online and on CD-ROM

1–10. Answers may vary. Samples are given.

Use the figure to name the following.

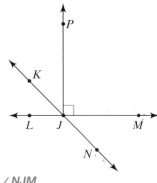

1. two lines
   $\overleftrightarrow{LM}$ and $\overleftrightarrow{KN}$

2. two rays
   $\overrightarrow{JP}$ and $\overrightarrow{NK}$

3. a right angle
   ∠PJM

4. an acute angle
   ∠PJK

5. an obtuse angle
   ∠PJN

6. a straight angle
   ∠LJM

7. a pair of vertical angles
   ∠KJL and ∠MJN

8. an angle congruent to ∠MJN
   ∠KJL

9. a pair of complementary angles
   ∠PJK and ∠KJL

10. a pair of supplementary angles ∠LJN and ∠NJM

Alternative Assessment

Each student in a pair draws and labels two parallel lines with a transversal and numbers the resulting angles. Partners exchange papers and identify the interior angles, exterior angles, and pairs of supplementary angles.

Test Prep

Resources
For additional practice with a variety of test item formats:
• Test Prep, p. 425
• Test-Taking Strategies, p. 421
• Test-Taking Strategies With Transparencies

Investigating Angles in a Triangle

For Use With Lesson 8-3

Technology

Geometry software is a fun way to investigate relationships among angles of a triangle. You can indicate "measure of angle A" with $m\angle A$.

Activity

Step 1   Draw a triangle. Label the vertices A, B, and C.

Step 2   Measure the three interior angles.

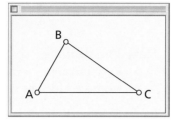

$m\angle BAC = 60.14°$
$m\angle ABC = 85.84°$
$m\angle BCA = 34.02°$

Step 3   Make a table to show the angles, their measures, and the sum of the measures.

Angle	Measurements
$\angle A$	60.14°
$\angle B$	85.84°
$\angle C$	34.02°
sum	180°

EXERCISES

1. Change the shape of the triangle by dragging A, B, or C. Make a new column in your table and find the sum of the angle measures. What happens to the sum of the angle measures?   It stays the same.

2. What seems to be true about the sum of the measures of the interior angles of a triangle?   They sum to 180°.

3. Extend one side of a triangle to make an *exterior angle of a triangle* as shown at the right.   3a–b. Check students' work.

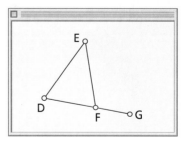

   a. What is the measure of $\angle EFG$?

   b. What is the sum of the measures of $\angle D$ and $\angle E$?

   c. Change the shape of the triangle. Find the measure of $\angle EFG$ and the sum of the measures of $\angle D$ and $\angle E$ again. What do you notice?   They are the same.

   d. What seems to be true of an exterior angle and the sum of the two angles of a triangle not adjacent to the exterior angle?   The sum of the two angles of a triangle not adjacent to the exterior angle is the same as the measure of the exterior angle.

   Technology

Investigating Angles in a Triangle

This feature presents ways for students to explore relationships among the angles of triangles. By manipulating the vertices of a triangle, students can learn more about the sum of the angle measures of triangles and of other polygons.

Materials

• geometry software

Teaching Notes

English Learners
Review the meaning of the terminology in the activity such as *vertices* and *interior angles*.

Error Prevention!

Make sure students create each vertex so that it can be dragged and is not fixed. Students should use the angle measuring feature of the computer software to display each angle measure and their sum.

Teaching Tip
As students manipulate the vertices of their triangles, ask:
• *When you drag a vertex, do only one or two angle measures change?* Sample: All three angles change.
• *If you drag a side of the triangle, would the angle measures change?* Sample: Yes, all three angles would change.

Exercises
Have students work in pairs on the exercises.

30.

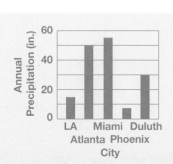

391

Lesson Preview

 Check Skills You'll Need

Classifying Angles
Lesson 8-2: Example 2. Extra
Practice, p. 649.

Lesson Resources

📁 **Teaching Resources**
Practice, Reteaching, Enrichment

👥 **Reaching All Students**
Practice Workbook 8-4
Spanish Practice Workbook 8-4
Guided Problem Solving 8-4
Technology Activities 14
Hands-On Activities 27

⏰ **Presentation Assistant Plus!**
Transparencies
• Check Skills You'll Need 8-4
• Problem of the Day 8-4
• Additional Examples 8-4
• Student Edition Answers 8-4
• Lesson Quiz 8-4
• Classroom Aid 20, 21
PH Presentation Pro CD-ROM 8-4

Computer Test Generator CD

💻 **Technology**
Resource Pro® CD-ROM
Computer Test Generator CD
PH Presentation Pro CD-ROM

💻 **www.PHSchool.com**
Student Site
• Teacher Web Code: aak-5500
• Self-grading Lesson Quiz

PH SuccessNet Teacher Center
• Lesson Planner
• Resources

Plus

What You'll Learn

OBJECTIVE 1 To classify triangles by their angles

OBJECTIVE 2 To classify triangles by their sides

. . . And Why

To identify triangles in game pieces, as in Example 4

 Check Skills You'll Need 🔍 For help, go to Lesson 8-2.

Classify each angle as *acute*, *right*, *obtuse*, or *straight*.

1. 45° acute 2. 105° obtuse 3. 60° acute 4. 100° obtuse
5. 90° right 6. 1° acute 7. 179° obtuse 8. 180° straight

New Vocabulary
• acute triangle • obtuse triangle
• right triangle • congruent segments • equilateral triangle
• isosceles triangle • scalene triangle

OBJECTIVE 1

📱 Interactive lesson includes instant self-check, tutorials, and activities.

Classifying Triangles by Angles

A *triangle* is a closed figure with three sides. The sides of every closed figure meet only at their endpoints. The sum of the measures of the angles of a triangle is 180°.

You can classify triangles by angle measures.

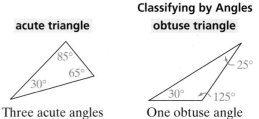

Classifying by Angles

| acute triangle | obtuse triangle | right triangle |

Three acute angles · One obtuse angle · One right angle

1 EXAMPLE Classifying Triangles by Angles

Classify each triangle by its angles.

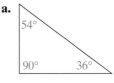

a. right triangle

b. obtuse triangle

c. acute triangle

✓ **Check Understanding** 1 a. Classify the triangle at the right by its angles. right triangle
b. A triangle has three equal angles. Classify the triangle by its angles. acute triangle

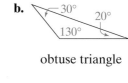 **Ongoing Assessment and Intervention**

Before the Lesson	During the Lesson	After the Lesson
Diagnose prerequisite skills using:	Monitor progress using:	Assess knowledge using:
• Check Skills You'll Need	• Check Understanding	• Lesson Quiz
	• Additional Examples	• Computer Test Generator CD
	• Test Prep	

② EXAMPLE Finding an Angle's Measure

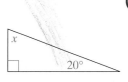

Algebra Find the value of x in the triangle at the left.

$$x + 20° + 90° = 180°$$ ← A right angle measures 90°.
$$x + 110° = 180°$$ ← Add 20° and 90°.
$$x + 110° - 110° = 180° - 110°$$ ← Subtract 110° from each side.
$$x = 70°$$ ← Simplify.

✔ **Check Understanding** ② Two angles of a triangle measure 58° and 72°. What is the measure of the third angle? **50°**

OBJECTIVE

2 Classifying Triangles by Sides

Segments that have the same length are **congruent segments.** You can classify triangles by the number of congruent segments or sides. Tick marks are often used to indicate congruent sides of a figure.

Real-World 🌐 Connection
This sign means "falling rocks."

Classifying by Sides

equilateral triangle | **isosceles triangle** | **scalene triangle**

Three congruent sides | At least two congruent sides | No congruent sides

You can sometimes classify a triangle in more than one way. For example, every equilateral triangle is also an isosceles triangle. When classifying triangles, use the most precise name.

③ EXAMPLE Classifying Triangles by Sides

Classify each triangle by its sides.

a. 4 4 6
isosceles triangle

b. 5.5 3.5 8
scalene triangle

c.
equilateral triangle

✔ **Check Understanding** ③
a. Classify the triangle at the right by its sides. **isosceles**
b. The sides of a triangle have lengths 5, 10, and 12 units. Classify it by its sides. **scalene**

👥 Reaching All Students

| **Below Level** Have students create their own triangles using cardstock. Students trade their triangles with a partner. They measure and classify their partner's triangle by its angles and its sides. | **Advanced Learners** *If you reduce the side lengths in a triangle proportionally, such as by $\frac{1}{3}$, how does its classification by its sides and its angles change?* **No change occurs.** | **English Learners** See note on page 394. **Inclusion** See note on page 394. |

---

2. Teach

Math Background

A *triangle* is a closed figure with three sides that form three angles. The sum of the measures of the angles of a triangle is 180°.

Triangles can be classified by their angle measures.

acute	3 acute angles
obtuse	1 obtuse angle
right	1 right angle

Triangles can also be classified by the number of congruent sides.

scalene	0 congruent sides
isosceles	at least 2 congruent sides
equilateral	3 congruent sides

Teaching Notes

① EXAMPLE Visual Learners

Have students examine the three triangles above Example 1. Ask:
- *Why can't a triangle have more than one obtuse angle?* Sample: The sum of the angles of the triangle would be greater than 180° because the sum of two obtuse angles is always greater than 180°.
- *Why can't an acute triangle have only one or two acute angles?* Sample: The third angle could be either 90° or obtuse.

PowerPoint

🖵 Additional Examples

① Classify each triangle by its angles.

a. 35° 110° 35°
obtuse

b. 60° 55° 65°
acute

② Two angles of a triangle measure 48° and 90°. What is the measure of the third angle? **42°**

③ Classify each triangle by its sides.

a.
isosceles

b. 2.3 5.5 5
scalene

393

Real-World Connection
Triominoes is a game played by matching numbers.

A triangle can be classified by both its angle measures and by the number of congruent sides it has.

4 **EXAMPLE** Real-World Problem Solving

Games Name the triangle formed by each triomino by its angles and its sides.

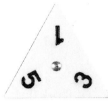

The triangle has three acute angles. It is acute.

The triangle has three congruent sides. It is equilateral.

✔ **Check Understanding** 4 Name the triangle shown at the right by its angles and its sides. **isoceles right triangle**

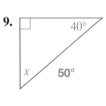

EXERCISES

? For more practice, see *Extra Practice*.

A **Practice by Example**

Classify each triangle by its angles.

Example 1 (page 392)

1. right
55°
35°

2.
85°
70° 25°
acute

3. obtuse
115°
45°
20°

Example 2 (page 393)

Algebra Find the value of *x* for triangles with the given angle measures.

4. $15°, 60°, x$ **105°**

5. $14°, x, 76°$ **90°**

6. $x, 60°, 61°$ **59°**

7.
x 115°
25° 40°

8. 65°
50°
65° x

9.
40°
x 50°

Example 3 (page 393)

Classify each triangle by its sides.

10.
13
5
12
scalene, right

11.
isosceles

12.
5 5
7
isosceles

13. triangle with sides 3, 3, 5 **isosceles**

14. triangle with sides 6, 9, 4 **scalene**

15. triangle with sides 11, 11, 11 **equilateral**

Example 4
(page 394)

Name each triangle by its angles and its sides.

16.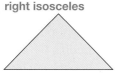
9   17.5
15
scalene, right

17. isosceles, obtuse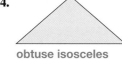
4
120°
4

scalene, acute
18.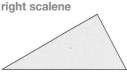
8.3   82°   6.9
43°   55°
10

B Apply Your Skills
19a. See margin.

19. **a. Drafting** Find the side lengths and angle measures of each drafting triangle at the right.

b. Classify each triangle according to its angle measures. right; right

c. Classify each triangle according to its sides.
scalene; isosceles

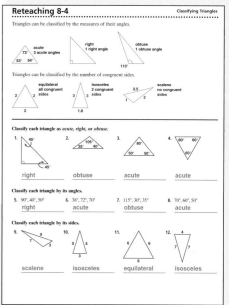

20. **Sailing** A triangular sail allows a boat to sail in any direction, even into the wind. Judging by appearance, give all names possible for the triangle in the photo. Answers may vary. Sample: acute, isosceles

21. **Writing in Math** Explain why you need to know the measures of all three angles of a triangle before you can name it by its angles. See below left.

Measure the angles and sides of each triangle. Then name each triangle by its angles and its sides. 22–25. Check students' measurements.

right isosceles
22.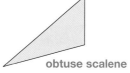

right scalene
23.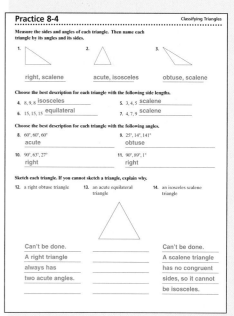

24.
obtuse isosceles

25.
obtuse scalene

Sketch each triangle.

26. an acute isosceles triangle

27. an obtuse scalene triangle

28. an acute scalene triangle

29. a right scalene triangle
26–29. See margin.

30. **Reasoning** Every equilateral triangle is also *equiangular*. That is, each of its angles has the same measure. Use the sum of the measures of the angles of a triangle to find the measure of each angle of an equilateral triangle. 60°

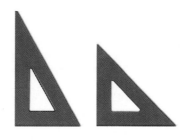
Real-World Connection
Triangular sails are used on sport sailing craft because they are easy to operate.

21. Answers may vary. Sample: Two angles of every triangle are acute. So you need the measure of the third angle to tell if a triangle is a right triangle or an obtuse triangle.

19a. sides $\frac{7}{8}$ in., $1\frac{1}{2}$ in., $1\frac{3}{4}$ in.; angles: 30°, 60°, 90° sides: $1\frac{1}{16}$ in., $1\frac{1}{16}$ in., $1\frac{1}{2}$ in; angles: 45°, 45°, 90°

26.

27–29. See back of book.

GPS Use the Guided Problem Solving worksheet with Exercise 20.

Assignment Guide

1 Objective 1
Ⓐ Ⓑ Core 1–9, 20–21

2 Objective 2
Ⓐ Ⓑ Core 10–19, 22–30
Ⓒ Extension 31–32

Test Prep 33–36
Mixed Review 37–41

Diversity
Exercise 20 Ask a volunteer who sails to explain what sailing involves and why they enjoy it.

Practice 8-4   Classifying Triangles
Measure the sides and angles of each triangle. Then name each triangle by its angles and its sides.

1.   2.   3.

right, scalene   acute, isosceles   obtuse, scalene

Choose the best description for each triangle with the following side lengths.

4. 8, 9, 8 isosceles   5. 3, 4, 5 scalene
6. 15, 15, 15 equilateral   7. 4, 7, 9 scalene

Choose the best description for each triangle with the following angles.

8. 60°, 60°, 60°   9. 25°, 14°, 141°
acute   obtuse
10. 90°, 63°, 27°   11. 90°, 89°, 1°
right   right

Sketch each triangle. If you cannot sketch a triangle, explain why.

12. a right obtuse triangle   13. an acute equilateral triangle   14. an isosceles scalene triangle

Can't be done.
A right triangle always has two acute angles.

Can't be done.
A scalene triangle has no congruent sides, so it cannot be isosceles.

Reteaching 8-4   Classifying Triangles
Triangles can be classified by the measures of their angles.

acute   right   obtuse
73° 3 acute angles   1 right angle   1 obtuse angle
53° 54°   110°

Triangles can be classified by the number of congruent sides.

equilateral   isosceles   scalene
all congruent sides   2 congruent sides   no congruent sides
2   2   3   3   2.5 1   2
2   1.8

Classify each triangle as *acute, right,* or *obtuse.*

1. 45°   2. 105°   3. 80°   4. 60° 60°
45°   35° 40°   50° 50°   60°
right   obtuse   acute   acute

5. 90°, 40°, 50°   6. 38°, 72°, 70°   7. 115°, 30°, 35°   8. 70°, 60°, 50°
right   acute   obtuse   acute

Classify each triangle by its sides.

9. 9   10.   11.   12. 4
9   3   6   7 7
7   3   5   6   6
scalene   isosceles   equilateral   isosceles

Lesson Quiz 8-4

Names each triangle by its angles and by its sides.

1.
12   4.8
11

right, scalene

2.
60°
60° 60°

acute, equilateral, isosceles

3.
30°
75°

acute, isosceles

4.
25°
120°   35°

obtuse, scalene

Alternative Assessment

Each student in a pair draws five different triangles. Partners exchange drawings and classify each other's triangles in as many ways as possible.

Test Prep

Resources

For additional practice with a variety of test item formats:
- Test Prep, p. 425
- Test-Taking Strategies, p. 421
- Test-Taking Strategies With Transparencies

Enrichment 8-4   Classifying Triangles
Critical Thinking

- $\overline{BH}$ is perpendicular to $\overline{DC}$, $\overline{HF}$ is perpendicular to $\overline{AJ}$, and $\overline{AJ}$ is parallel to $\overline{BH}$.
- The following angle pairs have the same measure: ∠DAB, ∠EBC; ∠BCH, ∠CHE, ∠HJF, ∠DGF, ∠DGE, ∠EGH; ∠EDG and ∠DEG.
- The measure of each angle of an equilateral triangle is always 60°. The measures of the angles opposite the equal sides of an isosceles triangle are also equal.

Use the diagram above and the information given to solve Exercises 1–8.

1. Identify three equilateral triangles.
   △ACJ, △DEG, △BCH

2. Identify six right angles.
   Sample answer: ∠DEB, ∠BEC, ∠CEH, ∠EHG, ∠DFG, ∠HFJ

Suppose line segment $\overline{BF}$ is drawn.

3. Would △BFH be right, acute, or obtuse?
   right

4. Would △BDF be right, acute, or obtuse?
   obtuse

Give the measures of the following angles.

5. ∠DEG 60°
6. ∠EBC 60°
7. ∠ECB 30°
8. ∠JHG 30°

---

31. Reasoning Cut out three narrow strips of paper measuring 2, 3, and 6 inches long. Is it possible to construct a triangle with these sides? If not, why not? **No; to form a triangle, the sum of the 2 shorter lengths must be greater than the third.**

32. Stretch Your Thinking Nathan is weighing blocks and balls. Each of the blocks weighs the same and each of the balls weighs the same. The weight of 4 blocks and 1 ball is the same as the weight of 2 blocks and 2 balls. Which is heavier, a block or a ball? How much heavier?
A ball; it is as heavy as 2 blocks.

Test Prep

Multiple Choice

Choose the best description for triangles with the following angle measures and side lengths.

33. angle measures: 45°, 45°, 90°; side lengths: 4 cm, 4 cm, and 5.7 cm **A**
   A. right isosceles   **B.** acute isosceles
   C. right scalene   **D.** acute scalene

34. angle measures: 60°, 60°, 60°; side lengths: 6 in., 6 in., 6 in. **H**
   F. acute isosceles   **G.** obtuse isosceles
   H. acute equilateral   **I.** obtuse equilateral

 **Take It to the NET**
Online lesson quiz at
www.PHSchool.com
Web Code: aaa-0804

35. angle measures: 84°, 48°, 48°; side lengths: 8 m, 6 m, 6 m **A**
   A. acute isosceles   **B.** obtuse isosceles
   C. acute scalene   **D.** obtuse scalene

Extended Response

36. Answer each question. Include a sketch.
   a. Can an isosceles triangle have three sides of equal length?
   b. Can an obtuse triangle have three sides of equal length?
   a–b. See margin.

Mixed Review

Lesson 7-5

37. The graph shows the results of a survey. Two hundred people were asked to choose their favorite dessert.
   a. How many people prefer pie? **50**
   b. How many prefer ice cream? **80**
   c. How many more people preferred ice cream than cake? **40**

Favorite Dessert

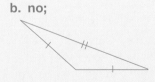

Ice cream 40%
Pie 25%
Cake 20%
15% Other

Lesson 6-5

A map has a scale of 1 in. : 12 mi. How many miles equal each of these lengths on the map?

38. 3 in. **36 mi**   **39.** 5.5 in. **66 mi**   **40.** 0.5 in. **6 mi**   **41.** $1\frac{1}{4}$ in. **15 mi**

36. **[4] a. yes;**

b. no;

[3] both answers correct, one sketch with a minor error

[2] answer and sketch to one part correct

[1] both answers correct, but no sketches

8-5 Exploring and Classifying Polygons

What You'll Learn

OBJECTIVE 1 To identify polygons

OBJECTIVE 2 To classify quadrilaterals

. . . And Why

To identify polygons in sports, as in Example 2

 Check Skills You'll Need

1-3. Answers may vary. Samples are given.
Name each of the following.

 For help, go to Lesson 8-1.

1. two segments parallel to $\overline{AB}$ $\overline{DC}$ and $\overline{FG}$

2. two segments skew to $\overline{DE}$ $\overline{CB}$ and $\overline{GH}$

3. two segments intersecting $\overline{BG}$ $\overline{FG}$ and $\overline{BC}$

New Vocabulary
- **polygon**
- **quadrilateral**
- **trapezoid**
- **parallelogram**
- **rectangle**
- **rhombus**
- **square**

---

1. Plan

Lesson Preview

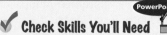 **PowerPoint**

 Check Skills You'll Need

Naming Parallel, Intersecting, and Skew Lines
Lesson 8-1: Example 3. Extra Practice, p. 649.

Lesson Resources

Teaching Resources
Practice, Reteaching, Enrichment

Reaching All Students
Practice Workbook 8-5
Spanish Practice Workbook 8-5
Guided Problem Solving 8-5
Hands-On Activities 28, 29

Presentation Assistant Plus!
Transparencies
- Check Skills You'll Need 8-5
- Problem of the Day 8-5
- Additional Examples 8-5
- Student Edition Answers 8-5
- Lesson Quiz 8-5
- Classroom Aid 20-22
PH Presentation Pro CD-ROM 8-5

PRENTICE HALL ASSESSMENT SYSTEM

Computer Test Generator CD

Technology
Resource Pro® CD-ROM
Computer Test Generator CD
PH Presentation Pro CD-ROM

www.PHSchool.com
Student Site
- Teacher Web Code: aak-5500
- Self-grading Lesson Quiz

PH SuccessNet Teacher Center
- Lesson Planner
- Resources

Plus **iTEXT**

OBJECTIVE 1

 **Interactive lesson includes instant self-check, tutorials, and activities.**

Identifying Polygons

A **polygon** is a closed figure that has three or more line segments that do not cross. See the examples below.

polygon   polygon   not a polygon   not a polygon

To name a polygon, just count the number of sides.

Polygon	Number of Sides
Triangle	3
Quadrilateral	4
Pentagon	5
Hexagon	6
Octagon	8
Decagon	10

1 EXAMPLE **Identifying Polygons**

Identify each polygon according to the number of sides.

a.    **b.**   **c.**

pentagon   octagon   quadrilateral

 Check Understanding 1 Name each polygon according to the number of sides.

a.   **b.**   **c.**

quadrilateral   hexagon   octagon

8-5 Exploring and Classifying Polygons   **397**

 Ongoing Assessment and Intervention

Before the Lesson
Diagnose prerequisite skills using:
- Check Skills You'll Need

During the Lesson
Monitor progress using:
- Check Understanding
- Additional Examples
- Test Prep

After the Lesson
Assess knowledge using:
- Lesson Quiz
- Computer Test Generator CD

2. Teach

Professional Development

Math Background

Polygons are closed figures formed by three or more line segments that intersect only at their vertices. Polygons are named by the number of sides. *Quadrilaterals* are four-sided polygons that can be further classified by parallel sides as a *trapezoid* or as a *parallelogram*, which includes a *rectangle*, a *rhombus*, and a *square*.

Teaching Notes

① EXAMPLE English Learners

Students can compare the names of polygons with the names of numbers in their native language. For instance, triangle, quadrilateral, octagon, and decagon come from the same roots as the numbers 3, 4, 8, and 10 in French and Spanish.

Tactile Learners

Have students form the different polygons on geoboards.

Geometry Connection

Names of other polygons include: heptagon (7 sides), nonagon (9 sides), and dodecagon (12 sides).

PowerPoint
Additional Examples

① Identify each polygon according to the number of sides.

a.   b.

hexagon   pentagon

② Write all the possible names for the quadrilateral. Then give the best name.
trapezoid

Closure

• *How can you classify polygons?*
by their number of sides
• *What are the five special quadrilaterals that have parallel sides?* trapezoid, parallelogram, rectangle, rhombus, square

398

OBJECTIVE
2 Classifying Quadrilaterals

Any polygon with four sides is called a **quadrilateral.** Some have special names depending on whether they have *one* or *two* pairs of parallel lines.

A **trapezoid** has exactly one pair of parallel lines.

A **parallelogram** has two pairs of parallel lines.

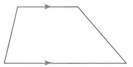   

Reading Math
Arrows on a drawing indicate parallel sides.

There are three special types of parallelograms.

A **rectangle** has four right angles.

A **rhombus** has four congruent sides.

A **square** has four right angles and four congruent sides.

② EXAMPLE   Real-World 🌐 Problem Solving

Baseball A baseball diamond is a quadrilateral. Write all of its possible names. Which is the best name? Explain.

Both pairs of opposite sides are parallel. It is a parallelogram.

The four angles are right angles. It is a rectangle.

The four sides are congruent. It is a rhombus.

This quadrilateral is best described as a square, because a square has four right angles and four congruent sides.

2b. Rectangle; answers may vary. Sample: A rectangle has four right angles and two pairs of parallel lines.

c. Yes; every square has 4 congruent sides.

✓ **Check Understanding** ②
parallelogram, rectangle
a. Write all the possible names for the quadrilateral at the right.
b. Which is the best name? Explain.
c. **Reasoning** Is every square a rhombus? Explain. b–c. See above left.

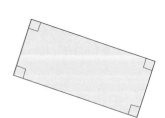

👥 Reaching All Students

| **Below Level** Have students create a table for the five special quadrilaterals. Students should draw 2 examples and 2 non-examples for each quadrilateral. | **Advanced Learners** Have students create a Venn diagram that shows the relationship of the five special quadrilaterals discussed in the lesson. | **English Learners** See note on page 398.
 Tactile Learners See note on page 398. |

A Practice by Example

Example 1
(page 397)

Identify each polygon according to the number of sides.

1.

pentagon

2.

decagon

3.

quadrilateral

Example 2
(page 398)

Write all the possible names for each quadrilateral. Then give the best name.

4.

quadrilateral, parallelogram,
rhombus; rhombus

5.

quadrilateral, parallelogram,
rectangle; rectangle

6.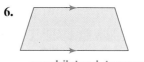

quadrilateral, trapezoid;
trapezoid

B Apply Your Skills

Use graph paper to draw an example of each quadrilateral.
7–11. **Check students' work.**

7. a parallelogram   8. a rectangle   9. a rhombus

10. a trapezoid   11. a quadrilateral with only one right angle

Real-World Connection

Scientists use the Raft of Treetops to work and sleep atop rain forests.

12. **a. Science** What shape is the Raft of Treetops platform at the left?
    b. Draw the polygon. Divide it into a quadrilateral and two triangles.
    12a. hexagon   b. See margin.
13. Draw a parallelogram that has a 30° angle.
    GPS 13. See margin.

Complete each sentence with *all, some,* or *no.*

Some

14. __?__ quadrilaterals are squares.

No

15. __?__ trapezoids are parallelograms.

16. __?__ rhombuses are quadrilaterals.   17. __?__ squares are rectangles.
All   All

18. **Writing in Math** Describe the difference between a figure that is *not* a polygon and one that is a polygon.
    Check students' work.

C Challenge

20.

19. **Patterns** A *diagonal* of a polygon is a segment that connects two vertices that are not next to each other. As shown at the right, a quadrilateral has two diagonals.

    diagonals

    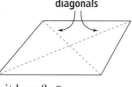

    a. Draw a pentagon. How many diagonals does it have? 5
    b. Draw a hexagon. How many diagonals does it have? 9
    c. Without drawing, predict the number of diagonals in an octagon. 20

20. **Stretch Your Thinking** Use the figure at the left. Which six sides of the small squares can you remove to leave only two squares?

12b. Answers may vary.
Sample:

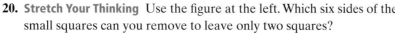

13.

GPS Use the Guided Problem Solving worksheet with Exercise 13.

Assignment Guide

1 Objective 1
   A B Core 1–3, 12, 18
   C Extension 19

2 Objective 2
   A B Core 4–11, 13–17
   C Extension 20

Test Prep 21–23
Mixed Review 24–28

Error Prevention!

Exercises 14–17 Have students justify each answer with drawings for *all* and *some* responses.

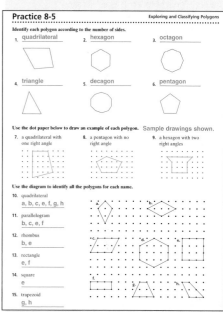

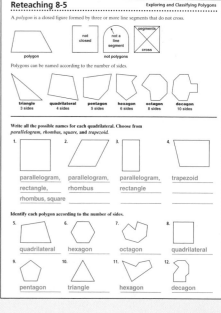

4. Assess

 PowerPoint Lesson Quiz 8-5

Identify each polygon. Write all the possible names.

1.
octagon

2.
hexagon

3.
quadrilateral, rhombus

4.
quadrilateral, trapezoid

Alternative Assessment

Each student in a pair draws several polygons, including quadrilaterals. Partners exchange papers and name each polygon using as many names as they can.

Test Prep

Resources
For additional practice with a variety of test item formats:
• Test Prep, p. 425
• Test-Taking Strategies, p. 421
• Test-Taking Strategies With Transparencies

Exercise 22 Elicit the fact that all quadrilaterals have four sides.

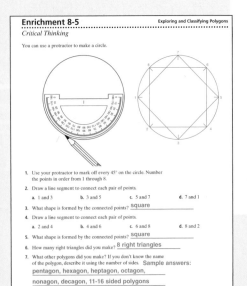

Enrichment 8-5   Exploring and Classifying Polygons
Critical Thinking

You can use a protractor to make a circle.

1. Use your protractor to mark off every 45° on the circle. Number the points in order from 1 through 8.
2. Draw a line segment to connect each pair of points.
   a. 1 and 3   b. 3 and 5   c. 5 and 7   d. 7 and 1
3. What shape is formed by the connected points? square
4. Draw a line segment to connect each pair of points.
   a. 2 and 4   b. 4 and 6   c. 6 and 8   d. 8 and 2
5. What shape is formed by the connected points? square
6. How many right triangles did you make? 8 right triangles
7. What other polygons did you make? If you don't know the name of the polygon, describe it using the number of sides. Sample answers:
   pentagon, hexagon, heptagon, octagon,
   nonagon, decagon, 11-16 sided polygons
8. Name the polygons that have congruent sides and congruent angles.
   quadrilateral, octagon

 **Test Prep**

Multiple Choice

21. Which name does NOT appear to describe quadrilateral *RSTU*? **C**
A. square   B. rhombus
C. trapezoid   D. parallelogram

 Take It to the NET
Online lesson quiz at
www.PHSchool.com
Web Code: aaa-0805

22. Which of the following polygons is NOT a quadrilateral? **I**
F. trapezoid   G. parallelogram   H. rhombus   I. pentagon

Short Response

23. Draw each of the following figures. Give the best name for each.
a. a quadrilateral with exactly one pair of parallel sides
b. a quadrilateral with four congruent sides and no right angles
23a–b. See margin.

○ **Mixed Review**

Lesson 7-6

24. What value is in cell B2? **90**

25. Which cell has the value 92? **C3**

26. Write a formula that will calculate the value in cell D3.
=(B3+C3)/2

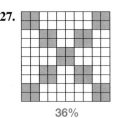

	A	B	C	D
1	Student	Test 1	Test 2	Mean
2	Antwon	90	70	■
3	Bianca	82	92	■

Lesson 6-6   **What percent of each grid is shaded?**

27.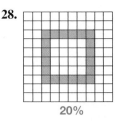
36%

28.
20%

◁ **Math at Work**
                                    Cartoonist

If you enjoy reading comics and draw well, a career as a cartoonist may be right for you. Some cartoonists produce comic strips meant for amusement. Others create illustrations for articles, books, or advertisements. Cartoonists use lines, angles, measures, and perspective to create cartoons.

Take It to the NET For more information about cartoonists, go to **www.PHSchool.com**.
Web Code: aab-2031

23. [2] a.
trapezoid

b.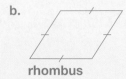
rhombus

[1] Drawings are mainly accurate with only minor errors. Best name is consistent with drawing.

8-6 Use Logical Reasoning

What You'll Learn

OBJECTIVE 1
To solve problems using logical reasoning

...And Why

To use reasoning to solve puzzles, as in Example 1

✓ **Check Skills You'll Need**   ? For help, go to Lesson 7-2.

Organize each set of data by making a frequency table.

1. goals in hockey games: 3, 2, 0, 0, 1, 2, 3, 3, 1, 1, 4, 2, 0 **1–3. See margin.**

2. test scores: 75, 100, 80, 80, 82, 85, 90, 90, 100, 80, 85, 90

3. water temperatures (°F): 80, 80, 82, 82, 85, 87, 88, 89, 87, 88

OBJECTIVE 1

Solving Problems Using Logical Reasoning

iTEXT Interactive lesson includes instant self-check, tutorials, and activities.

When to Use This Strategy You can **use logical reasoning** when you are given a series of clues or when you are playing a game.

1 EXAMPLE   Real-World 🌐 Problem Solving

	a	b	c
a	R	A	Y
b	A	R	E
c	Y	E	A

Puzzles The word square at the left shows three words read the same across and down. Use the clues below to complete the word square at the right.

a. Continues without end in opposite directions
b. Thought
c. Reports of recent events
d. Not difficult

	a	b	c	d
a				
b				
c				
d				

Read and Understand The goal is to complete a word square using the given clues.

1.

	a.	b.	c.	d.
a.	T	H	A	T
b.	H	E	X	A
c.	A	X	E	S
d.	T	A	S	K

Plan and Solve Copy the 4-by-4 grid. Fill in the words using the clues. The word "line" goes in row (a) and column (a). Complete the word square.

	a	b	c	d
a	L	I	N	E
b	I			
c	N			
d	E			

Look Back and Check Check that the words match the clues and that they all read the same across and down.

	a	b	c	d
a	L	I	N	E
b	I	D	E	A
c	N	E	W	S
d	E	A	S	Y

✓ **Check Understanding** ① Use these clues to complete a 4-by-4 word square.
a. This and _?_   b. Prefix meaning "six"
c. Plural of "axis"   d. Chore **a–d. See left.**

8-6

1. Plan

Lesson Preview

✓ **Check Skills You'll Need** 🖥
Making a Frequency Table
Lesson 7-2: Example 1. Extra Practice, p. 648.

Lesson Resources

📁 **Teaching Resources**
Practice, Reteaching, Enrichment

👥 **Reaching All Students**
Practice Workbook 8-6
Spanish Practice Workbook 8-6
Guided Problem Solving 8-6

⏱ **Presentation Assistant Plus!**
Transparencies
• Check Skills You'll Need 8-6
• Problem of the Day 8-6
• Additional Examples 8-6
• Student Edition Answers 8-6
• Lesson Quiz 8-6
• Classroom Aid 2
PH Presentation Pro CD-ROM 8-6

PRENTICE HALL
ASSESSMENT SYSTEM

Computer Test Generator CD

💻 **Technology**
Resource Pro® CD-ROM
Computer Test Generator CD
PH Presentation Pro CD-ROM

💻 **www.PHSchool.com**
Student Site
• Teacher Web Code: aak-5500
• Self-grading Lesson Quiz

PH SuccessNet Teacher Center
• Lesson Planner
• Resources

Plus iTEXT

Ongoing Assessment and Intervention

Before the Lesson
Diagnose prerequisite skills using:
• Check Skills You'll Need

During the Lesson
Monitor progress using:
• Check Understanding
• Additional Examples
• Test Prep

After the Lesson
Assess knowledge using:
• Lesson Quiz
• Computer Test Generator CD

1.

0	1	2	3	4

2–3. See back of book.

Math Background

Professional Development

Use logical reasoning is a problem-solving strategy that often supports other strategies like *look for a pattern*. However, in puzzle-like problems with a series of clues, *use logical reasoning* becomes the primary problem-solving strategy.

Teaching Notes

1 EXAMPLE Inclusion

Elicit the fact that the 4-by-4 word square contains exactly 4 four-letter words.

Error Prevention!

In Check Understanding 1, have students begin by filling-in the words they know.

2 EXAMPLE Diversity

Have students explain the different types of collections they have.

PowerPoint
Additional Examples

1 Use these clues to make a 4-by-4 word square.

a. metric standard unit for mass

b. seldom occurring or found

c. square units inside a figure

d. average for a set of data

G	R	A	M
R	A	R	E
A	R	E	A
M	E	A	N

2 Jude, Cecily, and Gloria each play one of the three bases in softball. Jude does not play 1st base. Gloria lives next door to the 1st base player. Gloria does not play 2nd base. Which girl plays each base? **1st: Cecily; 2nd: Jude; 3rd: Gloria**

Closure

When might you use logical reasoning to solve a problem?
Sample: when you are given a series of clues or when playing a game

402

---

2 EXAMPLE   Real-World 🌐 Problem Solving

Hobbies Anna, Bob, and Carlos each collect one of the following: sports cards, stamps, and coins. Bob's cousin collects stamps. Carlos had lunch with the coin and the stamp collectors. Decide what each person collects.

Read and Understand   The problem gives clues about the hobbies of Anna, Bob, and Carlos. The goal is to match each person with their hobby.

Plan and Solve   Make a table. Use the clues and record your conclusions.

- Bob's cousin collects stamps. ⟶
- Carlos had lunch with the coin ⟶ and stamp collectors.

	Cards	Stamps	Coins
Anna		Yes	
Bob		No	
Carlos	Yes	No	No

- Carlos must be the card collector. Anna must collect stamps.
- Complete the table. Bob must collect coins.

	Cards	Stamps	Coins
Anna	No	Yes	No
Bob	No	No	Yes
Carlos	Yes	No	No

Look Back and Check   Reread the problem. Make sure your solution matches all the facts given.

✓ **Check Understanding** 2 Janna, Georgine, and Tanika were born in Jamaica, Peru, and France. Janna has never been to France. Tanika plays softball with the girl from Jamaica, but not with the one who came from France. Where was each girl born?
Janna was born in Jamaica. Georgine was born in France. Tanika was born in Peru.

EXERCISES

❓ For more practice, see *Extra Practice*.

Ⓐ **Practice by Example**

Example 1 (page 401)

In each exercise, use the clues to complete a 4-by-4 word square.

1. **a.** Results of adding   **b.** One of something
   c. 5,280 feet   **d.** ___?___ -and-leaf plot

2. **a.** Unit of mass   **b.** Uncommon
   c. Measurement in square units   **d.** Average
                                  1–2. See margin.

Example 2 (page 402)

Solve each problem using logical reasoning.

3. Amy, Bill, and Chuck each have one bicycle. One bicycle is blue, one is green, and the other is red. Amy's brother rides a red bike. Chuck's bike is neither red nor green. Which bicycle does each person own?
Amy has a green bike. Bill has a red bike. Chuck has a blue bike.

👫 Reaching All Students

Below Level Have students make a table to record their pets. **Sample:**

Jane	2 cats		1 fish
Raul		2 dogs	
Bo	1 cat		

Advanced Learners Have students make five-letter and six-letter word squares that emphasize mathematics vocabulary.

Inclusion
See note on page 402.
Diversity
See note on page 402.

Need Help?
- Reread the problem.
- Identify the key facts and details.
- Tell the problem in your own words.
- Try a different strategy.
- Check your work.

6. Lamar = firefighter
   Camille = doctor
   Amelia = artist
   Jake = musician

4. Jane, Aldo, and Michelle play guitar, keyboards, and drums. Jane is the friend of the guitar player. Aldo lives next door to the drummer and works with the guitar player. Match each person with his or her instrument.   Jane plays the drums. Aldo plays the keyboard. Michelle plays the guitar.

 5. Track and Field In a race at the track meet, Sue outran Keisha. Debbie beat Alma but lost to Keisha. Who finished first? Sue

 6. Occupations Jake, Amelia, Camille, and Lamar each have an occupation represented by one of the objects below. Jake and Lamar did not go to medical school. Camille and Lamar buy the artist's paintings and listen to the musician's performances. Amelia does not play an instrument. What is each person's occupation? See left.

B **Apply Your Skills**

Use any standard strategy to solve each problem. Show your work.

Strategies

Draw a Diagram
Make a Graph
Make an Organized List
Make a Table and
   Look for a Pattern
Simulate a Problem
Solve a Simpler Problem
Try, Check, and Revise
Use Logical Reasoning
Work Backward
Write an Equation

 7. Collections Your friend decides to sort his collection of baseball
GPS cards. When he tries to put the cards in equal piles of two, he has one card left over. He also has one left over when he sorts the cards in piles of three or piles of four. But when he puts them in piles of seven, he has none left over. What is the least possible number of cards in your friend's collection? 49 cards

 8. Survey You ask 130 high school students how they earn money. Forty-five students babysit, 32 bag groceries, 28 do yard work, and 12 have after school office jobs. Each student who works at these jobs does only one kind of job, except for 15 who babysit and also do yard work.
   a. How many students babysit, do yard work, or do both? 58 students
   b. How many students do not have any of the jobs listed above? 28 students

9. 68, 60. Start with 65. Subtract 2 for next term. Add the next consecutive number from what you subtracted. Subtract the next consecutive number. Continue alternately adding and subtracting consecutive numbers.

 9. Writing in Math Find the missing numbers and describe the pattern.

   65, 63, 66, 62, 67, 61, ■, ■, 69, 59 . . . See left.

 10. Sports There are 20 students on the intramural tennis team. Eight students play only singles, and eight students play both singles and doubles. How many students play only doubles? 4 students

1.

	a.	b.	c.	d.
a.	S	U	M	S
b.	U	N	I	T
c.	M	I	L	E
d.	S	T	E	M

2.

	a.	b.	c.	d.
a.	G	R	A	M
b.	R	A	R	E
c.	A	R	E	A
d.	M	E	A	N

---

3. Practice

Assignment Guide

1 **Objective 1**
   A **B** Core 1–11
   C Extension 12–13

Test Prep 14–16
Mixed Review 17–19

Visual Learners
Exercises 3–10 Remind students to make a table and use the information in a completed row to fill-in the other rows.

Practice 8-6   Problem Solving: Use Logical Reasoning

Solve each problem using logical reasoning. Show your work.

1. A local restaurant features a three-course meal. For the first course, you can choose from soup, salad, cottage cheese, or coleslaw. For the second course, you can choose from beef, pork, chicken, or a vegetarian pasta dish. For the third course, you can choose from sherbet, rice pudding, or ice cream. How many different meals could you choose if you choose one item from each course?
   48 meals

2. In a sixth-grade class of 28 students, 23 like to watch basketball. Also, 15 like to watch baseball. Twelve in the class said they like to watch both sports. How many students in the class do not like to watch either sport?
   2 students

Use any strategy to solve each problem. Show your work.

3. Don has a pile of pennies. When he separates the pennies into stacks of two, he has one left over. When he separates the pennies into stacks of five, he has four left over. When he separates the pennies into stacks of seven, there is none left over. What is the least number of pennies that Don could have?
   49 pennies

4. Mara bought some flowers to plant in her garden. When she separated the plants into groups of three or five, she had one plant left over. When she separated the plants into groups of eight, she had none left over. What is the smallest number of plants that Mara could have bought?
   16 plants

5. Use the clues to make a 4-by-4 word square.
   a. a triangle has three
   b. a thought or opinion
   c. where lions sleep
   d. opposite of west

	a	b	c	d
a	S	I	D	E
b	I	D	E	A
c	D	E	N	S
d	E	A	S	T

Reteaching 8-6   Problem Solving: Use Logical Reasoning

Daniel, Sandy, Rita, and Joseph mixed up their class schedules. Each student has math class during a different period, and the schedules show math in period A, B, C, or D. Daniel knows he eats lunch during period C. Sandy sees Daniel arrive for math class just as she is leaving. Rita goes to math after eating lunch with Daniel. Which schedule belongs to each student?

Read and Understand

There are four different schedules for four students. Clues are given about which schedule belongs to each student. The goal is to match each student with a schedule.

Plan and Solve

Make a table. Label the schedules A, B, C, and D for the periods in which math appears. Use the clues to determine whether or not a student has a given schedule.

	A	B	C	D
Daniel	No	Yes	No	No
Sandy	Yes	No	No	No
Rita	No	No	No	Yes
Joseph	No	No	Yes	No

- Daniel eats lunch during period C. Write "No" in the box for Daniel and schedule C.
- Rita goes to math after eating lunch with Daniel. Rita must have math during period D.
- Sandy sees Daniel arrive for math just as she is leaving. To have math before Daniel, Sandy must go to math in period A. Daniel has math in period B.
- Complete the table. Joseph must have math in period C.

Look Back and Check

Reread the problem. Make sure your solution matches all the facts given.

Solve each problem using logical reasoning.

1. Patrick, Tony, and Neil live in a row of three houses on the same street. Walking past their houses, they pass a white house first, then a green house, then a blue house. Patrick lives next door to the green house. Tony does not live next door to his friend who lives in the blue house. Who lives in each house?
   Patrick in the blue house, Tony in the white house, and Neil in the green house

2. A landscaper is planting five types of flowers in a row. The daisies are not planted at either end of the row. The snapdragons are planted at one of the ends and are next to the daffodils. The tulips are only next to the hyacinths. The hyacinths are second in the row. In what order did the landscaper plant the flowers?
   tulips, hyacinths, daisies, daffodils, snapdragons

GPS Use the Guided Problem Solving worksheet with Exercise 7.

PowerPoint **Lesson Quiz 8-6**

Solve using logical reasoning.

1. Ron's, Sam's, and Todd's eyes are three different colors: blue, hazel, or brown. Ron does not have blue eyes. Sam does not have blue or hazel eyes. What color eyes does each boy have? **Ron: hazel; Sam: brown; Todd: blue**

Alternative Assessment

Each student in a pair writes a problem that can be solved by using logical reasoning. Have them use the Examples in the lesson as models. Partners exchange papers and solve each other's problem.

Test Prep

Resources

For additional practice with a variety of test item formats:
• Test Prep, p. 425
• Test-Taking Strategies, p. 421
• Test-Taking Strategies With Transparencies

Exercise 16 Suggest that students use *try, test, and revise* to solve the problem.

Enrichment 8-6   Problem Solving: Use Logical Reasoning
Critical Thinking

Of the 300 employees that work at an electronics store, 185 wear glasses, 92 own only a laptop computer, and 120 own only a desktop computer. Also, 45 wear glasses and own only a laptop computer, 25 wear glasses and own only a desktop computer, and 32 wear glasses and own a desktop and a laptop computer.

1. Complete the Venn Diagram to represent the information.
   Let circle A represent the number of people who own a laptop computer.
   Let circle B represent the number of people who own a desktop computer.
   Let circle C represent the number of people who wear glasses.

2. How many employees own a desktop computer and a laptop computer but do not wear glasses?
   0 employees

3. How many people do not wear glasses nor own a computer?
   37 employees

4. One of the employees who wears glasses and owns a laptop and a desktop computer sells his laptop to an employee who owns a desktop computer but does not wear glasses. Draw another Venn diagram to represent the employees at the store.

5. Another employee who wears glasses and owns only a desktop computer sells his computer to an employee who wears glasses but does not own a computer. Redraw your diagram from Exercise 4 to represent the employees at the store.

404

---

11. a. **Geometry** Draw a quadrilateral. Draw a segment to divide the quadrilateral into two triangles. Use your diagram to find the sum of the measures of the angles of a quadrilateral. **360°**

11b. 540°; 720°
c. 900°; 1080°
d. yes

   b. Draw a pentagon and a hexagon. Draw segments to divide each figure into the least possible number of triangles. Use your diagram to find the sum of the measures of the angles of a pentagon and a hexagon.

   c. Use your answers in parts (a) and (b) to predict the sums of the measures of the angles of a seven-sided figure and an octagon.

   d. **Data File, p. 371** Are your results the same as those in the table?
   11b–d. See left.

 Challenge 12. **Lemonade** To make lemonade, you need 3 cups of water for every 2 cups of lemon juice. You want to make 10 gallons of lemonade. How many cups of lemon juice do you need? **64 cups of lemon juice**

13. **Stretch Your Thinking** Marcus makes 3 flower arrangements in 4 hours. At this rate, how long will it take him to make 5 flower arrangements? **6 h 40 min**

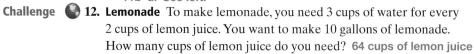 **Test Prep**

Multiple Choice

14. These are geomlets: These are not geomlets:

Which of these is a geomlet? **B**

A.   B.   C.   D.

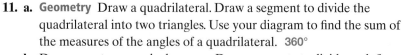 **Take It to the NET**
Online lesson quiz at
www.PHSchool.com
Web Code: aaa-0806

15. What day of the week is 263 days from Monday? **H**
   F. Monday   G. Wednesday   H. Friday   I. Sunday

Short Response

16. The sum of two numbers is 4.2. Their product is 4.4. Find the numbers. Explain how you found your answer. **See margin.**

Mixed Review

Lesson 7-7   **Make a stem-and-leaf plot of the data.**

17. 33, 42, 16, 45, 14, 28, 37, 16, 23, 33, 25, 16 **See margin.**

Lesson 5-8   **Complete each statement.**

18. 8,800 lb = ■ t ■ lb
   4   800

19. 18 qt = ■ gal ■ qt
   4   2

16. **[2]** 2 and 2.2; The product 4 is close to 4.4, so I thought to try numbers close to those that would give a product of 4. Since 4.4 is a little more than 4, I tried 2 and a number a little more than 2.

[1] correct answer with no explanation

17.

1	4 6 6 6
2	3 5 8
3	3 3 7
4	2 5

Key: 1 | 4 means 14

8-7 Congruent and Similar Figures

What You'll Learn

OBJECTIVE 1 To identify congruent figures

OBJECTIVE 2 To identify similar figures

. . . And Why

To identify similar figures in architecture, as in Example 3

✓ Check Skills You'll Need

? For help, go to Lesson 8-4.

Classify each triangle by its sides.

1.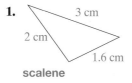
scalene

2.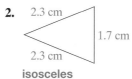
isosceles

3.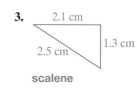
scalene

New Vocabulary
• congruent figures • similar figures

OBJECTIVE 1

ⓘ TEXT Interactive lesson includes instant self-check, tutorials, and activities.

Identifying Congruent Figures

Real-World 🌐 Connection

Notice the congruent triangles in this bridge in Pittsburgh, Pennsylvania.

Congruent figures have the same size and shape. Congruent figures have congruent *corresponding sides* and congruent *corresponding angles*.

Figures can be congruent even if one of the figures is turned or flipped. Suppose you copy and cut out the blue trapezoid. You could make it fit exactly over either green trapezoid. The matching sides and angles are the corresponding sides and angles.

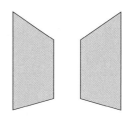

1 EXAMPLE Identifying Congruent Figures

Tell whether each triangle is congruent to triangle *PQR*.

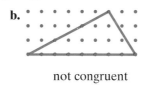

a.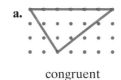
congruent

b.
not congruent

✓ Check Understanding ① Are the two trapezoids congruent to the first trapezoid?

a.
no

b.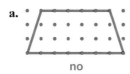
yes

📋 Ongoing Assessment and Intervention

Before the Lesson
Diagnose prerequisite skills using:
• Check Skills You'll Need

During the Lesson
Monitor progress using:
• Check Understanding
• Additional Examples
• Test Prep

After the Lesson
Assess knowledge using:
• Lesson Quiz
• Computer Test Generator CD

8-7

1. Plan

Lesson Preview

PowerPoint

✓ **Check Skills You'll Need**

Classifying Triangles by Sides
Lesson 8-4: Example 3. Extra Practice, p. 649.

Lesson Resources

Optional Materials
• dot paper

📁 **Teaching Resources**
Practice, Reteaching, Enrichment

👥 **Reaching All Students**
Practice Workbook 8-7
Spanish Practice Workbook 8-7
Guided Problem Solving 8-7
Hands-On Activities 23

⏱ **Presentation Assistant Plus!**
Transparencies
• Check Skills You'll Need 8-7
• Problem of the Day 8-7
• Additional Examples 8-7
• Student Edition Answers 8-7
• Lesson Quiz 8-7
• Classroom Aid 6, 20, 21
PH Presentation Pro CD-ROM 8-7

PRENTICE HALL ASSESSMENT SYSTEM

Computer Test Generator CD

💻 **Technology**
Resource Pro® CD-ROM
Computer Test Generator CD
PH Presentation Pro CD-ROM

💻 **www.PHSchool.com**
Student Site
• Teacher Web Code: aak-5500
• Self-grading Lesson Quiz

PH SuccessNet Teacher Center
• Lesson Planner
• Resources

Plus **ⓘ TEXT**

2. Teach

Professional Development

Math Background

Congruent figures have the same size and shape. Congruent figures may not appear congruent because they can be rotated and flipped. However, if you place congruent figures on top of one another—matching corresponding sides and corresponding angles—the figures exactly match. You can identify congruent figures if both their corresponding sides and corresponding angles are congruent.

Similar figures have the same shape but not necessarily the same size. So, corresponding angles are congruent but corresponding sides are proportional. This means congruent figures are similar but similar figures may not be congruent.

Teaching Notes

① EXAMPLE Visual Learners

Ask: *What transformation to △QPR gives the triangle in part a?* **a rotation** Make sure students understand that two figures can also be congruent when they are flipped instead of rotated.

Investigation (Optional)

For students who might have difficulty forming the larger triangle, have them work in small groups or use right triangles. Remind students that they can flip their triangles to form the larger triangle.

English Learners

Help students understand what is meant by "same shape." Similar figures can be reductions or enlargements, such as by a photocopier, that therefore retain the "same shape" even though they have different sizes.

② EXAMPLE Error Prevention

Emphasize that the proportions are formed using the corresponding sides. Students can write the proportions in different ways as long as the corresponding parts of the figures are corresponding terms in their proportions.

406

Investigation: Comparing Triangles

- Draw four identical triangles on dot paper and cut them out.
- Arrange the four cutout triangles to form a larger triangle that has the same shape as the original triangles. (None of the cutout triangles should overlap.)

1. How do the lengths of the sides of one of the original triangles and the lengths of the sides of the larger triangle compare? **They are proportional.**
2. How do the angles of one of the original triangles compare with the angles of the larger triangle? **They are the same.**

Similar figures have the same shape, but not necessarily the same size. Corresponding angles of similar figures are congruent. Lengths of corresponding sides of similar figures are proportional.

② EXAMPLE Identifying Similar Figures

Need Help?
For help with checking for proportions, go to Lesson 6-4.

Which triangles are similar to triangle *DEF*? Confirm your answer by finding whether the corresponding sides are proportional.

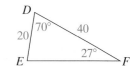

a.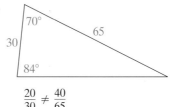

$\dfrac{20}{30} \neq \dfrac{40}{65}$

Not similar

b.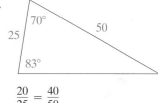

$\dfrac{20}{25} = \dfrac{40}{50}$

Similar

✓ **Check Understanding** ② Tell whether each triangle is similar to triangle *DEF* in Example 2.

a. **yes**

b. **no**

🖐 Reaching All Students

| **Below Level** Have students trace pattern blocks with irregular-shaped figures. Students should trace rotated figures as well a flipped figures. | **Advanced Learners** Have students find the values of *x* and *y* if △A is similar to △B. **x = 15, y = 8** 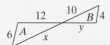 | **English Learners** See note on page 406. **Inclusion** See note on page 407. |

If the angles of two triangles are congruent, then the triangles are similar. The sides must also be congruent for the triangles to be congruent.

3 EXAMPLE   Real-World 🌎 Problem Solving

Architecture Are the triangles *ABC* and *CDE* congruent or similar? Explain.

Triangles *ABC* and *CDE* are not congruent because their corresponding sides are not congruent.

Triangles *ABC* and *CDE* appear to be similar, because their corresponding angles appear to be congruent.

The Rock and Roll Hall of Fame in Cleveland, Ohio.

✔ **Check Understanding** ③ Are the figures *congruent* or *similar*? Explain.

 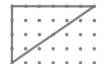

congruent and similar; all of their sides and angles are congruent.

EXERCISES

❓ For more practice, see *Extra Practice*.

A Practice by Example

Example 1 (page 405)

For each figure, tell whether it is congruent to trapezoid *ABDC*.

1. yes **2.** no

3. yes **4.** yes **5.** no

Example 2 (page 406)

Which rectangles are similar to rectangle *MNOP* at the left?

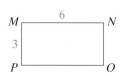

no   no   yes   yes
6. 5   **7.**   **8.** 1.5   **9.**
2   3   3   4
             4   2

407

---

3 EXAMPLE Inclusion

Ask: *Can a congruent figure also be similar? Explain.* **Sample:** Yes, because corresponding angles are congruent.

Tactile Learners
Have pairs of students work together to construct congruent and similar figures using geoboards. One partner constructs a figure and the other partner constructs both a congruent figure and a similar figure.

PowerPoint
Additional Examples

① Are the pentagons congruent? yes

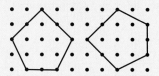

② Which triangle appears to be similar to △*HJK*? Confirm your answer by finding whether the corresponding sides are proportional.

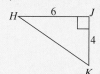

a.   **b.** 25
  3   20
   2

$\frac{4}{2} = \frac{6}{3}$ $\frac{4}{20} \neq \frac{6}{25}$
similar   not similar

③ Are the figures *congruent* or *similar*? Explain.

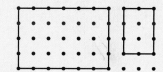

Similar; corresponding sides are proportional.

Closure

• *How do you identify congruent figures?* **Sample:** Congruent figures have congruent corresponding angles and congruent corresponding sides.

• *How do you identify similar figures?* **Sample:** Similar figures have congruent corresponding angles and proportional corresponding sides.

407

Assignment Guide

 Objective 1
- Ⓐ Ⓑ Core 1–5, 14–16, 21–22
- Ⓒ Extension 23

 Objective 2
- Ⓐ Ⓑ Core 6–13, 17–20
- Ⓒ Extension 24

Test Prep 25–27
Mixed Review 28–36

Exercise 1 Some students may have difficulty recognizing congruence for a figure that is flipped.

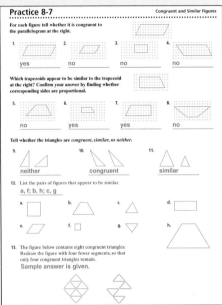

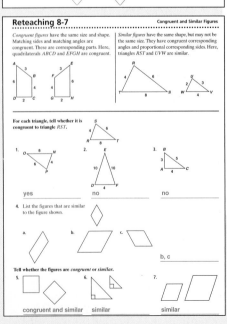

Example 3 (page 407)

Tell whether the triangles are *congruent*, *similar*, or *both*.

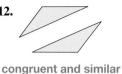

10. similar

11. similar

12. congruent and similar

🌎 **13. Home Repairs** Suppose you are replacing a window. Should the replacement be congruent to or similar to the original? Explain.
Congruent; the window must be exactly the same size.

Ⓑ **Apply Your Skills**

Match the congruent triangles. Choose A, B, or C.

14. A

15. C

16. B

A. **B.** **C.**

17. List the pairs of figures that are similar. If necessary, use a protractor to measure the angles. A and E, H and J

Need Help?
For help with measuring angles, see page 379.

A. 2 / 4   **B.** 2 / 2   **C.** 3 / 2 / 3   **D.** 1 / 2 / 2 / 1   **E.** 1 / 2

F. 2 / 3   **G.** 3   **H.** 3 / 2 / 2 / 2   **I.** 3 / 4   **J.** 2 / 4 / 4 / 6

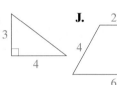

18. Triangles *MNO* and *PQR* are similar.

GPS **a.** List the pairs of congruent angles.

18a. ∠MNO and ∠PQR, ∠MON and ∠PRQ, ∠OMN and ∠RPQ

b. Write the proportions for the corresponding sides. $\frac{3}{12} = \frac{4}{16}$, $\frac{3}{12} = \frac{5}{20}$, $\frac{4}{16} = \frac{5}{20}$

19a. Check students' work.

19. a. Draw five rhombuses that are not congruent.

b. Are all rhombuses similar? Explain.
No; their angles may not be congruent.

20. **Writing in Math** Are congruent figures always similar figures? Explain.
Yes; their angles are always congruent and their sides are always proportional.

(**Algebra**) **Each pair of figures is congruent. Find *x*.**

21. 8 / 8 / 6 / x

22. 150 / 17° / 20 / 14° / x / 15

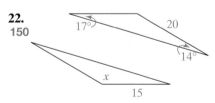

GPS Use the Guided Problem Solving worksheet with Exercise 18a.

23. Patterns How many congruent triangles are in the figure at the right? How many similar triangles? 4, 5

24. Stretch Your Thinking One sixth of a fraction is the same as one half of one fourth. What is the fraction?

$\frac{3}{4}$

Test Prep

Multiple Choice

25. Which figure below is NOT congruent to the figure at the left? **D**

A.　　　　**B.**　　　　**C.**　　　　**D.**

26. Which figure is congruent to triangle *PQR*? **I**

F. 　　　　**G.**

H. 　　　　**I.**

Q ... *P* ... *R*

**Take It to the NET**
Online lesson quiz at
www.PHSchool.com
Web Code: aaa-0807

Short Response

27. Use the similar figures at the right. Find each length.
a. $\overline{BA}$　　b. $\overline{BC}$
See margin.

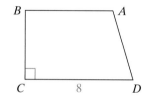

B ... *A*
F — 4 — *E*
3
G — 5 — *H*　　*C* — 8 — *D*

Mixed Review

Lesson 7-4

28. Make a line graph from the data in the table. See margin.

Net Profit per Week

Week	1	2	3	4	5
Store A	$1,500	$800	$700	$950	$1,000

Lesson 6-6

Write each fraction as a percent.

29. $\frac{90}{120}$ 75%　　**30.** $\frac{2}{5}$ 40%　　**31.** $\frac{4}{10}$ 40%　　**32.** $\frac{55}{88}$ 62.5%

33. $\frac{7}{8}$ 87.5%　　**34.** $\frac{15}{25}$ 60%　　**35.** $\frac{1}{4}$ 25%　　**36.** $\frac{7}{35}$ 20%

8-7　Congruent and Similar Figures　**409**

27. [2] a. $\frac{EF}{BA} = \frac{HG}{CD}$ so $\frac{4}{BA} = \frac{5}{8}$,
$5(BA) = 32$
$BA = 6.4$

b. $\frac{BC}{EH} = \frac{CD}{HG}$ so $\frac{BC}{3} = \frac{8}{5}$
$5(BC) = 24$
$BC = 4.8$

[1] no work shown

28.

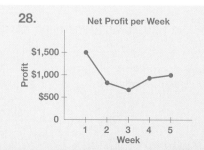

Net Profit per Week

 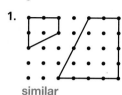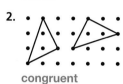

1. Plan

Lesson Preview

✓ **Check Skills You'll Need** PowerPoint

Identifying Congruent Figures
Lesson 8-7: Example 1. Extra
Practice, p. 649.

Lesson Resources

Optional Materials
• scissors

📁 **Teaching Resources**
Practice, Reteaching, Enrichment
Checkpoint Quiz 2

👥 **Reaching All Students**
Practice Workbook 8-8
Spanish Practice Workbook 8-8
Reading and Math Literacy 8C
Spanish Reading and Math
  Literacy 8C
Spanish Checkpoint Quiz 2
Guided Problem Solving 8-8

⏱ **Presentation Assistant Plus!**
Transparencies
• Check Skills You'll Need 8-8
• Problem of the Day 8-8
• Additional Examples 8-8
• Student Edition Answers 8-8
• Lesson Quiz 8-8
• Classroom Aid 6
PH Presentation Pro CD-ROM 8-8

PRENTICE HALL
ASSESSMENT SYSTEM

Checkpoint Quiz 2
Computer Test Generator CD

💻 **Technology**
Resource Pro® CD-ROM
Computer Test Generator CD
PH Presentation Pro CD-ROM

💻 **www.PHSchool.com**
Student Site
• Teacher Web Code: aak-5500
• Algebra Readiness Puzzle 8
• Self-grading Lesson Quiz

PH SuccessNet Teacher Center
• Lesson Planner
• Resources

Plus 📘 **iTEXT**
410

What You'll Learn

OBJECTIVE 1 To find lines of
symmetry

. . . And Why

To find a line of symmetry
in nature, as in Example 2

✓ **Check Skills You'll Need**
🔍 For help, go to Lesson 8-7.

Are the two figures congruent?

1. yes    **2.** yes

New Vocabulary • line symmetry • line of symmetry

OBJECTIVE 1 **Finding the Lines of Symmetry**

📘 **iTEXT** Interactive lesson includes instant self-check, tutorials, and activities.

Investigation: Symmetry

1. Fold a sheet of paper in half. Draw a design
   on one side of the fold line. With the paper
   still folded, cut out your design. Do not cut
   along the fold. Unfold the paper.
   Check students' work.
2. Are the designs on either side of the fold
   similar? Explain. *Yes; the two sides match.*

3. Fold another sheet of paper in half twice such
   that the fold lines intersect each other at
   right angles. Cut out a design on the corner
   that includes the fold lines. Unfold the paper.
   Check students' work.
4. How many similar shapes did you form? *4*

Real-World 🌐 Connection
The two butterfly wings are
similar. Their shapes are
symmetric.

You often see symmetry in nature like the butterfly at the left. You can also
find symmetrical designs in fabrics, flags, architecture, and art. Symmetry is
appealing to the eye.

A figure has **line symmetry** if a line can be drawn through the figure so that
each half is a mirror image of the other. This line is a **line of symmetry.** If
you fold a drawing on its line of symmetry, the two sides match.

✓ **INSTANT CHECK SYSTEM** **Ongoing Assessment and Intervention**

Before the Lesson	**During the Lesson**	**After the Lesson**
Diagnose prerequisite skills using:	Monitor progress using:	Assess knowledge using:
• Check Skills You'll Need	• Check Understanding	• Lesson Quiz
	• Additional Examples	• Computer Test Generator CD
	• Test Prep	• Chapter Checkpoint 2 (p. 414)

 **EXAMPLE** **Testing for Line Symmetry**

For each figure, is the dashed line a line of symmetry? Explain.

a.

b.

No, if you fold the figure along the line, the two parts do not match.

Yes, if you fold the figure along the line, the two parts match.

✔ **Check Understanding** 1 Is the red dashed line in the figure a line of symmetry? Explain.

No; if you fold the figure along the line, the two parts do not match.

Some figures have more than one line of symmetry.

2 **EXAMPLE** **Real-World** 🌐 **Problem Solving**

Nature How many lines of symmetry does each figure have? Draw them.

a.

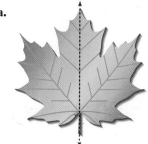

b.

The leaf has one line of symmetry.

The snowflake has 6 lines of symmetry.

✔ **Check Understanding** 2 How many lines of symmetry does each figure have? Trace the figure and draw the lines of symmetry.

a. 1

b. 4

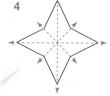

c. **Reasoning** How many lines of symmetry does a circle have? Explain your reasoning. Infinitely many; any line that goes through the center of a circle is a line of symmetry.

8-8 Line Symmetry **411**

Professional Development

Math Background

Both the natural world and the human built world are full of symmetry. A figure has *line symmetry* if a *line of symmetry* can be drawn that divides the figure into two mirror images. You can test a figure for line symmetry by folding it along the line of symmetry and seeing if the two halves match.

Teaching Notes

Investigation (Optional)
Make sure that the students' shapes start and end on the fold. In Step 3, make sure students' shapes start on one fold and end on the other fold.

2 **EXAMPLE** **Tactile Learners**

For Check Understanding 2, have students fold their traced figure along their proposed line of symmetry. Then have them hold the folded figure up to the light to observe if the two parts match.

PowerPoint
📽 Additional Examples

1 Is the dashed line shown in each figure a line of symmetry? Explain.

a.

b.

Yes, the two parts match.

No, the parts do not match.

2 How many lines of symmetry does each figure have? Trace the figure and draw the lines of symmetry.

a.

b.

two lines

six lines

Closure

When does a figure have line symmetry? Sample: when a line can be drawn through the figure so that each half is a mirror image of the other

411

👥 **Reaching All Students**

Below Level Introduce the lesson by having students list as many real-world objects as they can that exhibit symmetry. Point out that the long list shows mathematics is all around us.

Advanced Learners Have students fold a sheet of paper as in Step 3 of the Investigation. Students cut out figures that have 2, 4, 6, and 8 lines of symmetry. For 6 and 8 lines, some will not be folds.

Diversity See note on page 413.

Tactile Learners See note on page 411.

Assignment Guide

1 **Objective 1**
- Ⓐ Ⓑ Core 1–21
- Ⓒ Extension 22–25

Test Prep 26–29
Mixed Review 30–32

Error Prevention!

Exercises 1–12 Some students may confuse a line of symmetry with any line that divides a figure into two parts. Remind them that a line of symmetry divides a figure into two congruent parts.

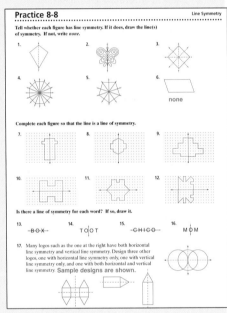

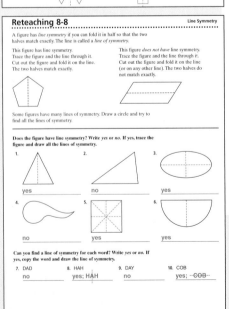

Ⓐ **Practice by Example**

1–6. See margin for explanations.

Is the dashed line in each figure a line of symmetry? Explain.

Example 1
(page 411)

1. no

2. yes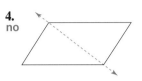

3. yes

4. no

5. yes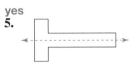

6. yes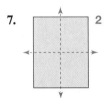

Example 2
(page 411)

How many lines of symmetry does each figure have? Trace the figure and draw the lines of symmetry.

7. 2

8. 1

9. 1

Tell whether each design has line symmetry.

10. no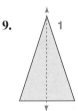

11. yes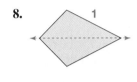

12. yes

Ⓑ **Apply Your Skills**

13. Which capital letters have at least one line of symmetry?

A B C D E F G H I J K L M
N O P Q R S T U V W X Y Z
A, B, C, D, E, H, I, K, M, O, T, U, V, W, X, Y

14. Open-Ended The word CODE has a horizontal line of symmetry. Find another word that has a horizontal line of symmetry. Check students' work.

◄--CODE--►

15. Open-Ended The word MOW has a vertical line of symmetry, when written vertically. Find another word that has a vertical line of symmetry when written vertically. Check students' work.

M
O
W

GPS Use the Guided Problem Solving worksheet with Exercise 19.

1. If you fold the figure along the line, the two parts do not match.

2. If you fold the figure along the line, the two parts match.

3. If you fold the figure along the line, the two parts match.

4. If you fold the figure along the line, the two parts do not match.

5. If you fold the figure along the line, the two parts match.

6. If you fold the figure along the line, the two parts match.

🌿 **Nature** Tell how many lines of symmetry each object has.

16.
5

17.
3

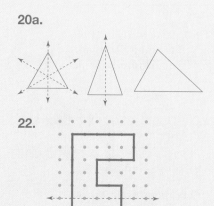

18a.

18. a. Trace the figure at the right and draw all lines of symmetry. **See left.**

b. Data File, page 371 Find the value of *x*. **135**

19.

19. Reasoning How many lines of symmetry does a square have? Draw a diagram to support your answer. **4; see left for diagram.**

20a.

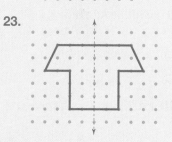

20. a. Draw a scalene, an equilateral, and an isosceles triangle. Draw all lines of symmetry for each triangle. **See margin.**

b. Writing in Math Describe the lines of symmetry in part (a). **See left.**

20b. The scalene triangle has no lines of symmetry. The lines of symmetry in the equilateral triangle go from each vertex to the center of the opposite side. The line of symmetry in the isosceles triangle extends from the center of the noncongruent side to the opposite corner.

🌐 **21. a. Flags** How many lines of symmetry are in each flag? Consider the design of each flag. **1; 2; 0**

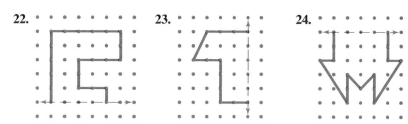

b. Open-Ended Design a flag that has at least one line of symmetry. **Check students' work.**

22.

C Challenge

Copy each figure on dot paper. Complete the figure so that the dashed line is a line of symmetry. **22–24. See margin.**

22.

23.

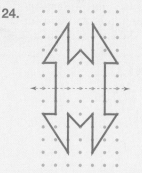

24.

25. Stretch Your Thinking A quadrilateral has one obtuse angle, one acute angle, and two consecutive right angles. What kind of quadrilateral is it? **a trapezoid**

PowerPoint Lesson Quiz 8-8

Is the dashed line shown in each figure a line of symmetry?

1. [circle with dashed line] no   2. [star with dashed line] yes

3. How many lines of symmetry does an equilateral triangle have? **3**

✔ Chapter Checkpoint

To check understanding of Lessons 8-4 to 8-8:

Checkpoint Quiz 2 (p. 414)

📁 **Teaching Resources**
Checkpoint Quiz 2 (also in Prentice Hall Assessment System)

👥 **Reaching All Students**
Reading and Math Literacy 8C

Spanish versions available

Alternative Assessment

Each student in a pair draws four figures on dot paper. Partners exchange figures and find and draw all the lines of symmetry.

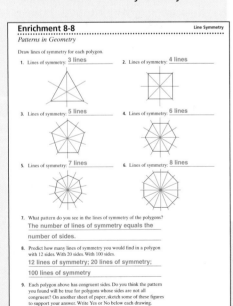

Test Prep

Gridded Response

26. How many lines of symmetry does a nonsquare rectangle have? 2

27. How many lines of symmetry does a nonsquare rhombus have? 2

 **Take It to the NET**
Online lesson quiz at
www.PHSchool.com
Web Code: aaa-0808

28. How many lines of symmetry does a trapezoid with two consecutive 60° angles have? 1

29. How many lines of symmetry does the word BOOK have? 1

● Mixed Review

Lesson 8-1 **Use the diagram to name each of the following.** 31–32. Answers may vary. Samples are given.

30. a different name for $\overline{AB}$ $\overline{BA}$

31. three noncollinear points *A*, *C*, and *D*

32. three rays $\overrightarrow{AC}$, $\overrightarrow{BC}$, $\overrightarrow{AD}$

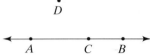

✔ Checkpoint Quiz 2   Lessons 8-4 through 8-8

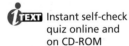 Instant self-check quiz online and on CD-ROM

Classify each triangle by its angles.

1. 20°, 60°, 100°
obtuse

2. 40°, 50°, 90°
right

3. 60°, 60°, 60°
acute

Classify each triangle by its sides.

4. 8, 9, and 8 units
isosceles

5. 3, 4, and 5 units
scalene

6. 10, 10, and 10 units
equilateral

7. The perimeter of an equilateral triangle is 12 m. Find the length of a side. 4 m

8. Fred, Matt, and Alison are a teacher, an artist, and a writer, though not necessarily in that order. Alison is the sister of the teacher. Matt has never met the teacher or the artist. Match each person to his or her job. Fred is the teacher. Matt is the writer. Alison is the artist.

Use the figures below for Exercises 9 and 10.

9. Which figures are similar?
B, D, and E

10. Which figures are congruent?
B and E

A. B. C. D. E.

Test Prep

Resources
A sheet of blank grids is available in the *Test-Taking Strategies With Transparencies* booklet. Give copies of this sheet to students so they can practice filling in grids.

For additional practice with a variety of test item formats:
• Test Prep, p. 425
• Test-Taking Strategies, p. 421
• Test-Taking Strategies With Transparencies

What You'll Learn

OBJECTIVE 1 To identify and draw translations and reflections

OBJECTIVE 2 To identify rotations

... And Why

To find rotations in nature, as in Example 3

✓ **Check Skills You'll Need** 🔎 For help, go to Lesson 8-8.

Trace each figure and draw the lines of symmetry.

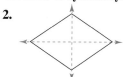

1. 2. 3.

New Vocabulary • image • translation • reflection
• line of reflection • rotation • center of rotation

Lesson Preview

✓ **Check Skills You'll Need** PowerPoint

Finding Lines of Symmetry
Lesson 8-8: Example 2. Extra Practice, p. 649.

Lesson Resources

Optional Materials
• graph paper

📁 **Teaching Resources**
Practice, Reteaching, Enrichment

👥 **Reaching All Students**
Practice Workbook 8-9
Spanish Practice Workbook 8-9
Guided Problem Solving 8-9
Hands-On Activities 41

⏱ **Presentation Assistant Plus!**
Transparencies
• Check Skills You'll Need 8-9
• Problem of the Day 8-9
• Additional Examples 8-9
• Student Edition Answers 8-9
• Lesson Quiz 8-9
• Classroom Aid 2
PH Presentation Pro CD-ROM 8-9

 **ASSESSMENT SYSTEM**

Computer Test Generator CD

💻 **Technology**
Resource Pro® CD-ROM
Computer Test Generator CD
PH Presentation Pro CD-ROM

💻 **www.PHSchool.com**
Student Site
• Teacher Web Code: aak-5500
• Self-grading Lesson Quiz

PH SuccessNet Teacher Center
• Lesson Planner
• Math Background
• Resources

Plus

OBJECTIVE 1

Drawing Translations and Reflections

 iTEXT Interactive lesson includes instant self-check, tutorials, and activities.

A *transformation* of a figure is a change in its position, shape, or size. The new figure is the **image** of the original. Three types of transformations change only the position of the figure. They are *translations*, *reflections*, and *rotations*.

A **translation,** or *slide*, is a transformation that moves every point of a figure the same distance and in the same direction.

Real-World 🌐 Connection

Quilters often translate one design to make a pattern.

The blue figure is the image of the black figure after a translation.

1 EXAMPLE **Identifying Translations**

Is the second figure a translation of the first figure?

a.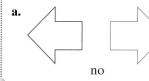

no

b.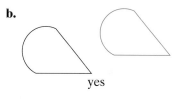

yes

✓ **Check Understanding** 1 Is the second figure a translation of the first figure? no

---

INSTANT CHECK ANALYSIS
Ongoing Assessment and Intervention

Before the Lesson
Diagnose prerequisite skills using:
• Check Skills You'll Need

During the Lesson
Monitor progress using:
• Check Understanding
• Additional Examples
• Test Prep

After the Lesson
Assess knowledge using:
• Lesson Quiz
• Computer Test Generator CD

Math Background

Professional Development

A *transformation* of a figure is a change in its position, shape, or size. The resulting figure is called an *image*. There are three rigid-motion transformations that change only the position of the figure: translations, reflections, and rotations.

A *translation*, or slide, moves every point of the figure the same distance in the same direction. A *reflection*, or flip, moves every point of the figure over a line, creating a mirror image with the *line of reflection* serving as the mirror. A *rotation*, or turn, moves every point of the figure about a fixed point called the *center of rotation*.

Teaching Notes

① EXAMPLE Inclusion

Ask: *When a figure is translated, what stays the same and what changes?* Sample: The shape and size stay the same but the location of all the points of the figure change by the same amount.

② EXAMPLE Visual Learners

Help students recognize that each point on Figure A is the same perpendicular distance from the line of reflection as its corresponding point in its image, Figure B. This relationship is exactly how images are formed in a mirror.

Alternative Method

For Check Understanding 2, have students fold each of their copied figures over the line of reflection to verify that their figures and images match. Students can hold their folded drawings to the light to better compare them.

Error Prevention!

Students may confuse translations and reflections. Relate *s*lide to translation and *f*lip to reflection. Use an everyday object, such as a book, to illustrate each transformation.

416

Real-World Connection
The reflecting pool gives an image of the Taj Mahal.

Another way to change the position of a figure is to reflect it. A **reflection,** or *flip*, is a transformation that flips a figure over a line. This line is the **line of reflection.** The new figure is a mirror image of the original.

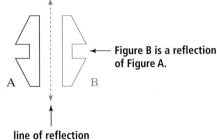

← Figure B is a reflection of Figure A.

A   B

line of reflection

② EXAMPLE Drawing Reflections

Draw the reflection of Figure A over the red line of reflection.

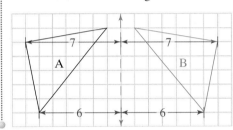

7   7

A   B

6   6

Use the grid to locate vertices equidistant from the line of reflection.

Then connect the vertices.

✔ **Check Understanding** ② Copy each diagram on graph paper and draw its reflection over the given line of reflection.

a. **b.**

OBJECTIVE

a–b. See back of book.

2 Identifying Rotations

A **rotation,** or *turn*, is a transformation that turns a figure about a point. This point stays fixed and is called the **center of rotation.**

The letter P is being rotated around the center of rotation. Each image is congruent to the original letter P.

Center of rotation

Clockwise rotation

📘 **Reading Math**
The hands of a clock rotate clockwise.

You can describe a rotation using degrees. The letter P has been rotated clockwise 90°, 180°, and 270°.

👥 Reaching All Students

| **Below Level** Provide students with pattern blocks to trace and manipulate to draw the three types of transformations. Emphasize the terms slides, flips, and turns instead of translations, reflections, and rotations. | **Advanced Learners** *Can a transformation appear to be both a reflection and a rotation? Explain giving an example.* Yes, if a figure has symmetry its reflection and rotation can have the same image. | **English Learners** See note on page 417. **Inclusion** See note on page 416. |

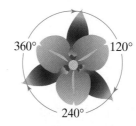

③ **EXAMPLE**   Real-World Problem Solving

Nature Through how many degrees can you rotate the flower so that the image and the original flower match?

The image matches the original flower after rotations of 120°, 240°, and 360°.

360°   120°

240°

✔ **Check Understanding** ③ Tell whether each figure is a rotation of the first shape below.

    a. no   **b.** yes   **c.** no

EXERCISES

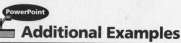 For more practice, see *Extra Practice.*

Ⓐ Practice by Example   **Is the second figure a translation of the first figure?**

Example 1
(page 415)   **1.** no    **2.** yes    **3.** yes

Example 2
(page 416)   **Copy each diagram on graph paper and draw its reflection over the given line of reflection.** 4–9. See margin.

4.   **5.**   **6.**

7.   **8.**   **9.**

Example 3
(page 417)   **Tell whether each figure is a rotation of the shape at the left.**

   **10.** no   **11.** no   **12.** yes   **13.** yes

4.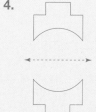

5.

6.

7–9. See back of book.

Teaching Tip
Review angle measures by relating 90° to a right angle and 180° to a straight angle.

③ **EXAMPLE** Tactile Learners
For Check Understanding 3, have students trace the figure. Then have students rotate their traced figure to see if any of three images match.

Technology Tip
Students can use geometry software to draw figures and perform translations, reflections, and rotations on them.

English Learners
Use plain language to help students distinguish between *flips* and *rotations*. Relate a flip over a line of symmetry to a flipped coin, which shows its two sides. Relate a rotation to a rolling coin that shows only one side.

PowerPoint
Additional Examples

① Is the second figure a translation of the first? yes

② Copy each figure and draw its reflection over the given line of reflection.
a. **b.**

③ Tell whether each figure is a rotation of the shape at the right.
a.  **b.** **c.**
yes   no   no

Closure

• *How do you identify a translation?* Sample: Translations move every point of a figure the same distance in the same direction.
• *How do you identify a reflection?* Sample: Reflections flip a figure over a line of reflection.
• *How do you identify a rotation?* Sample: Rotations turn a figure about a fixed point.

417

3. Practice

Assignment Guide

1 Objective 1
Ⓐ Ⓑ Core 1–9, 15, 17–19, 21–22, 24–25

2 Objective 2
Ⓐ Ⓑ Core 10–14, 16, 20, 23, 26
Ⓒ Extension 27–30

Test Prep 31–34
Mixed Review 35–39

Exercises 20–22 Encourage students to use graph paper to make accurate drawings.

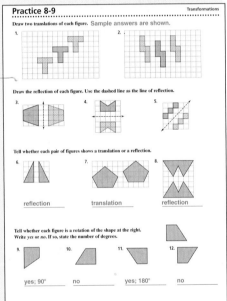

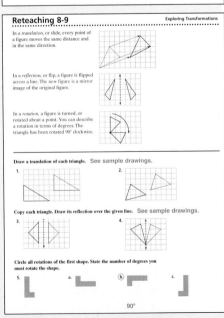

---

14. Through how many degrees can you rotate the figure at the right so that the image is in the same position? List all possibilities less than 360°. 90°, 180°, 270°

Ⓑ **Apply Your Skills**

15. **Writing in Math** Describe how translations and reflections are alike and how they are different. Include examples. **See margin.**

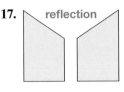

16. **Windmills** Describe the type of transformation the blades of a windmill make. rotation

Real-World 🌐 Connection
Windmills capture the energy of the wind.

Tell whether each pair of figures is a translation or a reflection.

17. reflection   **18.** translation   **19.** reflection

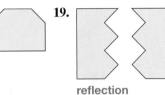

Make three copies of the figure below for Exercises 20–22.
20–22. See left.

20. Draw any 90° clockwise rotation of the figure.

21. Draw a translation of the figure.

22. Draw a line of reflection below the figure. Then draw the reflection of the figure over the line.

23. What clockwise rotation of a figure will produce the same image as a counterclockwise rotation of 180°? 180°
GPS

20.

21.

22.

Copy the figures onto graph paper. Then draw the line of reflection.
24–25. See back of book.

24.   **25.**

26. **Interior Design** Describe a translation of the figure in the fabric.
See below left.

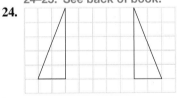

26. Answers may vary. Sample: directly left, directly right, up and slightly to the right

GPS Use the Guided Problem Solving worksheet with Exercise 23.

15. Translations and reflections are alike because the figures stay the same size and shape. They are different because in a translation the object's orientation does not change, while in a reflection its orientation is reversed.

Reflection

Translation

State the least number of degrees you must rotate the figure so the image fits exactly over the given figure.

27. a square 90°

28. a rhombus that is not a square 180°

29. an equilateral triangle 120°

30. Open-Ended Design a pattern that consists of translations, reflections, and rotations of one basic figure. Explain in words how to find each transformation in your design. **Check students' work.**

Test Prep

Multiple Choice

Use the figure at the right for Exercises 31–33.

31. Which choice shows a translation of the figure? B

A.   B.   C.   D.

32. Which choice shows a reflection of the figure over a vertical line? H

F.   G.   H.   I.

Take It to the NET
Online lesson quiz at
www.PHSchool.com
Web Code: aaa-0809

33. Which choice shows a rotation of the figure?

A.   B.   C.   D.   A

Extended Response

34. Draw a parallelogram that is not a rectangle. Show its reflection over a vertical line. Also show its image after a 90° clockwise rotation.
See margin.

Mixed Review

Lesson 6-8

Estimate the sales tax and total cost for each item. The sales tax rate is 8%.

35. a magazine that costs $3.75
$.32, $4.07

36. a snowboard that costs $119
$9.60, $128.60

Lesson 4-6

Solve each equation.

37. $x + 5\frac{2}{9} = 14\frac{1}{3}$ $9\frac{1}{9}$

38. $27\frac{1}{2} = x + 5\frac{3}{4}$ $21\frac{3}{4}$

39. $25 - 17\frac{2}{3} = x$ $7\frac{1}{3}$

34. [4]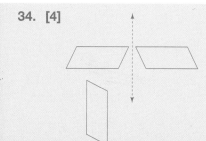

[3] minor error in either transformation

[2] one correct response

[1] incorrect shape with one correct transformation

PowerPoint **Lesson Quiz 8-9**

Identify each transformation as a *translation*, *reflection*, or *rotation*.

1.   **2.**

translation   rotation

3.   **4.**

reflection   reflection

Alternative Assessment

Each student in a pair draws a right triangle and its image when the triangle is rotated three different ways, reflected three different ways, and translated three different ways. Partners exchange papers and identify each image as a translation, reflection, or rotation.

Test Prep

Resources
For additional practice with a variety of test item formats:
• Test Prep, p. 425
• Test-Taking Strategies, p. 421
• Test-Taking Strategies With Transparencies

Enrichment 8-9 Transformations
Visual Thinking

Each grid shows a letter after a transformation. For each letter, describe the type of transformation needed to get the letter in the correct orientation. Use the transformed letters to fill in the blank to the statement below. Sample answers are shown.

When a figure undergoes a transformation, the new figure is the IMAGE of the original figure.

1. The letter is I
Describe the transformation.
The letter has to be rotated clockwise 90°.

2. The letter is M
Describe the transformation.
The letter has to be reflected across the *x*-axis.

3. The letter is A
Describe the transformation.
The letter has to be translated to the origin.

4. The letter is G
Describe the transformation.
The letter has to be rotated counterclockwise 180°.

5. The letter is E
Describe the transformation.
The letter has to be reflected across the *y*-axis.

Tessellations

In this feature, students examine and make arrangements called tessellations.

Optional Materials

- rulers
- scissors
- crayons or color markers
- pattern blocks

Teaching Notes

Teaching Tip

After discussing what a tessellation is, ask students to describe where they have seen them. **mosaic work, floor tiles, jigsaw puzzles, honeycombs, M.C. Escher artworks, etc.**

To prepare students to work with tessellations, draw six congruent right triangles on the board. Ask students to name the shapes they can make by combining them. **Sample: rectangles, parallelograms, trapezoids**

English Learners

Point out to students that tessellate comes from the Latin *tessellare*, which means to pave with *tesserae*, or tiles.

Exercises

Exercises 2–5 Remind students that figures tessellate only if they are congruent and cover a section *completely* without any gaps or overlaps.

A *tessellation* is a pattern of repeated, congruent shapes. It covers a surface without gaps or overlaps. You can make a tessellation using just one figure, or several different figures that fit together. The M. C. Escher tessellation at the right uses three shapes: a bird, a sting ray, and a turtle.

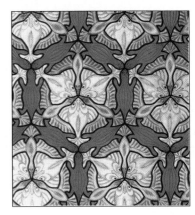

 EXAMPLE

Can you use this one figure to make a tessellation? Use a drawing to explain.

Yes. In the drawing at the right, the figure covers the surface with no gaps or overlaps.

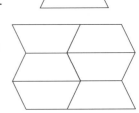

Activity

Make a tessellation.

a. Draw a $1\frac{1}{2}$-inch square and cut it out.

b. Inside the square, draw a trapezoid and a triangle with one side of each shape on the side of the square.

c. Cut out the figures and move each to the opposite side of the square. Tape them in place.

d. Trace the figure repeatedly to make a tessellation.

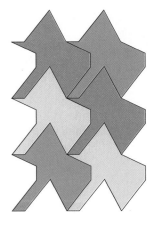

EXERCISES

1. Repeat the Activity using two other shapes inside the square. **Check students' work.**

Does each figure tessellate? Use a drawing to support your answer. 2–5. **Check students' work.**

2. yes

3. yes

4. no

5. yes

Often, you can find a solution to a problem more easily if you draw a diagram to show the information in the problem.

1 EXAMPLE

$\overleftrightarrow{MN}$ and $\overleftrightarrow{RS}$ intersect at point W. List two pairs of vertical angles.

Step 1 Draw a diagram of the intersecting lines to visualize the information.

Step 2 List the pairs of vertical angles in your diagram.

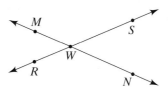

$\angle MWS$ and $\angle RWN$ form vertical angles.
$\angle RWM$ and $\angle NWS$ form vertical angles.

2 EXAMPLE

Rectangle A and rectangle B share an edge of 16 inches. The shorter side of rectangle A is 8 inches. The longer side of rectangle B is 34 inches. Are the two rectangles similar?

Step 1 Draw a diagram of the two rectangles to visualize the information.

Step 2 Use a proportion to determine whether the rectangles are similar.

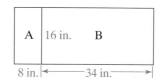

Shorter side of A → $\quad \dfrac{8}{16} \overset{?}{=} \dfrac{16}{34}$ ← Shorter side of B
Longer side of A → $\quad$ ← Longer side of B

$$\dfrac{8}{16} \neq \dfrac{8}{17}$$

The sides are not proportional, so the two rectangles are not similar.

EXERCISES

Draw a diagram to solve each problem.

1. $\overleftrightarrow{AF}$ and $\overleftrightarrow{DT}$ intersect at K. List two pairs of adjacent angles.
Answers may vary. Sample: $\angle AKT$ and $\angle TKF$; $\angle DKF$ and $\angle FKT$

2. a. How many different types of quadrilaterals can two congruent isosceles right triangles form if they share a side? **2**

b. Name these quadrilaterals. **square, parallelogram**

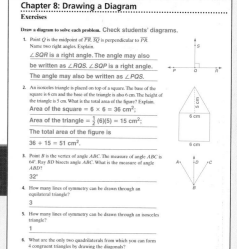
421

Resources

Student Edition
Extra Practice, Ch. 8, p. 649
English/Spanish Glossary, p. 669
Table of Symbols, p. 666

 Reaching All Students
Reading and Math Literacy 8D
Spanish Reading and Math
Literacy 8D

PRENTICE HALL
ASSESSMENT SYSTEM

Test Preparation
• Chapter 8 practice in test
formats

www.PHSchool.com
Student Site
• Self-grading vocabulary test

PH SuccessNet Teacher Center
• Resources

Plus **i TEXT**

Vocabulary

acute angle (p. 380)	line of reflection (p. 416)	right triangle (p. 392)
acute triangle (p. 392)	line of symmetry (p. 410)	rotation (p. 416)
angle (p. 379)	line symmetry (p. 410)	scalene triangle (p. 393)
center of rotation (p. 416)	obtuse angle (p. 380)	segment (p. 373)
collinear (p. 374)	obtuse triangle (p. 392)	similar figures (p. 406)
complementary angles (p. 386)	parallel lines (p. 374)	skew lines (p. 374)
congruent angles (p. 387)	parallelogram (p. 398)	square (p. 398)
congruent figures (p. 405)	perpendicular lines (p. 380)	straight angle (p. 380)
congruent segments (p. 393)	plane (p. 374)	supplementary angles (p. 386)
degrees (p. 379)	point (p. 373)	
equilateral triangle (p. 393)	polygon (p. 397)	translation (p. 415)
exterior angles (p. 387)	quadrilateral (p. 398)	transversal (p. 387)
image (p. 415)	ray (p. 373)	trapezoid (p. 398)
interior angles (p. 387)	rectangle (p. 398)	vertex (p. 379)
intersecting lines (p. 374)	reflection (p. 416)	vertical angles (p. 387)
isosceles triangle (p. 393)	rhombus (p. 398)	
line (p. 373)	right angle (p. 380)	

Reading Math:
Understanding Vocabulary

Choose the correct term to complete each sentence.

1. The measure of an (acute, obtuse) angle is between 90° and 180°.
   obtuse

2. An (isosceles, equilateral) triangle has three congruent sides.
   equilateral

Take It to the NET
Online vocabulary quiz
at **www.PHSchool.com**
Web Code: aaj-0851

3. Lines that intersect to form right angles are (skew, perpendicular).
   perpendicular

4. A (rectangle, rhombus) always has four right angles.
   rectangle

5. A (ray, line) extends in two opposite directions without end.
   line

Skills and Concepts

8-1 Objectives

▼ To name points, lines, segments, and rays

▼ To identify parallel, intersecting, and skew lines

A **point** has no size, only location. A **line** continues without end in opposite directions. A **segment** is part of a line and has two endpoints. A **ray** is part of a line and has one endpoint.

If a line can be drawn through a set of points, the points are **collinear.** **Parallel lines** are lines in the same plane that do not intersect. **Skew lines** lie in different planes. 6–8. Answers may vary. Samples are given.

6. Name three collinear points.
   Sample: *A; B; C*

7. Name two parallel lines.
   Sample: $\overleftrightarrow{EF}$ and $\overleftrightarrow{AB}$

8. Name two rays with endpoint B.
   Sample: $\overrightarrow{BC}$, $\overrightarrow{BA}$

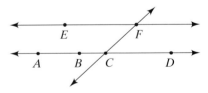

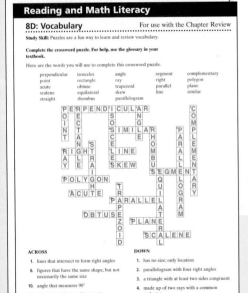

Spanish Reading and Math Literacy

Reading and Math Literacy

8D: Vocabulary For use with the Chapter Review
Study Skill: Puzzles are a fun way to learn and review vocabulary.

Complete the crossword puzzle. For help, use the glossary in your textbook.

Here are the words you will use to complete this crossword puzzle.

perpendicular	isosceles	angle	segment	complementary
point	rectangle	ray	right	polygon
acute	obtuse	trapezoid	parallel	plane
scalene	equilateral	skew	line	similar
straight	rhombus	parallelogram		

ACROSS
1. lines that intersect to form right angles
6. figures that have the same shape, but not necessarily the same size
10. angle that measures 90°
11. continues without end in opposite directions
12. lines that lie in different planes

DOWN
1. has no size; only location
2. parallelogram with four right angles
3. a triangle with at least two sides congruent
4. made up of two rays with a common endpoint
5. two angles, the sum of whose measure is 90°
7. parallelogram with four congruent sides

8-2 and 8-3 Objectives

▼ To measure and classify angles

▼ To find complements and supplements

▼ To identify special pairs of angles

Two rays with a common endpoint form an **angle.** Angles are classified as **acute, right, obtuse,** or **straight. Congruent angles** have the same measure.

Two intersecting lines form two pairs of **vertical angles.** The sum of the measures of two **complementary angles** is 90°. The sum of the measures of two **supplementary angles** is 180°.

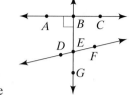

Name each of the following.
9–12. Answers may vary. Samples are given.

9. a pair of vertical angles
∠*DEG* and ∠*BEF*

10. a transversal
$\overleftrightarrow{BE}$

11. two congruent angles
∠*ABE* and ∠*EBC*

12. an acute angle
∠*DEG*

8-4 and 8-5 Objectives

▼ To classify triangles by their angles

▼ To classify triangles by their sides

▼ To identify polygons

▼ To classify quadrilaterals

You can classify a triangle by its angles as **acute, obtuse,** or **right.** You can classify a triangle by its sides as **scalene, isosceles,** or **equilateral.**

Polygons with four sides are called **quadrilaterals.** Three special types of **parallelograms** are the **rhombus, rectangle,** and **square.**

Give the best name for each polygon.

13.

rectangle

14.

hexagon

15.

pentagon

8-6 Objective

▼ To solve problems using logical reasoning

You can *use logical reasoning* when you are given a series of clues to solve a problem.

16. Of 26 students, 3 read *The Yearling* and *Where the Red Fern Grows*, 11 students read only the first book, and 7 students read neither book. How many students read only the second book? **5 students**

8-7, 8-8, and 8-9 Objectives

▼ To identify congruent figures

▼ To identify similar figures

▼ To find lines of symmetry

▼ To identify and draw translations and reflections

▼ To identify rotations

Congruent figures have the same size and shape. **Similar** figures have the same shape, but not necessarily the same size. **Translations, reflections,** and **rotations** are transformations that change the position of a figure.

Do the triangles appear to be congruent or similar?

17.
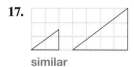
similar

18.
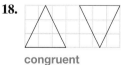
congruent

19. Draw a translation and a reflection of the figure shown. **See margin.**

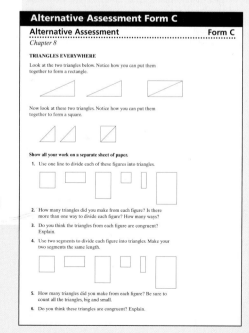

19. Answers may vary. Sample:

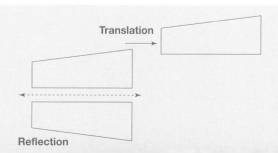

Translation

Reflection

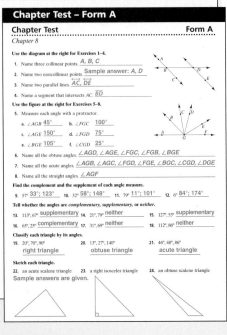

1. Draw three noncollinear points. Label them
X, Y, and Z. Draw $\overleftrightarrow{XY}$ and $\overrightarrow{YZ}$.
See margin.

**Measure each angle. Then classify it as *acute,
right, obtuse,* or *straight*.**

2. ▲ right

3. acute

4. obtuse

5. obtuse

**Find the complement and supplement of each
angle measure.**

6. 72° 18°, 108°

7. 42° 48°, 138°

Classify each triangle as *acute, right,* or *obtuse*.

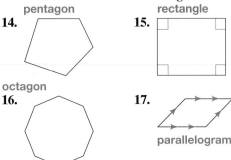

8. 27° 41° 112° obtuse

9. 55° 35° right

**Classify each triangle as *scalene, isosceles,* or
equilateral.**

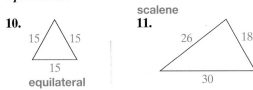

10. 15 15 15 equilateral

11. scalene 26 18 30

12. Draw a quadrilateral with the given number
of lines of symmetry.
a. 0   **b.** 1   **c.** 2   **d.** 4
Check students' work.

13. **Pizza** Who ate the pizza? Al says, "I didn't.
Neither did Bob." Bob says, "Cathie ate it.
Al didn't." Cathie says, "I didn't eat it. Bob
did!" If the person who ate the pizza lied,
and the others told the truth, then who ate
the pizza? Explain. **See margin.**

Write the best name for each figure.

pentagon
14.

rectangle
15.

octagon
16.

17.
parallelogram

18. **Writing in Math** Describe how congruent
figures and similar figures are alike and how
they are different. **See margin.**

**How many lines of symmetry does each
quadrilateral have?**

19. 1

20. 2

Use the shape below for Exercises 21–22.

21. Draw a translation of the shape.
See margin.

22. Draw a reflection of the shape. Show the line
of reflection. **See margin.**

13. Cathie. Answers may
vary. Sample: If Cathie
lied, then she did and
Bob didn't. Bob tells the
truth saying Cathie ate it
and not Al. Al tells the
truth in saying neither he
nor Al ate the pizza.

18. Congruent and similar
figures both have the
same shape. Congruent
figures are also the same
size.

21.

22.
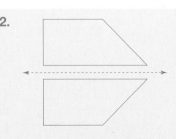

Test Prep

Multiple Choice

Choose the best answer.

1. What information does the circle graph below NOT tell you about Jen? **C**

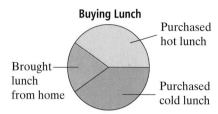

Buying Lunch

Purchased hot lunch

Brought lunch from home

Purchased cold lunch

A. Jen purchased lunch more often than she brought it from home.

B. Jen purchased hot lunches about as often as cold lunches.

C. Jen brought lunch from home more often than she purchased cold lunch.

D. Jen purchased hot lunch more often than she brought lunch from home.

2. A hot air balloon is 2,250 feet in the air. It is scheduled to land at 3:30 P.M. It descends 90 feet every minute. When should the balloonist start descending? **G**
   F. 3:55 P.M.   G. 3:05 P.M.
   H. 2:55 P.M.   I. 2:45 P.M.

3. In order to conclude that *MNOP* is a rhombus, what do you need to know? **D**
   A. $\overline{MO}$ is perpendicular to $\overline{NP}$.
   B. $\overline{MO}$ has length 8.
   C. $\overline{NP}$ and $\overline{MO}$ are congruent.
   D. $\overline{MP}$ and $\overline{PO}$ each have length 8.

4. Which set of decimals is ordered from least to greatest? **G**
   F. 0.2, 0.02, 0.22   G. 0.15, 0.51, 1.05
   H. 0.24, 0.3, 0.05   I. 0.49, 0.4, 0.05

5. The Amazon River in South America carries one sixth of Earth's water that flows into oceans. About what percent is this? **A**
   A. 17%   B. 12.5%   C. 10%   D. 6%

6. Which is ordered from least to greatest? **H**
   F. $\frac{3}{7}, \frac{5}{7}, \frac{7}{11}$ G. $\frac{1}{4}, \frac{1}{2}, \frac{2}{5}$
   H. $\frac{1}{3}, \frac{2}{3}, \frac{4}{5}$ I. $\frac{1}{8}, \frac{2}{5}, \frac{3}{10}$

Gridded Response

7. $31.2 \times \blacksquare = 0.0312$. What is $\blacksquare$?   **0.001**

8. What is the value of $3 + 4 \times 2^3$?   **35**

9. What is the degree measurement of a supplement of a 32° angle?   **148**

10. The greatest angle in a right triangle measures __?__ degrees.   **90**

Short Response

11. Which of the mean, median, mode, or range is the greatest for these data? Explain.
    81, 70, 95, 73, 74, 91, 86, 74
    See margin.

12. a. Bagels cost $6 per dozen. Find the cost of 5 bagels. Use a proportion.   **a–b. See back of book.**
    b. Find the unit cost for a bagel.

Extended Response

13. Could the two triangles below be similar? Explain.   **See margin.**

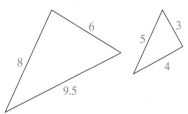

Item	1	2	3	4	5	6	7	8	9	10	11	12	13
Lesson	7-5	2-4	8-5	1-3	6-6	3-7	1-8	2-8	8-3	8-4	7-1	6-4	8-7

11. [2] mean. mean: 80.5, median: 77.5, mode: 74, range: 25 OR a correct explanation including   mean, median, mode, and range

    [1] correct values for 3 of the 4 terms

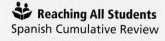
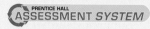

13. [4] No, the ratio of the smallest sides is $\frac{3}{6}$; the ratio of the longest sides is $\frac{5}{9.5}$. These ratios do not form a proportion, so the corresponding sides are not proportional.

    [3] correct answer, but incomplete explanation

    [2] correct answer, but no explanation

    [1] incorrect answer with explanation based on sides with measures 6, 8 and 3, 4

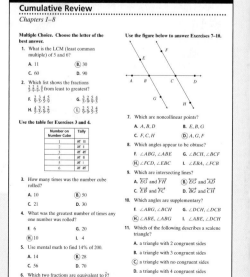

Cumulative Review

425

Building Outside the Box

Students will use data from these two pages to answer the questions posed here in Put It All Together.

Activating Prior Knowledge

Guide students to understand that a blueprint is a scale drawing and is essential to architects and builders. Ask students to share any experiences they have had examining blueprints.

Teaching Notes

Have volunteers read aloud the information about blueprints. If possible, provide students with copies of floor plans from the real estate section of the newspaper or from brochures. Discuss what the drawings do and do not show. Then ask students to describe what a blueprint of your classroom would show.

Career Connection

Discuss with students that modern architects can be creative and experimental in their designs but they must be careful and thorough in their engineering and construction plans. If you can, have an architect or landscape architect visit the class to answer students' questions about their fields.

Architecture Connection

Invite interested students to choose a famous architect and learn more about his or her work. Possible names include: Frank Lloyd Wright, Antonio Gaudi, Frank Geary, I. M. Pei, Phillip Johnson, Frederick Law Olmstead, Rem Koolhaas, Zaha Hadid, and Julia Morgan.

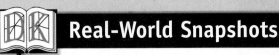
Building Outside the Box

Applying Geometry Before your home was built, it was probably drawn as a two-dimensional plan, or blueprint. A blueprint lets an architect experiment on paper with different ideas. The architect can discuss these ideas with the owner before construction begins. A blueprint also gives clear directions to a contractor on what to build. Most houses and apartments are rectangles with rectangular rooms, but they can be any shape.

Using a Blueprint

Builders read blueprints and translate the two-dimensional notes into three-dimensional buildings. A builder refers to a blueprint many times a day during the building process.

Reading a Blueprint

A blueprint shows the layout of individual floors of your home in $\frac{1}{4}$-inch to 1-foot scale. It includes the dimensions of each room and closet and provides a key so you know what various symbols mean.

1a. trapezoid

b. kitchen - hexagon
bedroom - trapezoid
computer & games room - parallelogram
bathroom - triangle
family room - pentagon

2. Answers may vary.
Sample:
Bedrooms
Bathrooms
Kitchen
TV room
Computer room
porch
living room

4. Check students' work.

5. Rooms with angles less or greater than 90° make it difficult to create wide spaces; the rectangular shape is very efficient.

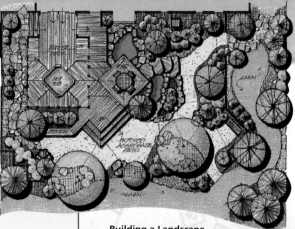

Put It All Together

Materials ruler

1. The blueprint shows a home where no room is rectangular.
   a. What shape is the home?
   b. Identify the shape of each room.

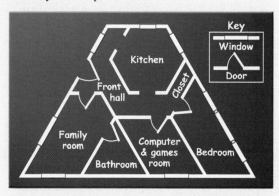

2. **Open-Ended** Suppose you are designing your own home. Make a list of the rooms you would like to include. Feel free to include rooms for hobbies or other special interests.

3. Make a rough sketch of the home, showing the shape and location of each room.
   • Use at least five different shapes from this chapter.
   • Include at least two rooms that are congruent to each other. Make one a translation or rotation of the other.
   • Remember to include hallways and doorways so that people can get into the rooms!

4. Use a ruler to make a final drawing of your design. Show windows and doors using the key in the blueprint. Label the rooms. Add furniture to your drawing if you wish.

5. <u>**Writing in Math**</u> Why do you think homes usually have rectangular rooms?

Take It to the NET For more information about architecture, go to **www.PHSchool.com**.
Web Code: aae-0853

Building a Landscape
Landscape architects use flowers, bushes, and trees to make a pleasing environment around a building.

Help students, as needed, to interpret the blueprint. Guide them, for instance, to understand where the doors and windows are. Then invite comments on the sizes and shapes of the rooms. Ask: *If this were a scale drawing of the floor of a home, what scale might have been used?* Have students use a ruler and work with a partner to choose a sensible scale. Have them defend their choice. **Sample: 1 in. = 20 ft**

Inclusion
Review different shapes and angles with students, as well as the concepts of congruence and transformations. Ask:
• *What can you say about two rooms that are congruent?* **Sample: they are the exact same size and shape**
• *Are there any rooms in your own home that are congruent, or that are translations or rotations of one another?* **Answers will vary.**

Exercise 1 Have students work in pairs. Students should then work independently on Exercises 2–4 but can consult one another.

Exercise 4 Students may have an easier time with this task if they work on graph paper. If you wish students to make their drawings to scale, suggest that they work on centimeter graph paper, using the simple scale of 1 cm = 1 m. Have students present their blueprints. Make sure they identify the shapes that appear in the drawings.

3.

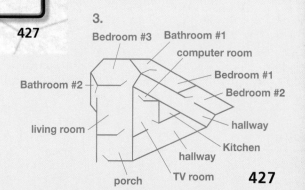

Geometry and Measurement

Chapter at a Glance

9-1
Metric Units of Length, Mass, and Capacity *pp. 431–435*

Objectives
1. Using Metric Units of Length
2. Choosing Units for Mass and Capacity

New Vocabulary
metric system, meter, mass, gram, capacity, liter

Optional Materials
metric ruler

NCTM Standards
1, 4, 6, 7, 8, 9, 10

Local Standards

9-2
Converting Units in the Metric System *pp. 436–439*

Objectives
1. Converting Metric Measurements

NCTM Standards
1, 4, 6, 7, 8, 9, 10

Local Standards

9-3
Perimeters and Areas of Rectangles *pp. 440–445*

Objectives
1. Estimating Areas of Irregular Shapes by Using Squares
2. Finding Perimeters and Areas of Rectangles

New Vocabulary
area, perimeter

NCTM Standards
1, 2, 3, 4, 6, 7, 8, 9, 10

Local Standards

9-4
Areas of Parallelograms and Triangles *pp. 446–450*

Objectives
1. Finding the Areas of Parallelograms and Triangles
2. Finding the Areas of Complex Figures

New Vocabulary
base of a parallelogram, height of a parallelogram, base of a triangle, height of a triangle

NCTM Standards
1, 2, 3, 4, 6, 7, 8, 9, 10

Local Standards

✓ **Checkpoint Quiz 1**

9-5
Circles and Circumference *pp. 452–455*

Objectives
1. Identifying Parts of a Circle
2. Finding Circumference

New Vocabulary
circle, radius, chord, diameter, circumference

NCTM Standards
1, 2, 3, 4, 6, 7, 8, 9, 10

Local Standards

9-6
Area of a Circle *pp. 456–459*

Objectives
1. Finding the Area of a Circle

NCTM Standards
1, 2, 3, 4, 6, 7, 8, 9, 10

Local Standards

9-7
Three-Dimensional Figures and Spatial Reasoning *pp. 462–466*

Objectives
1. Identifying Three-Dimensional Figures

New Vocabulary
three-dimensional figures, faces, prism, cube, pyramid, cylinder, cone, sphere, net

NCTM Standards
1, 3, 6, 7, 8, 9, 10

Local Standards

9-8
Surface Areas of Prisms and Cylinders *pp. 467–471*

Objectives
1. Finding the Surface Area of a Prism
2. Finding the Surface Area of a Cylinder

New Vocabulary
surface area

NCTM Standards
1, 2, 3, 4, 6, 7, 8, 9, 10

Local Standards

9-9
Volumes of Rectangular Prisms and Cylinders *pp. 472–476*

Objectives
1. Finding the Volume of a Rectangular Prism
2. Finding the Volume of a Cylinder

New Vocabulary
volume, cubic unit

NCTM Standards
1, 2, 3, 4, 6, 7, 8, 9, 10

Local Standards

✓ **Checkpoint Quiz 2**

9-10 Problem Solving
Work Backward *pp. 477–480*

Objectives
1. Solving Problems by Working Backward

NCTM Standards
1, 6, 7, 8, 9, 10

Local Standards

Reaching All Students

Additional Instructional Options in Chapter 9

Reading and Math Literacy

Reading Math

Using Concept Maps to Connect Ideas p. 460

Reading Math hints, pp. 441, 452, 458

Reading Comprehension, p. 485

Understanding Vocabulary, p. 482

Writing in Math

Daily Writing Practice, pp. 434, 438, 444, 449, 454, 458, 465, 470, 475, 479, 484

Above Level

C Challenge exercises

pp. 435, 439, 445, 450, 455, 459, 465, 471, 475, 479

Hands-On and Technology

Investigations

Comparing Areas, p. 446

Exploring Circles, p. 451

Views of Three-Dimensional Objects, p. 461

Making Three-Dimensional Figures, p. 464

Activities and Projects

Real-World Snapshots

Applying Measurement pp. 486–487

Chapter Project

Go Fish, p. 640

Test Prep

Daily Test Prep

pp. 435, 439, 445, 450, 455, 459, 466, 471, 475, 479

Test-Taking Strategies

Using Estimation, p. 481

Test Prep

Reading Comprehension, p. 485

Chapter Assessment

Checkpoint Quiz

pp. 450, 476

Chapter Review

pp. 482–483

Chapter Test

p. 484

Pacing Options

This chart suggests pacing only for the core lessons and their parts. It is provided as a possible guide. It will help you determine how much time you have in your schedule to cover the additional features and assessment, as described at the left.

Day	Traditional 45-minute class periods	Block 90-minute class periods
1	9-1 ▽ ▽	9-1 ▽ ▽ 9-2 ▽
2	9-2 ▽	9-3 ▽ ▽
3	9-3 ▽	9-4 ▽ ▽
4	9-3 ▽	9-5 ▽ ▽
5	9-4 ▽	9-6 ▽ 9-7 ▽ ▽
6	9-4 ▽	9-8 ▽ ▽
7	9-5 ▽	9-9 ▽ ▽
8	9-5 ▽	9-10 ▽
9	9-6 ▽	
10	9-7 ▽	
11	9-8 ▽	
12	9-8 ▽	
13	9-9 ▽ ▽	
14	9-10 ▽	

NCTM STANDARDS 2000

1 Number and Operations	6 Problem Solving
2 Algebra	7 Reasoning and Proof
3 Geometry	8 Communication
4 Measurement	9 Connections
5 Data Analysis and Probability	10 Representation

Math Background

Skills Trace

BEFORE Chapter 9
Grade 5 presented metric units of measure and basic perimeter and area calculations.

DURING Chapter 9
Course 1 reviews measurement and extends it to finding the surface area and volume of three-dimensional figures.

AFTER Chapter 9
Throughout this course students apply geometric reasoning and measurement skills to solve real-world problems.

9-1 Metric Units of Length, Mass, and Capacity

Math Understandings
- The metric system uses prefixes to relate the sizes of units to standard units.
- Mass (metric system) refers to the amount of matter in an object and does not vary from place to place. Weight (customary system) refers to the gravitational force exerted by the given amount of substance, and it differs, for example, on Earth and on the Moon.

The **metric system** of measurement is a decimal system. The standard unit of length in the metric system is the **meter (m)**. **Mass** is a measure of the amount of matter in a object. The standard unit of mass is the **gram (g)**. **Capacity** is a measure of the amount of liquid an object holds. The standard unit of capacity is the **liter (L)**.

Common Metric Units With Examples.

Unit	Relationship	Example
kilogram (kg)	1,000 g	mass of 4 videos
gram (g)	1 g	mass of paper clip
milligram (mg)	0.001 g	mass of grain of salt
kiloliter (kL)	1,000 L	water for 2 bathtubs
liter (L)	1 L	a bottle of juice
milliliter (mL)	0.001 L	2 dewdrops

9-2 Converting Units in the Metric System

Math Understandings
- You can rewrite one metric unit as another metric unit within a measurement type (length, capacity, mass) by multiplying or dividing by a power of 10.
- To convert to smaller units, you multiply. To convert to larger units, you divide.

Length	Mass	Capacity
1,000 m = 1 km	1,000 g = 1 kg	1,000 L = 1 kL
100 cm = 1 m		
1,000 mm = 1 m	1,000 mg = 1 g	1,000 mL = 1 L
10 mm = 1 cm		

Example: Convert 236 grams to kilograms.
236 g ÷ 1,000 = 0.236 kg

9-3, 9-4 Perimeters and Areas of Rectangles Areas of Parallelograms and Triangles

Math Understandings
- You can estimate the area of any figure by using a grid and counting the number of squares it covers.
- Perimeters and other linear measures use linear units such as feet and meters. You measure area in square units.
- You can find the area of an irregular figure by separating it into familiar figures, finding the area of each smaller figure, and adding the areas together.

Any side can be considered the **base of a parallelogram**. The **height of a parallelogram** is the perpendicular distance from one base to another. Any side can be the **base of a triangle**. The **height of a triangle** is the length of the perpendicular segment from a vertex to the base opposite that vertex.

Area of a Parallelogram	Area of a Triangle
$A = bh$	$A = \frac{1}{2}bh$

9-5, 9-6 Circles and Circumference / Area of a Circle

Prism **Pyramid** **Cylinder** **Cone** **Sphere**

Math Understandings

- For every circle, the ratio of the circumference, C, to the diameter, d, is the same.
- Although the ratio $\frac{C}{d}$, or π, is not exactly equal to $\frac{22}{7}$ or to 3.14, you can use these numbers as a good approximation of the value of π when you solve problems.

A **circle** is a set of points in a plane, each of which is the same distance from a given point called the *center*. The distance around a circle is its **circumference**.

Circumference of a Circle	Area of a Circle
$C = \pi d = 2\pi r$	$A = \pi r^2$

9-7 Three-Dimensional Figures and Spatial Reasoning

Math Understandings

- A three-dimensional figure has the three dimensions of length, width, and height.
- You name a prism by the shape of its bases. You name a pyramid by the type of base it has.

A **three-dimensional figure** is a figure that does not lie in a plane. A **prism** is a three-dimensional figure with two parallel and congruent faces that are polygons. The prism that has six congruent faces that are squares is a **cube**. A **pyramid** is a three-dimensional figure with one polygon for a base. All of the other faces are triangles. The cylinder, cone and sphere do not use polygons for bases.

9-8, 9-9 Surface Areas of Prisms and Cylinders / Volumes of Rectangular Prisms and Cylinders

Math Understandings

- You can use a net, or pattern that you can fold to form a three-dimensional figure, to find the surface area of a prism.

The **surface area** of a three-dimensional figure is the sum of the areas of its surfaces. The surface area of a rectangular prism is the sum of the areas of the six rectangles in its net. The surface area of a cylinder is the sum of the area of the rectangle and two circles in its net.

The **volume** of a three-dimensional figure is the number of cubic units needed to fill the space inside the figure. The **cubic unit** is the amount of space in a cube that measures 1 unit long by 1 unit wide by 1 unit high.

Volume of a Prism
Volume = Area of Base x height $V = Bh$ 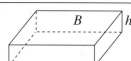

9-10 Work Backwards

Some problems involve a series of steps that lead to a final result. If you are asked to find the initial amount, you can *work backward* from the final result by using inverse operations.

Additional Professional Development Opportunities

Chapter 9 Math Background notes:
pp. 432, 437, 441, 447, 453, 457, 463, 468, 473, 478

SkyLight Professional Development

Additional resources available from SkyLight Professional Development:

On-site courses, workshops, summer institutes. Online courses and chat rooms. Videocassettes and books. Visit www.skylightedu.com.

Ongoing Assessment and Intervention

The *Prentice Hall Mathematics* program provides many options for assessment in the Student Edition, Teacher's Edition, and teaching resources. From these options you may choose instructional materials that are appropriate for your students and that support your district's curriculum requirements.

Daily Assessment

 Instant Check System™ in Chapter 9

Allows students to check their own learning before, during, and after each lesson.

Diagnosing Readiness before the chapter (p. 430)

Check Skills You'll Need exercises in each lesson (pp. 431, 436, 440, 446, 452 456, 462, 467, 472, 477)

Check Understanding questions with each Example (pp. 431, 432, 433, 436, 437, 440, 441, 442, 447, 448, 452, 453, 457, 463, 467, 468, 469, 472, 473, 478)

Checkpoint Quiz (pp. 450, 476)

Formal Assessment

Assessment in the Student Text and in Additional Resources

Assess student progress throughout the Course 1 textbook and with blackline masters and CD-ROM.

Student Edition
- Chapter 9 Review, with Vocabulary, Skills, and Concepts Review, pp. 482–483
- Chapter 9 Test, p. 484

Assessment Resources
- Checkpoint Quizzes 1 & 2
- Chapter Test, forms A & B
- Chapter Alternative Assessment

Spanish versions available.

 Computer Test Generator CD-ROM
- Instant Chapter Tests™—pre-made tests with items that vary every time you print.
- Online Testing allows you to give tests online and receive progress reports.
- Prepare students by making tests based on standardized test objectives.

Algebra Readiness Tests
- Includes Basic Skills Tests and Concept-Readiness Tests.
- Assess understanding of skills and concepts needed for success in algebra.

Intervention

 Skills Intervention Kit

Online Intervention
Integrated within the iText, this online intervention system includes diagnostic tests and prescribed remediation, plus reports to track student mastery.

A *complete* system for the student who is struggling with course-level work

Eight intervention units cover core skills and allow you to:
- **Diagnose** students' gaps in basic skills
- **Prescribe** an individualized course of study
- **Monitor** student progress

Includes print workbooks, tutorial CD-ROM, teacher editions, progress folders, and more. *Available in Spanish.*

How to Use with Chapter 9

9-2	Measurement, Skills 1–2
9-3	Measurement, Skill 8
9-4	Measurement, Skills 9–11
9-5	Measurement, Skill 13
9-6	Measurement, Skill 14
9-7	Geometry, Skill 14
9-8	Measurement, Skills 15–16
9-9	Measurement, Skills 17, 21

Standardized Test Preparation

The *Prentice Hall Mathematics* program integrates preparation for high-stakes standardized tests in every lesson of the Student Edition and continues this support in the Prentice Hall Assessment System.

Test Prep

In Student Text, Chapter 9

Teaches students strategies and gives them practice with all the test item formats they will encounter on high-stakes tests.

Test Prep exercises in each lesson (pp. 435, 439, 445, 450, 455, 459, 466, 471, 475, 479)

Test-Taking Strategies (Using Estimation, p. 481)

Test Prep (Reading Comprehension, p. 485)

A three-step approach to preparing students for high stakes, national, and state exams.

1 Diagnose & Prescribe

Content Diagnostic Tests
- Diagnose strengths and weaknesses with ongoing benchmark tests.
- Prescribe individualized reteaching opportunities.

2 Review & Reteach

Skills and Concepts Review
- Provides reteaching worksheets with instruction and practice for each skill.
- Includes course prerequisite skills.

3 Practice & Assess

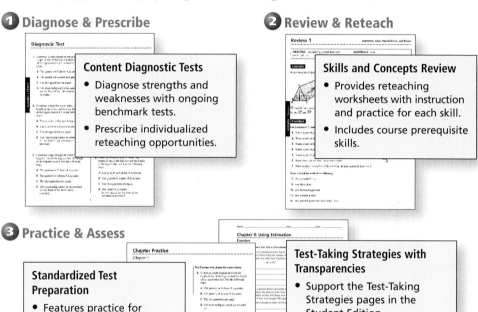

Standardized Test Preparation
- Features practice for national standardized exams.
- Includes practice tests for NAEP, SAT10, ITBS, and Terra Nova.

Test-Taking Strategies with Transparencies
- Support the Test-Taking Strategies pages in the Student Edition.
- Provide a transparency and a worksheet for each strategy.

Correlation to Standardized Tests

Lesson		NAEP	Terra Nova CAT6	CTBS	ITBS	SAT10	Local Test
9-1	Metric Units of Length, Mass, and Capacity	M2c				■	
9-2	Changing Units in the Metric System	M2c					
9-3	Perimeters and Area of Rectangles	M1c	■	■	■	■	
9-4	Areas of Parallelograms and Triangles	M1h	■	■		■	
9-5	Circles and Circumference	M1h					
9-6	Area of a Circle	M1h					
9-7	Three-Dimensional Figures and Spatial Reasoning	G1c, G1e, G1f	■	■		■	
9-8	Surface Areas of Prisms and Cylinders	M1j					
9-9	Volumes of Rectangular Prisms and Cylinders	M1j		■			
9-10	Problem Solving: Work Backward						

NAEP National Assessment of Educational Progress
CAT6/Terra Nova California Achievement Test, 6th Ed.

CTBS/Terra Nova Comprehensive Test of Basic Skills
ITBS Iowa Test of Basic Skills, Form M.

SAT10 Stanford Achievement Test, 10th Ed.

Program Resources

	Resources in Grab & Go™ Files				Resources for Reaching All Students				Spanish Resources			Presentation Assistant Plus! — Transparencies					Prentice Hall Presentation Pro CD-ROM
	Practice	Reteach	Enrich	Checkpt Quiz	Reading & Math Literacy	Technology Activities	Hands-On Activities	Guided Problem Solving	Practice	Reading & Math Literacy	Checkpt Quiz	Skills Check	Problem of the Day	Additional Examples	Answers to Exercises	Lesson Quiz	
9-1	■	■	■		■		■	■	■			■	■	■	■	■	■
9-2	■	■	■				■	■	■			■	■	■	■	■	■
9-3	■	■	■				■	■	■			■	■	■	■	■	■
9-4	■	■	■	■	■		■	■	■	■	■	■	■	■	■	■	■
9-5	■	■	■				■	■	■			■	■	■	■	■	■
9-6	■	■	■				■	■	■			■	■	■	■	■	■
9-7	■	■	■				■	■	■			■	■	■	■	■	■
9-8	■	■	■			■		■	■			■	■	■	■	■	■
9-9	■	■	■	■	■		■	■	■		■	■	■	■	■	■	■
9-10	■	■	■					■	■			■	■	■	■	■	■
For the Chapter	Chapter Projects, Chapter Tests, Alternative Assessment, Cumulative Review, Cumulative Assessment				**On web site only:** Home Activities, Interdisciplinary Activities, Algebra Readiness Puzzles				Spanish Chapter Tests, Alternative Assessment, Cumulative Review, Cumulative Assessment			Classroom Aid Transparencies					

Also available for use with the chapter:

 **PRENTICE HALL ASSESSMENT SYSTEM** *See page 428F.*

- Practice Workbook
- Solution Key
- MathNotes folder

- For teacher support and access to student Web materials, use the Web Code aak-5500.
- For additional online and technology resources, see *below*.

Technology

 iTEXT **Online and on CD-ROM**

Complete Interactive Student Text online and on CD-ROM—with instant feedback assessment, tutorial help, dynamic activities, instructional and real-world videos, audio, and additional practice.

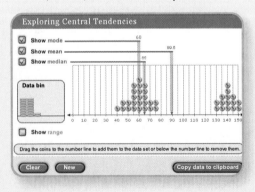

www.PHSchool.com For Students

Use Web codes for easy access to online activities, chapter projects, self-grading lesson quizzes, chapter tests, vocabulary quizzes, updated data sources, graphing calculator procedures, and more.

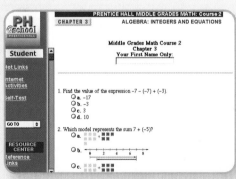

PH SuccessNet **For Teachers**

Online lesson planning with built-in state correlations, all the teaching resources, complete reference library, your own calendar and Teacher Web page, professional development, and more.

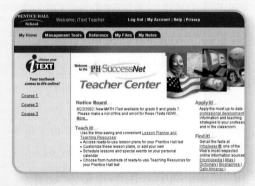

Presentation Assistant Plus!

The *Prentice Hall Presentation Assistant Plus!* provides you with the material you need to teach a lesson from beginning to end. Two easy-to-use formats—Transparencies and PowerPoint®—allow you to present a lesson the way you are most comfortable.

Transparencies

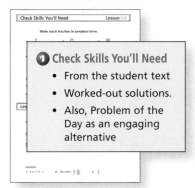

❶ Check Skills You'll Need
- From the student text
- Worked-out solutions.
- Also, Problem of the Day as an engaging alternative

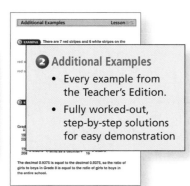

❷ Additional Examples
- Every example from the Teacher's Edition.
- Fully worked-out, step-by-step solutions for easy demonstration

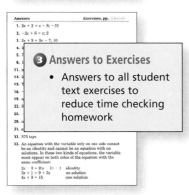

❸ Answers to Exercises
- Answers to all student text exercises to reduce time checking homework

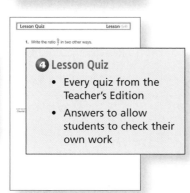

❹ Lesson Quiz
- Every quiz from the Teacher's Edition
- Answers to allow students to check their own work

 PowerPoint Throughout the Teacher's Edition, this symbol indicates material that is available in the Presentation Assistant Plus!

 PowerPoint ## Prentice Hall Presentation Pro CD-ROM

- Includes all Transparencies.
- Conveniently organized by lesson so you can easily ❶ Introduce, ❷ Teach, ❸ Check Homework, and ❹ Assess each lesson.
- Animated examples allow step-by-step instruction at your own pace.
- Easy to edit so you can create custom presentations.

Teaching Chapter 9 Using Presentation Assistant Plus!

	❶ Introduce	❷ Teach	❸ Check Homework	❹ Assess
	Check Skills You'll Need	Additional Examples	Student Edition Answers	Lesson Quiz
9-1	p. 75	p. 117	✔	p. 75
9-2	p. 76	pp. 118–119	✔	p. 76
9-3	p. 77	pp. 120–122	✔	p. 77
9-4	p. 78	pp. 123–124	✔	p. 78
9-5	p. 79	pp. 125–126	✔	p. 79
9-6	p. 80	p. 127	✔	p. 80
9-7	p. 81	p. 128	✔	p. 81
9-8	p. 82	pp. 129–131	✔	p. 82
9-9	p. 83	pp. 132–133	✔	p. 83
9-10	p. 84	p. 134	✔	p. 84

 ### Prentice Hall Presentation Pro

CD-ROM with dynamic PowerPoint® presentations for every lesson. Helps you introduce and develop concepts, check homework, and assess progress. Part of Presentation Assistant Plus! *(See above.)*

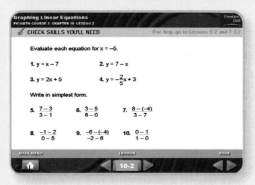

 ### Computer Test Generator

CD-ROM to create practice sheets and tests for course objectives and standardized tests. Includes Instant Chapter Tests™, online testing, and student reports. Part of the PH Assessment System. *(See page 428F.)*

Resource Pro® with Planning Express®

CD-ROM with a lesson planning tool that allows you to import state and local objectives. Includes electronic versions of all the teaching resources.

Chapter Resources

Reading and Math Support

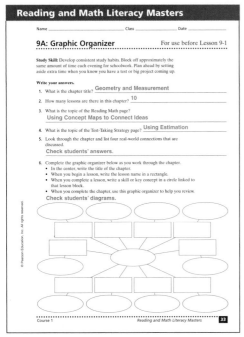

Reading and Math Literacy Masters

9A: Graphic Organizer — For use before Lesson 9-1

Study Skill: Develop consistent study habits. Block off approximately the same amount of time each evening for schoolwork. Plan ahead by setting aside extra time when you know you have a test or big project coming up.

Write your answers.

1. What is the chapter title? Geometry and Measurement
2. How many lessons are there in this chapter? 10
3. What is the topic of the Reading Math page? Using Concept Maps to Connect Ideas
4. What is the topic of the Test-Taking Strategy page? Using Estimation
5. Look through the chapter and list four real-world connections that are discussed. Check students' answers.
6. Complete the graphic organizer below as you work through the chapter.
   - In the center, write the title of the chapter.
   - When you begin a lesson, write the lesson name in a rectangle.
   - When you complete a lesson, write a skill or key concept in a circle linked to that lesson block.
   - When you complete the chapter, use this graphic organizer to help you review.
   Check students' diagrams.

Course 1 — Reading and Math Literacy Masters — 33

Available in Spanish

Reading and Math Literacy Masters

9B: Reading Comprehension — For use after Lesson 9-4

Study Skill: Pay attention in class and when reading so information does not slip out of your "short-term memory."

Read the paragraph below and answer the questions.

Elephants are the largest living land animals. There are two species of elephants, the African and the Asian. Elephants are vegetarians and eat up to 440 pounds of plants per day. They use their tusks to strip bark from trees and their trunks to pull up plants and pick leaves. They drink about 26 gallons of water per day. At birth a baby elephant measures about three feet high and weighs approximately 265 pounds. At six years of age, an elephant can weigh as much as 2,200 pounds. Although an elephant consumes a great deal of food, it has only 6 teeth at a time. When a tooth wears away or falls out, another one grows in its place. During a lifetime, four full sets of teeth are lost.

1. What is the paragraph about? characteristics of elephants
2. What are the two species of elephants? African and Asian
3. If one lb is equal to 0.454 kg, how many kilograms of plants can an elephant eat in one day? 199.76 kg
4. According to the paragraph, how much weight does an elephant gain in the first six years of life? 2,200 − 265 = 1,935 pounds
5. How many teeth can an elephant have in its lifetime? 4 × 6 = 24
6. Which statistic measures a volume? 26 gallons of water
7. How many quarts of water does an elephant drink in one day? 26 gallons × 4 quart/gallon = 104 quarts
8. If one in. is equal to 2.54 cm, how many centimeters tall is a baby elephant when it is born? 91.44 cm
9. How does an elephant get its food? They use their tusks to strip bark from trees and their trunks to pull up plants and pick leaves.

34 — Reading and Math Literacy Masters — Course 1

Available in Spanish

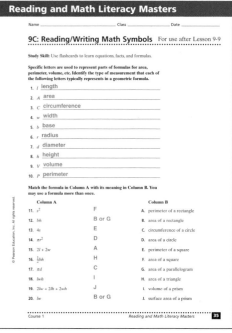

Reading and Math Literacy Masters

9C: Reading/Writing Math Symbols — For use after Lesson 9-9

Study Skill: Use flashcards to learn equations, facts, and formulas.

Specific letters are used to represent parts of formulas for area, perimeter, volume, etc. Identify the type of measurement that each of the following letters typically represents in a geometric formula.

1. l — length
2. A — area
3. C — circumference
4. w — width
5. b — base
6. r — radius
7. d — diameter
8. h — height
9. V — volume
10. P — perimeter

Match the formula in Column A with its meaning in Column B. You may use a formula more than once.

	Column A		Column B
11.	s^2	F	A. perimeter of a rectangle
12.	bh	B or G	B. area of a rectangle
13.	$4s$	E	C. circumference of a circle
14.	πr^2	D	D. area of a circle
15.	$2l + 2w$	A	E. perimeter of a square
16.	$\frac{1}{2}bh$	H	F. area of a square
17.	πd	C	G. area of a parallelogram
18.	lwh	I	H. area of a triangle
19.	$2lw + 2lh + 2wh$	J	I. volume of a prism
20.	lw	B or G	J. surface area of a prism

Course 1 — Reading and Math Literacy Masters — 35

Available in Spanish

Problem Solving

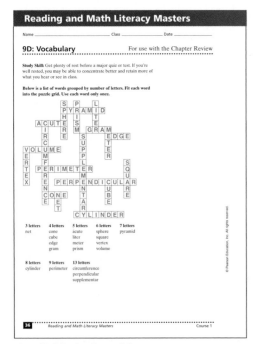

Reading and Math Literacy Masters

9D: Vocabulary — For use with the Chapter Review

Study Skill: Get plenty of rest before a major quiz or test. If you're well rested, you will be able to concentrate better and retain more of what you hear or see in class.

Below is a list of words grouped by number of letters. Fit each word into the puzzle grid. Use each word only once.

3 letters	4 letters	5 letters	6 letters	7 letters
net	cone	acute	sphere	pyramid
	cube	liter	square	
	edge	meter	vertex	
	gram	prism	volume	

8 letters	9 letters	13 letters
cylinder	perimeter	circumference
		perpendicular
		supplementar

36 — Reading and Math Literacy Masters — Course 1

Available in Spanish

Guided Problem Solving Masters

9-1 • Guided Problem Solving

Student Page 434, Exercise 40:

Estimation The width of a door is about 1 meter. How can you estimate the length of a wall that contains the door?

Read and Understand

1. What are you being asked to do? Estimate the length of the wall.

Plan and Solve

2. How wide is the door? about 1 m
3. How can you use the width of the door to estimate the length of the wall?
   Method 1: Estimate how many doors would fit along the wall. Then multiply that value by 1 m.
   Method 2: Use a piece of string whose width matches the width of the door. See how many times you can lay the string end-to-end from one end of the wall to the other end.

Look Back and Check

4. What would be an approximate length of a wall in terms of the width of the door if about 6 doors would fit along the length of the wall? 6 m

Solve Another Problem

5. The height of a window is approximately 3 feet. How can you estimate the height of a wall that contains the window? Compare the height of the window with the height of the wall. Estimate how many windows would fit on the wall. Multiply this value by 3.

Course 1 — Guided Problem Solving — 71

Guided Problem Solving Masters

9-2 • Guided Problem Solving

Student Page 438, Exercise 23:

Physics Light travels at approximately 299,792,458 meters per second. Approximately how many kilometers does light travel in one second?

Read and Understand

1. What are you being asked to do? Find the number of kilometers light travels in one second.
2. Which is larger, a meter or a kilometer? a kilometer

Plan and Solve

3. How many meters does light travel in one second? 299,792,458 m
4. Will the number of kilometers light travels in one second be bigger or smaller than the answer in Step 3? smaller
5. What number do you divide meters by to get kilometers? 1,000
6. Divide the answer in Step 3 by the answer in Step 5. 299,732.458
7. Approximately how many kilometers does light travel in one second? 299,732 km

Look Back and Check

8. How can you check your answer? Multiply your answer by 1,000.

Solve Another Problem

9. A boulder weighs 44,320 grams. Approximately how many kilograms does the boulder weigh? 44,320 ÷ 1,000 ≈ 44; 44 kg

72 — Guided Problem Solving — Course 1

Name _____ Class _____ Date _____

9-3 • Guided Problem Solving

[GPS] **Student Page 444, Exercise 21:**

Stamps The world's smallest stamp, shown at the right, measured 0.31 inch by 0.37 inch. Find the area of the stamp.

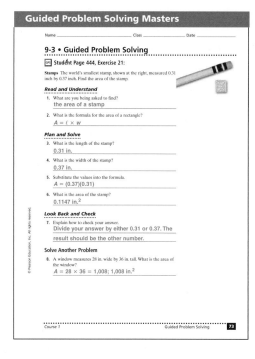

Read and Understand

1. What are you being asked to find?
   the area of a stamp

2. What is the formula for the area of a rectangle?
   $A = \ell \times w$

Plan and Solve

3. What is the length of the stamp?
   0.31 in.

4. What is the width of the stamp?
   0.37 in.

5. Substitute the values into the formula.
   $A = (0.37)(0.31)$

6. What is the area of the stamp?
   0.1147 in.^2

Look Back and Check

7. Explain how to check your answer.
   Divide your answer by either 0.31 or 0.37. The
   result should be the other number.

Solve Another Problem

8. A window measures 28 in. wide by 36 in. tall. What is the area of the window?
   $A = 28 \times 36 = 1,008; 1,008 \text{ in.}^2$

Name _____ Class _____ Date _____

9-4 • Guided Problem Solving

[GPS] **Student Page 449, Exercise 25:**

Algebra A parallelogram has an area of 66 square inches and a base length of 5 inches. What is the height of the parallelogram?

Read and Understand

1. What are you being asked to find?
   the height of a parallelogram

2. What information are you given?
   the area of the parallelogram and the length
   of the base

Plan and Solve

3. Write the formula you will use to find the area of a parallelogram.
   $A = bh$

4. Substitute the values you know into the formula.
   $66 = 5h$

5. What operation do you use to find the height?
   division

6. What is the height of the parallelogram?
   $\frac{66}{5} = 13.2; 13.2$ in.

Look Back and Check

7. Check your answer. Explain your method.
   Sample answers: Multiply the answer by 5. The
   product is 66, so the answer checks.

Solve Another Problem

8. A parallelogram has an area of 96 cm and a height of 4 cm. What is the base length of the parallelogram?
   $A = bh; 96 = 4b; b = 24; 24$ cm

Name _____ Class _____ Date _____

9-5 • Guided Problem Solving

[GPS] **Student Page 454, Exercise 19:**

Hoops A dog trainer uses hoops with diameters of 24 and 30 inches. What is the difference between their circumferences? Use 3 for π.

Read and Understand

1. What do you need to know in order to answer the question?
   the circumference of each hoop

2. How do you find the circumference of a circle when you know the diameter?
   Sample answer: Use the formula $C = \pi d$.

Plan and Solve

3. What is the diameter of each hoop?
   24 in.; 30 in.

4. What is the circumference of the 24 in. hoop?
   $24 \times 3 = 72; 72$ in.

5. What is the circumference of the 30 in. hoop?
   $30 \times 3 = 90; 90$ in.

6. What is the difference between their circumferences?
   $90 - 72 = 18; 18$ in.

Look Back and Check

7. What unit should your final answer have? Why?
   inches; circumference is a length, like
   perimeter.

Solve Another Problem

8. Included in the china Jill and Ed received for their wedding were dinner plates and salad plates. The dinner plates have a diameter of 10 in. and the salad plates have a diameter of 7 in. What is the difference between their circumferences? Use 3 for π.
   $30 \text{ in.} - 21 \text{ in.} = 9; 9$ in.

Name _____ Class _____ Date _____

9-6 • Guided Problem Solving

[GPS] **Student Page 458, Exercise 20:**

Communications You can pick up the radio signal for station WAER FM 88 in Syracuse, New York, within a 45-mile radius of the station. What is the approximate area of the broadcast region? Use 3.14 for π.

Read and Understand

1. What are you being asked to find?
   the area of the broadcast region

2. Write the formula you use to find the area of a circle.
   $A = \pi r^2$

Plan and Solve

3. What is the radius of the broadcast area?
   45 miles

4. Substitute the values into the area formula.
   $A = (3.14)(45)^2$

5. Evaluate the formula to find the area of the broadcast region to the nearest square mile.
   $A = 6,358$ square miles

Look Back and Check

6. Use a radius of 50 and 3 for π to estimate the area. Then use a radius of 40 and 3 for π to estimate the area. Is your answer reasonable? Why?
   The answer is reasonable because 6,358
   square miles is between the estimates of 4,800
   square miles and 7,500 square miles.

Solve Another Problem

7. The lead investigator in a search for a boat tells the coastguard to search everywhere within 5 miles of the last known location of the boat. What is the area of search region? Use 3.14 for π.
   $A = (3.14)(5)^2 = 78.5$; the area of the search
   region is 78.5 square miles.

Name _____ Class _____ Date _____

9-7 • Guided Problem Solving

[GPS] **Student Page 465, Exercise 24:**

Name the figure. Then find the number of faces, vertices, and edges in the figure.

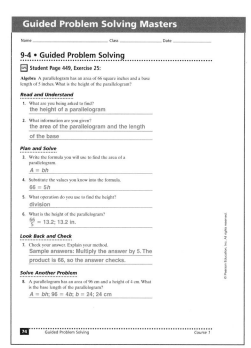

Read and Understand

1. What is a face?
   A face is a plane on a prism.

2. What is a vertex?
   A vertex is a point where two or three
   edges intersect.

3. What is an edge?
   An edge is a line formed by the intersection of
   two faces.

Plan and Solve

4. How many bases does the figure have? 2 bases
5. Does this make the figure a pyramid or a prism? prism
6. What is the shape of the bases? trapezoid
7. Name the figure. trapezoidal prism
8. How many faces are there total? 6 faces
9. How many vertices are there? 8 vertices
10. How many edges are there? 12 edges

Look Back and Check

11. How do you know the figure is not a pyramid?
    It has two bases.

Solve Another Problem

12. Name the figure. Then find the number of faces, vertices, and edges in the figure.
    trapezoidal pyramid; 5 faces; 5 vertices; 8
    edges

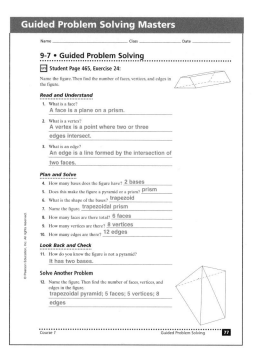

Name _____ Class _____ Date _____

9-8 • Guided Problem Solving

[GPS] **Student Page 470, Exercise 15:**

Writing in Math Suppose each dimension of a rectangular prism is doubled. How is the surface area affected?

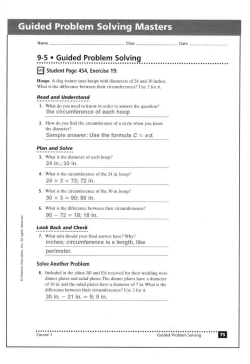

Read and Understand

1. Write the formula used to find the surface area of a rectangular prism.
   $SA = 2(\ell \times w) + 2(w \times h) + 2(\ell \times h)$

2. To double a number means to multiply that number by what value?
   two

Plan and Solve

3. Multiply each dimension by 2 and substitute it into the surface area formula from Step 1.
   $SA = 2(2\ell \times 2w) + 2(2w \times 2h) + 2(2\ell \times 2h)$

4. Simplify the formula.
   $SA = 8(\ell \times w) + 8(w \times h) + 8(\ell \times h)$

5. Instead of multiplying the area of each face by 2, multiply by what number?
   8

6. How is the surface area affected when each dimension is doubled?
   The surface area is quadrupled.

Look Back and Check

7. Explain another way to solve this problem.
   Think of each face separately. Double each
   dimension. Then, calculate the surface area.

Solve Another Problem

8. Suppose each dimension of a rectangular prism is tripled. How is the surface area affected?
   The surface area is 9 times greater.

Activities and Projects

Name _____ Class _____ Date _____

9-9 • Guided Problem Solving

GPS Student Page 475, Exercise 16:

Trucks A rectangular truck bed has a (length of 20 feet), a (width of 8 feet), and a (height of 7 feet). A cylindrical truck tank has (a radius of 3.5 feet) and a (length of 22 feet). Find each (volume). Use 3.14 for π.

Read and Understand

1. Circle the information you will need to solve the problem.

2. Write the formula used to find the volume of a rectangular solid and of a cylinder.
   Rectangular solid, $V = \ell \times w \times h$; cylinder,
   $V = \pi \times r^2 \times h$

Plan and Solve

3. Substitute the values for the length, width, and height into the formula for the volume of a rectangular solid. What is the volume?
   1,120 cubic feet

4. Substitute the values for the radius and length into the formula for the volume of a cylinder. What is the volume? Use 3.14 for π.
   846.23 cubic feet

5. What are the units for the volume of a solid?
   cubic units

Look Back and Check

6. How can you check your answer?
   Sample answer: Round the measurements and let π = 3. Use mental math to estimate each volume. Check your answer for reasonableness.

Solve Another Problem

7. A silo is 32 feet tall and has a diameter of 12 feet. What is the volume of the silo? Use 3.14 for π.
   3,617.28 cubic feet

Name _____ Class _____ Date _____

9-10 • Guided Problem Solving

GPS Student Page 478, Exercise 4:

Entertainment At the Plex Cinema, every 15th customer gets a free ticket. Every 10th customer gets free popcorn. Of 418 ticket buyers, how many received both prizes?

Read and Understand

1. What are you being asked to find?
   the number of customers who received both the free ticket and the free popcorn

2. Which two problem solving strategies should you use to help you to solve this problem?
   Sample answer: Solve a simpler problem and look for a pattern.

Plan and Solve

3. Find the common multiples of 10 and 15 between 1 and 100. Out of the first 100 customers, how many people won both prizes?
   3 people

4. How many people out of 299 people did won both prizes? **9 people**

5. Is 300 divisible by both 10 and 15? **yes**

6. How many people out of 418 people are there who won both prizes ? **13 people**

Look Back and Check

7. Is your answer reasonable? Explain.
   Yes; 10 and 15 have 13 common multiples between 1 and 418.

Solve Another Problem

8. Lara is working a double shift at the hospital. Every 30 minutes she drinks a glass of milk, and every 45 minutes she eats some grapes. If her shift is 15 hours long, how many times did she have both a glass of milk and some grapes?
   10 times; see Answers.

Name _____ Class _____ Date _____

Activity 8: Area and Perimeter Patterns

Materials needed: graph paper

The tables below give the formula for area and perimeter for several rectangles. Draw each rectangle on graph paper. Then copy and complete the tables by finding the area and perimeter of each rectangle. Look for patterns to fill in missing information. Use this information to answer the questions about patterns.

RECTANGLE	AREA (A) = $l \times w$	PERIMETER = $2(l + w)$
Rectangle 1	4 × 1 =	2(4 + 1) =
Rectangle 2	4 × 2 =	2(4 + 2) =
Rectangle 3		2(4 + 3) =
Rectangle 4	4 × 4 =	

1. Describe the pattern you see in
   a. the lengths and widths of the rectangles.
   b. the areas of the rectangles.
   c. the perimeters of the rectangles.

2. Creating a line graph is a good way of discovering a pattern. Make a double-line graph showing area and perimeter for Rectangles 1–4. Use the graph to answer these questions:
   a. Which pattern of numbers is increasing the most, those for area or those for perimeter?
   b. Extend the lines on the graph. If the table was extended to include more rectangles, what would their area and perimeter measure?
   c. Add two rows to the tables above, and continue the pattern.
   d. What happens to the lines for area and perimeter on the graph?
   e. Does your graph support your conclusion in Step 1?

3. Calculate the area and perimeter for a 2 × 2 rectangle and a 3 × 3 rectangle. Do the values fit the pattern in Step 1? Explain.

Sample pages; see p. G for complete list.

Name _____ Class _____ Date _____

Activity 30: Metric Conversions

Materials needed: both metric and U.S. customary scales, rulers, and measuring containers

Work in pairs.

CONVERSION CHART

From U.S. Customary to Metric			From Metric to U.S. Customary		
If you know	Multiply by	To find:	If you know	multiply by	to find
inches	2.54	centimeters	centimeters	0.39	inches
inches	25.4	millimeters	millimeters	0.04	inches
feet	0.305	meters (m)	meters	3.28	feet
feet	30.48	centimeters	centimeters	0.033	feet
yards	0.91	meters	meters	1.09	yards
ounces	28.35	grams (g)	grams	0.035	ounces
pounds	0.45	kilograms	kilograms	2.21	pounds
fluid ounces	29.57	milliliters	milliliters	0.03	fluid ounces
cups	0.24	liters	liters	4.23	cups
pints	0.47	liters	liters	2.11	pints
quarts	0.95	liters	liters	1.06	quarts
gallons	3.79	liters	liters	0.26	gallons

1. a. Find classroom objects to measure using U.S. customary units.
   b. Use the chart to convert the measurement from U.S. customary to metric.
   c. Check your answer by measuring the same object using the metric measure.

2. a. Find classroom objects to measure using metric units.
   b. Use the chart to convert the measurement from metric to U.S. customary.
   c. Check your answers by measuring the same object using U.S. customary measures.

3. With your partner, make a list of the advantages and disadvantages of using the metric or U.S. customary system of units.

Name _____ Class _____ Date _____

Activity 34: Exploring Rectangular Prisms

Materials needed: scissors, tape, ruler, graph paper

Work in small groups of 3–4 students.

Draw these nets on graph paper. Cut them out and fold them along the inside segments. Tape the edges together to form a solid.

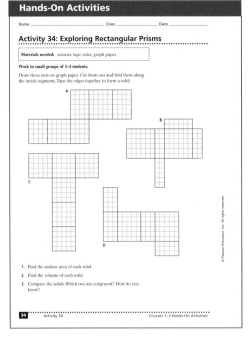

1. Find the surface area of each solid.
2. Find the volume of each solid.
3. Compare the solids. Which two are congruent? How do you know?

Name _____ Class _____ Date _____

Finding Surface Areas of Cylinders   Activity 15

Use your scientific calculator to do this activity.

Example: Find the surface area of the cylinder to the nearest square meter.

① With the calculator, you can find the surface area of a cylinder in one step. Remember, you must find the area of the two circular ends ($2\pi r^2$), and the area of the rectangle that forms the sides ($2\pi rh$).

② Enter [(] 2 [×] 6 [.] 2 8 [x^2] [)]. *Do not press* [ENTER] *yet.* This part of the expression calculates the area of the two circular ends of the cylinder.

③ Next, enter [+] [(] 2 [×] 6 [.] 2 8 [×] 3 2 [)] and then press [ENTER]. The second part of the expression finds the area of the rectangular part of the cylinder. After you press [ENTER], the number 1510.467695 shows on the screen.

Rounded to the nearest square meter, the surface area of the cylinder is 1,510 m².

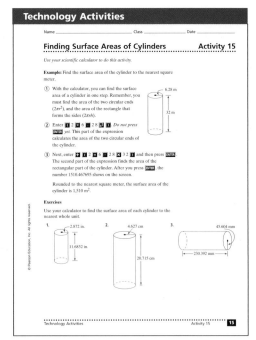

Exercises

Use your calculator to find the surface area of each cylinder to the nearest whole unit.

428K

Name _____ Class _____ Date _____

Chapter 9 Project: Go Fish

Design an Aquarium

Beginning the Chapter Project

Have you ever spent time gazing into an aquarium full of fish? You can get lost in thought as you look through the glass watching the fish. Many people enjoy having an aquarium because they feel peaceful while observing nature in this miniature form.

In this chapter project, you will design an aquarium for your classroom. You should consider how many fish you want in the aquarium. Also consider the size of each type of fish that you plan to place in the aquarium. As part of your final project, you will create a drawing of your proposed aquarium.

Activities

Activity 1: Investigating and Planning   Check students' work.

To begin the project, make a list of the types of fish you might like to have in the aquarium.

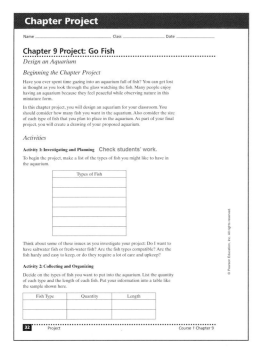

Types of Fish

Think about some of these issues as you investigate your project: Do I want to have saltwater fish or fresh-water fish? Are the fish types compatible? Are the fish hardy and easy to keep, or do they require a lot of care and upkeep?

Activity 2: Collecting and Organizing

Decide on the types of fish you want to put into the aquarium. List the quantity of each type and the length of each fish. Put your information into a table like the sample shown here.

Fish Type	Quantity	Length

Name _____ Class _____ Date _____

Chapter 9 Project: Go Fish (continued)

Activity 3: Calculating

A fish needs at least 20 square inches of water surface on the top of the tank for each inch of body length. Based on the sum of the lengths of all of your fish, find out what the area of the water surface should be in your aquarium. Use this number to figure out a possible length and width for the tank.

Activity 4: Designing

Determine the length, width, and height of your aquarium. Multiply these measurements to find the volume of the aquarium. Measure the length, width, and height of your classroom. Decide if your aquarium will fit comfortably in the classroom or if you will have to make adjustments.

Finishing the Project

Make a drawing of your aquarium. Label each dimension and present the drawing to your class. Include a table showing the types and quantities of fish that will be in the aquarium.

Be sure your work is neat and clear. Show your data and calculations. Write any explanations that you think are necessary.

Reflect and Revise

Ask a classmate to review your project with you. Are your calculations correct? Did you make the correct adjustments? Is your drawing clearly presented? If necessary, make changes to improve your aquarium.

Extending the Project

Research the living environment needed for each type of pet, such as a gerbil, a rabbit, a snake, etc. Find out how much sunlight, water, and food the pet needs. Design a living arrangement that would best house one of these pets. Explain how your design would change if you had two of that same type of pets sharing the same living space.

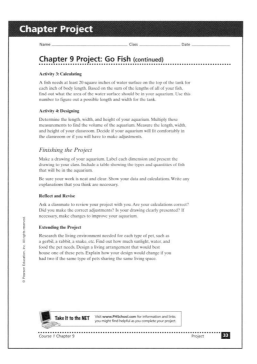 **Take It to the NET** Visit www.PHSchool.com for information and links you might find helpful as you complete your project.

Name _____ Class _____ Date _____

Chapter Project Manager

Chapter 9: Go Fish

Getting Started

Read about the project. As you work on it, you will need several sheets of paper. You may also use a spreadsheet program if one is available. Keep all your work for the project in a folder, along with this Project Manager.

Checklist

☐ Activity 1: investigating and planning
☐ Activity 2: collecting and organizing
☐ Activity 3: calculating
☐ Activity 4: designing
☐ Recommendations

Suggestions

☐ Distinguish between fresh-water and saltwater fish.
☐ Ask your parents to take you to a pet store to learn the lengths and compatibility of various types of fish.
☐ Look at previous exercises to remember how to calculate area and volume.
☐ Be sure you use the same units of measure when comparing the volume of the aquarium to the volume of the classroom.
☐ Draw your aquarium in three dimensions so your classmates have a good visual representation of your plan.

Scoring Rubric

3 Number of fish and their total length are accurately calculated. Size of aquarium is adequate for classroom and fish. Drawing is neat and accurately labeled.

2 Number of fish and the sum of their lengths are accurately calculated. Size of aquarium is adequate for classroom and fish. Drawing is sloppy and not labeled.

1 Number of fish and the sum of their lengths are calculated with some degree of error. Size of aquarium is adequate for either classroom or fish. Drawing is sloppy or missing.

0 Number of fish and their total length are inaccurately calculated. Size of aquarium is not appropriate. Drawing is missing.

Your Evaluation of Project Evaluate your work, based on the Scoring Rubric.

Teacher's Evaluation of Project

Transparencies

Name _____ Class _____ Date _____

Chapter Project Teacher Notes

Chapter 9: Go Fish

About the Project Students will have an opportunity to apply their knowledge of geometry and measurement to design an aquarium for the classroom.

Introducing the Project

Discuss the kinds of fish students might be able to have in an aquarium. Distinguish between saltwater and fresh-water fish. Talk about the number of fish an aquarium might hold and other equipment you might need, such as a heater and a filter. Talk about fish types that are compatible and types that are not compatible.

Activity 1: Investigating and Planning

Encourage students to use a spreadsheet program to help organize and tabulate their data.

Activity 2: Collecting and Organizing

Encourage students to use the Internet for research. They can look up, for example, the words, *aquarium, fish behavior,* and *measurement* to help them complete their tables.

Activity 3: Calculating

Point out to students that all measurements must have the same units in order to accurately compare their calculations.

Activity 4: Designing

Allow students to estimate or round to the nearest whole number for ease with computations. Show students how to draw a rectangular prism to help them with the drawing of their aquarium.

Finishing the Project

You may wish to plan a project day on which students share their completed projects. Encourage students to explain their design. Have them explain how understanding geometry helped them design an appropriately sized aquarium.

 **Take It to the NET** Visit www.PHSchool.com for information, student links, and teacher support for this project.

Problem of the Day	Lesson 9-1

Find the next three terms in this number pattern and describe the pattern.

3.75, 3.81, 3.87, 3.93, . . .

Answer

3.99, 4.05, 4.11; Start with 3.75 and add 0.06 repeatedly.

Problem of the Day	Lesson 9-2

Write five numbers that round to 6.

Answers may vary

any number from 5.5 to 6.4

Problem of the Day	Lesson 9-3

Rounded to the nearest ounce, Jack's basketball weighs 22 oz. What is the least and most it could weigh, in tenths of an ounce?

Answer

21.5 oz; 22.4 oz

Problem of the Day	Lesson 9-4

If a certain number is squared and then multiplied by 3, the result is 48. What was the original number?

Answer

4

Problem of the Day	Lesson 9-5

Write in order from least to greatest:

0.00602, 0.0062, 0.0620, 0.00600

Answer

0.00600, 0.00602, 0.0062, 0.0620

Problem of the Day	Lesson 9-6

Choose the appropriate graph:

a. You own a fish store. You want to compare one week's sales of salmon and swordfish.

b. You have examined your diet and want to show what parts of the food you have consumed belong to each of the four basic food groups.

Answer

a. bar graph   b. circle graph

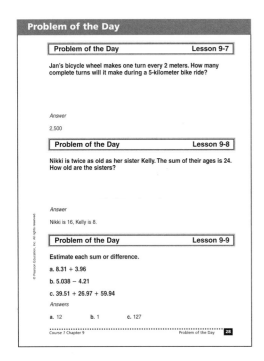

Problem of the Day — **Lesson 9-7**

Jan's bicycle wheel makes one turn every 2 meters. How many complete turns will it make during a 5-kilometer bike ride?

Answer

2,500

Problem of the Day — **Lesson 9-8**

Nikki is twice as old as her sister Kelly. The sum of their ages is 24. How old are the sisters?

Answer

Nikki is 16, Kelly is 8.

Problem of the Day — **Lesson 9-9**

Estimate each sum or difference.

a. $8.31 + 3.96$

b. $5.038 - 4.21$

c. $39.51 + 26.97 + 59.94$

Answers

a. 12   b. 1   c. 127

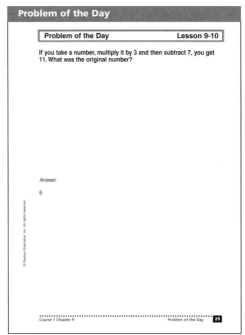

Problem of the Day — **Lesson 9-10**

If you take a number, multiply it by 3 and then subtract 7, you get 11. What was the original number?

Answer

6

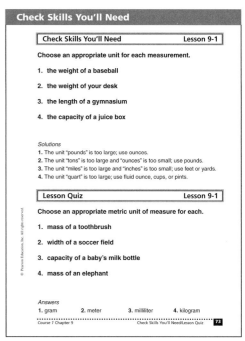

Check Skills You'll Need — **Lesson 9-1**

Choose an appropriate unit for each measurement.

1. the weight of a baseball

2. the weight of your desk

3. the length of a gymnasium

4. the capacity of a juice box

Solutions

1. The unit "pounds" is too large; use ounces.
2. The unit "tons" is too large and "ounces" is too small; use pounds.
3. The unit "miles" is too large and "inches" is too small; use feet or yards.
4. The unit "quart" is too large; use fluid ounce, cups, or pints.

Lesson Quiz — **Lesson 9-1**

Choose an appropriate metric unit of measure for each.

1. mass of a toothbrush

2. width of a soccer field

3. capacity of a baby's milk bottle

4. mass of an elephant

Answers

1. gram   2. meter   3. milliliter   4. kilogram

Sample page; see p. H for complete list.

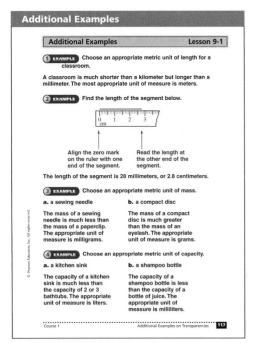

Additional Examples — **Lesson 9-1**

1 EXAMPLE Choose an appropriate metric unit of length for a classroom.

A classroom is much shorter than a kilometer but longer than a millimeter. The most appropriate unit of measure is meters.

2 EXAMPLE Find the length of the segment below.

Align the zero mark on the ruler with one end of the segment.

Read the length at the other end of the segment.

The length of the segment is 28 millimeters, or 2.8 centimeters.

3 EXAMPLE Choose an appropriate metric unit of mass.

a. a sewing needle

The mass of a sewing needle is much less than the mass of a paperclip. The appropriate unit of measure is milligrams.

b. a compact disc

The mass of a compact disc is much greater than the mass of an eyelash. The appropriate unit of measure is grams.

4 EXAMPLE Choose an appropriate metric unit of capacity.

a. a kitchen sink

The capacity of a kitchen sink is much less than the capacity of 2 or 3 bathtubs. The appropriate unit of measure is liters.

b. a shampoo bottle

The capacity of a shampoo bottle is less than the capacity of a bottle of juice. The appropriate unit of measure is milliliters.

Sample page; see p. H for complete list.

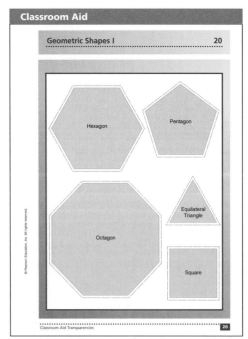

Geometric Shapes I — 20

Hexagon

Pentagon

Equilateral Triangle

Octagon

Square

Sample page.

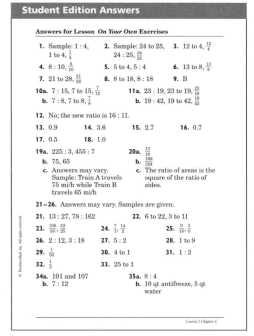

Answers for Lesson *On Your Own* Exercises

1. Sample: 1 : 4, 1 to 4, $\frac{1}{4}$

2. Sample: 24 to 25, 24 : 25, $\frac{24}{25}$

3. 12 to 4, $\frac{12}{4}$

4. 8 : 10, $\frac{8}{10}$

5. 5 to 4, 5 : 4

6. 13 to 8, $\frac{13}{8}$

7. 21 to 28, $\frac{21}{28}$

8. 8 to 18, 8 : 18

9. B

10a. 7 : 15, 7 to 15, $\frac{7}{15}$
   b. 7 : 8, 7 to 8, $\frac{7}{8}$

11a. 23 : 19, 23 to 19, $\frac{23}{19}$
   b. 19 : 42, 19 to 42, $\frac{19}{42}$

12. No; the new ratio is 16 : 11.

13. 0.9   14. 3.6   15. 2.7   16. 0.7

17. 0.5   18. 1.0

19a. 225 : 3, 455 : 7
   b. 75, 65
   c. Answers may vary. Sample: Train A travels 75 mi/h while Train B travels 65 mi/h

20a. $\frac{13}{18}$
   b. $\frac{169}{324}$
   c. The ratio of areas is the square of the ratio of sides.

21–26. Answers may vary. Samples are given.

21. 13 : 27, 78 : 162   22. 6 to 22, 3 to 11

23. $\frac{106}{50}$, $\frac{53}{25}$ 24. $\frac{7}{1}$, $\frac{14}{2}$ 25. $\frac{9}{18}$, $\frac{3}{6}$

26. 2 : 12, 3 : 18   27. 5 : 2   28. 1 to 9

29. $\frac{1}{50}$ 30. 4 to 1   31. 1 : 2

32. $\frac{1}{3}$ 33. 25 to 1

34a. 101 and 107
   b. 7 : 12

35a. 8 : 4
   b. 10 qt antifreeze, 5 qt water

Sample page; see p. H for complete list.

Assessment

Lesson Quiz

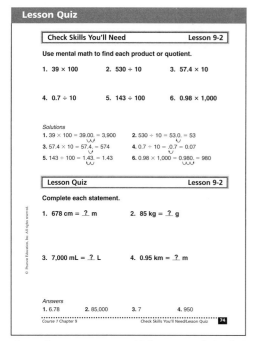

Sample page; see p. H for complete list.

Checkpoint Quizzes

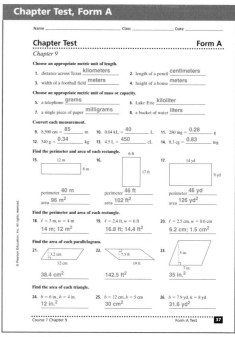

Available in Spanish

Chapter Test, Form A

Available in Spanish

Chapter Test, Form A

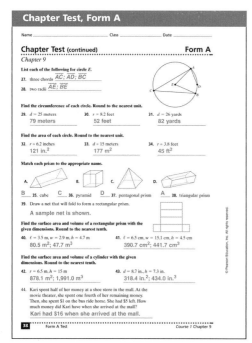

Available in Spanish

Chapter Test, Form B

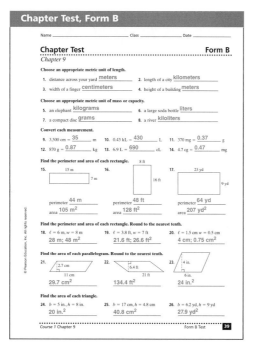

Available in Spanish

Chapter Test, Form B

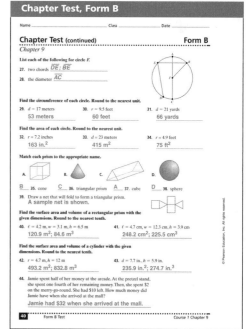

Available in Spanish

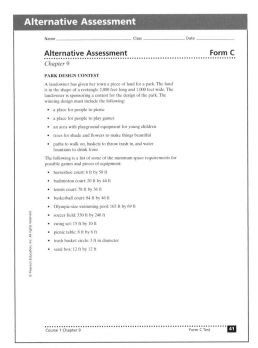
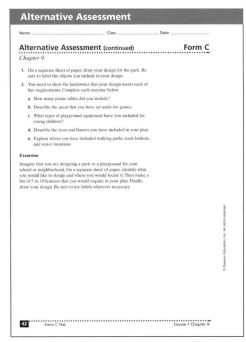
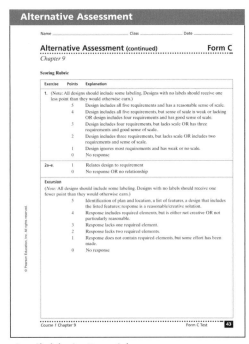

Available in Spanish

Available in Spanish

Available in Spanish

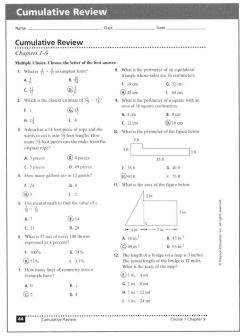
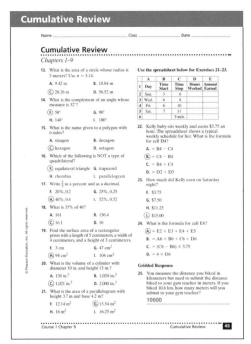
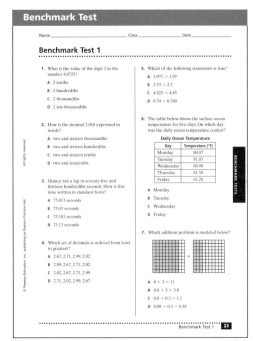

Available in Spanish

Available in Spanish

On PH Website

Test-Taking Strategies transparency

Test-Taking Strategies: Using Estimation

Sometimes you can estimate to find the answer.

Example	Find the sum: 0.75 + 8.23 + 5.5		
A. 15.53	B. 14.48	C. 9.53	D. 21.23

Estimate: Round to the nearest whole number.

$$0.75 + 8.23 + 5.5$$
$$1 + 8 + 6 = 15$$

Both A and B are near 15, so round to the nearest tenth.

$0.8 + 8.2 + 5.5$ must be less than 15.

The answer is 14.48, or choice B.

Estimate to find the answer. Explain your reasoning.

1. The area of a square with side 2.7 cm is

   A. 5.4 cm²   B. 7.29 cm²   C. 54 cm²   D. 72.9 cm².

2. Reese went grocery shopping to buy spaghetti sauce, spaghetti noodles, and a loaf of french bread. These items cost \$1.59, \$1.79, and \$1.89. About how much should Reese's grocery bill be?

   F. less than \$5   G. between \$5 and \$6
   H. between \$6 and \$7   I. more than \$7

Transparency 10

Test-Taking Strategies worksheet

Name _____ Class _____ Date _____

Chapter 9: Using Estimation
Exercises

Estimate each answer. Use 3 for π. Use estimation to eliminate choices.

1. The diameter of a cylindrical water barrel is 2.2 feet. The height of the barrel is 2.8 feet. Find the volume of the water barrel to the nearest tenth of a cubic foot. Explain your reasoning.

   A. 3.6 ft³   B. 6.4 ft³   C. 9.4 ft³   D. 12.9 ft³

   Estimate first. Since the diameter is 2.2 feet, the radius is 1.1 feet. The height is 2.8 feet, which can be rounded to 3 feet. Use 3 for π, 1 for r, and 3 for h in the formula for volume. $V = Bh = \pi r^2 h$; $V \approx 3 \cdot 1^2 \cdot 3 \approx 9$ ft³

   Choice C is closer to the estimate than the other choices.

2. Lisa is having a special dinner and needs to make tablecloths for 10 large round tables. She plans to add 2 feet to the diameter of the tables for the tablecloths, so they will drape over the edges. The diameter of each table is 7.8 feet. Lisa bought 500 square feet of material.

   a. Does she have enough to make all 10 tablecloths? Explain.

   Estimate using the formula for area. The diameter of each tablecloth will be 7.8 + 2 = 9.8 feet, so the radius will be 4.9 feet. Use 5 feet as an estimate. Use 3 for π. $A = \pi r^2$; $A \approx 3 \cdot 5^2$; $A \approx 75$ ft²; she will need approximately 75 square feet for each table. Since there are 10 tables, she will need 750 square feet of material. So, she does not have enough material.

   b. If not, approximately how much more material will she need to buy? about 250 ft²

3. The diameter of a round garden is 12 feet. To the nearest square foot, how much plastic would be required to cover the garden?

   F. 36 ft²   G. 48 ft²   H. 72 ft²   I. 108 ft²

4. To the nearest centimeter, find the circumference of a circle with a 5-centimeter radius.

   A. 15 cm   B. 24 cm   C. 30 cm   D. 75 cm

5. What is the approximate volume of a bucket that has a diameter of 10 inches and is 12 inches tall? 900 in.³

Test-Taking Strategies   Course 1   **9**

Home Activities

in math class …

We have been learning about measurement. In particular, we have studied linear measurements, area of polygons, and area of circles. Here is a list of some of the skills and concepts we have studied.

- Perimeter
- Converting in the metric system
- Using conversion factors
- Area of squares, rectangles, parallelograms, and triangles
- Discovering π
- Area of circles

Home Activities

Here are some activities you can do with your child that use these math skills and concepts.

Have your child find the area of some of the windows and doors in your home. Discuss what the area could be used for, such as buying curtains or blinds for the windows, and paint for the door. Measure each shape at least twice for accuracy. If discrepancies occur, have your child suggest why. Next, measure the diameter of circular objects that are in your home and find the areas. Possible items to measure are plates, bowls, clock faces, or barometer faces.

To find the area of a circular shape, such as a paper plate with a diameter of 8 inches, your child must first divide the diameter by 2 to find the radius. Then your child can use the formula $A = \pi r^2$, with $\pi = 3.14$, to find the area: $A = 3.14 \times 4 \times 4 = 50.24$ in.²

Finally, have your child make an irregular shape by placing some books next to each other in an L-shaped or other non-rectangular or non-square design. Encourage your child to find the area of the shape using more than one method.

Use with Chapter 9

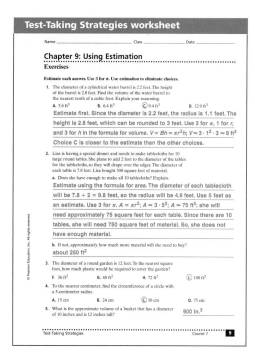

Available in Spanish
Web Code: aak-5500

Interdisciplinary Activities

Name _____   *Math and Social Studies*

Welcome to the Round House

Find the area of a circle as it relates to houses that have circular bases.

Look around at your classroom. Then picture the different rooms in your home. These rooms, whether large or small, share some things. They usually have four walls, a floor, and a ceiling. While most rooms around the world are built this way, there are some exceptions, such as the *igloo* and the *teepee*.

The Inuit people (once called Eskimos) who live in central and western Canada used to build snow igloos as their permanent winter homes. Today, few Inuit people build snow igloos unless they are taking long journeys and need a temporary shelter.

Igloos are built from blocks of snow. Typically, each block is 2 to 3 feet long and 1 to 2 feet wide. The igloo is dome-shaped, and its base is circular. It usually has a diameter of about 8 feet and a height of 12 feet. A sheet of ice covering a hole in the side of the igloo forms a

window. The igloo has a narrow tunnel opening. The tunnel stops the cold wind from coming inside the igloo. Seal oil lamps are used for light and heat. A small hole punched through the top of the igloo allows just enough fresh air to come into the igloo. A platform, built inside the igloo and covered with furs, is used as a bed.

Like the igloo, the teepee also has a circular base. The Plains Indians of North America lived in teepees, which are portable, cone-shaped tents. Portable homes were important for the Plains Indians, because they often moved their camps to follow the animals they hunted, such as buffalo and deer. Their teepees were constructed of three long poles tied at the top and stuck in the ground as a tripod. The Indians stretched buffalo hides across the poles. Typically, the Indians covered a teepee with as many as 20 buffalo hides. The teepee was about 10 feet high and had a diameter of 15 feet.

Type of Housing	Diameter of Base of Structure	Circumference of Base of Structure
snow igloo	8 feet	
teepee	15 feet	

1. Determine the circumference of the snow igloo and the teepee and record your answers in the table above. Use 3.14 for π.

2. Knowing the diameter of the floor of the snow igloo and the teepee, you can also determine the floor area of each structure. Calculate and write the radius and area of each structure in the table below. Use 3.14 for π.

Type of Housing	Radius of Circular Floor	Area of Circular Floor
snow igloo		
teepee		

Use with Chapter 9

Available in Spanish
Web Code: aak-5500

Interdisciplinary Activities

Name _____   *Math and Social Studies*

3. The snow igloo and the teepee are one-room structures. One family unit of Inuit people lived in an igloo, and one family unit of Plains Indians lived in a teepee. A family unit usually included a husband, a wife, and their children. Calculate the area of your bedroom and compare it to the areas of the snow igloo and the teepee. Would the circular floor area of a snow igloo or a teepee fit in your bedroom? Explain your answer. Can you imagine your home consisting of just the room in which you sleep?

4. The Plains Indians also built a dome-shaped structure called a sweat lodge. Tree branches were used to form the dome, and hides were placed over the branches. Sweat lodges were usually 4 feet high and had circular bases. In the middle of the lodge was a circular fire pit. Hot rocks were placed in the pit. Water was poured over the rocks to make steam. A group of men or women crowded into the lodge, where they sat around the fire pit and meditated, prayed, or chanted. Imagine that you are in a sweat lodge that has a floor area of 78.5 square feet.

   a. What is the diameter of the floor area? Explain how you got your answer. Use 3.14 for π.

b. If the fire pit in this sweat lodge had a diameter of 1.5 feet, how much floor area was left on which to sit?

c. To get a sense of how close Native Americans sat in the sweat lodge, you decide to sit with several of your friends on 78.5 square feet of floor space. On your classroom floor, use chalk or tape to create a circle that encloses 78.5 square feet. In the middle of the circle, use chalk or tape to create a circle that encloses the area of the fire pit. Sitting as close together as possible, find out how many people will fit within the circle and around the fire pit.

5. What factors determined the size of the igloo and teepee?

6. Why do you suppose the Inuits and the Plains Indians chose structures with circular bases?

7. Why is an understanding of how to find the area of a circle useful to someone studying the Inuit and Plains Indians?

Use with Chapter 9

Available in Spanish
Web Code: aak-5500

Algebra Readiness Puzzles

Name _____   Class _____   Date _____

Figure It Out   Puzzle 9

Geometry and Measurement

Find the area and perimeter of each figure. Match the letter to the solution at the bottom to find the answer to the following riddle.

What did the acorn say to the squirrel?

6 cm (square)   6 cm

Perimeter _____ G
Area _____ T

42 cm, 26 cm, 68 cm, 100 cm (triangle)

Perimeter _____ R
Area _____ Y

35 cm, 60 cm (rectangle)

Perimeter _____ E
Area _____ A

50 cm, 40 cm, 50 cm, 60 cm (triangle)

Perimeter _____ M
Area _____ I

0.1 m, 50 cm, 36 cm, 34.8 cm, 0.1 m (parallelogram)

Perimeter _____ O
Area _____ S

24 cm	190 cm	190 cm	1,200 cm²	160 cm	2,100 cm²
36 cm²	210 cm	190 cm	190 cm		

© Pearson Education, Inc.   Algebra Readiness Puzzles   9

Web Code: aak-5500

Geometry and Measurement

Chapter 9 Overview

In this chapter students begin by working with metric measurements. Then they apply their geometric understandings as they learn to find perimeters, areas, volumes, and surface areas of geometric figures.

 Reading Math
- Using Concept Maps to Connect Ideas, p. 460
- **Vocabulary:** A complete list, plus exercises, in the Chapter Review, p. 482
- **Illustrated Glossary:** Examples for each vocabulary term, plus definitions in English and Spanish, on p. 669

 Test-Taking Strategies
Using Estimation, p. 481

 Real-World Problem Solving
- **Strategies:** Work Backward, pp. 477–480
- **Real-World Snapshots:** The Shape of Buildings to Come, pp. 486–487
- **Chapter Project:** Go Fish, p. 640

 www.PHSchool.com
Internet support includes:
- Self-grading Vocabulary and Chapter 9 Tests
- Activity Masters
- Chapter Project support
- Chapter Planner
- Ch. 9 Resources

Plus **iTEXT**

Geometry and Measurement

Lessons

Key Vocabulary

- area (p. 440)
- chord (p. 452)
- circle (p. 452)
- circumference (p. 453)
- diameter (p. 452)
- metric system (p. 431)
- perimeter (p. 441)
- prism (p. 462)
- radius (p. 452)
- surface area (p. 468)
- volume (p. 472)

Real-World Snapshots

The Air Force Academy Chapel was built from 1956 to 1962 in Colorado Springs, Colorado. It stands 150 feet tall and has 17 spires that soar toward the sky like fighter jets. The frame was made from 100 tetrahedrons measuring 75 feet long.

Data File
Great Buildings

Building	Length (meters)	Width (meters)	Height (meters)
Great Pyramid of Khufu Giza, Egypt	230	230	146
Louvre Pyramid Paris, France	35.4	35.4	21.64
Taj Mahal (platform) Agra, India	100	100	6

You will use the data above in this chapter:

• p. 470   Lesson 9-8
• p. 475   Lesson 9-9

 Real-World Snapshots On pages 486 and 487, you will solve problems involving buildings.

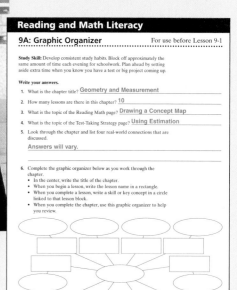

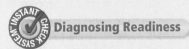

Diagnosing Readiness

Students will find answers to these exercises in the back of their textbooks.

Prescribing Intervention
For intervention, direct students to:

Choosing Appropriate Units of Measurement
Lesson 5-7: Examples 1–3.
Extra Practice, p. 646.

Changing Units
Lesson 5-8: Examples 1–3.
Extra Practice, p. 646.

Classifying Polygons
Lesson 8-5: Examples 1–2.
Extra Practice, p. 649.

Chapter 9 Preview

Where You've Been

● In Chapter 5, you worked with the customary system of measurement.

● In Chapter 8, you classified angles and polygons.

Where You're Going

● In Chapter 9, you will use the metric system of measurement and compare different units.

● Applying what you learn, you will identify three-dimensional figures as seen in architecture.

Teepees are shaped like pyramids or cones.

 Instant self-check online and on CD-ROM

Diagnosing Readiness

? **For help, go to the lesson in green.**

Choosing Appropriate Units of Measurement (Lesson 5-7)

Choose an appropriate unit for each measurement.

1. weight of a newborn baby   pounds

2. capacity of a train's oil car   gallons

3. distance to the sun   miles

4. length of your hand   inches

Changing Units (Lesson 5-8)

Complete each statement.

5. ■ oz = 9 lb   **144**

6. 46 in. = ■ ft $3\frac{5}{6}$

7. $7\frac{1}{4}$ c = ■ pt $3\frac{5}{8}$

8. 4,500 lb = ■ t $2\frac{1}{4}$

9. ■ pt = 13 qt   **26**

10. 7,920 ft = ■ mi $1\frac{1}{2}$

Use <, =, or > to complete each statement.

11. 14 ft ■ 4 yd   **>**

12. $2\frac{1}{2}$ gal ■ 11 qt   **<**

13. 5 c ■ 37 fl oz   **>**

14. 3 yd ■ 108 ft   **<**

15. $14\frac{1}{4}$ lb ■ 9,000 t   **<**

16. 65 c ■ $16\frac{1}{4}$ qt   **=**

Classifying Polygons (Lessons 8-4 and 8-5)

Classify each triangle or quadrilateral. Classify each triangle by its sides.

17.

rhombus

18.

isosceles triangle

19.

trapezoid

Metric Units of Length, Mass, and Capacity

1. Plan

What You'll Learn

OBJECTIVE 1 To use metric units of length

OBJECTIVE 2 To choose units for mass and capacity

. . . And Why

To choose appropriate units of mass, as in Example 3

 Check Skills You'll Need For help, go to Lesson 5-7.

Choose an appropriate unit for each measurement.

1. the weight of a baseball   ounces
2. the weight of your desk   pounds
3. the length of a gymnasium feet; (Yards would also be appropriate.)
4. the capacity of a juice box pints; (Cups or fluid ounces would also be appropriate.)

New Vocabulary • **metric system** • **meter** • **mass** • **gram** • **capacity** • **liter**

Lesson Preview

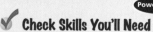

✔ **Check Skills You'll Need**
Choosing Appropriate Customary Units
Lesson 5-7: Examples 1–3. Extra Practice, p. 646.

Lesson Resources

Optional Materials
• metric rulers

📁 **Teaching Resources**
Practice, Reteaching, Enrichment

👥 **Reaching All Students**
Practice Workbook 9-1
Spanish Practice Workbook 9-1
Guided Problem Solving 9-1
Hands-On Activities 30

⏱ **Presentation Assistant Plus!**
Transparencies
• Check Skills You'll Need 9-1
• Problem of the Day 9-1
• Additional Examples 9-1
• Student Edition Answers 9-1
• Lesson Quiz 9-1
PH Presentation Pro CD-ROM 9-1

ASSESSMENT SYSTEM
Computer Test Generator CD

💻 **Technology**
Resource Pro® CD-ROM
Computer Test Generator CD
PH Presentation Pro CD-ROM

💻 **www.PHSchool.com**
Student Site
• Teacher Web Code: aak-5500
• Self-grading Lesson Quiz

PH SuccessNet Teacher Center
• Lesson Planner
• Resources

Plus 🔲**TEXT**

OBJECTIVE 1

Using Metric Units of Length

Metric Prefixes

Prefix	Meaning
kilo-	1,000
centi-	$\frac{1}{100}$ or 0.01
milli-	$\frac{1}{1,000}$ or 0.001

In Chapter 5, you worked with units in the customary system such as yards, pounds, and gallons. The **metric system** of measurement is a decimal system. It uses prefixes to relate the sizes of units to standard units. The table at the left shows the most common prefixes.

The standard unit of length in the metric system is the **meter (m)**. A meter is a little longer than a yard.

Metric Units of Length

Unit	Relationship to a Meter	Example
kilometer (km)	1 km = 1,000 meters	2.5 times around an indoor track
meter (m)	1 meter	height of a doorknob from the floor
centimeter (cm)	1 cm = 0.01 meter	thickness of a CD case
millimeter (mm)	1 mm = 0.001 meter	thickness of a CD

1 **EXAMPLE**   Choosing a Unit of Length   Real World

Choose an appropriate metric unit of length for a pencil.

A pencil is much shorter than a meter but much longer than a millimeter. The most appropriate unit of measure is centimeters.

✔ **Check Understanding** ① Choose an appropriate metric unit of length for a city block.   meter

---

 Ongoing Assessment and Intervention

Before the Lesson	**During the Lesson**	**After the Lesson**
Diagnose prerequisite skills using:	**Monitor progress using:**	**Assess knowledge using:**
• Check Skills You'll Need	• Check Understanding	• Lesson Quiz
	• Additional Examples	• Computer Test Generator CD
	• Test Prep	

2. Teach

Math Background

Three basic units of measure in the metric system are the *meter* for measuring length, the *gram* for measuring mass, and the *liter* for measuring liquid capacity. Each basic unit is formally defined in terms of a physical property that is constant throughout the world. For instance, the meter is defined as the distance that light travels in a vacuum in $\frac{1}{299,792,458}$ s.

The metric system is the most widely used measurement system in the world. It is also known as *SI*, from the first two words of the French name for the system, *Système International d'Unités*.

Teaching Notes

English Learners

To help students learn the metric prefixes, discuss the meanings of familiar words that have the same prefixes or the same roots. For instance, just as a *cent* is one hundredth of a dollar, a *centimeter* is one hundredth of a meter.

① EXAMPLE Diversity

In the United States, the customary system remains the predominant system of measurement. Students who have lived outside the United States, however, might be quite familiar with the metric system. Encourage these students to share their knowledge of the metric system with the class. For instance, as you introduce each unit, you might ask these students to give examples of everyday situations in which that unit is used.

② EXAMPLE Error Prevention!

In Check Understanding 2a–c, some students might make an incorrect measurement because they lined up the left end of the segment with the left end of the ruler instead of the zero mark.

432

---

② EXAMPLE Using a Metric Ruler

Find the length of the segment in millimeters and in centimeters.

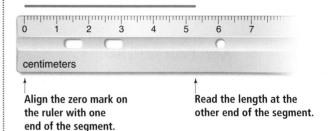

Align the zero mark on the ruler with one end of the segment.

Read the length at the other end of the segment.

● The length of the segment is 53 millimeters, or 5.3 centimeters.

✓ **Check Understanding** ② Use a metric ruler to find each length in millimeters and in centimeters.

    a. —————— 20 mm or 2 cm

    b. ———————— 36 mm or 3.6 cm

    c. ———————————————— 79 mm or 7.9 cm

OBJECTIVE

▷ 2 Choosing Units for Mass and Capacity

Real-World 🌐 Connection

The mass of a small paperclip is 1 gram. The mass of a penny is about 2.5 grams.

Solids are sometimes measured in units of mass. **Mass** is a measure of the amount of matter in an object. The standard unit of mass is the **gram (g)**.

Unit of Mass	Relationship to a Gram	Example
kilogram (kg)	1 kg = 1,000 grams	mass of 4 videocassettes
gram (g)	1 gram	mass of a small paper clip
milligram (mg)	1 mg = 0.001 gram	mass of an eyelash

③ EXAMPLE Choosing a Unit of Mass 🌐 Real World

Choose an appropriate metric unit of mass.

a. a pea

    A pea has about the same mass as a paperclip. The appropriate unit of measure is grams.

b. a baby

    The mass of a baby is much greater than the mass of a paperclip. The appropriate unit of measure is kilograms.

✓ **Check Understanding** ③ Choose an appropriate metric unit of mass.

    a. a car **kilograms**   b. a desk **kilograms**

    c. a robin's feather **milligrams**   d. a pencil **grams**

👥 Reaching All Students

Below Level Have students draw segments with lengths 14 cm, 14 mm, 1.4 cm, and 140 mm. Ask them to identify which pairs of measures name equal lengths. **14 cm and 140 mm; 14 mm and 1.4 cm**	**Advanced Learners** Give students several measures. Have them identify objects around the school with those approximate measures. For example: about 6,000 kg **mass of school bus** about 30 L **capacity of wastebasket**	**English Learners** See note on page 432. **Diversity** See note on page 432.

Liquids are measured by units of capacity. **Capacity** is a measure of the amount of liquid an object holds. The standard unit of capacity is the **liter (L).** A liter is a little more than a quart.

Unit of Capacity	Relationship to a Liter	Example
kiloliter (kL)	1 kL = 1,000 liters	water to fill 2 or 3 bathtubs
liter (L)	1 liter	a bottle of juice
milliliter (mL)	1 mL = 0.001 liter	2 dewdrops

4 EXAMPLE Choosing a Unit of Capacity Real World

Choose an appropriate metric unit of capacity.

a. a bottle cap

A bottle cap holds about 10 to 20 drops of water. The appropriate unit of measure is milliliters.

b. a swimming pool

The capacity of a swimming pool is much greater than the capacity of a bottle of juice. The appropriate unit of measure is kiloliters.

✔ **Check Understanding** ④ Choose an appropriate metric unit of capacity.

a. a car's fuel tank
liters

b. a pond
kiloliters

c. a test tube
milliliters

EXERCISES

? For more practice, see *Extra Practice*.

A Practice by Example 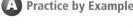 **Choose an appropriate metric unit of length.**
1–6. Answers may vary. Samples are given.

Example 1
(page 431)

1. width of a highway
meters

2. length of an eyelash
millimeters

3. height of your desk
centimeters

4. width of your finger
millimeters

5. width of your classroom door
centimeters

6. distance across the state of Ohio
kilometers

Example 2
(page 432)

Use a metric ruler to find each length in millimeters and in centimeters.

7. ——
12 mm or 1.2 cm

8. ————
27 mm or 2.7 cm

9. ———
20 mm or 2 cm

10. —————
108 mm or 10.8 cm

Example 3
(page 432) **Choose an appropriate metric unit of mass.**

11. a garbage can
kilograms

12. a pin
milligrams

13. a chair
kilograms

14. a pay phone
kilograms

15. a potato
grams

16. a shirt button
milligrams

9-1 Metric Units of Length, Mass, and Capacity **433**

Assignment Guide

1 Objective 1
Ⓐ Ⓑ Core 1–10, 25, 27, 29, 31, 37, 40, 46
Ⓒ Extension 49

2 Objective 2
Ⓐ Ⓑ Core 11–24, 26, 28, 30, 32–36, 38–39, 41–45, 47
Ⓒ Extension 48, 50

Test Prep 51–54
Mixed Review 55–63

Practice 9-1 — Metric Units of Length, Mass, and Capacity

Choose an appropriate metric unit of length.

1. the height of an office building — meter
2. the width of a page of a text — centimeter
3. the length of an ant — millimeter
4. the depth of a lake — meter

Use a metric ruler to find each length in millimeters and in centimeters.

5. 30 mm; 3 cm
6. 24 mm; 2.4 cm
7. 42 mm; 4.2 cm

Choose an appropriate metric unit of mass.

8. a grain of rice — milligram
9. a bag of groceries — kilogram
10. a feather — milligram
11. a cat — kilogram
12. a leaf — milligram
13. an eraser — gram

Choose an appropriate metric unit of capacity.

14. a gasoline tank — liter
15. a coffee mug — milliliter
16. 6 raindrops — milliliter
17. a pitcher of juice — liter
18. a swimming pool — kiloliter
19. a can of paint — liter

Is each measurement reasonable? Write *True* or *False*.

20. The mass of the horse is about 500 kg. — true
21. Jean drank 5.8 L of juice at breakfast. — false
22. A mug holds 250 mL of hot chocolate. — true
23. A penny is about 3 kg. — false
24. A teaspoon holds about 5 L. — false
25. A textbook is about 1 kg. — true
26. The mass of a nail is about 500 g. — false
27. A soccer field is about 5 m long. — false

Reteaching 9-1 — Metric Units of Length, Mass, and Capacity

The standard unit of length in the metric system is the *meter*.

millimeter (mm)	= 0.001 meter
centimeter (cm)	= 0.01 meter
meter (m)	= 1 meter
kilometer (km)	= 1,000 meters

A length can be named using different metric units. The point marked on the ruler is 2.7 centimeters.

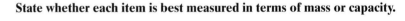

Since each centimeter is 10 millimeters, the point is also 27 millimeters.

In the metric system, solids can be measured in units of *mass*.

milligram (mg)	= 0.001 gram
gram (g)	= 1 gram
kilogram (kg)	= 1,000 grams

The standard unit of mass is the *gram*.
• The mass of a vitamin pill may be measured in milligrams.
• A thumbtack has a mass of about 1 gram.
• A full liter bottle of soda has a mass of about 1 kilogram.

Liquids are measured in units of *capacity*.

milliliter (mL)	= 0.001 liter
liter (L)	= 1 liter
kiloliter (kL)	= 1,000 liters

The standard unit of capacity is the *liter*.
• The capacity of a soup spoon is measured in milliliters.
• A 1-liter soda bottle can fill about four average-sized glasses.
• Water in a river is measured in kiloliters.

Choose an appropriate metric unit of length.

1. distance across the end of a pencil — millimeters
2. length of a thumb — centimeters
3. distance from your home to Australia — kilometers
4. width of a swimming pool — meters

Choose an appropriate metric unit of mass.

5. the mass of a tooth — milligrams
6. the mass of a puppy — grams

Choose an appropriate metric unit of capacity.

7. the capacity of a bucket of water — liters
8. the amount of water in a pond — kiloliters

Example 4 (page 433) 🌐 **Choose an appropriate metric unit of capacity.**

17. a watering can — liters
18. a juice box — milliliters
19. a large lake — kiloliters
20. a bucket of paint — liters
21. an oil truck — kiloliters
22. a glass of milk — milliliters

Ⓑ **Apply Your Skills**

Complete the following.

23. 1 g = ▨ kg — 0.001
24. 1 mL = ▨ L — 0.001
25. ▨ cm = 1 m — 100
26. ▨ L = 1 kL — 1,000
27. 1 m = ▨ mm — 1,000
28. ▨ g = 1 mg — 0.001

🌐 **Is each measurement reasonable? Explain.** 29–33. Explanations may vary.

29. A sidewalk is 30 kilometers wide. **No; a sidewalk would be measured in centimeters or meters.**
30. A ladybug has a mass of 4 kilograms. **No; a ladybug would be measured in milligrams.**
31. A giraffe is 550 centimeters tall. **Yes; giraffes are very tall.**
32. A truck has a mass of 1,200 kilograms. **Yes; trucks are very large.**
33. A cow produces 500 kiloliters of milk each day. **No; a cow's milk would be measured in liters per day.**

True or *False*? If false, explain why.

34. 1,000 mg = 1 g **true**
35. 100 kg = 100,000 g **true**
36. 10 L = 1,000 mL **false; 10L = 10,000 mL**
37. 1 mm = 10 cm **false; 1 cm = 10 mm**

38. **Error Analysis** Explain and correct the error in each statement. 38a–b. See margin.
    a. A tennis ball has a mass of about 58 milliliters.
    b. A dime has a capacity of about 2.5 grams.

39. **Writing in Math** Explain the difference between mass and capacity. Give an example of each. **See margin.**

40. **Estimation** The width of a door is about 1 meter. How can you estimate the length of a wall that contains the door? **See left.**

State whether each item is best measured in terms of mass or capacity.

41. a bottle of lamp oil **capacity**
42. a newspaper **mass**
43. a bag of oranges **mass**
44. water in a fish tank **capacity**

Open-Ended Name two items for which each unit might be used.
Answers may vary. 45. See margin for sample. 46–47. See back of book.

45. milligram
46. centimeter
47. kilogram

Real-World 🌐 **Connection**

An adult giraffe can reach over 5 meters in height.

40. Answers may vary. Sample: Use a piece of string whose length matches the width of the door (1 m). Count how many times you can lay that string end-to-end from one end of the wall to the other.

GPS Use the Guided Problem Solving worksheet with Exercise 40.

38a. Milliliters measure capacity. A tennis ball has a mass of about 58 grams.

b. Grams measure mass. A dime has a mass of about 2.5 grams.

39. Answers may vary. Sample: Mass is the amount of matter in an object; capacity is a measure of the amount of liquid an object holds. A plastic bottle might have a mass of 10 g, but a capacity of 1L.

45. Sample: small insects such as a flea or mite

 Challenge 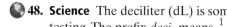 **48. Science** The deciliter (dL) is sometimes used in medical laboratory testing. The prefix *deci-* means $\frac{1}{10}$, or 0.1. Complete the following.

a. 15 L = ■ dL
150

b. 49 dL = ■ L
4.9

c. 273 dL = ■ L
27.3

49. Reasoning Ancient Egyptians based measures of length on the cubit, palm, and digit. The cubit (forearm) was the length from the elbow to the fingers. The palm was the width of the palm excluding the thumb. The digit was the width of the finger. List some advantages and disadvantages of using such a system of measurement. **See margin.**

50. Stretch Your Thinking Gerri started with the number 15. She multiplied by 3, divided by some number, and then added 10. The result was 15. By what number did Gerri divide? **9**

 **Test Prep**

Multiple Choice

51. Which of the following items would NOT be best measured in terms of mass? **C**

A. bread **B.** a box of rice **C.** orange juice **D.** popcorn

Take It to the NET
Online lesson quiz at
www.PHSchool.com
Web Code: aaa-0901

52. Which should be used to measure a baseball bat's length? **G**

F. millimeter **G.** centimeter **H.** liter **I.** kilometer

53. Which should be used to measure a backpack's mass? **D**

A. milligram **B.** centimeter **C.** gram **D.** kilogram

Short Response

54. You have two 650-milliliter bottles of lotion. **See back of book.**

a. Will the lotion from the two bottles fit in a 1-liter container?

b. Explain in words how you found your answer.

 **Mixed Review**

Lesson 8-3 **Find the complement and the supplement of each angle.**

55. 44° 46°; 136° **56.** 16° 74°; 164° **57.** 81° 9°; 99° **58.** 62.5° 27.5°; 117.5°

Lesson 6-3 **Find the value that completes each proportion.**

59. $\frac{4}{5} = \frac{68}{■}$ 85 **60.** $\frac{10}{13} = \frac{■}{65}$ 50 **61.** $\frac{288}{■} = \frac{6}{11}$ 528 **62.** $\frac{■}{162} = \frac{2}{3}$ 108

63. $\frac{3}{\$5.67} = \frac{18}{\$34.02}$

 63. Consumer Issues Three pounds of peaches cost $5.67. You need 18 pounds of peaches to make pies for a bake sale. How much will you spend on peaches? Write and solve a proportion. **See left.**

49. Answers may vary. Sample: Advantages: The system was helpful in developing a "sense" of measure, since measures were related to the human body. The system had units useful for small, medium, and large objects.; **Disadvantages:** Exact measurements and conversions between units were probably difficult. If the units were redefined each time a new ruler took power, record keeping and interpretation were probably confusing.

 Lesson Quiz 9-1

Choose an appropriate metric unit of measure for each.

1. mass of a toothbrush **gram**

2. width of a soccer field **meter**

3. capacity of a baby's milk bottle **milliliter**

4. mass of an elephant **kilogram**

Alternative Assessment

Students work together in pairs to estimate and record the length and mass of several classroom objects. Partners then use metric rulers and a balance scale to find and record the actual measurements. Ask partners to share their estimates and measurements with the class.

Test Prep

Resources
For additional practice with a variety of test item formats:
• Test Prep, p. 485
• Test-Taking Strategies, p. 481
• Test-Taking Strategies With Transparencies

Enrichment 9-1 Metric Units of Length, Mass, and Capacity
Visual Thinking

Optical illusions occur when the human eye and brain perceive something that is not really true. Look at the pictures below. Answer the questions. Then check your answers by measuring.

1. Circle the railroad tie that is longest.
Check students' answers.

2. Measure the ties. Which is longest? Was there an illusion? If so, what was the illusion?
The ties are the same length. The illusion is that the ties get longer as the track recedes.

3. Circle the square that is larger. Check students' answers.

4. Measure the squares. Which is larger? Was there an illusion? If so, what was the illusion?
The squares are the same size. The illusion is that the square on the right is larger.

5. Shade the center circle that is larger. Check students' answers.

6. Measure the center circles. Which is larger? Was there an illusion? If so, what was the illusion?
The center circles are the same size. The illusion is that the circle surrounded by smaller circles is larger.

Converting Units in the Metric System

Lesson Preview

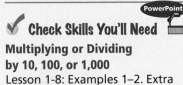

✓ Check Skills You'll Need

Multiplying or Dividing by 10, 100, or 1,000
Lesson 1-8: Examples 1–2. Extra Practice, p. 642.

Lesson Resources

📁 **Teaching Resources**
Practice, Reteaching, Enrichment

👥 **Reaching All Students**
Practice Workbook 9-2
Spanish Practice Workbook 9-2
Guided Problem Solving 9-2

⏰ **Presentation Assistant Plus!**
Transparencies
• Check Skills You'll Need 9-2
• Problem of the Day 9-2
• Additional Examples 9-2
• Student Edition Answers 9-2
• Lesson Quiz 9-2
PH Presentation Pro CD-ROM 9-2

PRENTICE HALL
ASSESSMENT SYSTEM

Computer Test Generator CD

💻 **Technology**
Resource Pro® CD-ROM
Computer Test Generator CD
PH Presentation Pro CD-ROM

💻 **www.PHSchool.com**
Student Site
• Teacher Web Code: aak-5500
• Self-grading Lesson Quiz

PH SuccessNet Teacher Center
• Lesson Planner
• Resources

Plus **iTEXT**

What You'll Learn

OBJECTIVE 1 To convert metric measurements

. . . And Why

To find distances, as in Example 2

✓ **Check Skills You'll Need**   ❓ For help, go to Lesson 1-8.

Use mental math to find each product or quotient.

1. 39×100 **3,900**
2. $530 \div 10$ **53**
3. 57.4×10 **574**
4. $0.7 \div 10$ **0.07**
5. $143 \div 100$ **1.43**
6. $0.98 \times 1,000$ **980**

OBJECTIVE 1

iTEXT Interactive lesson includes instant self-check, tutorials, and activities.

Converting Metric Measurements

You can rewrite one metric unit as another metric unit by multiplying or dividing by a power of 10. Multiply to change from larger units to smaller units. Divide to change from smaller units to larger units.

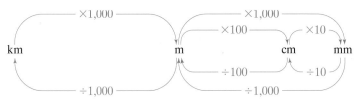

You can think of converting to smaller units as creating many small units from a larger unit. To do this, you must multiply. You should end up with more smaller units than you had larger units.

1 EXAMPLE Converting to Smaller Units

Convert 3.2 meters to centimeters.

The meter is a larger unit than the centimeter. To convert meters to centimeters, multiply by 100.

$3.2 \times 100 = 3.20$ ← To multiply by 100, move the decimal point 2 places to the right.

$3.2 \text{ m} = 320 \text{ cm}$

1a. 150 mm

b. 837,000 m

c. 5 m is greater; 1 m = 1,000 mm, but 5 m = 5,000 mm.

✓ **Check Understanding** ① Convert each measurement. 1a–b–c. See above left.
a. 15 centimeters to millimeters   **b.** 837 kilometers to meters
c. **Number Sense** Which measurement is greater: 500 millimeters or 5 meters? Explain.

Ongoing Assessment and Intervention

Before the Lesson	During the Lesson	After the Lesson
Diagnose prerequisite skills using:	Monitor progress using:	Assess knowledge using:
• Check Skills You'll Need	• Check Understanding • Additional Examples • Test Prep	• Lesson Quiz • Computer Test Generator CD

You can think of converting to larger units as combining many small units. To do this, you must divide. You should end up with fewer larger units than you had smaller units.

2 EXAMPLE Converting to Larger Units Real World

Geography The distance from the equator to the North Pole along Earth's surface is approximately 10,000,000 meters. What is the approximate distance in kilometers?

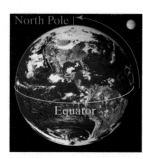

The meter is a smaller unit than the kilometer. So to convert meters to kilometers, divide by 1,000.

$$10{,}000{,}000 \div 1{,}000 = 10{,}000.000$$ ← **To divide by 1,000, move the decimal point 3 places to the left.**

The equator is about 10,000 kilometers from the North Pole.

✓ **Check Understanding** 2 Convert each measurement.
7.5 cm
a. 0.5 centimeter to meters **0.005 m** b. 75 millimeters to centimeters
c. A sprinter runs 60,000 meters each week to train for a 400-meter race. How many kilometers does the sprinter run each week? **60 km**

You can also convert grams or liters to related units.

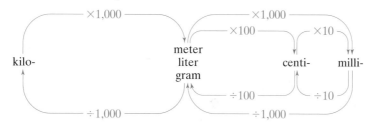

3 EXAMPLE Converting Units of Mass or Capacity

Complete each statement.

a. $0.035 \text{ kg} = \blacksquare \text{ g}$

To convert kilograms to grams, multiply by 1,000.

$$0.035 \times 1{,}000 = 0.035. \rightarrow 35 \text{ grams}$$ ← **To multiply by 1,000, move the decimal point 3 places to the right.**

b. $325 \text{ cL} = \blacksquare \text{ L}$

To convert centiliters to liters, divide by 100.

$$325 \div 100 = 3.25. \rightarrow 3.25 \text{ liters}$$ ← **To divide by 100, move the decimal point 2 places to the left.**

✓ **Check Understanding** 3 Complete each statement.
a. $15 \text{ mg} = \blacksquare \text{ g}$ b. $386 \text{ L} = \blacksquare \text{ kL}$ c. $8.2 \text{ cg} = \blacksquare \text{ g}$
 0.015   0.386   0.082

�* Reaching All Students

| **Below Level** Give students several pairs of exercises like these.

$8 \text{ cm} = \blacksquare \text{ mm}$ **80** $3 \text{ mL} = \blacksquare \text{ L}$ **0.003**
$8 \text{ mm} = \blacksquare \text{ cm}$ **0.8** $3 \text{ L} = \blacksquare \text{ mL}$ **3,000** | **Advanced Learners** One megameter (1 Mm) is one million meters. Write a number to make each statement true.

$5.2 \text{ Mm} = \blacksquare \text{ m}$ **5,200,000**
$7.6 \text{ m} = \blacksquare \text{ Mm}$ **0.0000076** | **Tactile Learners** See note on page 437.

Error Prevention See note on page 438. |

---

2. Teach

 Professional Development

Math Background

The metric system of measurement is a decimal system. This means that all metric units for a given type of measure are related to each other by powers of ten. So conversions between units can be accomplished by multiplying or dividing by 10, 100, 1,000, and so on. Many people consider the relative ease of these calculations to be a major advantage of the metric system over the customary system of measurement.

Teaching Notes

Tactile Learners
Before discussing the examples, give students metric rulers and have them perform several conversions by sight. For instance, have them locate the mark for 4 cm and count the number of millimeters. **40 mm** Similarly, have them count 60 mm and identify the number of centimeters. **6 cm**

PowerPoint
🖳 **Additional Examples**

1 Convert 41 centimeters to millimeters. **410 mm**

2 Convert each measurement.
  a. 4,201 meters to kilometers **4.201 km**
  b. 195 centimeters to meters **1.95 m**

3 Complete each statement.
  a. $125 \text{ g} = \blacksquare \text{ kg}$ **0.125**
  b. $8.4 \text{ L} = \blacksquare \text{ mL}$ **8,400**

Closure

• *How do you convert a metric measurement from one unit to another?* Multiply or divide by the appropriate power of 10.

• *How do you decide whether to multiply or divide?* Multiply to convert from a larger unit to a smaller unit. Divide to convert from a smaller unit to a larger unit.

437

3. Practice

Assignment Guide

1 Objective 1
Ⓐ Ⓑ Core 1–34
Ⓒ Extension 35–39

Test Prep 40–43
Mixed Review 44–48

Error Prevention!

Exercise 1 A student who gives the answer "13,000 m" might believe that inserting three zeros is equivalent to moving the decimal point three places to the right.

EXERCISES

Ⓐ **Practice by Example**

Example 1
(page 436)

Convert each measurement. Exercise 1 has been started for you.

1. 1.3 kilometers to meters
$1.3 \times 1,000 = \blacksquare$ **1,300 m**

2. 83 grams to centigrams
8,300 cg

3. 6,000 meters to centimeters
600,000 cm

4. 0.5 liter to milliliters
500 mL

5. 65 kilograms to grams
65,000 g

6. 59 centimeters to millimeters
590 mm

Example 2
(page 437)

Convert each measurement. Exercise 7 has been started for you.

7. 206 centimeters to meters
$206 \div 100 = \blacksquare$ **2.06 m**

8. 142 liters to kiloliters
0.142 kL

9. 83 milligrams to grams
0.083 g

10. 7.5 millimeters to centimeters
0.75 cm

11. 6,900 milliliters to liters
6.9 L

12. 0.31 centigram to grams
0.0031 g

🌐 **13. Animals** One of the world's longest dogs measured 240 centimeters. How many meters long was this dog? **2.4 m**

Example 3
(page 437)

Complete each statement.

14. $3,070 \text{ mm} = \blacksquare \text{ m}$
3.07

15. $586 \text{ cg} = \blacksquare \text{ g}$
5.86

16. $0.61 \text{ km} = \blacksquare \text{ m}$
610

17. $0.04 \text{ m} = \blacksquare \text{ cm}$
4

18. $4,500 \text{ g} = \blacksquare \text{ mg}$
4,500,000

19. $6.4 \text{ kL} = \blacksquare \text{ L}$
6,400

20. $150 \text{ cL} = \blacksquare \text{ L}$
1.5

21. $120 \text{ mg} = \blacksquare \text{ g}$
0.12

22. $35,000 \text{ L} = \blacksquare \text{ mL}$
35,000,000

Ⓑ **Apply Your Skills**

🌐 **23. Physics** Light travels at approximately 299,792,458 meters per second.
[GPS] Approximately how many kilometers does light travel in one second?
about 299,792.458 km (or about 300,000 km)

🌐 **24. Waves** The world's largest wave was about 0.524 kilometer tall. How many meters tall is this? **524 m**

Convert each measurement to meters, liters, or grams.

25. 8 kL
8,000 L

26. 7,000 mg
7 g

27. 0.24 km
240 m

28. 34,000 cm
340 m

29. 0.07 cL
0.0007 L

30. 52 kg
52,000 g

31. 8.6 mm
0.0086 m

32. 41.5 cg
0.415 g

33. ⟨ **Algebra** ⟩ You have *x* kilograms of peaches. Write an expression for how many grams of peaches you have. **1,000x grams**

34. <u>**Writing in Math**</u> When you convert metric measurements, how do you decide whether to multiply or divide? **See margin.**

Real-World 🌐 **Connection**

The height of this wave is about 5 meters.

[GPS] Use the Guided Problem Solving worksheet with Exercise 23.

34. Answers may vary. Sample: If you are converting to a smaller unit, then you multiply. If you are converting to a larger unit, then you divide.

Practice 9-2   Converting Units in the Metric System

Convert each measurement to meters.

1. 800 mm   **2.** 50 cm   **3.** 2.6 km   **4.** 7 km   **5.** 250 mm
  0.8   0.5 m   2,600 m   7,000 m   0.25 m

6. 35 km   **7.** 40 mm   **8.** 300 cm   **9.** 1.8 km   **10.** 450 cm
  35,000 m   0.04 m   3 m   1,800 m   4.5 m

Convert each measurement to liters.

11. 160 mL   **12.** 0.36 kL   **13.** 0.002 kL   **14.** 240.9 mL   **15.** 368.5 mL
  0.16 L   360 L   2 L   0.2409 L   0.3685 L

16. 8 kL   **17.** 80 mL   **18.** 17.3 mL   **19.** 0.09 kL   **20.** 330 mL
  8,000 L   0.08 L   0.0173 L   90 L   0.33 L

Convert each measurement to grams.

21. 4,000 mg   **22.** 7 kg   **23.** 56,000 mg   **24.** 0.19 kg   **25.** 754.8 mg
  4 g   7,000 g   56 g   190 g   0.7548 g

26. 600 mg   **27.** 90 kg   **28.** 2,800 mg   **29.** 0.4 kg   **30.** 58.1 mg
  0.6 g   90,000 g   2.8 g   400 g   0.0581 g

Convert each measurement.

31. ? km = 3,400 m   **32.** 420 mL = ? cL   **33.** 37 cm = ? m
  3.4   42   3.7

34. 5,100 mg = ? cg   **35.** 77.8 mm = ? cm   **36.** 9.5 kL = ? L
  510   7.78   9,500

37. 2.564 kg = ? g   **38.** ? m = 400,000 cm   **39.** 948 mm = ? cm
  2,564   4,000   94.8

40. ? mL = 0.648 cL   **41.** ? kg = 6,000 g   **42.** ? L = 0.1678 kL
  6.48   6   167.8

Reteaching 9-2   Converting Units in the Metric System

The most common metric units use the prefixes *kilo-*, *centi-*, and *milli-*.

Prefix	Meaning	Examples
kilo-	1,000	kilometer (1,000 m), kilogram (1,000 g), kiloliter (1,000 L)
centi-	$\frac{1}{100}$ or 0.01	centimeter (or 0.01 m), centigram (or 0.01 g), centiliter (or 0.01 L)
milli-	$\frac{1}{1,000}$ or 0.001	millimeter (or 0.001 m), milligram (or 0.001 g), milliliter (or 0.001 L)

Multiply to convert from larger units to smaller units.

Convert 4.7 kilometers to meters.

• A kilometer is larger than a meter. Multiply.
• Since 1 km = 1,000 m, multiply by 1,000.
  4.7 × 1,000 = 4,700
  4.7 km = 4,700 m
• Or use mental math. Multiply by 1,000 by moving the decimal point three places to the *right*.
  4.7 → 4,700

Divide to convert from smaller units.

Convert 347 milliliters to liters.

• A milliliter is smaller than a liter. Divide.
• Since 1,000 mL = 1 L, divide by 1,000.
  347 ÷ 1,000 = 0.347
  347 mL = 0.347 L
• Or use mental math. Divide by 1,000 by moving the decimal point three places to the *left*.
  347 → 0.347

Convert each measurement to meters.

1. 2.5 km   2,500 m   **2.** 371 m   3.71 m   **3.** 490 mm   0.49 m
4. 48 cm   0.48 m   **5.** 4 km   4,000 m   **6.** 1,500 mm   1.5 m

Convert each measurement to liters.

7. 0.6 kL   600 L   **8.** 799 mL   7.99 L   **9.** 0.9 mL   0.0009 L
10. 35.6 mL   0.0356 L   **11.** 0.006 kL   6 L   **12.** 1.8 cL   0.018 L

Convert each measurement to grams.

13. 4 kg   4,000 g   **14.** 661 cg   6.61 g   **15.** 1,500 mg   1.5 g
16. 2 cg   0.02 g   **17.** 1.95 kg   1,950 g   **18.** 2.3 mg   0.0023 g

Convert each measurement.

19. 19 mL = 0.019 L   **20.** 5.5 kg = 5,500 g   **21.** 4.9 cL = 0.049 L
22. 730 mg = 0.73 g   **23.** 0.06 kL = 60 L   **24.** 2,540 mm = 254 cm

438

C Challenge   **Complete each statement.**

35. 1.2 kL = ■ mL   **36.** ■ km = 300,000 cm   **37.** ■ mL = 0.5 kL
1,200,000   3   500,000

38. **Stretch Your Thinking** Draw the three squares at the right without lifting your pencil from the paper, retracing, or crossing any lines. **See left.**

38. start
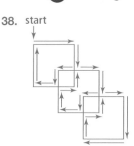

39. **Nutrition** A cup of whole milk has 8.5 grams of fat. A cup of skim milk has 400 milligrams of fat. Find the difference in fat content per cup. **8.1 g**

Test Prep

Multiple Choice

40. Which is NOT equivalent to the others? **A**
A. 355.5 cm   **B.** 35.55 m   **C.** 0.03555 km   **D.** 35,550 mm

41. Which mass is least? **F**
F. 1,560 mg   **G.** 13.2 kg   **H.** 30,000 cg   **I.** 7,428 g

42. Which container could hold 80,000 milliliters? **A**
A. 0.5-kiloliter drum   **B.** 500-milliliter beaker
C. 48-liter fuel tank   **D.** 2-liter bottle

43a–b. See margin.

Extended Response

Take It to the NET
Online lesson quiz at
www.PHSchool.com
Web Code: aaa-0902

43. A bottle is supposed to contain 1 liter of juice. The table shows several quality control test measurements.
  a. Write each measurement in liters.
  b. Which measurement is closest to 1 liter?

Test #	Measurement
1	1,002.3 mL
2	100.1 cL
3	0.000997 kL

Mixed Review

Lesson 8-4   **Name each triangle by its angles and its sides.**

44.   **45.**   **46.**

right isosceles triangle

acute triangle
equilateral triangle

scalene triangle
obtuse triangle

Lesson 6-5   **Write each scale as a ratio in simplest form.**

47. a 2-foot model of a 122-foot field **1 : 61**

48. a 7-inch model of a 40-inch oven **7 : 40**

9-2 Converting Units in the Metric System   **439**

---

43. [4] a. 1.0023 L, 1.001 L, 0.997 L

b. 1.001 cL; explanations may vary. Sample: All of the other measurements are close to 1 L.

[3] one minor error

[2] one part incorrect

[1] no work shown

Perimeters and Areas of Rectangles

What You'll Learn

OBJECTIVE 1 To estimate areas

OBJECTIVE 2 To find perimeters and areas of rectangles

. . . And Why

To install a fence, as in Example 2

✓ **Check Skills You'll Need** ❓ For help, go to Lesson 2-8.

Simplify each expression.

1. 4^2 16 **2.** 6^2 36 **3.** 9^2 81

4. 5.4^2 29.16 **5.** 1.6^2 2.56 **6.** 10^2 100

New Vocabulary • area • perimeter

OBJECTIVE 1

 iTEXT Interactive lesson includes instant self-check, tutorials, and activities.

Estimating Areas of Irregular Shapes by Using Squares

The **area** of a figure is the number of square units the figure contains. You can estimate the area of any figure by using a grid and counting the number of squares it covers.

1 EXAMPLE **Estimating the Area of an Irregular Shape** 🌎 Real World

Estimate the area of the state of Indiana. Each square represents 5,760 square kilometers.

Count squares that are full, almost full, about half full, or almost empty.

13 ← Thirteen squares are full.

2 ← Two squares are almost full, and two are almost empty.

$\left(3 \times \frac{1}{2}\right) = 1\frac{1}{2}$ ← Three squares are about half full.

$16\frac{1}{2}$ ← Total number of squares

About $16\frac{1}{2}$ or 16.5 squares are covered. Each square represents 5,760 square kilometers. So, the area of Indiana is about $16.5 \times 5,760$, or 95,040 square kilometers.

✓ **Check Understanding** ① Estimate the area of the lake. Each square represents 9 square miles.

1. Answers may vary. Sample: about 144 square miles

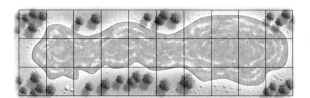

 Ongoing Assessment and Intervention

Before the Lesson
Diagnose prerequisite skills using:
• Check Skills You'll Need

During the Lesson
Monitor progress using:
• Check Understanding
• Additional Examples
• Test Prep

After the Lesson
Assess knowledge using:
• Lesson Quiz
• Computer Test Generator CD

The **perimeter** of a figure is the distance around the figure. You can find the perimeter P of a rectangle by adding its length, width, length, and width as you go around the rectangle.

$$P = \ell + w + \ell + w$$

Thus, the perimeter is twice ℓ plus twice w. Or you could find the perimeter by first adding ℓ and w and then finding twice their sum.

$$P = 2\ell + 2w \quad \text{or} \quad P = 2(\ell + w)$$

You can find the area A of a rectangle by multiplying the length ℓ and the width w.

Key Concepts | **Perimeter and Area of a Rectangle**

$P = 2(\ell + w)$

$A = \ell \times w$

Reading Math

Read the symbol ft² as "square feet."

Common units for length and width are feet (ft), yards (yd), and meters (m). Common units for area are square feet (ft^2), square yards (yd^2), and square meters (m^2).

2 EXAMPLE Finding Perimeter and Area **Real World**

Landscaping Mr. Vostal is planting a garden and installing a fence around his rectangular backyard. Find the perimeter and area of his backyard.

70 ft

House | Backyard | 25 ft ← The length is 70 ft.
The width is 25 ft.

$P = 2(\ell + w)$ ← Use the formula for perimeter.

$\quad = 2(70 + 25)$ ← Substitute 70 for ℓ and 25 for w.

$\quad = 2 \times 95$ ← Add.

$\quad = 190$ ← Multiply.

$A = \ell \times w$ ← Use the formula for area.

$\quad = 70 \times 25$ ← Substitute 70 for ℓ and 25 for w.

$\quad = 1,750$ ← Multiply.

● The perimeter is 190 feet. The area is 1,750 square feet.

Real-World ● Connection

A gardener needs to know the area of a garden to determine available space for plants.

✔ **Check Understanding** **2** Find the perimeter and area of a rectangle with a length of 8 feet and a width of 5 feet. **$P = 26$ ft, $A = 40$ ft²**

---

2. Teach

Professional Development

Math Background

The *perimeter* of a plane figure is the distance around it. Perimeter is measured in *linear units*, such as inches, centimeters, and feet. In contrast, the *area* of a plane figure is the amount of space it encloses. No matter what the shape of the plane figure, its area is measured in *square units*, such as square inches, square centimeters, and square feet.

Teaching Notes

1 EXAMPLE Tactile Learners

Students can use small square tiles to model the rectangle in Check Understanding 1a. Point out that each tile represents *nine square feet*, and that one side of a tile represents *three feet*.

PowerPoint

Additional Examples

1 Estimate the area of the pond shown below. Each square represents 8 square yards.

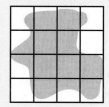

about 80 square yards

2 To renovate their bedroom, the Novaks are carpeting the floor and pasting a wallpaper border along the top of each wall. Find the perimeter and area of their bedroom.

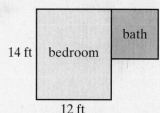

bath

14 ft | bedroom

12 ft

perimeter: 52 ft; area: 168 ft²

👥 **Reaching All Students**

| **Below Level** Give students a sheet of several rectangles and squares drawn on square grids. Have them find the area and perimeter of each figure by counting. | **Advanced Learners** Find all possible whole-number widths and lengths for a rectangle with area 36. **1, 36; 2, 18; 3, 12; 4, 9; 6, 6** Which combination of length/width gives the smallest perimeter? **6, 6** | **English Learners** See note on page 442. **Visual Learners** See note on page 444. |

A square is a rectangle with four sides of equal length. The perimeter of a square is 4 times the length of its side *s*, or 4*s*. The area is $s \times s$, or s^2.

> **Key Concepts** | **Perimeter and Area of a Square**
>
> Perimeter: $P = 4s$
>
> Area: $A = s^2$
>
>

EXAMPLE 3 — Finding the Area of a Square

The perimeter of a square is 32 centimeters. Find its area.

Use the perimeter formula.   Use the area formula.

$$P = 4s \qquad\qquad\qquad A = s^2$$
$$32 = 4s \qquad\qquad\qquad\quad = 8^2$$
$$\frac{32}{4} = \frac{4s}{4} \qquad\qquad\qquad = 64$$
$$8 = s$$

The area of the square is 64 square centimeters, or 64 cm².

✓ **Check Understanding** 3 Find the area of each square given the side *s* or the perimeter *P*.

a. $s = 7$ inches   **49 in.²**   **b.** $P = 24$ feet   **36 ft²**

More Than One Way

Leon and Lauren run laps around the school playground. The playground is 310 feet long and 215 feet wide. How many laps should Leon and Lauren run around the playground to run about 1 mile?

> **Leon's Method**
>
> I can draw a model of the playground and label each side. Then I'll add the four sides to find the length of one lap.
>
> $310 + 215 + 310 + 215 = 1,050$
>
> So, each lap I run is 1,050 feet. Since 1 mile contains 5,280 feet, I must divide to find the number of laps I should run.
>
> $5,280 \div 1,050 \approx 5$
>
> I should run 5 laps around the playground to run about 1 mile.

Lauren's Method

I can use the formula for perimeter. I'll substitute 310 feet for the length and 215 feet for the width.

$$P = 2(\ell + w)$$
$$= 2(310 + 215)$$
$$= 2 \times 525$$
$$= 1,050$$

The perimeter of the playground is 1,050 feet. There are 5,280 feet in a mile. To find the number of laps I should run, I'll divide.

$$5,280 \div 1,050 \approx 5$$

I should run 5 laps around the playground to run about 1 mile.

Choose a Method

Baseball diamonds have the shape of a square. Major League diamonds are 90 feet on each side. Little League baseball diamonds are 60 feet on each side. What is the difference in running distance for a home run (once around the diamond) in each league? Describe your method.

120 feet; check students' methods.

EXERCISES

? **For more practice, see** *Extra Practice.*

A Practice by Example

Example 1
(page 440)

Estimate the area of each figure. Each square represents 1 square inch.
1–6. Answers may vary. Samples are given.

1.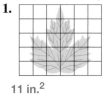

11 in.²

2.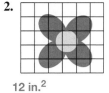

12 in.²

3.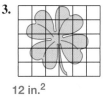

12 in.²

Estimate the area of each figure. Each square represents 4 square feet.

4.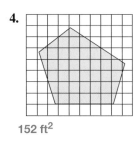

152 ft²

5.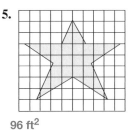

96 ft²

6.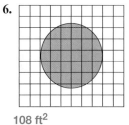

108 ft²

 GPS Use the Guided Problem Solving worksheet with Exercise 21.

Assignment Guide

1 **Objective 1**
Ⓐ Ⓑ Core 1–6, 20

2 **Objective 2**
Ⓐ Ⓑ Core 7–19, 21–32
Ⓒ Extension 33–34

Test Prep 35–38
Mixed Review 39–44

Error Prevention!

Exercises 4–6 Watch for students who count the number of squares but forget to multiply by 4.

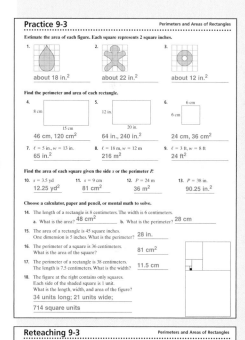

Practice 9-3   Perimeters and Areas of Rectangles

Estimate the area of each figure. Each square represents 2 square inches.

1. about 18 in.²
2. about 22 in.²
3. about 12 in.²

Find the perimeter and area of each rectangle.

4. 8 cm, 15 cm — 46 cm, 120 cm²
5. 12 in., 20 in. — 64 in., 240 in.²
6. 6 cm, 6 cm — 24 cm, 36 cm²
7. $\ell = 5$ in., $w = 13$ in. — 65 in.²
8. $\ell = 18$ m, $w = 12$ m — 216 m²
9. $\ell = 3$ ft, $w = 8$ ft — 24 ft²

Find the area of each square given the side s or the perimeter P.

10. $s = 3.5$ yd — 12.25 yd²
11. $s = 9$ cm — 81 cm²
12. $P = 24$ m — 36 m²
13. $P = 38$ in. — 90.25 in.²

Choose a calculator, paper and pencil, or mental math to solve.

14. The length of a rectangle is 8 centimeters. The width is 6 centimeters.
    a. What is the area? 48 cm²   b. What is the perimeter? 28 cm
15. The area of a rectangle is 45 square inches. One dimension is 5 inches. What is the perimeter? 28 in.
16. The perimeter of a square is 36 centimeters. What is the area of the square? 81 cm²
17. The perimeter of a rectangle is 38 centimeters. The length is 7.5 centimeters. What is the width? 11.5 cm
18. The figure at the right contains only squares. Each side of the shaded square is 1 unit. What is the length, width, and area of the figure? 34 units long; 21 units wide; 714 square units

Reteaching 9-3   Perimeters and Areas of Rectangles

Perimeter

The *perimeter* of a figure is the sum of the lengths of its sides. Opposite sides of a rectangle are equal. To find the perimeter, add the 2 lengths (ℓ) and the 2 widths (w).

$$P = \ell + \ell + w + w \text{ or } P = 2\ell + 2w$$

Find the perimeter.

$$P = 2\ell + 2w$$
$$= 2(14) + 2(9)$$
$$= 28 + 18 = 46$$

The perimeter is 46 centimeters.

Area

The *area* of a figure is the number of square units needed to cover the figure. To find the area of a rectangle, multiply the length (ℓ) and the width (w).

$$A = \ell \times w$$

Find the area.

$$A = \ell \times w$$
$$= 6 \times 5$$
$$= 30$$

The area is 30 square meters.

Estimate the area of each figure. Each square represents 1 square inch.

1. $A \approx 12\frac{1}{2}$ in.²
2. $A \approx 6$ in.²
3. $A \approx 14$ in.²

Find the perimeter and area of each rectangle or square.

4. $\ell = 12$ cm, $w = 2$ cm — 28 cm; 24 cm²
5. $\ell = 9$ ft, $w = 7.5$ ft — 33 ft; 67.5 ft²
6. $\ell = 2.5$ m, $w = 2.5$ m — 10 m; 6.25 m²
7. $\ell = 5.5$ in., $w = 5.5$ in. — 22 in.; 30.25 in.²
8. $\ell = 6.2$ in., $w = 3.4$ in. — 19.2 in.; 21.08 in.²
9. $\ell = 4.5$ ft, $w = 0.75$ ft — 10.5 ft; 3.375 ft²
10. $\ell = 8$ cm, $w = 8$ cm — 32 cm; 64 cm²
11. $\ell = 10.5$ m, $w = 5.2$ m — 31.4 m; 54.6 m²
12. $\ell = 22$ in., $w = 9$ in. — 62 in.; 198 in.²
13. What is the area of a square with a perimeter of 60 meters? 225 m²

Example 2
(page 441)

Find the perimeter and area of each rectangle.

7.
4 in.
4 in.

$P = 16$ in., $A = 16$ in.^{2}

8.
4 ft
9 ft

$P = 26$ ft, $A = 36$ ft^2

9.
16 m
8 m

$P = 48$ m, $A = 128$ m^2

10. $\ell = 12$ in., $w = 7$ in.
$P = 38$ in., $A = 84$ in.^{2}

11. $\ell = 8$ ft, $w = 5$ ft
$P = 26$ ft, $A = 40$ ft^2

12. $\ell = 13$ in., $w = 9.5$ in.
$P = 45$ in., $A = 123.5$ in.^{2}

13. $\ell = 1.5$ m, $w = 0.25$ m
$P = 3.5$ m, $A = 0.375$ m^2

Example 3
(page 442)

Find the area of each square given the side s or the perimeter P.

14. $s = 2$ yd   4 yd^2 **15.** $s = 5$ m   25 m^2 **16.** $s = 14.2$ ft   201.64 ft^2

17. $P = 20$ cm   25 cm^2 **18.** $P = 48$ in.   144 in.^{2} **19.** $P = 10$ mm   6.25 mm^2

B Apply Your Skills

20. Open-Ended On graph paper, trace your hand with your fingers spread apart. Estimate the area of your hand.   **Check students' work.**

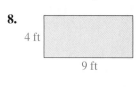

21. Stamps The world's smallest stamp, shown at the left, measured
[GPS] 0.31 inch by 0.37 inch. Find the area of the stamp.   **0.1147 in.^{2}**

Real-World Connection

The world's smallest stamp was issued in Colombia from 1863 to 1866.

Use a centimeter ruler to measure the length and width of each rectangle to the nearest millimeter. Then find the perimeter and area.

22.

98 mm; 570 mm^2

23.

70 mm; 294 mm^2

24.

84 mm; 425 mm^2

25. a. Draw and label as many rectangles as you can with a perimeter of 24 units. Use only whole units.   **Check students' drawings**

b. Find the area of each rectangle. Record your data in a table like the one shown below.   **See margin.**

Length	Width	Perimeter	Area
11 units	1 unit	24 units	11 square units

c. What do you notice about the rectangle with the greatest area?
   It is a square.

26. The area increases from 13.5 in.^{2} to 54 in.^{2}, which is 4 times the area of the original rectangle.

26. Number Sense A rectangle has a length of 4.5 inches and a width of 3 inches. How would the area change if you doubled both dimensions?
See left.

27. Writing in Math Suppose you know the area of a rectangle. Can you then find its perimeter? Use examples to explain why or why not.
See margin.

25b.

L	W	P	A
11	1	24	11
10	2	24	20
9	3	24	27
8	4	24	32
7	5	24	35
6	6	24	36

27. Answers may vary. Sample: Knowing the area alone is not enough information to find the perimeter. For example, if the area is 20 square units, you cannot tell whether the dimensions are 10-by-2 or 5-by-4.

28. Recreation The area of a rectangular swimming pool is 32 square meters. One side is 4 meters. What is the perimeter of the pool?
24 m

Find the perimeter and area of each rectangle.

29. $\ell = 2.8$ m, $w = 4.4$ m
$P = 14.4$ m; $A = 12.32$ m^2

30. $\ell = 5.6$ ft, $w = 8.7$ ft
$P = 28.6$ ft; $A = 48.72$ ft^2

31. $\ell = \frac{3}{4}$ in., $w = \frac{4}{5}$ in.
$P = 3\frac{1}{10}$ in.; $A = \frac{3}{5}$ in.^{2}

32. $\ell = 2\frac{1}{3}$ in., $w = 4\frac{1}{6}$ in.
$P = 13$ in.; $A = 9\frac{13}{18}$ in.^{2}

 Challenge

33. Reasoning How many square feet are in a square yard? How many square inches are in a square yard? Justify your answer using diagrams.
See margin.

34. Stretch Your Thinking At a food store, $\frac{1}{2}$ of the customers paid for their purchases by check. Of the remaining customers, $\frac{2}{3}$ paid with a credit card, and the rest paid cash. What fraction of the customers paid cash?
$\frac{1}{6}$

Test Prep

Multiple Choice

35. Each square represents 100 square meters. Which is the best estimate for the area of the lake? **C**
A. 14.5 m^2 **B.** 150 m^2
C. 1,400 m^2 **D.** 3,000 m^2

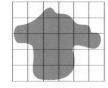

Take It to the NET
Online lesson quiz at
www.PHSchool.com
Web Code: aaa-0903

36. A square has an area of 25 square meters. What is its perimeter? **H**
F. 5 meters   **G.** 6.25 meters   **H.** 20 meters   **I.** 25 meters

37. Wanda would like a garden with an area of 18 square feet. Her garden space is 6 feet long. How wide should she make the garden?
A. 3 feet **A**   **B.** 48 feet   **C.** 54 feet   **D.** 108 feet

Short Response

38. The area of a movie screen is 576 square feet. The ratio of the area of the screen to its width is 16 : 1. **(a)** Write a proportion to find the width of the screen. **(b)** Solve your proportion. See back of book.

Mixed Review

Lesson 6-6

Write each fraction as a percent.

39. $\frac{3}{4}$ 75%   **40.** $\frac{17}{25}$ 68%   **41.** $\frac{13}{20}$ 65%   **42.** $\frac{2}{5}$ 40%   **43.** $\frac{23}{50}$ 46%

Lesson 6-5

44. A map's scale is 1 centimeter : 10 kilometers. How many centimeters on the map represent an actual distance of 25 kilometers? **2.5 cm**

33. There are 3 ft × 3 ft, or 9 ft^2, in 1 yd^2.

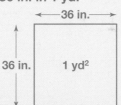

There are 12 in. in 1 ft or 36 in. in 1 yd.

←——36 in.——→

36 in.   1 yd^2

So, 1 yd^2 equals 36 in. × 36 in., or 1,296 in.^{2}.

Enrichment 9-3   Perimeters and Areas of Rectangles
Patterns in Geometry

You have learned that perimeter is the distance around the outside of a figure. Consider how the perimeter of a rectangle changes when you change the lengths of its sides.

1. What is the perimeter of the rectangle? **12 ft**
2. Write the length of each side of the rectangle when each side is doubled.
3. Find the perimeter of the new rectangle. **24 ft**
4. What happens to the perimeter of the rectangle if the length of each side is doubled?
It is doubled.
5. Write the length of each side of the rectangle when each side is tripled.
6. Find the perimeter of the new rectangle. **36 ft**
7. What happens to the perimeter of the rectangle if the length of each side is halved?
It is halved.
8. What happens to the perimeter of a rectangle when each side is multiplied by the same factor?
The perimeter is multiplied by the same factor.
9. Do you think the relationship will be the same if the length of each side is increased by 2 units? Give an example to prove or disprove your theory.
No; the rectangle above would have a perimeter of 20 units, which is 8 units more than that of the original rectangle.
10. What is the perimeter of the top rectangle above if you add 3 units to each side? If you add 4 units?
24 ft; 28 ft
11. Write an expression for the perimeter of the top rectangle above if you add x units to each side
12 + 4x

445

Lesson Preview

 Check Skills You'll Need

Classifying Quadrilaterals
Lesson 8-5: Example 2. Extra
Practice, p. 649.

Lesson Resources

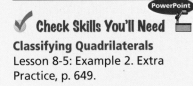

📁 **Teaching Resources**
Practice, Reteaching, Enrichment
Checkpoint Quiz 1

👥 **Reaching All Students**
Practice Workbook 9-4
Spanish Practice Workbook 9-4
Reading and Math Literacy 9B
Spanish Reading and Math
 Literacy 9B
Spanish Checkpoint Quiz 1
Guided Problem Solving 9-4
Hands-On Activities 32

⏰ **Presentation Assistant Plus!**
Transparencies
• Check Skills You'll Need 9-4
• Problem of the Day 9-4
• Additional Examples 9-4
• Student Edition Answers 9-4
• Lesson Quiz 9-4
• Classroom Aid 2, 20, 21
PH Presentation Pro CD-ROM 9-4

(ASSESSMENT *SYSTEM*)

Checkpoint Quiz 1
Computer Test Generator CD

💻 **Technology**
Resource Pro® CD-ROM
Computer Test Generator CD
PH Presentation Pro CD-ROM

💻 **www.PHSchool.com**
Student Site
• Teacher Web Code: aak-5500
• Algebra Readiness Puzzles 9
• Self-grading Lesson Quiz

PH SuccessNet Teacher Center
• Lesson Planner
• Resources

Plus

Areas of Parallelograms and Triangles

What You'll Learn

▽**OBJECTIVE 1** To find the areas of parallelograms and triangles

▽**OBJECTIVE 2** To find the areas of complex figures

... And Why

To find the area of a plot of land, as in Example 2

✓ **Check Skills You'll Need**

❓ For help, go to Lesson 8-5.
1–3. See back of book.

Write all the possible names for each quadrilateral. Then give the best name.

1.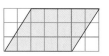

2.

3.

New Vocabulary
• base of a parallelogram   • height of a parallelogram
• base of a triangle   • height of a triangle

▽**OBJECTIVE 1**

Finding the Areas of Parallelograms and Triangles

(*i*TEXT) Interactive lesson includes instant self-check, tutorials, and activities.

Investigation: Comparing Areas

• On graph paper, draw a parallelogram that is not a rectangle. Draw a perpendicular segment from one vertex to the base.

• Cut out the parallelogram. Cut along the perpendicular segment. Rearrange the two figures to form a rectangle.

1. a. What is the area of the rectangle? Answers may vary.
   b. What do you think was the area of the original parallelogram?
   c. Repeat this activity. Make two different-sized parallelograms. Are the results similar? Check students' work.

1b. The areas are the same; the pieces were just rearranged.

Any side can be considered the **base of a parallelogram.** The **height of a parallelogram** is the perpendicular distance between opposite bases. The area of a parallelogram is the product of the base and the height.

Key Concepts **Area of a Parallelogram**

$A = b \times h$

446 Chapter 9 Geometry and Measurement

Ongoing Assessment and Intervention

Before the Lesson
Diagnose prerequisite skills using:
• Check Skills You'll Need

During the Lesson
Monitor progress using:
• Check Understanding
• Additional Examples
• Test Prep

After the Lesson
Assess knowledge using:
• Lesson Quiz
• Computer Test Generator CD
• Chapter Checkpoint 1 (p. 450)

1 EXAMPLE Finding the Area of a Parallelogram

Find the area of the parallelogram.

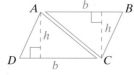

$A = b \times h$ ← Use the formula for the area of a parallelogram.

$= 5 \times 3$ ← Substitute 5 for b and 3 for h.

$= 15$ ← Simplify.

● The area of the parallelogram is 15 square meters.

✔ **Check Understanding** **1** Find the area of each parallelogram given the base b and the height h.
 a. $b = 14\,m, h = 5\,m$ **70 m²** **b.** $b = 30\,ft, h = 17.3\,ft$ **519 ft²**

Any side can be the **base of a triangle.**
The **height of a triangle** is the length
of the perpendicular segment from a vertex
to the base opposite that vertex.

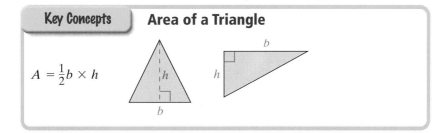

The area of a triangle is half of the area of a
parallelogram with the same base length and height.

Key Concepts **Area of a Triangle**

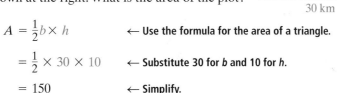

$A = \frac{1}{2}b \times h$

2 EXAMPLE Finding the Area of a Triangle

Real World

Conservation A conservation group plans to buy
a triangular plot of land. A diagram of the plot
is shown at the right. What is the area of the plot?

10 km
30 km

$A = \frac{1}{2}b \times h$ ← Use the formula for the area of a triangle.

$= \frac{1}{2} \times 30 \times 10$ ← Substitute 30 for b and 10 for h.

$= 150$ ← Simplify.

● The area of the plot is 150 square kilometers.

2a. 259.5 m²

✔ **Check Understanding** **2 a.** A triangle has a base of 30 meters and a height of 17.3 meters. Find its area.
 b. Number Sense Suppose the base of the triangular plot of land in
 Example 2 were doubled. How would the area of the plot change?
 The area would double.

9-4 Areas of Parallelograms and Triangles **447**

Real-World ● Connection

Conservation groups buy
land to preserve its natural
state.

2. Teach

Professional Development

Math Background

Students generally remember the area formula for a rectangle, $A = \ell \times w$, because it is so easily derived from a visual image. That is, given a rectangle with a whole-number length ℓ and width w, it is not difficult to imagine it enclosing $\ell \times w$ squares on a grid. This lesson provides students with visual images that can help them to derive the area formulas for a parallelogram and a triangle from the rectangle area formula.

Teaching Notes

Investigation (Optional)
To make their parallelograms, suggest that students first draw two horizontal segments, counting very carefully to make sure the segments are equal in length. When they connect the endpoints of the horizontal segments, the resulting figure will be a parallelogram.

2 EXAMPLE Teaching Tip

The height of a triangle is also called its *altitude*. Students who have studied triangles in previous years might have learned this term.

Error Prevention!

In calculating the area of a triangle, students might multiply the base and height but forget to multiply by $\frac{1}{2}$. Encourage them to always begin their work by writing the formula, as demonstrated in Example 2.

PowerPoint
Additional Examples

1 Find the area of the parallelogram. 26.4 in.²

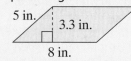
5 in. 3.3 in.
8 in.

2 A park is a triangular plot of land. The plot has a base of 214 m and a height of 70 m. What is the area of the plot? 7,490 m²

447

③ EXAMPLE Alternative Method

Often there is more than one way to split a complex figure. Students might notice that the area of this figure can also be found as follows.

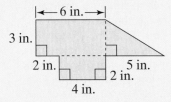

larger rectangle: $A = 6 \times 3 = 18$ in.^{2}
smaller rectangle: $A = 4 \times 2 = 8$ in.^{2}
triangle: $A = \frac{1}{2}(5 \times 3) = 7.5$ in.^{2}
total area: $18 + 8 + 7.5 = 33.5$ in.^{2}

Careers
The boundaries of a plot of land often form a complex figure. Locating these boundaries and measuring them precisely is the job of a *surveyor*. The surveyor then uses the measurements to prepare a drawing and write a description of the plot for legal documents such as deeds and leases. To determine the area of the plot, a surveyor might use the technique that is taught in Example 3.

PowerPoint
🖳 **Additional Examples**

③ Find the area of the figure. **56 m²**

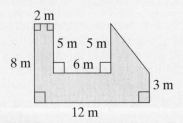

Closure

- *How do you find the area of a parallelogram?* Find the product of the base and height.
- *How do you find the area of a triangle?* Find half the product of the base and height
- *How do you find the area of a complex figure?* Split the figure into smaller polygons. Then find the area of each polygon and add.

448

Sometimes it helps to split a figure into smaller polygons. Then you can find the area of each polygon and add.

③ EXAMPLE Finding the Area of a Complex Figure

Find the area of the figure below.

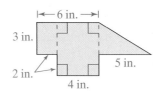

Split the polygon into two ← rectangles and a triangle, as shown by the dashed lines.

Area of smaller rectangle: $3 \times 2 = 6$, or 6 in.^{2}
Area of larger rectangle: $5 \times 4 = 20$, or 20 in.^{2} ← Find the area of each polygon.
Area of triangle: $\frac{1}{2}(5 \times 3) = \frac{1}{2} \times 15$, or 7.5 in.^{2}

○ The total area is $6 + 20 + 7.5$, or 33.5 square inches.

✔ **Check Understanding** ③ **a.** Find the area of the complex figure at the right. **16m²**
b. Reasoning Show another way to split the figure in Example 3 to find the area. **See margin.**

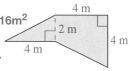

EXERCISES

❓ For more practice, see *Extra Practice.*

Ⓐ **Practice by Example**

Find the area of each parallelogram. Exercise 1 has been started for you.

Example 1
(page 447)

1.
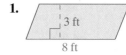
$A = b \times h = 8 \times 3$
24 ft²

2.
4 m
4 m
16 m²

3.
12 in.
6 in.
72 in.²

Example 2
(page 447)

Find the area of each triangle. Exercise 4 has been started for you.

4.
40 cm²
5 cm
16 cm
$A = \frac{1}{2}b \times h$
$= \frac{1}{2} \times 16 \times 5$

5.
31.5 m²
9 m
7 m

6. 99 yd²
11 yd
18 yd

448 **Chapter 9** Geometry and Measurement

3b. Answers may vary.
Sample:

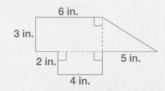

7. Art Kaitlyn is sprinkling glitter on a card. The area where she has applied the glue is a triangle with a base of 5 centimeters and a height of 10 centimeters. How large is the area she plans to glitter? **25 cm²**

Example 3
(page 448)

Find the area of each complex figure.

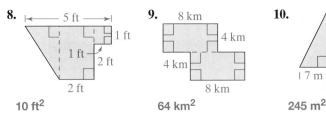

8. 5 ft, 1 ft, 1 ft, 2 ft, 2 ft
10 ft²

9. 8 km, 4 km, 4 km, 8 km
64 km²

10. 7 m | 7 m | 9 m | 10 m |
245 m²

B **Apply Your Skills**

11. Food A triangular cracker has a base of 4 centimeters and a height of 3.5 centimeters. What is the area of the cracker? **7 cm²**

12. Parking Each space at the left has a width of 8.5 feet and a length of 22 feet. Find the area of a parking space. **187 ft²**

Real-World Connection

Parking spaces are sometimes shaped like parallelograms.

Find the area of each figure.

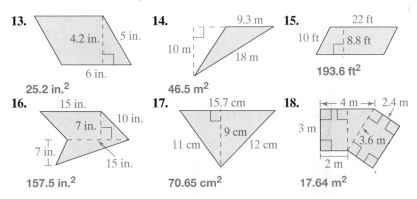

13. 4.2 in., 5 in., 6 in.
25.2 in.²

14. 9.3 m, 10 m, 18 m
46.5 m²

15. 22 ft, 10 ft, 8.8 ft
193.6 ft²

16. 15 in., 7 in., 10 in., 7 in., 15 in.
157.5 in.²

17. 15.7 cm, 11 cm, 9 cm, 12 cm
70.65 cm²

18. 4 m, 2.4 m, 3 m, 3.6 m, 2 m
17.64 m²

Find the area of a parallelogram and a triangle with the given dimensions.

19. $b = 4$ ft, $h = 9$ ft
36 ft²; 18 ft²

20. $b = 20$ yd, $h = 34$ yd
680 yd²; 340 yd²

21. $b = 3.5$ m, $h = 7$ m
24.5 m²; 12.25 m²

22. $b = 5.3$ ft, $h = 6.5$ ft
34.45 ft²; 17.225 ft²

23. Number Sense Two parallelograms have the same base length. The height of the first is half the height of the second. What is the ratio of the area of the smaller parallelogram to the area of the larger one?
1 : 2

24. Answers may vary. Sample: Divide the perimeter by 3 to get the base b. Then use $A = \frac{1}{2}bh$.

24. Writing in Math Suppose you know the perimeter and the height of an equilateral triangle. Explain how you would find the area of the triangle.

25. Algebra A parallelogram has an area of 66 square inches and a base
GPS length of 5 inches. What is the height of the parallelogram? **13.2 in.**

 Use the Guided Problem Solving worksheet with Exercise 25.

Assignment Guide

1 **Objective 1**
Ⓐ Ⓑ Core 1–7, 11–15, 17, 19–25

2 **Objective 2**
Ⓐ Ⓑ Core 8–10, 16, 18
Ⓒ Extension 26–27

Test Prep 30–33
Mixed Review 34–38

Tactile Learners
Exercises 13–14 Students can use geoboards to help find these areas.

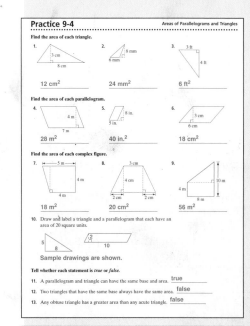

Practice 9-4 — Areas of Parallelograms and Triangles

Find the area of each triangle.

1. 3 cm, 8 cm — **12 cm²**
2. 8 mm, 6 mm — **24 mm²**
3. 3 ft, 4 ft — **6 ft²**

Find the area of each parallelogram.

4. 4 m, 7 m — **28 m²**
5. 8 in., 5 in. — **40 in.²**
6. 3 cm, 6 cm — **18 cm²**

Find the area of each complex figure.

7. 5 m, 4 m — **18 m²**
8. 3 cm, 4 cm, 4 m — **20 cm²**
9. 4 m, 8 m, 10 m — **56 m²**

10. Draw and label a triangle and a parallelogram that each have an area of 20 square units.
Sample drawings are shown.

Tell whether each statement is *true* or *false*.

11. A parallelogram and triangle can have the same base and area. **true**
12. Two triangles that have the same base always have the same area. **false**
13. Any obtuse triangle has a greater area than any acute triangle. **false**

Reteaching 9-4 — Areas of Parallelograms and Triangles

Parallelogram
To find the area of a parallelogram, multiply base times height.
$A = b \times h$

Triangle
The area of a triangle is $\frac{1}{2}$ times the base times the height.
$A = \frac{1}{2}b \times h$

Find the area of the parallelogram.
$h = 6$ cm, $b = 3$ cm
$A = b \times h$
$= 3 \times 6$
$= 18$
The area is 18 square centimeters.

Find the area of the triangle.
$h = 6$ cm, $b = 3$ cm
$A = \frac{1}{2} \times b \times h$
$= \frac{1}{2} \times 3 \times 6$
$= 9$
The area is 9 square centimeters.

Find the area of each parallelogram.

1. $b = 6$ ft, $h = 8$ ft — **48 ft²**
2. $b = 12$ in., $h = 9$ in. — **108 in.²**
3. $b = 6$ yd, $h = 12$ yd — **72 yd²**
4. $b = 2.8$ in., $h = 3.4$ in. — **9.52 in.²**
5. $b = 31$ yd, $h = 19$ yd — **589 yd²**
6. $b = 4.5$ m, $h = 4.5$ m — **20.25 m²**
7. $b = 15$ cm, $h = 7$ cm — **105 cm²**
8. $b = 8.3$ ft, $h = 11.7$ ft — **97.11 ft²**
9. $b = 14.4$ m, $h = 6.5$ m — **93.6 m²**

Find the area of each triangle.

10. $b = 8$ cm, $h = 14$ cm — **56 cm²**
11. $b = 7$ in., $h = 18$ in. — **63 in.²**
12. $b = 11$ m, $h = 4.6$ m — **25.3 m²**
13. $b = 6.4$ ft, $h = 3.5$ ft — **11.2 ft²**
14. $b = 104$ in., $h = 55$ in. — **2,860 in.²**
15. $b = 5.9$ cm, $h = 4.2$ cm — **12.39 cm²**
16. $b = 1.7$ m, $h = 3.3$ m — **2.805 m²**
17. $b = 5.8$ yd, $h = 5.8$ yd — **16.82 yd²**
18. $b = 8.6$ in., $h = 0.8$ in. — **3.44 in.²**

449

Find the area of each.

1. parallelogram: b = 6 in., h = 17 in. **102 in.²**

2. triangle: b = 8 cm, h = 19 cm **76 cm²**

Chapter Checkpoint

To check understanding of Lessons 9-1 to 9-4:

Checkpoint Quiz 1 (p. 450)

📁 **Teaching Resources**
Checkpoint Quiz 1 (also in Prentice Hall Assessment System)

👥 **Reaching All Students**
Reading and Math Literacy 9B

Spanish versions available

Test Prep

Resources
For additional practice with a variety of test item formats:
• Test Prep, p. 485
• Test-Taking Strategies, p. 481
• Test-Taking Strategies With Transparencies

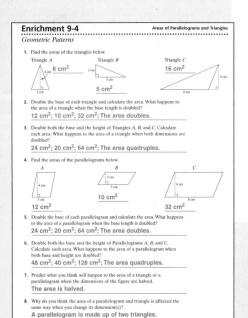

C Challenge

26. Draw the trapezoid at the right. Split it into two triangles with 3-centimeter heights. Then find the area of the trapezoid. **15 cm²**

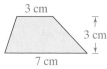
3 cm / 3 cm / 7 cm

27. **Stretch Your Thinking** An 8-foot wide walkway surrounds a rectangular pool that is 20 feet by 30 feet. Find the area of the walkway. **1,056 ft²**

Test Prep

Multiple Choice

28. What is the area of the figure at the right in square feet? **D**
    A. 7   **B.** 8   **C.** 9   **D.** 10

    5 ft / 4 ft

29. A parallelogram has a height of 6 inches and a base length of 8.5 inches. What is its area? **I**
    F. 2.5 in.²   **G.** 14.5 in.²   **H.** 25.5 in.²   **I.** 51 in.²

Take It to the NET
Online lesson quiz at
www.PHSchool.com
Web Code: aaa-0904

30. A triangle has an area of 42 square meters and a base length of 7 meters. What is the height of the triangle? **C**
    A. 6 m   **B.** 7 m   **C.** 12 m   **D.** 14 m

Short Response

31. The area of a rectangular space is 128 square feet. **31a–b. See margin.**
    a. Find all the possible pairs of whole-number dimensions in feet.
    b. Explain which pair allows enough space for a car to park.

Mixed Review

Lesson 8-6 32. **Clothing** You have 2 pairs of pants, 3 sweaters, and 6 shirts. How many days can you wear a different outfit consisting of a pair of pants, a sweater, and a shirt before you wear the same one again? **36 days**

Lesson 6-7 **Find each answer.**

33. 50% of 492   34. 35% of 84   35. 15% of 120 **18**   36. 11% of 500 **55**
    246   **29.4**

Checkpoint Quiz 1   Lessons 9-1 through 9-4

 TEXT Instant self-check quiz online and on CD-ROM

Convert each measurement to meters, liters, or grams.

1. 62 milliliters **0.062 L**   2. 4.3 kilograms **4,300 g**   3. 178 centimeters **1.78 m**

Find the area of a figure with the given dimensions.

4. square: s = 8.5 cm **72.25 cm²**   5. triangle: b = 4 mi, h = 9 mi **18 mi²**

Alternative Assessment

Each student in a pair draws and labels a parallelogram, a triangle, and a complex figure similar to those in the Examples. Partners exchange drawings and find the area of each figure.

31. [2] a. 1 × 128, 2 × 64, 4 × 32, 8 × 16

b. 8 × 16; spaces less than 8 ft wide are too narrow.

[1] one part correct

 **Exploring Circles**

For Use With Lesson 9-5

Recall that the perimeter of a figure is the distance around the figure. In Lesson 9-3, you learned the formula for the perimeter of a rectangle and a square. In this Investigation, you will explore the distance around a circle.

Activity

Materials: several circular objects, metric tape measure **1–5. Check students' work.**

1. Find several circular objects, such as a can or a wastebasket.

2. Copy the table shown below.

Object	Distance around the circle	Distance across the circle	Distance around the circle / Distance across the circle

3. Measure the longest distance across each circle to the nearest tenth. Record the results in your table.

4. Measure the distance around each circle by wrapping the tape measure around the outside of each circle. Measure to the nearest tenth. Record the results in your table.

5. **Calculator** Find the ratio $\frac{\text{Distance around the circle}}{\text{Distance across the circle}}$ for each circle to the nearest tenth. Record the results in your table.

6. **Patterns** What do you notice about the relationship between the distance around a circle and the distance across a circle? **The distance around the circle is about 3 times the distance across.**

7. **Algebra** Suppose the distance across a circle is x. Write an expression to approximate the distance around the circle. **Sample: 3.1x**

8. **a.** In the diagram at the right, the distance across the circle is the same as the side length of the square. Use your expression from Exercise 7 to estimate the distance around the circle. **18.6 cm**
   b. Find the perimeter of the square. **24 cm**
   c. What is the difference between your distance around the circle and the perimeter of the square? **5.4 cm**

6 cm

Investigation Exploring Circles **451**

 Investigation

Exploring Circles

In this feature, students measure to investigate the relationship between the circumference and diameter of any circle. In Lesson 9-5 that follows, students formally learn the terms radius, diameter, and circumference, as well as the meaning of *pi*.

Materials

- metric tape measure
- calculator
- several circular objects

Teaching Notes

For any circle, the ratio of the circumference to its diameter is *pi*, which is about 3.14. Expect student measurements of that ratio to approximate this number.

Guide students to understand that the *distance across the circle* refers to the line segment that passes through the center of the circle. It is the largest measure possible across the circle.

Error Prevention!

Review and demonstrate how to measure something to the nearest tenth of a centimeter (nearest mm), and how to round decimals to the nearest hundredth.

Teaching Tip

Have students work with partners to make and record their measurements. Students should take turns measuring and recording the measurements.

Exercises

Exercise 7 As an extension, ask: *If the distance around a circle is* y, *what is the distance across the circle?* **Sample:** $\frac{y}{3}$

451

Circles and Circumference

Lesson Preview

✓ Check Skills You'll Need

Multiplying a Whole Number by a Decimal
Lesson 1-7: Example 1. Extra Practice, p. 642.

Lesson Resources

📁 **Teaching Resources**
Practice, Reteaching, Enrichment

👥 **Reaching All Students**
Practice Workbook 9-5
Spanish Practice Workbook 9-5
Guided Problem Solving 9-5
Hands-On Activities 37

⏱ **Presentation Assistant Plus!**
Transparencies
• Check Skills You'll Need 9-5
• Problem of the Day 9-5
• Additional Examples 9-5
• Student Edition Answers 9-5
• Lesson Quiz 9-5
• Classroom Aid 4, 11, 20, 21
PH Presentation Pro CD-ROM 9-5

PRENTICE HALL
ASSESSMENT SYSTEM

Computer Test Generator CD

💻 **Technology**
Resource Pro® CD-ROM
Computer Test Generator CD
PH Presentation Pro CD-ROM

💻 **www.PHSchool.com**
Student Site
• Teacher Web Code: aak-5500
• Self-grading Lesson Quiz

PH SuccessNet Teacher Center
• Lesson Planner
• Resources

Plus **i TEXT**

452

What You'll Learn

OBJECTIVE 1 To identify parts of a circle

OBJECTIVE 2 To find circumference

. . . And Why

To find the circumference of an archery target, as in Example 3

✓ Check Skills You'll Need

❓ For help, go to Lesson 1-7.

Find each product.

1. 2×3.14 6.28

2. 3.14×8 25.12

3. 3.14×50 157

4. $2 \times 3.14 \times 35$ 219.8

5. 3.14×12 37.68

6. $2 \times 3.14 \times 10$ 62.8

New Vocabulary
• circle • radius • chord • diameter
• circumference

OBJECTIVE 1

 Interactive lesson includes instant self-check, tutorials, and activities.

Identifying Parts of a Circle

A **circle** is the set of points in a plane that are the same distance from a given point called the *center*. A circle is named after its center point.

Reading Math
Radii (RAY dee eye) is the plural of *radius*.

A **radius** is a segment that connects the center to the circle.

A **chord** is a segment that has both endpoints on the circle.

A **diameter** is a chord that passes through the center of a circle.

Center

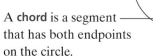

1 EXAMPLE **Identifying Parts of a Circle**

a. List the radii shown in circle P.

The radii are $\overline{PA}$, $\overline{PB}$, $\overline{PC}$, and $\overline{PD}$.

b. List the chords shown in circle P.

The chords are $\overline{AB}$, $\overline{BC}$, $\overline{CD}$, $\overline{DA}$, $\overline{AC}$, and $\overline{BD}$.

✓ **Check Understanding** 1 List the diameters shown in circle P. *$\overline{AC}$, $\overline{BD}$*

In Example 1, the diameter $\overline{AC}$ consists of two radii $\overline{PA}$ and $\overline{PC}$. So, the length of a diameter of a circle is twice the length of a radius. Of course, this means that the radius is half the length of a diameter!

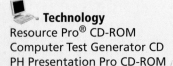 **Ongoing Assessment and Intervention**

Before the Lesson	During the Lesson	After the Lesson
Diagnose prerequisite skills using: • Check Skills You'll Need	Monitor progress using: • Check Understanding • Additional Examples • Test Prep	Assess knowledge using: • Lesson Quiz • Computer Test Generator CD

 **EXAMPLE** **Finding Radius and Diameter** Real World

Amusement Parks The diameter of a Ferris wheel is 250 feet. How long is its radius?

$$r = \frac{1}{2} \times 250 \quad \leftarrow \text{The radius is half the diameter.}$$

$$= 125 \quad \leftarrow \text{Simplify.}$$

● The radius of the Ferris wheel is 125 feet.

✓ **Check Understanding** ② Find the unknown length for a circle with the given dimension.

a. $d = 8$ cm, $r = \blacksquare$ 4 cm   **b.** $r = 10$ in., $d = \blacksquare$ 20 in.

OBJECTIVE

2 **Finding Circumference**

The distance around a circle is its **circumference.** The ratio of the circumference C of a circle to its diameter d is the same for *every* circle. The symbol π (read "pi") represents this ratio. So, $\pi = \frac{C}{d}$.

Pi is a nonrepeating, nonterminating decimal. Two approximations for π are 3.14 and $\frac{22}{7}$. Use $\frac{22}{7}$ when measurements are a multiple of 7 or use fractions. You can also use the π key on a calculator.

You can rewrite the relationship $\pi = \frac{C}{d}$ as $C = \pi \times d$, or πd.

Key Concepts	**Circumference of a Circle**

$$C = \pi d$$
$$C = 2\pi r$$

③ **EXAMPLE** **Finding the Circumference of a Circle** Real World

Archery A regulation archery target has a circle with a 48-inch diameter. Find the circumference of a regulation target to the nearest inch.

$$C = \pi d \quad \leftarrow \text{Use the formula for the circumference of a circle.}$$

$$\approx 3.14 \times 48 \quad \leftarrow \text{Substitute 48 for } d \text{ and 3.14 for } \pi.$$

$$= 150.72 \quad \leftarrow \text{Multiply.}$$

● The circumference of a regulation target is about 151 inches.

✓ **Check Understanding** ③ Find the circumference of a circle with a diameter of 5.8 centimeters. Round to the nearest centimeter. **18 cm**

 **Reaching All Students**

Below Level Have students measure the diameter of a circular object and find its circumference using $C = \pi d$. Have them check the result by wrapping string around the circumference and measuring the string.	**Advanced Learners** This figure is formed by a square and a *semicircle* (half of a circle). Find the perimeter of the figure to the nearest meter. **37 m** |←8m→|	**Auditory Learners** See note on page 453. **Error Prevention** See note on page 454.

---

2. Teach

Professional Development

Math Background

The perimeter of a polygon can be found by adding the lengths of its sides. However, this method does not work for a circle, since a circle does not have sides. The perimeter of a circle, called its *circumference*, must either be measured directly or calculated using one of the formulas taught in this lesson.

Teaching Notes

① **EXAMPLE** **Auditory Learners**

Some students might be confused by the pronunciation of the word *chord*. Point out that the initial sound is the same as the sound of *ch* in the word *chorus*.

PowerPoint

Additional Examples

①

a. List the radii shown in circle *R*. $\overline{RB}, \overline{RD}, \overline{RE}$

b. List the chords shown in circle *R*. $\overline{AB}, \overline{CD}, \overline{BD}$

② On July 22, 2002, the world's largest wooden nickel was unveiled in San Antonio, Texas. The radius of the wooden nickel is 80 inches. What is its diameter? **160 inches**

③ The surface of one type of trampoline is bounded by a circular frame with a 7-foot radius. Find the circumference of the frame to the nearest foot. **44 feet**

Closure

• *What is a chord and what is a diameter?* A chord is any segment with endpoints on the circle. A diameter is a chord that passes through the center of the circle.

• *How do you find the circumference of a circle?* Multiply the diameter by π, or double the radius and then multiply by π.

453

Assignment Guide

Objective 1
Ⓐ Ⓑ Core 1–7

Objective 2
Ⓐ Ⓑ Core 8–25
Ⓒ Extension 26–27

Test Prep 28–31
Mixed Review 32–37

Error Prevention!

Exercises 9–14 Some students might substitute the length of a radius for d in the formula $C = \pi d$.

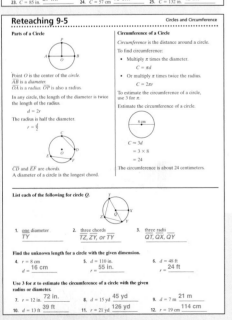

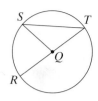

Ⓐ **Practice by Example**

List each of the following for circle Q.

Example 1
(page 452)

1. three radii
$\overline{QR}, \overline{QS}, \overline{QT}$

2. one diameter
$\overline{RT}$

3. two chords
$\overline{RT}, \overline{ST}$

Example 2
(page 453)

Find the unknown length for a circle with the given dimension.

4. $r = 35$ mi, $d =$ ▦ 70 mi

5. $d = 6.8$ yd, $r =$ ▦ 3.4 yd

6. $r = 18$ ft, $d =$ ▦ 36 ft

7. $d = 0.25$ km, $r =$ ▦ 0.125 km

Example 3
(page 453)

Find the circumference of each circle. Round to the nearest unit. Exercise 8 has been started for you.

8. 38 m (12 m)

$C = \pi d$
$C \approx 3.14(12)$

9. 16 in. (5 in.)

10. 72 ft (23 ft)

11. 57 cm (9 cm)

12. 188 m (30 m)

13. 88 mi (14 mi)

🌐 **14. Tanks** A circular water tank has a radius of 3.9 meters. What is the circumference of the tank? **about 24.5 m**

Ⓑ **Apply Your Skills**

Find the circumference of each circle with the given radius or diameter. Use $\frac{22}{7}$ for π.

15. $d = 28$ mi
88 mi

16. $r = 7$ ft
44 ft

17. $d = 14$ m
44 m

18. $r = \frac{5}{8}$ mi
$3\frac{13}{14}$ mi

🌐 **19. Hoops** A dog trainer uses hoops with diameters of 24 and 30 inches.
GPS What is the difference between their circumferences? Use 3 for π. **18 in.**

Find the radius and diameter of a circle with the given circumference. Use 3.14 for π. Round to the nearest tenth.

20. 192 ft
30.6 ft; 61.1 ft

21. 1,273 m
202.7 m; 405.4 m

22. 3.75 in.
0.6 in.; 1.2 in.

23. 12.4 mi
2.0 mi; 3.9 mi

Real-World Connection

Dogs can jump through hoops that are only a little larger than their bodies.

24. Writing in Math A pebble got stuck in a bicycle's tire and left a mark in the track made by the tire every 69 inches. Explain how you would find the circumference of the tire. **See margin.**

 GPS Use the Guided Problem Solving worksheet with Exercise 19.

24. Answers may vary. Sample: The pebble makes a mark along the circumference during every rotation. So, the circumference is 69 inches.

Practice 9-5 — Circles and Circumference

List each of the following for circle O.

1. three radii $\overline{OJ}, \overline{OL}, \overline{OK}$
2. one diameter $\overline{JK}$
3. two chords $\overline{JK}, \overline{LK}$

Find the unknown length for a circle with the given dimension.

4. $r = 4$ in.; $d = \underline{?}$ 8 in.
5. $d = 15$ cm; $r = \underline{?}$ 7.5 cm
6. $d = 9$ mm; $r = \underline{?}$ 4.5 mm
7. $r = 12$ mm; $d = \underline{?}$ 24 mm

Find the circumference of each circle. Round to the nearest unit.

8. 5 mm 31 mm
9. 11 in. 69 in.
10. 5 m 3 m
11. 23 ft 72 ft
12. 6 cm 19 cm
13. 15 in. 47 in.

Estimate the circumference of each circle with the given radius or diameter. Use 3 for π.

14. $d = 4$ in. about 12 in.
15. $d = 8$ cm about 24 cm
16. $r = 6$ m about 36 m
17. $r = 10$ ft about 60 ft
18. $r = 3$ in. about 18 in.
19. $d = 20$ cm about 60 cm

Find the diameter of a circle with the given circumference. Round to the nearest unit.

20. $C = 128$ ft 41 ft
21. $C = 36$ cm 11 cm
22. $C = 200$ m 64 m
23. $C = 85$ in. 27 in.
24. $C = 57$ cm 18 cm
25. $C = 132$ in. 42 in.

Reteaching 9-5 — Circles and Circumference

Parts of a Circle

Point O is the center of the *circle*.
$\overline{AB}$ is a *diameter*.
$\overline{OA}$ is a *radius*. $\overline{OP}$ is also a radius.
In any circle, the length of the diameter is twice the length of the radius.
$d = 2r$
The radius is half the diameter.
$r = \frac{d}{2}$

$\overline{CD}$ and $\overline{EF}$ are *chords*.
A diameter of a circle is the longest chord.

Circumference of a Circle

Circumference is the distance around a circle.
To find circumference:
- Multiply π times the diameter.
$C = \pi d$
- Or multiply π times twice the radius.
$C = 2\pi r$
To estimate the circumference of a circle, use 3 for π.

Estimate the circumference of a circle.
8 cm
$C \approx 3d$
$= 3 \times 8$
$= 24$
The circumference is about 24 centimeters.

List each of the following for circle Q.

1. one diameter $\overline{TY}$
2. three chords $\overline{TZ}, \overline{ZY},$ or $\overline{TY}$
3. three radii $\overline{QT}, \overline{QX}, \overline{QY}$

Find the unknown length for a circle with the given dimension.

4. $r = 8$ cm $d = 16$ cm
5. $d = 110$ in. $r = 55$ in.
6. $d = 48$ ft $r = 24$ ft

Use 3 for π to estimate the circumference of a circle with the given radius or diameter.

7. $r = 12$ in. 72 in.
8. $d = 15$ yd 45 yd
9. $d = 7$ m 21 m
10. $d = 13$ ft 39 ft
11. $r = 21$ yd 126 yd
12. $r = 19$ cm 114 cm

25. Math in the Media Read the cartoon below.

Foxtrot *by Bill Amend*

a. Use the value of π from the cartoon to find the circumference of a circle with a diameter of 48 inches. **150.79632 in.**

25b. They cannot finish; the decimal π goes on forever.

b. **Reasoning** How many more pumpkins are needed to finish the "pumpkin pi"? Explain your answer. **See left.**

C Challenge  **26. Bicycles** The diameter of a bicycle wheel is 3 feet. How far will the bicycle travel when the wheel makes one full turn? **about 9.4 ft**

27. Stretch Your Thinking You fold a square sheet of paper in half. Then you cut along the fold. The perimeter of each of the rectangles formed is 18 inches. What was the area of the original square sheet of paper? **36 in.²**

Test Prep

Gridded Response

28. What is the radius of a circle with a diameter of 8.46 kilometers? Round to the nearest hundredth kilometer. **4.23**

29. The diameter of a circle is 2.24 centimeters. What is the circumference? Use 3.14 for π and round to nearest hundredth. **7.03**

Take It to the NET
Online lesson quiz at
www.PHSchool.com
Web Code: aaa-0905

30. The circumference of the circle is 11 meters. What is the diameter of the circle to the nearest tenth meter? **3.5**

31. The circumference of a circle is 48 inches. Suppose the radius of the circle is doubled. What is the new circumference to the nearest inch? **96**

Mixed Review

Lesson 7-1 **Find the median of each data set.**

32. 50, 20, 42, 45, 48, 50 **46.5**   **33.** 8.0, 7.5, 6.6, 7.8, 7.5 **7.5**

Lesson 6-8 **34.** Estimate a 15% tip for a $35.90 restaurant bill. **about $5.40**

 PowerPoint Lesson Quiz 9-5

Find the unknown length of each circle.

1. $r = 5.4$ m, $d = $ ■ **10.8 m**

2. $d = 68$ cm, $r = $ ■ **34 cm**

Find the circumference of each circle to the nearest unit.

3. $d = 20$ in. **63 in.**

4. $r = 35$ mm **220 mm**

Alternative Assessment

Each student in a pair draws several circles and labels the length of their radii or diameters. Partners exchange drawings and find the circumference of each other's circles.

Test Prep

Resources
A sheet of blank grids is available in the *Test-Taking Strategies With Transparencies* booklet. Give copies of this sheet to students so they can practice filling in grids.

For additional practice with a variety of test item formats:
• Test Prep, p. 485
• Test-Taking Strategies, p. 481
• Test-Taking Strategies With Transparencies

Enrichment 9-5   Circles and Circumference
Geometric Relationships

A sand dollar is an animal that lives slightly buried in the sand of shallow coastal waters. Its thin, circular body is about 2 to 4 inches wide.

a. What are the smallest and largest circumferences of sand dollars? What is the range of circumferences?

b. What are the smallest and largest areas of sand dollars? What is the range of areas?

1. What mathematical term describes the "width" of a circle?
diameter

2. What radius will you use to find the measures of the smaller sand dollar? 1 inch

3. What radius will you use to find the measures of the larger sand dollar? 2 inches

4. Find the circumference of each sand dollar, in terms of pi. Then calculate the approximate measure using 3.14 for pi.
smaller sand dollar: 2π or 6.28 inches;
larger sand dollar: 4π or 12.56 inches

5. What does it mean to find the *range* of the values?
Find the difference between the greatest value and the least value.

6. Write an equation to find the range of the sand dollar circumferences, *R*, in terms of pi. Then calculate the approximate range.
R = 4π − 2π; R = 2π; The approximate range of circumferences for sand dollars is 6.28 inches.

7. Find the area of each sand dollar, in terms of pi. Then calculate the approximate measure using 3.14 for pi.
smaller sand dollar: π or 3.14 in.²;
larger sand dollar: 4π or 12.56 in.²

8. Write an equation to find the range of the sand dollar areas, in terms of pi. Then calculate the approximate range.
R = 4π − π; R = 3π; The approximate range of areas for sand dollars is 9.42 in.².

Lesson Preview

✓ **Check Skills You'll Need**

Simplifying Expressions With Exponents
Lesson 2-8: Examples 3–4. Extra Practice, p. 643.

Lesson Resources

📁 **Teaching Resources**
Practice, Reteaching, Enrichment

👥 **Reaching All Students**
Practice Workbook 9-6
Spanish Practice Workbook 9-6
Guided Problem Solving 9-6

⏰ **Presentation Assistant Plus!**
Transparencies
• Check Skills You'll Need 9-6
• Problem of the Day 9-6
• Additional Examples 9-6
• Student Edition Answers 9-6
• Lesson Quiz 9-6
• Classroom Aid 20, 21
PH Presentation Pro CD-ROM 9-6

ASSESSMENT SYSTEM

Computer Test Generator CD

💻 **Technology**
Resource Pro® CD-ROM
Computer Test Generator CD
PH Presentation Pro CD-ROM

💻 **www.PHSchool.com**
Student Site
• Teacher Web Code: aak-5500
• Self-grading Lesson Quiz

PH SuccessNet Teacher Center
• Lesson Planner
• Resources

Plus 📘**TEXT**

456

9-6 Area of a Circle

3.02 Identify the radius, diameter, chord, center, and circumference of a circle; determine the relationships among them.

What You'll Learn

OBJECTIVE 1 To find the area of a circle

...And Why

To find the area of a mirror, as in Example 2

✓ **Check Skills You'll Need**

Simplify each expression.

1. 7^2 49
2. 5^2 25
3. $(7 - 3)^2$ 16
4. $(6 + 4)^2$ 100
5. $9 + 3^2$ 18
6. 12^2 144

❓ For help, go to Lesson 2-8.

📘**TEXT** Interactive lesson includes instant self-check, tutorials, and activities.

Finding the Area of a Circle

Suppose you cut a circle into equal-sized wedges. You can rearrange the wedges into a figure that resembles a parallelogram.

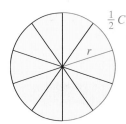
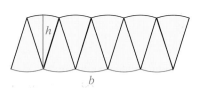

The base of the parallelogram is half the circumference of the circle, or πr. The height of the parallelogram is the same length as the circle's radius.

$A = b \times h$ ← Use the formula for the area of a parallelogram.

$= \pi r \times r$ ← Substitute πr for b and r for h.

$= \pi r^2$ ← Simplify.

? Need Help?
For help finding the area of a parallelogram, go to Lesson 9-4.

This suggests a formula for the area of a circle.

Key Concepts | **Area of a Circle**

$$A = \pi r^2$$

When you are estimating to check for reasonableness, you can use 3 for the value of π.

456 Chapter 9 Geometry and Measurement

Ongoing Assessment and Intervention

Before the Lesson
Diagnose prerequisite skills using:
• Check Skills You'll Need

During the Lesson
Monitor progress using:
• Check Understanding
• Additional Examples
• Test Prep

After the Lesson
Assess knowledge using:
• Lesson Quiz
• Computer Test Generator CD

Find the area of the circle at the right.

5 ft

Estimate Use 3 for π. So, $A \approx 3 \times 5^2$, or 75 square feet.

$$A = \pi r^2 \qquad \leftarrow \text{ Use the formula for the area of a circle.}$$

$$\approx 3.14 \times 5^2 \qquad \leftarrow \text{ Substitute 5 for } r \text{ and 3.14 for } \pi.$$

$$= 78.5 \qquad \leftarrow \text{ Multiply.}$$

The area is about 78.5 square feet.

Check for Reasonableness The estimate, 75 square feet, is close to 78.5 square feet. So the answer is reasonable.

✓ **Check Understanding** ① Find the area of each circle. Use 3.14 for π .

a.

12 km

452.16 km²

b.

3 in.

28.26 in.²

c.

8 yd

50.24 yd²

When the radius or diameter of a circle is a multiple of 7 or a fraction, you might want to use $\frac{22}{7}$ for π.

2 EXAMPLE Real-World 🌐 Problem Solving

Real-World 🌐 Connection

Circular mirrors are used to build telescopes.

Mirrors Find the area of the circular mirror at the left with a diameter of 14 inches. Use $\frac{22}{7}$ for π.

The radius is half of the diameter, or 7 inches.

$$A = \pi r^2 \qquad \leftarrow \text{ Use the formula for the area of a circle.}$$

$$\approx \frac{22}{7} \times 7^2 \qquad \leftarrow \text{ Use } \frac{22}{7} \text{ for } \pi \text{ and 7 for } r.$$

$$= \frac{22}{\underset{1}{7}} \times \overset{7}{49} \qquad \leftarrow \text{ Divide 7 and 49 by their GCF, 7.}$$

$$= 154 \qquad \leftarrow \text{ Multiply.}$$

The area of the mirror is about 154 square inches.

✓ **Check Understanding** ② Find the area of each circle. Use $\frac{22}{7}$ for π.

2a. 1,386 m²

2b. 616 cm²

2c. 38.5 mi²

a.

21 m

b.
28 cm

c.
$3\frac{1}{2}$ mi

d. Find the area of a 14-inch large pizza. Use $\frac{22}{7}$ for π. 154 in.²

👥 Reaching All Students

Below Level Have students identify the radius and diameter of the circle whose area is $\pi \times 8^2$ square units. **radius = 8 units, diameter = 16 units** Have them calculate the area using 3.14 for π. **about 201 square units**

Advanced Learners Find the radius, diameter, and circumference of a circle that has an area of 314 ft². Use 3.14 for π. **radius ≈ 10 ft; diameter ≈ 20 ft; circumference ≈ 62.8 ft**

Inclusion See note on page 458. **Visual Learners** See note on page 457.

---

2. Teach

Professional Development

Math Background

In a geometry course, the formula for the area of a circle is usually derived by considering a circle as a regular polygon of infinitely many sides. The derivation presented in this lesson—imagining a circle cut apart and rearranged to look like a parallelogram—provides an alternative that is within the grasp of younger children.

Teaching Notes

② EXAMPLE Visual Learners

Before discussing Example 2, give each student a circle of diameter 14 units drawn on a grid, as shown below. Have them estimate the area of the circle using the method taught in Lesson 9-3. After discussing Example 2, have them compare their estimates to 154 in.², the area found by using the formula.

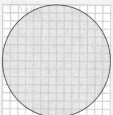

Error Prevention!

In Check Understanding 2d, watch for students who square the diameter.

📽 **PowerPoint**

Additional Examples

① Find the area of a circle with diameter 18 inches. Round to the nearest tenth. **about 254 square inches**

② Find the area of a circular flower bed with radius 7 feet. Use $\frac{22}{7}$ for π. **about 154 square feet**

Closure

Explain how to find the area of a circle. **Square the radius and multiply by pi.**

457

3. Practice

Assignment Guide

▼ Objective 1
- **Ⓐ Ⓑ Core 1–22**
- **Ⓒ Extension 23–26**

Test Prep 27–30
Mixed Review 31–33

Inclusion

Exercises 1–10 Some students might not see the difference between the circumference formula $C = 2\pi r$ and the area formula $A = \pi r^2$. Suggest that they use the forms $C = 2 \times \pi \times r$ and $A = \pi \times r \times r$.

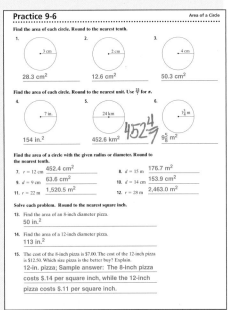

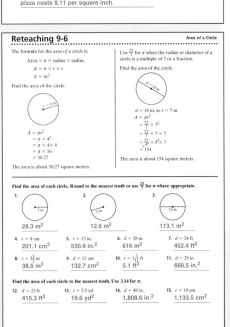

 **EXERCISES**

For more practice, see *Extra Practice*.

Ⓐ Practice by Example

Example 1
page 457

Find the area of each circle. Use 3.14 for π. Round to the nearest tenth. Exercise 1 has been started for you.

1. 8 mm — 201.0 mm²   **2.** 25 in. — 1962.5 in.²   **3.** 37 ft — 4,298.7 ft²

$A = \pi r^2$
$\approx 3.14 \times 8^2$

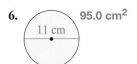

4. 26 km — 530.7 km²   **5.** 30 yd — 706.5 yd²   **6.** 11 cm — 95.0 cm²

Example 2
page 457

Find the area of each circle. Use $\frac{22}{7}$ for π.

7. $2\frac{1}{3}$ mm — $17\frac{1}{9}$ mm²   **8.** $4\frac{1}{2}$ in. — $63\frac{9}{14}$ in.²   **9.** 21 mi — $346\frac{1}{2}$ mi²

🌐 **10. Camping** Campers arrange stones in a circle around their campfire site. The circle has a diameter of 14 feet. Find the area of the site.
about 154 ft²   *153.9 or 153.86*

Ⓑ Apply Your Skills

Mental Math Estimate the area of each circle. Use 3 for π.

11. $r = 2$ in.   **12.** $d = 6$ mm   **13.** $r = 20$ cm   **14.** $d = 16$ ft
   12 in.²   27 mm²   1,200 cm²   192 ft²

Find the area of each circle. Use 3.14 for π and round to the nearest tenth.

15. $r = 1.1$ mi   **16.** $d = 2.4$ cm   **17.** $r = 0.5$ m   **18.** $d = 13.7$ ft
   3.8 mi²   4.5 cm²   0.8 m²   147.3 ft²

Reading Math

The prefix *semi-* means "half." A semicircle is one half of a circle.

🌐 **19. Games** The hopscotch drawing at the right is composed of squares and a semicircle. Suppose the side lengths of each square are 2 feet. Find the area of the hopscotch drawing.
about 38.28 ft²

🌐 **20. Communications** You can pick up the radio signal for station
GPS WAER FM 88 in Syracuse, New York, within a 45-mile radius of the station. What is the approximate area of the broadcast region? Use 3.14 for π. about 6,359 mi² *6358.5*

21. a pan with a radius of 10 in., which has a diameter of 20 in.

21. Writing in Math Which is larger: a pan with a radius of 10 inches, or a pan with the same depth and a diameter of 18 inches? Explain.

22. Find the area of a circle with a circumference of 31.4 units.
about 78.5 units²

458   **Chapter 9** Geometry and Measurement

GPS Use the Guided Problem Solving worksheet with Exercise 20.

Find the area of each yellow region. Use 3.14 for π.

23.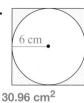

30.96 cm²

24.

65.94 m²

25.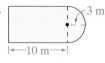

74.13 m²

26. **Stretch Your Thinking** The diameter of a circle is tripled. How does this affect the area of the circle? When the diameter is tripled, the area becomes 9 times as much.

Test Prep

Reading Comprehension Read the passage and answer the questions below.

Follow the Sun

The Aztecs used their accurate knowledge of astronomy and mathematics to make a calendar called the Sun Stone. They carved the calendar on a circular stone 3.6 meters in diameter. The Aztecs began working on the calendar in 1427 and completed the work in 1479. The center circle of the stone shows the face of Tonatiuh, the Aztec sun god. The 20 squares in the second ring name the 20 days of each Aztec month. There were 18 Aztec months.

Take It to the NET
Online lesson quiz at
www.PHSchool.com
Web Code: aaa-0906

27. Find the area of the Sun Stone. Use 3.14 for π. about 10.17 m²

28. How long did it take the Aztecs to complete the calendar?
about 52 years

29. How many days were in the Aztec calendar? 360 days

Multiple Choice

30. Which is the best estimate for the area of a circle with a diameter of 5.8 yards? B
   A. 18 yd²   B. 26 yd²   C. 36 yd²   D. 108 yd²

Mixed Review

Lesson 8-8   **Trace the figure and draw the lines of symmetry.**

31.

32.

33.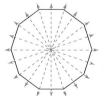

 **Lesson Quiz 9-6**

Find the area of each circle. Round to the nearest whole unit.

1. $r = 5$ cm 79 cm²

2. $r = 7$ m 154 m²

3. $d = 18$ in. 254 in.²

4. $d = 30$ ft 707 ft²

Alternative Assessment

Each student in a pair draws several circles and labels the lengths of the radii or diameters. Partners exchange circles and use 3 or $\frac{22}{7}$ for π to find the areas to the nearest whole unit.

Test Prep

Resources
For additional practice with a variety of test item formats:
• Test Prep, p. 485
• Test-Taking Strategies, p. 481
• Test-Taking Strategies With Transparencies

Exercise 30 Ask: *What is the radius of a circle with a diameter of 5.8 yards?* 2.9 yards

---

Enrichment 9-6   Area of a Circle
Patterns in Geometry

The area of a circle can be determined using the formula $A = \pi \times r^2$, where r is the radius. What happens to the area of the circle when the measurements of the radius change? Use 3.14 for π.

1. Find the area of the circles with the following radii.
   1 inch 3.14 in.²   2 inches 12.56 in.²   3 inches 28.26 in.²
   4 inches 50.24 in.²   5 inches 78.5 in.²   6 inches 113.04 in.²

2. What is the difference between the areas of circles with these radii?
   1 and 2 inches 9.42 in.²
   2 and 3 inches 15.7 in.²
   3 and 4 inches 21.98 in.²
   4 and 5 inches 28.26 in.²
   5 and 6 inches 35.54 in.²

3. Write the differences in order from least to greatest. Then find the difference between the differences.
   9.42 in.², 15.7 in.², 21.98 in.², 28.26 in.², 34.54 in.²
   6.28 in.², 6.28 in.², 6.28 in.², 6.28 in.²

4. What pattern do you see?
   All the differences are 6.28 in.².

5. How is the number 6.28 related to the radii or to π?
   $6.28 = 2 \times 3.14 \approx 2 \times \pi$.

6. What is the area of a circle with a 9-inch radius?
   ≈ 254.34 in.²

7. Would you rather use the pattern or the formula to find area? Why?
   Sample answer: The formula; you can use it for any circle without calculating areas of other circles.

Using Concept Maps to Connect Ideas

Graphic organizers provide visual representations of knowledge organized into patterns. They are valuable teaching tools that get students actively involved in their learning and help them to develop their critical thinking skills. A concept map is a graphic organizer that shows the relationship between a main concept and supporting details. It is particularly useful for instruction in mathematics vocabulary.

Optional Materials

• Classroom Aid 1

Teaching Notes

Discuss with students the importance of learning and correctly using precise math vocabulary. Then explain what a concept map is and how they can use one to help them focus on, understand, and remember new terms.

Discuss the sample concept map given in the example. Guide students to see the links between the "image position" oval and the specific types of transformations that are connected to it with line segments.

English Learners

Graphic organizers are particularly helpful to English language learners. Invite students to work in small groups to use the concept map and to create their own. Help them to organize the information. You may wish to modify the map to meet the language needs of your students.

Exercises

Check students' maps. Invite volunteers to display theirs, and to explain the choices they made. Invite students to suggest other kinds of graphic organizers they could use to the same purpose.

Reading Math Using Concept Maps to Connect Ideas

One way to show connections among ideas is to draw a diagram called a concept map. The lines in a concept map connect related ideas.

EXAMPLE

Make a concept map with the terms from Chapter 8 related to transformations.

center of rotation
reflection
rotation
translation
transformation
line of reflection

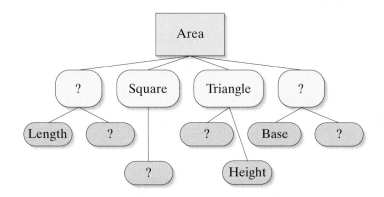

EXERCISES

1–2. See back of book.

1. Copy the concept map at the right. Fill in the ovals using the appropriate terms listed below. Include area formulas on your concept map.

area	triangle
parallelogram	rectangle
square	base
height	length
width	side

2. Use the list below to make a concept map for circles.

circle	circumference
radius	area of a circle
diameter	π

Investigation

Views of Three-Dimensional Objects

For Use With Lesson 9-7

Stack 6 blocks as shown at the right. The number of blocks you can "see" depends on how you look at the stack. The *front view*, the *right side view*, and the *top view* of the stack of blocks are shown below.

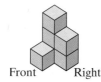

Front   Right

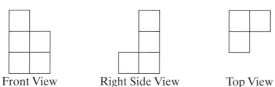

Front View   Right Side View   Top View

EXAMPLE

Use the drawings below. How many blocks are possible in the stack?

Front View   Right Side View   Top View

Use blocks to make a stack that matches each view. Count the blocks.

Two possible stacks have 10 and 11 blocks.

4.   5.

EXERCISES

1. See margin. 2–3. See back of book.

Draw the front, right side, and top views of each figure.

1.   2. 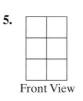   3.

Use the drawings below. Draw a possible stack of blocks.   4–5. See above.

4.

Front View   Right Side View   Top View

5.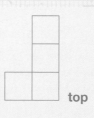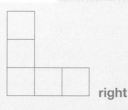

Front View   Right Side View   Top View

1.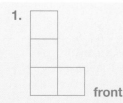

front   right   top

Investigation

Views of Three-Dimensional Objects

In this Investigation, students draw front, right side, and top views of stacks of blocks. This activity serves as an introduction to two-dimensional views of three-dimensional figures that is presented in Lesson 9-7.

Optional Materials

- cube-shaped blocks
- graph paper
- Classroom Aid 2, 6

Resources

Student Manipulatives Kit

Teaching Notes

Point out to students that each of the three views—front, right, and top—show only what is visible from that point of view. Ask:
- *If you had only one view of a stack of blocks, can you know how many blocks are in the stack?* Sample: no
- *If you had only two views of a stack of blocks, can you know how many blocks are in the stack?* Sample: Maybe, but not necessarily.

EXAMPLE Visual Learners

Elicit the fact that each block is a cube and that they are all the same size. Also point out that the blocks are touching and placed directly on top of other blocks.

Exercises
Exercises 1–3 Emphasize that students need to label each of their views as front, right side, or top.

Teaching Tip
Have students combine their blocks to build a "sculpture." They then draw the front, right side, and top views and try to use their views to count the blocks.

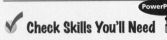
Lesson Preview

✓ **Check Skills You'll Need**

Identifying Polygons
Lesson 8-5: Example 1. Extra Practice, p. 649.

Lesson Resources

📁 **Teaching Resources**
Practice, Reteaching, Enrichment

👥 **Reaching All Students**
Practice Workbook 9-7
Spanish Practice Workbook 9-7
Guided Problem Solving 9-7
Hands-On Activities 33, 35

⏱ **Presentation Assistant Plus!**
Transparencies
• Check Skills You'll Need 9-7
• Problem of the Day 9-7
• Additional Examples 9-7
• Student Edition Answers 9-7
• Lesson Quiz 9-7
• Classroom Aid 2, 20, 21
PH Presentation Pro CD-ROM 9-7

PRENTICE HALL
ASSESSMENT SYSTEM

Computer Test Generator CD

💻 **Technology**
Resource Pro® CD-ROM
Computer Test Generator CD
PH Presentation Pro CD-ROM

💻 **www.PHSchool.com**
Student Site
• Teacher Web Code: aak-5500
• Self-grading Lesson Quiz

PH SuccessNet Teacher Center
• Lesson Planner
• Resources

Plus

What You'll Learn

OBJECTIVE 1 To identify three-dimensional figures

. . . And Why

To identify building shapes, as in Example 2

✓ **Check Skills You'll Need**   ❓ For help, go to Lesson 8-5.

Identify each type of polygon according to the numbers of sides.

1.

hexagon

2.

quadrilateral

3.

triangle

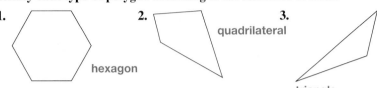

New Vocabulary • three-dimensional figure • prism • cube
• pyramid • cylinder • cone • sphere • net

OBJECTIVE
1

Identifying Three-Dimensional Figures

iTEXT Interactive lesson includes instant self-check, tutorials, and activities.

Three-dimensional figures make up the world around you from your school building to your pencil. A **three-dimensional figure** is a figure that does not lie in a plane. It has three dimensions: length, width, and height.

The flat surfaces of a three-dimensional figure are called **faces**.

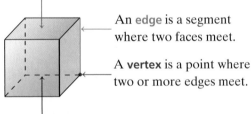

An **edge** is a segment where two faces meet.

A **vertex** is a point where two or more edges meet.

When you draw three-dimensional figures, use dashed lines to indicate "hidden" edges.

A **prism** is a three-dimensional figure with two parallel and congruent faces that are polygons. These faces are called bases. The prism above is a **cube.** All of its faces are congruent.

Base Shape	Name of Prism
Triangle	Triangular Prism
Rectangle	Rectangular Prism
Pentagon	Pentagonal Prism
Hexagon	Hexagonal Prism
Heptagon	Heptagonal Prism
Octagon	Octagonal Prism

← You name a prism by the shape of its bases.

✓ **Ongoing Assessment and Intervention**

Before the Lesson
Diagnose prerequisite skills using:
• Check Skills You'll Need

During the Lesson
Monitor progress using:
• Check Understanding
• Additional Examples
• Test Prep

After the Lesson
Assess knowledge using:
• Lesson Quiz
• Computer Test Generator CD

1 EXAMPLE Naming Prisms

Name the prism shown.

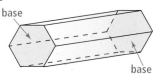

base

base

Each base is a hexagon. So the figure is a hexagonal prism.

✔ **Check Understanding** (1) Name each prism.

1a. pentagonal prism

1b. rectangular prism

1c. triangular prism

a. **b.**  **c.**

d. Reasoning In these prisms, what shape is any face that is not the base?
rectangle

A **pyramid** is a three-dimensional figure with one polygon for a base. All of the other faces are triangles. You name a pyramid by its base.

Other three dimensional figures do not use polygons for bases.

rectangular pyramid

A **cylinder** has two congruent parallel bases that are circles.

A **cone** has one circular base and one vertex.

A **sphere** has no base.

Test-Prep Tip
When naming a 3-D figure, notice the shape of its base, and whether or not its faces meet at one vertex.

2 EXAMPLE Identifying Three-Dimensional Figures 🌐 Real World

Museum The American Museum of Natural History in New York City is shown at the right. Name one of the three-dimensional figures in the photo.

One of the figures in the photo is a sphere.

✔ **Check Understanding** (2) **a.** Name another three-dimensional figure in the photo. rectangular prism

b. Reasoning How are a cylinder and a cone alike? How are they different? See back of book.

👥 Reaching All Students

Below Level Have students list the names of as many different polygons as they can. Next to the name of each polygon, have them write its number of sides. Allow them to refer to this list when naming prisms and pyramids.

Advanced Learners Draw a complex figure that is made of two or more three-dimensional figures. **Sample: cone and cylinder**

Inclusion See note on page 463.

Tactile Learners See note on page 463.

---

2. Teach

🔵 Professional Development

Math Background

Plane figures such as polygons and circles lie entirely within a plane. They generally can be described by two measurements, length and width, and so they are called *two-dimensional figures*. In this lesson, students examine figures that extend beyond a plane into space. These *space figures* have an added dimension, often referred to as *depth*. For this reason, they are called *three-dimensional figures*.

Teaching Notes

1 EXAMPLE Inclusion

Point out that a prism does not necessarily rest on its base, as is shown for the hexagonal prism.

Tactile Learners
Let students "see with their hands" by passing around examples of the three-dimensional figures.

Teaching Tip
Challenge students in small groups to write as many real-world examples as they can of cylinders, cones, and spheres.

Investigation (Optional)
Make sure students have written a prediction for the name of the net before working on the model.

🔵 PowerPoint
💻 Additional Examples

(1) Name the prism shown.
octagonal prism

(2) Name the three-dimensional figure shown. rectangular pyramid

Closure

What is a three-dimensional figure? a geometric figure that has length, width, and height

463

3. Practice

Assignment Guide

1 Objective 1

Ⓐ Ⓑ Core 1–26

Ⓒ Extension 27–29

Test Prep 30–33
Mixed Review 34–38

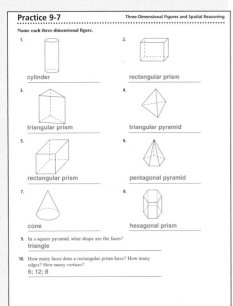

Practice 9-7 — Three-Dimensional Figures and Spatial Reasoning

Name each three-dimensional figure.

1. cylinder
2. rectangular prism
3. triangular prism
4. triangular pyramid
5. rectangular prism
6. pentagonal pyramid
7. cone
8. hexagonal prism

9. In a square pyramid, what shape are the faces?
triangle

10. How many faces does a rectangular prism have? How many edges? How many vertices?
6; 12; 8

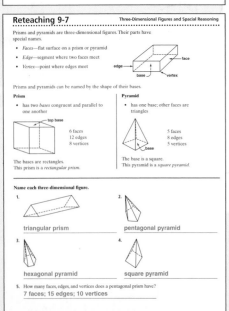

Reteaching 9-7 — Three-Dimensional Figures and Spacial Reasoning

Prisms and pyramids are three-dimensional figures. Their parts have special names.

• *Faces*—flat surface on a prism or pyramid
• *Edge*—segment where two faces meet
• *Vertex*—point where edges meet

Prisms and pyramids can be named by the shape of their bases.

Prism
• has two *bases* congruent and parallel to one another

6 faces
12 edges
8 vertices

The bases are rectangles.
This prism is a *rectangular prism*.

Pyramid
• has one base; other faces are triangles

5 faces
8 edges
5 vertices

The base is a square.
This pyramid is a *square pyramid*.

Name each three-dimensional figure.

1. triangular prism
2. pentagonal pyramid
3. hexagonal pyramid
4. square pyramid

5. How many faces, edges, and vertices does a pentagonal prism have?
7 faces; 15 edges; 10 vertices

464

Investigation: Making Three-Dimensional Figures

A **net** is a pattern that you can fold to form a three-dimensional figure.

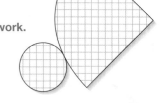

1. a. Name the three-dimensional figure you can form from the net shown. **cone**
   b. Copy the net onto graph paper. Cut, fold, and tape it to check your answer to part (a). **Check students' work.**

2. **Spatial Reasoning** Draw a net that will fold to form each given figure.
   a. rectangular prism   b. cylinder

2a–b. Check students' work.

EXERCISES

? For more practice, see *Extra Practice*.

Ⓐ Practice by Example

Name each prism.

Example 1
(page 463)

1.
triangular prism

2.
hexagonal prism

3.
rectangular prism

4.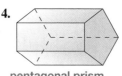
pentagonal prism

5.
cube, rectangular prism

6.
octagonal prism

Example 2
(page 463)

Name each figure.

7.  cylinder

8. rectangular pyramid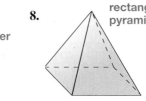

9.  cone

10.
hexagonal pyramid

11.
sphere

12.
triangular pyramid

GPS Use the Guided Problem Solving worksheet with Exercise 24.

2a. Check students' work.

b. Check students' work.

Investigation

1a. cone

b. Check students' work.

B Apply Your Skills 🌐 **Structures** Name the three-dimensional figure in each photo.

13.
sphere

14.
pyramid

15.
rectangular prism

16.
cone

Sketch each three-dimensional figure on graph paper. 17–22. See margin.

17. rectangular prism   18. cone   19. hexagonal prism

20. cylinder   21. triangular pyramid   22. cube

23. Answers may vary. Sample: One face of the figure is a square. The other four faces are triangles that have a common vertex.

23. **Writing in Math** Describe the shape of a square pyramid. See left.

24. Name the figure. Then find the
[GPS] number of faces, vertices, and
edges in the figure. **trapezoidal prism;
6 faces, 8 vertices, 12 edges**

🌐 **Art** You can use translations to draw three-dimensional figures.

Step 1
Draw a figure on graph paper.

Step 2
Translate the figure.

Step 3
Connect each vertex with its image.

Step 4
Use dashes for hidden lines.

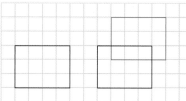

25–27. Check students' work.
25. Start with a triangle. Draw a three-dimensional figure.

26. Start with a pentagon. Draw a three-dimensional figure.

C Challenge
27. Describe the translation used in the example above. Redraw the rectangle. Use a different translation to draw the figure.

Error Prevention!

Exercises 1–12 Students might confuse the names of the figures, particularly since the words *prism* and *pyramid* have the same initial letter, as do the words *cylinder* and *cone*. Furthermore the words *cylinder* and *sphere* have the same initial sound. Lead a discussion in which students share methods they have devised for learning the names.

20.

21.

22.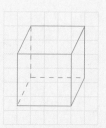

17.

18.

19.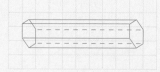

Name each figure.

1.

triangular pyramid

2.

rectangular prism

Alternative Assessment

Each student in a pair names a prism for their partner to draw. Partners draw the prisms on graph paper by following the guidelines provided in Exercises 25–26.

Test Prep

Resources

For additional practice with a variety of test item formats:
• Test Prep, p. 485
• Test-Taking Strategies, p. 481
• Test-Taking Strategies With Transparencies

36.

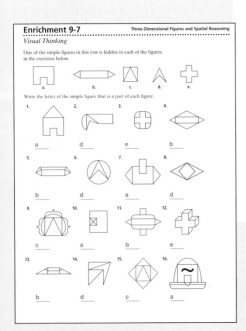

Enrichment 9-7 — Three-Dimensional Figures and Spatial Reasoning
Visual Thinking

28. **Algebra** The formula $F + V - E = 2$ shows the relationship between the faces (F), the vertices (V), and the edges (E) of prisms and pyramids. Use the figure shown at the left to verify the formula.
$5 + 5 - 8 = 2$

29. **Stretch Your Thinking** The figure at the right has an area of 180 square inches and consists of 5 congruent squares. Rearrange the squares to make a figure with a perimeter of 60 inches. **See margin.**

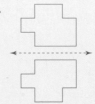

Test Prep

Multiple Choice

30. Which figure does NOT have a rectangular face? **D**
A. cube
B. triangular prism
C. rectangular pyramid
D. cone

31. Which figure is a rectangular pyramid? **G**

F.   **G.**   **H.**   **I.**

Take It to the NET
Online lesson quiz at
www.PHSchool.com
Web Code: aaa-0907

32. Which figure has more than five faces (including bases)? **D**
A. square pyramid
B. triangular prism
C. triangular pyramid
D. rectangular prism

33. How many edges does a pentagonal pyramid have? **H**
F. 5
G. 8
H. 10
I. 13

Mixed Review

Lesson 8-9
Copy each diagram on graph paper and draw its reflection over the given line of reflection. **34–36. See margin.**

34.   **35.**   **36.**

Lesson 6-9
Solve each problem by writing an equation.

37. If the sales tax is 6%, how much tax do you pay for a $15.99 CD? **$.96**

38. A T-shirt that originally costs $20 is 30% off. What is the sale price? **$14**

29. Answers may vary. Sample:

34.

35.

Surface Areas of Prisms and Cylinders

What You'll Learn

OBJECTIVE 1 To find the surface area of a prism

OBJECTIVE 2 To find the surface area of a cylinder

. . . And Why

To find the surface area of a juice box, as in Example 2

✓ **Check Skills You'll Need**   ? For help, go to Lesson 9-6.

Find the area of each circle. Use 3.14 for π.

1.

16 m

200.96 m²

2.

2 yd

12.56 yd²

3.

40 mm

5,024 mm²

New Vocabulary • surface area

Lesson Preview

PowerPoint

✓ **Check Skills You'll Need**

Finding the Area of a Circle
Lesson 9-6: Example 1. Extra Practice, p. 650.

Lesson Resources

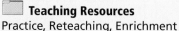

📁 **Teaching Resources**
Practice, Reteaching, Enrichment

👥 **Reaching All Students**
Practice Workbook 9-8
Spanish Practice Workbook 9-8
Guided Problem Solving 9-8
Technology Activities 15
Hands-On Activities 34

⏱ **Presentation Assistant Plus!**
Transparencies
• Check Skills You'll Need 9-8
• Problem of the Day 9-8
• Additional Examples 9-8
• Student Edition Answers 9-8
• Lesson Quiz 9-8
• Classroom Aid 20, 21
PH Presentation Pro CD-ROM 9-8

PRENTICE HALL
ASSESSMENT SYSTEM

Computer Test Generator CD

💻 **Technology**
Resource Pro® CD-ROM
Computer Test Generator CD
PH Presentation Pro CD-ROM

💻 **www.PHSchool.com**
Student Site
• Teacher Web Code: aak-5500
• Self-grading Lesson Quiz

PH SuccessNet Teacher Center
• Lesson Planner
• Resources

Plus 📱**iTEXT**

OBJECTIVE 1

iTEXT Interactive lesson includes instant self-check, tutorials, and activities.

Finding the Surface Area of a Prism

A *net* is a pattern you can fold to form a three-dimensional figure. Package designers use nets like the one below to make boxes.

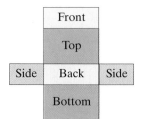

	Front	
	Top	
Side	Back	Side
	Bottom	

1 EXAMPLE **Drawing a Net**

Draw a net for the triangular prism at the left.

Step 1 Draw one base.

Step 2 Draw one face that connects the two bases.

Step 3 Draw the other base.

Step 4 Draw the remaining faces.

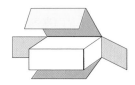
Back
Left side | Bottom | Right side
Front

✓ **Check Understanding** ① Draw a net for a cube.

1. Answers may vary. Sample:

Ongoing Assessment and Intervention

Before the Lesson
Diagnose prerequisite skills using:
• Check Skills You'll Need

During the Lesson
Monitor progress using:
• Check Understanding
• Additional Examples
• Test Prep

After the Lesson
Assess knowledge using:
• Lesson Quiz
• Computer Test Generator CD

Math Background

Prisms and cylinders are three-dimensional figures. However, an important measure associated with them is two-dimensional. This measure is *surface area*. In later courses, students will be expected to learn formulas for calculating surface areas. In this lesson, however, students determine surface areas primarily by relating the length, width, and height of the three-dimensional figure to its two-dimensional net.

Teaching Notes

Inclusion

Finding surface area is a multi-step process. Some students might have trouble perceiving the steps and applying them in the correct order. For each figure studied in this lesson—rectangular prism, triangular prism, and cylinder—identify a set of simple steps for finding the surface area. Create a fill-in-the-blanks template of the steps that students can use until they assimilate the process.

① EXAMPLE Teaching Tip

Use Check Understanding 1 to emphasize that there are more than one possible net for most three-dimensional solids.

② EXAMPLE Tactile Learners

Some students might have difficulty visualizing the three pairs of congruent faces. Before discussing the example, give students empty cereal boxes. Have them cut the boxes apart and match the congruent faces.

Error Prevention!

In Check Understanding 2a–b, watch for students who confuse the dimensions of different pairs of faces. Suggest that they list the dimensions of each face, as shown in Step 2 of Example 2, and to check that each dimension is correct before multiplying.

Real-World Connection

Careers Package designers design attractive and cost-efficient packages.

The **surface area** of a three-dimensional figure is the sum of the areas of its surfaces. You can use a net to find the surface area of a prism.

② EXAMPLE Finding the Surface Area of a Prism Real World

Package Design Find the surface area of the juice box at the right.

Step 1 Draw and label a net for the prism.

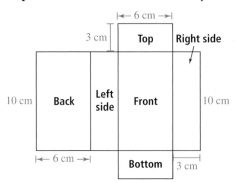

Step 2 Find and add the areas of all the rectangles.

Top	Back	Left	Front	Right	Bottom
3×6	10×6	10×3	10×6	10×3	3×6
$= 18$	60	30	60	30	18

$= 216$

● The surface area of the juice box is 216 square centimeters.

✓ **Check Understanding** ② Find the surface area of each prism.

a.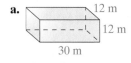

1,728 m²

b.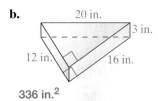

336 in.²

OBJECTIVE

2 Finding the Surface Area of a Cylinder

If you carefully peel a label off of a can as shown, you will see that the label is a rectangle.

The width of the rectangle is the height of the can.

The base length of the rectangle is the circumference of the can.

👥 Reaching All Students

Below Level Give students this net for a rectangular prism. Have them use the net to find the surface area. 216 square units

Advanced Learners The figure is half of a cylinder. Find its surface area. about 668 in.²

Inclusion See note on page 468.

Tactile Learners See notes on pages 468 and 469.

Suppose you draw a net of the cylinder that is the actual vegetable can. You will see that the can is a rectangle and two circles.

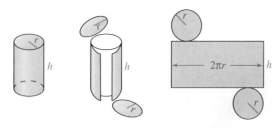

You can find the surface area of a cylinder by finding the area of its net.

③ EXAMPLE   Finding the Surface Area of a Cylinder

Find the surface area of the cylinder. Use 3.14 for π.

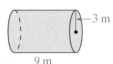

Step 1 Draw and label a net for the cylinder.

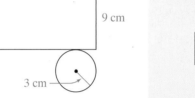

Step 2 Find the area of one circle.

$A = \pi r^2$ ← **Use the formula.**

$\approx 3.14 \times 3^2$ ← **Substitute 3 for r and 3.14 for π.**

$= 28.26$ ← **Multiply.**

≈ 28.3 ← **Round to the nearest tenth.**

Need Help?
The formula for the circumference of a circle is $C = \pi d$.

Step 3 Find the area of the rectangle.

$A = l \times w$ ← **Use the formula.**

$= \pi d \times h$ ← **The length of the rectangle is the circumference of the circle. The width of the rectangle is the height of the cylinder.**

$\approx 3.14(6) \times 9$ ← **Substitute 6 for d, 9 for h, and 3.14 for π.**

$= 169.56$ ← **Multiply.**

≈ 169.6 ← **Round to the nearest tenth.**

Step 4 Add the areas of the rectangles and the two circles.

$$28.3 + 169.6 + 28.3 = 226.2$$

The surface area of the cylinder is about 226.2 square centimeters.

✔ **Check Understanding** ③ **a. Reasoning** Explain how the formula S.A. $= 2\pi r^2 + C \times h$ can be used to find the surface area of the cylinder at the right. **See margin.**

b. Find the surface area of the cylinder. Use 3.14 for π. Round to the nearest tenth. **96.6 in.^{2}**

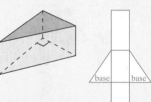

Check Understanding

3a. The areas of the top and bottom of the can are πr^2. The area around the can is the product of the height of the can and the distance around the can. The distance around the can is the circumference of the can, so the area around the can is Ch.

---

③ **EXAMPLE** Tactile Learners

In the net for a cylinder, students might not understand why the length of the rectangle is equal to the circumference of one of the circles. To help them see the relationship, have them cut apart a cylindrical cardboard carton, such as a rolled oats container.

Error Prevention!

When finding the surface area of a cylinder, students might calculate the correct area for one circular base, but forget that they must account for two of these bases in determining the total surface area.

PowerPoint
Additional Examples

① Draw a net for the triangular prism shown.

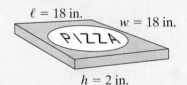

② Find the surface area of the pizza box. **792 in.^{2}**

$\ell = 18$ in. $w = 18$ in.

$h = 2$ in.

③ Find the surface area of the cylinder. Round to the nearest tenth. **about 565.5 ft^2**

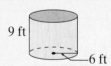

9 ft   6 ft

Closure

• *What is the surface area of a three-dimensional figure?* **the sum of the areas of all its surfaces**

• *How do you find the surface area of a prism or cylinder?* **Find the area of its net.**

3. Practice

Assignment Guide

1 **Objective 1**
Ⓐ Ⓑ Core 1–9, 14–21
Ⓒ Extension 22–23

2 **Objective 2**
Ⓐ Ⓑ Core 10–13

Test Prep 24–27
Mixed Review 28–34

Teaching Tip
Exercise 15 Suggest that students double the dimensions of the prisms in Exercises 3 and 5 and calculate the new surface areas.

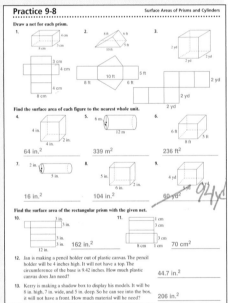
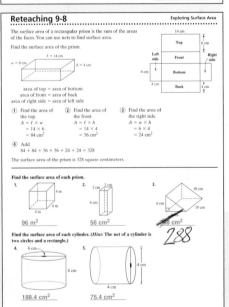

Ⓐ **Practice by Example**

Draw a net for each three-dimensional figure. 1–2. See margin.
3. See back of book.

Example 1
(page 467)

1. 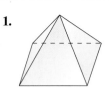 **2.** 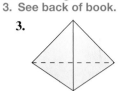 **3.**

Example 2
(page 468)

Find the surface area of each prism.

4. 78 cm²
5. 520 m²
6. 216 ft²

4. 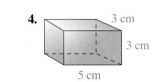 3 cm / 3 cm / 5 cm

5. 8 m / 17 m / 15 m / 10 m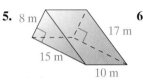

6. 6 ft / 6 ft / 6 ft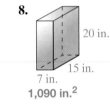

7. 9 m / 8 m / 12 m
552 m²

8. 20 in. / 15 in. / 7 in.
1,090 in.²

9. 7.1 in. / 10.9 in. / 7.1 in. / 13 in.
297.49 in.²

Example 3
(page 469)

Find the surface area of each cylinder. Use 3.14 for π.

10. 4 cm / 10 cm
351.68 cm²

11. 6 m / 5 m
414.48 m²

12. 24 ft / 16 ft
1,607.68 ft²

Ⓑ **Apply Your Skills** 🏠 **Household Objects** **Find the surface area of each object.**

13.  BATTERY / 3.2 cm / ⟵ 5.5 cm ⟶
about 71.3 cm²

14. Spaghetti / 7 cm / 27 cm / 3 cm
582 cm²

15. Writing in Math Suppose each dimension of a rectangular prism is
🔲GPS doubled. How is the surface area affected? **The surface area of the prism with doubled dimensions is four times the surface area of the original prism.**

16. Data File, p. 429 Find the surface area of the platform of the Taj Mahal.
22,400 m²

Find the surface area of a rectangular prism with the given dimensions.

17. ℓ = 2.2 m, w = 3 m, h = 11 m
127.6 m²

18. ℓ = 5 in., w = 6.3 in., h = 8 in.
243.8 in.²

470 **Chapter 9** Geometry and Measurement

🔲GPS Use the Guided Problem Solving worksheet with Exercise 15.

1.

2.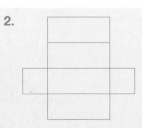

Find the surface area of each figure. A small cube measures 1 cm on a side.

19.

14 cm²

20.

24 cm²

21.

28 cm²

C **Challenge**

22. **Reasoning** The surface area of a cube is 54 square inches. What is the length of each edge? **3 in.**

23. **Stretch Your Thinking** Terri's cube has a surface area of 6 square centimeters. Each edge of Quinn's cube is twice as long as each edge of Terri's cube. What is the surface area of Quinn's cube? **24 cm²**

Test Prep

Multiple Choice

24. What is the approximate surface area of the cylinder at the right? **C**
   A. 12 square meters   **B.** 25 square meters
   C. 125 square meters   **D.** 175 square meters

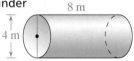

Take It to the NET
Online lesson quiz at
www.PHSchool.com
Web Code: aaa-0908

25. What is the surface area of a cube whose edges are *s* units long? **H**
   F. s^2 **G.** $3s^2$ **H.** $6s^2$ **I.** s^3

26. Which of the following CANNOT be the dimensions **C** of the piece of wrapping paper used to wrap the box?
   A. 20 by 28 inches   **B.** 36 by 18 inches
   C. 40 by 10 inches   **D.** 24 by 24 inches

4 in.
9 in.
15 in.

Extended Response

27. **a.** What is the surface area of the triangular prism at the right?
   b. Explain how you found your answer.

27a–b. See margin.

25 ft
7 ft
24 ft
40 ft

Mixed Review

Lesson 9-3

Find the area of each square given the side *s* or the perimeter *P*.

28. $s = 7$ km   29. $s = 12.6$ in.   30. $P = 36$ ft   31. $P = 18$ yd
   49 km²   158.76 in.²   81 ft²   20.25 yd²

Lesson 9-1

Choose an appropriate metric unit of measure.

32. capacity of a pond   33. capacity of a thimble   34. mass of a pencil
   kiloliters   milliliters   grams

9-8 Surface Areas of Prisms and Cylinders   **471**

27. [4] a. 2,408 ft²
   b. Find the area of one of the triangular ends $\left(\frac{1}{2} \times 7 \times 4\right)$ and multiply by 2 to get 168 ft². Then find the areas of

the three rectangular faces
($7 \times 40 = 280$ ft²,
$24 \times 40 = 960$ ft²,
$25 \times 40 = 1,000$ ft²).
Add all the areas to get a total of 2,408 ft²

for the surface area.

[3] one computational error
[2] incorrect explanation
[1] no work shown

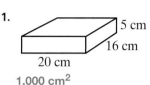 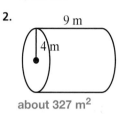
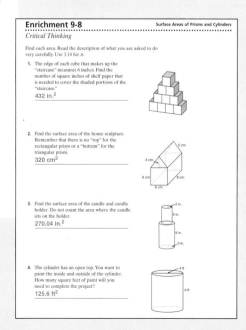
471

Volumes of Rectangular Prisms and Cylinders

Lesson Preview

Check Skills You'll Need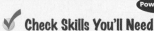

Finding the Area of a Parallelogram and a Triangle
Lesson 9-4: Examples 1–2. Extra Practice, p. 650.

Lesson Resources

  Teaching Resources
Practice, Reteaching, Enrichment
Checkpoint Quiz 2

Reaching All Students
Practice Workbook 9-9
Spanish Practice Workbook 9-9
Reading and Math Literacy 9C
Spanish Reading and Math
   Literacy 9C
Spanish Checkpoint Quiz 2
Guided Problem Solving 9-9
Hands-On Activities 34, 38

Presentation Assistant Plus!
Transparencies
• Check Skills You'll Need 9-9
• Problem of the Day 9-9
• Additional Examples 9-9
• Student Edition Answers 9-9
• Lesson Quiz 9-9
• Classroom Aid 20, 21
PH Presentation Pro CD-ROM 9-9

PRENTICE HALL
ASSESSMENT SYSTEM

Checkpoint Quiz 2
Computer Test Generator CD

Technology
Resource Pro® CD-ROM
Computer Test Generator CD
PH Presentation Pro CD-ROM

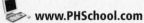 **www.PHSchool.com**
Student Site
• Teacher Web Code: aak-5500
• Self-grading Lesson Quiz

PH SuccessNet Teacher Center
• Lesson Planner
• Resources

Plus **iTEXT**

What You'll Learn

OBJECTIVE 1 To find the volume of a rectangular prism

OBJECTIVE 2 To find the volume of a cylinder

. . . And Why

To find the volume of a fish tank, as in Example 2

Check Skills You'll Need

For help, go to Lesson 9-4.

Find the area of each figure.

1.
2 yd
8 yd²
4 yd

2.
20 km
500 km²
50 km

New Vocabulary • volume • cubic unit

iTEXT Interactive lesson includes instant self-check, tutorials, and activities.

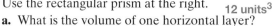

OBJECTIVE 1 Finding the Volume of a Rectangular Prism

The **volume** of a three-dimensional figure is the number of cubic units needed to fill the space inside the figure. A **cubic unit** is the amount of space in a cube that measures 1 unit long by 1 unit wide by 1 unit high.

1 EXAMPLE Counting Cubes to Find Volume

Find the volume of the rectangular prism.

Each layer of the prism is 3 cubes by 5 cubes. This equals 3×5, or 15 cubes. The prism is 4 layers tall. So, the prism has a total of 4×15, or 60 cubes.

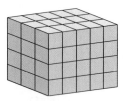

The volume of the prism is 60 cubic units.

✓ Check Understanding ① Use the rectangular prism at the right. 12 units³
   a. What is the volume of one horizontal layer?
   b. What is the volume of the entire prism? 36 units³
   c. **Number Sense** How would the volume change if the number of layers were doubled? **The volume would double.**

Key Concepts **Volume of a Prism**

$$\text{Volume} = \text{Area of Base} \times \text{height}$$
$$V = B \times h$$

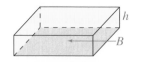

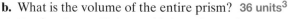

Ongoing Assessment and Intervention

Before the Lesson	**During the Lesson**	**After the Lesson**
Diagnose prerequisite skills using:	Monitor progress using:	Assess knowledge using:
• Check Skills You'll Need	• Check Understanding • Additional Examples • Test Prep	• Lesson Quiz • Computer Test Generator CD • Chapter Checkpoint 2 (p. 476)

For a rectangular prism, the area of a base is $\ell \times w$, since the base is a rectangle. So, the volume formula becomes $V = \ell \times w \times h$. Common cubic units used in measuring volume are cubic centimeters (cm^3), cubic inches, (in.^3), and cubic feet (ft^3).

10 in.

12 in.

20 in.

 EXAMPLE **Finding the Volume of a Prism** Real World

Fish Tanks Find the volume of the fish tank shown at the left.

$V = \ell \times w \times h$ ← Use the formula for the volume of a rectangular prism.

    $= 20 \times 10 \times 12$ ← Substitute 20 for ℓ, 10 for w, and 12 for h.

    $= 2{,}400$ ← Multiply.

The volume is about 2,400 cubic centimeters, or 2,400 cm^3.

 Check Understanding Find the volume of a rectangular prism with a length of 8 meters, a width of 7 meters, and a height of 10 meters. **560 m^3**

OBJECTIVE

2 **Finding the Volume of a Cylinder**

The formula $V = B \times h$ applies to cylinders as well as to prisms. Since the base of the cylinder is a circle, use $A = \pi r^2$ to find the area of the base. Then multiply by the height to find the volume of the cylinder.

1.4 in.

6 in.

3 **EXAMPLE** **Finding the Volume of a Cylinder** Real World

Food Find the volume of the can of Parmesan cheese at the left. Round to the nearest tenth.

Step 1 Find the area of the base.

    Area of Base $= \pi \times r^2$ ← Use $A = \pi r^2$ to find the area of the base.

           $\approx 3.14 \times 1.4^2$ ← Substitute 1.4 for r and 3.14 for π.

           $= 6.1544$ ← Multiply.

Step 2 Find the volume.

    Volume $= B \times h$

          $\approx 6.1544 \times 6$ ← Substitute 6.1544 for B and 6 for h.

          $= 36.9264$ ← Multiply.

The volume is about 36.9 cubic inches, or 36.9 in.^3.

 Check Understanding **3** Find the volume of a cylinder with a radius of 4 inches and a height of 9 inches. Round to the nearest cubic inch. **452 in.^3**

 **Reaching All Students**

| **Below Level** Have students build as many different prisms as they can using 48 small cubes. **possible dimensions:** $1 \times 1 \times 48$, $1 \times 2 \times 24$, $1 \times 3 \times 16$, $1 \times 4 \times 12$, $1 \times 6 \times 8$, $2 \times 2 \times 12$, $2 \times 3 \times 8$, $2 \times 4 \times 6$, $3 \times 4 \times 4$ | **Advanced Learners** A fish tank is a rectangular prism with length 36 in., width 18 in., and height 24 in. What is the volume of this tank in gallons if one gallon of water is 231 in.^3? **about 67 gal** | **Alternative Method** See note on page 473. **Error Prevention** See note on page 475. |

2. Teach

 Professional Development

Math Background

The area of a two-dimensional figure is the number of square units it encloses on a plane surface. *Volume* is the comparable measure in three dimensions. That is, the volume of a three-dimensional figure is the number of cubic units it encloses in space.

Teaching Notes

3 **EXAMPLE** **Alternative Method**

When $\pi \times r^2$ is substituted into the general volume formula $V = B \times h$, you arrive at a special formula for the volume of a cylinder, namely $V = \pi \times r^2 \times h$. Some students might find it easier to find volumes of cylinders using this formula.

PowerPoint

Additional Examples

1 Find the volume of the rectangular prism shown. **72 cubic units**

2 Find the volume of the storage container shown. **1,800 in.^3**

9 in.

10 in.

20 in.

3 Find the volume of the can of tuna. Round to the nearest tenth. **about 175.9 cm^3**

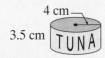

4 cm

3.5 cm TUNA

Closure

• *How do you find the volume of a rectangular prism?* Use the formula $V = \ell \times w \times h$.

• *How do you find the volume of a cylinder?* Find the area of the circular base using $A = \pi \times r^2$; multiply the result by the height.

473

3. Practice

Assignment Guide

1 **Objective 1**
  Ⓐ Ⓑ Core 1–8, 14, 16–19, 24
  Ⓒ Extension 25

2 **Objective 2**
  Ⓐ Ⓑ Core 9–13,15, 20–23
  Ⓒ Extension 26–27

Test Prep 28–31
Mixed Review 32–36

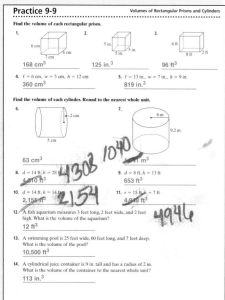
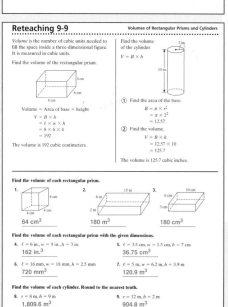
474

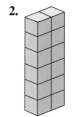 **EXERCISES**   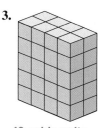 **For more practice, see** *Extra Practice.*

Ⓐ **Practice by Example**

Find the volume of each rectangular prism.

Example 1
(page 472)

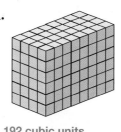

1. 192 cubic units

2. 12 cubic units

3. 40 cubic units

Example 2
(page 473)

Find the volume of each rectangular prism.

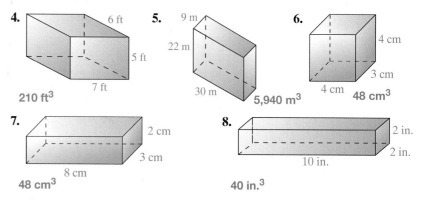

4. 6 ft, 5 ft, 7 ft — 210 ft³

5. 9 m, 22 m, 30 m — 5,940 m³

6. 4 cm, 3 cm, 4 cm — 48 cm³

7. 2 cm, 3 cm, 8 cm — 48 cm³

8. 2 in., 2 in., 10 in. — 40 in.³

Example 3
(page 473)

Find the volume of each cylinder. Use 3.14 for π and round to the nearest tenth. Exercise 9 has been started for you.

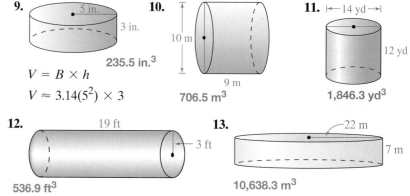

9. 5 in., 3 in. — 235.5 in.³
$$V = B \times h$$
$$V \approx 3.14(5^2) \times 3$$

10. 10 m, 9 m — 706.5 m³

11. 14 yd, 12 yd — 1,846.3 yd³

12. 19 ft, 3 ft — 536.9 ft³

13. 22 m, 7 m — 10,638.3 m³

Ⓑ **Apply Your Skills**

🌐 **14. Architecture** The shape of a monument is a hexagonal prism. The area of the base is 5.4 square feet and the height is 13 feet. Find the volume.
70.2 ft³

🌐 **15. Straws** A straw has the shape of a cylinder. Find the volume of a straw with a radius of 3 millimeters and a height of 200 millimeters.
about 5,652 mm³

474 Chapter 9   Geometry and Measurement

GPS Use the Guided Problem Solving worksheet with Exercise 16.

18. The volume of the second prism would double because h in the formula $A = bh$ would double.

16. **Trucks** A rectangular truck bed has a length of 20 feet, a width of 8 feet, and a height of 7 feet. A cylindrical truck tank has a radius of 3.5 feet and a length of 22 feet. Find each volume. Use 3.14 for π.
1,120 ft³; 846.23 ft³

17. **Number Sense** How would the volume of a cube change if its dimensions were doubled? What if the dimensions were halved?
See margin.

18. **Writing in Math** Two rectangular prisms have the same base area. The second prism has twice the height of the first prism. How do their volumes compare? How do you know? See below left.

19. **Data File, p. 429** Find the volume of the Great Pyramid of Khufu using the formula Volume $= \frac{1}{3} \times$ length $\times$ width $\times$ height.
about 2,574,467 m³

Find the volume of each rectangular prism or cylinder with the given dimensions. Round to the nearest hundredth, if necessary.

20. $\ell = 6$ m, $w = 4.3$ m, $h = 11$ m
283.8 m³

21. $\ell = 3.2$ ft, $w = 2$ ft, $h = 9.4$ ft
60.16 ft³

22. $r = 8.1$ cm, $h = 4$ cm
824.48 cm³

23. $r = 2.4$ in., $h = 5.4$ in.
97.72 in.³

24. **Reasoning** One ton of coal fills a bin that is 3 feet by 4 feet by 4 feet. Find the dimensions of a bin that would hold 2 tons of coal.
Answers may vary. Sample: 6 feet by 4 feet by 4 feet

Challenge 25. **Swimming Pools** A swimming pool is 24 meters long and 16 meters wide. The average depth of the water is 2.5 meters. How many 2-liter bottles of water would be needed to fill the pool? (*Hint:* 1 m³ = 1,000 L) 480,000

26. **Algebra** Find the height of a cylinder with a volume of 85 cubic feet and a radius of 2.6 feet. about 4 ft

27. **Stretch Your Thinking** Items at a garage sale cost $1, $2, and $5. Marty spent $21. He bought one more $2 item than $1 items. He bought twice as many $2 items as $5 items. How many of each item did he buy?
3 $1 items, 4 $2 items, and 2 $5 items

Test Prep

Multiple Choice

28. A cylinder has a radius of 7 feet and a height of 14 feet. What is its approximate volume in cubic feet? D
A. 294 B. 333 C. 686 D. 2,155

29. A rectangular prism is 2 meters long, 50 centimeters wide, and 1 meter high. What is its volume? F
F. 1 cubic meter G. 100 cubic centimeters
H. 100 cubic meters I. 10,000 cubic centimeters

17. The volume would be 8 times greater. The volume would be $\frac{1}{8}$ as much.

 **Lesson Quiz 9-9**

1. Find the volume of a rectangular prism with dimensions of $\ell = 15$ in., $w = 13$ in., and $h = 8$ in. **1,560 in.^{3}**

2. Find the volume of a cylinder with dimensions $r = 6$ mm, and $h = 21$ mm. Use 3.14 for π. Round to the nearest tenth. **about 2,373.8 mm^3**

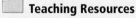 **Chapter Checkpoint**

To check understanding of Lessons 9-5 to 9-9:

Checkpoint Quiz 2 (p. 476)

📁 **Teaching Resources**
Checkpoint Quiz 2 (also in Prentice Hall Assessment System)

Reaching All Students
Reading and Math Literacy 9C

Spanish versions available

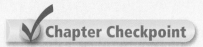

Enrichment 9-9   Volumes of Rectangular Prisms and Cylinders
Critical Thinking

A company needs to select a container to package coffee. The container cannot be wider than 10 inches and it needs to be shorter than 14 inches. There are no restrictions on the length. Each container needs to hold at least 1,500 cubic inches of coffee grounds but not more than 1,680 cubic inches. The containers the company is considering are shown in the table. Which container meets their requirements?

container	shape	length	width	height	diameter
A	cube	—	9.5 in.	—	—
B	box	10 in.	12 in.	13 in.	—
C	cylinder	—	—	12 in.	9 in.
D	box	16 in.	8 in.	12 in.	—
E	can	—	—	13 in.	9.5 in.

1. The container cannot be wider than 10 inches and it must be shorter than 14 inches. Give some examples of measures of widths and heights that are acceptable.
   width: from 0.1 in. to 10 in.; height: from 0.1 in. to 14 in.

2. Knowing the restrictions on the container, which container can you immediately eliminate? Why?
   Container B; width of 12 in. is greater than 10 in.

3. Is Container A an acceptable choice? Explain.
   No; the volume of Container A is 857.4 in.^{3}, which is too small.

4. Knowing the restrictions on length and width, would any cube-shaped container be acceptable for the coffee grounds? Explain.
   No; a width no greater than 10 inches gives a volume of 1,000 in.^{3}, which is less than the minimum volume range required.

5. Would either of the cylindrical-shaped containers be acceptable? Explain.
   Yes; the volume of container B is 1,560 in.^{3}, but the volume of container E is about 884 in.^{3}.

6. Which containers have you eliminated? Of the remaining choice(s), which is acceptable? Explain.
   Containers A, C, and E have been eliminated.
   Containers B and D are acceptable because their width, height, and volume are acceptable.

476

---

30. Each cube of the rectangular prism at the right measures 1 inch on each edge. If the top level of cubes is removed, what is the volume of the remaining prism? **B**

    A. 40 cubic inches   **B.** 45 cubic inches
    C. 48 cubic inches   **D.** 60 cubic inches
    31a–b. See back of book.

 Take It to the NET
Online lesson quiz at
www.PHSchool.com
Web Code: aaa-0909

Extended Response

31. a. Find all possible rectangular prisms that have a volume of 18 cubic centimeters and whole-number dimensions.
    b. For which dimensions does the prism have the most surface area?

 **Mixed Review**

Lesson 9-6 🌐 **32. Pets** A dog is tied to a post with a 10-foot rope. The dog gets exercise by running in a circle. (Assume that the rope does not wrap around the post.) What is the circumference of the circle the dog makes? Round to the nearest tenth. **62.8 ft**

Lesson 9-3 **Find the area of each square with the given perimeter.**

33. 12 m **9 m^2**   34. 24 ft **36 ft^2**   35. 34 cm **72.25 cm^2**   36. 25 in. **39.0625 in.^{2}**

 **Checkpoint Quiz 2**   **Lessons 9-5 through 9-9**

📱 Instant self-check quiz online and on CD-ROM

Name each figure.

1.
2.
3.
4.

triangular pyramid   cone   pentagonal pyramid   hexagonal prism

Use the rectangular prism at the left for Exercises 5 and 6.

5. Find the surface area. **62 cm^2**   6. Find the volume. **30 cm^3**

3 cm   2 cm   5 cm

Use the cylinder at the right for Exercises 7–10.
Use 3.14 for π. Round to the nearest tenth.

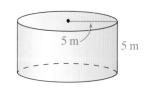
5 m   5 m

7. Find the circumference of the circular base. **31.4 m**
8. Find the area of the circular base. **78.5 m^2**
9. Find the surface area. **314.0 m^2**   10. Find the volume. **392.5 m^3**

476   Chapter 9   Geometry and Measurement

Alternative Assessment

Each student uses the drawings of prisms and cylinders that they made in the Alternative Assessment for Lesson 9-8. Students then find the volume of each of the figures.

Test Prep

Resources
For additional practice with a variety of test item formats:
• Test Prep, p. 485
• Test-Taking Strategies, p. 481
• Test-Taking Strategies With Transparencies

9-10 Work Backward

What You'll Learn

OBJECTIVE 1
To solve problems by working backward

... And Why

To solve problems involving money, as in Example 1

✔ Check Skills You'll Need

? For help, go to Lesson 1-10.

Find the value of each expression.

1. $3 \times (5 + 7)$ **36**

2. $36 \div 3 - 5$ **7**

3. $68 \div 4 - 8$ **9**

4. $(9 + 8) \times 4$ **68**

5. $14 + (13 \times 7)$ **105**

6. $105 - 13 \times 7$ **14**

OBJECTIVE 1

(TEXT) Interactive lesson includes instant self-check, tutorials, and activities.

Solving Problems by Working Backward

When to Use This Strategy Some problems involve a series of steps that lead to a final result. If you are asked to find the initial amount, you can *work backward* from the final result by using inverse operations.

1 EXAMPLE Real-World 🌐 Problem Solving

Real-World 🌐 Connection

Natural habitats in zoos help protect some endangered species.

Zoo Luis went to the zoo for a school trip. He paid $5 for admission. He spent $14 at the souvenir shop. When he got home, he had $18 left. How much money did he start with?

Read and Understand You know how much money Luis had when he got home. You know how much he spent. You want to know how much he had when he started.

Plan and Solve To find the amount Luis had when he started, begin with the amount he had at the end. Then work backward.

To undo the amounts that Luis spent, add.

$18 ← **Luis had $18 left at the end.**

$18 + $5 = $23 ← **He spent $5 on admission. Add.**

$23 + $14 = $37 ← **He spent $14 at the souvenir shop. Add.**

Luis started with $37.

Look Back and Check Read the problem again. Start with $37. Subtract the amounts as Luis spends money in the problem. $37 − $5 − $14 = $18. The answer checks. ✔

Lesson Preview

PowerPoint

✔ **Check Skills You'll Need** 🖥

Finding the Value of Expressions
Lesson 1-10: Example 1. Extra Practice, p. 642.

Lesson Resources

📁 **Teaching Resources**
Practice, Reteaching, Enrichment

👥 **Reaching All Students**
Practice Workbook 9-10
Spanish Practice Workbook 9-10
Guided Problem Solving 9-10

🕐 **Presentation Assistant Plus!**
Transparencies
• Check Skills You'll Need 9-10
• Problem of the Day 9-10
• Additional Examples 9-10
• Student Edition Answers 9-10
• Lesson Quiz 9-10
PH Presentation Pro CD-ROM 9-10

PRENTICE HALL ASSESSMENT SYSTEM

Computer Test Generator CD

💻 **Technology**
Resource Pro® CD-ROM
Computer Test Generator CD
PH Presentation Pro CD-ROM

💻 **www.PHSchool.com**
Student Site
• Teacher Web Code: aak-5500
• Self-grading Lesson Quiz

PH SuccessNet Teacher Center
• Lesson Planner
• Resources

Plus (TEXT)

Ongoing Assessment and Intervention

Before the Lesson
Diagnose prerequisite skills using:
• Check Skills You'll Need

During the Lesson
Monitor progress using:
• Check Understanding
• Additional Examples
• Test Prep

After the Lesson
Assess knowledge using:
• Lesson Quiz
• Computer Test Generator CD

477

Math Background

Many problems give a set of initial conditions and the student is expected to arrive at a result. In other problems, the result is given and the student's task is to determine what the initial conditions must have been. Such problems can be solved by using inverse operations to reverse the steps that led to the result. This process is called the *work backward* strategy.

Teaching Notes

1 EXAMPLE Tactile Learners

Have students act out the steps of the solution using play money.

Error Prevention!

Students might not be able to identify the appropriate inverse operations because they cannot identify the original operations within the language of the problem. Suggest that they summarize the given problem in a diagram like this one for Check Understanding 1.

Read Forward

? pencils	21 pencils ↑
− 7 pencils	+ 7 pencils
+ 5 pencils	− 5 pencils
− 3 pencils	+ 3 pencils
16 pencils	16 pencils

Work Backward

Additional Examples

1. Ali baked some cookies. She gave a dozen to her friend. She gave half the remaining cookies to her mother, and she kept the rest. The next day, she ate four of the cookies that she kept. A dozen cookies were left. How many cookies did Ali bake? **44 cookies**

Closure

How do you solve a problem by working backward? Start with the final result. Use inverse operations until you find the initial amount.

✔ **Check Understanding** **1** A teacher lends 7 pencils to her students in the morning, collects 5 before lunch, and gives out 3 after lunch. At the end of the day, she has 16 pencils. How many pencils did the teacher have at the start of the day? **21 pencils**

EXERCISES

? For more practice, see *Extra Practice*.

A Practice by Example

Example 1
(page 477)

Need Help?
- Reread the problem.
- Identify the key facts and details.
- Tell the problem in your own words.
- Try a different strategy.
- Check your work.

Work backward to solve each problem.

1. You divide a number by 2, add 7, and then multiply by 5. The result is 50. What is the number? **6**

2. **Shopping** Brenda spent half her money at a store in the mall. At another store, she spent half her remaining money and $6 more. She had $2 left. How much did Brenda have when she arrived at the mall? **$32**

3. **Money** The checkbook shows amounts subtracted from an account (checks) and amounts added (deposits). How much was in the account before the $25 check was written? **$89.25**

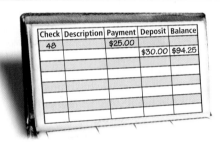

Check	Description	Payment	Deposit	Balance
48		$25.00		
			$30.00	$94.25

B Apply Your Skills

Strategies

Draw a Diagram
Make a Graph
Make an Organized List
Make a Table and Look for a Pattern
Simulate a Problem
Solve a Simpler Problem
Try, Check, and Revise
Use Logical Reasoning
Work Backward
Write an Equation

Use any strategy to solve each problem. Show your work.

4. **Entertainment** At the Plex Cinema, every 15th customer gets a free ticket. Every 10th customer gets free popcorn. Of 418 ticket buyers, how many received both prizes? **13 ticket buyers**

5. **Baking** Henry bakes some muffins. He eats two. He puts half of the muffins away. He divides the remaining muffins among his 3 sisters. Each sister receives 3 muffins. How many muffins did Henry bake? **20 muffins**

6. **Hobbies** Kai sold half his baseball cards to Ana, half of the remaining cards to Joe, and the last 10 to Chip. How many cards were sold? **40 cards**

7. **Transportation** A local bus picked up 3 passengers at its first stop. At every stop thereafter, it picked up 2 more passengers than at the previous stop. How many passengers got on at the fifth stop? **11 passengers**

Reaching All Students

Below Level Review the concept of inverse operations by having students solve simple equations like these.

$c - 12 = 36$ $c = 48$ $7k = 42$ $k = 6$
$r + 8 = 22$ $r = 14$ $\frac{m}{4} = 24$ $m = 96$

Advanced Learners Ann had the same number of cards as Dan. Ann gave 12 of her cards to Dan. Now Dan has twice as many cards as Ann. How many cards did each have at the start? **36 cards each**

Tactile Learners See note on page 478.
Auditory Learners See note on page 479.

Use any strategy to solve each problem. Show your work.

 8. a. Money Taesha has $1.35 in nickels and dimes. She has a total of 15 coins. How many of each coin does she have? **3 nickels, 12 dimes**

b. Writing in Math Explain how you solved this problem.

8b. Answers may vary. Sample: make an organized list.

 **9. Biology** A bacterial population doubles in size every 6 minutes. After 2 hours, the population is 8,000. When was the population 4,000? **6 minutes before the end of the 2-hour period**

10. Calendar Jeffrey's birthday is circled below. His cousin Marianne was born in the same year and turns 12 on April 19. What day of the week does Marianne turn 12? **Sunday**

March						
S	M	T	W	T	F	S
1	2	3	4	5	6	7
8	9	10	11	12	13	14
15	16	17	18	19	20	21
22	23	24	25	26	27	28
29	30	31				

11. Health Of 25 students, 11 need a dental check-up and 17 need an eye exam. Five students don't need either. How many students need both a dental check-up and an eye exam? **8 students**

C **Challenge**

12. Box A has 9 green balls and 4 red balls. Box B has 12 green balls and 5 red balls. Suppose you want the fraction of green balls in Box A to equal the fraction of red balls in Box B. How many green balls must you move from Box A to Box B? **8 green balls**

13. Stretch Your Thinking Suppose you have 4 lengths of chain with 3 links each. How should you cut and rejoin only 3 links so that the 4 lengths form one circular chain with 12 links? **See back of book.**

Test Prep

Multiple Choice

14. The diameter of a circle is 8 meters. What is the approximate circumference of the circle? **C**

A. 4 meters   **B.** 12 meters   **C.** 24 meters   **D.** 32 meters

Take It to the NET
Online lesson quiz at
www.PHSchool.com
Web Code: aaa-0910

15. The ratio of the circumferences of two circles is 1:2. What is the ratio of the radii of the circles? **F**

F. 1:2   **G.** 1:4   **H.** 1:5   **I.** 1:10

9-10 Work Backward **479**

GPS Use the Guided Problem Solving worksheet with Exercise 4.

---

3. Practice

Assignment Guide

1 Objective 1
 A **B** Core 1–11
 C Extension 12–13

Test Prep 14–17
Mixed Review 18–25

Auditory Learners
Exercises 1–7 Have students use vocal emphasis to identify the reverse steps. For Exercise 1 they might say, "The problem *ends* with 50, so I *start* with 50. The problem *multiplies* by 5, so I *divide* by 5. It then *adds* 7, so I *subtract* 7. . . ."

Practice 9-10   Problem Solving: Work Backward

Work backward to solve each problem.

1. At the end of a board game, Al had 57 game dollars. During the game he had won $200, lost $150, won $25, lost $10, and lost $35. How much money did Al have at the start?
$27

2. Jan spent half of the money she had on a coat. She spent half of what remained on a dress. Next, she spent half of what remained on a pair of boots. She returned home with $57. How much money did Jan have before shopping?
$456

3. Bill gathered some eggs on Monday. On Tuesday, he gathered half as many eggs, plus an egg, as he gathered on Monday. On Wednesday, he gathered half the difference of the number of eggs he gathered on Monday and Tuesday, plus an egg. If he gathered 5 eggs on Wednesday, how many eggs did Bill gather on Monday?
18 eggs

4. Carli spent a third of her money, and then spent $4 more. She then spent half of what money remained. It cost her $1 for the bus ride home. She then had $5 left. How much money did she start with?
$24

5. Mick picked a number, doubled it, added 8, divided by 4, and had a result of 12. What number did Mick pick?
20

6. It takes Jenni 50 minutes to get ready for school. The drive to school takes 15 minutes. She needs 8 minutes to get to her locker, then to her first class. If school begins at 8:30 A.M., what is the latest Jenni should get up in the morning?
7:17 A.M.

7. On May 31, Hayden's uncle and grandfather came to visit him. Hayden's grandfather visits every three days, and his uncle visits every twelve days. What is the first day in May that both visited Hayden on the same day?
May 7

Reteaching 9-10   Problem Solving: Work Backward

The store manager recorded 80 greeting cards sold on Friday. The day before she had sold one-half that number. On Wednesday, she sold 25 more than on Thursday. On Monday and Tuesday she sold a total of twice what she sold on Wednesday. How many cards did she sell during the 5 days?

Read and Understand | What does the problem ask you to find? *You need to find the total number of cards sold during the 5 days.*

Plan and Solve | How can you find the number sold on each day? *Use the information given in the problem. Work backward from that information to find the number sold on Thursday, then Wednesday, and finally, the total on Tuesday and Monday.*

Work backward.

	Cards sold on Friday	80
	80 ÷ 2 sold on Thursday	40
	40 + 25 sold on Wednesday	65
	2 × 65 sold on Monday and Tuesday	+ 130
		315

She sold 315 cards.

Look Back and Check | Write the number of cards sold as a mathematical expression. Solve by using the order of operations.
80 + (80 ÷ 2) + (40 + 25) + (2 × 65) = 315

Work backward to solve each problem.

1. On Friday, the diner served 56 ears of corn. On Thursday, the diner served one-half as much corn as on Friday. On Wednesday, the diner served two times as much as on Thursday. On Tuesday, the diner served one-half of what it had served on Wednesday. How much corn did the diner serve during the 4 days?
168 ears

2. On Thursday, the diner served 42 pounds of green beans. On Wednesday, the diner served one-third that amount. On both Tuesday and Monday, the diner served one-half the amount it had served on Wednesday. How many pounds of beans did the diner serve during the 4 days?
70 lb

3. On Friday, the diner served 60 baked potatoes. On both Tuesday and Thursday, the diner served one-fifth that amount. On both Monday and Wednesday, it served one-sixth of Thursday's amount. How many baked potatoes were served during the 5 days?
88 potatoes

4. The diner served 32 pounds of salad on Saturday night. On both Friday and Thursday, one-half that amount was served. On Wednesday, one-eighth of Saturday's amount was served. How many pounds of salad did the diner serve during the 4 days?
68 lb

Work backward to solve each problem.

1. You multiply a number by 9, add 10, and then subtract 5. The result is 113. What is the number? **12**

2. Amy bought a parka for $58.95, a pair of mittens for $6.79, and a scarf for $8.50. When she paid the cashier, she received $5.76 in change. How much money did Amy give the cashier? **$80.00**

Alternative Assessment

Each student in a pair writes a problem that can be solved by the strategy *work backward*. Partners exchange problems and solve.

Test Prep

Resources

For additional practice with a variety of test item formats:
- Test Prep, p. 485
- Test-Taking Strategies, p. 481
- Test-Taking Strategies With Transparencies

Enrichment 9-10 — Problem Solving: Work Backward
Patterns in Geometry

1. The radius of the center circle in the dart game is 1 inch. Each larger circle has a radius that is 1 inch greater than the next smallest circle. Complete the table by finding the area of each ring in the target. (Use π = 3.14.) Then find the ratio of each ring to Ring 1 expressed as a fraction.

Ring	Area	Ratio
1	28.26 in.²	1
2	21.98 in.²	7/9
3	15.7 in.²	5/9
4	9.42 in.²	3/9
5	3.14 in.²	1/9

2. What pattern do you see in the table?
The ratio decreases by 2/9 for each ring as you move from the outer ring to the middle circle.

3. The side length of the smallest square measures 2 inches. Each larger square has a side length that is twice the side length of the next smaller square. Complete the table by finding the area of each square. Then find the ratio of the area of square 1 to the area of each larger square expressed as a fraction.

Figure	Side Length	Area	Ratio
1	2 in.	4 in.²	1
2	4 in.	16 in.²	1/4
3	8 in.	64 in.²	1/16
4	16 in.	256 in.²	1/64
5	32 in.	1,024 in.²	1/256

4. What pattern do you see in the table?
Sample answer: As the side length doubles, the area increases by a factor of 4.

480

---

16. A circular mirror has a diameter of 12 inches. What is the circumference of the mirror? Round to the nearest inch. Use 3.14 for π. **B**

A. 24 inches   **B.** 38 inches   **C.** 113 inches   **D.** 452 inches

Short Response   **17.** The diameter of a bicycle's wheel is 28 inches. About how many times does each wheel make a complete turn when the bicycle travels 1,000 feet? **See margin.**

Mixed Review

Lesson 9-2   **Convert each measurement.**

18. 2.4 kilometers to meters **2,400 m**   **19.** 452 milligrams to centigrams **45.2 c...**

20. 26,400 liters to kiloliters **26.4 kL**   **21.** 0.79 meter to centimeters **79 cm**

Lesson 7-5   **Sketch a circle graph for the given percents.** **22–23. See margin.**

22. 25%, 30%, 45%   **23.** 3%, 37%, 50%, 10%

Lesson 7-3   **Solve each problem by making an organized list.**

24. Use each of the digits 2, 3, 4, and 5 exactly once. How many 4-digit numbers can you form? **24**

25. How many ways can you divide 3 different books among 2 people? Each person must have at least 1 book. **6 ways**

Math at Work

Event Planner

Event planners organize and arrange all the details for parties, business meetings, and other group activities. Their responsibilities include finding the place, choosing the menu, and decorating the tables for an event.

Geometry is useful to event planners as they determine dimensions for room sizes, arrange rectangular or circular tables, and plan serving areas.

Take It to the NET For more information on event planners, go to **www.PHSchool.com**.
Web Code: aab-2031

17. [2] the tire makes one complete circle every $28\pi \approx 87.96$ in., or 7.33 ft. Divide 1,000 by 7.33 to find about 136 revolutions.

[1] Explanation is missing.

22. Answers may vary. Sample:

23. Answers may vary. Sample:

Using Estimation

Estimating may help you find an answer, check an answer, or eliminate one or more answer choices.

1 EXAMPLE

The diameter of a circular plate is 9 inches. Find its area to the nearest tenth.
- **A.** 14.1 square inches
- **B.** 28.3 square inches
- **C.** 63.6 square inches
- **D.** 254.3 square inches

Since the diameter is 9 inches, the radius is 4.5 inches, or about 5 inches.

$$A = \pi r^2$$
$$\approx 3 \times 5^2 \qquad \leftarrow \text{ Substitute 3 for } \pi \text{ and 5 for } r.$$
$$= 3 \times 25, \text{ or 75 square inches} \quad \leftarrow \text{ Simplify.}$$

Only choice C is close to the estimate, so the correct answer is C.

2 EXAMPLE

Eve has 50 feet of edging. What is the diameter of the largest flowerbed she can make? Round to the nearest tenth.
- **F.** 15.7 feet
- **G.** 15.9 feet
- **H.** 157.1 feet
- **I.** 159.2 feet

$$C = \pi d \quad \leftarrow \text{ Use the formula for the circumference of a circle.}$$
$$50 \approx 3d \quad \leftarrow \text{ Estimate by substituting 50 for } C \text{ and 3 for } \pi.$$
$$\frac{50}{3} \approx \frac{3d}{3} \quad \leftarrow \text{ Divide each side by 3.}$$
$$16.7 \text{ feet} \approx d \quad \leftarrow \text{ Simplify. Round to the nearest tenth.}$$

You can eliminate choices H and I because they are not near the estimate.

EXERCISES

Estimate each answer. Then tell which answer choice(s) you can eliminate.

1. What value is closest to the area of a circle with a 3-inch radius? **27 sq. in.; A, B, and D**
   - **A.** 9 square inches
   - **B.** 19 square inches
   - **C.** 28 square inches
   - **D.** 113 square inches

2. To the nearest inch, find the circumference of a circle with a 3-inch radius. **18 in.; F, H, and I**
   - **F.** 9 inches
   - **G.** 19 inches
   - **H.** 28 inches
   - **I.** 113 inches

3. To the nearest tenth, how many more square inches of pizza are in a pizza with a 14-inch diameter than in a pizza with a 12-inch diameter? **39 sq. in.; A, B, and D**
   - **A.** 13 square inches
   - **B.** 21.3 square inches
   - **C.** 40.8 square inches
   - **D.** 163.3 square inches

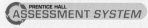

Resources

Student Edition
Extra Practice, Ch. 9, p. 650
English/Spanish Glossary, p. 669
Table of Symbols, p. 666

 Reaching All Students
Reading and Math Literacy 9D
Spanish Reading and Math
    Literacy 9D

 PRENTICE HALL
ASSESSMENT SYSTEM

Test Preparation
• Chapter 9 practice in test
   formats

 www.PHSchool.com
Student Site
• Self-grading vocabulary test

PH SuccessNet Teacher Center
• Resources

Plus **iTEXT**

Chapter Review

Vocabulary

area (p. 440)	cylinder (p. 463)	metric system (p. 431)
base of a parallelogram (p. 446)	diameter (p. 452)	net (p. 464)
base of a triangle (p. 447)	faces (p. 462)	perimeter (p. 441)
capacity (p. 433)	gram (p. 432)	prism (p. 462)
chord (p. 452)	height of a parallelogram	pyramid (p. 463)
circle (p. 452)	(p. 446)	radius (p. 452)
circumference (p. 453)	height of a triangle (p. 447)	sphere (p. 463)
cone (p. 463)	liter (p. 433)	surface area (p. 468)
cube (p. 462)	mass (p. 432)	three-dimensional figure (p. 462)
cubic unit (p. 472)	meter (p. 431)	volume (p. 472)

 Reading Math:
Understanding
Vocabulary

Choose the vocabulary term that best completes each sentence.

1. A rectangular prism has three pairs of congruent and parallel __?__. **faces**

2. A __?__ is a three-dimensional figure with one base. **pyramid OR cone**

Take It to the NET
Online vocabulary quiz
at www.PHSchool.com
Web Code: aaj-0951

3. The standard unit of __?__ in the metric system is the gram. **mass**

4. A __?__ is a segment that connects a circle to its center. **radius**

5. __?__ is the number of cubic units inside a three-dimensional figure. **Volume**

Skills and Concepts

9-1 and 9-2 Objectives

▼ To use metric units of
   length

▼ To use metric units for
   mass and capacity

The standard units of measurement in the **metric system** are the **meter (m)**, the **gram (g)**, and the **liter (L)**. You can convert one metric unit to another by multiplying or dividing by a power of 10.

Complete each statement.

6. $0.3 \text{ kg} = \blacksquare \text{ g}$ **300**   7. $150 \text{ cm} = \blacksquare \text{ m}$ **1.5**   8. $57,000 \text{ mL} = \blacksquare \text{ L}$ **57**

9-3 and 9-4 Objectives

▼ To estimate areas

▼ To find perimeters
   and areas of
   rectangles

▼ To find the areas of
   parallelograms and
   triangles

▼ To find the areas of
   complex figures

The **area** of a figure is the number of square units inside the figure. The formula for the area of a parallelogram is $A = b \times h$. The formula for the area of a triangle is $A = \frac{1}{2}b \times h$.

Find the perimeter and the area of each figure.

9.
6 ft
7 ft
8 ft
30 ft; 48 ft²

10.
15.2 m
29 m
24.7 m
68.9 m; 187.72 m²

11.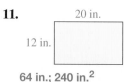
20 in.
12 in.
64 in.; 240 in.²

9-5 and 9-6 Objectives

▼ To identify parts of a circle

▼ To find circumference

▼ To find the area of a circle

A **circle** has three kinds of segments: **radius, chord,** and **diameter.** The distance around a circle is the **circumference.** The symbol π represents the ratio $\dfrac{\text{circumference}}{\text{diameter}}$.

Circumference: $C = \pi d$ or $C = 2\pi r$ Area: $A = \pi r^2$

Use circle O for Exercises 12–16. Use 3.14 for π.

12. Name three chords.   **13.** Name a diameter. $\overline{XV}$
$\overline{XV}, \overline{YW}, \overline{VW}$

14. Name three radii.   **15.** Find the circumference.
$\overline{OV}, \overline{OX}, \overline{OY}$ 31.4 in.

16. Find the area of the circle. Round to the nearest square inch.
79 in.^{2}

9-7 Objective

▼ To identify three-dimensional figures

A **prism** is a **three-dimensional figure** with two parallel and congruent **faces** that are polygons. A **pyramid** has triangular faces and one base that is a polygon. You name a prism or a pyramid by the shape of its bases.

Name each figure.

17.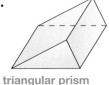

18.

19.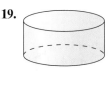

triangular prism   rectangular pyramid   cylinder

9-8 and 9-9 Objectives

▼ To find the surface area of a prism

▼ To find the surface area of a cylinder

▼ To find the volume of a rectangular prism

▼ To find the volume of a cylinder

The **surface area** of a three-dimensional figure is the sum of the areas of all its faces. The **volume** of a three-dimensional figure is the number of cubic units needed to fill the space inside the figure. The formula for the volume of a prism or a cylinder is $V = B \times h$, where B is the area of the base.

Find the surface area and volume of each figure. Use 3.14 for π.

20.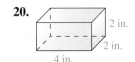

40 in.^{2}; 16 in.^{3}

21.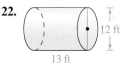

122 m^2; 84 m^3

22.

715.92 ft^2; 1,469.52 ft^3

9-10 Objective

▼ To solve problems by working backward

Some problems involve a series of steps that lead to an end result. To find the initial amount, you can work backward.

23. Travel Tina's family is planning a trip to visit relatives. It will take six hours of driving. Her family will also make two 45-minute stops. If they want to arrive at 4:30 P.M., at what time should they leave? 9:00 A.M.

Chapter
9
Chapter Test

Take It to the NET
Online chapter test at
www.PHSchool.com
Web Code: aaa-0952

Choose an appropriate metric unit for each measurement.

1. length of a car **meters**

2. capacity of a cup **milliliters**

3. length of a skateboard **centimeters**

4. mass of a boat **kilograms**

Convert each measurement.

5. 672 millimeters to centimeters **67.2 cm**

6. 25,040 milliliters to liters **25.04 L**

7. 35.1 kilograms to grams **35,100 g**

8. 125 liters to kiloliters **0.125 kL**

9. 42.9 meters to centimeters **4,290 cm**

Estimate the area of each figure. Each square represents 4 square centimeters.
10–11. Answers may vary.

10.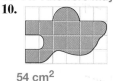
54 cm²

11.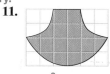
52 cm²

Find the area of each figure.

12.
189 mm²

13.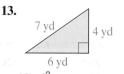
12 yd²

14.
56 m²

15.
117 in.²

16. **Writing in Math** Which is larger: a pie plate with a radius of 5 inches, or a pie plate with a diameter of 9 inches? Explain. **See margin.**

Find the circumference and area of each circle. Round to the nearest tenth.

17.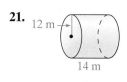
C ≈ 94.2 ft, *A* ≈ 706.5 ft²

18. *C* ≈ 56.52 km, *A* ≈ 254.34 km²
18 km

19. **Food** A rectangular cracker has a length of 5 centimeters and an area of 20 square centimeters. Find its perimeter. **18 cm**

20. **Manufacturing** A factory fills cans with tomato juice. A can has a radius of 2 inches and a height of 8 inches. Find its volume. **about 100.5 in.³**

Find the surface area of each figure.

21.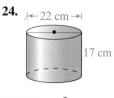
12 m, 14 m
1,959.36 m²

22.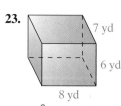
2 in., 13 in., 5 in., 12 in.
120 106 in.²

Find the volume of each figure.

23. 7 yd, 6 yd, 8 yd
336 yd³

24. 22 cm, 17 cm
6,458.98 cm³

25. Suppose you add 2 to a number, subtract 5, and then multiply by 3. The result is 24. What is the number? **11**

26. The volume of a rectangular prism is 504 square centimeters. The area of the base is 72 square centimeters. Find the height of the prism. **7 cm**

16. A pie plate with a radius of 5 inches, since the diameter of the plate is 2 × 5, or 10 inches.

Reading Comprehension Read each passage below. Then answer each question based on what you have read.

Clock Face The Clock Tower of the Palace of Westminster in London—what people often call "Big Ben"—is about 316 feet tall. The tower has four sides, each with a large clock. Each clock face is a circle about 22 feet in diameter. The minute hands are about 12 feet long, measuring from the center of the clock face to the tip of the hand. The Clock Tower can be seen from many parts of the city.

1. Which expression represents the circumference of the circle that the tip of one of the minute hands traces out in an hour? **D**
A. 6π **B.** 10π **C.** 12π **D.** 24π

2. If the minute hand were twice as long, how much farther would it travel every hour? **H**
F. half as far   **G.** the same distance
H. twice as far   **I.** four times as far

3. Which expression represents the area of one of the clock faces? **B**
A. $10 \cdot 10 \cdot \pi$ **B.** $11 \cdot 11 \cdot \pi$
C. $20 \cdot 20 \cdot \pi$ **D.** $22 \cdot 22 \cdot \pi$

4. If the radius of the clock face were twice as long, how many times greater would the area of the face be? **H**
F. the same   **G.** two times
H. four times   **I.** eight times

Mountain Math It takes about $1\frac{1}{2}$ hours to get from Al's house to Mount Monadnock. First you go west 40 miles on the state highway. Then you turn right and go north another 30 miles, and you're there. On a clear day you can see the tallest buildings in Al's hometown from the top of the mountain.

5. Which choice below does NOT correctly identify a point in this diagram? **A**

A. Q is Al's house.   **B.** R is Al's house.
C. P is at the right turn.   **D.** Q is the mountain.

6. How long will it take Al to drive to Mount Monadnock if he averages a rate of 56 miles per hour for the whole trip? **G**
F. 1 hour   **G.** 1.25 hours
H. 1.5 hours   **I.** 1.75 hours

7. How many miles is the trip from Al's house to Mount Monadnock? **D**
A. 30 miles   **B.** 40 miles
C. 50 miles   **D.** 70 miles

8. The odometer on Al's car shows how many miles the car travels. If the odometer shows 12,350 miles as Al leaves home, what will it show after a round trip to the mountain? **G**
F. 12,000 miles   **G.** 12,490 miles
H. 12,520 miles   **I.** 12,900 miles

Chapter 9 Test Prep **485**

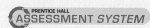

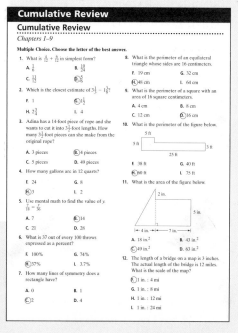

The Shape of Buildings to Come

Students will use data from these two pages to answer the questions posed here in Put It All Together.

Activating Prior Knowledge
Examples of buildings and structures with surprising shapes and sizes abound in America. Have students describe some they have seen. Students may point to museums which often are outstanding examples of imaginative architecture.

Teaching Notes
Have volunteers read the captions for the pictures. Discuss that in this activity, students will explore different arrangements that can be made using the same shapes.

Inclusion
Review the distinction between surface area and volume. Make or draw a row of 4 small squares as students do the same at their seats. Demonstrate that the volume is $4 \times 1 \times 1$, or 4 cubic units, but that the figure has 6 surfaces and that its surface area is $4(4 \times 1) + 2(1 \times 1)$, or 18 square units.

Science Connection
Have interested students do research to find out the history of Biospheres 1 and 2. Have them report on these experimental habitats and discuss what the scientists learned from these experiments.

486

The Shape of Buildings to Come

Applying Measurement When architects design office or apartment buildings, they know that people will want as many windows as possible. The footprint, or area that a building covers, has a lot to do with the arrangement of the windows. For example, a large square building may have inside rooms with no windows. Architects can change the shape of the footprint to make more outside walls.

Let the Sun in
This modern glass building connects two Victorian-era office buildings.

Straw-Bale Construction
College students in Wisconsin designed and built this straw-bale house. Wheat, oats, barley, rice, rye, and flax are all desirable straws for bale walls.

Straw bale   Frame

Biosphere 2
Originally constructed as a miniature Earth, Biosphere 2 is now a research facility. It covers 3.15 acres and includes five different environments: a coastal desert, a marsh, a grassy plain, a rain forest, and an ocean.

Rain forest

Grassy plain

Ocean

Kitchen

486

---

1. A = 16 square units
   P = 34 units

   A = 16 square units
   P = 20 units

   A = 16 square units
   P = 16 units

2. Answers may vary. Samples are given:

Put It All Together

Materials graph paper

1. Draw three rectangular footprints that you can make using 16 squares. Find each area and perimeter.

Footprint using 4 squares

2. **Open-Ended** Draw several non-rectangular footprints that use 16 squares. Be creative! Find each perimeter.

3. **a.** Use 16 squares. Draw a square footprint with an open area in the center.
   b. Find the outside perimeter. Find the inside perimeter. Then find the total perimeter.
   c. **Reasoning** Why might an architect use a design like this for a building? Explain.

4. Consider all the footprints you have drawn. What arrangement of 16 squares gives the greatest total perimeter? The least total perimeter?

5. Buildings A, B, and C at the right are rectangular.
   a. Copy and complete the table. Calculate the volume and total exposed area of each building. (Include the top and four faces, but not the base.) How does the shape affect the surface area?
   b. Which shape gives the most space for windows? Which gives the least? Explain.

Building Entry

These binoculars are four stories tall and made from steel tubing and cement. Each barrel is a conference room with a circular skylight at the top.

Building Data

Building	ℓ	w	h	Volume	Exposed Surface Area
A	3	2	4	■	■
B	6	2	2	■	■
C	1	3	8	■	■

Marsh
Library
Living quarters
Tree research buildings
Control room
Air supply

Take It to the NET For more information about architecture, go to **www.PHSchool.com**.
Web Code: aae-0953

P = 24 units

P = 22

P = 34 units

5a. Volume   Exposed Surface Area
A   24   46 square units
B   24   44 square units
C   24   67 square units

b. C, B. The tall shape with fewer 'interior' cubes gives the most window options.

487

Put It All Together

Have students work in pairs to answer the questions. Discuss and have volunteers demonstrate the idea that in many cases several different figures can be formed using the same number of 2-dimensional or 3-dimensional shapes. Elicit that figures formed with the same number of shapes can have different perimeters, areas, or volumes.

Exercise 2 Guide students to understand that arrangements can be the same but not appear to look congruent. For example, they might be flipped or rotated. Provide examples of this idea using 4-square arrangements.

Tactile Learners
Exercises 1–4 Some students may have more success with the activity if they manipulate models, like pattern blocks, to construct the different shapes.

Exercise 5 Students can use centimeter squares or other cubes to build the figures.

3a.
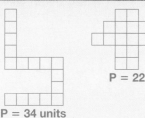

b. outside perimeter = 20 units;
   inside perimeter = 12 units;
   total perimeter = 32 units

c. The architect may want an open courtyard or garden in the center, or the architect may want every room to have a window-view.

4. the 1 × 16 rectangle; the 4 × 4 rectangle

487

CHAPTER 10 Integers

Chapter at a Glance

10-1 Using a Number Line
pp. 491–495

Objectives
1. Graphing Integers on a Number Line
2. Comparing and Ordering Integers

New Vocabulary
opposites, integers, absolute value

Optional Materials
calculator

NCTM Standards
1, 3, 6, 7, 8, 9, 10

Local Standards

10-2 Algebra — Adding Integers
pp. 497–501

Objectives
1. Adding Integers With the Same Sign
2. Adding Integers With Different Signs

NCTM Standards
1, 3, 6, 7, 8, 9, 10

Local Standards

10-3 Algebra — Subtracting Integers
pp. 503–508

Objectives
1. Subtracting Integers
2. Solving Equations With Integers

NCTM Standards
1, 3, 6, 7, 8, 9, 10

Local Standards

10-4 Algebra — Multiplying Integers
pp. 509–512

Objectives
1. Multiplying Integers

NCTM Standards
1, 3, 6, 7, 8, 9, 10

Local Standards

10-5 Algebra — Dividing Integers
pp. 513–516

Objectives
1. Dividing Integers
2. Solving Equations

NCTM Standards
1, 2, 3, 6, 7, 8, 9, 10

Local Standards

✓ Checkpoint Quiz 1

10-6 Algebra — Graphing in the Coordinate Plane
pp. 518–521

Objectives
1. Naming Coordinates
2. Graphing Points on a Coordinate Plane

New Vocabulary
coordinate plane, quadrants, origin, ordered pair

Optional Materials
graph paper

NCTM Standards
1, 3, 6, 7, 8, 9, 10

Local Standards

10-7 Algebra — Applications of Integers
pp. 523–526

Objectives
1. Finding Profit and Loss
2. Drawing and Interpreting Graphs

Optional Materials
graph paper

NCTM Standards
1, 3, 6, 7, 8, 9, 10

Local Standards

10-8 Algebra — Graphing Functions
pp. 527–532

Objectives
1. Making a Function Table
2. Graphing Functions

New Vocabulary
function

Optional Materials
graph paper, straightedge

NCTM Standards
1, 2, 3, 6, 7, 8, 9, 10

Local Standards

10-9 Problem Solving — Make a Graph
pp. 533–535

Objectives
1. Making a Graph

Optional Materials
graph paper, straightedge

NCTM Standards
1, 2, 3, 6, 7, 8, 9, 10

Local Standards

✓ Checkpoint Quiz 2

Reading and Math Literacy

Reading Math

Understanding Word Problems, p. 517

Reading Math hints, pp. 492, 497, 503, 518

Understanding Vocabulary, p. 538

Writing in Math

Writing to Justify Steps, p. 536

Daily Writing Practice, pp. 494, 501, 506, 515, 520, 526, 531, 535, 540

Above Level

Challenge exercises

pp. 495, 501, 507, 512, 516, 521, 526, 531, 535

Extension

Reflections in the Coordinate Plane, p. 522

Hands-On and Technology

Investigations

Modeling Addition of Integers, p. 496

Modeling Subtraction of Integers, p. 502

Connecting Division to Multiplication, p. 513

Activities and Projects

Real-World Snapshots

Applying Integers pp. 542–543

Chapter Project

The Time of Your Life, p. 640

Test Prep

Daily Test Prep

pp. 495, 501, 507, 512, 516, 521, 526, 532, 535

Test-Taking Strategies

Using a Variable, p. 537

Test Prep

Cumulative Review (Chapters 1-10), p. 541

Chapter Assessment

Checkpoint Quiz

pp. 516, 532

Chapter Review

pp. 538–539

Chapter Test

p. 540

Pacing Options

This chart suggests pacing only for the core lessons and their parts. It is provided as a possible guide. It will help you determine how much time you have in your schedule to cover the additional features and assessment, as described at the left.

Day	Traditional 45-minute class periods	Block 90-minute class periods
1	10-1 ▽	10-1 ▽ ▽
2	10-1 ▽	10-2 ▽ ▽
3	10-2 ▽	10-3 ▽ ▽
4	10-2 ▽	10-4 ▽ 10-5 ▽
5	10-3 ▽	10-5 ▽ 10-6 ▽ ▽
6	10-3 ▽	10-7 ▽ ▽ 10-8 ▽
7	10-4 ▽	10-8 ▽ 10-9 ▽
8	10-5 ▽	
9	10-5 ▽	
10	10-6 ▽ ▽	
11	10-7 ▽	
12	10-7 ▽	
13	10-8 ▽	
14	10-8 ▽	
15	10-9 ▽	

NCTM STANDARDS 2000

1 Number and Operations	6 Problem Solving
2 Algebra	7 Reasoning and Proof
3 Geometry	8 Communication
4 Measurement	9 Connections
5 Data Analysis and Probability	10 Representation

Math Background

Skills Trace

BEFORE Chapter 10

Grade 5 presented integers computations.

DURING Chapter 10

Course 1 extends the four operations with integers to graphing in the coordinate plane and introduces functions.

AFTER Chapter 10

Throughout this course students apply number patterns to solve real-world patterns.

10-1 10-2 Using a Number Line Adding Integers

Math Understandings

- Integers are the set of counting numbers (positive integers), their opposites (negative integers), and zero (neither positive nor negative).
- Two opposites have the same absolute value. The opposite of 0 is 0.
- As you move from left to right on a horizontal number line, the integers become greater.
- You can use a number line to model adding integers.

Two numbers are **opposites** if they are the same distance from 0 on a number line, but in opposite directions. **Integers** are the set of positive whole numbers, their opposites, and 0. The **absolute value** of a number is its distance from 0 on a number line.

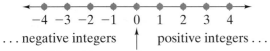

... negative integers   positive integers ...

0 is neither positive nor negative.

Adding Integers With the Same Sign The sum of two positive integers is positive. The sum of two negative integers is negative.

Example: $2 + 3 = 5$ $-2 + (-3) = -5$

Adding Integers With Different Signs To add integers with different signs, first find the absolute value of each integer. Then, subtract the lesser absolute value from the greater. The sum has the sign of the integer with the greater absolute value.

Example:

$2 + (-3) = \blacksquare$ $-2 + 3 = \blacksquare$

$|2| = 2$ and $|-3| = 3$ $|-2| = 2$ and $|3| = 3$

$3 - 2 = 1$ $3 - 2 = 1$

Use the sign of -3.   Use the sign of 3.

So, $2 + (-3) = -1$.   So, $-2 + 3 = 1$.

10-3 Subtracting Integers

Math Understandings

- Subtracting an integer gives the same result as adding its opposite.
- You can solve addition and subtraction equations with integers using the same methods you used to solve equations with whole numbers.

Subtracting Integers You subtract an integer by adding its opposite.

Example:
$10 - 6 = 10 + (-6) = 4$
$10 - (-6) = 10 + 6 = 16$
$-10 - 6 = -10 + (-6) = -16$
$-10 - (-6) = -10 + 6 = -4$

10-4 10-5 Multiplying Integers Dividing Integers

Math Understandings

- You can think of multiplication as repeated addition.
- Multiplication and division are inverse operations because they undo each other.
- The rules for finding the sign of a quotient when dividing two integers are similar to the rules for finding the sign of a product when multiplying integers.
- You can solve multiplication and division equations with integers using the same methods you used to solve equations with whole numbers.

Multiplying Integers
The product of two integers with the *same* sign is positive.
The product of two integers with *different* signs is negative.
Examples: $4 \times 5 = 20$ $4 \times (-5) = -20$
$-4 \times (-5) = 20$ $-4 \times 5 = -20$

Dividing Integers
The quotient of two integers with the *same* sign is positive.
The quotient of two integers with *different* signs is negative.
Examples: $20 \div 4 = 5$ $20 \div (-4) = -5$
$-20 \div (-4) = 5$ $-20 \div 4 = -5$

10-6 Graphing in the Coordinate Plane

Math Understandings

- You can name any point on a coordinate plane by an ordered pair of numbers, and you can graph any ordered pair of real numbers as a point on the plane.
- An ordered pair (x, y) is ordered because you always name the horizontal coordinate first. If you reverse the order, you change the location of the point that the pair names.

The **coordinate plane** is formed by the intersection of two number lines. The plane is divided into four regions, called **quadrants**. The **origin** is the place where the two number lines intersect. An **ordered pair** is a pair of numbers that describes the location of a point in a coordinate plane.

10-7 Applications of Integers

Math Understandings

- You can use line graphs to look at trends of monthly balances.

In business, money received is *income* and money spent is *expenses*. A balance is a company's *profit* or *loss*. A positive balance means that there is a profit. A negative balance means that there is a loss.

10-8 Graphing Functions

Math Understandings

- You can represent the relationship between two quantities using a table, a rule, or a graph.

A **function** is a rule that assigns exactly one output value to each input value. You can show a function relationship on a coordinate plane by graphing the input (x) on the horizontal axis and the output (y) on the vertical axis. When the points you graph for a function lie along a line, this type of function is a *linear function*.

Example: Make a table and graph the function $y = x - 1$.

Input	−2	0	2	4
Output	−3	−1	1	3

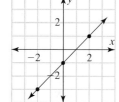

10-9 Make a Graph

Making a graph can help you find relationships between data in a problem.

Additional Professional Development Opportunities

Chapter 10 Math Background notes: pp. 492, 498, 504, 510, 514, 519, 524, 528

SkyLight Professional Development

Additional resources available from SkyLight Professional Development:

On-site courses, workshops, summer institutes. Online courses and chat rooms. Videocassettes and books. Visit www.skylightedu.com.

Ongoing Assessment and Intervention

The *Prentice Hall Mathematics* program provides many options for assessment in the Student Edition, Teacher's Edition, and teaching resources. From these options you may choose instructional materials that are appropriate for your students and that support your district's curriculum requirements.

Daily Assessment

✓ Instant Check System™ in Chapter 10

Allows students to check their own learning before, during, and after each lesson.

Diagnosing Readiness before the chapter (p. 490)

Check Skills You'll Need exercises in each lesson (pp. 491, 497, 503, 509, 513, 518, 523, 527, 533)

Check Understanding questions with each Example (pp. 491, 492, 493, 498, 499, 503, 504, 505, 510, 514, 518, 519, 523, 524, 527, 528, 533)

Checkpoint Quiz (pp. 516, 532)

Formal Assessment

Assessment in the Student Text and in Additional Resources

Assess student progress throughout the Course 1 textbook and with blackline masters and CD-ROM.

Student Edition
- Chapter 10 Review, with Vocabulary, Skills, and Concepts Review, pp. 538-539
- Chapter 10 Test, p. 540

Assessment Resources
- Checkpoint Quizzes 1 & 2
- Chapter Test, forms A & B
- Chapter Alternative Assessment
Spanish versions available.

 Computer Test Generator CD-ROM
- Instant Chapter Tests™—pre-made tests with items that vary every time you print.
- Online Testing allows you to give tests online and receive progress reports.
- Prepare students by making tests based on standardized test objectives.

Algebra Readiness Tests
- Includes Basic Skills Tests and Concept-Readiness Tests.
- Assess understanding of skills and concepts needed for success in algebra.

Intervention

Skills Intervention Kit

Online Intervention
Integrated within the iText, this online intervention system includes diagnostic tests and prescribed remediation, plus reports to track student mastery.

A *complete* system for the student who is struggling with course-level work

Eight intervention units cover core skills and allow you to:
- **Diagnose** students' gaps in basic skills
- **Prescribe** an individualized course of study
- **Monitor** student progress

Includes print workbooks, tutorial CD-ROM, teacher editions, progress folders, and more. *Available in Spanish.*

How to Use with Chapter 10

10-1	Pre-Algebra Basics, Skills 1–3
10-2	Pre-Algebra Basics, Skill 4
10-3	Pre-Algebra Basics, Skill 5
10-4	Pre-Algebra Basics, Skill 6
10-5	Pre-Algebra Basics, Skill 7
10-6	Pre-Algebra Basics, Skill 15
10-7	Pre-Algebra Basics, Skill 8

Standardized Test Preparation

The *Prentice Hall Mathematics* program integrates preparation for high-stakes standardized tests in every lesson of the Student Edition and continues this support in the Prentice Hall Assessment System.

Test Prep

In Student Text, Chapter 10

Teaches students strategies and gives them practice with all the test item formats they will encounter on high-stakes tests.

Test Prep exercises in each lesson (pp. 495, 501, 507, 512, 516, 521, 526, 532, 535)

Test-Taking Strategies Using a Variable, p. 537

Test Prep Cumulative Review (Chapters 1–10), p. 541

PRENTICE HALL
ASSESSMENT *SYSTEM*

A three-step approach to preparing students for high stakes, national, and state exams.

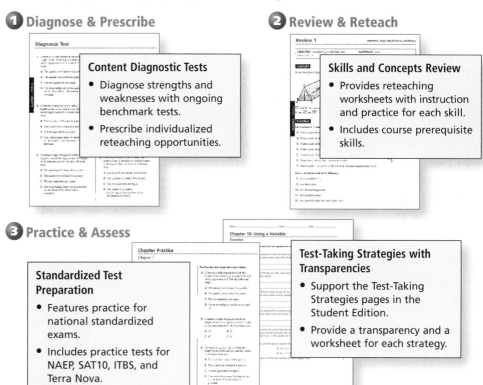

1 Diagnose & Prescribe

Content Diagnostic Tests
- Diagnose strengths and weaknesses with ongoing benchmark tests.
- Prescribe individualized reteaching opportunities.

2 Review & Reteach

Skills and Concepts Review
- Provides reteaching worksheets with instruction and practice for each skill.
- Includes course prerequisite skills.

3 Practice & Assess

Standardized Test Preparation
- Features practice for national standardized exams.
- Includes practice tests for NAEP, SAT10, ITBS, and Terra Nova.

Test-Taking Strategies with Transparencies
- Support the Test-Taking Strategies pages in the Student Edition.
- Provide a transparency and a worksheet for each strategy.

Correlation to Standardized Tests

Lesson		NAEP	Terra Nova CAT6	Terra Nova CTBS	ITBS	SAT10	Local Test
10-1	Using a Number Line	N1a, N1i, N1j					
10-2	Adding Integers	N3a		■			
10-3	Subtracting Integers	N3a		■			
10-4	Multiplying Integers	N3a		■			
10-5	Dividing Integers	N3a		■			
10-6	Graphing in the Coordinate Plane	A2c, A2d	■			■	
10-7	Applications of Integers	A2c, A2d					
10-8	Graphing Functions	A2a, A2b					
10-9	Problem Solving: Make a Graph						

NAEP National Assessment of Educational Progress
CAT6/Terra Nova California Achievement Test, 6th Ed.

CTBS/Terra Nova Comprehensive Test of Basic Skills
ITBS Iowa Test of Basic Skills, Form M.

SAT10 Stanford Achievement Test, 10th Ed.

Program Resources

	Resources in Grab & Go™ Files				Resources for Reaching All Students				Spanish Resources			Presentation Assistant Plus! Transparencies					Prentice Hall Presentation Pro CD-ROM
	Practice	Reteach	Enrich	Checkpt Quiz	Reading & Math Literacy	Technology Activities	Hands-On Activities	Guided Problem Solving	Practice	Reading & Math Literacy	Checkpt Quiz	Skills Check	Problem of the Day	Additional Examples	Answers to Exercises	Lesson Quiz	
10-1	■	■	■		■			■	■			■	■	■	■	■	■
10-2	■	■	■					■	■			■	■	■	■	■	■
10-3	■	■	■				■	■	■			■	■	■	■	■	■
10-4	■	■	■					■	■			■	■	■	■	■	■
10-5	■	■	■	■	■	■		■	■	■		■	■	■	■	■	■
10-6	■	■	■					■	■			■	■	■	■	■	■
10-7	■	■	■					■	■			■	■	■	■	■	■
10-8	■	■	■	■		■		■	■		■	■	■	■	■	■	■
10-9	■	■	■					■	■			■	■	■	■	■	■
For the Chapter	Chapter Projects, Chapter Tests, Alternative Assessment, Cumulative Review, Cumulative Assessment				On web site only: Home Activities, Interdisciplinary Activities, Algebra Readiness Puzzles				Spanish Chapter Tests, Alternative Assessment, Cumulative Review, Cumulative Assessment			Classroom Aid Transparencies					

Also available for use with the chapter:

 **PRENTICE HALL ASSESSMENT SYSTEM** *See page 488F.*

- Practice Workbook
- Solution Key
- MathNotes folder

- For teacher support and access to student Web materials, use the Web Code aak-5500.
- For additional online and technology resources, *see below*.

Technology

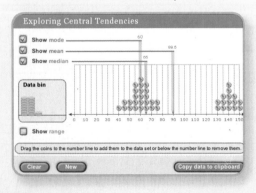 **iTEXT Online and on CD-ROM**

Complete Interactive Student Text online and on CD-ROM—with instant feedback assessment, tutorial help, dynamic activities, instructional and real-world videos, audio, and additional practice.

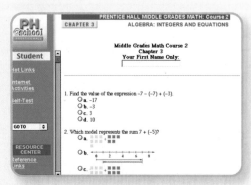 **www.PHSchool.com For Students**

Use Web codes for easy access to online activities, chapter projects, self-grading lesson quizzes, chapter tests, vocabulary quizzes, updated data sources, graphing calculator procedures, and more.

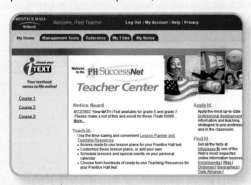 **PH SuccessNet For Teachers**

Online lesson planning with built-in state correlations, all the teaching resources, complete reference library, your own calendar and Teacher Web page, professional development, and more.

488G

Presentation Assistant Plus!

The *Prentice Hall Presentation Assistant Plus!* provides you with the material you need to teach a lesson from beginning to end. Two easy-to-use formats—Transparencies and PowerPoint®—allow you to present a lesson the way you are most comfortable.

 Transparencies

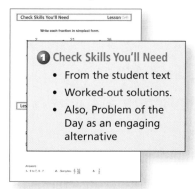

1 Check Skills You'll Need
- From the student text
- Worked-out solutions.
- Also, Problem of the Day as an engaging alternative

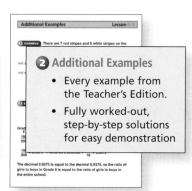

2 Additional Examples
- Every example from the Teacher's Edition.
- Fully worked-out, step-by-step solutions for easy demonstration

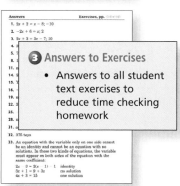

3 Answers to Exercises
- Answers to all student text exercises to reduce time checking homework

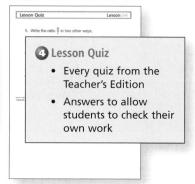

4 Lesson Quiz
- Every quiz from the Teacher's Edition
- Answers to allow students to check their own work

 Throughout the Teacher's Edition, this symbol indicates material that is available in the Presentation Assistant Plus!

 Prentice Hall Presentation Pro CD-ROM

- Includes all Transparencies.
- Conveniently organized by lesson so you can easily **1** Introduce, **2** Teach, **3** Check Homework, and **4** Assess each lesson.
- Animated examples allow step-by-step instruction at your own pace.
- Easy to edit so you can create custom presentations.

Teaching Chapter 10 Using Presentation Assistant Plus!

	1 Introduce	**2 Teach**	**3 Check Homework**	**4 Assess**
	Check Skills You'll Need	Additional Examples	Student Edition Answers	Lesson Quiz
10-1	p. 85	pp. 135–137	✔	p. 85
10-2	p. 86	pp. 138–140	✔	p. 86
10-3	p. 87	pp. 141–142	✔	p. 87
10-4	p. 88	p. 143	✔	p. 88
10-5	p. 89	p. 144	✔	p. 89
10-6	p. 90	pp. 145–146	✔	p. 90
10-7	p. 91	pp. 147–148	✔	p. 92
10-8	p. 93	pp. 149–150	✔	p. 93
10-9	p. 94	p. 151	✔	p. 94

Prentice Hall Presentation Pro

CD-ROM with dynamic PowerPoint® presentations for every lesson. Helps you introduce and develop concepts, check homework, and assess progress. Part of Presentation Assistant Plus! *(See above.)*

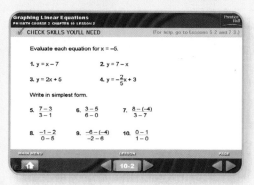

Computer Test Generator

CD-ROM to create practice sheets and tests for course objectives and standardized tests. Includes Instant Chapter Tests™, online testing, and student reports. Part of the PH Assessment System. *(See page 488F.)*

Resource Pro® with Planning Express®

CD-ROM with a lesson planning tool that allows you to import state and local objectives. Includes electronic versions of all the teaching resources.

Chapter Resources

Reading and Math Support

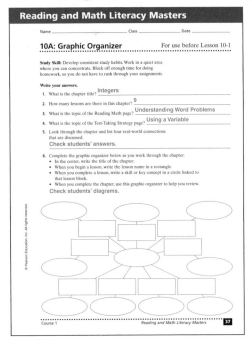

Available in Spanish

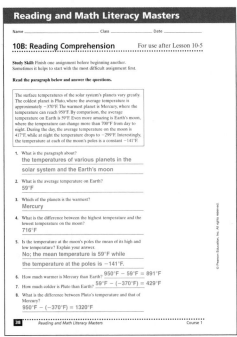

Available in Spanish

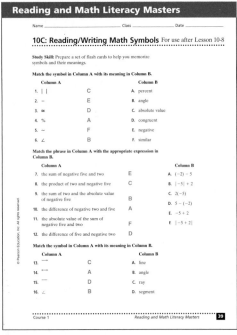

Available in Spanish

Problem Solving

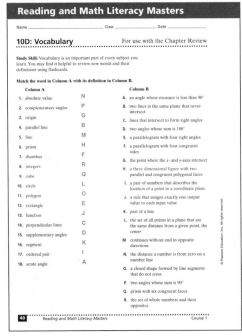

Available in Spanish

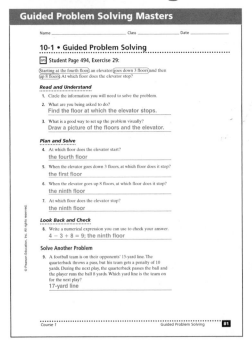

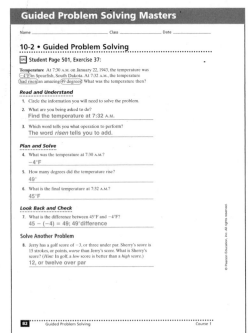

Name _____ Class _____ Date _____

10-3 • Guided Problem Solving

GPS Student Page 506, Exercise 30:

Hiking A hiker is at the top of Lost Mine Peak. The elevation of the peak is 6,850 feet. The beginning of the Lost Mine trail has an elevation of 5,600 feet. What is the trail's change in elevation?

Read and Understand

1. What are you being asked to do?
Determine the trail's change in elevation.

2. What operation do you use to represent change?
subtraction

Plan and Solve

3. What is the elevation of the peak?
6,850 feet

4. What is the elevation of the trail at the beginning?
5,600 feet

5. Write an expression you can use to find the change in elevation.
6,850 − 5,600

6. What is the trail's change in elevation?
1,250 feet

Look Back and Check

7. How can you check your answer?
Add your answer to 5,600 to get 6,850, the
starting elevation.

Solve Another Problem

8. Sarah's savings account has $325 in it before she deposited her $255 paycheck. She then wrote the following checks: $20 for a parking ticket, $35 for her electric bill, $111 for her phone bill, $65 for her cable bill, and $89 for her new cell phone. Does Sarah have enough money left to buy a $150 DVD player? Explain.
Yes; she has $260 left.

Name _____ Class _____ Date _____

10-4 • Guided Problem Solving

GPS Student Page 511, Exercise 15:

Ballooning Hot air balloons generally descend at a rate of 200 to 400 feet per minute. A balloon descends 235 feet per minute for 4 minutes. Write an integer to express the balloon's total movement.

Read and Understand

1. What are you being asked to do?
Write an integer to express the balloon's
movement.

2. Which word describes the direction of the balloon?
descends

3. Will the integer be positive or negative?
negative

Plan and Solve

4. Each minute the balloon descends how many feet?
235 feet

5. How many minutes is the balloon descending?
4 minutes

6. What is $235 \frac{\text{feet}}{\text{minute}} \cdot 4$ minutes?
940 feet

7. Write an integer to express the balloon's movement.
−940

Look Back and Check

8. What is $940 \text{ feet} \div 235 \frac{\text{feet}}{\text{minute}}$?
4 minutes

Solve Another Problem

9. A submarine dives for 5 seconds at 130 feet per second. Write an integer to express the submarine's movement.
−650 feet

Name _____ Class _____ Date _____

10-5 • Guided Problem Solving

GPS Student Page 515, Exercise 22:

Stocks The value of a share of stock decreased $30 over the last 5 days. Find the average rate of change in dollars per day.

Read and Understand

1. Circle the information you will need to solve the problem.

2. What are you being asked to do?
Find which integer represents the average
decrease in stock value each day.

3. What operation will you perform to find the answer?
division

Plan and Solve

4. How much did the stock decrease total?
$30

5. How many days did you watch the stock?
5 days

6. What is the average decrease?
$6 per day

7. What integer represents the average decrease in dollars per day?
−6

Look Back and Check

8. What is −6 · 5? Does the answer make sense?
−30; yes

Solve Another Problem

9. Emma makes $18 per hour for providing technical support for an Internet provider. Emma works every day for 6 hours. After 2½ months, how much will she make? (*Note:* Assume 1 month = 30 days.)
$8,100

Name _____ Class _____ Date _____

10-6 • Guided Problem Solving

GPS Student Page 520, Exercise 24:

Geometry A symmetrical four-pointed star has eight corner points. Seven of the points are (−1, 1), (0, 3), (1, 1), (3, 0), (1, −1), (0, −3), (−1, −1). What are the coordinates of the missing point?

Read and Understand

1. What does *symmetrical* mean?
A symmetrical figure has the same shape on
both sides of a line of symmetry.

2. What is a good way to set up the problem visually?
Plot the seven points on a coordinate plane.

Plan and Solve

3. What point is symmetrical to (−1, 1) over the *y*-axis?
(1, 1)

4. What point is symmetrical to (−1, −1) over the *y*-axis?
(1, −1)

5. What point is symmetrical to (3, 0) over the *y*-axis?
(−3, 0)

6. What is the missing point?
(−3, 0)

Look Back and Check

7. Does the point (−3, 0) form a four-point star with the other seven points?
yes

Solve Another Problem

8. A five-pointed star that is symmetric over the *y*-axis has ten corner points. Eight of the points are (−1, 1), (0, 3), (1, 1), (3, 1), (1, −1), (0, −1), (−2, −3), (−3, 1). What are the coordinates of the missing points?
(−1, −1) and (2, −3)

Name _____ Class _____ Date _____

10-7 • Guided Problem Solving

GPS Student Page 526, Exercise 16:

You receive a total of $125 for your birthday. You spend $20 on a sweater, $15 on a CD, $8 on a book, $12 on a pair of sunglasses, and $35 on a bicycle helmet. How much money do you have left?

Read and Understand

1. Circle the information you will need to solve the problem.

2. What are you being asked to do?
Find how much money you have left.

Plan and Solve

3. How much money did you receive?
$125

4. How much money did you spend?
$90

5. Write an expression for how much you have left.
125 − 90

6. How much money do you have left?
$35

Look Back and Check

7. How can you check your answer?
Add the amount spent to the answer for Step 6
to get $125.

Solve Another Problem

8. Helen received some cash for her birthday. She spent $14.30 on a CD and donated $25 to a charity. She put half of what was left into her savings account. She has $17.85 left. How much money did she receive on her birthday?
$75

Name _____ Class _____ Date _____

10-8 • Guided Problem Solving

GPS Student Page 531, Exercise 21:

Business Suppose you want to start a cookie business. You know that it will cost $600 to buy the oven and materials you need. You decide to charge $.75 for each cookie. The function $p = 0.75C - 600$ relates profit p to the number of cookies sold C.

a. What will your profit or loss be if you sell 400 cookies? 500 cookies?

b. How many cookies must you sell to break even?

Read and Understand

1. What is *profit*?
The amount of money you make after you
pay for expenses.

2. How will you use the equation to answer part *a* and part *b*?
For part *a*, substitute 400 and 500 for the number of
cookies sold and then simplify. For part *b*, substitute 0
for the profit and solve for the number of cookies sold.

Plan and Solve

3. Substitute 400 for *C* and solve for *p*. What is the profit? −$300

4. Substitute 500 for *C* and solve for *p*. What is the profit? −$225

5. What value represents breaking even? 0

6. Do you substitute this for *p* or *C*? *p*

7. How many cookies must you sell to break even? 800 cookies

Look Back and Check

8. What is $(0.75 \cdot 800) - 600$? 0

Solve Another Problem

9. Distance is a function of time. Suppose you walk at a rate of 2 miles per hour. Write an equation for the distance *d* if you walk for *t* hours and use it to determine the distance you will walk after 10 hours.
d = 2*t*; 20 miles

Activities and Projects

Name _____ Class _____ Date _____

10-9 • Guided Problem Solving

GPS Student Page 534, Exercise 4:

Music Nate, Nina, Nancy, and Ned are in the school orchestra. Each person plays one of the instruments shown to the right. Nate does not play a wind instrument. Nina broke a string. Nancy sits next to the trumpet player, and Nate sits behind him. Which instrument does each person play?

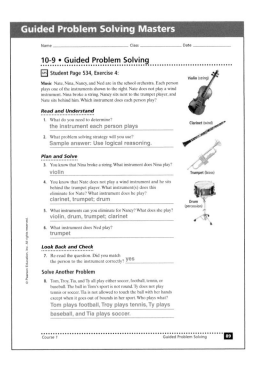

Violin (string)

Clarinet (wind)

Trumpet (brass)

Drum (percussion)

Read and Understand

1. What do you need to determine?
   the instrument each person plays

2. What problem solving strategy will you use?
   Sample answer: Use logical reasoning.

Plan and Solve

3. You know that Nina broke a string. What instrument does Nina play?
   violin

4. You know that Nate does not play a wind instrument and he sits behind the trumpet player. What instrument(s) does this eliminate for Nate? What instrument does he play?
   clarinet, trumpet; drum

5. What instruments can you eliminate for Nancy? What does she play?
   violin, drum, trumpet; clarinet

6. What instrument does Ned play?
   trumpet

Look Back and Check

7. Re-read the question. Did you match the person to the instrument correctly? yes

Solve Another Problem

8. Tom, Troy, Tia, and Ty all play either soccer, football, tennis, or baseball. The ball in Tom's sport is not round. Ty does not play tennis or soccer. Tia is not allowed to touch the ball with her hands except when it goes out of bounds in her sport. Who plays what?
   Tom plays football, Troy plays tennis, Ty plays baseball, and Tia plays soccer.

Name _____ Class _____ Date _____

Activity 5: A Classroom Coordinate Plane

Materials needed: small flag, index cards

Work as a class.

1. Follow your teacher's directions and place your classroom desks in a large rectangular grid. Your teacher will identify which rows will represent the x- and y-axis and will place a flag on the desk in the center to represent the origin.

2. Using the front of the room as the top of the grid, determine where on the coordinate plane you are sitting. Write the coordinates of your desk on an index card. Be sure to pay attention to the location of the origin. For example, if you are sitting two desks to the left and one desk in front of the origin, your coordinates will be (−2, 1). Place all the cards in a pile.

3. a. Will any coordinate pairs appear more than once in the pile?
   b. What would duplicate pairs mean? Explain.

4. As a class, check each pair of coordinates and then place all the cards in a pile.

5. Take turns calling out four pairs of coordinates. Keep a list of the coordinates called. If your desk is located at one of the coordinate pairs that is called, stand up.

6. After the four pairs of coordinates have been called, look around and name the quadrilateral that has been formed. Write the name of the quadrilateral with the list of its coordinates on the board or on the overhead.

7. After you name the quadrilateral, the students who are standing sit. Play another round, calling out another set of four pairs of coordinates.

8. After another round, work in small groups to determine the coordinates need to form a parallelogram, a square, and a trapezoid.

9. Compare your quadrilaterals to those of other groups.

10. What are some ways you can classify your quadrilaterals as the same or different using coordinates?

Name _____ Class _____ Date _____

Activity 39: Integers

Materials needed: sheets of $8\frac{1}{2} \times 11$ in. paper with all the integers from −6 to 6 written on them, one integer per paper (13 sheets), box

As a "warm up" for this activity, review these rules of operations with integers:

- When you add two negative integers, disregard the negative signs. Add the numbers and make the resulting quantity negative.
- When you add two integers, one of which is negative and the other positive, subtract the lesser number from the greater number. The sign of the answer will be the same as that of the greater number.
- When you subtract integers when the second number is negative, add the opposite of the number, and follow the rules for adding integers.

1. Your class will be divided into two teams, Team 1 and Team 2. If your teacher calls your name to be a member of Team 1, draw a slip of paper from the box.

2. When all of the members of Team 1 have drawn a piece of paper, arrange yourselves in a human number line. Your position on the number line should be based on the number you drew, with the person who drew the smallest number standing farthest to the left and the one who drew the largest number standing farthest to the right. Hold your paper up so the members of the class can see your number.

3. Your teacher will call out two integers whose sum is on the number line. If either of the numbers is the one you drew, step forward.

4. If you are a member of Team 2 and your teacher calls your name, add the two integers that were called and instruct your classmate who represents that integer on the number line to step forward.

5. Your classmates will determine if you are correct. If so, your team receives one point. If you are incorrect, the other team receives one point if they can correctly identify the student who should have stepped forward.

6. Complete five rounds of adding integers and five rounds of subtracting integers. Keep a tally of each team's points. Then, Team 1 and Team 2 will trade places.

7. Begin the next round by putting the numbers back into the box. Each member of Team 2 draws a slip of paper from the box. (Add or remove integers from the number line depending on the number of students.) Repeat Steps 2–6.

8. The team with the most points at the end of the game wins.

Name _____ Class _____ Date _____

Dividing Integers   Activity 16

Use your graphing calculator to do this activity.

Example 1: Find the quotient: $−1,137,466 \div 3,278$.

① When you enter negative integers, be careful to use the **[−]** key (the negative key) instead of the **[−]** key (the subtract key). Press **[−]** and then **[−]**. Notice the difference between the two signs on the screen. The **[−]** key produces the negative sign, which is smaller and slightly higher than the minus sign, which is produced by the **[−]** key.

② Press **CLEAR**. Enter **[−]** 1 1 3 7 4 6 6 **[÷]** 3 2 7 8 and press **ENTER**.

③ The quotient, −347, is shown on the screen.

Example 2: Find the mean for the set of data.

$−37, −22, −17, −2, 6, 12$

① Press **LIST**. If there is any data already entered into any of the lists, to clear each list, highlight the title and press **CLEAR** then **ENTER**.

② Enter the data above into the L1 list. Remember to use the **[−]** key for the negative sign before negative integers. Press **ENTER** after each entry.

③ Press **2nd** [STAT]. Use the right arrow key to highlight **MATH**, then press 3 to select **mean(**.

④ On the screen, you will see **mean(**. Press **2nd** [STAT] **1: L1** to select L1. Press **ENTER**. You now see the mean of L1, which is −10.

Exercises

Find each quotient.

1. $2,986,812 \div 652$ 2. $−3,951,494 \div −2,746$ 3. $−18,429,464 \div 2,386$

4. $29,846,880 \div 8,460$ 5. $−40,922,148 \div −4,107$ 6. $−54,994,305 \div 5,315$

Find the mean of each set of data.

7. $−12, −9, −8, −3, 7, 16$ 8. $−68, −51, −47, −32, 24, 41, 70$

Name _____ Class _____ Date _____

Graphing a Function   Activity 17

Use your graphing calculator to do this activity.

Example: Make a table and graph the function $y = 2x + 2$. Use x values −2, −1, 0, 1, 2.

① To turn off any old plots, press **2nd** [PLOT] **4: PlotsOff** and press **ENTER**.

② Press **Y=**. If there are any functions already entered, highlight them and press **CLEAR**.

③ Next to \Y1 =, enter 2 **[x]** 2 and press **ENTER**.

④ Press **2nd** [TABLE]. Scroll until you can see x values of −2, −1, 0, 1, 2. Use the x- and y-values from this table to complete your table.

⑤ Next, use the values in the table to plot points on the coordinate plane and complete the graph for $y = 2x + 2$. The graph of this function is in the picture below.

$y = 2x + 2$

Input	Output
−2	−2
−1	0
0	2
1	4
2	6

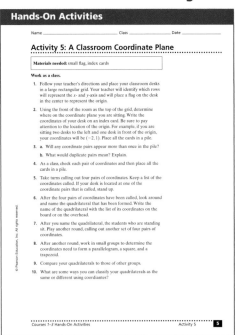

⑤ Press **ZOOM 6: ZStandard** to graph the function on the calculator. Compare it to your graph. The graphs should be the same.

Exercises

Make a table and graph each function. Use x-values −2, −1, 0, 1, 2.

1. $y = 3x + 2$ 2. $y = 4x − 1$

3. $y = \frac{x}{3}$ 4. $y = −x + 1$

5. $y = −\frac{4}{3} − 3$ 6. $y = −\frac{4}{3} + 2$

Name _____ Class _____ Date _____

Chapter 10 Project: The Time of Your Life

Draw a Time Line

Beginning the Chapter Project

Do you know an older person who has lived an interesting life? That person could probably tell you a lot of stories about his or her life. You can tell stories about your life, too. You may not have lived as long, but there have been important events in your past, and there will be others in your future.

Your project will be to build a time line of your life—past, present, and future. Think about the time lines you have seen in your social studies classes. You will have a chance to apply math skills such as ratios, measurements, scale drawings, and integers.

Activities

Activity 1: Calculating   Check students' work.

Plan a time line about 3 feet long. It should show a timeline of about 80 years. Use what you learned about ratios and scale drawings in Chapter 6 to choose a scale for your time line. What distance will you use between the one-year marks?

Activity 2: Drawing

Draw your time line on a sheet of paper about 3 feet long. Use marks of different lengths for the one-year, five-year, and ten-year divisions. Label the current year "0" so that your past lies on the negative side of the time line and your future lies on the positive side.

Activity 3: Graphing

Make a list of entries for your time line. Include milestones such as learning to walk or crawl. Add events that have shaped who you are, such as making new friends, learning valuable lessons, or gaining new skills or confidence. Place these events on the negative side of your time line.

Name _____ Class _____ Date _____

Chapter 10 Project: The Time of Your Life (continued)

Finishing the Project

Complete the time line for your future. List events or changes that you think will be important. What do you think will happen to you? What do you want to happen? Consider events like getting married and having children. Show the time line to your classmates. Explain all the events you chose. Be sure to make the time line attractive and detailed.

Reflect and Revise

Review your time line with a classmate, friend, or family member. Did you choose an appropriate scale? Does your time line have enough details? Is it attractive? If necessary, make changes to improve your time line.

Extending the Project

As a gift, create a time line for an elderly person. Choose a grandparent, great aunt or uncle, or an elderly friend. Create a list of questions that you should ask in order to get the information you need to create a time line for his or her life. Then take a tape recorder and interview the person of your choice. If you do not have a tape recorder, take notes as the person answers your questions. Try to get as much information about the person's life as possible.

After you leave the interview, organize your notes and write down important dates in the history of that person's life. Create and complete a time line for your person. Present it to him or her as a gift once you have finished.

Take It to the NET Visit www.PHSchool.com for information and links you might find helpful as you complete your project.

Name _____ Class _____ Date _____

Chapter Project Manager

Chapter 10: The Time of Your Life

Getting Started

Read about the project. As you work on it, you will need several sheets of paper. If available, a spreadsheet program can be used. Keep all your work for the project in a folder, along with this Project Manager.

Checklist	Suggestions
☐ Activity 1: calculating	☐ Decide on the increments of the time line. Make sure to make the time line to scale.
☐ Activity 2: drawing	☐ Make sure to get poster board that measures three feet. Look to place the "0" further to the left as there will be more future than past events.
☐ Activity 3: graphing	☐ Create a list of possible milestones. (i.e. marriage, children, college graduation)
☐ Recommendations	☐ When creating the time line, be sure to include realistic goals and be sure that the time line is drawn with an appropriate incremental scale.

Scoring Rubric

3 You correctly calculate a scale and apply it to your time line. You locate events in the past on the negative side, and you list events or changes you think might happen in your future on the positive side. Your time line is detailed, interesting, and attractive.

2 You correctly apply a scale to your time line, and you locate events on both the negative and positive sides. Your details are adequate, and your time line is readable.

1 Your scale is incorrect, your time line is unorganized, or you include too few details.

0 You do not create a time line.

Your Evaluation of Project Evaluate your work, based on the Scoring Rubric.

Teacher's Evaluation of Project

Name _____ Class _____ Date _____

Chapter Project Teacher Notes

Chapter 10: The Time of Your Life

About the Project

The Chapter Project allows students to use their knowledge of integers and graphing to make a time line showing the past, present, and future.

Introducing the Project

Share with students some milestones in your own life. Draw sample time line of your life onto the board. You might also want to include a time line of someone similar in age to yourself but whom the students are familiar with. For instance, you might show them a time line of the President's life, or perhaps a movie star, or a local celebrity.

Activity 1: Calculating

Have students explain their reasons for choosing their scales.

Activity 2: Drawing

Encourage students to recall important events to list on the negative side of the time line. Suggest that students include hopes of things to come and predictions about future events on the positive side.

Activity 3: Graphing

Suggest that students make a two-column table with ages in the first column and events related to the age in the second column. The table will help them organize the information before they put it on their time line.

Finishing the Project

You may wish to plan a project day on which students share their completed projects. Encourage students to explain their process as well as their product.

Take It to the NET Visit www.PHSchool.com for information, student links, and teacher support for this project.

Transparencies

Problem of the Day — Lesson 10-1

Grace is tying carnations into bunches of one dozen. If she has 336 carnations, how many bunches can she make? Will she have any carnations left over? Explain.

Answer

28 bunches; none left over; 336 is divisible by 12.

Problem of the Day — Lesson 10-2

Mr. Vega spent $64.75 for five light fixtures and $12.50 for four light switches. Each light fixture cost the same amount. How much did each light fixture cost?

Answer

$12.95

Problem of the Day — Lesson 10-3

Harold spent $6.99 on a CD and twice that amount on a book. He has $9.03 left. How much did he have before making the purchase?

Answer

$30

Problem of the Day — Lesson 10-4

What kind of graph represents a whole broken into its parts?

Answer

circle graph

Problem of the Day — Lesson 10-5

Solve the equation:

$-4 + y = 2.$

Answer

$y = 6$

Problem of the Day — Lesson 10-6

Calculate the interest if you borrow $200 for 2 years at a simple interest rate of 12% per year.

Answer

$48

Problem of the Day — Lesson 10-7

Write each number that makes these number sequences true.

a. $(6 \times 7) -$? $= 35$ b. $23 -$? $= 23$

c. $9 +$? $= 21$ d. $8 \times$? $= 56$

Answer

a. 7   b. 0   c. 12   d. 7

Problem of the Day — Lesson 10-8

Draw a triangle and place a dot directly above the midpoint of one of the sides. Then connect each vertex to that point. What three-dimensional figure have you drawn?

Answer

triangular pyramid

Problem of the Day — Lesson 10-9

A soccer player is preparing for a tournament by running 3 miles every day for 6 weeks The first week her run took 21 minutes and 40 seconds. Each week she trimmed 25 seconds off her time. How long did the 3-mile run take her during the last week?

Answer

19 minutes 35 seconds

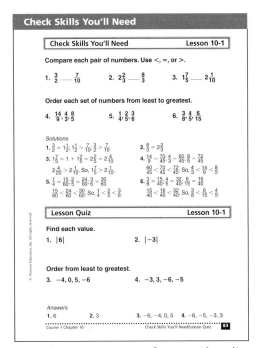

Check Skills You'll Need — Lesson 10-1

Compare each pair of numbers. Use <, =, or >.

1. $\frac{3}{2}$ —— $\frac{7}{10}$ 2. $2\frac{2}{3}$ —— $\frac{8}{3}$ 3. $1\frac{7}{5}$ —— $2\frac{1}{10}$

Order each set of numbers from least to greatest.

4. $\frac{14}{9}, \frac{4}{3}, \frac{8}{5}$ 5. $\frac{1}{4}, \frac{2}{5}, \frac{3}{6}$ 6. $\frac{3}{8}, \frac{4}{5}, \frac{6}{15}$

Solutions

1. $\frac{3}{2} = 1\frac{1}{2}; 1\frac{1}{2} > \frac{7}{10}; \frac{3}{2} > \frac{7}{10}$ 2. $\frac{8}{3} = 2\frac{2}{3}$

3. $1\frac{7}{5} = 1 + 1\frac{2}{5} = 2\frac{4}{5}$ 4. $\frac{14}{9} = \frac{70}{45}, \frac{4}{3} = \frac{60}{45}, \frac{8}{5} = \frac{72}{45}$
   $2\frac{4}{20} > 2\frac{1}{10}.$ So, $1\frac{7}{5} > 2\frac{1}{10}.$ $\frac{60}{45} < \frac{70}{45} < \frac{72}{45}.$ So, $\frac{4}{3} < \frac{14}{9} < \frac{8}{5}.$

5. $\frac{1}{4} = \frac{15}{60}, \frac{2}{5} = \frac{24}{60}, \frac{3}{6} = \frac{30}{60}$ 6. $\frac{3}{8} = \frac{15}{40}, \frac{4}{5} = \frac{32}{40}, \frac{6}{15} = \frac{16}{40}$
   $\frac{15}{60} < \frac{24}{60} < \frac{30}{60}.$ So, $\frac{1}{4} < \frac{2}{5} < \frac{3}{6}.$ $\frac{15}{40} < \frac{16}{40} < \frac{32}{40}.$ So, $\frac{3}{8} < \frac{6}{15} < \frac{4}{5}.$

Lesson Quiz — Lesson 10-1

Find each value.

1. $|6|$ 2. $|-3|$

Order from least to greatest.

3. $-4, 0, 5, -6$ 4. $-3, 3, -6, -5$

Answers

1. 6   2. 3   3. $-6, -4, 0, 5$ 4. $-6, -5, -3, 3$

Sample page; see p. H for complete list.

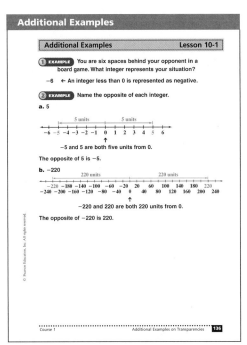

Additional Examples — Lesson 10-1

1 EXAMPLE You are six spaces behind your opponent in a board game. What integer represents your situation?

-6 ← An integer less than 0 is represented as negative.

2 EXAMPLE Name the opposite of each integer.

a. 5

-5 and 5 are both five units from 0.

The opposite of 5 is -5.

b. -220

-220 and 220 are both 220 units from 0.

The opposite of -220 is 220.

Sample page; see p. H for complete list.

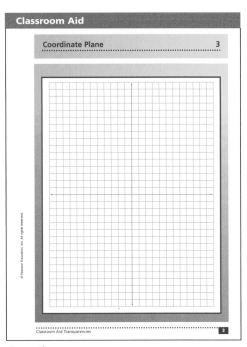

Coordinate Plane — 3

Sample page.

Assessment

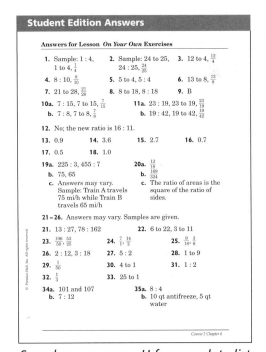

Answers for Lesson *On Your Own* Exercises

1. Sample: 1 : 4, 1 to 4, $\frac{1}{4}$ 2. Sample: 24 to 25, 24 : 25, $\frac{24}{25}$ 3. 12 to 4, $\frac{12}{4}$

4. 8 : 10, $\frac{8}{10}$ 5. 5 to 4, 5 : 4   6. 13 to 8, $\frac{13}{8}$

7. 21 to 28, $\frac{21}{28}$ 8. 8 to 18, 8 : 18   9. B

10a. 7 : 15, 7 to 15, $\frac{7}{15}$ 11a. 23 : 19, 23 to 19, $\frac{23}{19}$
  b. 7 : 8, 7 to 8, $\frac{7}{8}$ b. 19 : 42, 19 to 42, $\frac{19}{42}$

12. No; the new ratio is 16 : 11.

13. 0.9   14. 3.6   15. 2.7   16. 0.7

17. 0.5   18. 1.0

19a. 225 : 3, 455 : 7   20a. $\frac{13}{18}$
  b. 75, 65   b. $\frac{169}{324}$
  c. Answers may vary. Sample: Train A travels 75 mi/h while Train B travels 65 mi/h   c. The ratio of areas is the square of the ratio of sides.

21–26. Answers may vary. Samples are given.

21. 13 : 27, 78 : 162   22. 6 to 22, 3 to 11

23. $\frac{106}{50}, \frac{53}{25}$ 24. $\frac{7}{1}, \frac{14}{2}$ 25. $\frac{9}{18}, \frac{3}{6}$

26. 2 : 12, 3 : 18   27. 5 : 2   28. 1 to 9

29. $\frac{1}{50}$ 30. 4 to 1   31. 1 : 2

32. $\frac{1}{3}$ 33. 25 to 1

34a. 101 and 107   35a. 8 : 4
  b. 7 : 12   b. 10 qt antifreeze, 5 qt water

Sample page; see p. H for complete list.

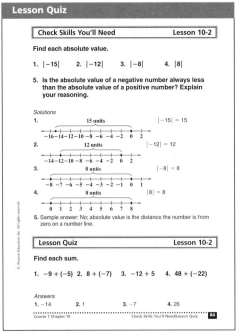

Check Skills You'll Need — Lesson 10-2

Find each absolute value.

1. $|-15|$ 2. $|-12|$ 3. $|-8|$ 4. $|8|$

5. Is the absolute value of a negative number always less than the absolute value of a positive number? Explain your reasoning.

Solutions

1. 15 units; $|-15| = 15$
2. 12 units; $|-12| = 12$
3. 8 units; $|-8| = 8$
4. 8 units; $|8| = 8$

5. Sample answer: No; absolute value is the distance the number is from zero on a number line.

Lesson Quiz — Lesson 10-2

Find each sum.

1. $-9 + (-5)$ 2. $8 + (-7)$ 3. $-12 + 5$ 4. $48 + (-22)$

Answers

1. -14 2. 1   3. -7 4. 26

Sample page; see p. H for complete list.

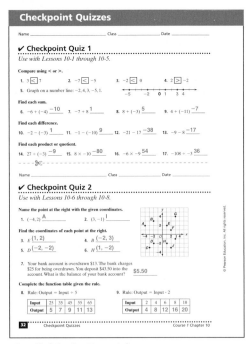

Name _____ Class _____ Date _____

✔ Checkpoint Quiz 1

Use with Lessons 10-1 through 10-5.

Compare using < or >.

1. 3 < 7   2. -7 < -5 3. -2 < 0   4. 2 > -2

5. Graph on a number line: $-2, 4, 3, -5, 1.$

Find each sum.

6. $-6 + (-4)$ -10 7. $-7 + 8$ 1   8. $8 + (-3)$ 5   9. $4 + (-11)$ -7

Find each difference.

10. $-2 - (-3)$ 1   11. $-1 - (-10)$ 9   12. $-21 - 17$ -38 13. $-9 - 8$ -17

Find each product or quotient.

14. $27 \div (-3)$ -9 15. 8×-10 -80 16. -6×-9 54   17. $-108 \div -3$ 36

Name _____ Class _____ Date _____

✔ Checkpoint Quiz 2

Use with Lessons 10-6 through 10-8.

Name the point at the right with the given coordinates.

1. $(-4, 2)$ A   2. $(3, -1)$ F

Find the coordinates of each point at the right.

3. E $(1, 2)$ 4. B $(-2, 3)$
5. D $(-2, -2)$ 6. H $(1, -2)$

7. Your bank account is overdrawn $13. The bank charges $25 for being overdrawn. You deposit $43.50 into the account. What is the balance of your bank account? $5.50

Complete the function table given the rule.

8. Rule: Output = Input ÷ 5

Input	25	35	45	55	65
Output	5	7	9	11	13

9. Rule: Output = Input · 2

Input	2	4	6	8	10
Output	4	8	12	16	20

Available in Spanish

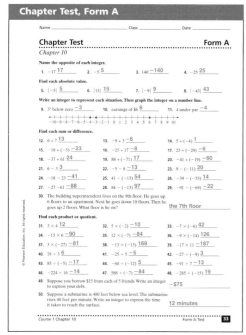

Available in Spanish

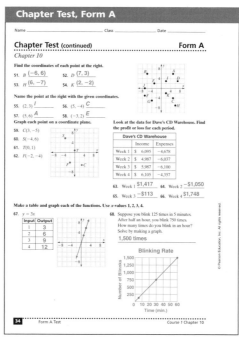

Available in Spanish

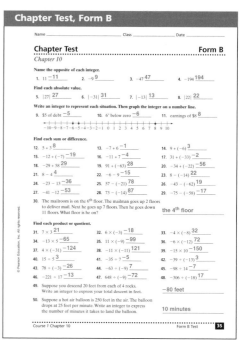

Available in Spanish

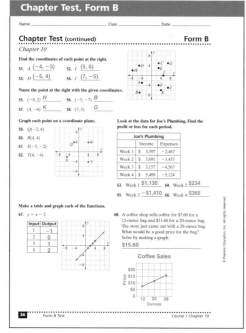

Available in Spanish

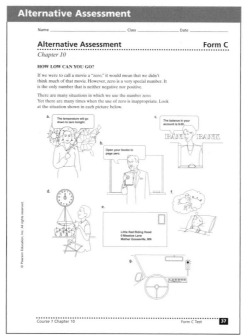

Available in Spanish

Available in Spanish

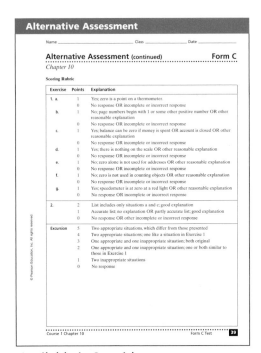

Name _____ Class _____ Date _____

Alternative Assessment (continued)　　　　**Form C**

Chapter 10

Scoring Rubric

Exercise	Points	Explanation
1. a.	1	Yes; zero is a point on a thermometer.
	0	No response OR incomplete or incorrect response
b.	1	No; page numbers begin with 1 or some other positive number OR other reasonable explanation
	0	No response OR incomplete or incorrect response
c.	1	Yes; balance can be zero if money is spent OR account is closed OR other reasonable explanation
	0	No response OR incomplete or incorrect response
d.	1	Yes; there is nothing on the scale OR other reasonable explanation
	0	No response OR incomplete or incorrect response
e.	1	No; zero is not used for addresses OR other reasonable explanation
	0	No response OR incomplete or incorrect response
f.	1	No; zero is not used in counting objects OR other reasonable explanation
	0	No response OR incomplete or incorrect response
g.	1	Yes; speedometer is at zero at a red light OR other reasonable explanation
	0	No response OR incomplete or incorrect response
2.	2	List includes only situations a and c; good explanation
	1	Accurate list; no explanation OR partly accurate list; good explanation
	0	No response OR other incomplete or incorrect response
Excursion	5	Two appropriate situations, which differ from those presented
	4	Two appropriate situations; one like a situation in Exercise 1
	3	One appropriate and one inappropriate situation; both original
	2	One appropriate and one inappropriate situation; one or both similar to those in Exercise 1
	1	Two inappropriate situations
	0	No response

Course 1 Chapter 10　　　　Form C Test　　**39**

Available in Spanish

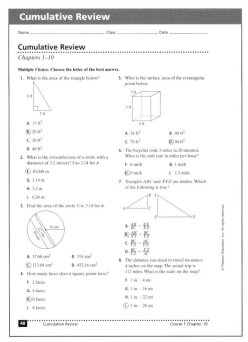

Name _____ Class _____ Date _____

Cumulative Review

Chapters 1–10

Multiple Choice. Choose the letter of the best answer.

1. What is the area of the triangle below?

   A. 13 ft²
   B. 20 ft²
   C. 30 ft²
   D. 40 ft²

2. What is the circumference of a circle with a diameter of 3.2 meters? Use 3.14 for π.

   F. 10.048 m
   G. 3.14 m
   H. 3.2 m
   I. 6.28 m

3. Find the area of the circle. Use 3.14 for π.

   A. 37.68 cm²
   B. 314 cm²
   C. 113.04 cm²
   D. 452.16 cm²

4. How many faces does a square prism have?

   F. 2 faces
   G. 4 faces
   H. 6 faces
   I. 8 faces

5. What is the surface area of the rectangular prism below?

   A. 24 ft²
   B. 40 ft²
   C. 70 ft²
   D. 94 ft²

6. The bicyclist rode 3 miles in 20 minutes. What is the unit rate in miles per hour?

   F. 6 mi/h
   G. 1 mi/h
   H. 9 mi/h
   I. 1.5 mi/h

7. Triangles ABC and XYZ are similar. Which of the following is true?

   A. $\frac{AB}{BC} = \frac{XY}{YZ}$
   B. $\frac{AB}{YZ} = \frac{BC}{XY}$
   C. $\frac{BC}{YZ} = \frac{XY}{AB}$
   D. $\frac{BC}{YZ} = \frac{XZ}{AC}$

8. The distance you need to travel measures 4 inches on the map. The actual trip is 112 miles. What is the scale on the map?

   F. 1 in. : 4 mi
   G. 1 in. : 16 mi
   H. 1 in. : 22 mi
   I. 1 in. : 28 mi

40　Cumulative Review　　　　Course 1 Chapter 10

Available in Spanish

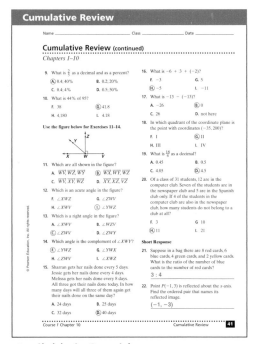

Name _____ Class _____ Date _____

Cumulative Review (continued)

Chapters 1–10

9. What is $\frac{2}{5}$ as a decimal and as a percent?

   A. 0.4; 40%
   B. 0.2; 20%
   C. 0.4; 4%
   D. 0.5; 50%

10. What is 44% of 95?

   F. 38
   G. 41.8
   H. 4,180
   I. 4.18

Use the figure below for Exercises 11–14.

11. Which are all shown in the figure?

   A. $\overline{WV}, \overline{WZ}, \overline{WY}$
   B. $\overline{WX}, \overline{WY}, \overline{WZ}$
   C. $\overline{WV}, \overline{XY}, \overline{WZ}$
   D. $\overline{XY}, \overline{XZ}, \overline{VZ}$

12. Which is an acute angle in the figure?

   F. ∠XWZ
   G. ∠ZWV
   H. ∠XWV
   I. ∠YWZ

13. Which is a right angle in the figure?

   A. ∠XWV
   B. ∠WZV
   C. ∠ZWV
   D. ∠ZWY

14. Which angle is the complement of ∠XWY?

   F. ∠YWZ
   G. ∠YWX
   H. ∠ZWV
   I. ∠XWZ

15. Sharran gets her nails done every 5 days. Jessie gets her nails done every 4 days. Melissa gets her nails done every 8 days. All three got their nails done today. In how many days will all three of them again get their nails done on the same day?

   A. 24 days
   B. 25 days
   C. 32 days
   D. 40 days

16. What is −6 + 3 + (−2)?

   F. −3
   G. 5
   H. −5
   I. −11

17. What is −13 − (−13)?

   A. −26
   B. 0
   C. 26
   D. not here

18. In which quadrant of the coordinate plane is the point with coordinates (−35, 200)?

   F. I
   G. II
   H. III
   I. IV

19. What is $\frac{18}{4}$ as a decimal?

   A. 0.45
   B. 0.5
   C. 4.05
   D. 4.5

20. Of a class of 31 students, 12 are in the computer club. Seven of the students are in the newspaper club and 5 are in the Spanish club only. If 4 of the students in the computer club are also in the newspaper club, how many students do not belong to a club at all?

   F. 3
   G. 10
   H. 11
   I. 21

Short Response

21. Suppose in a bag there are 8 red cards, 6 blue cards, 4 green cards, and 2 yellow cards. What is the ratio of the number of blue cards to the number of red cards?

   3 : 4

22. Point P(−1, 3) is reflected about the x-axis. Find the ordered pair that names its reflected image.

   (−1, −3)

Course 1 Chapter 10　　　　Cumulative Review　**41**

Available in Spanish

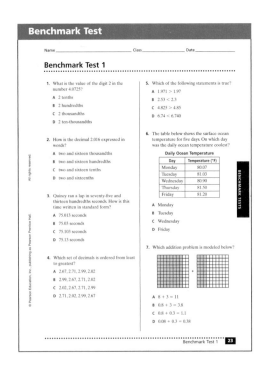

Name _____ Class _____ Date _____

Benchmark Test 1

1. What is the value of the digit 2 in the number 4.0725?

   A. 2 tenths
   B. 2 hundredths
   C. 2 thousandths
   D. 2 ten-thousandths

2. How is the decimal 2.016 expressed in words?

   A. two and sixteen thousandths
   B. two and sixteen hundredths
   C. two and sixteen tenths
   D. two and sixteenths

3. Quincy ran a lap in seventy-five and thirteen hundredths seconds. How is this time written in standard form?

   A. 75.013 seconds
   B. 75.03 seconds
   C. 75.103 seconds
   D. 75.13 seconds

4. Which set of decimals is ordered from least to greatest?

   A. 2.67, 2.71, 2.99, 2.02
   B. 2.99, 2.67, 2.71, 2.02
   C. 2.02, 2.67, 2.71, 2.99
   D. 2.71, 2.02, 2.99, 2.67

5. Which of the following statements is true?

   A. 1.971 > 1.97
   B. 2.53 < 2.3
   C. 4.825 > 4.85
   D. 6.74 < 6.740

6. The table below shows the surface ocean temperature for five days. On which day was the daily ocean temperature coolest?

   Daily Ocean Temperature

Day	Temperature (°F)
Monday	80.07
Tuesday	81.03
Wednesday	80.90
Thursday	81.50
Friday	81.20

   A. Monday
   B. Tuesday
   C. Wednesday
   D. Friday

7. Which addition problem is modeled below?

   A. 8 + 3 = 11
   B. 0.8 + 3 = 3.8
   C. 0.8 + 0.3 = 1.1
   D. 0.08 + 0.3 = 0.38

BENCHMARK TESTS

Benchmark Test 1　**23**

Test-Taking Strategies: Using a Variable

You can solve many problems by using a variable to represent an unknown quantity.

Let the variable be the quantity that you are looking for.

Examples

Let x = the number of hours worked.

Let t = the amount of time spent.

Let A = the area of the backyard.

Then use the variable to write an equation.

You attend a cheerleading clinic with your team every Saturday morning. The clinic costs $6.50 per person. It costs $78 for your entire team to attend the clinic. How many cheerleaders are on your team?

Let c = the number of cheerleaders.

Write and solve an equation to find the number of cheerleaders.

$6.50c = 78$

$\frac{6.50c}{6.50} = \frac{78}{6.50}$　　There are 12 cheerleaders on your team.

$c = 12$

Define a variable. Then, write and solve an equation for each problem.

1. An illustrator charges $75 per picture. Find the total number of pictures in a children's book if the illustrator earned $3,000.

2. There are 12 songs on a CD. The CD lasts 42 minutes. About how long is the average song on the CD?

Transparency 11

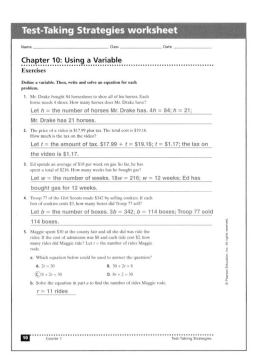

Name _____ Class _____ Date _____

Chapter 10: Using a Variable

Exercises

Define a variable. Then, write and solve an equation for each problem.

1. Mr. Drake bought 84 horseshoes to shoe all of his horses. Each horse needs 4 shoes. How many horses does Mr. Drake have?

   Let h = the number of horses Mr. Drake has. 4h = 84; h = 21;

   Mr. Drake has 21 horses.

2. The price of a video is $17.99 plus tax. The total cost is $19.16. How much is the tax on the video?

   Let t = the amount of tax. $17.99 + t = $19.16; t = $1.17; the tax on

   the video is $1.17.

3. Ed spends an average of $18 per week on gas. So far, he has spent a total of $216. How many weeks has he bought gas?

   Let w = the number of weeks. 18w = 216; w = 12 weeks; Ed has

   bought gas for 12 weeks.

4. Troop 77 of the Girl Scouts made $342 by selling cookies. If each box of cookies costs $3, how many boxes did Troop 77 sell?

   Let b = the number of boxes. 3b = 342; b = 114 boxes; Troop 77 sold

   114 boxes.

5. Maggie spent $30 at the county fair and all she did was ride the rides. If the cost of admission was $8 and each ride cost $2, how many rides did Maggie ride? Let r = the number of rides Maggie rode.

   a. Which equation below could be used to answer the question?

   A. 2r = 30
   B. 30 + 2r = 8
   C. 8 + 2r = 30
   D. 8r + 2 = 30

   b. Solve the equation in part a to find the number of rides Maggie rode.

   r = 11 rides

10　Course 1　　　　Test-Taking Strategies

On PH Website

in math class ...

We have been learning about integers and the coordinate plane. Here is a list of some of the skills and concepts we have studied.

◆ Understanding integers
◆ Adding and subtracting integers
◆ Multiplying and dividing integers
◆ The coordinate plane
◆ Graphing equations

Home Activities

Here are some activities you can do with your child that use these math skills and concepts.

Use your local news, a weather service, or the Internet to find the temperature each day for a week. Record the actual temperature for the day that you start and then use integers to record the temperature change between days in a table. At the end of the week, have your child tell you the actual temperature of each day for which there is an integer in the table.

In the table below, the actual temperatures for Monday through Friday are: 88°F, 86°F, 83°F, 87°F, and 88°F.

Starting temperature: 85°F

Day	Temperature Change
Monday	+3
Tuesday	-2
Wednesday	-3
Thursday	+4
Friday	+1

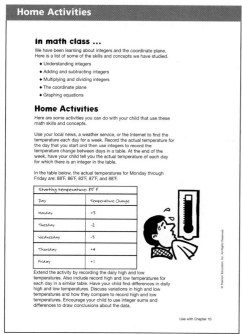

Extend the activity by recording the daily high and low temperatures. Also include record high and low temperatures for each day in a similar table. Have your child find differences in daily high and low temperatures. Discuss variations in high and low temperatures and how they compare to record high and low temperatures. Encourage your child to use integer sums and differences to draw conclusions about the data.

Use with Chapter 10

Available in Spanish;
Web Code: aak-5500

Name _____   ***Math and Social Studies***

TAKE IT TO THE BANK

Use integers and positive and negative numbers in banking.

Banking has a long history. In ancient Rome, people went to money changers to borrow money, to deposit money, and to get bills of credit. Bills of credit were similar to today's checks. The money changers were so important to Roman commerce that an entire Roman street, called the Street of Janus, was set aside for money changing. During the Renaissance (between 1400 and 1600), money changers did business from benches in the street. The Italian word for bench is *banca*, from which comes the English word, *bank*.

In England during the early 1600s, goldsmiths were the bankers. Goldsmiths were people who made and repaired articles of gold. The goldsmiths kept money and other valuables in safe care for their customers. Over time, the goldsmiths noticed that the value of the deposits left in their care remained at a steady level. There were about as many deposits as there were withdrawals. (A *withdrawal* is the process by which money is taken out of a bank account.)

Apparently, people wanted only enough money to meet their everyday needs. They left the rest with the goldsmiths. The goldsmiths realized that they could use the money left in their safe keeping to make additional profits. They could lend the money to people and charge a fee—interest—as the cost for borrowing the money. The goldsmiths also allowed their customers to transfer any part of the money in their account to another person's account. This seems to be the beginning of modern check writing.

Modern banks provide many services. The most common ones are savings accounts, loans, and checking accounts. A checking account is an account in which a person deposits money and then writes checks against that money. For example, a person who deposits $300 into a checking account may write up to $300 worth of checks. If that person writes checks for more than $300, the checks are said to be "bad," because there is not enough money in his or her account to cover the check.

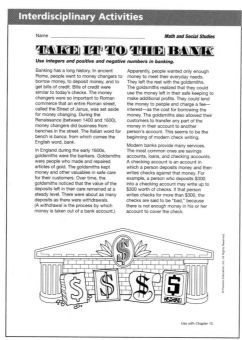

Use with Chapter 10

Available in Spanish;
Web Code: aak-5500

Name _____   ***Math and Social Studies***

Item	Cost	Cost Rounded	Balance in Checking Account	Balance in Checking Account Rounded	+ or −	Do you have enough money?
sneakers	$99.95	$100	$86.79	$90	−$10	no
video game	$43.50		$217.14			
dinner at a restaurant	$17.23		$3.89			
CD	$11.99		$41.08			
baseball cap	$22.50		$25.62			
bicycle	$269.79		$177.45			

1. Complete the table by rounding to decide whether you have enough money in your checking account to pay for an item. If you have enough, select the positive sign and write the rounded amount of money you will have left after writing the check. If you do not have enough money, select the negative sign and write the rounded amount of money you will owe the account. An example has been provided to help you get started. Round each number so there is only one non-zero digit.

2. When is an amount of money an integer and when is it not an integer? Include an example of each in your explanation.

3. When people make deposits, they add money to their checking account. When people write checks, they subtract money from their checking account. How can checkbook activities be expressed on a number line?

_____
_____
_____
_____

4. Why do you think banking has existed for at least 2,000 years?

_____
_____
_____
_____
_____

5. a. Research ways that banks have helped to shape history.

   b. Visit or call your local bank to find out their rules about checking accounts. Find out such things as how old a person must be to open a checking account and the penalties for writing bad checks. Also, find out about overdraft protection and how it can help a person to avoid writing bad checks.

Use with Chapter 10

Available in Spanish;
Web Code: aak-5500

Name _____ Class _____ Date _____

Integer Puzzles   Puzzle 39

Use the given numbers to make each equation true.

3	5	7	⁻3	⁻5	⁻7

1. ____ + ____ = ⁻4
2. ____ + ____ = 8
3. ____ + ____ = 2
4. ____ + ____ = ⁻2
5. ____ + ____ = ⁻12
6. ____ + ____ = ⁻2
7. ____ + ____ = 12
8. ____ + ____ = 10
9. ____ + ____ = ⁻8
10. ____ + ____ = ⁻10

2	6	9	⁻2	⁻6	⁻9

11. ____ + ____ = ⁻11
12. ____ + ____ = ⁻7
13. ____ + ____ = 4
14. ____ + ____ = ⁻4
15. ____ + ____ = 15
16. ____ + ____ = ⁻15
17. ____ + ____ = 7
18. ____ + ____ = 7
19. ____ + ____ = 3
20. ____ + ____ = 11
21. ____ + ____ = 8
22. ____ + ____ = ⁻3

Make eight different addition equations using the given numbers for the addends. Then find each sum.

3	4	8	⁻3	⁻4	⁻8

23. ____ + ____ = ____
24. ____ + ____ = ____
25. ____ + ____ = ____
26. ____ + ____ = ____
27. ____ + ____ = ____
28. ____ + ____ = ____
29. ____ + ____ = ____
30. ____ + ____ = ____

Algebra Readiness Puzzles   39

Web Code: aak-5500

Name _____ Class _____ Date _____

Coordinate Geometry   Puzzle 97

Refer to the graph at the right for 1 through 4.

1. Write the coordinates of each point.
   A: (2 , 1)
   B: (____, ____)
   C: (____, ____)

2. Add 5 to each coordinate of points A, B, and C.
   A': (7 , 6)
   B': (____, ____)
   C': (____, ____)

3. Draw a triangle with new points A', B', and C' as vertices.

4. Are the two triangles congruent? ____

Refer to the graph at the right for 5 through 8.

5. Write the coordinates of each point.
   X: (____, ____)
   Y: (____, ____)
   Z: (____, ____)

6. Subtract 4 from each coordinate of points X, Y, and Z.
   X': (____, ____)
   Y': (____, ____)
   Z': (____, ____)

7. Draw a triangle with new points X', Y', and Z' as vertices.

8. Are the two triangles congruent? ____

Algebra Readiness Puzzles   97

Web Code: aak-5500

CHAPTER 10

Integers

Chapter 10 Overview

In this chapter students study integers and explore common applications of integers. First they examine integers using a number line. Next they add, subtract, multiply, and divide integers. Finally, they graph integers and functions containing integers on a coordinate plane.

 Reading Math
- **Understanding Word Problems,** p. 517
- **Vocabulary:** A complete list, plus exercises, in the Chapter Review, p. 538
- **Illustrated Glossary:** Examples for each vocabulary term, plus definitions in English and Spanish, on p. 669

 **Writing in Math**
Writing to Justify Steps, p. 536

Test-Taking Strategies
Using a Variable, p. 537

 **Real-World Problem Solving**
- **Strategies:** Make a Graph, pp. 533–535
- **Real-World Snapshots:** Peaks and Valleys, pp. 542–543
- **Chapter Project:** The Time of Your Life, p. 640

 www.PHSchool.com
Internet support includes:
- Self-grading Vocabulary and Chapter 10 Tests
- Activity Masters
- Chapter Project support
- Chapter Planner
- Ch. 10 Resources

Plus **iTEXT**

CHAPTER 10

Integers

Key Vocabulary
- absolute value (p. 492)
- coordinate plane (p. 518)
- function (p. 527)
- integers (p. 491)
- opposites (p. 491)
- ordered pair (p. 518)
- origin (p. 518)
- quadrants (p. 518)

Real-World Snapshots

The temperature of lava flow can range between 1,250°F and 2,250°F. From the surface toward the center of Earth, the temperature gets even hotter than this.

Data File
Selected Earth Temperatures

Location	Temperature (°F)	Elevation (feet)
Vostok Station, Antarctica	−129 (record low)	11,220
Colossal Cave, Arizona	70 (constant)	3,660
El Azizia, Libya	136 (record high)	367
Land surface (average)	47.3	2,559
Sea surface (average)	60.9	0
Upper mantle	932	Above −2,196,480
Lower mantle	3,632	−2,900,000 to −2,196,480
Outer core	9,032	−5,100,000 to −2,900,000
Inner core	12,632	Below −5,100,000

SOURCE: National Oceanic and Atmospheric Administration, *Glossary of Geology*

You will use the data above in this chapter:
- p. 500   Lesson 10-2
- p. 507   Lesson 10-3

 Real-World Snapshots On pages 542 and 543, you will solve problems involving elevation.

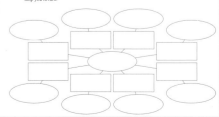

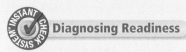

Chapter 10 Preview

Where You've Been

● In Chapter 1, you added, subtracted, multiplied, and divided decimal numbers greater than or equal to 0.

● In Chapters 4 and 5, you did the same for fractions.

Where You're Going

● In Chapter 10, you will add, subtract, multiply, and divide integers.

● You will graph in the coordinate plane.

● You will see how businesses and stock markets use integers.

● Applying what you learn, you use positive and negative integers in problems related to the weather.

Meteorologists use integers every day to report the temperature.

Instant self-check
online and on CD-ROM

Diagnosing Readiness

For help, go to the lesson in green.

Algebra **Solving Addition and Subtraction Equations** (Lesson 2-6)

Solve each equation.

1. $a - 31 = 8$ 39

2. $b + 12 = 43$ 31

3. $c - 16 = 84$ 100

4. $d + 13 = 92$ 79

5. $e - 23 = 8$ 31

6. $f + 45 = 163$ 118

Algebra **Solving Multiplication and Division Equations** (Lesson 2-7)

Solve each equation.

7. $7g = 42$ 6

8. $h \div 6 = 11$ 66

9. $8j = 32$ 4

10. $k \div 9 = 8$ 72

11. $16m = 240$ 15

12. $n \div 14 = 18$ 252

Comparing and Ordering Fractions (Lesson 3-7)

Compare each pair of numbers. Use $<$, $=$, or $>$.

13. $\frac{1}{3} \blacksquare \frac{2}{5}$ $<$

14. $\frac{3}{4} \blacksquare \frac{2}{3}$ $>$

15. $\frac{2}{16} \blacksquare \frac{1}{8}$ $=$

Order each set of numbers from least to greatest.

16. $\frac{1}{8}, \frac{1}{3}, \frac{1}{12}$ $\frac{1}{12}, \frac{1}{8}, \frac{1}{3}$

17. $\frac{4}{9}, \frac{5}{6}, \frac{7}{12}$ $\frac{4}{9}, \frac{7}{12}, \frac{5}{6}$

18. $\frac{1}{4}, \frac{6}{7}, \frac{1}{2}$ $\frac{1}{4}, \frac{1}{2}, \frac{6}{7}$

 10-1

Using a Number Line

What You'll Learn

 OBJECTIVE 1 To graph integers on a number line

OBJECTIVE 2 To compare and order integers

. . . And Why

To compare game scores, as in Example 5

 Check Skills You'll Need   For help, go to Lesson 3-7.

Compare each pair of numbers. Use <, =, or >.

1. $\frac{3}{2}$ ■ $\frac{7}{10}$ >

2. $2\frac{2}{3}$ ■ $\frac{8}{3}$ =

3. $1\frac{7}{5}$ ■ $2\frac{1}{10}$ >

Order each set of numbers from least to greatest.

4. $\frac{14}{9}, \frac{4}{3}, \frac{8}{5}$ $\frac{4}{3}, \frac{14}{9}, \frac{8}{5}$

5. $\frac{1}{4}, \frac{2}{5}, \frac{3}{6}$ $\frac{1}{4}, \frac{2}{5}, \frac{3}{6}$

6. $\frac{3}{8}, \frac{4}{5}, \frac{6}{15}$ $\frac{3}{8}, \frac{6}{15}, \frac{4}{5}$

New Vocabulary   • opposites   • integers   • absolute value

Lesson Preview

 PowerPoint

Check Skills You'll Need
Comparing and Ordering Fractions
Lesson 3-7: Examples 1–3. Extra Practice p. 644.

Lesson Resources

📁 **Teaching Resources**
Practice, Reteaching, Enrichment

👥 **Reaching All Students**
Practice Workbook 10-1
Spanish Practice Workbook 10-1
Guided Problem Solving 10-1
Hands-On Activities 39

⏱ **Presentation Assistant Plus!**
Transparencies
• Check Skills You'll Need 10-1
• Problem of the Day 10-1
• Additional Examples 10-1
• Student Edition Answers 10-1
• Lesson Quiz 10-1
• Classroom Aid 7
PH Presentation Pro CD-ROM 10-1

 PRENTICE HALL ASSESSMENT SYSTEM

Computer Test Generator CD

 Technology
Resource Pro® CD-ROM
Computer Test Generator CD
PH Presentation Pro CD-ROM

 www.PHSchool.com
Student Site
• Teacher Web Code: aak-5500
• Self-grading Lesson Quiz

PH SuccessNet Teacher Center
• Lesson Planner
• Resources

 Plus 📘**TEXT**

 OBJECTIVE 1   **Graphing Integers on a Number Line**

📘**TEXT** Interactive lesson includes instant self-check, tutorials, and activities.

Suppose you play tug-of-war against the team on the left shown below. Your team begins by gaining 2 feet. The position of the flag is positive 2 feet, or +2. The expression +2 is usually written simply as 2.

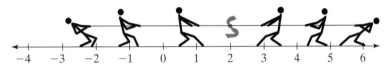

If, instead, your team begins by losing 2 feet, the position of the flag would be negative 2 feet, or −2. These positions can be graphed on a number line.

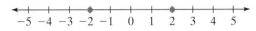

The numbers 2 and −2 are opposites. Two numbers are **opposites** if they are the same distance from 0 on a number line but in opposite directions. **Integers** are the set of positive whole numbers, their opposites, and 0. The opposite of 0 is 0.

Real-World Connection
The "smoke" that makes a performance exciting is actually from dry ice.

1 EXAMPLE   **Representing Situations With Integers** 🌐 **Real World**

Dry Ice Dry ice is composed of pressurized carbon dioxide that has a freezing point of 190 degrees below zero Fahrenheit. Use an integer to represent the freezing point of dry ice.

   −190   ← An integer less than 0 is represented as negative.

✔ **Check Understanding** ① The altitude of New Orleans, Louisiana, is 8 feet below sea level. Use an integer to represent this altitude.   −8

⚡ **Ongoing Assessment and Intervention**

Before the Lesson
Diagnose prerequisite skills using:
• Check Skills You'll Need

During the Lesson
Monitor progress using:
• Check Understanding
• Additional Examples
• Test Prep

After the Lesson
Assess knowledge using:
• Lesson Quiz
• Computer Test Generator CD

Math Background

A number line can be helpful to compare and order integers. A number line also exemplifies the concepts of opposites and absolute value. Numbers that are *opposites* are the same distance from 0 on a number line. So, the sum of two opposites, such as −3 and 3, is always 0. The *absolute value* of a number is its distance from 0 on a number line. This means that the absolute value of both 5 and −5 is 5; both numbers are 5 positions from 0 on a number line. Absolute value is never negative because it expresses a distance.

The *integers* are the numbers . . . , −3, −2, −1, 0, 1, 2, 3, ... Integers can be pictured as points on a number line. To the right of 0 are the positive integers 1, 2, 3, . . . and to the left of 0 are the negative integers −1, −2, −3, ... Zero is neither positive nor negative. As you move from left to right on a number line, the integers become larger.

Teaching Notes

① EXAMPLE Inclusion

Help students identify words associated with negative (*below, less, loss, fewer*) and with positive (*more, add, greater*) values.

② EXAMPLE English Learners

Use plain language to help students understand what opposite events are. For instance, "in and out," "open and close," or "going up and coming down" are opposite events.

Error Prevention!

Some students might think that an opposite number must be negative. Ask:
- What is the opposite of 4? −4
- What is the opposite of −4? 4
- What does it mean that 4 and −4 are opposites? They are the same distance from 0 on a number line but in opposite directions.

492

Calculator Hint

You can use the (−) key or the +/− key on your calculator to express an opposite.

② EXAMPLE Identifying Opposites

Name the opposite of 3.

← −3 and 3 are both three units from 0.

The opposite of 3 is −3.

✓ **Check Understanding ②** Name the opposite of −5. 5

The **absolute value** of a number is its distance from 0 on a number line. You write "the absolute value of negative 3" as $|-3|$. Opposites have the same absolute value.

③ EXAMPLE Finding Absolute Values

Find $|-4|$ and $|2|$.

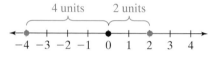

Since −4 is four units from 0, $|-4| = 4$. Since 2 is two units from 0, $|2| = 2$.

✓ **Check Understanding ③ a.** Find $|-1|$. 1   **b.** Find $|7|$. 7   **c.** Find $|-9|$. 9

OBJECTIVE

2 Comparing and Ordering Integers

You can use a number line to compare integers.

Reading Math

As you read from left to right on a horizontal number line, the integers become greater.

… negative integers   positive integers …

0 is neither positive nor negative.

④ EXAMPLE Comparing Integers

Compare −4 and −6.

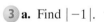

← Graph −4 and −6 on the same number line.

Since −6 is to the left of −4 on the number line, −6 < −4.

✓ **Check Understanding ④** Compare using < or >.   **a.** 5 ▓ −3   **b.** −12 ▓ 9

👥 Reaching All Students

| **Below Level** Create a number line for Check Understanding 5. Students can place the numbers on the line. They can move their fingers from left to right. Remind them that movement to the right shows a greater integer. | **Advanced Learners** Have students compare absolute value such as these.

$\|-(-(-9))\| \ \blacksquare \ 0 \ >$
$-\|-65\| \ \blacksquare \ -\|56\| \ <$
$-\|-32\|\| \ \blacksquare \ -(-\|-23\|) \ <$ | **English Learners** See note on page 492.
Inclusion See note on page 492. |

You can also use a number line to help you order integers from least to greatest.

5 **EXAMPLE** **Ordering Integers** Real World

Games In a trivia game, points are deducted for incorrect answers. Four teams participate in the game. Order the scores from least to greatest.

Use one hundred as the number line unit.

$$\xleftarrow{\quad} \underset{-400}{\bullet}\ |\ \underset{-300}{\bullet}\ |\ \underset{-200}{\bullet}\ |\ \underset{-100}{}\ |\ \underset{0}{}\ |\ \underset{100}{}\ |\ \underset{200}{}\ |\ \underset{300}{\bullet}\ |\ \underset{400}{} \xrightarrow{\quad}$$

$-400, -200, 100, 300$ ← Write the scores in order from left to right.

In order from least to greatest, the scores are $-400, -200, 100,$ and 300.

Tigers	−200
Bulldogs	+300
Lions	−400
Spartans	+100

✓ **Check Understanding** **5** Order these scores from least to greatest: $-25, 100, -50, 75$.
–50, –25, 75, 100

EXERCISES

? For more practice, see *Extra Practice*.

A **Practice by Example**

Example 1
(page 491)

Use an integer to represent each situation.

1. earnings of $15   15   **2.** 14°F below zero   −14   **3.** a debt of $25   −25

Example 2
(page 492)

Name the opposite of each integer.

4. 13   −13   **5.** −8   8   **6.** 150   −150   **7.** −1   1

Example 3
(page 492)

Find each absolute value.

8. $|-4|$ 4   **9.** $|17|$ 17   **10.** $|-65|$ 65   **11.** $|0|$ 0

Example 4
(page 492)

Compare using < or >.

12. $2 \; \blacksquare \; -12$ **13.** $-9 \; \blacksquare \; -17$ **14.** $-23 \; \blacksquare \; -4$ **15.** $-7 \; \blacksquare \; 0$
   >   >   <   <

Example 5
(page 493)

16. Weather The coldest temperatures on record for five Alaskan cities are $-62°F, -70°F, -54°F, -75°F,$ and $-56°F.$ Write the temperatures in order from coldest to warmest.   **−75°F, −70°F, −62°F, −56°F, −54°F**

Auditory Learners
To help students distinguish between positive and negative integers, have them use the word *positive* when naming positive integers. For instance, have them read 3 as "positive three."

5 **EXAMPLE** **Tactile Learners**

Tactile learners may benefit from manipulating numbers on a number line. Have students draw a number line on the board or on a roll of paper. Students can write the numbers in the exercises on self-stick notes and place them on the number line in the correct order. Remind students that they are working with integers, not absolute values of integers.

PowerPoint
Additional Examples

1 You are six spaces behind your opponent in a board game. What integer represents your situation? −6

2 Name the opposite of each integer.
   a. 5 −5   **b.** −220 220

3 Find each absolute value.
   a. $|-19|$ 19
   b. $|67|$ 67

4 Compare −12 and −10.
   −12 < −10

5 Order from least to greatest.
   a. 16, −2, −35, 68, −10
      −35, −10, −2, 16, 68
   b. −87, −14, 41, −104, 78
      −104, −87, −14, 41, 78

Closure

- *What are integers?* Integers are the set of positive whole numbers, their opposites, and 0.
- Explain the difference between an opposite number and an absolute value. The opposite of a number is the number that is the same distance from 0 on the opposite side of the number line, such as 4 and −4. The absolute value is the distance from 0 to the integer on the number line. An absolute value is never negative.

Assignment Guide

 Objective 1
(A) (B) Core 1–11, 17–26
(C) Extension 34

 Objective 2
(A) (B) Core 12–16, 27–32
(C) Extension 33, 35

Test Prep 36–39
Mixed Review 40–44

Exercises 8–11 Use these exercises to review the difference between opposite integers and absolute values.

Practice 10-1   Using a Number Line

Use an integer to represent each situation.
1. spent $23 _−23_   2. lost 12 yards _−12_   3. deposit of $58 _58_

Name the opposite of each integer.
4. 16 _−16_   5. −12 _12_   6. 100 _−100_   7. 75 _−75_

Find each absolute value.
8. |−5| _5_   9. |13| _13_   10. |25| _25_   11. |−7| _7_

Compare using < or >.
12. −5 [<] 8   13. 13 [>] −14   14. −11 [>] −19
15. Order the temperatures from least to greatest. _−25°F, −3°F, 32°F, 34°F, 78°F_
  • The temperature was 25°F below zero.
  • The pool temperature was 78°F.
  • Water freezes at 32°F.
  • The low temperature in December is −3°F.
  • The temperature in the refrigerator was 34°F.
16. Graph these integers on the number line: −4, 9, 1, −2, 3.

Name the integer represented by each point on the number line.
17. J _−3_   18. K _4_
19. L _2_   20. M _−6_
Name an integer between the given integers. Sample answers are given.
21. −2, 9 _1_   22. 3, −12 _−6_   23. −7, −11 _−9_
Complete with an integer that makes the statement true. Samples answers are given.
24. −9 > _−12_   25. _7_ > 3   26. 0 > _−5_
Think of the days of a week as integers. Let today be 0, and let days in the past be negative and days in the future be positive.
27. If today is Tuesday, what integer stands for last Sunday? _−2_
28. If today is Wednesday, what integer stands for next Saturday? _3_
29. If today is Friday, what integer stands for last Saturday? _−6_
30. If today is Monday, what integer stands for next Monday? _7_

Reteaching 10-1   Using a Number Line

The numbers . . . −3, −2, −1, 0, +1, +2, +3, ... are *integers*.
Integers are the set of positive whole numbers, their opposites, and 0.

The absolute value of a number is its distance from 0 on a number line. |−4| = 4. *Opposite integers*, like −4 and 4, are the same distance from 0.

Compare −2 and 1.
For two integers on a number line, the greater integer is farther to the right.
① Locate −2 and 1 on the number line.
② Find that 1 is farther to the right.
③ Write 1 > −2 (1 is greater than −2), or −2 < 1 (−2 is less than 1.)

Name the opposite of each integer.
1. 7 _−7_   2. −212 _212_   3. 49 _−49_
4. 1,991 _−1,991_   5. −78 _78_   6. 16 _−16_

Compare using < or >.
7. 6 [>] 3   8. 2 [<] 8   9. −2 [<] 2   10. 9 [>] −9
11. 0 [<] 5   12. −9 [<] −5   13. 0 [<] 10   14. −5 [<] −2
15. 7 [>] −9   16. −5 [<] −1   17. 6 [>] −6   18. −12 [<] 0
19. 8 [>] −3   20. −1 [>] −2   21. −5 [<] 4   22. −3 [<] −2

Find each absolute value.
23. |−2| _2_   24. |−100| _100_   25. |−16| _16_
26. |8| _8_   27. |−25| _25_   28. |−250| _250_
29. |16| _16_   30. |12| _12_   31. |75| _75_

(B) **Apply Your Skills** **17. Time Line** A time line is a number line that shows dates.

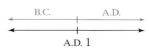

Draw a time line from 2000 B.C. to A.D. 2000. Mark the time line in intervals of 500 years. Then place the following events on the time line.

See margin.

776 B.C.   First Olympic Games held.
1600 B.C.   Stonehenge is completed.
A.D. 1492   Columbus lands in America.
1190 B.C.   The city of Troy falls to Greek warriors.
A.D. 1971   First microcomputer introduced.
A.D. 1565   Oldest settlement in North America started at St. Augustine.

Write an integer that represents each situation. Then graph the integer on a number line. 18–21. See margin for number line.

18. You climb 3 flights of stairs. **3**   19. You spend $7 for a gift. **−7**

20. The temperature falls 10 degrees. **−10**   21. You earn $6 babysitting. **6**

Name two numbers that have the given number as their absolute value.

22. 3 **−3, 3**   23. 22 **−22, 22**   24. 101 **−101, 101**   25. 2,004 **−2,004; 2,004**

26. **Writing in Math** Can the absolute value of a number ever be negative? Explain your reasoning.

 27. **Weather** List the following temperatures from least to greatest.

  • Normal body temperature is about 37°C.
  • An average winter day on the polar ice cap is −25°C.
  • The warmest day on record in Canada was 45°C.
  • Ski resorts make artificial snow at 0°C, the temperature at which water freezes.
  • The coldest day on record in Texas was −31°C.
    −31°C, −25°C, 0°C, 37°C, 45°C

28. **Divers** Dean dives 17 feet below the surface of Canyon Lake. Janet dives 25 feet below the lake's surface. Who dives farther below the lake's surface? **Janet**

29. Starting at the fourth floor, an elevator goes down 3 floors and then up 8 floors. At which floor does the elevator stop? **9th Floor** [GPS]

Compare using <, =, or >.

30. |−9| **>** |8| 31. |13| **=** |−13| 32. |0| **<** |−4|

26. Answers may vary. Sample: No; the absolute value of a number gives its distance from 0 on the number line, and distances are never negative.

[GPS] Use the Guided Problem Solving worksheet with Exercise 29.

18–21. (number line from −10 to 10)

17. (time line)
Troy Falls (to Greek warriors)   First Olympics   Columbus   Micro-Computer
2000 B.C.   1000 B.C.   A.D. 1000   A.D. 2000
Stonehenge   Oldest Settlement in North America at St. Augustine

33. Number Sense Compare using < or >.
    a. If $a > b$, then the opposite of a ■ the opposite of b.   <
    b. If $a < b$, then the opposite of a ■ the opposite of b.   >

34. Answers may vary. Sample: Place 3 marks between 200 and 300 to divide the segment into 4 equal-size segments. The mark closest to 200 is the mark for 225.

34. Reasoning Explain how to locate 225 on the number line below.

35. Stretch Your Thinking In a tug-of-war game, four sixth graders can tug as hard as five fifth graders. Two fifth graders and one sixth grader can tug as hard as one dog. One dog and three fifth graders compete against four sixth graders. Who will win? **The dog and the three fifth graders will win.**

Test Prep

Multiple Choice

36. Which statement is NOT true? **C**
  A. $-9 < -7$ **B.** $-3 < 5$ **C.** $-5 > -3$ **D.** $-2 < 6$

37. When multiplied by $\frac{1}{3}$, which number has a product that is an integer? **G**
  F. 5   **G.** 6   **H.** 7   **I.** 8

Take It to the NET
Online lesson quiz at
www.PHSchool.com
Web Code: aaa-1001

38. Order -2, 4, 0, and -6 from least to greatest. **D**
  A. 4, 0, -2, -6 **B.** -6, 4, 0, -2 **C.** 0, -2, 4, -6 **D.** -6, -2, 0, 4

Short Response

39. Write three numbers that are between -4 and -6. Are all of these numbers integers? Explain. **See margin.**

Mixed Review

Lesson 9-4   **Find the area of each parallelogram.**

40.
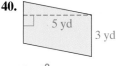
5 yd / 3 yd
15 yd²

41.
6 km / 9 km
54 km²

42.

6.5 m / 4 m
26 m²

Lesson 7-4   **Use the data in the table at the right.**

43. Which waterfall has the greatest height? the least height?
Angel Falls; Dudhsagar Falls

44. Which waterfalls are between 2,000 feet and 2,500 feet?
Piemans Falls and Yosemite Falls

Height of Waterfalls

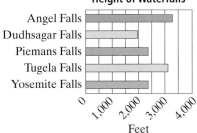

---

39. **[2] Answers may vary.**
Sample: $-5\frac{1}{2}$, -5, $-4\frac{2}{3}$;
$-5\frac{1}{2}$ and $-4\frac{2}{3}$ are not integers because they are not opposites of whole numbers; -5 is an integer because it is the opposite of a whole number.
[1] correct answer with no explanation

Enrichment 10-1   Using a Number Line
Critical Thinking

Is the deepest point in the ocean further from sea level than the top of the highest mountain in the world?

Use the table of highest and lowest points on land and in the ocean to answer this question as well as the other exercises that follow. Distances are measured from sea level.

ELEVATION

Mountain	Location	Meters		Name	Ocean	Meters
Kilimanjaro	Africa	5,995		Java Trench	Indian Ocean	$-7,125$
Aconcagua	South America	6,960		Challenger Deep	Pacific Ocean	$-10,924$
Everest	Asia	8,850		Puerto Rico Trench	Atlantic Ocean	$-8,648$
McKinley	North America	6,194		Eurasia Basin	Artic Ocean	$-5,450$
Vinson Massif	Antarctica	4,897				
Elbrus	Europe	5,640				

1. Where is the deepest point in the ocean? What is the elevation?
Challenger Deep, Pacific Ocean; $-10,924$ meters below sea level

2. Where is the highest mountain in the world? What is the elevation?
Mt. Everest, Asia; 8,850 meters above sea level

3. If you made a number line and plotted the elevations in the table, what would 0 represent? What would the points to the left of 0 represent? What would the points to the right of 0 represent?
0 would represent sea level; the points to the left of 0 would represent below sea level; the points to the right of 0 would represent above sea level.

4. Which is further from sea level, the elevation of the deepest point in the ocean or the elevation of the top of the highest mountain? Explain.
the deepest point in the ocean since $-10,924$ meters is further from zero on a number line than 8,850 meters.

5. If Mt. Kilimanjaro was placed in the Java Trench in the Indian Ocean, would the top of its peak be under water or above water? Explain.
The trench is 7,125 meters deep and the mountain is 5,995 meters tall. All of Mt. Kilimanjaro would be covered.

Modeling Addition of Integers

Students use models to add integers with like signs and with different signs.

Optional Materials

• counters in two colors

Resources

Student Manipulatives Kit

Teaching Notes

Teaching Tip
To prepare students for adding integers, write pairs of integers on the board. Have students identify the one that is farther from zero.

Have students work in pairs to model the additions. Choose one color for positive integers and the second for negative integers. One student can lay out the positive counters and the other, the negative counters. Ask: *Why does removing a zero pair leave a sum unchanged?* **Zero is the identity element for addition; adding zero will not change the sum.**

English Learners
Make sure students understand the phrase *zero pair*. Use plain language to communicate that a zero pair represents a sum of 0.

 Investigation **Modeling Addition of Integers**

Activity

1. Find 5 + 2.   Show 5 "+" chips.   There are 7 "+" chips.
Then add 2 "+" chips.   So, 5 + 2 = 7.

2. Find −5 + (−2).   Show 5 "−" chips.   There are 7 "−" chips.
Then add 2 "−" chips.   So, −5 + (−2) = −7.

To add integers with different signs, use zero pairs. These chips ⊕ ⊖ are a *zero pair* because ⊕ + ⊖ = 0. Removing a zero pair does not change the sum.

3. Find 5 + (−2).   Show 5 "+" chips.   Pair the "+" and "−" chips.   There are 3 "+" chips left.
Then add 2 "−" chips.   Remove the pairs.   So, 5 + (−2) = 3.

4. Find −5 + 2.   Show 5 "−" chips.   Pair "+" and "−" chips.   There are 3 "−" chips left.
Then add 2 "+" chips.   Remove the pairs.   So, −5 + 2 = −3.

EXERCISES

Use chips or mental math to help you add the following integers.

1. 4 + 5 9

2. 6 + (−3) 3

3. −2 + (−3) −5

4. −2 + 2 0

5. 13 + (−8) 5

6. −4 + 3 −1

7. −7 + (−2) −9

8. 8 + (−11) −3

9. Write a rule for adding each of the following: (a) two positive integers, (b) two negative integers, and (c) two integers with different signs.
9a–c. Answers may vary. See margin for samples.

9a. To add two positive integers, add their absolute values. The result is the desired sum.

b. To add two negative integers, add their absolute values. The opposite of the result is the desired sum.

c. To add two integers with different signs, find the difference of the absolute values. Use the sign of the number with the greater absolute value. If the absolute values are equal, the sum is zero.

10-2 Adding Integers

What You'll Learn

OBJECTIVE 1 To add integers with the same signs

OBJECTIVE 2 To add integers with different signs

. . . And Why

To determine the result of a contest, as in Example 5

 **Check Skills You'll Need**   For help, go to Lesson 10-1.

Find each absolute value.

1. $|-15|$ 15   **2.** $|-12|$ 12   **3.** $|-8|$ 8   **4.** $|8|$ 8

5. Is the absolute value of a negative number always less than the absolute value of a positive number? Explain your reasoning. Answers may vary. Sample: No; absolute value is the distance the number is from zero on a number line.

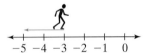 Interactive lesson includes instant self-check, tutorials, and activities.

Lesson Preview

 Check Skills You'll Need

Finding Absolute Values
Lesson 10-1: Example 3. Extra Practice p. 651.

Lesson Resources

Teaching Resources
Practice, Reteaching, Enrichment

Reaching All Students
Practice Workbook 10-2
Spanish Practice Workbook 10-2
Guided Problem Solving 10-2
Hands-On Activities 39

Presentation Assistant Plus!
Transparencies
• Check Skills You'll Need 10-2
• Problem of the Day 10-2
• Additional Examples 10-2
• Student Edition Answers 10-2
• Lesson Quiz 10-2
• Classroom Aid 7, 37
PH Presentation Pro CD-ROM 10-2

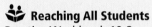 **ASSESSMENT SYSTEM**

Computer Test Generator CD

Technology
Resource Pro® CD-ROM
Computer Test Generator CD
PH Presentation Pro CD-ROM

www.PHSchool.com
Student Site
• Teacher Web Code: aak-5500
• Algebra Readiness Puzzles 10, 39
• Self-grading Lesson Quiz

PH SuccessNet Teacher Center
• Lesson Planner
• Resources

Plus

OBJECTIVE

1 Adding Integers With the Same Signs

You can use a number line to model the addition of integers. You start at 0, facing the positive direction. You move forward for a positive integer or backward for a negative integer. Here is how to find $3 + 2$.

Start at 0. Face the positive direction. Move forward 3 units for 3.

Then move forward 2 more units for 2. You stop at 5.

So, $3 + 2 = 5$. Notice that the sum of two positive integers is positive.

1 EXAMPLE Using a Number Line

Find $-3 + (-2)$.

Reading Math
Parentheses are used in $-3 + (-2)$ to show that a negative number is being added.

Start at 0. Face the positive direction. Move backward 3 units for -3.

Then move backward 2 more units for -2. You stop at -5.

So, $-3 + (-2) = -5$.

 Check Understanding 1 Find each sum. Use a number line.
  a. $-1 + (-3)$ −4   **b.** $2 + 10$ 12   **c.** $(-5) + (-4)$ −9
  d. Number Sense The sum of two negative integers is __?__. negative

 Ongoing Assessment and Intervention

Before the Lesson	During the Lesson	After the Lesson
Diagnose prerequisite skills using:	Monitor progress using:	Assess knowledge using:
• Check Skills You'll Need	• Check Understanding • Additional Examples • Test Prep	• Lesson Quiz • Computer Test Generator CD

Math Background

The addition of integers can be modeled as a series of moves on a number line with zero as the starting point. Positive numbers are shown as moves to the right. Negative numbers are shown as moves to the left. The ending point of the last move indicates the sum.

Positive and negative integers are often called *signed* numbers. A pair of numbers that are both positive or both negative have the *same sign*. When adding numbers with the same sign, every move on a number line is in the same direction. So, the sum of positive numbers is always positive and the sum of negative numbers is always negative.

The sum of numbers with *different signs*, such as a positive number and a negative number, can be positive, negative, or 0. When adding two numbers with different signs, the sum has the sign of the integer with the greater absolute value.

Teaching Notes

① EXAMPLE Tactile Learners

Tactile learners may benefit from actually walking the number line. Use the squares indicated by classroom tiles or mark a number line with tape or chalk on the floor. Have students "walk" the additions.

Error Prevention!

Point out that bars are used for absolute value and parentheses are used to show a negative number. Make sure students are not confusing these signs.

Inclusion

Students can usually understand that going "forward" on a number line means that integers are increasing in value and that going "backward" means that integers are decreasing in value. Emphasize, however, that students must start at 0 and face forward, or the positive direction.

498

Key Concepts **Adding Integers With the Same Sign**

The sum of two positive integers is positive. The sum of two negative integers is negative.

Examples: $2 + 3 = 5$ $-2 + (-3) = -5$

---

② EXAMPLE Adding Integers With the Same Sign

Find each sum.

a. $9 + 18$

$9 + 18 = 27$
↑
The sum of two positive integers is positive.

b. $-3 + (-7)$

$-3 + (-7) = -10$
↑
The sum of two negative integers is negative.

✓ **Check Understanding** ② Find each sum. **a.** $7 + 9$ **16** **b.** $-9 + (-12)$ **−21**

OBJECTIVE

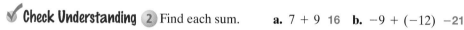

2 Adding Integers With Different Signs

You can also use a number line to model the addition of integers with different signs. Here is how to find $3 + (-2)$.

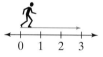 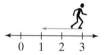

Start at 0, and face the positive direction. Move forward 3 units for 3.

Then move backward 2 units for −2. You stop at 1.

So, $3 + (-2) = 1$.

---

③ EXAMPLE Using a Number Line

Find $-3 + 2$. Use a number line.

Start at 0, and face the positive direction. Move backward 3 units for −3.

Then move forward 2 units for 2. You stop at −1.

So, $-3 + 2 = -1$.

✓ **Check Understanding** ③ Use a number line to find each sum. **a.** $4 + (-1)$ **3** **b.** $-1 + 4$ **3**

 Reaching All Students

Below Level Give students addition problems and have them use a number line to find each sum.	**Advanced Learners** Students write two expressions whose sum is −8. They use two negative integers for one expression, and a positive and a negative integer for the other.	**Inclusion** See note on page 498.
$5 + 2$ **7** $5 + (-2)$ **3** $-5 + (-2)$ **−7** $-5 + 2$ **−3**	Sample: $-2 + (-6)$; $4 + (-12)$	**Alternative Method** See note on page 499.

Consider the following:

$$3 - 2 = 1 \rightarrow 3 + (-2) = 1$$
$$4 - 1 = 3 \rightarrow 4 + (-1) = 3$$

As you can see, adding integers with different signs is related to subtraction.

Reading Math

Positive 3 can be written as +3 or 3. In either case, its sign is positive. Zero has no sign.

Key Concepts   Adding Integers With Different Signs

To add integers with different signs, first find the absolute value of each integer. Then, subtract the lesser absolute value from the greater. The sum has the sign of the integer with the greater absolute value.

Examples: $2 + (-3) = -1$ $-2 + 3 = 1$

4 EXAMPLE   Adding Integers With Different Signs

a. Find $8 + (-5)$.

$$|8| = 8$$
$$|-5| = 5$$
$$8 - 5 = 3$$
$$8 + (-5) = 3$$

← Find the absolute values of the integers. →

← Subtract the absolute values. →

← The sum has the sign of the integer with the greater absolute value. →

b. Find $-9 + 6$.

$$|-9| = 9$$
$$|6| = 6$$
$$9 - 6 = 3$$
$$-9 + 6 = -3$$

✔ **Check Understanding** 4 Find each sum.

a. $7 + (-10)$ −3   **b.** $-11 + 4$ −7   **c.** $12 + (-3)$ 9

d. Number Sense How can you tell whether a sum will be positive or negative before adding? If the integer with the greatest absolute value is negative, then the sum will be negative.

5 EXAMPLE   Real-World Problem Solving

Real-World Connection

The world record for a frog jumping three times is 21 feet $5\frac{3}{4}$ inches.

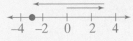

Frog-Jumping Contest Suppose you enter your frog in a jumping contest. The judge records each jump. A jump toward the finish line is a positive number. A jump away from the finish line is a negative number.

Your frog jumps 4 feet toward the finish line. Then he jumps 6 feet away. What is the result of these jumps?

$$|4| = 4 \text{ and } |-6| = 6$$ ← Find the absolute value of each integer.
$$6 - 4 = 2$$ ← Subtract the absolute values.
$$4 + (-6) = -2.$$ ← Since −6 has the greater absolute value, the sum is negative.

The result of the frog's jumps is −2 feet.

✔ **Check Understanding** 5 **Reasoning** What would have been the result if the frog jumped 4 feet away from the finish line and then 6 feet toward it? 2 ft

3 EXAMPLE Alternative Method

Model $3 + (-2)$ with small objects like pencils. Remind students that adding a negative number is like "taking away." Remove two of the objects to illustrate the problem.

Additional Examples

1 Use a number line to find each sum.
   a. 5 + 2 7

   b. −3 + (−5) −8

2 Find each sum.
   a. 9 + 9 18
   b. −6 + (−10) −16

3 Use a number line to find each sum.
   a. −4 + 7 3

   b. 3 + (−6) −3

4 Find each sum.
   a. 8 + (−10) −2
   b. −4 + 16 12

5 A painter is painting a tall building. She climbs up 26 rungs of a ladder. Then she climbs down 14 rungs. What is her current position? 26 + (−14) = 12; She is on the 12th rung.

Closure

• Explain how to add integers with the same sign. Sample: Add the integers. The sum of two positive integers is positive. The sum of two negative integers is negative.

• Explain how to add integers with different signs. Sample: First find the absolute value of each integer. Then subtract the lesser absolute value from the greater. The sum has the sign of the integer with the greater absolute value.

3. Practice

Assignment Guide

1 Objective 1
  Ⓐ Ⓑ Core 1–12, 34

2 Objective 2
  Ⓐ Ⓑ Core 13–26, 27–33, 35–37
  Ⓒ Extension 38–39

Test Prep 40–43
Mixed Review 44–48

Exercises 1–24 Have students decide whether each sum will be positive or negative before adding.

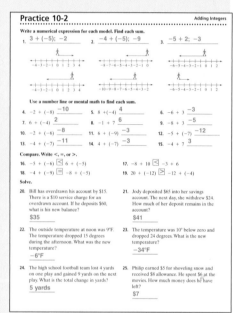

Ⓐ **Practice by Example**

Use a number line to find each sum.

Example 1
(page 497)

1. $3 + 7$ 10
2. $-8 + (-1)$ −9
3. $-7 + (-7)$ −14
4. $-3 + (-5)$ −8
5. $6 + 5$ 11
6. $-4 + (-4)$ −8

Example 2
(page 498)

Find each sum.

7. $-31 + (-16)$ −47
8. $-12 + (-9)$ −21
9. $13 + 29$ 42
10. $91 + 28$ 119
11. $-47 + (-41)$ −88
12. $-51 + (-9)$ −60

Example 3
(page 498)

Use a number line to find each sum.

13. $-5 + 9$ 4
14. $-8 + 3$ −5
15. $7 + (-7)$ 0
16. $6 + (-4)$ 2
17. $-3 + 5$ 2
18. $8 + (-1)$ 7

Example 4
(page 499)

Find each sum.

19. $16 + (-5)$ 11
20. $-48 + 78$ 30
21. $89 + (-176)$ −87
22. $23 + (-15)$ 8
23. $-8 + 72$ 64
24. $18 + (-39)$ −21

Example 5
(page 499)

25. A submarine is 64 feet below sea level. The submarine then rises 19 feet. What integer describes the position of the submarine? −45

 26. Football A football team gains 6 yards on one play. On the next play, the team loses 11 yards. What is the result of these two plays?
5-yd loss

Ⓑ **Apply Your Skills**

Find each sum.

27. $-6 + (-11) + 7$ −10
28. $(-8) + 12 + (-5)$ −1
29. $8 + (-1) + (-6)$ 1
30. $-2 + 6 + (-3)$ 1

31. Open-Ended Write an addition exercise involving a positive integer and a negative integer with each type of sum. 31a–c. Answers may vary.
  a. negative
    $17 + (-19) = -2$
  b. zero
    $13 + (-13) = 0$
  c. positive
    $-40 + 60 = 20$

32. Data File, p. 489 What is the lowest recorded temperature in Florida if it is 127°F warmer than the record low in Antarctica? −2°F

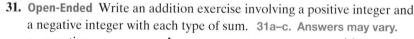

Real-World Connection

The John Hancock Tower in Boston has 60 floors.

 33. Office Buildings Suppose the mail center of the Hancock Tower is on the 15th floor. A clerk delivers mail by going up 5 floors, down 3 floors, and then down another 4 floors. Where is the clerk in relation to the mail center? $15 + 5 + (-3) + (-4) = 13$; 2 floors below the mail center

500 Chapter 10 Integers

GPS Use the Guided Problem Solving worksheet with Exercise 37.

Compare. Write <, =, or >.

34. $-7 + (-3)$ ▊ $7 + 3$
<

35. $5 + (-5)$ ▊ $-1 + 1$
=

36. <u>Writing in Math</u> Explain how to find the sum of -41 and 48. **See margin.**

37. Temperature At 7:30 A.M. on January 22, 1943, the temperature was $-4°F$ in Spearfish, South Dakota. At 7:32 A.M. the temperature had risen an amazing 49 degrees! What was the temperature then? **45°F**

C **Challenge**

38. Puzzles Copy the square at the right. Place the integers $-4, -3, -2, -1, 0, 1, 2, 3,$ and 4 in the boxes so that the vertical, horizontal, and diagonal sums are 0.
Placement of numbers may vary. Sample:

3	−4	1
−2	0	2
−1	4	−3

39. Stretch Your Thinking A four-digit number is a multiple of 9. The first two digits are the same and the last two digits are 58. What is the number? **7,758**

Test Prep

Multiple Choice

40. Which expression has a sum of -8? **B**

   A. $-12 + (-4)$ **B.** $-11 + 3$ **C.** $-5 + 3$ **D.** $9 + (-1)$

41. Which expresson does NOT have a sum of -3? **I**

   F. $-4 + 1$ **G.** $-2 + (-1)$ **H.** $7 + (-10)$ **I.** $6 + (-3)$

Take It to the NET
Online lesson quiz at
www.PHSchool.com
Web Code: aaa-1002

42. At 6:00 A.M., the temperature was $-10°F$. Four hours later the temperature had risen 21 degrees. What was the temperature then?

   A. $-31°F$ **B.** $-11°F$ **C.** $11°F$ **D.** $31°F$ **C**

Short Response

43. The top of a mountain is 425 feet above sea level. The base of the mountain is 654 feet below sea level. What is the height of the mountain? Include a diagram that supports your answer. **[2] 1,079 ft; Diagrams may vary. See margin for sample. [1] correct answer with no diagram**

Mixed Review

Lesson 9-5

Name each of the following for circle J at the right.

44. radii
$\overline{JC}, \overline{JD}, \overline{JE}, \overline{JF}, \overline{JG}, \overline{JH}$

45. diameters
$\overline{CF}, \overline{DG}, \overline{EH}$

46. chords
$\overline{CD}, \overline{DE}, \overline{EF}, \overline{FG}, \overline{GH}, \overline{HC},$
$\overline{CF}, \overline{DG}, \overline{EH}$

47. the center
J

Lesson 9-4

48. Find the area of a triangle with a base of 12 cm and a height of 6 cm. **36 cm²**

---

36. Answers may vary. Sample: First find the absolute value of each integer. The absolute value of -41 is 41 and of 48 is 48. Then find the difference of the absolute values. The difference of the absolute values is 7. The sum has the sign of 48.

43.

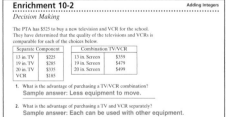

425 ft
1,079 ft
Sea Level
654 ft

PowerPoint Lesson Quiz 10-2

Find each sum.

1. $-9 + (-5)$ **−14**

2. $8 + (-7)$ **1**

3. $-12 + 5$ **−7**

4. $48 + (-22)$ **26**

Alternative Assessment

Provide student pairs with counters or integer chips. Have partners take turns using the integer chips to model the additions in Exercises 1–24. On partner models the addition; the other partner records the sum.

Test Prep

Resources

For additional practice with a variety of test item formats:
• Test-Prep, p. 541
• Test-Taking Strategies, p. 537
• Test-Taking Strategies With Transparencies

Modeling Subtraction of Integers

Students use models to subtract integers.

Optional Materials

• counters in two colors

Resources

Student Manipulatives Kit

Teaching Notes

Teaching Tip
Remind students about the meaning of *zero pair*. Ask: *When you subtract an integer from an integer with a different sign, what counters must you add to your model?* You must add a zero pair—the same number of positive and negative counters as the absolute value of the number you are subtracting.

Tactile Learners
Invite students to model the subtraction of positive and negative integers. For instance, to show −5 − (−2), give 5 students one sheet of colored paper each and have them stand in the front of the room. Ask 2 students to sit down on the floor to represent subtracting −2. Students can see that −5 − (−2) is −3.

Alternative Method
Students place a marker on a number line to represent an integer from which another integer is being subtracted. Discuss that a move representing subtraction of a positive integer is to the left. A move representing subtraction of a negative integer is to the right. The number of spaces moved is equal to the absolute value of the integer being subtracted. Guide students to compare this subtraction method with the number-line method they used to add integers.

 Investigation **Modeling Subtraction of Integers**

For Use With Lesson 10-3

● **Activity**

1. Find 5 − 2.   Show 5 "+" chips.   Take away 2 "+" chips.   There are 3 "+" chips. So, 5 − 2 = 3.

2. Find −5 − (−2). Show 5 "−" chips.   Take away 2 "−" chips.   There are 3 "−" chips. So, −5 − (−2) = −3.

Remember that ⊕ and ⊖ are a zero pair. Sometimes you need to insert zero pairs in order to subtract.

3. Find 5 − (−2).   Show 5 "+" chips.   Insert two zero pairs. Then take away 2 "−" chips.   There are 7 "+" chips left. So, 5 − (−2) = 7.

4. Find −5 − 2.   Show 5 "−" chips.   Insert two zero pairs. Then take away 2 "+" chips.   There are 7 "−" chips left. So, −5 − 2 = −7.

 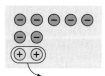

EXERCISES

Use chips or mental math to help you subtract the following integers.

1. 8 − 6 2	**2.** −4 − (−3) −1	**3.** 5 − 8 −3	**4.** −3 − 7 −10
5. −6 − 2 −8	**6.** 5 − (−9) 14	**7.** −8 − (−13) 5	**8.** −5 − (−8) 3

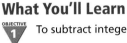

Subtracting Integers

What You'll Learn

 OBJECTIVE 1 To subtract integers

OBJECTIVE 2 To solve equations with integers

. . . And Why

To find a change in depth, as in Example 3

 Check Skills You'll Need

For help, go to Lesson 2-6.

Solve each equation.

1. $a + 15 = 32$ 17
2. $b + 13 = 44$ 31
3. $c + 16 = 23$ 7
4. $d + 88 = 88$ 0
5. $105 + e = 263$ 158
6. $f + 315 = 495$ 180

7. Estimate the value of x if $x + 26.8 = 65$. about 38

Lesson Preview

Check Skills You'll Need

Solving Equations by Subtracting
Lesson 2-6: Example 1. Extra Practice p. 643.

Lesson Resources

Teaching Resources
Practice, Reteaching, Enrichment

Reaching All Students
Practice Workbook 10-3
Spanish Practice Workbook 10-3
Guided Problem Solving 10-3
Hands-On Activities 39

Presentation Assistant Plus!
Transparencies
• Check Skills You'll Need 10-3
• Problem of the Day 10-3
• Additional Examples 10-3
• Student Edition Answers 10-3
• Lesson Quiz 10-3
• Classroom Aid 7, 37
PH Presentation Pro CD-ROM 10-3

PRENTICE HALL ASSESSMENT SYSTEM

Computer Test Generator CD

Technology
Resource Pro® CD-ROM
Computer Test Generator CD
PH Presentation Pro CD-ROM

www.PHSchool.com
Student Site
• Teacher Web Code: aak-5500
• Self-grading Lesson Quiz

PH SuccessNet Teacher Center
• Lesson Planner
• Resources

Plus *i*TEXT

OBJECTIVE 1 Subtracting Integers

On a number line, the subtraction operation tells you to turn around and face the negative direction. Here is how to find $3 - 2$ using a number line.

  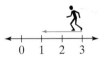

Start at 0. Face the positive direction. Move forward 3 units for 3.

The subtraction sign tells you to turn around.

Then move forward 2 units for 2. You stop at 1.

So, $3 - 2 = 1$.

Reading Math

$3 - (-2)$ is read "3 minus negative 2."

1 EXAMPLE Using a Number Line to Subtract Integers

Find $3 - (-2)$.

 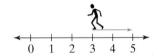

Start at 0. Face the positive direction. Move forward 3 units for 3.

For subtraction, turn around. Then move backward 2 units for −2. You stop at 5.

So, $3 - (-2) = 5$.

Check Understanding **1** Use a number line for each subtraction.
a. $4 - 1$ 3
b. $4 - (-1)$ 5
c. $3 - (-5)$ 8
d. Number Sense What seems to happen when you subtract a negative? It is the same as adding the opposite.

 Ongoing Assessment and Intervention

Before the Lesson
Diagnose prerequisite skills using:
• Check Skills You'll Need

During the Lesson
Monitor progress using:
• Check Understanding
• Additional Examples
• Test Prep

After the Lesson
Assess knowledge using:
• Lesson Quiz
• Computer Test Generator CD

Math Background

The subtraction of integers can be modeled on a number line. Zero is the starting point and the ending point of the last move indicates the difference. Positive numbers are shown as moves to the right. Negative numbers are shown as moves to the left. A subtraction operation changes the direction of movement for the number that follows it. This change of direction represents how you subtract an integer by adding its opposite.

Teaching Notes

Tactile Learners

Students may better understand the concept of subtracting integers if they "walk" the number line. Use squares on the floor or a number line made of tape or chalk. As a volunteer reads the steps for 3 − 2, students can model the subtraction by walking the number line.

Auditory Learners

Auditory learners may benefit from "talking out" the examples in the *Key Concepts* section. Model 10 − 6 for students: "I start at 0 and face the positive direction. I walk forward ten steps. I then turn around and walk 6 steps in the other direction. I stop at 4. So 10 − 6 is 4." Have students "talk out" the other examples. Remind students that they can quietly talk through problems when they work on their own.

Visual Learners

Use arrows to help students visualize the changes.

$$10 \quad - \quad 6$$
$$\downarrow \qquad \downarrow$$
$$10 \quad + \quad (-6)$$

Teaching Tip

Have students practice rewriting subtraction problems as addition problems.

$$6 - 2 \quad 6 + (-2)$$
$$-4 - 3 \quad -4 + (-3)$$
$$-2 - (-4) \quad -2 + 4$$
$$-6 - 6 \quad -6 + (-6)$$

There are similarities between addition and subtraction sentences.

$$3 + (-2) = 1 \quad \rightarrow \quad 3 - 2 = 1$$

Subtracting an integer gives the same result as adding its opposite.

> **Key Concepts** | **Subtracting Integers**
>
> You subtract an integer by adding its opposite.
>
> **Examples:**
>
> $10 - 6 = 10 + (-6)$ $\qquad$ $10 - (-6) = 10 + 6$
>
> $-10 - 6 = -10 + (-6)$ $\qquad$ $-10 - (-6) = -10 + 6$

② EXAMPLE   Subtracting Integers

Need Help?
For help adding integers, go to Lesson 10-2.

a. Find $-10 - (-4)$.

$$-10 - (-4) = -10 + 4 \quad \leftarrow \text{To subtract } -4, \text{ add its opposite, } 4.$$
$$= -6 \qquad \leftarrow \text{Simplify.}$$

b. Find $-2 - 7$.

$$-2 - 7 = -2 + (-7) \quad \leftarrow \text{To subtract } 7, \text{ add its opposite, } -7.$$
$$= -9 \qquad \leftarrow \text{Simplify.}$$

✔ **Check Understanding** ② Find each difference.

a. $9 - (-3)$ **12** $\qquad$ **b.** $-6 - (-2)$ **−4** $\qquad$ **c.** $-3 - 5$ **−8**

d. Number Sense How can you tell that the difference of two numbers will be positive or negative without doing the computation? **See margin.**

③ EXAMPLE   Real-World 🌐 Problem Solving

Real-World 🌐 Connection

Alvin has a safe diving depth of about 13,000 feet.

Submarines The research submarine *Alvin* was 1,500 feet below sea level (−1,500). It then moved to 1,872 feet below sea level (−1,872). How many feet did *Alvin* descend?

Find $-1,872 - (-1,500)$.

$$-1,872 - (-1,500) = -1,872 + 1,500 \quad \leftarrow \begin{array}{l} \text{To subtract } -1,500, \\ \text{add its opposite.} \end{array}$$
$$= -372 \qquad \leftarrow \text{Simplify.}$$

Alvin is 372 feet farther below sea level.

✔ **Check Understanding** ③ Suppose *Alvin* moved from 1,872 feet below sea level to a position of 1,250 feet below sea level (−1,250). How many feet did it move? **622 ft**

👥 Reaching All Students

| **Below Level** Give students practice changing subtraction problems into addition problems as shown below. $\quad$ $5 - 3$ $5 + (-3)$ $\quad$ $-4 - 3$ $-4 + (-3)$ $\quad$ $6 - (-6)$ $6 + 6$ $\quad$ $-3 - (-4)$ $-3 + 4$ | **Advanced Learners** Dora received a check for $250, a check for $200, a bill for $80, and a bill for $122. The net result was $153. Did Dora have an additional check or a bill? For what amount? **a bill for $95** | **Inclusion** See notes on pages 505 and 506. **Visual Learners** See note on pages 504 and 505. |

OBJECTIVE

2 Solving Equations With Integers

You can solve addition and subtraction equations using integers. You can write either of the following to solve $t + 9 = 5$.

$$t + 9 = 5 \qquad \text{or} \qquad t + 9 - 9 = 5 - 9$$
$$\underline{ -9 \quad -9}$$

4 **EXAMPLE** **Solving Equations With Integers**

Solve each equation.

a. $t + 9 = 5$

$t + 9 - 9 = 5 - 9$ ← Subtract 9 from each side.

$t = 5 + (-9)$ ← To subtract 9, add its oppposite.

$t = -4$ ← Simplify.

b. $a - 7 = -12$

$a - 7 + 7 = -12 + 7$ ← Add 7 to each side.

$a = -5$ ← Simplify.

✔ **Check Understanding** **4** Solve each equation. **a.** $b + 14 = 8$ **−6** **b.** $c - 15 = -5$ **10**

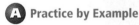

EXERCISES

❓ For more practice, see *Extra Practice*.

A Practice by Example

Use a number line. Find each difference.

Example 1
(page 503)

1. $6 - (-2)$ **8**   **2.** $5 - 3$ **2**   **3.** $-4 - (-1)$ **−3**

4. $-1 - (-1)$ **0**   **5.** $7 - (-2)$ **9**   **6.** $-4 - 3$ **−7**

Example 2
(page 504)

Find each difference.

7. $-9 - 7$ **−16**   **8.** $81 - 106$ **−25**   **9.** $12 - (-17)$ **29**

10. $43 - (-21)$ **64**   **11.** $-24 - (-12)$ **−12**   **12.** $-25 - (-57)$ **32**

Example 3
(page 504)

🌎 **13. Geography** The water level of the Dead Sea dropped from 1,280 feet below sea level in 1930 to 1,360 feet below sea level in 1999. Find the difference in the two readings. **80 ft**

🌎 **14. Bank Accounts** You have a balance of $13 in your bank account. You write a check for $17. What is the balance in your account? **−$4**

2d. If the first number is larger than the second number, the difference will be positive. The difference will be negative if either the second number is larger OR they are both negative and the second number has a smaller absolute value.

2 **EXAMPLE** **Error Prevention**

Students may confuse opposites with absolute values. Remind students that to subtract integers, they should add the opposite. Opposite integers can be positive or negative.

Inclusion

Help students understand that they must make two changes when rewriting a subtraction as an addition.
1) The minus sign is changed to a plus sign, and
2) the second number is changed to its opposite.

3 **EXAMPLE** **Visual Learners**

Have a volunteer draw a vertical number line on the board and label it with the given information.

Technology Tip

You might have students explore addition and subtraction of integers on their calculators. Help them to distinguish between the calculator's subtraction key and the opposite or negative sign .

PowerPoint
Additional Examples

1 Use a number line to find $4 - (-4)$. **8**

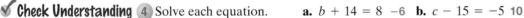

2 Find each difference.
a. $-5 - (-7)$ **2**
b. $-9 - 6$ **−15**

3 Juan owes his sister $14. She told him to subtract $8 of what he owes if he feeds the dog. Write an integer to show how much Juan will owe if he feeds the dog. **−6**

4 Solve each equation.
a. $x + 8 = 5$ **−3**
b. $y - 11 = -1$ **10**

Closure

What is the rule for subtracting integers? To subtract an integer, add its opposite.

505

Assignment Guide

1 Objective 1
Ⓐ Ⓑ Core 1–14, 21–29, 31–33, 36–40
Ⓒ Extension 41–44

2 Objective 2
Ⓐ Ⓑ Core 15–20, 30, 34–35
Ⓒ Extension 45

Test Prep 46–49
Mixed Review 50–55

Inclusion
Exercise 28 Make sure students understand time zones.

Example 4
(page 505)

Solve each equation.

15. $t + 12 = 9$ −3   **16.** $v − 6 = −4$ 2   **17.** $−3 + c = −8$ −5

18. $12 + r = −11$ −23   **19.** $w − 18 = −13$ 5   **20.** $s − 16 = −25$ −9

Ⓑ Apply Your Skills

Subtract.

21. $17 − 18$ −1   **22.** $55 − (−81)$ 136   **23.** $−18 − 13$ −43 — 12

24. $54 − (−81)$ 135   **25.** $23 − (−18)$ 41   **26.** $16 − 28 − (−38)$ 26

🌐 **27. Bank Accounts** You receive a $150 check, a $300 bill, a $250 bill, an $80 check, and a $105 check. By how much will your bank account change when you deposit the checks and pay the bills? −$215

🌐 **28. Time Zones** Greenwich, England is located on the 0° meridian, also called the prime meridian. Standard time all over the world is computed in relation to Greenwich Mean Time (GMT). The table at the right indicates the number of hours from the GMT for each city. Suppose it is 1:30 P.M. in Greenwich. Find the time for each city. **See margin.**

Cairo, Egypt	+2
Honolulu, Hawaii	−10
Lima, Peru	−5
London, England	0
Los Angeles, U.S.A.	−8
Paris, France	+1
Sydney, Australia	+10
Tokyo, Japan	+9
Washington, D.C., U.S.A.	−5

29. Writing in Math Explain how to find the difference $−15 − 26$. **See margin.**

Real-World 🌐 Connection

This home is divided by the prime meridian. The two sides of the house are in different time zones.

🌐 **30. Hiking** A hiker is at the top of Lost Mine Peak. The elevation of the peak is 6,850 feet. The beginning of the Lost Mine trail has an elevation of 5,600 feet. What is the trail's change in elevation? **1,250 ft**

Determine whether each statement is *always, sometimes,* or *never* true.

31. (positive integer) − (negative integer) = (negative integer)
never

32. (positive integer) − (positive integer) = (positive integer)
sometimes

33. (any positive integer) − (its opposite) = zero   never

🌐 **34. Entertainment** After the first round in a game show, a contestant has 250 points. At the end of the second round, the contestant has −300 points. How did the score change during the second round?
−550 points

🌐 **35. Golf** In golf, par represents an average score. Suppose you are 2 under par at the end of 9 holes. At the end of 18 holes, you are 5 under par. What was your score on the last 9 holes?
3 under par

GPS Use the Guided Problem Solving worksheet with Exercise 30.

28. Cairo, 3:30 PM; Honolulu, 3:30 AM; Lima, 8:30 AM; London, 1:30 PM; Los Angeles, 5:30 AM; Paris, 2:30 PM; Sydney, 11:30

PM; Tokyo, 10:30 PM; Washington, D.C., 8:30 AM

29. Answers may vary. Sample: Subtract an integer by adding its opposite. To subtract 26 from −15, add −26 to

−15. $−15 + (−26) = −41$.

---

36. Number Sense Is the subtraction of integers commutative? In other words, is $a - b$ equal to $b - a$ for all integer values of a and b? Explain. **See margin.**

37. Data File, p. 489 Find the difference between the record low and the record high temperatures. **265°F**

Need Help?
The range is the difference between the greatest and the least value in a set of data.

Find the range for each set of data.

38. $-3, 12, -6, -15, 8$ **27**

39. $25, 31, 20, 0, -3, -18$ **49**

40. $13, 29, -32, 8, 30, -19, -4, 3$ **62**

 Challenge

Compare using $<$, $=$, or $>$.

41. $|8 - (-2)| \; \overset{>}{\blacksquare} \; |8| - |-2|$

42. $|-4 + 8| \; \overset{<}{\blacksquare} \; |-4| + |8|$

43. $|-3 + (-1)| \; \overset{=}{\blacksquare} \; |-3| + |-1|$

44. Answers may vary. Sample: Yes; change the number being subtracted to the sum of the number before the subtraction and another integer. The first number minus the second number is zero, and zero minus the third number is the answer; check students' work.

44. Reasoning Suppose your friend says that she has discovered a new method that can be used to subtract integers. Below is the subtraction of $6 - 8$ using her method.

$$6 - 8 = 6 - (6 + 2) = (6 - 6) - 2 = 0 - 2 = -2$$

Is your friend's method correct? Explain her method in words. Test the method with other numbers.

45. Stretch Your Thinking Tomorrow will not be Monday or Friday. Today is not Tuesday or Wednesday. Yesterday was not Thursday or Sunday. What day was yesterday? **Friday**

Test Prep

Multiple Choice

46. Which expression does NOT have a difference of -5? **B**

A. $10 - 15$ **B.** $-2 - 7$ **C.** $-7 - (-2)$ **D.** $-4 - 1$

Take It to the NET
Online lesson quiz at
www.PHSchool.com
Web Code: aaa-1003

47. The low temperature for a city is $-8°F$. The high temperature on the same day is $12°F$. What is the range in temperatures for that day? **F**

F. $-20°F$ **G.** $-4°F$ **H.** $4°F$ **I.** $20°F$

48. You have $40 in your bank account. You deposit $12 and then later withdraw $23. How much money do you have in your account? **D**

A. $-$29   **B.** $-$5   **C.** $5   **D.** $29

Short Response

49. During a winter storm, the temperature fell to $7°F$ below zero. By noon, the temperature was $8°F$ above zero. **(a)** Explain how you would find the number of degrees the temperature rose. **(b)** Find how much the temperature rose. **See margin.**

36. No; answers may vary. Sample: $3 - 7 = -4$, $7 - 3 = 4$, $-4 \neq 4$.

49. [2] a. I would add the absolute values of both numbers; this will be the change in temperature.

b. The temperature rose $15°F$.

[1] incorrect result OR incorrect explanation

PowerPoint Lesson Quiz 10-3

Find each difference.

1. $3 - 6$ **−3**

2. $-7 - 8$ **−15**

3. $10 - (-4)$ **14**

4. $-9 - (-9)$ **0**

5. Solve $x + 7 = -5$. **−12**

Alternative Assessment

Provide student pairs with integer chips. Partners use the integer chips to model the subtractions in Exercises 1–12. One student models the exercise; the other students records the difference.

Test Prep

Resources
For additional practice with a variety of test item formats:
- Test-Prep, p. 541
- Test-Taking Strategies, p. 537
- Test-Taking Strategies With Transparencies

508

Lesson 8-1 **Name each of the following using the diagram at the right.**
50–52. Answers may vary.
50. three noncollinear points *A, D, E*

51. three rays $\overrightarrow{AB}, \overrightarrow{AD}, \overrightarrow{DE}$

52. three segments $\overline{AB}, \overline{AD}, \overline{DC}$

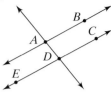

Lesson 7-6 **The spreadsheet gives the number of cars parked in two parking lots for a three-day county fair.**

53. Write a formula that will calculate the total cars parked in the two lots on Friday. **= B2 + C2**

54. Write a formula that will calculate the total cars parked in Lot X for the three days. **= B2 + B3 + B4**

55. Write a formula that will calculate the total cars parked in the two lots for the three days. **= B2 + B3 + B4 + C2 + C3 + C4**

	A	B	C	D
1	Day	Lot X (cars)	Lot Y (cars)	
2	Fri.	89	112	
3	Sat.	205	226	
4	Sun.	195	176	
5				

Practice Game
A Race to the End

What You'll Need
- game board
- two different-colored number cubes
- two different-colored place markers

How to Play
- Each of two players places his or her marker on 0.
- Designate one cube to represent positive integers and the other cube to represent negative integers.
- One player rolls the two number cubes.
- The player adds the integers shown on the cubes and then moves his or her marker the number of spaces and direction indicated by the sum.
- Players take turns rolling the number cubes and moving their markers.
- The first player who reaches or goes past either end of the board wins.

508 **Chapter 10** Integers

Multiplying Integers

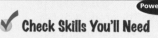
Algebra

1. Plan

Lesson Preview

✓ **Check Skills You'll Need** PowerPoint

Adding Integers With the Same Sign
Lesson 10-2: Example 2. Extra Practice p. 651.

Lesson Resources

📁 **Teaching Resources**
Practice, Reteaching, Enrichment

👥 **Reaching All Students**
Practice Workbook 10-4
Spanish Practice Workbook 10-4
Guided Problem Solving 10-4

⏱ **Presentation Assistant Plus!**
Transparencies
• Check Skills You'll Need 10-4
• Problem of the Day 10-4
• Additional Examples 10-4
• Student Edition Answers 10-4
• Lesson Quiz 10-4
• Classroom Aid 7
PH Presentation Pro CD-ROM 10-4

PRENTICE HALL
ASSESSMENT SYSTEM

Computer Test Generator CD

💻 **Technology**
Resource Pro® CD-ROM
Computer Test Generator CD
PH Presentation Pro CD-ROM

💻 **www.PHSchool.com**
Student Site
• Teacher Web Code: aak-5500
• Self-grading Lesson Quiz

PH SuccessNet Teacher Center
• Lesson Planner
• Resources

Plus iTEXT

What You'll Learn

OBJECTIVE 1 To multiply integers

. . . And Why

To find the change in stock prices, as in Example 3

✓ **Check Skills You'll Need** ❓ For help, go to Lesson 10-2.

Find each sum.

1. $-4 + (-4)$ **-8** **2.** $32 + 32$ **64**

3. $-14 + (-14)$ **-28** **4.** $-45 + (-45)$ **-90**

5. $81 + 81$ **162** **6.** $-23 + (-23)$ **-46**

OBJECTIVE 1

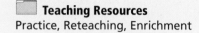 **Interactive lesson includes instant self-check, tutorials, and activities.**

Multiplying Integers

Recall that multiplication can be thought of as repeated addition. You can use a number line to multiply integers. Always start at 0.

3×2 means three groups of 2 each: $3 \times 2 = 6$.

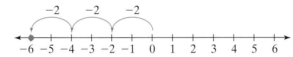

$3 \times (-2)$ means three groups of -2 each: $3 \times (-2) = -6$.

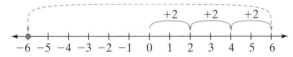

Recall that the integers 3 and -3 are opposites. You can think of -3×2 as the *opposite* of three groups of 2 each. Therefore, $-3 \times 2 = -6$.

You can think of $-3 \times (-2)$ as the *opposite* of three groups of -2 each. Since $3 \times (-2) = -6$, then $-3 \times (-2) = 6$.

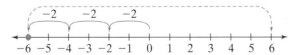

Real-World 🌐 Connection

Skydivers multiply time (positive) by their rate of descent (negative) to determine when to open their parachutes.

INSTANT CHECK

Ongoing Assessment and Intervention

Before the Lesson	**During the Lesson**	**After the Lesson**
Diagnose prerequisite skills using:	Monitor progress using:	Assess knowledge using:
• Check Skills You'll Need	• Check Understanding	• Lesson Quiz
	• Additional Examples	• Computer Test Generator CD
	• Test Prep	

Professional Development

Math Background

When two positive integers are multiplied, or when two negative integers are multiplied, the product is always a positive integer. The product of two integers with *different signs* is always *negative*.

Teaching Notes

2 EXAMPLE Inclusion

Have students predict what the sign of each product will be before they make any calculations.

3 EXAMPLE Diversity

Use plain language to explain that *stocks* are certificates of partial ownership that corporations sell to raise money for improvements. The value of the stock may go up, down, or stay the same.

Error Prevention!

Students might confuse the rules for multiplying integers with the rules for adding integers.

PowerPoint

Additional Examples

1 Use a number line to find $5 \times (-2)$. **−10**

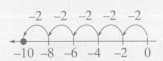

2 Find each product.

a. $-2 \times (-6)$ **12**

b. -7×2 **−14**

3 The value on a telephone calling card decreases 20¢ for each minute used. Write an integer to express the change in the card's value for a 4-minute call. **−80**

Closure

What are the rules for multiplying two integers? The product of two integers with the same sign is positive. The product of two integers with different signs is negative.

510

---

1 EXAMPLE **Using a Number Line to Multiply Integers**

Use a number line to find $4 \times (-3)$.

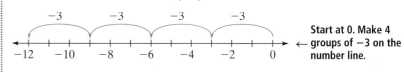

Start at 0. Make 4 ← groups of −3 on the number line.

The sum of 4 groups of −3 is −12. So, $4 \times (-3) = -12$.

✔ **Check Understanding 1** Use a number line to find each product.
a. $3 \times (-4)$ **−12**   **b.** $-3 \times (-4)$ **12**   **c.** -4×3 **−12**

To multiply integers without using a number line, remember the following rules.

Key Concepts	Multiplying Integers

The product of two integers with the *same* sign is positive.
The product of two integers with *different* signs is negative.

Examples: $4 \times 5 = 20$ $4 \times (-5) = -20$
    $-4 \times (-5) = 20$ $-4 \times 5 = -20$

2 EXAMPLE **Multiplying Integers**

a. Find $6 \times (-2)$.   **b.** Find $-5 \times (-2)$.

$6 \times (-2) = -12$ ← different signs, negative product $-5 \times (-2) = 10$ ← same signs, positive product

✔ **Check Understanding 2** Find each product.
a. -6×7 **−42**   **b.** $-9 \times (-3)$ **27**   **c.** $5 \times (-3)$ **−15**

3 EXAMPLE **Real-World**  **Problem Solving**

Stock Market A share of stock fell $2 in value each day for five days. Write an integer to express the change in the stock's value over the five days.

$(-2) \times 5 = -10$ ← Use a negative number to represent a stock losing value.

The amount, −$10, expresses the change in the stock's value.

✔ **Check Understanding 3** Over four hours, the temperature drops 5°F each hour. Write an integer to express the total drop in temperature.   **−20**

👥 Reaching All Students

Below Level Provide students with several exercises like these.	Advanced Learners Have students place the correct operational symbols in each equation:	English Learners See note on page 511.
5×3 15 -5×3 **−15** $-5 \times (-3)$ **15** $5 \times (-3)$ **−15**	$6 \; \overset{+}{\blacksquare} \; (-2) \; \overset{\times}{\blacksquare} \; 5 \; \overset{-}{\blacksquare} \; 12 \; \overset{÷}{\blacksquare} \; (-3) = 0$ $-14 \; \blacksquare \; 2 \; \blacksquare \; 6 \; \blacksquare \; 14 \; \blacksquare \; (-7) = -28$ $\underset{-}{} \quad \underset{\times}{} \quad \underset{+}{} \quad \underset{÷}{}$	**Inclusion** See note on page 510.

Here is a summary of how to determine the sign of the products of integers.

Multiplication of Integers

positive	×	positive	=	positive
negative	×	negative	=	positive
positive	×	negative	=	negative
negative	×	positive	=	negative

3. Practice

Assignment Guide

1 Objective 1
Ⓐ Ⓑ Core 1–23
Ⓒ Extension 24–26

Test Prep 27–30
Mixed Review 31–38

English Learners
Exercise 15 Make sure students know that *descend* indicates the balloon drops lower.

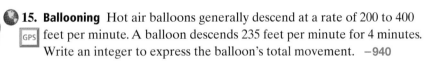

EXERCISES

 For more practice, see *Extra Practice*.

Ⓐ Practice by Example

Example 1
(page 510)

Use a number line to find each product.

1. 6 × 3 18   **2.** −4 × (−2) 8   **3.** 5 × (−2) −10   **4.** 2 × 7 14

Examples 2, 3
(page 510)

Find each product.

5. −3 × 5 −15   **6.** 11 × (−2) −22 **7.** 7 × 12 84   **8.** (−4) × 5
                                                                          −20

9. −6 × (−9)   **10.** 15 × (−4)   **11.** −25 × (−5)   **12.** −16 × 4
54   −60   125   −64

13. Suppose you want to withdraw $5 from your savings account each week for 4 weeks. What integer expresses the total change to your account?
−$20

Ⓑ Apply Your Skills

14. A temperature that is first recorded at −2°F falls three degrees per hour. What is the temperature at the end of four hours? −14°F

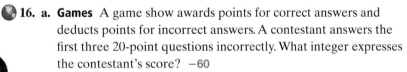

15. Ballooning Hot air balloons generally descend at a rate of 200 to 400 feet per minute. A balloon descends 235 feet per minute for 4 minutes. Write an integer to express the balloon's total movement. −940

16. a. Games A game show awards points for correct answers and deducts points for incorrect answers. A contestant answers the first three 20-point questions incorrectly. What integer expresses the contestant's score? −60

b. The contestant then gets the next four 10-point questions correct. Write an integer to express the final score. −20

17. Number Sense Is the product of three negative integers positive or negative? What is the product of four negative integers?
negative; positive

Find each product.

18. 5 × 22 × 2 220   **19.** 12 × (−12) × (−1)   **20.** 5 × (−8) × 4
                                     144   −160

21. −3 × (−4) × (−5)   **22.** −6 × 8 × (−2)   **23.** 7 × 3 × (−3)
−60   96   −63

10-4 Multiplying Integers **511**

GPS Use the Guided Problem Solving worksheet with Exercise 15.

Practice 10-4   Multiplying Integers

Use a number line to find each product.

1. 5 × 2	2. −4 × 3	3. 6 × (−2)	4. −3 × (−2)
10	−12	−12	6

Find each product.

5. 7 × 8	6. −5 × 7	7. 4 × (−8)	8. −8 × (−2)
56	−35	−32	16

9. 11 × (−6)	10. −7 × 6	11. −8 × (−8)	12. 10 × 4
−66	−42	64	40

13. 21 × 13	14. −15 × 12	15. −25 × (−14)	16. 10 × (−25)
273	−180	350	2250

Find the missing number.

17. 3 × _?_ = −6	18. 4 × _?_ = −4	19. _?_ × (−4) = −8
−2	−1	2

20. −3 × _?_ = 9	21. −9 × (−2) = _?_	22. _?_ × (−2) = −18
−3	18	9

23. Your teacher purchases 24 pastries for a class celebration, at $2 each. What integer expresses the amount he paid?
48

24. Temperatures have been falling steadily at 5°F each day. What integer expresses the change in temperature in degrees 7 days from today?
−35

25. A submarine starts at the surface of the Pacific Ocean and descends 60 feet every hour. What integer expresses the submarine's depth in feet after 6 hours?
−360

26. A skydiver falls at approximately 10 meters per second. Write a number sentence to express how many meters he will fall in 40 seconds.
−10 × 40; −400

Reteaching 10-4   Multiplying Integers

When two integers have like signs, the product will always be positive.

Both integers are positive: 3 × 4 = 12
Both integers are negative: −3 × (−4) = 12

When two integers have different signs, the product will always be negative.

One integer positive, one negative: 3 × (−4) = −12
One integer negative, one positive: −3 × 4 = −12

Example 1: Find −8 × 3.   *Example 2:* Find (−10) × (−20).

① Determine the product.   ① Determine the product.
  8 × 3 = 24   10 × 20 = 200

② Determine the sign of the product. Since   ② Determine the sign of the product. Since
  one integer is negative and one is positive,   both integers are negative, the product is
  the product is negative.   positive.

③ So, −8 × 3 = −24.   ③ So, (−10) × (−20) = 200.

Find each product.

1. 7 × (−4)	2. −5 × (−9)	3. −11 × 2
−28	45	−22

4. 8 × (−9)	5. 15 × (−3)	6. −7 × (−6)
−72	−45	42

7. −12 × 6	8. 13 × (−5)	9. −10 × (−2)
−72	−65	20

10. A dog lost 2 pounds three weeks in a row. What integer expresses the total change in the dog's weight? −6 pounds

Find each quotient.

11. 18 × (−6)	12. −35 × (−7)	13. −15 × 3
−108	245	−45

14. 28 × (−4)	15. 25 × (−5)	16. −27 × (−9)
−112	−125	243

17. −12 × 4	18. 33 × (−11)	19. −50 × (−2)
−48	−363	100

Lesson Quiz 10-4

Find each product.

1. -8×7 **−56**

2. $-7 \times (-3)$ **21**

3. $3 \times (-6)$ **−18**

4. $9 \times 5 \times (-2)$ **−90**

Alternative Assessment

Each student in a pair writes five integer multiplication problems. Students exchange papers and predict whether each product will be positive or negative. Partners then find each product.

Test Prep

Resources

For additional practice with a variety of test item formats:
• Test-Prep, p. 541
• Test-Taking Strategies, p. 537
• Test-Taking Strategies With Transparencies

  Challenge

24. Reasoning When you add a positive and negative integer, sometimes you get a positive result and sometimes you get a negative result. Is this true for multiplying a positive and negative integer? Explain. **See margin.**

25. Stretch Your Thinking Find the value of the expression below. Then change one of the operation symbols in the expression so that the new value is four times the original value. **10; $81 - 12 - 13 - 14 + 15 - 17$**
$= 40; 40 = 4 \times 10$

$$81 - 12 - 13 - 14 - 15 - 17$$

26. Copy and complete the pyramid at the right so that each number represents the product of the two numbers directly beneath it.

26.

−14,580			
−108	135		
12	−9	−15	
−4	−3	3	−5

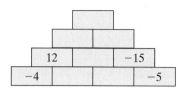

(pyramid: top; 12, −15; −4, , −5)

Test Prep

Multiple Choice

27. What is the product of -6 and -8? **D**
   A. -48 B. -14 C. 14 D. 48

Take It to the NET
Online lesson quiz at
www.PHSchool.com
Web Code: aaa-1004

28. Which expression does NOT have a value of -24? **G**
   F. -8×3 G. $-12 \times (-2)$ H. $6 \times (-4)$ I. $24 \times (-1)$

29. Which expression has the greatest product? **A**
   A. $-4 \times (-8)$ B. -2×25 C. $4 \times (-12)$ D. 6×5

Short Response

30. Suppose you spent $12 to go to a football game. Then you earned $6 each day for three days. **Answers may vary. See margin for sample.**
   a. Write an expression that represents this situation.
   b. Simplify your expression.

Mixed Review

Lesson 9-7   **Identify the three-dimensional figures.**

31.   **32.**   **33.**   **34.**

rectangular pyramid   cylinder   cone   triangular pyramid

Lesson 8-3   **Find the complement and the supplement of each angle.**

35. $50°$ **40°; 130°**   **36.** $19°$ **71°; 161°**   **37.** $67°$ **23°; 113°**   **38.** $81°$ **9°; 99°**

512   Chapter 10   Integers

---

24. Answers may vary.
Sample: No; multiplying
a positive and a negative
integer always results in
a negative integer.

30. Sample:
[2] a. $-12 + (3 \times 6)$

(OR equivalent
expression)

b. $-12 + (18) = 6$
(OR equivalent
stage)

[1] incorrect expression
OR incorrect
simplification

10-5 Dividing Integers

What You'll Learn

OBJECTIVE 1 To divide integers

OBJECTIVE 2 To solve equations

...And Why

To find an average rate of change, as in Example 3

 Check Skills You'll Need

? For help, go to Lesson 2-7.

Solve each equation.

1. $q \div 8 = 72$ **576**
2. $3r = 24$ **8**
3. $s \div 6 = 42$ **252**
4. $18x = 108$ **6**
5. $y \div 6 = 90$ **540**
6. $22z = 66$ **3**

Lesson Preview

 Check Skills You'll Need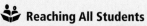

Solving by Multiplying or Dividing Equations
Lesson 2-7: Examples 1, 3. Extra Practice p. 643.

Lesson Resources

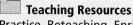

📁 **Teaching Resources**
Practice, Reteaching, Enrichment
Checkpoint Quiz 1

👥 **Reaching All Students**
Practice Workbook 10-5
Spanish Practice Workbook 10-5
Reading and Math Literacy 10B
Spanish Reading and Math
  Literacy 10B
Spanish Checkpoint Quiz 1
Guided Problem Solving 10-5
Technology Activities 16

⏱ **Presentation Assistant Plus!**
Transparencies
• Check Skills You'll Need 10-5
• Problem of the Day 10-5
• Additional Examples 10-5
• Student Edition Answers 10-5
• Lesson Quiz 10-5
PH Presentation Pro CD-ROM 10-5

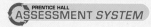

Checkpoint Quiz 1
Computer Test Generator CD

💻 **Technology**
Resource Pro® CD-ROM
Computer Test Generator CD
PH Presentation Pro CD-ROM

💻 **www.PHSchool.com**
Student Site
• Teacher Web Code: aak-5500
• Algebra Readiness Puzzles 97
• Self-grading Lesson Quiz

PH SuccessNet Teacher Center
• Lesson Planner
• Resources

Plus

OBJECTIVE 1
Dividing Integers

iTEXT Interactive lesson includes instant self-check, tutorials, and activities.

Investigation: Connecting Division to Multiplication

1. Copy and complete each of the following.

   a. $3 \times 4 = 12$
   $12 \div 4 = \blacksquare$ **3**
   $12 \div 3 = \blacksquare$ **4**

   b. $3 \times (-4) = -12$
   $-12 \div (-4) = \blacksquare$ **3**
   $-12 \div 3 = \blacksquare$ **-4**

   c. $-3 \times (-4) = 12$
   $12 \div (-4) = \blacksquare$ **-3**
   $12 \div (-3) = \blacksquare$ **-4**

2. What is the sign of the quotient of two numbers with the same sign? **positive**

3. What is the sign of the quotient of two numbers with different signs? **negative**

Since $4 \times 3 = 12$, we know that $12 \div 3 = 4$. So the rules for finding the sign of a quotient when dividing two integers are similar to the rules for finding a product when multiplying integers.

> **Key Concepts** **Dividing Integers**
>
> The quotient of two integers with the *same* sign is positive.
> The quotient of two integers with *different* signs is negative.
>
> **Examples:** $20 \div 4 = 5$ $20 \div (-4) = -5$
> $-20 \div (-4) = 5$ $-20 \div 4 = -5$

Ongoing Assessment and Intervention

Before the Lesson
Diagnose prerequisite skills using:
• Check Skills You'll Need

During the Lesson
Monitor progress using:
• Check Understanding
• Additional Examples
• Test Prep

After the Lesson
Assess knowledge using:
• Lesson Quiz
• Computer Test Generator CD
• Chapter Checkpoint 1 (p. 516)

Math Background

The rules for dividing integers are comparable to the rules for multiplying integers—the quotient of two integers with the same sign is positive and the quotient of two integers with different signs is negative. The rules for multiplying and dividing integers can be used to solve equations that have negative integers.

Teaching Notes

Investigation (Optional)
Have students explain why the sign of each product in i–iii is correct before they complete the division statements.

① EXAMPLE Teaching Tip

Ask: *How are the rules for multiplying integers different from the rules for dividing integers?* The rules are the same: same sign, positive result; different signs, negative result.

③ EXAMPLE Inclusion

You may want to point out that the fraction bar represents division. So $\frac{m}{5}$ is the same as $m \div 5$.

PowerPoint

📖 Additional Examples

① Find each quotient.

  a. $-33 \div (-3)$ **11**

  b. $24 \div (-6)$ **−4**

② Solve each equation.

  a. $\frac{x}{5} = -6$ **−30**

  b. $-8y = 24$ **−3**

③ In a 2-hour period, the wind speed decreased from 28 mph to 18 mph. If the speed decreased the same amount each hour, how much did the wind speed change each hour? **−5 mph each hour**

Closure

What are the rules for dividing two integers? Sample: The quotient of two integers with the same sign is positive. The quotient of two integers with different signs is negative.

514

---

① EXAMPLE Dividing Integers

  a. Find $-15 \div (-3)$.   **b.** Find $-24 \div 8$.

  $-15 \div (-3) = 5$ ← same signs, positive quotient $-24 \div 8 = -3$ ← different signs, negative quotient

✔ **Check Understanding** ① Find each quotient.   **a.** $-24 \div 6$ **−4** **b.** $-36 \div (-2)$ **18**

OBJECTIVE

② Solving Equations

You can solve multiplication and division equations with integers using the same methods you used to solve equations with whole numbers.

② EXAMPLE Solving Equations with Integers

  a. Solve $-3n = -18$.   **b.** Solve $\frac{m}{5} = -7$.

  $-3n = -18$ $\frac{m}{5} = -7$

  $\dfrac{-3n}{-3} = \dfrac{-18}{-3}$ ← Divide each side by −3. $5 \times \dfrac{m}{5} = 5 \times (-7)$ ← Multiply each side by 5.

  $n = 6$ ← Simplify. $m = -35$ ← Simplify.

✔ **Check Understanding** ② Solve each equation.   **a.** $-6z = 36$ **b.** $\frac{u}{7} = -4$

                                                      $z = -6$ $u = -28$

You can use division of integers to find an average rate of change.

③ EXAMPLE Real-World 🌐 Problem Solving

Weather The temperature changed from 0 degrees to -56 degrees over 4 hours. Find the average rate of change in degrees per hour.

Words	total change	divided by	number of hours	equals	average change per hour

Let r = the average rate of change in degrees per hour.

Equation	-56	$\div$	4	$=$	r

  $-56 \div 4 = r$

  $-14 = r$ ← Simplify.

FRIDAY FORECAST EARLY EVENING

Real-World 🌐 Connection

Careers Meteorologists analyze and predict changes in the weather.

The temperature changed at an average rate of -14 degrees per hour.

✔ **Check Understanding** ③ The value of a share of stock decreased \$20 over the last 5 days. Find the average rate of change in dollars per day. **−4**

👥 Reaching All Students

Below Level Provide students with several exercises like these.	**Advanced Learners** Have students solve multi-step integer equations such as shown.	**Inclusion** See note on page 514.
$10 \div 5$ **2** $-10 \div 5$ **−2** $-10 \div (-5)$ **2** $10 \div (-5)$ **−2**	$-4y - 6 = 50$ **−14** $-5x - 4 = -29$ **5** $-\frac{x}{2} + 3 = 13$ **−20**	**Error Prevention** See note on page 515.

A **Practice by Example**

Find each quotient.

Example 1
(page 514)

1. $18 \div 6$ 3   **2.** $-25 \div (-5)$ 5   **3.** $10 \div 2$ 5   **4.** $-15 \div 3$ −5

5. $-12 \div 4$ −3   **6.** $100 \div (-20)$ −5   **7.** $64 \div 8$ 8   **8.** $156 \div (-13)$ −12

Example 2
(page 514)

Solve each equation.

9. $-4y = -64$ 16

10. $\frac{s}{5} = -6$ −30

11. $7h = -84$ −12

12. $\frac{k}{3} = 12$ 36

Example 3
(page 514)

Find the average rate of change for each situation.

13. decreases \$15 over 5 days
−\$3/day

14. climbs 72 stairs in 4 minutes
18 stairs/min

15. sinks 160 feet in 20 seconds
−8 ft/s

16. loses 36 pounds over 12 weeks
−3 lb/week

17. Weather Over three hours, the temperature decreased 6 degrees. Find the average rate of change in degrees per hour. −2° per hour

B **Apply Your Skills**

Find the mean for each set of data.

18. $-4, -1, 0, 3, 7$ 1

19. $-12, -9, -2, 8, 15, 19$ 3.17

20. $-24, -13, -5, 10$ −8

21. $-8, -7, -5, -3, 3, 5, 7, 8$ 0

22. Stocks The value of a share of stock decreased \$30 over the last 5 days.
GPS Find the average rate of change in dollars per day.
−6

23. Scuba Diving Suppose a scuba diver is 100 feet below sea level. The diver rises to the surface at a rate of 25 feet per minute. Use integers to write an expression that represents the time it takes the diver to reach the surface. $100 - 25m$, m = minutes taken.

Simplify each expression.

30. Explanations may vary. Sample: It will be less than zero because the quotient of two numbers with different signs is always negative.

24. $14 + 63 \div (-7)$ 5

25. $(-10) \div 2 - 12$ −17
−9

26. $4 + (-2) \div (-1)$ 6

27. $3 + 5 \times (-2) - (-4) \div (-2)$

28. $28 - 14 \div (-2)$ 35

29. $6 \times (-3) + 4 \div (-2)$ −20

30. Writing in Math Explain how you know without computing that the quotient $-400 \div 25$ is greater than or less than 0. See above left.

GPS Use the Guided Problem Solving worksheet with Exercise 22.

Assignment Guide

1 **Objective 1**
Ⓐ Ⓑ Core 1–8, 18–21, 24–30
Ⓒ Extension 31–32

2 **Objective 2**
Ⓐ Ⓑ Core 9–17, 22–23

Test Prep 33–36
Mixed Review 37–41

Error Prevention!

Exercises 1–8 Have students predict what the sign of each quotient will be before calculating.

Practice 10-5 — Dividing Integers

Find each quotient.

1. $14 \div 7$ 2
2. $21 \div (-3)$ −7
3. $-15 \div 5$ −3
4. $-27 \div (-9)$ 3
5. $45 \div (-9)$ −5
6. $-42 \div 6$ −7
7. $-105 \div (-15)$ 7
8. $63 \div (-9)$ −7
9. $108 \div 6$ 18
10. $-204 \div 17$ −12
11. $240 \div (-15)$ −16
12. $-252 \div (-12)$ 21

Solve each equation.

13. $-6x = -24$ 4
14. $\frac{t}{4} = -32$ −128
15. $5m = 45$ 9
16. $3b = -27$ −9
17. $\frac{c}{2} = -17$ −34
18. $\frac{q}{4} = 4$ 16
19. $-15 = 3z$ −5
20. $-2x = 100$ −50
21. $-22 = \frac{m}{11}$ −242

Represent each rule of change with an integer.

22. spends \$300 in 5 days   −\$60 per day
23. runs 800 feet in 4 minutes   200 feet/minute
24. descends 45 yards in 15 sec   −3 feet/second
25. lose 26 ounces of baby fat in 13 months   −2 ounces/month
26. Juan's baseball card collection was worth \$800. Over the last 5 years, the collection decreased \$300 in value. What integer represents the average decrease in value each year?   −\$60 per year
27. Florence purchased stock for \$20 per share. After 6 days, the stock is worth \$32 per share. What integer represents the average increase in stock value each day?   \$2 per day
28. A freight train starts out at 0 miles per hour. After 15 miles the train is traveling 90 miles per hour. What integer represents the average increase in speed per mile?   6 mi/h per mile

Reteaching 10-5 — Dividing Integers

When two integers have like signs, the quotient will always be positive.
Both integers are positive: $8 \div 2 = 4$
Both integers are negative: $-8 \div (-2) = 4$

When two integers have different signs, the quotient will always be negative.
One integer positive, one negative: $8 \div (-2) = -4$
One integer negative, one positive: $-8 \div 4 = -2$

Example 1: Find $-24 \div 8$.
① Determine the quotient.
   $24 \div 8 = 3$
② Determine the sign of the quotient. Since one integer is negative and one is positive, the quotient is negative.
③ So, $-24 \div 8 = 3$.

Example 2: Find $35 \div (-7)$.
① Determine the quotient.
   $35 \div 7 = 5$
② Determine the sign of the quotient. Since one integer is positive and one is negative, the quotient is negative.
③ So, $35 \div (-7) = -5$.

Find each quotient.

1. $18 \div (-6)$ −3
2. $-35 \div (-7)$ 5
3. $-15 \div 3$ −5
4. $28 \div (-4)$ −7
5. $25 \div (-5)$ −5
6. $-27 \div (-9)$ 3
7. $-12 \div 4$ −3
8. $33 \div (-11)$ −3
9. $-50 \div (-25)$ 2

Solve each equation.

10. $-2y = 12$ $y = -6$
11. $\frac{p}{10} = -6$ $p = -60$
12. $-10y = -100$ $y = 10$
13. $7x = -28$ $x = -4$
14. $-6x = 36$ $x = -6$
15. $\frac{s}{2} = -14$ $s = 28$
16. $\frac{x}{8} = -12$ $y = -96$
17. $4x = -24$ $x = -6$
18. $3x = 30$ $x = 10$
19. A ship sank at a rate of 90 feet in 10 seconds. Represent the rate of change with an integer.   −9 ft/s

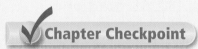 **Lesson Quiz 10-5**

Find each quotient.

1. $-27 \div (-3)$ **9**

2. $30 \div (-6)$ **−5**

Solve each equation.

3. $\frac{x}{5} = -8$ **−40**

4. $-8y = 24$ **−3**

✔ **Chapter Checkpoint**

To check understanding of Lessons 10-1 to 10-5:

Checkpoint Quiz 1 (p. 516)

📁 **Teaching Resources**
Checkpoint Quiz 1 (also in Prentice Hall Assessment System)

👥 **Reaching All Students**
Reading and Math Literacy 10B

Spanish versions available

Alternative Assessment

Each student in a pair writes several integer division exercises. Students exchange papers and find each quotient.

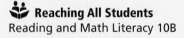

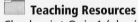

516

C **Challenge**

31. Reasoning Is the division of integers commutative? Give examples to support your answer. **No; $3 \div 1 = 3$ but $1 \div 3 \neq 3$.**

32. Number Sense Is the mean of five negative numbers positive or negative? Explain your reasoning. **Negative; the sum of five negative numbers is negative. The sum divided by 5 will also be negative.**

Test Prep

Gridded Response

Take It to the NET
Online lesson quiz at
www.PHSchool.com
Web Code: aaa-1005

33. What integer represents a rise of 500 feet per minute for 10 minutes? **5,000**

34. What is the solution to $-5x = -80$? **16**

35. What is the mean of 14, 6, −8, −12, and 10? **2**

36. What is the range of 19, −5, 0, −15, 27 and 9? **42**

⚪ Mixed Review

Lesson 9-9   **Find the volume of each rectangular prism.**

37.
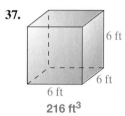
6 ft
6 ft
6 ft
216 ft³

38.
3 in.
3 in.
15 in.
135 in.³

39.
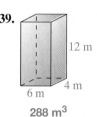
12 m
6 m
4 m
288 m³

Lesson 9-8   **Find the surface area of each rectangular prism with the given dimensions.**

40. $\ell = 5$ cm, $w = 3$ cm, $h = 4$ cm
94 cm²

41. $\ell = 9$ in., $w = 6$ in., $h = 7$ in.
318 in.²

✔ **Checkpoint Quiz 1**   **Lessons 10-1 through 10-5**

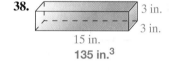 Instant self-check quiz online and on CD-ROM

Find each answer.

1. $-8 + 5$ **−3**

2. $-4 - (-2)$ **−2**

3. $-10 + (-2)$ **−12**

4. $-9 + 3$ **−6**

5. $-10 - 2$ **−12**

6. $12 \times (-3)$ **−36**

7. -8×2 **−16**

8. $14 \div (-2)$ **−7**

9. $-21 \div (-3)$ **7**

10. What integer represents a change of −2 degrees per hour for 10 hours? **−20**

Test Prep

Resources
A sheet of blank grids is available in the *Test-Taking Strategies With Transparencies* booklet. Give copies of this sheet to students so they can practice filling in the grids.

For additional practice with a variety of test item formats:
• Test-Prep, p. 541
• Test-Taking Strategies, p. 537
• Test-Taking Strategies With Transparencies

Understanding Word Problems

For Use With Lesson 10-4

Some problems contain *too little information*. You can use the problem-solving plan to decide if you have enough information to solve a problem. Ask yourself, "What do I know?" and "What do I need to find out?"

EXAMPLE

Elevators in a building travel an average of 1,000 feet per minute. From the first floor, a messenger takes an elevator to floors in this order: 7, 5, and 1. About how many minutes does the messenger spend on the elevator?

Read and Understand Read for understanding. Summarize the problem.

What do I know?
- The elevators travel about 1,000 feet per minute.
- The messenger has traveled:
  7 − 1 = 6, or 6 floors up;
  5 − 7 = −2, or 2 floors down;
  1 − 5 = −4, or 4 floors down.

What do I need to find out?
- The number of minutes the messenger spent on the elevator.

Do I have enough information to solve the problem? If not, what is missing?
No. I need to know the height of a floor, in feet.

Read and Understand is the first step in problem solving. Here it helps you identify that the problem cannot be solved.

EXERCISES

For each problem, write answers for "What do I know?" and "What do I need to find out?" Identify any missing information. 1–2. See margin.

1. A.J. bought three shirts for a total of $48. How much did A.J. pay for each shirt?

2. A distributor shipped 3,000 CDs to several stores. All stores received the same number of CDs. How many CDs did each store receive?

3. The formula for converting degrees Celsius to degrees Fahrenheit is $F = \frac{9}{5} C + 32$. Convert 150°C to degrees Fahrenheit. See above.

3. What I know: the conversion formula is $F = \frac{9}{5}C + 32$; What I need to find out: the conversion of 150°C into degrees Fahrenheit; there is no missing information.

1. What I know: three shirts cost $48; What I need to find out: how much each shirt cost; there is not enough information to solve the problem because I need to know if each of the shirts is priced the same as the others.

2. What I know: a distributor shipped 3,000 CDs to several stores, all stores received the same number of CDs; What I need to find out: how many CDs each store received; there is not enough information to solve the problem because the exact number of stores is missing.

517

10-6

1. Plan

Lesson Preview

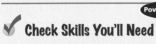

✓ Check Skills You'll Need

Graphing Integers
Lesson 10-1: Example 1. Extra Practice p. 651.

Lesson Resources

Optional Materials
• graph paper

 Teaching Resources
Practice, Reteaching, Enrichment

 **Reaching All Students**
Practice Workbook 10-6
Spanish Practice Workbook 10-6
Guided Problem Solving 10-6
Hands-On Activities 5

⏱ Presentation Assistant Plus!
Transparencies
• Check Skills You'll Need 10-6
• Problem of the Day 10-6
• Additional Examples 10-6
• Student Edition Answers 10-6
• Lesson Quiz 10-6
• Classroom Aid 3
PH Presentation Pro CD-ROM 10-6

PRENTICE HALL ASSESSMENT SYSTEM

Computer Test Generator CD

💻 Technology
Resource Pro® CD-ROM
Computer Test Generator CD
PH Presentation Pro CD-ROM

💻 www.PHSchool.com
Student Site
• Teacher Web Code: aak-5500
• Self-grading Lesson Quiz

PH SuccessNet Teacher Center
• Lesson Planner
• Resources

Plus **iTEXT**

What You'll Learn

OBJECTIVE 1 To name coordinates

OBJECTIVE 2 To graph points on a coordinate plane

. . . And Why

To name the coordinates on a map, as in Example 3

✓ Check Skills You'll Need ❓ For help, go to Lesson 10-1.

Graph each integer on a number line. 1–6. See back of book.

1. −2   **2.** 3   **3.** 0
4. −6   **5.** −1   **6.** −4

New Vocabulary • coordinate plane • quadrants • origin • ordered pair

iTEXT Interactive lesson includes instant self-check, tutorials, and activities.

OBJECTIVE 1 Naming Coordinates

> **Reading Math**
> The plural of *axis* is *axes*.

The **coordinate plane** is formed by the intersection of two number lines. The plane is divided into four regions, called **quadrants**. The **origin** is the place where the two number lines intersect.

An **ordered pair** is a pair of numbers that describes the location of a point in a coordinate plane. The ordered pair $(0, 0)$ describes the origin.

The *x*-coordinate tells how far to move left or right along the *x*-axis. x y The *y*-coordinate tells how far to move up or down along the *y*-axis.

1 EXAMPLE Naming Coordinates

Find the coordinates of point *B*.

Point *B* is 3 units to the left of the *y*-axis. So, the *x*-coordinate is –3. Point *B* is 2 units above the *x*-axis. So, the *y*-coordinate is 2.

The coordinates of point *B* are $(-3, 2)$.

✓ Check Understanding 1 Find the coordinates of each point in the coordinate plane.
  a. *C* C(1, 3)   **b.** *D* D(−2, −3)   **c.** *E* E(2, −2)

518 Chapter 10 Integers

 **Ongoing Assessment and Intervention**

Before the Lesson	During the Lesson	After the Lesson
Diagnose prerequisite skills using:	**Monitor progress using:**	**Assess knowledge using:**
• Check Skills You'll Need	• Check Understanding	• Lesson Quiz
	• Additional Examples	• Computer Test Generator CD
	• Test Prep	

You can graph points given their coordinates. You move right from the origin to graph a positive *x*-coordinate and left from the origin to graph a negative *x*-coordinate. You move up from the *x*-axis to graph a positive *y*-coordinate and down from the *x*-axis to graph a negative *y*-coordinate.

2 EXAMPLE Graphing Ordered Pairs

a. Graph point $P(3, -2)$ on a coordinate plane.

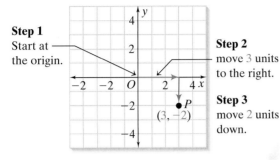

Step 1
Start at the origin.

Step 2
move 3 units to the right.

Step 3
move 2 units down.

P
$(3, -2)$

✓ **Check Understanding** ② Graph each point on the same coordinate plane.   See back of book.

   a. $A(-4, -4)$ b. $B(-3, 2)$ c. $C(1, -2)$

3 EXAMPLE Using Map Coordinates   🌎 **Real World**

Test-Prep Tip
Look back at your answer. Make sure it checks in the original problem.

Maps A student drew a map of certain locations in relationship to his home.

  a. Identify the coordinates of the library.

     The library is located at $(-2, 1)$.

  b. Suppose you leave the library and walk 2 blocks north and then 4 blocks east. At which building are you located?

     You are at the grocery store.

  c. What are the coordinates of the building in part (b)?

     The coordinates of the grocery store are $(2, 3)$.

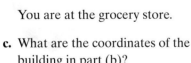

✓ **Check Understanding** ③ Suppose you leave the library and walk 2 blocks south and then 5 blocks east.

  a. At which building are you located? **City Hall**

  b. What are the coordinates of the building? **(3, −1)**

👥 Reaching All Students

| **Below Level** Have students graph these points in a coordinate plane. Have them connect the points in order. Ask: *What is the figure?*

 (4, 3), (−3, 3), (4, −3), (−3, −3)
 rectangle | **Advanced Learners** A square has coordinates (3, 3) and (−3, −3). *What are the missing coordinates?* (−3, 3), (3, −3) | **Tactile Learners** See note on page 519.
 Error Prevention See notes on page 520. |

---

2. Teach

Professional Development

Math Background

A coordinate plane is formed by two number lines—one horizontal and one vertical. The *origin* describes the point where the two axes intersect. An ordered pair of numbers describes the location of a point in the coordinate plane. For instance, the point (0, 0) describes the origin.

Teaching Notes

① EXAMPLE Tactile Learners

Some students may find it easier to locate coordinates by placing their fingers on a graph and tracing the corresponding horizontal and vertical lines until they meet at the coordinates of the point.

PowerPoint

🖥 **Additional Examples**

Use the coordinate grid for Questions 1–3.

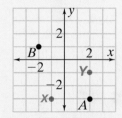

① Find the coordinates of each point.

  a. *A* (2, −3)   b. *B* (−2, 1)

② Graph each point in a coordinate plane. **see coordinate grid above**

  a. *X*(−1, −3)   b. *Y*(2, −1)

③ Use the coordinate grid. If you travel 2 units down and 3 units right from *B*, what are the coordinates of the point? **(1, −1)**

Closure

• *What is the origin in the coordinate plane?* (0, 0), the point where the two axes intersect

• *Which number comes first in an ordered pair?* the *x*-coordinate, the number of horizontal units from the origin

519

3. Practice

Assignment Guide

 Objective 1
Ⓐ Ⓑ Core 1–8, 23, 25

Objective 2
Ⓐ Ⓑ Core 9–22, 24, 26–27
Ⓒ Extension 28–29

Test Prep 30–33
Mixed Review 34

Error Prevention!

Exercises 9–14 Give students this visual aid to help them plot points.

$$\begin{array}{c|c} (-,+) & (+,+) \\ \hline (-,-) & (+,-) \end{array}$$

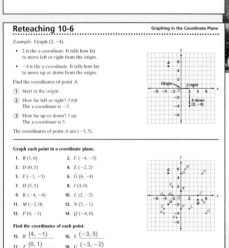

Practice 10-6   Graphing in the Coordinate Plane

Name the point with the given coordinates in the coordinate plane at the right.
1. (2, 3) _B_   2. (−4, 0) _F_
3. (−3, −5) _I_   4. (0, 6) _H_
5. (3, 5) _L_   6. (4, 0) _K_

Find the coordinates of each point at the right.
7. _J_ (3, −5)   8. _E_ (0, 4)
9. _D_ (3, 2)   10. _A_ (6, 0)
11. _G_ (−3, 2) 12. _C_ (−2, 3)

Graph each point on a coordinate plane.
13. A (8, −4)   14. B (−4, 8)
15. C (4, 8)   16. D (−8, −4)
17. E (8, 4)   18. F (−4, −8)
19. A taxi begins at (4, −3). It travels 3 blocks west and 5 blocks north to pick up a customer. What are the customer's coordinates?
(1, 2)
20. A moving truck fills up a shipment at an old address, at (−2, 1). It travels 7 blocks south and 6 blocks east to the new address. What is the location of the new address?
(4, −6)

Use the coordinate plane below. Sample answers are given.
21. Graph four points on the coordinate plane so that when the points are connected in order, the shape is a rectangle. List the coordinates of the points.
A(2, 5), B(6, 5), C(2, 3), D(6, 3)
22. Graph four points on the coordinate plane so that when the points are connected in order, the shape is a parallelogram that is not a rectangle. List the coordinates of the points.
E(−7, −4), F(−5, −2), G(−2, −2), H(−4, −4)

Reteaching 10-6   Graphing in the Coordinate Plane

Example: Graph (2, −4).
• 2 is the x-coordinate. It tells how far to move left or right from the origin.
• −4 is the y-coordinate. It tells how far to move up or down from the origin.
Find the coordinates of point A.
① Start at the origin.
② How far left or right? 3 left
  The x-coordinate is −3.
③ How far up or down? 5 up
  The y-coordinate is 5.
The coordinates of point A are (−3, 5).

Graph each point in a coordinate plane.
1. B (1, 6)   2. C (−4, −3)
3. D (0, 5)   4. E (−2, 2)
5. F (−1, −5) 6. G (6, −4)
7. H (5, 5)   8. J (4, 0)
9. K (−4, −4) 10. L (2, −3)
11. M (−2, 0) 12. N (5, −1)
13. P (0, −3) 14. Q (−4, 0)

Find the coordinates of each point.
15. R (4, −1) 16. S (−3, 5)
17. T (0, 1)   18. U (−3, −2)

Look at the coordinate grid above.
19. If you travel 7 units down from S, at which point will you be located?
_U_
20. If you travel 4 units right from T and 2 units down, at which point will you be located?
_R_

520

? For more practice, see *Extra Practice*.

Ⓐ **Practice by Example**

Find the coordinates of each point at the right.

Example 1
(page 518)

1. _B_ (−3, 1)   2. _D_ (−1, 1)

3. _K_ (3, 2)   4. _Q_ (0, 3)

Name the point with the given coordinates in the coordinate plane at the right.

5. (1, 2) _A_   6. (−2, −2) _P_

7. (3, −3) _J_   8. (0, −3) _C_

Example 2
(page 519)

Graph each point on the same coordinate plane.   9–14. See back of book.

9. $A(1, 5)$ 10. $B(-5, -3)$ 11. $C(2, -4)$

12. $D(-2, 3)$ 13. $E(1, -4)$ 14. $F(-5, 5)$

Example 3
(page 519)

🌐 **Use the map at the right.**

15. If you travel 2 units north of the library and 4 units east, where are you located?
grocery store

16. Find the coordinates of each building.
  a. Post office   **b.** School
  (−6, −1)   (0, 4)

Ⓑ **Apply Your Skills**

Graph each point on the same coordinate plane.   17–20. See margin.

17. $(0, 3)$ 18. $(-4, 0)$ 19. $(-4, -2)$ 20. $(5, 3)$

21. Your cousin is located at $(-5, -2)$. He rides his scooter 3 blocks west and then 1 block south to the park. What are the coordinates of the park? **(−8, −3)**

22. A police car begins at $(-2, 8)$. It travels 10 blocks south and 6 blocks east to the court house. What are the coordinates of the court house? **(4, −2)**

23. **Writing in Math** Describe how you would locate the following points on a coordinate plane. 23a–b. Answers may vary. See margin for samples.
  a. $(0, -8)$ **b.** $(-6, 3)$

24. **Geometry** A symmetrical four-pointed star has eight corner [GPS] points. Seven of the points are $(-1, 1), (0, 3), (1, 1), (3, 0), (1, -1), (0, -3), (-1, -1)$. What are the coordinates of the missing point? **(−3, 0)**

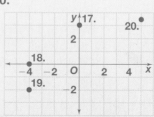

Real-World 🌐 Connection

When riding a scooter, wear a helmet and other safety gear to minimize the risk of injury.

520   Chapter 10   Integers

[GPS] Use the Guided Problem Solving worksheet with Exercise 24.

17–20.

23. Samples:
  a. Start at the origin. Move down the y-axis 8 units.
  b. Start at the origin. Move left 6 units; then move up 3 units.

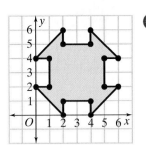

25. Quilt Making Quilt designers use coordinate grids to design patterns. Find the coordinates of the pattern points at the left. **See margin.**

26. Writing in Math What do all points located on the *x*-axis have in common? What do all points located on the *y*-axis have in common? Explain. **Answers may vary. Sample: Their second coordinates are all 0; their first coordinates are all 0.**

27. Reasoning Is the order of the coordinates in an ordered pair important? Explain. **See margin.**

 Challenge

28. An oil tanker is located at (8, −8). Another oil tanker is located at (14, −8). How far apart are the two tankers? **6 units**

29. Stretch Your Thinking Suppose you make corn muffins. Your family eats $\frac{1}{3}$ of them. You give $\frac{1}{4}$ of the remaining muffins to a friend. You have 9 muffins left. How many muffins did you make? **18 muffins**

Test Prep

Reading Comprehension Read the following passage and answer the questions below.

Where on Earth Are You?

Geographers have given Earth a coordinate system so that locations can be described easily. Imagine a coordinate plane wrapped around the planet. The horizontal axis is the equator, and the vertical axis is the prime meridian.

Distances on Earth's coordinate system are measured in degrees. Degrees north or south of the equator are called degrees of latitude. Degrees east or west of the prime meridian are called degrees of longitude.

30. On Earth's coordinate system, what is the vertical axis? **prime meridian**

31. On Earth's coordinate system, what is the horizontal axis? **equator**

32. On what continent is the location 20° N latitude, 20° E longitude? **Africa**

33. On what continent is the location 45° N latitude, 5° E longitude? **Europe**

Take It to the NET
Online lesson quiz at
www.PHSchool.com
Web Code: aaa-1006

Mixed Review

Lesson 9-6 **34.** What is the circumference and area of a circle with radius of 6 millimeters? Round to the nearest millimeter.
C = 38 mm; A = 113 mm²

Lesson 7-8 **35.** Distances of 10 feet, 23 feet, 16 feet, 55 feet, and 21 feet have a mean of 25 feet. Is this statistic misleading? Explain. **See margin.**

25. (0, 2), (1, 2), (1, 4), (0, 4), (2, 6), (2, 5), (4, 5), (4, 6), (6, 4), (5, 4), (5, 2), (6, 2), (4, 0), (4, 1), (2, 1), (2, 0)

27. Yes; answers may vary. Sample: The first coordinate tells you where to move along the *x*-axis and the second coordinate tells you how far to move along the *y*-axis.

35. The statistic is misleading because four of the tire distances are less than 25 feet.

521

4. Assess

PowerPoint **Lesson Quiz 10-6**

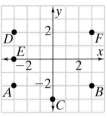

Find the coordinates of each point.

1. *A* (−3 −2) **2.** *F* (3, 2)

Name each point with the given coordinates.

3. (−3, 2) *D* **4.** (0, −3) *C*

Alternative Assessment

Using all four quadrants, each student in a pair plots six points and labels the points *A* through *F*. Partners exchange papers and name the coordinates of each point.

Test Prep

For additional practice with a variety of test item formats:
• Test-Prep, p. 541
• Test-Taking Strategies, p. 537
• Test-Taking Strategies With Transparencies

Enrichment 10-6 Graphing in the Coordinate Plane
Critical Thinking

One item that Cheryl had to find on a treasure hunt was located at the point (3, 4) on the map. When Cheryl got there, she realized she had the map upside down. How many units left, right, up, and down on the map should Cheryl walk to find the correct location?

1. Mark (3, 4) on the coordinate plane. Label it *A*.
2. Turn this page upside down. Imagine that the graph was scaled in the usual way. Then mark (3, 4). Label it *B*.
3. Turn your page to original position. Follow the grid lines to mark the shortest path between the *B* and *A*.

4. Does your path go up or down? How many units?
   up; 8 units
5. Does your path go left or right? How many units?
   right; 6 units
6. Are there other paths that you could choose? Explain.
   Yes; one path could start out going right, then up.
7. What is the relationship between the number of units the path takes and the original coordinates?
   The path is two times the value of each coordinate.
8. One item that Norm had to find on a treasure hunt was located at the point (−2, 5) on the map. When Norm got there, he realized he had the map upside down. How many units left, right, up, and down on the map should Norm walk to find the correct location?
   up 10, left 4

Reflections in the Coordinate Plane

Students use a coordinate plane to explore transformations, or movements, of geometric figures.

Optional Materials

- graph paper
- Classroom Aid 2–3

Teaching Notes

English Learners
Review the meanings of the words *congruent*, *parallelogram*, and *quadrant*.

Tactile Learners
For students having difficulty visualizing the reflections, have them copy the parallelograms on a coordinate grid. Then have them fold their papers over one axis, and hold their paper up to the light. The figures should match exactly.

① EXAMPLE Inclusion

Have students list the ordered pairs of the vertices of the parallelograms that are in Quadrants III and IV. They will find the same relationships as for Quadrants I and II.

② EXAMPLE Teaching Tip

Have students use the ordered pairs for the parallelograms in Quadrants II and III to see if the same relationship exists between *x*-coordinates and *y*-coordinates. It does.

The grid at the right shows four congruent parallelograms.

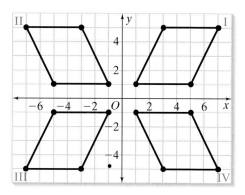

① EXAMPLE

List the ordered pairs of the vertices of the parallelogram that are in Quadrants I and II. Find a pattern.

Quadrant I	
x	y
1	1
3	5
7	5
5	1

Quadrant II	
x	y
−1	1
−3	5
−7	5
−5	1

All corresponding *x*-coordinates are opposites and all corresponding *y*-coordinates are the same.

② EXAMPLE

List the ordered pairs of the vertices of the parallelogram that are in Quadrants I and IV. Find a pattern.

Quadrant I	
x	y
1	1
3	5
7	5
5	1

Quadrant IV	
x	y
1	−1
3	−5
7	−5
5	−1

All corresponding *x*-coordinates are the same and all corresponding *y*-coordinates are opposites.

EXERCISES

Plot the given points and connect them in order. Reflect the figure over the *y*-axis. Then reflect the original figure over the *x*-axis. 1–3. See back of book.

1. $(2, 2), (4, 6), (6, 2), (2, 2)$

2. $(-1, -1), (-1, -6), (-7, -6), (-1, -1)$

3. $(1, -1), (4, -1), (4, -3), (3, -4), (2, -4), (1, -3), (1, -1)$

10-7

Applications of Integers

What You'll Learn

 OBJECTIVE 1 To find profit and loss

 OBJECTIVE 2 To draw and interpret graphs

...And Why

To find profit or loss for a business, as in Example 1

 Check Skills You'll Need

For help, go to Lesson 10-2.

Find each sum.

1. 12 + 26 **38**
2. 18 + (−9) **9**
3. 41 + (−54) **−13**
4. −19 + (−9) **−28**
5. −32 + 18 **−14**
6. 26 + (−32) **−6**
7. −18 + (−13) **−31**
8. −25 + (−34) **−59**
9. −16 + 42 **26**

Lesson Preview

Check Skills You'll Need

Adding Integers
Lesson 10-2: Examples 2, 4. Extra Practice p. 651.

Lesson Resources

 **Optional Materials**
• graph paper

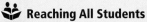 **Teaching Resources**
Practice, Reteaching, Enrichment

Reaching All Students
Practice Workbook 10-7
Spanish Practice Workbook 10-7
Guided Problem Solving 10-7

Presentation Assistant Plus!
Transparencies
• Check Skills You'll Need 10-7
• Problem of the Day 10-7
• Additional Examples 10-7
• Student Edition Answers 10-7
• Lesson Quiz 10-7
PH Presentation Pro CD-ROM 10-7

ASSESSMENT SYSTEM
Computer Test Generator CD

Technology
Resource Pro® CD-ROM
Computer Test Generator CD
PH Presentation Pro CD-ROM

www.PHSchool.com
Student Site
• Teacher Web Code: aak-5500
• Self-grading Lesson Quiz

PH SuccessNet Teacher Center
• Lesson Planner
• Resources

Plus

OBJECTIVE 1
Finding Profit and Loss

Interactive lesson includes instant self-check, tutorials, and activities.

Businesses keep track of money they receive and money they spend. Money received is called *income*. Money spent is called *expenses*.

A balance is a company's profit or loss. To find a balance, add the income (positive numbers) and the expenses (negative numbers).

A positive balance means that there is a profit. A negative balance means that there is a loss.

 EXAMPLE Finding Profit or Loss   **Real World**

Small Business Find Flower Mania's profit or loss for February.

Income and Expenses for Flower Mania		
Month	Income	Expenses
Jan.	$11,917	−$14,803
Feb.	$12,739	−$9,482
Mar.	$11,775	−$10,954
Apr.	$13,620	−$15,149

$12,739 + (−$9,482) = $3,257   ← **Add income and expenses for February.**

Flower Mania had a profit of $3,257 for February.

Real-World Connection

Careers Small business owners make up more than 90% of all businesses in the United States.

 Check Understanding 1 Find the profit or loss for each period.

a. January **−$2,886**
b. March **$821**
c. April **−$1,529**
d. January through April **−$337**

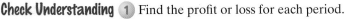

Ongoing Assessment and Intervention

Before the Lesson
Diagnose prerequisite skills using:
• Check Skills You'll Need

During the Lesson
Monitor progress using:
• Check Understanding
• Additional Examples
• Test Prep

After the Lesson
Assess knowledge using:
• Lesson Quiz
• Computer Test Generator CD

Math Background

To make a useful graph, choose appropriate *scales* and *intervals* for the data. The scale is the units used, such as time or dollar amounts. The interval is the distance between values on a scale such as $5 or $100 increments.

Teaching Notes

2 EXAMPLE Error Prevention

Help students determine what scale and interval to use for each axis. Guide them to estimate where to plot points that lie between labeled tick marks.

PowerPoint

Additional Examples

1 Find the profit or loss for each month.

Month	Income	Expenses
Sept	$1,250	−$1,250
Oct	$3,200	−$2,550
Nov	$4,250	−$3,570
Dec	$2,530	−$2,840

a. Sept. $0 b. Oct. $650

c. Nov. $680 d. Dec. −$310

2 Draw a line graph based on your answers to Example 1a–d. In which month did the greatest profit occur?
November

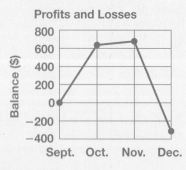

Closure

How do you find a profit and a loss? Add the income and expenses. A positive balance means a profit and a negative balance means a loss.

524

You can use line graphs to look at the trends of monthly balances.

2 EXAMPLE Drawing and Interpreting Graphs   Real World

Business Draw a line graph of the monthly profits and losses for Beth's Hobby Shop. In which month did the greatest profit occur?

Profit/Loss in 2003 for Beth's Hobby Shop; by Month					
Month	Profit/Loss	Month	Profit/Loss	Month	Profit/Loss
Jan.	−$1,917	May	−$150	Sept.	−$417
Feb.	−$682	June	$250	Oct.	−$824
Mar.	$303	July	$933	Nov.	$1,566
Apr.	$781	Aug.	$1,110	Dec.	$1,945

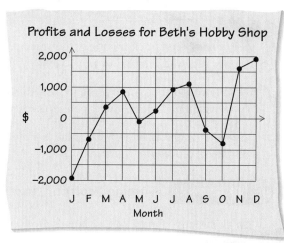

The balances vary from −$1,917 to $1,945. So make a scale from −$2,000 to $2,000. Use intervals of $500.

Real-World Connection
Many hobby shops provide pottery lessons.

● Beth's Hobby Shop had the greatest profit in December.

✓ **Check Understanding** **2** In which months did the company show a profit?
March, April, June, July, August, November, December

EXERCISES

? For more practice, see *Extra Practice*.

A Practice by Example

Look at the data for Rad's Books. Find the profit or loss for each period.

Example 1
(page 523)

1. Week 1 −$2,256 **2.** Week 2 $984

3. Week 3 $194 **4.** Week 4 −$1,196

Income and Expenses for Rad's Books		
Week	Income	Expenses
Week 1	$4,257	−$6,513
Week 2	$3,840	−$2,856
Week 3	$4,109	−$3,915
Week 4	$3,725	−$4,921

👥 Reaching All Students

Below Level Give students two number and have them make a reasonable scale as shown. **Answers may vary.**
−$328 and $562 −$400 to $600
−$4,563 and $2,091 −$5,000 to $2,500

Advanced Learners Mel babysits, charging $2 per hour per child. Twice a week she sits 2 children for 3 hours, 3 children for 1 hour, and 2 children for 4 hours. What are her weekly earnings? $34

English Learners See note on page 525.
Error Prevention See notes on page 524.

Example 2
(page 524)

5. The table at the right gives the income and expenses for several days.
  a. Find the profit or loss for each day.   **See left.**
  b. Draw a line graph to show the profits and losses.   **See below left.**
  c. On what day was the profit the greatest? The loss the greatest?
  Tuesday; Friday

5a. Monday: $9;
Tuesday: $18;
Wednesday: −$9;
Thursday: $17;
Friday: −$12;
Saturday: −$1

Day	Income	Expenses
Mon.	$94	−$85
Tues.	$78	−$60
Wed.	$13	−$22
Thurs.	$90	−$73
Fri.	$37	−$49
Sat.	$15	−$16

B Apply Your Skills

6. a. Accounting Determine the balance after each transaction of the checking account shown below.   **$197; $149; $124; −$11; $204**
  b. What was the greatest balance? The least?   **$204; −$11**

5b.
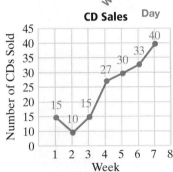

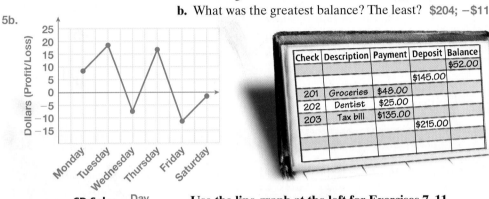

CD Sales   **Day**

Use the line graph at the left for Exercises 7–11.

7. How many CDs were sold in the first week?   **15**

8. How many CDs were sold in the fifth week?   **30**

9. How many more CDs were sold in the sixth week than were sold in the second week?   **23**

10. In which two weeks were the same number of CDs sold?   **weeks 1 and 3**

11. Which week showed a drop in the number of CDs sold?   **week 2**

Population Use the table for Exercises 12–14.

City	Population (in thousands)					
	1950	1960	1970	1980	1990	2000
Miami, Fla.	249	292	335	347	359	362
Rochester, N.Y.	322	319	296	242	232	220

12. Graph the data on the same grid. Use a different line for each city.
  See margin.
13. Use the line graph you created in Exercise 12. Which city shows a positive trend in population? A negative trend?   **Miami; Rochester**

14. In 1950, which city had a larger population, Miami or Rochester?
  Rochester

12.

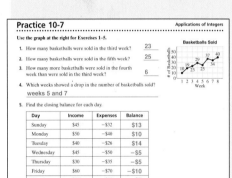

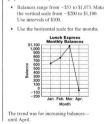

Use the Guided Problem Solving worksheet with Exercise 16.

PowerPoint Lesson Quiz 10-7

Find the profit or loss for each month.

Month	Income	Expenses
May	$2,575	−$3,325
June	$3,280	−$4,850
July	$5,210	−$3,960
Aug.	$5,460	−$2,430

1. May
−$750

2. June
−$1,570

3. July
$1,250

4. Aug.
$3,030

5. Draw a line graph based on your answers to 1–4.

Profits and Losses

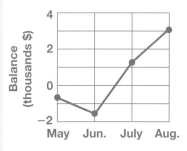

Test Prep

Resources

For additional practice with a variety of test item formats:
- Test-Prep, p. 541
- Test-Taking Strategies, p. 537
- Test-Taking Strategies With Transparencies

Enrichment 10-7   Applications of Integers
Charting Information

You work as a self-employed barber. Your gross receipts for the year totaled $22,050 and you had clients return $1,275 worth of hair products. Your expenses for the year included $1,245 worth of repairs, utility bills of $550, $11,000 in fees, $675 in depreciation, $1,420 worth of supplies, $5,700 in car expenses, $325 worth of advertising, $975 in office expenses, and legal bills of $2,600.

1. Shown below is a modified and simplified version of the tax form you must complete when you file your taxes. Complete the form.

Modified Schedule C
Profit or Loss From Business

Part I	INCOME	
1	Gross Receipts or Sales	$22,050
2	Returns	$1,275
3	Gross profit. Subtract line 2 from line 1	$20,775
4	Other income	$0
5	Gross income. Add lines 4 and 5	$20,775
Part II	EXPENSES	
6	Advertising	$325
7	Car expenses	$5,700
8	Commissions and fees	$11,000
9	Depreciation	$675
10	Insurance	$0
11	Interest paid	$0
12	Legal services	$2,600
13	Office expenses	$975
14	Rentals	$0
15	Repairs	$1,245
16	Supplies	$1,420
17	Travel	$0
18	Utilities	$550
19	Other	$0
20	Total Expenses. Add lines 6 through 19.	$24,490
21	Total profit or loss Subtract line 20 from line 5.	−$3,715

2. Did your business make a profit? Explain.
No; the business had a loss of −$3,715.

---

15. A company has made a profit if its total expenses are less than its total income.

15. **Writing in Math** Explain how you can determine whether a company has made a profit.

16. You receive a total of $125 for your birthday. You spend $20 on a sweater, $15 on a CD, $8 on a book, $12 on a pair of sunglasses, and $35 on a bicycle helmet. How much money do you have left? **$35**

 Challenge

17. Predictions may vary. Sample: 315 million. See back of book for graph.

17. The table at the right shows the population of the United States every twenty years from 1900 to 2000. Make a graph of the data. Then use the graph to predict the population in 2010.

18. **Stretch Your Thinking** A number is divided by 8. When 7 is subtracted from the doubled quotient, the answer is −1. What is the number? **24**

Year	Population (in millions)
1900	76
1920	106
1940	132
1960	179
1980	227
2000	281

Test Prep

Multiple Choice

19. What is the difference between the average low surface temperature of Earth of −89°C and the average high surface temperature of 58°C? **C**
A. 13°C   B. 31°C   C. 147°C   D. 174°C

Take It to the NET
Online lesson quiz at
www.PHSchool.com
Web Code: aaa-1007

20. Suppose you earn $15 each time you cut your neighbor's lawn. You cut the lawn 18 times. How much money do you earn? **I**
F. $3   G. $33   H. $180   I. $270

21. What is the profit or loss for income of $7,892 and expenses of $1,698? **B**
A. $6,194 loss   B. $6,194 profit   C. $9,590 loss   D. $9,590 profit

Extended Response

22. Jordan bought a DVD for $5. He sold it for $10, and then bought it back for $15. Finally, he sold it for $20. Express Jordan's transactions using integers. How much money did he make or lose? **See margin.**

Mixed Review

Lesson 8-2   Classify each angle as *acute*, *obtuse*, *right*, or *straight*.

23. 15° acute   **24.** 123° obtuse   **25.** 54° acute   **26.** 90° right

27. 173° obtuse   **28.** 180° straight   **29.** 175° obtuse   **30.** 45° acute

Lesson 2-6   Solve each equation.

31. $d + 25 = 39$ **14**   **32.** $n − 13 = 74$ **87**

Alternative Assessment

Each student in a pair writes a word problem similar to Exercise 5. Partners exchange problems and then solve them. Have partners discuss how they solved each other's problem.

22. [4] −5 + 10 = 5, 5 − 15 = −10, −10 + 20 = 10; $10

[3] final answer missing OR one minor error in work

[2] expressions missing

[1] two minor errors

10-8 Graphing Functions

What You'll Learn

OBJECTIVE 1 To make a function table

OBJECTIVE 2 To graph functions

...And Why

To find the points scored in a game, as in Example 3

 Check Skills You'll Need   For help, go to Lesson 2-2.

Evaluate the expression for $x = 3$.

1. $8 + x$ **11**
2. $4x$ **12**
3. $18 \div x$ **6**
4. $21 - x$ **18**
5. $42 \div x$ **14**
6. $x + 47$ **50**
7. $79 - x$ **76**
8. $11x$ **33**

New Vocabulary • function

OBJECTIVE 1

Making a Function Table

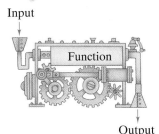

Input → Function → Output

Imagine you have a machine. You can put any number, or input, into the machine. The machine will perform an operation on the number and provide a result, or output. A **function** is a rule that assigns exactly one output value to each input value.

Suppose you tell the machine to multiply by 4. A function table, like the one at the right, shows the input and output values.

Input	Output
3	12
−7	−28

1 EXAMPLE **Completing a Function Table**

Complete the function table if the rule is Output = Input · (−2).

Input	Output
−1	2
1	−2
3	−6

← Multiply −1 by −2. Place 2 in the Output column.
← Multiply 1 by −2. Place −2 in the Output column.
← Multiply 3 by −2. Place −6 in the Output column.

✔ **Check Understanding** ① Complete the function table given the rule.

a. Rule:
Output = Input ÷ 4

Input	Output
16	4
−24	−6
36	9

b. Rule:
Output = Input − 8

Input	Output
−6	−14
−1	−9
4	−4

Ongoing Assessment and Intervention

Before the Lesson	During the Lesson	After the Lesson
Diagnose prerequisite skills using:	**Monitor progress using:**	**Assess knowledge using:**
• Check Skills You'll Need	• Check Understanding	• Lesson Quiz
	• Additional Examples	• Computer Test Generator CD
	• Test Prep	• Chapter Checkpoint 2 (p. 532)

Lesson Preview

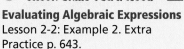

✔ **Check Skills You'll Need**

Evaluating Algebraic Expressions
Lesson 2-2: Example 2. Extra Practice p. 643.

Lesson Resources

Optional Materials
• graph paper
• straightedge

📁 **Teaching Resources**
Practice, Reteaching, Enrichment
Checkpoint Quiz 2

Reaching All Students
Practice Workbook 10-8
Spanish Practice Workbook 10-8
Reading and Math Literacy 10C
Spanish Reading and Math Literacy 10C
Spanish Checkpoint Quiz 2
Guided Problem Solving 10-8
Technology Activities 17

🕐 **Presentation Assistant Plus!**
Transparencies
• Check Skills You'll Need 10-8
• Problem of the Day 10-8
• Additional Examples 10-8
• Student Edition Answers 10-8
• Lesson Quiz 10-8
• Classroom Aid 2, 3, 36
PH Presentation Pro CD-ROM 10-8

 PRENTICE HALL ASSESSMENT SYSTEM

Checkpoint Quiz 2
Computer Test Generator CD

💻 **Technology**
Resource Pro® CD-ROM
Computer Test Generator CD
PH Presentation Pro CD-ROM

 www.PHSchool.com
Student Site
• Teacher Web Code: aak-5500
• Self-grading Lesson Quiz

PH SuccessNet Teacher Center
• Lesson Planner
• Resources

Plus

527

Math Background

A *function* is a rule that assigns each input number to exactly one output number. So the output number *depends* on the input number. A function table shows input and output values for a particular function.

The input and output values in a table can be graphed as ordered pairs on a coordinate grid. The input is graphed on the horizontal axis and the output on the vertical axis. If the graphed points lie along a line, the function is called a *linear function*. Functions can also be expressed using algebraic equations. So functions can be expressed in tables, graphs, word rules, and algebraic rules.

Teaching Notes

Inclusion
Help students understand the significance of the function machine. The input enters a machine, such as a toaster, it is acted upon in a particular way, and the output is the result.

1 EXAMPLE Alternative Method

Some students may need to write the substitution equation for each input to find the corresponding output. Have them write the middle column shown below.

Input	Input · (−2)	Output
−1	−1 · (−2) =	2
1	1 · (−2) =	−2
3	3 (−2) =	−6

2 EXAMPLE Teaching Tip

Help students understand that y depends on the value of x. Elicit the fact that students substitute values for x (input) to find the corresponding y-values (output).

Music Connection
Musical instruments apply function relationships. For example, a flute's pitch depends on the number of holes that are closed and a violin's pitch depends on the length of string.

528

You can write the function rule in Example 1 using variables.

$$\text{Output} = \text{Input} \cdot (-2)$$
$$y = x \cdot (-2) \text{ or } y = -2x$$

You can show function relationships on the coordinate plane. Graph the input (x) on the horizontal axis. Graph the output (y) on the vertical axis.

2 EXAMPLE Graphing a Function

Make a table and use it to graph some points of the function $y = x + 3$.

Input (x)	Output (y)
−2	1
−1	2
0	3
1	4
2	5

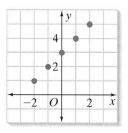

✓ **Check Understanding** ② Make a table and use it to graph some points of the function $y = x - 3$. **See margin.**

In Example 2, the points lie along a line. This type of function is a *linear function*. When you graph functions, you can join the points with a line. In real-world situations you can use the line to see trends or make predictions.

3 EXAMPLE Real-World 🌐 Problem Solving

Salaries Workers at a grocery store start off making $7 an hour. The function $m = 7h$ shows how the money they earn relates to the number of hours they work. Make a table and graph the function.

Hours Worked	Money Earned (dollars)
1	7
2	14
3	21
4	28

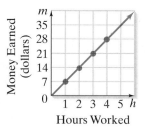

✓ **Check Understanding** ③ Suppose a car is driven at a steady rate of 45 miles per hour. The function $d = 45t$ shows how time t relates to distance d. Make a table and graph the function. **Tables may vary. See back of book.**

👥 Reaching All Students

| **Below Level** Have students complete function tables for the values −3, −1, 0, 2, and 5 for function rules as shown.

Add 1 −2, 0, 1, 3, 6
Divide by (−1) 3, 1, 0, −2, −5
Subtract 3 −6, −4, −3, −1, 2 | **Advanced Learners** The input integers for a function rule are 0, 4, and 8. The output is 2, 10, and 18. Write an equation for the function rule. $y = 2x + 2$ | **English Learners** See note on page 531.
Inclusion See note on page 528. |

More Than One Way

A pizza delivery person receives $5 each day he reports to work plus $2 for each pizza delivered. This can be expressed as the function $y = 5 + 2x$, where y = earnings and x = number of pizzas delivered. How much will the delivery person earn if he delivers 25 pizzas?

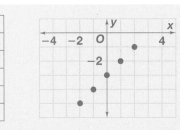

Jessica's Method

I can evaluate the equation to find the amount the delivery person earns. To do this, I replace x with the 25 pizzas delivered.

$y = 5 + 2x$ ← Write the equation.

$y = 5 + 2(25)$ ← Substitute 25 for x.

$y = 55$

The delivery person will earn $55 for delivering 25 pizzas.

Leon's Method

If I make a table and a graph, I can look at the graph to tell how much the delivery person earns for delivering different numbers of pizzas.

x	y
0	5
5	15
10	25
15	35

Delivery Earnings

All the points lie on a line, so I can use the graph to find the amount earned for 25 pizzas delivered. The y-value for $x = 25$ is 55. So the delivery person earned $55.

Choose a Method

Tracy is a member of a discount CD club. Paying an annual fee of $30 allows her to buy CDs for $4 each. The function $y = 30 + 4x$ models this situation. If Tracy buys 15 CDs during the year, what will be her total cost? Describe your method and explain why you chose it.

$90; answers may vary. Sample: I substituted 15 for x in the second equation and solved for y; I chose this method because it was easier than making a table or graph.

2.

x	y
−2	−5
−1	−4
0	−3
1	−2
2	−1

Discuss the difference between a solid line and a dashed line. Many real-world situations are not continuous, so a dashed line is used to indicate that values between plotted points are not acceptable solutions.

PowerPoint

Additional Examples

1 Complete the function table given the rule: Output = Input ÷ (−3).

Input	−9	−3	12	15
Output	3	1	−4	−5

2 Make a table and graph the function $y = -2x$.

Input	−2	−1	0	1	2
Output	4	2	0	−2	−4

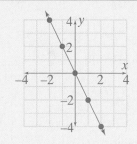

3 Henry receives $8.00 per hour for babysitting two children. The function $e = 8h$ shows how the earnings e relate to the number of hours h that Henry babysits. Make a table and graph the function.

Hours	1	2	3	4
Earnings ($)	8	16	24	32

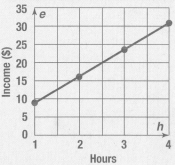

Closure

- *What is a function?* a rule that assigns exactly one output value to each input value
- *When might you not connect the points of a function graph?* when not every point on the line represents a solution

529

3. Practice

Assignment Guide

1 Objective 1
Ⓐ Ⓑ Core 1–3, 17–21

2 Objective 2
Ⓐ Ⓑ Core 4–16, 22–28
Ⓒ Extension 29–31

Test Prep 32–35
Mixed Review 36–40

Error Prevention!

Exercise 11 Students may not know which variable is graphed along the *x*-axis. Give them the phrase "*y* is a function of *x*."

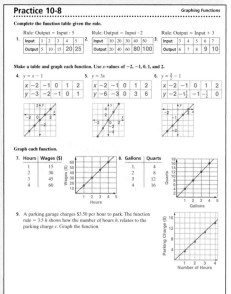

Ⓐ **Practice by Example**

Complete the function table given the rule.

Example 1 (page 527)

1. Rule:
Output = Input + 4

Input	Output	
−5	▪	−1
8	▪	12
31	▪	35

2. Rule:
Output = Input − 4

Input	Output	
−2	▪	−6
5	▪	1
14	▪	10

3. Rule:
Output = Input · (−8)

Input	Output	
−3	▪	24
4	▪	−32
9	▪	−72

Examples 2, 3 (page 528)

Make a table and graph each function. Use *x*-values −2, −1, 0, 1, 2.
4–9. See back of book.

4. $y = x + 2$ **5.** $y = x - 2$ **6.** $y = 2x$

7. $y = \frac{x}{2}$ **8.** $y = \frac{x}{2} + 1$ **9.** $y = -\frac{x}{2}$

🌐 **10. Library** Suppose each day a library book is over due, the fine is $.25. The function $f = 0.25d$ shows how the number of days d, relates to the fine f. Make a table and graph the function. **See back of book.**

Ⓑ **Apply Your Skills**

Make a table and graph each function. Use *x*-values −2, −1, 0, 1, 2.
11–16. See back of book.

11. $y = 2x + 1$ **12.** $y = 2x - 1$ **13.** $y = -2x + 1$

14. $y = -2x - 1$ **15.** $y = 3x + 4$ **16.** $y = -4x + 3$

17. Suppose you buy T-shirts for $9 each. You have a coupon that gives you $2 off your total purchase. The function $p = 9t - 2$ shows how price p relates to the number of T-shirts t. Find the final price of seven T-shirts. $61

🌐 **18. Sports** A store sells kicking tees by mail for $3 each. There is a shipping charge of $5 no matter how many tees are ordered. Make a table to find the total price for the purchase of 2, 3, 4, and 5 tees. See margin.

Complete each function table. Then write a rule for the function.

19.

Input	Output
3	5
4	6
5	7
6	▪ 8
7	▪ 9

Output = Input + 2

20.

Input	Output
10	2
15	3
20	4
25	▪ 5
30	▪ 6

Output = Input ÷ 5

GPS Use the Guided Problem Solving worksheet with Exercise 21.

18.

Number of Tees	Total Price ($)
2	11
3	14
4	17
5	20

21. Business Suppose you want to start a cookie business. You know that it will cost $600 to buy the oven and materials you need. You decide to charge $.75 for each cookie. The function $p = 0.75C - 600$ relates profit p to the number of cookies sold C.   −$300; −$225
   a. What will your profit or loss be if you sell 400 cookies? 500 cookies?
   b. How many cookies must you sell to break even? **800 cookies**

Make a table and graph each function. 22–25. **See back of book.**

22. $y = 2x - 12$ **23.** $y = 4x - 13$

24. $y = 0.5x + 1$ **25.** $y = 3x - 6$

 Tell whether each function is *linear* or *not linear*. Explain your answers. 26–28. **See at left.**

26. Linear; the graph is a line.

27. Not linear; the graph is not a line.

28. Not linear; the graph is not a line.

26. $y = x$

27. $y = x^2$

28. $y = \frac{1}{x}$

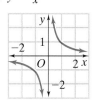

C Challenge ● **29. Business** Three companies offer to sew your team name, TIGERS, on your team uniforms. Pro Lettering charges $2 per letter. Uniforms-R-Us charges $1 per letter plus a fee of $5 per uniform. Speedy Lettering charges a fee of $12 per uniform for any amount of letters. Which graph shows the fees of the company that would charge the least per uniform? **Graph A**

A.
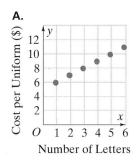
Number of Letters

B.
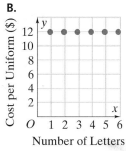
Number of Letters

C.
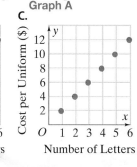
Number of Letters

30. a. Graph $y = -2x$ and $y = -x^2$ on the same grid. **30a–c. See margin.**
   b. What points do the graphs have in common?
   c. Describe how the graphs are different.

31. Stretch Your Thinking A fraction's numerator is 3 less than its denominator. Its reciprocal is 4 times its value. It is greater than 0. What is the fraction? $\frac{3}{6}$

English Learners
Exercise 21 Completion of this exercise depends heavily on students' understanding of English. Use plain language to convey the important information in the exercise including the term *break even*. You might also pair students learning English with fluent speakers.

30a.
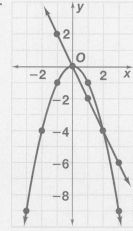

b. (0, 0) and (2, −4)

c. Answers may vary. Sample: The graph of $y = -2x$ is a straight line. The graph of $y = -x^2$ is a curve. The graph of $y = -x^2$ is symmetric with respect to the y-axis, but the graph of $y = -2x$ is not.

Lesson Quiz 10-8

1. Complete the function table given the rule: Output = Input · (−4).

Input	−3	0	6
Output	12	0	−24

2. Make a table and graph the function $y = \frac{x}{2} - 1$.

Input	−2	0	2	4
Output	−2	−1	0	1

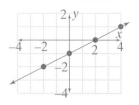

 Chapter Checkpoint

To check understanding of Lessons 10-6 to 10-8:

Checkpoint Quiz 2 (p. 532)

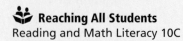 **Teaching Resources**
Checkpoint Quiz 2 (also in Prentice Hall Assessment System)

Reaching All Students
Reading and Math Literacy 10C

Spanish versions available

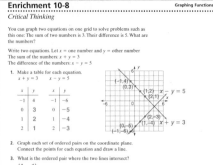

Enrichment 10-8   Graphing Functions
Critical Thinking

You can graph two equations on one grid to solve problems such as this one: The sum of two numbers is 3. Their difference is 5. What are the numbers?

Write two equations. Let x = one number and y = other number
The sum of the numbers: $x + y = 3$
The difference of the numbers: $x - y = 5$

1. Make a table for each equation.
   $x + y = 3$ $x - y = 5$

2. Graph each set of ordered pairs on the coordinate plane. Connect the points for each equation and draw a line.

3. What is the ordered pair where the two lines intersect?
   $(4, -1)$

4. Substitute the coordinates of the ordered pair in Exercise 3 into each equation. Show your equations.
   $4 + (-1) = 3; 4 - (-1) = 5$

5. What is the solution to the problem?
   The numbers are 4 and −1.

The sum of two numbers is 4. Their difference is −2. What are the numbers?

6. Write equations for each condition.
   $x + y = 4; x - y = -2$

7. Graph each equation. What are the numbers?
   The numbers are 1 and 3.

Multiple Choice

32. Which rule could define a function with an input of 4 and an output of 9? **C**
    A. Subtract 5. B. Multiply by 2. C. Add 5. D. Divide by 3.

33. Use the function table at the right to find the value of y when $x = 6$. **I**
    F. 9 G. 10.5 H. 13.5 I. 15

x	y
2	5
3	7.5
4	10
5	12.5

Take It to the NET
Online lesson quiz at
www.PHSchool.com
Web Code: aaa-1008

34. What is the input of a function whose rule is *subtract 3* and whose output is 5? **C**
    A. −2 B. 2 C. 8 D. 15

Short Response

35. Do the graphs of the functions $y = x + 2$ and $y = x - 2$ have any points in common? Explain. See back of book.

Mixed Review

Lesson 9-10   **Solve the problem by working backward.**

36. Suppose your family is planning a trip to a resort. It will take 5 hours of driving. Your family is planning to make three $\frac{1}{2}$ hour stops. They want to arrive at 3:30 P.M. What time should they plan to leave? 9:00 A.M.

Lesson 7-7   **Use the stem-and-leaf plot for Exercises 37–40.**

37. What is the lowest value? 13

38. What is the median? 28

39. What is the mode? 25

40. Find the range. 36

```
1 | 3 7
2 | 5 5 8 9
3 | 1 2
4 | 9
Key: 1 | 3 means 13
```

Checkpoint Quiz 2   **Lessons 10-6 through 10-8**

 Instant self-check quiz online and on CD-ROM

Graph each point on a coordinate plane. 1–2. See back of book.

1. $(-6, 2)$
2. $(0, -6)$

3. Use the table to find the profit or loss for Monday through Wednesday. −$1,293

Day	Income	Expenses
Monday	$948	−$1,285
Tuesday	$523	−$406
Wednesday	$672	−$1,745

Make a table and graph each function. Use x-values $-2, -1, 0, 1, 2$.
4–5. See back of book.

4. $y = x - 7$
5. $y = \frac{x}{2} - 1$

Alternative Assessment

Each student in a pair writes a linear function such as $y = 2x - 3$. Partners exchange papers and make a table and graph of their partner's function rule.

Test Prep

Resources
For additional practice with a variety of test item formats:
• Test-Prep, p. 541
• Test-Taking Strategies, p. 537
• Test-Taking Strategies With Transparencies

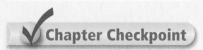

10-9

Make a Graph

Problem Solving

What You'll Learn

OBJECTIVE 1 To solve problems by making a graph

. . . And Why

To make predictions using a graph, as in Example 1

✓ Check Skills You'll Need

? For help, go to Lesson 10-8.

Complete the function table for the given rule.

1. Rule: Output = Input + 8

Input	Output
-6	■ 2
0	■ 8
8	■ 16

2. Rule: Output = Input ÷ (−2)

Input	Output
-8	■ 4
2	■ -1
14	■ -7

OBJECTIVE 1  Making a Graph

 Interactive lesson includes instant self-check, tutorials, and activities.

When to Use This Strategy Making a graph can help you find relationships between data.

① EXAMPLE Making a Graph 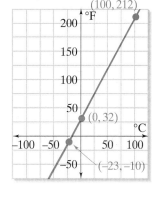 Real World

Temperature The average January temperature in Fairbanks, Alaska, is −23°C. Water freezes at 0°C (32°F) and boils at 100°C (212°F). Use a graph to estimate the average January temperature in degrees Fahrenheit in Fairbanks.

Read and Understand Water freezes at 0°C (32°F) and boils at 100°C (212°F). You need to find −23°C in degrees Fahrenheit.

Plan and Solve To approximate −23°C in degrees Fahrenheit, *make a graph.* You know two pairs of equivalent temperatures. Write the ordered pairs as (0, 32) and (100, 212).

Connect the points with a line. The Fahrenheit temperature is about −10° when the Celsius temperature is −23°.

Look Back and Check Using number sense, since −23°C is less than 0°C and −10°F is less than 32°F, the answer is reasonable.

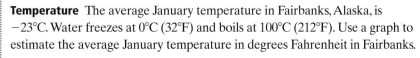

✓ **Check Understanding** ① Use the graph to estimate 22°C in degrees Fahrenheit. **about 70°F**

10-9 Make a Graph **533**

Ongoing Assessment and Intervention

Before the Lesson
Diagnose prerequisite skills using:
• Check Skills You'll Need

During the Lesson
Monitor progress using:
• Check Understanding
• Additional Examples
• Test Prep

After the Lesson
Assess knowledge using:
• Lesson Quiz
• Computer Test Generator CD

10-9

1. Plan

Lesson Preview

✓ **Check Skills You'll Need**
Completing a Function Table
Lesson 10-8: Example 1. Extra Practice p. 651.

Lesson Resources

Optional Materials
• graph paper
• straightedge

Teaching Support includes:
Practice, Reteaching, Enrichment Assessment, Reading & Literacy, Activities, Transparencies, Technology, CD-ROMs, Spanish, and More

See pp. 488G–488H for a complete list of resources for this lesson.

• www.PHSchool.com
• Teacher Web Code: aak-5500

Plus i TEXT

2. Teach

Math Background

You can find approximate solutions to problems by making and interpreting a graph.

Additional Examples

① Marie weighed two objects in class. She found that a 1-lb object was 0.45 kg. A 4-lb object was 1.8 kg. Use a graph to find the weight (mass) in kg of a 2.5-lb object. **about 1.1 kg**

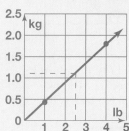

Closure

How can making a graph help you solve a problem? Making a graph helps you visualize data. It also helps you find an approximate answer when you know some values, but not all.

3. Practice

Assignment Guide

1 Objective 1

Ⓐ Ⓑ Core 1–7

Ⓒ Extension 8–9

Test Prep 10–13

Mixed Review 14–19

Error Prevention!

Exercises 1–3 Have students identify what each axis represents and then find a appropriate scale.

4. Assess

 Lesson Quiz 10-9

Solve by making a graph.

1. Asaro was given $1,000 worth of stock in 2001. By 2004, the stock was worth $1,750. If the value of the stock increases at a constant rate, what is its worth in 2006? **$2,250** See back of book.

Alternative Assessment

Each student in a pair writes a word problem that can be solved by making a graph. Partners exchange papers and solve each other's problem. Partners check each other's graphs.

Test Prep

Resources

For additional practice with a variety of test item formats:
• Test-Prep, p. 541
• Test-Taking Strategies, p. 537
• Test-Taking Strategies With Transparencies

534

EXERCISES

Ⓐ **Practice by Example**

Example 1
(page 533)

Need Help?
• Reread the problem.
• Identify the key facts and details.
• Tell the problem in your own words.
• Try a different strategy.
• Check your work.

Solve each problem by making a graph. 1–3. See back of book.

1. The water pressure at a depth of 100 feet in the ocean is 45 pounds per square inch. At a depth of 500 feet, the pressure is 225 pounds per square inch. What is the water pressure at a depth of 800 feet?

 2. **Speed Limits** Mr. Zeller lives in New Zealand where speed limits are measured in kilometers per hour. While visiting the United States, Mr. Zeller drives along a road with a speed limit of 65 miles per hour. Use the signs below. Estimate 65 miles per hour in kilometers per hour.

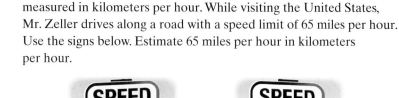

3. A car slowed to a stop at a constant rate. After 5 seconds, the car was traveling 30 miles per hour. After 8 seconds, the car was traveling 12 miles per hour.
   a. How fast was the car moving before the driver applied the brakes?
   b. After how many seconds did the car come to a complete stop?

Ⓑ **Apply Your Skills**

Strategies

Draw a Diagram
Make a Graph
Make an Organized List
Make a Table and Look for a Pattern
Simulate a Problem
Solve a Simpler Problem
Try, Check, and Revise
Use Logical Reasoning
Work Backward
Write an Equation

Choose a strategy to solve each problem.

4. **Music** Nate, Nina, Nancy, and Ned sit in a row in the school orchestra. Each person plays one of the instruments shown below. Nate does not play a wind instrument. Nina broke a string. Nancy sits next to the trumpet player and Nate sits behind him. Which instrument does each person play?
See back of book.

Violin (string)   Clarinet (wind)   Trumpet (brass)   Drum (percussion)

5. **Clocks** The clock in Bloomfield's central square loses 10 minutes every 2 days. On May 1, the clock showed the correct time. If the clock continues to lose time at the same rate, on what date will the clock again show the correct time? September 22

👥 Reaching All Students

| **Below Level** Have students plot pairs of points and connect them. Then have them find other points that appear to lie on the line. Sample: (2, 5) and (6, 15) (0, 0), (4, 10), (8, 20) | **Advanced Learners** A video arcade charges $10 admission and $1 per game. Another arcade charges $6 admission and $2 per game. After how many games are the costs the same? **4 games** | **Error Prevention** See note on page 534. |

6. **Writing in Math** At 10:00 A.M., Rick left camp on his bicycle riding at an average rate of 12 miles per hour. He traveled for 30 miles before he stopped. What time did he stop? Justify your steps. **12:30 P.M; see margin for justification.**

7. An ice cream parlor charges $2.40 for a 12-ounce shake and $3.60 for a 20-ounce shake. The parlor has just come out with a 16-ounce shake. What do you suggest the parlor should charge for the new size?
Answers may vary. Sample: about $3.04

C **Challenge**

8. The average blink of an eye takes $\frac{1}{5}$ of a second. You blink 25 times per minute. If you travel at an average speed of 50 miles per hour for 12 hours, how many miles will you travel with your eyes closed? **50 mi**

9. **Stretch Your Thinking** Write 47 as the sum of 3 different prime numbers. How many different combinations are there?
Answers may vary. Sample: 17 + 23 + 7; 9

Test Prep

Multiple Choice

Use the coordinate plane at the right.

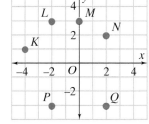

10. Which coordinates describes point K? **C**
   A. (4, 1) B. (4, −1)
   C. (−4, 1) D. (−4, −1)

11. Which point is located at (0, 3)? **I**
   F. L G. P H. Q I. M

12. Which point is 6 units left and 4 units up from point Q?
   A. N B. M C. K D. L **C**

Short Response

Take It to the NET
Online lesson quiz at
www.PHSchool.com
Web Code: aaa-1009

13. Look at the number line at the right.

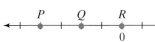

   a. Which point represents the opposite of point S?
   b. Which point represents the number with the greatest absolute value?
   [2] a. Q
   b. P
   [1] one part correct

Mixed Review

Lesson 10-1 Order the integers from least to greatest.

14. 4, −8, −10, 12
   −10, −8, 4, 12

15. 0, 3, −6, 19
   −6, 0, 3, 19

16. −1, 2, −3, 4
   −3, −1, 2, 4

Lesson 8-4 Classify each triangle with the given side lengths by its sides.

17. 7, 7, 7
   equilateral

18. 4, 15, 12
   scalene

19. 8, 9, 8
   isosceles

6. 30 miles at 12 miles per hour takes $2\frac{1}{2}$ hours. $2\frac{1}{2}$ hours from 10 A.M. is 12:30 P.M.

Use the Guided Problem Solving worksheet with Exercise 4.

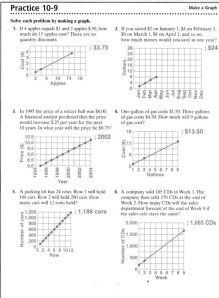

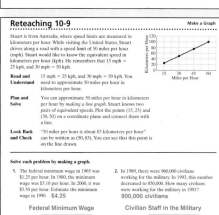

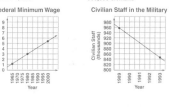

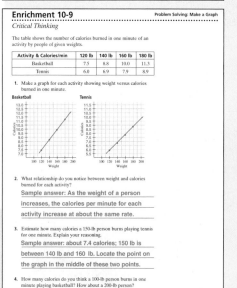

Writing to Justify Steps

Students need to be able to write coherently when formulating and sharing their mathematical thoughts and methods. In this feature, they are introduced to the practice of justifying steps taken to solve a problem—in this case, how to solve a problem involving distance, rate, and time.

Teaching Notes

Discuss with students the importance of being able to communicate mathematical ideas effectively. Elicit from them that carefully recording the steps they take to solve a problem can help them to organize, clarify, and refine their thinking.

EXAMPLE **Teaching Tip**

Emphasize the importance of expressing mathematical thinking clearly and succinctly, as shown in the Example. For instance, point out the use of "Division Property of Equality" rather than writing "dividing the same number from both sides of an equation does not change the equality."

English Learners

Guide students to understand the ordinary English meaning of the term "justify." Explain that to justify a step means to show the correct mathematical reason for doing it, such as to simplify an expression that is not in simplest form.

Exercises

Have students work independently on the exercises. Then have them share their written justifications with a group of classmates. Ask students to adjust their work based upon the group discussion. Guide them to look for ways to make their reasoning more explicit and concise.

Some problems ask you to justify your steps. That means you must explain the reasons for going from one step to the next step. Some steps require a property you have learned. Other steps are procedures, like simplifying.

EXAMPLE

Here is one way you could solve Exercise 6 in Lesson 10-9, with the reason for each step.

6. **Writing in Math** At 10:00 A.M., Rick left camp on his bicycle riding at an average rate of 12 miles per hour. He traveled for 30 miles before he stopped. What time did he stop? Justify your steps.

Rick traveled at an average rate of 12 miles per hour for 30 miles. Let t stand for the time he travels. Use the equation $12t = 30$.

Steps	Reasons
$12t = 30$	This is the equation to be solved.
$\frac{12t}{12} = \frac{30}{12}$	Divide each side by 12.
$t = 2\frac{1}{2}$	Simplify and write the fraction as a mixed number.
$10:00$	Starting time
$\underline{+\ 2:30}$ $12:30$	Write $2\frac{1}{2}$ hours as 2 hours and 30 minutes or 2:30. Then add the times.

Rick will stop at 12:30. This is afternoon, so it is 12:30 P.M.

EXERCISES

Justify each step.

1.
$$8 = 2x - 3$$
$$8 + 3 = 2x - 3 + 3 \quad \text{Add 3 to each side.}$$
$$11 = 2x \quad \text{Simplify.}$$
$$\frac{11}{2} = \frac{2x}{2} \quad \text{Divide each side by 2.}$$
$$5\frac{1}{2} = x \quad \text{Simplify.}$$

2.
$$\frac{1}{2}x = 15$$
$$2\left(\frac{1}{2}\right)x = 2 \cdot 15 \quad \text{Multiply each side by 2.}$$
$$x = 30 \quad \text{Simplify.}$$

3. Ten pounds of potatoes cost $2.55. How much will 6 pounds cost? Write and solve a proportion. Justify your steps. **See margin.**

3. $\frac{10}{2.55} = \frac{6}{c}$ Write the equation.

$10c = 6(2.55)$ Cross multiply.

$10c = 15.30$ Simplify.

$\frac{10c}{10} = \frac{15.30}{10}$ Divide each side by 10.

$c = 1.53$ Simplify.

6 pounds of potatoes cost $1.53.

Using a Variable

The problem-solving strategy **_write an equation_** can help you solve many problems when you are taking tests. Use a variable to represent the quantity that you are looking for. Then write an equation.

EXAMPLE

Admission to the county fair is $4.50 per person. The Rodriguez family pays $22.50 for admission to the fair. How many people are in the Rodriguez family?

Words	cost per person	times	number of people	=	total cost

Let n = the number of people.

Equation	4.50	·	n	=	22.50

$$4.50n = 22.50 \quad \leftarrow \text{Write the equation.}$$

$$\frac{4.50n}{4.50} = \frac{22.50}{4.50} \quad \leftarrow \text{Divide each side by 4.50.}$$

$$n = 5 \quad \leftarrow \text{Simplify.}$$

There are 5 people in the Rodriguez family.

EXERCISES

Write and solve an equation for each situation. 1–4. Equations may vary. Samples are given.

1. Stephanie scores 17 points in the first half of a basketball game. She scores 25 points in all during the game. How many points did she score in the second half of the game? $17 + g = 25$; 8 points

2. Suppose you pass out programs at a ballet. You have 178 programs twenty minutes before the ballet starts. You have 39 programs five minutes before the ballet starts. How many programs do you pass out during the 15 minutes? $39 + p = 178$; 139 programs

3. Suppose you want to make double-decker peanut butter and jelly sandwiches. You need 3 pieces of bread for each sandwich. If you make 18 sandwiches, how many pieces of bread will you need? $18 \times 3 = b$; 54 pieces of bread

4. Russell volunteers 36 hours at a local hospital. He volunteers over a period of 15 weekends. What is the average number of hours he volunteers each weekend? $36 \div 15 = h$; 2.4 hours each weekend

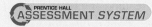
Using a Variable

This feature shows students the advantages of using a variable to solve problems involving an unknown quantity.

Resources

PRENTICE HALL
ASSESSMENT SYSTEM

Test-Taking Strategies With Transparencies
• Transparency 11
• Practice sheet, p. 10

Teaching Notes

EXAMPLE Teaching Tip

Point out that any lower-case letter can be used to represent an unknown quantity. However, emphasize that it is reasonable to choose easy-to-recall letters, such as _p_ for _person_ or _g_ for _granola bars._

Ask: _What is the advantage of choosing a variable and writing an equation to solve a word problem?_ Sample: Writing an equation is a good way to organize the information given.

Test-Taking Strategies With Transparencies

Chapter 10: Using a Variable
Exercises

Define a variable. Then, write and solve an equation for each problem.

1. Mr. Drake bought 84 horseshoes to shoe all of his horses. Each horse needs 4 shoes. How many horses does Mr. Drake have?
   Let _h_ = the number of horses Mr. Drake has. $4h = 84$; $h = 21$; Mr. Drake has 21 horses.

2. The price of a video is $17.99 plus tax. The total cost is $19.16. How much is the tax on the video?
   Let _t_ = the amount of tax. $17.99 + t = $19.16; $t = $1.17; the tax on the video is $1.17.

3. Ed spends an average of $18 per week on gas. So far, he has spent a total of $216. How many weeks has he bought gas?
   Let _w_ = the number of weeks. $18w = 216$; $w = 12$ weeks; Ed has bought gas for 12 weeks.

4. Troop 77 of the Girl Scouts made $342 by selling cookies. If each box of cookies costs $3, how many boxes did Troop 77 sell?
   Let _b_ = the number of boxes. $3b = 342$; $b = 114$ boxes; Troop 77 sold 114 boxes.

5. Maggie spent $30 at the county fair and all she did was ride the rides. If the cost of admission was $8 and each ride cost $2, how many rides did Maggie ride? Let _r_ = the number of rides Maggie rode.
   a. Which equation below could be used to answer the question?
      A. $2r = 30$ B. $30 + 2r = 8$
      C. $8 + 2r = 30$ D. $8r + 2 = 30$
   b. Solve the equation in part _a_ to find the number of rides Maggie rode.
      $r = 11$ rides

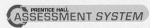

Vocabulary

absolute value (p. 492)   **integers** (p. 491)   **origin** (p. 518)
coordinate plane (p. 518)   **opposites** (p. 491)   **quadrants** (p. 518)
function (p. 527)   **ordered pair** (p. 518)

 Reading Math:
Understanding
Vocabulary

Take It to the NET
Online vocabulary quiz
at **www.PHSchool.com**
Web Code: aaj-1051

Choose the vocabulary term that best completes each sentence.

1. A __?__ assigns one output value to each input value. **function**

2. $(8, -4)$ and $(-2, -3)$ are examples of __?__. **ordered pairs**

3. The numbers $-4, -2, -1, 0,$ and 3 are __?__. **integers**

4. __?__ are the regions of the coordinate plane. **quadrants**

5. -3 and 3 are __?__. **opposites**

Skills and Concepts

10-1 Objectives
▼ To graph integers on
  a number line
▼ To compare and order
  integers

Integers are the set of positive whole numbers, their opposites, and 0. The
distance from 0 on a number line is the **absolute value** of a number.

Compare using < or >.

6. $|-5|$ ▓ $|4|$ 7. -8 ▓ 12 8. 4 ▓ $|-9|$ 9. -12 ▓ -14
    $>$ $<$ $<$ $>$

Order from least to greatest.

10. $-1, 1, 2, -2$ 11. $0, -4, 5, -6$ 12. $-3, 5, -7, 9$
    $-2, -1, 1, 2$ $-6, -4, 0, 5,$ $-7, -3, 5, 9$

10-2 and 10-3 Objectives
▼ To add integers with
  the same signs
▼ To add integers with
  different signs
▼ To subtract integers
▼ To solve equations
  with integers

The sum of two positive integers is positive. The sum of two negative
integers is negative. The sum of integers with different signs is found by
subtracting the lesser absolute value from the greater. The sum has the sign
of the number with the greater absolute value.

You subtract an integer by adding its opposite.

Find each sum or difference.

13. $3 + 8$ 11   14. $5 + (-9)$ -4 15. $-4 + 2$ -2 16. $-7 + (-6)$ -13

17. $11 - 3$ 8   18. $2 - (-6)$ 8   19. $-7 - 4$ -11 20. $-10 - (-2)$ -8

10-4 and 10-5 Objectives

▼ To multiply integers

▼ To divide integers

▼ To solve equations

The product of two integers with the same sign is positive. The product of two integers with different signs is negative.

The quotient of two integers with the same sign is positive. The quotient of two integers with different signs is negative.

Find each product or quotient.

21. 4×9 36   **22.** $7 \times (-3)$ −21 **23.** -5×2 −10   **24.** $-6 \times (-8)$
                                                                         48

25. $16 \div 4$ 4   **26.** $25 \div (-5)$ −5 **27.** $-32 \div 8$ −4   **28.** $-49 \div (-7)$
                                                                         7

10-6 Objectives

▼ To name coordinates

▼ To graph points on a coordinate plane

A **coordinate plane** is formed by the intersection of an *x*-axis and *y*-axis at the **origin.** An **ordered pair** identifies the location of a point. The *x*- and *y*-axes divide the coordinate plane into four regions called **quadrants.**

Graph each point on the same coordinate plane. 29–32. See back of book.

29. $A(0, 6)$ **30.** $B(5, -4)$ **31.** $C(-6, 1)$ **32.** $D(-2, -3)$

10-7 Objectives

▼ To find profit and loss

▼ To draw and interpret graphs

The sum of a business's income and expenses is called a balance. A positive balance is a profit. A negative balance is a loss.

Use the table at the right.

33. Find the total balance for the four months. $26,286

34. Did Pie in the Sky Balloons have a profit or a loss during that time? profit

Pie in the Sky Balloons	
Month	Profit/Loss
January	−$985
February	$10,241
March	−$209
April	$17,239

10-8 and 10-9 Objectives

▼ To make a function table

▼ To graph functions

▼ To solve problems by making a graph

A **function** is a rule that assigns exactly one **output** value to each **input** value.

35. For the function rule "output = input × 5," what is the output for the input 8? 40

Make a table and graph each function. Use *x*-values −2, −1, 0, 1, and 2.
36–38. See margin.

36. $y = x + 3$ **37.** $y = 2x - 3$ **38.** $y = \dfrac{x}{4}$

39. Last year the ticket price for Fun Times Theme Park was $12. This year the price is $16. The rate of increase remains the same. Make a graph to find the ticket price three years from now. See margin.

Chapter Review

36.

x	y
−2	1
−1	2
0	3
1	4
2	5

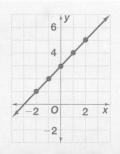

37.

x	y
−2	−7
−1	−5
0	−3
1	−1
2	1

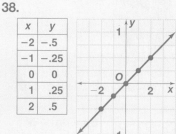

38.

x	y
−2	−.5
−1	−.25
0	0
1	.25
2	.5

39.

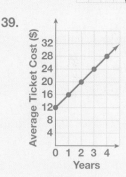

$28

539

Teaching Resources
Ch. 10 Test, Forms A & B
Ch. 10 Alternative Assessment,
Form C

Reaching All Students
Spanish Ch. 10 Test, Forms A & B
Spanish Ch. 10 Alternative
Assessment, Form C

PRENTICE HALL
ASSESSMENT SYSTEM

Assessment Resources
• Ch. 10 Test, Forms A & B
• Ch. 10 Alternative Assessment,
Form C

Computer Test Generator CD
• Ch. 10 Instant Chapter Test™
• Make your own Ch. 10 test

www.PHSchool.com
Student Site
• Self-grading Ch. 10 test

PH SuccessNet Teacher Center
• Resources

Plus *i*TEXT

Chapter 10 — Chapter Test

Take It to the NET
Online chapter test at
www.PHSchool.com
Web Code: aaa-1052

1. What integer represents 7°F below 0°F? −7

2. Name the opposite of each integer.
   a. 89 −89   b. −100 100

Compare using <, >, or =.

3. 18 ■ −24 >   4. −15 ■ −9 <   5. 27 ■ −27 >

6. Order the integers from least to greatest.
   3, −1, −13, 5, 0 −13, −1, 0, 3, 5

7. **Writing in Math** Define *absolute value* and illustrate with a number line. **See margin.**

Find each sum.

8. 9 + (−4) 5   9. −13 + 6 −7   10. −7 + (−5) −12

Find each difference.

11. 1 − (−7) 8   12. −2 − 8 −10

13. −3 − (−3) 0   14. 3 − 9 −6

15. Solve d + 6 = −3. −9

16. **Temperature** The temperature is 18°F at 1:00 A.M. The temperature falls 22 degrees by 6:00 A.M. Find the temperature at 6:00 A.M. −4°F

17. On a math quiz worth 50 points, a student misses 2 points on the first section, 3 points on the second, 2 points on the fourth, and 1 point on the last. Find the student's score. 42

Find each product.

18. 5 × (−4) −20   19. −3 × (−6) 18   20. −2 × 7 −14

21. 9 ÷ (−3) −3   22. −5 ÷ (−5) 1   23. −12 ÷ 4 −3

Use the coordinate plane for Exercises 24 and 25.

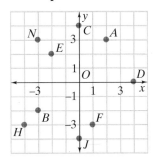

24. Name the point with the given coordinates.
    a. (0, 4) C   b. (−3, 3) N   c. (−4, −3) H

25. Write the coordinates for each point.
    a. A (2, 3)   b. B (−3, −2)   c. F (1, −3)   d. J (0, −4)

26. Graph each point on a coordinate plane.
    a. (−2, −3)   b. (4, −5)   c. (2, 6)
    26a–c. See back book.

27. a. Use the data below find Royale Bakery's profit or loss for each month. 27a–b. See back of book.
    b. Graph the profit and loss data.

Income and Expenses for Royale Bakery		
Month	**Income**	**Expenses**
Jan.	$1,314	−$828
Feb.	$2,120	−$120
Mar.	$1,019	−$1,285
Apr.	$1,438	−$765

28. Make a table and draw a graph for the linear function y = x − 3. **See margin.**

29. **Estimation** A mountain climber starts at 50 feet above sea level at 7:00 A.M. At 11:00 A.M., she is 210 feet above sea level. If she maintains a steady rate, estimate her height above sea level at 12:30 P.M.
    about 270 ft above sea level

---

7. **Answers may vary. Sample:** The absolute value of a number is its distance from 0 on a number line. −5 is 5 units from 0 on a number line, so its absolute value is 5.

5 is 5 units from 0 on a number line, so its absolute value is also 5.

5 units 5 units

−5 0 5

28.
x	y
−2	−5
−1	−4
0	−3
1	−2
2	−1

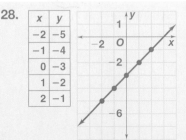

Test Prep

Test Prep

Students must be able to extract information from reading passages, answer multiple-choice questions, and construct responses in order to be successful in current state and national assessments.

Multiple Choice

Choose the correct letter.

1. Evaluate the expression $b - a - 8$ when $a = 7$ and $b = 24$. **C**
A. -25 B. -9 C. 9 D. 11

2. Which amount is the same as $1\frac{1}{2}$ pints? **G**
F. 25 fluid ounces G. 3 cups
H. $\frac{3}{5}$ quart I. $\frac{1}{8}$ gallon

3. Suppose you purchase 9 peaches, 6 oranges, 12 pears, and 8 plums. What is the ratio of plums to pears? **A**
A. $\frac{2}{3}$ B. 9 to 12 C. 12:8 D. 4:2

4. Find the median of the following set of data: 9, 19, 9, 17, 13, 14, 11, 9, 13. **I**
F. 9 G. 10 H. $12\frac{2}{3}$ I. 13

5. Suppose you have a fresh lemonade stand. You spend $7 on the lemons, sugar, and cups. During the day, you sell 12 cups of lemonade for $.50 each. What is your profit or loss? **A**
A. $-$1 B. $-$.50 C. $0 D. $1

6. Which of the following is the area of a circle with a diameter of 9 inches? Round to the nearest square unit. **H**
F. 28 in^2 G. 57 in^2
H. 64 in^2 I. 254 in^2

7. Simplify: $-8 + 9 \div 3$. **A**
A. $-\frac{1}{3}$ B. $\frac{1}{3}$ C. 5 D. -5

8. Which statement is false? **H**
F. A square is always a rectangle.
G. Some rectangles are rhombuses.
H. All quadrilaterals are parallelograms.
I. A square is always a rhombus.

9. Which equation is NOT correct? **D**
A. $\frac{3}{4} + 2\frac{1}{2} = 3\frac{1}{4}$ B. $3\frac{4}{5} - \frac{6}{8} = 3\frac{1}{20}$
C. $1\frac{7}{8} + 1\frac{5}{6} = 3\frac{17}{24}$ D. $5\frac{2}{5} - 2\frac{1}{3} = 3\frac{1}{10}$

10. Find the volume of a rectangular prism with the dimensions: $\ell = 10$ m, $w = 7$ m, $h = 8$ m.
F. $V = 25$ m^3 G. $V = 56$ m^3
H. $V = 70$ m^3 I. $V = 560$ m^3
I

11. The angles of 4 triangles have the following measures. Which of the triangles is obtuse?
A. $86°, 53°, 41°$ B. $89°, 45.5°, 45.5°$
C. $123°, 32°, 25°$ D. $74°, 71°, 35°$
C

Gridded Response

12. How many kilometers are in 120 meters? **0.12**

13. Jack saves $32.75 from his newspaper delivery job. On Saturday, he spends $19.52 of his savings on a CD. How much does he have left? **13.23**

Short Response

14–15. See back of book.

14. On a scale drawing, the scale shown is 1 inch to 10 feet. The length of a room is 2.5 inches on the drawing. Make a sketch and find the actual length of the room.

15. Write an integer to represent three degrees Fahrenheit below zero. Then graph the integer on a number line.

Extended Response

16a–b. See margin.

16. a. A parallelogram has a base of 9 inches and a height of 7 inches. Find its area.
b. The base and the height of the parallelogram are doubled. Is the area doubled? Explain.

16. **[4]** a. 63 in.^{2};
  b. $b \times h = 9 \times 7 = 63$ in.^{2};
  double the base:
  $b \times 2 = 9 \times 2 = 18$ in.; double the height:
  $h \times 2 = 7 \times 2 =$

14 in.;
$b \times h = 18 \times 14 = 252$ in.^{2}

The area in part (a) is one quarter the area in part (b) because $63 \times 4 = 252$.

16. **[3]** appropriate methods, but a computational error

[2] did not double the base and height accordingly OR no explanation given

Resources

Teaching Resources
Cumulative Review

Reaching All Students
Spanish Cumulative Review

PRENTICE HALL
ASSESSMENT SYSTEM

Test Preparation
• Ch. 10 standardized test prep

Assessment Resources
• Cumulative Review

Computer Test Generator CD
• Standardized test prep

www.PHSchool.com
• Standardized test prep
• Resources

Plus **TEXT**

16. [1] correct areas given without work shown

Peaks and Valleys

Students will use data from these two pages and from page 489 to answer the questions posed here in Put It All Together.

Activating Prior Knowledge

Have students share any experiences they have had at high (or low) altitudes and in very warm and cold temperatures. Have them describe the effects of these extremes of elevation and temperature.

Teaching Notes

Have volunteers read aloud the data about the variety of places shown on these pages. Discuss the information presented. Ask: *Suppose you stood at the base of Mt. Whitney and looked up at its summit. How many feet above you do you think its peak stands?* Sample: Because you are already standing high above sea level, the top of the mountain would actually be *much less* than 14,495 feet higher.

Number Sense Connection

Remind students that there are 5,280 feet in a mile. You might want to convert some elevations into miles.

Diversity

Invite students who have lived outside the United States to describe places familiar to them in terms of their altitudes and temperatures.

542

Real-World Snapshots

Peaks and Valleys

Applying Integers Elevations in the United States vary from tens of thousands of feet above sea level to several hundred feet below sea level. Aerial photography and relief maps show these differences clearly.

Seattle, Washington

Mt. Whitney, California
Elevation: 14,495 feet
Highest point in the contiguous United States.

Las Vegas, Nevada

Death Valley, California
Elevation: −282 feet
Annual temperature: high 90.5°F, low 62.2°F
Lowest point in the contiguous United States.

Pacific Ocean
Elevation: Sea level (0 feet)

Put It All Together

Data File **Use the information on these two pages and on page 489 to answer these questions.**

1. Which featured location has the highest elevation? The lowest elevation?

2. **a.** How much higher is the elevation of Vostok Station, Antarctica, than the elevation of Death Valley, California?

   b. How much higher is the elevation of New Orleans, Louisiana, than the elevation of Death Valley, California?

3. Which location has an elevation 5,512 feet lower than Colorado Springs, Colorado? Show your work.
   A. Colossal Cave, Arizona   **B.** Detroit, Michigan
   C. Houston, Texas   **D.** New Orleans, Louisiana

4. Which location has an elevation 16 feet higher than New Orleans, Louisiana? Show your work.
   A. Atlantic Ocean   **B.** Death Valley, California
   C. Key West, Florida   **D.** Long Island, New York

5. **Reasoning** Which of these places do you think has the highest elevation: Boston, Massachusetts; Denver, Colorado; Memphis, Tennessee? Explain.

Take It to the NET For more information about geography, go to **www.PHSchool.com**.
Web Code: aae-1053

542

---

1. Mt. Whitney; Death Valley

2a. 11,502 ft

   b. 274 ft

3. B. Detroit, Michigan
   $6145 - 5512 = x$
   $633 = x$

4. C. Keywest, Florida
   $y - 16 = -8$
   $y = 8$

5. Answers may vary. Sample: Denver, Colorado Boston, Massachusetts is on the coast and therefore is at about sea level; Memphis, Tennessee is on the Mississippi River and should be fairly low in elevation. Denver, Colorado is located near Colorado Springs, which has an elevation of over 6,000 ft.

Detroit, Michigan
Elevation: 633 feet
Annual temperature:
high 58.4°F, low 41°F

Minneapolis,
Minnesota

Boston,
Massachusetts

Long Island, New York
Elevation: 16 feet
Annual temperature:
high 61.2°F, low 43.5°F

Denver, Colorado

**Colorado Springs,
Colorado**
Elevation: 6,145 feet
Annual temperature:
high 61.8°F, low 33.7°F

Chicago,
Illinois

Washington, DC

Oklahoma City,
Oklahoma

Memphis,
Tennessee

New Orleans, Louisiana
Elevation: −8 feet
Annual temperature:
high 78°F, low 59.6°F

Atlantic Ocean
Elevation: Sea level (0 feet)

Houston, Texas
Elevation: 96 feet
Annual temperature:
high79.4°F, low 58.2°F

Key West, Florida Keys
Elevation: 8 feet
Annual temperature:
high 82.9°F, low 73.2°F

543

Put It All Together

Have students work in pairs to answer the questions. Begin by asking a volunteer to explain the difference between a relief map and a political map. Discuss reasons for using either kind.

Exercise 5 Suggest that students use a relief map of the United States to answer these questions, or that they use a road atlas and make inferences from it based on a city's proximity to mountains or sea shores.

Geography Connection
Invite students to identify the highest and lowest points in your state, as well as the warmest and coldest places. Ask them to compare this with some of the data presented on these pages.

Exploring Probability

Chapter at a Glance

11-1

Probability
pp. 547–551

Objectives
▼ Finding Probabilities of Events

New Vocabulary
eqally likely outcomes, event, probability of an event

NCTM Standards
1, 3, 5, 6, 7, 8, 9, 10

Local Standards

11-2

Experimental Probability
pp. 553–557

Objectives
▼ Finding Experimental Probabilities

New Vocabulary
experimental probability

Optional Materials
number cubes

NCTM Standards
1, 5, 6, 7, 8, 9, 10

Local Standards

11-3

Making Predictions From Data
pp. 558–562

Objectives
▼ Making Predictions From Probabilities
② Making Predictions Based on Samples

New Vocabulary
populaton, sample

Optional Materials
number cubes

NCTM Standards
1, 2, 5, 6, 7, 8, 9, 10

Local Standards

✓ Checkpoint Quiz 1

11-4 [Problem Solving]

Simulate a Problem
pp. 563–566

Objectives
▼ Solving Problems by Simulation

NCTM Standards
1, 5, 6, 7, 8, 9, 10

Local Standards

11-5

Tree Diagrams and the Counting Principle
pp. 568–573

Objectives
▼ Using Tree Diagrams
② Using the Counting Principle

New Vocabulary
tree diagram, counting principle

NCTM Standards
1, 2, 3, 5, 6, 7, 8, 9, 10

Local Standards

11-6

Exploring Permutations
pp. 574–578

Objectives
▼ Finding Permutations
② Counting Permutations

New Vocabulary
permutation

NCTM Standards
1, 3, 5, 6, 7, 8, 9, 10

Local Standards

✓ Checkpoint Quiz 2

11-7

Independent Events
pp. 580–584

Objectives
▼ Identifying Independent Events
② Finding Probabilities of Compound Independent Events

New Vocabulary
independent events, compound events

NCTM Standards
1, 2, 5, 6, 7, 8, 9, 10

Local Standards

Reaching All Students

Additional Instructional Options in Chapter 11

Reading and Math Literacy

📖 Reading Math

Understanding Word problems, p. 579

Reading Math hints, pp. 550, 577, 581

Reading Comprehension, p. 589

Understanding Vocabulary, p. 586

✏️ Writing in Math

Daily Writing Practice, pp. 549, 556, 561, 565, 567, 572, 577, 582, 588

Above Level

C Challenge exercises

pp. 551, 557, 561, 566, 572, 577, 583

⬤ Extension

Odds, p. 552

Hands-On and Technology

🔍 Investigations

Exploring probabilities, p. 553

Making Predictions, p. 558

Exploring Order, p. 574

💻 Technology

Simulations, p. 567

Activities and Projects

📖 Real-World Snapshots

Applying Probability pp. 590–591

📁 Chapter Project

Now Playing, p. 641

Test Prep

📝 Daily Test Prep

pp. 551, 557, 562, 566, 573, 577, 583

📝 Test-Taking Strategies

Answering True-False Questions, p. 585

📝 Test Prep

Reading Comprehension, p. 589

Chapter Assessment

✔️ Checkpoint Quiz

pp. 562, 578

⬤ Chapter Review

pp. 586–587

⬤ Chapter Test

p. 588

Pacing Options

This chart suggests pacing only for the core lessons and their parts. It is provided as a possible guide. It will help you determine how much time you have in your schedule to cover the additional features and assessment, as described at the left.

Day	Traditional 45-minute class periods	Block 90-minute class periods
1	11-1 ▽	11-1 ▽
2	11-2 ▽	11-2 ▽
3	11-3 ▽	11-3 ▽ ▽
		11-4 ▽
4	11-3 ▽	11-5 ▽ ▽
5	11-4 ▽	11-6 ▽ ▽
6	11-5 ▽	11-7 ▽ ▽
7	11-5 ▽	
8	11-6 ▽	
9	11-6 ▽	
10	11-7 ▽	
11	11-7 ▽	

NCTM STANDARDS 2000	
1 Number and Operations	6 Problem Solving
2 Algebra	7 Reasoning and Proof
3 Geometry	8 Communication
4 Measurement	9 Connections
5 Data Analysis and Probability	10 Representation

Math Background

Skills Trace

BEFORE Chapter 11
Grade 5 presented basic probability concepts.

DURING Chapter 11
Course 1 extends probability to simulations, tree diagrams, the counting principle, permutations, and independent events.

AFTER Chapter 11
Throughout this course students build a foundation for probability.

11-1 Probability

> **Math Understandings**
> - In mathematics, probability is expressed as a number from 0 to 1 that estimates how often an event will occur.
> - You can write probabilities as fractions, decimals, or percents.

When you toss a fair coin once, each outcome, heads and tails, is just as likely to occur as the other. Outcomes that have the same chance of occurring are called **equally likely outcomes**. An **event** is a collection of possible outcomes. The **probability of an event**, written P(event), is a number that describes how likely it is that the event will occur.

> **Probability of an Event**
>
> $$P(\text{event}) = \frac{\text{number of favorable outcomes}}{\text{total number of possible outcomes}}$$

When the probability of an event is 0, the event is impossible. When the probability of an event is 1, the event is certain to happen.

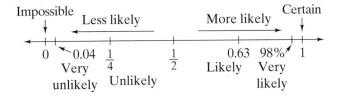

11-2 Experimental Probability

> **Math Understandings**
> - Experimental probability is based on the results of an actual experiment; theoretical probability is based on the assumption that certain outcomes are equally likely.

When you find a probability based on data you collect, you are finding experimental probability.

> **Experimental Probability**
>
> $$P(\text{event}) = \frac{\text{number of times an event occurs}}{\text{total number of trials}}$$

A *fair* coin or number cube generates equally likely outcomes. If coins, cubes, or spinners are unevenly made, they may *not* be fair.

11-3 Making Predictions from Data

> **Math Understandings**
> - Probabilities can help you make predictions about the outcome of an experiment. However, they do not guarantee what will actually occur.
> - The probability of an event may not be a good predictor of what will happen in a small number of cases. The laws of probability are more likely to predict what will happen when you survey a very large number of events.

To predict the number of times an event will occur, multiply the probability of the event by the total number of trials.

$$P(\text{event}) \times \frac{\text{total number}}{\text{of trials}} = \frac{\text{number of predicted}}{\text{successes}}$$

A **population** is a group about which you want information. A **sample** is a part of the population. To make predictions, a sample can *represent* the population.

11-4 Simulate a Problem

Sometimes it is difficult to collect data from an actual situation. Instead, you may be able to use a simulation. A **simulation** of a real-world situation is a model used to find experimental probabilities. You can use number cubes, spinners, and computers to model real-world situations.

11-5 ## Tree Diagrams and the Counting Principle

Math Understandings
- You can use the Counting Principle to find the number of ways to make one choice followed by a second choice.

You can use a **tree diagram** to find the probability of two or more events.

Example: This tree diagram shows the possible outcomes from rolling a number cube and then tossing a coin. What is the probability that you will get an even number and tails? The diagram shows that there are 3 outcomes for these two events.

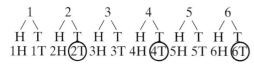

You can use the **counting principle** to find a large number of outcomes.

Counting Principle

Suppose there are m ways of making one choice and n ways of making a second choice. Then there are $m \times n$ ways to make the first choice followed by the second choice.

 11-6 ## Exploring Permutations

Math Understandings
- Order makes a difference in permutations.
- You can use an organized list, a tree diagram, or the counting principle to find the number of permutations.

An arrangement of objects in a particular order is called a **permutation**.

Example: To find the number of different orders in which you can arrange the four letters in STOP, you have four choices for the first letter, and then 3 remaining choices for the second letter, and so on. The number of permutations for the four letters is $4 \times 3 \times 2 \times 1$ or 24.

 11-7 ## Independent Events

Math Understandings
- Two events are independent if one event does not affect the probability of the other event.
- It is a fallacy that, when tossing a fair coin, you are more likely to get heads after tossing a series of tails. The probability remains one out of two.

When the occurrence of one event does not affect the probability of another event, the two are **independent events**. A **compound event** consists of two or more separate events.

Probability of Independent Events

If A and B are independent events, then
$P(A, \text{then } B) = P(A) \times P(B)$.

Example: If you roll a six-sided number cube two times, the probability of rolling a two followed by a two is $\frac{1}{6} \times \frac{1}{6}$, or $\frac{1}{36}$.

Additional Professional Development Opportunities

Chapter 11 Math Background notes: pp. 548, 554, 559, 564, 569, 575, 581

Additional resources available from SkyLight Professional Development:

On-site courses, workshops, summer institutes. Online courses and chat rooms. Videocassettes and books. Visit www.skylightedu.com.

Ongoing Assessment and Intervention

The *Prentice Hall Mathematics* program provides many options for assessment in the Student Edition, Teacher's Edition, and teaching resources. From these options you may choose instructional materials that are appropriate for your students and that support your district's curriculum requirements.

Daily Assessment

 Instant Check System™ in Chapter 11

Allows students to check their own learning before, during, and after each lesson.

Diagnosing Readiness before the chapter (p. 546)

Check Skills You'll Need exercises in each lesson (pp. 547, 553, 558, 563, 568, 574, 580)

Check Understanding questions with each Example (pp. 548, 554, 559, 564, 568, 569, 574, 575, 580, 581)

Checkpoint Quiz (pp. 562, 578)

Formal Assessment

Assessment in the Student Text and in Additional Resources

Assess student progress throughout the Course 1 textbook and with blackline masters and CD-ROM.

Student Edition
- Chapter 11 Review, with Vocabulary, Skills, and Concepts Review, pp. 586–587
- Chapter 11 Test, p. 588

Assessment Resources
- Checkpoint Quizzes 1 & 2
- Chapter Test, forms A & B
- Chapter Alternative Assessment

Spanish versions available.

Computer Test Generator CD-ROM
- Instant Chapter Tests™—pre-made tests with items that vary every time you print.
- Online Testing allows you to give tests online and receive progress reports.
- Prepare students by making tests based on standardized test objectives.

Algebra Readiness Tests
- Includes Basic Skills Tests and Concept-Readiness Tests.
- Assess understanding of skills and concepts needed for success in algebra.

Intervention

Skills Intervention Kit

 Online Intervention
Integrated within the iText, this online intervention system includes diagnostic tests and prescribed remediation, plus reports to track student mastery.

A *complete* system for the student who is struggling with course-level work

Eight intervention units cover core skills and allow you to:
- **Diagnose** students' gaps in basic skills
- **Prescribe** an individualized course of study
- **Monitor** student progress

Includes print workbooks, tutorial CD-ROM, teacher editions, progress folders, and more. *Available in Spanish.*

How to Use with Chapter 11

11-1 Ratio, Proportion, and Percent, Skill 11
11-2 Number Theory and Fraction Concepts, Skill 12
11-3 Ratio, Proportion, and Percent, Skill 6
11-5 Whole Numbers, Skills 14, 16
11-6 Whole Numbers, Skills 14, 16
11-7 Operations with Fractions, Skill 10

Standardized Test Preparation

The *Prentice Hall Mathematics* program integrates preparation for high-stakes standardized tests in every lesson of the Student Edition and continues this support in the Prentice Hall Assessment System.

Test Prep

In Student Text, Chapter 11

Teaches students strategies and gives them practice with all the test item formats they will encounter on high-stakes tests.

Test Prep exercises in each lesson (pp. 551, 557, 562, 566, 573, 577, 583)

Test-Taking Strategies Answering True-False Questions, p. 585

Test Prep Reading Comprehension, p. 589

A three-step approach to preparing students for high stakes, national, and state exams.

1 Diagnose & Prescribe

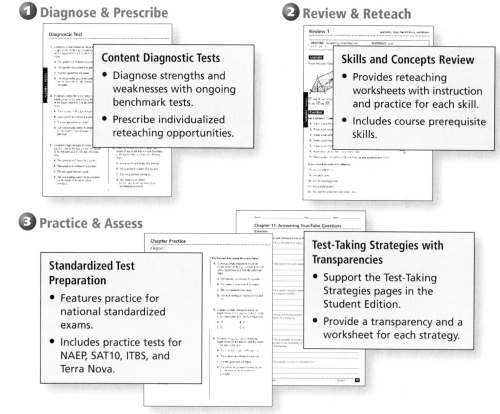

Content Diagnostic Tests

- Diagnose strengths and weaknesses with ongoing benchmark tests.
- Prescribe individualized reteaching opportunities.

2 Review & Reteach

Skills and Concepts Review

- Provides reteaching worksheets with instruction and practice for each skill.
- Includes course prerequisite skills.

3 Practice & Assess

Standardized Test Preparation

- Features practice for national standardized exams.
- Includes practice tests for NAEP, SAT10, ITBS, and Terra Nova.

Test-Taking Strategies with Transparencies

- Support the Test-Taking Strategies pages in the Student Edition.
- Provide a transparency and a worksheet for each strategy.

Correlation to Standardized Tests

Lesson		NAEP	Terra Nova		ITBS	SAT10	Local Test
			CAT6	CTBS			
11-1	Probability	D4a-D4c	■	■		■	
11-2	Experimental Probability	D4c, D4d		■		■	
11-3	Making Predictions From Data	D4c, D4d		■			
11-4	Problem Solving: Simulate a Problem	D4c		■			
11-5	Tree Diagrams and the Counting Principle	D4e, D4f		■		■	
11-6	Exploring Permutations	D4e		■		■	
11-7	Independent Events	D4b		■			

NAEP National Assessment of Educational Progress
CAT6/Terra Nova California Achievement Test, 6th Ed.

CTBS/Terra Nova Comprehensive Test of Basic Skills
ITBS Iowa Test of Basic Skills, Form M.

SAT10 Stanford Achievement Test, 10th Ed.

Program Resources

	Resources in Grab & Go™ Files				Resources for Reaching All Students				Spanish Resources			Transparencies					Presentation Assistant Plus!
	Practice	Reteach	Enrich	Checkpt Quiz	Reading & Math Literacy	Technology Activities	Hands-On Activities	Guided Problem Solving	Practice	Reading & Math Literacy	Checkpt Quiz	Skills Check	Problem of the Day	Additional Examples	Answers to Exercises	Lesson Quiz	Prentice Hall Presentation Pro CD-ROM
11-1	■	■	■		■		■	■	■			■	■	■	■	■	■
11-2	■	■	■		■		■	■	■			■	■	■	■	■	■
11-3	■	■	■		■			■	■		■	■	■	■	■	■	■
11-4	■	■	■			■		■	■			■	■	■	■	■	■
11-5	■	■	■					■	■			■	■	■	■	■	■
11-6	■	■	■	■	■			■	■		■	■	■	■	■	■	■
11-7								■				■	■	■	■	■	■
For the Chapter	Chapter Projects, Chapter Tests, Alternative Assessment, Cumulative Review, Cumulative Assessment				On web site only: Home Activities, Interdisciplinary Activities, Algebra Readiness Puzzles				Spanish Chapter Tests, Alternative Assessment, Cumulative Review, Cumulative Assessment			Classroom Aid Transparencies					

Also available for use with the chapter:

 PRENTICE HALL **ASSESSMENT SYSTEM** *See page 544F.*

- Practice Workbook
- Solution Key
- MathNotes folder

- For teacher support and access to student Web materials, use the Web Code aak-5500.
- For additional online and technology resources, *see below*.

 Technology

iTEXT Online and on CD-ROM

Complete Interactive Student Text online and on CD-ROM—with instant feedback assessment, tutorial help, dynamic activities, instructional and real-world videos, audio, and additional practice.

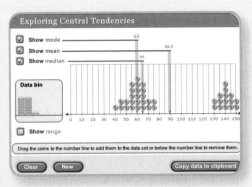

www.PHSchool.com For Students

Use Web codes for easy access to online activities, chapter projects, self-grading lesson quizzes, chapter tests, vocabulary quizzes, updated data sources, graphing calculator procedures, and more.

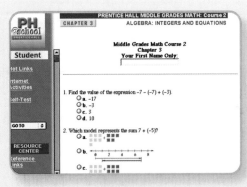

PH SuccessNet For Teachers

Online lesson planning with built-in state correlations, all the teaching resources, complete reference library, your own calendar and Teacher Web page, professional development, and more.

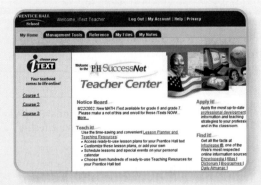

Presentation Assistant Plus!

The *Prentice Hall Presentation Assistant Plus!* provides you with the material you need to teach a lesson from beginning to end. Two easy-to-use formats—Transparencies and PowerPoint®—allow you to present a lesson the way you are most comfortable.

Transparencies

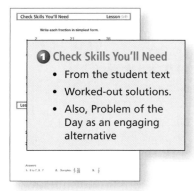

1 Check Skills You'll Need
- From the student text
- Worked-out solutions.
- Also, Problem of the Day as an engaging alternative

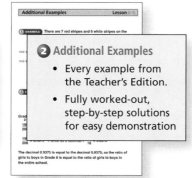

2 Additional Examples
- Every example from the Teacher's Edition.
- Fully worked-out, step-by-step solutions for easy demonstration

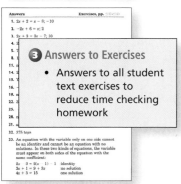

3 Answers to Exercises
- Answers to all student text exercises to reduce time checking homework

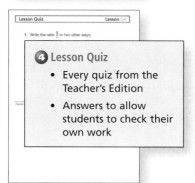

4 Lesson Quiz
- Every quiz from the Teacher's Edition
- Answers to allow students to check their own work

  PowerPoint Throughout the Teacher's Edition, this symbol indicates material that is available in the Presentation Assistant Plus!

 PowerPoint **Prentice Hall Presentation Pro CD-ROM**

- Includes all Transparencies.
- Conveniently organized by lesson so you can easily **1** Introduce, **2** Teach, **3** Check Homework, and **4** Assess each lesson.
- Animated examples allow step-by-step instruction at your own pace.
- Easy to edit so you can create custom presentations.

Teaching Chapter 11 Using Presentation Assistant Plus!

	1 Introduce	**2** Teach	**3** Check Homework	**4** Assess
	Check Skills You'll Need	Additional Examples	Student Edition Answers	Lesson Quiz
11-1	p. 94	p. 152	✔	p. 94
11-2	p. 95	p. 153	✔	p. 95
11-3	p. 96	p. 154	✔	p. 96
11-4	p. 97	pp. 155–157	✔	p. 97
11-5	p. 98	pp. 158–159	✔	p. 98
11-6	p. 99	p. 160	✔	p. 99
11-7	p. 100	pp. 161–162	✔	p. 100

Prentice Hall Presentation Pro

CD-ROM with dynamic PowerPoint® presentations for every lesson. Helps you introduce and develop concepts, check homework, and assess progress. Part of Presentation Assistant Plus! *(See above.)*

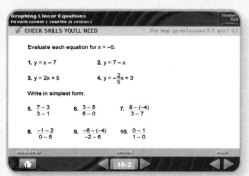

Computer Test Generator

CD-ROM to create practice sheets and tests for course objectives and standardized tests. Includes Instant Chapter Tests™, online testing, and student reports. Part of the PH Assessment System. *(See page 544F.)*

Resource Pro® with Planning Express®

CD-ROM with a lesson planning tool that allows you to import state and local objectives. Includes electronic versions of all the teaching resources.

Chapter Resources

Reading and Math Support

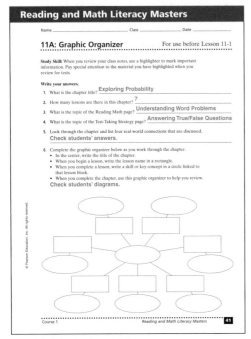

Name _____ Class _____ Date _____

11-3 • Guided Problem Solving

GPS Student Page 561, Exercise 22:

A sample of 100 gadgets is selected from the day's production of 5,000 gadgets. In the sample, 7 are defective. Predict the number of faulty gadgets in the day's production.

Read and Understand

1. What are you being asked to find?
   the number of faulty gadgets in the day's
   production

2. What do you need to use to solve this problem?
   a proportion

Plan and Solve

3. Write a ratio of the number of faulty gadgets to the number in the sample.
   $\frac{7}{100}$

4. Let n represent the number of faulty gadgets in the day's production. Write a ratio of the number of faulty gadgets to the number in the day's production.
   $\frac{n}{5,000}$

5. Create a proportion with the two ratios in Steps 3 and 4. Then solve the proportion.
   $\frac{7}{100} = \frac{n}{5,000}; n = 350$

6. Predict the number of faulty gadgets in the day's production.
   350 gadgets

Look Back and Check

7. Explain how to check your answer.
   Divide the answer by $\frac{7}{100}$ to get 5,000.

Solve Another Problem

8. A sample of 50 CDs is selected from the day's production of 300 CDs. In the sample, 4 are defective. Predict the number of faulty CDs in the day's production.
   $\frac{4}{50} = \frac{n}{300}; n = 24; 24$ CDs will be faulty.

Name _____ Class _____ Date _____

11-4 • Guided Problem Solving

GPS Student Page 566, Exercise 8:

Collecting Each box of a cereal brand contains one of four prizes. A box costs $3.50. You want to collect all four prizes. What is the least amount of money you may need to spend to get all four prizes?

Read and Understand

1. What are you being asked to find?
   The least amount of money you need to spend
   to get all four prizes.

Plan and Solve

2. What is the probability of getting one of the prizes?
   $\frac{1}{4}$

3. What is the least number of boxes you need to buy to get all 4 prizes?
   4 boxes

4. If each box costs $3.50, what is the least amount of money it will cost you?
   $13.50

Look Back and Check

5. How likely is it that you get all four prizes in the first four boxes you buy?
   not likely

Solve Another Problem

6. A fifth prize was added to the cereal boxes. What is the least amount of money you may need to spend to get all five prizes?
   $17

Name _____ Class _____ Date _____

11-5 • Guided Problem Solving

GPS Student Page 572, Exercise 14:

Games To play a game, you spin a spinner and take a card. The spinner has equal sections that tell you to move 1, 2, 3, or 4 spaces. The cards read *Free Turn*, *Lose a Turn*, or *No Change*. Find the probability that you move 3 spaces and lose a turn.

Read and Understand

1. Before you find the probability, what do you have to find?
   the total number of possible outcomes.

2. What are the two methods you can use to solve this problem?
   Draw a tree diagram or use the counting
   principle.

Plan and Solve

3. How many outcomes are possible on the spinner? 4

4. How many outcomes are possible with the cards? 3

5. Using the counting principle, how may total outcomes are possible?
   $4 \times 3 = 12$ outcomes

6. How many outcomes result in moving 3 spaces and losing a turn?
   1 outcome

7. What is the probability that you move 3 spaces and lose a turn?
   $\frac{1}{12}$

Look Back and Check

8. How would you use a tree diagram to answer this question?
   For each spinner number, there are 3 possible cards.
   Show each spinner number branching to all 3 cards.

Solve Another Problem

9. In this same game, what is the probability that you move 3 spaces and take any of the 3 cards?
   $\frac{3}{12} = \frac{1}{4}$

Name _____ Class _____ Date _____

11-6 • Guided Problem Solving

GPS Student Page 576, Exercise 14:

Fitness A body builder plans to do four different exercises in his workout. In how many ways can he complete his workout?

Read and Understand

1. What is a permutation?
   A permutation is an arrangement of objects in
   a particular order.

2. What are some methods you can use to find the number of permutations?
   lists, tree diagram, counting principle

Plan and Solve

3. How many choices does he have for his first exercise? 4 choices

4. After he completes the first exercise, how many choices does he have for his second exercise? 3 choices

5. After he completes the second exercise, how many choices does he have for his third exercise? 2 choices

6. After he completes the third exercise, how many choices does he have for his fourth exercise? 1 choice

7. Use the counting principle to find how many ways he can complete his workout?
   $4 \times 3 \times 2 \times 1 = 24$ ways

Look Back and Check

8. Is you answer reasonable? How can you confirm your answer?
   Yes; by making a list or a tree diagram, you
   can confirm that there are 24 ways.

Solve Another Problem

9. The body builder pulled a muscle and can only do three different exercises in his workout. In how many ways can he complete his workout?
   6 ways

Name _____ Class _____ Date _____

11-7 • Guided Problem Solving

GPS Student Page 582, Exercise 15:

Biology Assume two parents are equally likely to have a boy or a girl. Find the probability they will have a girl and then a boy.

Read and Understand

1. What does it mean for two events to be equally likely?
   Both events have the same probability occurring.

2. How would you describe the events of having a girl and then having a boy?
   independent events

Plan and Solve

3. What is the probability of a couple having a girl?
   $\frac{1}{2}$

4. What is the probability of a couple having a boy?
   $\frac{1}{2}$

5. Write an expression to find the probability of a couple having a girl and then having a boy.
   $\frac{1}{2} \times \frac{1}{2}$

6. Find the probability that a couple will have a girl and then have a boy.
   $\frac{1}{4}$

Look Back and Check

7. List all of the possible outcomes of a couple having two children. What is the probability that they will have a girl and then a boy. Does your answer check?
   boy, boy; boy, girl; girl, boy; girl, girl; yes.

Solve Another Problem

8. Find the probability that a couple will have a girl another boy, and then another girl.
   $\frac{1}{2} \times \frac{1}{2} \times \frac{1}{2} = \frac{1}{8}$

Activities and Projects

Name _____ Class _____ Date _____

Activity 42: Exploring Order

Materials needed: four index cards per student

1. Write each of the first four letters of your first name on the index cards, one letter per card. If you have a letter in your name that repeats, use the next letter in your name. For example, if your name is Matthew, don't use M-A-T-T, use M-A-T-H. If your first name does not have enough letters, use letters from your last name. For example, Sara Smith would use S-A-R-M.

2. Copy the table below.

Number of Letters	Number of Ways to Arrange the Letters
1	1
2	
3	
4	
5	
6	

3. a. Choose two of the cards and put the other two aside. On a sheet of paper, write all of the different orders in which you can arrange the letters.

   b. Count the number of different ways you can arrange the letters and record your answer in the table.

4. Next, choose three of the cards and list the different ways you can arrange the letters. Use your cards to help you find all of the arrangements by scrambling the letters. Compare each new arrangement to the arrangements already on your list. When you have found all of the arrangements, record the number in your table.

5. a. Make a list of arrangements for four cards. Record the number of arrangements in your table.

   b. Look at your results. Use multiplication to find a pattern relating the number of letters to the number of arrangements. Write an expression for your pattern using n letters.

6. Use the pattern you found in Step 7 to calculate how many ways you can arrange five letters and six letters. Write your answers in the table.

Sample pages; see p. G for complete list.

Hands-On Activities

Name ________________ Class ________ Date ________

Activity 43: Fair or Unfair

Materials needed: index cards, box

Work in pairs.

1. Write each letter of the words STATISTICS and GEOMETRY on an index card, one letter per card. Place all the cards in a box and mix them up. The player who most recently had a birthday is Player A. The other is Player B.
2. Without looking, pull one index card out of the box. If the letter on the card is a vowel, Player A gets a point. If the letter on the card is a consonant, Player B gets a point. Place the card back in the box and mix the cards up. Keep a tally of your points in a table like the one shown below.

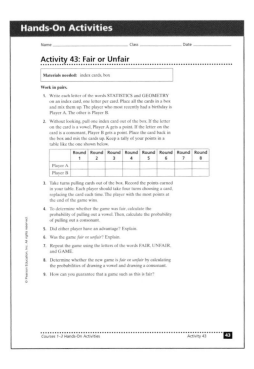

	Round 1	Round 2	Round 3	Round 4	Round 5	Round 6	Round 7	Round 8
Player A								
Player B								

3. Take turns pulling cards out of the box. Record the points earned in your table. Each player should take four turns choosing a card, replacing the card each time. The player with the most points at the end of the game wins.
4. To determine whether the game was fair, calculate the probability of pulling out a vowel. Then, calculate the probability of pulling out a consonant.
5. Did either player have an advantage? Explain.
6. Was the game *fair* or *unfair*? Explain.
7. Repeat the game using the letters of the words FAIR, UNFAIR, and GAME.
8. Determine whether the new game is *fair* or *unfair* by calculating the probabilities of drawing a vowel and drawing a consonant.
9. How can you guarantee that a game such as this is fair?

Hands-On Activities

Name ________________ Class ________ Date ________

Activity 44: Using Random Samples

Materials needed: 100 beads in 4 colors, paper bag

1. Copy the table below. List the colors of your beads in place of the labels Color A, Color B, Color C, and Color D.

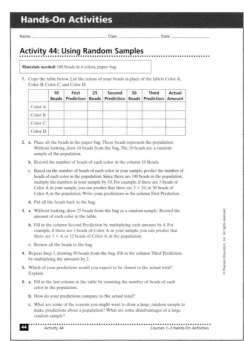

	10 Beads	First Prediction	25 Beads	Second Prediction	50 Beads	Third Prediction	Actual Amount
Color A							
Color B							
Color C							
Color D							

2. a. Place all the beads in the paper bag. These beads represent the population. Without looking, draw 10 beads from the bag. The 10 beads are a random sample of the population.
   b. Record the number of beads of each color in the column 10 Beads.
   c. Based on the number of beads of each color in your sample, predict the number of beads of each color in the population. Since there are 100 beads in the population, multiply the numbers in your sample by 10. For example, if there are 3 beads of Color A in your sample, you can predict that there are 3×10, or 30 beads of Color A in the population. Write your predictions in the column First Prediction.
   d. Put all the beads back in the bag.
3. a. Without looking, draw 25 beads from the bag as a random sample. Record the amount of each color in the table.
   b. Fill in the column Second Prediction by multiplying each amount by 4. For example, if there are 3 beads of Color A in your sample, you can predict that there are 3×4, or 12 beads of Color A in the population.
   c. Return all the beads to the bag.
4. Repeat Step 3, drawing 50 beads from the bag. Fill in the column Third Prediction by multiplying the amounts by 2.
5. Which of your predictions would you expect to be closest to the actual total? Explain.
6. a. Fill in the last column in the table by counting the number of beads of each color in the population.
   b. How do your predictions compare to the actual total?
   c. What are some of the reasons you might want to draw a large, random sample to make predictions about a population? What are some disadvantages of a large random sample?

Hands-On Activities

Name ________________ Class ________ Date ________

Activity 46: Experimental Probability

Materials needed: five sheets of used paper, large and small empty wastebaskets

1. Crumple four sheets of used paper into four paper balls.
2. Your teacher has placed a wastebasket at the front of the room. Wait until it is your turn, then stand 6 feet from the basket and try to throw all of your paper balls into the basket, one at a time.
3. As students are throwing, keep a tally of the throws that go in and those that do not in a table, such as the one below. Record the total number of balls that went in and the total number of misses for the class.

Student	Balls That Went In	Misses	Balls Thrown
Example	I	III	4
1			
2			
3			
TOTAL			

4. a. If you randomly chose one ball, how can you find the probability that it went in the basket? Calculate the probability using your results.
   b. If you randomly chose one ball, how can you find the probability that it did *not* go in the basket? Calculate the probability using your results.
   c. Based on these probabilities, how can you calculate the number of balls expected to go in the basket if a student throws 50 paper balls? Calculate this number.
5. a. How would a smaller basket change the probability of a single paper ball going in the basket?
   b. Repeat the experiment with one paper ball and a small wastebasket. Calculate the probability of a single ball going in the basket. Does your calculation support your prediction?
6. List two ways you could change this experiment, so that the probability of throwing a paper ball into the basket would increase.

Technology Activities

Name ________________ Class ________ Date ________

Random Numbers — Activity 18

Use your scientific calculator to do this activity.

Example: Elena usually has a $\frac{1}{4}$ chance of hitting free throws in her basketball games. Conduct a simulation to find out how many free throws she is likely to make in 100 attempts.

① For this simulation, program the calculator to generate a random number from 1 to 4. Let 1 be a successful free throw, and 2, 3, and 4 be unsuccessful free throws.

② Press [2nd] [>Op1]. On the screen you see **OP1 =**.

③ Press [PRB] and then use the right arrow key to move along the menu to the right until you highlight **RANDI**. Then press [ENTER]. Make sure you highlight **RANDI** and not **RANDI!** You should see **OP1 = RANDI(** on the screen.

④ Now enter 1 [2nd] [,] 4 [)] and press [ENTER]. You have created and stored a program to generate a random number from 1 to 4, so you can use it over and over again.

⑤ Press [OP1] to start the operation, or program. On the screen you see **RANDI(1, 4)** at the top. On the second line, on the left, you see trial number (1). On the right, you see the random number that the computer generated: a 1, 2, 3, or 4.

⑥ Make a table to record the results. If the number on the right is 1, record a Yes as attempt 1, because a 1 represents a successful shot. If the number on the right was a 2, 3, or 4, record a No because those numbers represent missed shots.

⑦ Repeat this procedure until you've done 100 trials.

⑧ Count the number of successful shots. Record that number as a fraction with a denominator of 100, and simplify to find the experimental probability. For example, if there were 28 successful shots, the experimental probability is $\frac{28}{100}$ or $\frac{7}{25}$.

Exercise

Conduct a simulation to find the experimental probability for rolling a sum of seven on two number cubes in 100 trials. Record your data in a table like the one below.

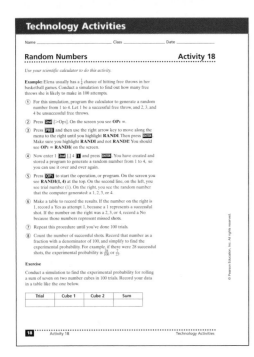

Trial	Cube 1	Cube 2	Sum

Chapter Project

Name ________________ Class ________ Date ________

Chapter 11 Project: Now Playing

Design a Three-Choice System

Beginning the Chapter Project

Suppose you and a friend have to choose among three movies, and you can't make up your mind. Should you flip a coin? You'd probably agree that assigning "heads" to one movie, "tails" to the second, and "lands on edge" to the third would not give the third movie much of a chance. What should you do?

Your project will be to design a device or system that is equally fair to three different outcomes. You will test your system to make sure each outcome can be expected one third of the time over a large number of trials.

Activities

Activity 1: Simulating Check students' work.

Design a method of choosing among three different movies. Use a computer, a list of random digits, a spinner, or number cubes to simulate the situation. Test your method for 100 trials and record your data in a table. Use the data to find the experimental probability of each outcome.

Activity 2: Designing

Design a three-dimensional shape that would result in three equally likely outcomes. (Refer back to Lesson 9-7 if necessary.) How would you use the shape so that a fair situation results? Test this method for 100 trials and record your data. Use the data to find the experimental probability of each outcome.

Activity 3: Analyzing

Compare the experimental method you used in Activity 2 with the one you used in Activity 1. Which method do you prefer? Using your preferred method, conduct and record 150 more trials. Then compare the experimental probability of each event to its theoretical probability. Do you think you made the right decision?

Chapter Project

Name ________________ Class ________ Date ________

Chapter 11 Project: Now playing

Finishing the Project

Imagine you are a salesman and you want to sell your three-choice system to your classmates. They will base their decision to buy based on the strength of your tests, the data collected, and your explanation of the system. Prepare a presentation that demonstrates or explains your system.

Reflect and Revise

Give a practice presentation to a friend or family member. Is your data believable and clearly presented? Are your calculations correct? Is your chosen system the best choice? If necessary, make changes to improve your system and your presentation.

Extending the Project

Design a system to simulate two independent decisions: you and a friend have to choose among three movies, and then you will choose to walk or bike to the theater. Use the model you just created to simulate the possibility of three equally likely events occurring (choosing between the movies), and create another type of simulation to model the equally likely choices of biking or walking. Test your method for 20 trials and record your data. Use the data to find the experimental probability of each outcome.

Take It to the NET Visit www.PHSchool.com for information and links you might find helpful as you complete your project.

Transparencies

Chapter Project

Name _____ Class _____ Date _____

Chapter Project Manager
Chapter 11: Now Playing

Getting Started

Read about the project. As you work on it, you will need several sheets of paper. If available, a spreadsheet program also can be used. Keep all your work for the project in a folder, along with this Project Manager.

Checklist	Suggestions
☐ Activity 1: simulating	☐ Spinners, number cubes, and computers are all useful for collecting data.
☐ Activity 2: designing	☐ Review three-dimensional objects to create a three-choice system.
☐ Activity 3: analyzing	☐ Use tables and experimental probability calculations to help deciding on a system.

Scoring Rubric

3 You design two three-choice systems, one based on random numbers and one based on a three-dimensional shape. You collect data from each system, and you find the experimental probability of the different outcomes. You collect additional data for one of your systems, and you prepare a presentation explaining your tests and calculations. You prove that your chosen system works for choosing among three equally likely outcomes.

2 You collect an adequate amount of data from the two systems you designed. You choose one system and collect additional data. You find the experimental probabilities of the three possible outcomes.

1 You complete only one three-outcome system. You collect data and attempt to find the experimental probabilities of the three possible outcomes.

0 You do not devise a three-outcome system, you do not collect an adequate amount of data, or you do not find the required experimental probabilities.

Your Evaluation of Project Evaluate your work, based on the Scoring Rubric.

Teacher's Evaluation of Project

24 Project — Course 1 Chapter 11

Chapter Project

Name _____ Class _____ Date _____

Chapter Project Teacher Notes
Chapter 11: Now Playing

About the Project

The Chapter Project challenges students to use their knowledge of gathering data and finding probability to design a three-outcome device.

Introducing the Project

Ask students:
- *Have you ever used a system to generate outcomes? Describe the system.*
- *How can a system be equally fair to three different outcomes?*
- *How do you think you would go about designing such a system?*

Activity 1: Simulating

Students should choose one method to conduct their trials. Have students save their tables for use later in the chapter.

Activity 2: Designing

Students who are visual learners may enjoy creating net patterns of their three-dimensional shapes. Students can use random number charts, spinners, or number cubes in their trials. Make sure students save their results.

Activity 3: Analyzing

Ask students to compare and contrast the two methods that they used. Then have them write a general statement that explains why they prefer one method over the other.

Finishing the Project

You may wish to plan a project day in which students share their completed projects. Encourage students to explain their processes as well as their products.

Have students review their methods for gathering data, making graphs, and analyzing data for the projects.

Take It to the NET Visit www.PHSchool.com for information, student links, and teacher support for this project.

Course 1 Chapter 11 — Project **25**

Problem of the Day

Problem of the Day	**Lesson 11-1**

Evaluate each expression when $a = 4$ and $b = 9$.

a. $(4 + b) - a$

b. $(b + a) \cdot 6$

c. $(a \cdot b) + (a + b)$

Answer

a. 9 b. 78 c. 49

Problem of the Day	**Lesson 11-2**

Stacy paid $12.00 for 15 juice bars at a fair. How much did each bar cost?

Answer

$.80

Problem of the Day	**Lesson 11-3**

At an amusement park, deluxe hamburgers cost $2.75 each. How many can Antria buy with a $20 bill? How much change will she receive?

Answer

7 hamburgers; $.75 change

Course 1 Chapter 11 — Problem of the Day **33**

Problem of the Day

Problem of the Day	**Lesson 11-4**

In each case, which one of the quantities is the most reasonable estimate?

a. shoes: 1 milligram, 1 gram, 1 kilogram

b. horse: 500 milligrams, 500 grams, 500 kilograms

c. bucket: 10 milliliters, 10 liters, 10 kiloliters

Answers

a. 1 kilogram b. 500 kilograms c. 10 liters

Problem of the Day	**Lesson 11-5**

If you tossed a coin 200 times, what is the mathematical probability of getting a head on the 143rd toss?

Answer

$P(\text{head}) = \frac{1}{2}$

Problem of the Day	**Lesson 11-6**

In a group of eight people, each person shakes hands once with each of the other people in the group. How many handshakes are exchanged?

Answer

28

Course 1 Chapter 11 — Problem of the Day **34**

Problem of the Day

Problem of the Day	**Lesson 11-7**

Sixteen teams play in a tournament. Each team plays until it loses. How many games must be played to determine the winner?

Answer

15 games

Course 1 Chapter 11 — Problem of the Day **35**

Check Skills You'll Need

Check Skills You'll Need	**Lesson 11-1**

Write each number as a percent.

1. 0.32   2. $\frac{9}{25}$ 3. $\frac{2}{5}$

4. $\frac{11}{50}$ 5. 0.02   6. $\frac{17}{20}$

Solutions

1. $0.32 = 32\%$
2. $\frac{9}{25} = \frac{9 \times 4}{25 \times 4} = \frac{36}{100} = 36\%$
3. $\frac{2}{5} = \frac{2 \times 20}{5 \times 20} = \frac{40}{100} = 40\%$
4. $\frac{11}{50} = \frac{11 \times 2}{50 \times 2} = \frac{22}{100} = 22\%$
5. $0.02 = 2\%$
6. $\frac{17}{20} = \frac{17 \times 5}{20 \times 5} = \frac{85}{100} = 85\%$

Lesson Quiz	**Lesson 11-1**

A box contains 3 red markers, 4 green markers, 2 purple markers, 2 black markers, and 1 blue marker. You pick a marker at random. Find the probability of each event. Write each answer as a fraction, a decimal, and a percent.

1. $P(\text{green})$ 2. $P(\text{purple or blue})$

3. $P(\text{pink})$ 4. $P(\text{blue})$

Answers

1. $\frac{1}{3}$, 0.33, 33%   2. $\frac{1}{4}$, 0.25, 25%
3. 0, 0, 0%   4. $\frac{1}{12}$, 0.08, 8%

Course 1 Chapter 11 — Check Skills You'll Need/Lesson Quiz **93**

Sample page; see p. H for complete list.

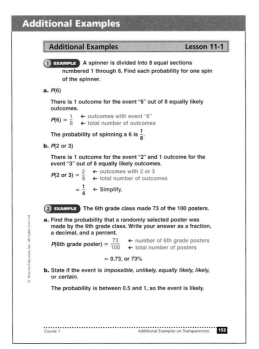

Sample page; see p. H for complete list.

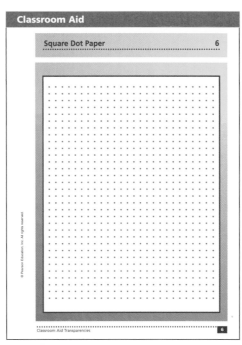

Sample page.

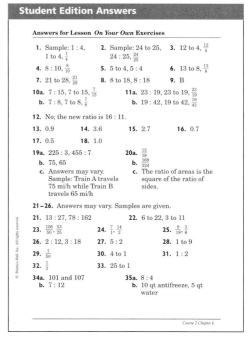

Sample page; see p. H for complete list.

Assessment

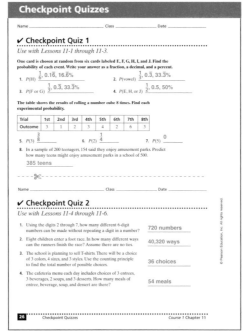

Sample page; see p. H for complete list.

Available in Spanish

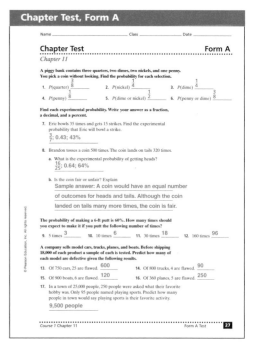

Available in Spanish

Name _____ Class _____ Date _____

Chapter Test (continued)   **Form A**
Chapter 11

18. Explain how using a spinner would help find the experimental probability that a soccer player will score a goal on a penalty kick. Suppose the player makes 75% of his penalty kicks.

If the player makes 75% of his penalty kicks, then 3 of 4 equal sections on a spinner will represent a score, and the fourth, a miss. The results of spinning the spinner will be the experimental probability that the player will score.

A baseball team is selecting their uniforms. They can choose from black or gold pants, T-shirts or mesh jerseys, and a solid-colored hat or a striped hat.

black pants — T-shirts — solid hat / striped hat; mesh jerseys — solid hat / striped hat

19. Draw a tree diagram to show the possible outcomes.

20. Find the probability that the team selects a solid-colored hat? $\frac{1}{2}$

gold pants — T-shirts — solid hat / striped hat; mesh jerseys — solid hat / striped hat

Find each probability using the counting principle.

21. In how many ways can the letters of the word CUBE be arranged? **24**

22. In how many ways can 7 dancers be arranged for a photo? **5,040**

23. There are two types of buns, three kinds of cheeses, two different onions, and three types of tomatoes. How many different cheeseburgers can you make? **36 cheeseburgers**

24. How many different ways can you arrange 7 people shoulder-to-shoulder in a line? **5,040 ways**

25. Suppose you roll a number cube three times. What is the probability that you will roll a 5, then a 2, then an even number? $\frac{1}{72}$

Decide whether or not the events are independent.

26. You open the refrigerator and pull out an apple. Then you take out an orange. **not independent**

27. It is Tuesday. It is raining today. **independent**

28. Your parents have blond hair. You have blond hair. **not independent**

Available in Spanish

Name _____ Class _____ Date _____

Chapter Test   **Form B**
Chapter 11

A piggy bank contains one quarter, three dimes, five nickels, and one penny. You pick a coin without looking. Find the probability for each selection.

1. P(quarter) $\frac{1}{10}$

2. P(nickel) $\frac{1}{2}$

3. P(dime) $\frac{3}{10}$

4. P(dime or nickel) $\frac{4}{5}$

5. P(penny) $\frac{1}{10}$

6. P(penny or dime) $\frac{2}{5}$

Find each experimental probability. Write your answer as a fraction, a decimal, and a percent.

7. During a tennis match Erin serves 45 times and gets 10 aces. Find the experimental probability that Erin will serve an ace. $\frac{2}{9}$; 0.22; 22%

8. Beau tosses a coin 360 times. The coin lands on tails 120 times.

a. What is the experimental probability of getting heads? $\frac{1}{3}$; 0.33; 33%.

b. Is the coin fair or unfair?
Sample answer: A coin would have an equal number of outcomes for heads and tails. Although the coin landed on tails fewer times, the coin is fair.

The probability of hitting the bullseye in a game of darts is 20%. How many times should you expect to hit the bullseye if you throw a dart the following number of times?

9. 15 times **3**

10. 35 times **7**

11. 60 times **12**

12. 480 times **96**

A company sells printers, scanners, faxes, and phones. Before shipping 26,000 of each product, a sample of each is tested. Predict how many of each item are defective given the following results.

13. Of 260 printers, 20 are flawed. **2,000**

14. Of 450 faxes, 9 are flawed. **520**

15. Of 1,200 scanners, 6 are flawed. **130**

16. Of 650 phones, 5 are flawed. **200**

17. In a town of 32,000 people, 640 people were asked what their favorite sport was. Only 223 people named baseball. Predict how many people in the entire town would say baseball is their favorite sport. **11,150 people**

Available in Spanish

Name _____ Class _____ Date _____

Chapter Test (continued)   **Form B**
Chapter 11

18. Explain how using a coin would help find the experimental probability that a family has 3 boys.

If heads is a boy, then tails is a girl. The results of the coin toss will be the experimental probability that the child is a boy. Unless all three are heads, the simulation fails.

A band is selecting a new song to play. They can choose from jazz, classic, or rock. The song can either be 2 minutes or 3 minutes in length, and the song may or may not need the string section of the band.

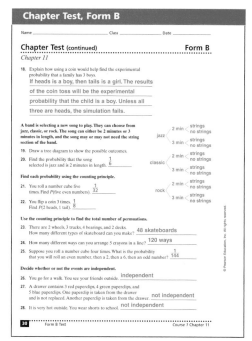

jazz — 2 min — strings / no strings; 3 min — strings / no strings
classic — 2 min — strings / no strings; 3 min — strings / no strings
rock — 2 min — strings / no strings; 3 min — strings / no strings

19. Draw a tree diagram to show the possible outcomes.

20. Find the probability that the song selected is jazz and is 2 minutes in length. $\frac{1}{6}$

Find each probability using the counting principle.

21. You roll a number cube five times. Find P(five even numbers). $\frac{1}{32}$

22. You flip a coin 3 times. Find P(2 heads, 1 tail). $\frac{1}{8}$

Use the counting principle to find the total number of permutations.

23. There are 2 wheels, 3 trucks, 4 bearings, and 2 decks. How many different types of skateboard can you make? **48 skateboards**

24. How many different ways can you arrange 5 crayons in a line? **120 ways**

25. Suppose you roll a number cube four times. What is the probability that you will roll an even number, then a 2, then a 6, then an odd number? $\frac{1}{144}$

Decide whether or not the events are independent.

26. You go for a walk. You see your friends outside. **independent**

27. A drawer contains 3 red paperclips, 4 green paperclips, and 5 blue paperclips. One paperclip is taken from the drawer and is not replaced. Another paperclip is taken from the drawer. **not independent**

28. It is very hot outside. You wear shorts to school. **not independent**

Available in Spanish

Name _____ Class _____ Date _____

Alternative Assessment   **Form C**
Chapter 11

TODAY'S PROBABLY A WEEKDAY

Keita Marshall woke up and rolled over in bed. Sunlight was streaming in the window, and Keita smiled. "It's going to be a nice day," she thought to herself.

"But what day is it going to be?" she wondered. She wasn't quite awake and couldn't remember what day it was.

"It's probably a weekday," Keita thought.

Show all your work on a separate sheet of paper.

1. Was Keita's guess a logical one? Is it more likely to be a weekday or a weekend day? Explain.

2. "I wish it were Saturday today," Keita sighed. Help Keita figure out the probability of it being Saturday. Express the probability as a fraction, a decimal, and a percent. Explain your thinking.

3. Then Keita had one more thought. "Maybe today is my birthday. It's probably not, but I wish it were."

Keita's birthday is December 5. What is the chance that it is Keita's birthday? Express the probability as a fraction and explain how you found the numerator and the denominator. Explain your thinking.

Available in Spanish

Name _____ Class _____ Date _____

Alternative Assessment (continued)   **Form C**
Chapter 11

4. Keita covered her face with her pillow and went back to sleep. Minutes later, her mother was calling her. "Hurry up, Keita. If you don't hurry, you'll probably miss the bus."

What will Keita probably do next? Explain.

Excursion

In some states, a license plate has three letters followed by three numbers. What is the probability that Keita's brother Joe will get a license plate with his name on it? Write the probability as a fraction and explain how you found the numerator and denominator.

Available in Spanish

Name _____ Class _____ Date _____

Alternative Assessment (continued)   **Form C**
Chapter 11

Scoring Rubric

Exercise	Points	Explanation
1.	3	Weekday chosen as more likely; correct explanation comparing number of weekdays and weekend days
	2	Weekday chosen as more likely but explanation incomplete OR weekend day chosen as more likely but with good explanation
	1	Weekday chosen but without explanation OR weekend day chosen with weak explanation
	0	No response OR weekend day chosen without explanation
2.	3	Correct figures ($\frac{1}{7}$, 0.1429, and 14.29% (the decimal and percent could be rounded more); with good explanation
	2	Correct figures with weak explanation
	1	Correct figures without explanation OR incorrect figures but good explanation OR good explanation without figures
	0	Other incorrect response
3.	3	Correct fraction ($\frac{1}{365}$) based on one birthday a year and number of days in the year; good explanation
	2	Correct fraction with weak explanation OR incorrect fraction with correct explanation of numerator and denominator
	1	Correct fraction without explanation OR incorrect fraction with weak explanation
	0	Other incorrect response
4.	1	Any reasonable statement: get up; go to school; fall back to sleep; miss the bus; etc., with sound reasoning
	0	No response OR response unrelated to question
Excursion	5	Correct fraction ($\frac{1}{26 \times 26 \times 26} \times 5 \frac{1}{10 \times 10 \times 10}$) and good explanation
	4	Correct explanation but incorrect fraction
	3	Correct fraction with weak explanation OR correct explanation but fraction not given
	2	Correct fraction with no explanation
	1	Incorrect fraction with weak explanation
	0	No response

Available in Spanish

Name _____ Class _____ Date _____

Cumulative Review
Chapters 1–11

Multiple Choice. Choose the letter of the best answer.

1. What are the next three numbers in this pattern? 2, 8, 14, 20, . . .
   - A. 26, 32, 38
   - B. 30, 44, 56
   - C. 26, 38, 48
   - D. 31, 37, 44

Use the figure below for Exercises 2–4.

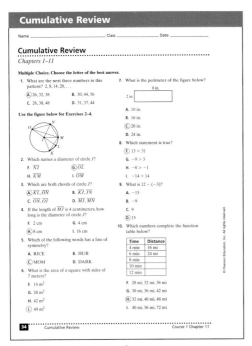

2. Which names a diameter of circle J?
   - F. $\overline{NJ}$
   - G. $\overline{OL}$
   - H. $\overline{KM}$
   - I. $\overline{OM}$

3. Which are both chords of circle J?
   - A. $\overline{KL}, \overline{ON}$
   - B. $\overline{KJ}, \overline{JN}$
   - C. $\overline{ON}, \overline{OJ}$
   - D. $\overline{MJ}, \overline{MN}$

4. If the length of $\overline{MJ}$ is 4 centimeters, how long is the diameter of circle J?
   - F. 2 cm
   - G. 4 cm
   - H. 8 cm
   - I. 16 cm

5. Which of the following words has a line of symmetry?
   - A. RICE
   - B. HUB
   - C. MOM
   - D. DARK

6. What is the area of a square with sides of 7 meters?
   - F. 14 m²
   - G. 28 m²
   - H. 42 m²
   - I. 49 m²

7. What is the perimeter of the figure below?

   8 in.

   2 in.

   - A. 10 in.
   - B. 16 in.
   - C. 20 in.
   - D. 24 in.

8. Which statement is true?
   - F. 13 < 31
   - G. −9 > 3
   - H. −8 > −1
   - I. −14 > 14

9. What is 12 − (−3)?
   - A. −15
   - B. −9
   - C. 9
   - D. 15

10. Which numbers complete the function table below?

Time	Distance
4 min	16 mi
6 min	24 mi
8 min	
10 min	
12 min	

   - F. 28 mi, 32 mi, 36 mi
   - G. 30 mi, 36 mi, 42 mi
   - H. 32 mi, 40 mi, 48 mi
   - I. 40 mi, 56 mi, 72 mi

Available in Spanish

Name _____ Class _____ Date _____

Cumulative Review (continued)
Chapters 1–11

11. What is the best name for the triangle shown?

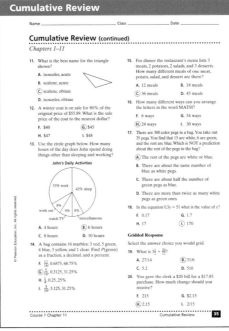

   - A. isosceles, acute
   - B. scalene, acute
   - C. scalene, obtuse
   - D. isosceles, obtuse

12. A winter coat is on sale for 80% of the original price of $55.89. What is the sale price of the coat to the nearest dollar?
   - F. $40
   - G. $45
   - H. $47
   - I. $48

13. Use the circle graph below. How many hours of the day does John spend doing things other than sleeping and working?

   John's Daily Activities

   - 33% work
   - 42% sleep
   - work out 8%
   - 9% watch TV
   - 8% miscellaneous

   - A. 4 hours
   - B. 6 hours
   - C. 8 hours
   - D. 10 hours

14. A bag contains 16 marbles: 3 red, 5 green, 4 blue, 3 yellow, and 1 clear. Find P(green) as a fraction, a decimal, and a percent.
   - F. $\frac{11}{16}$, 0.6875, 68.75%
   - G. $\frac{5}{16}$, 0.3125, 31.25%
   - H. $\frac{1}{4}$, 0.25, 25%
   - I. $\frac{5}{16}$, 3.125, 31.25%

15. For dinner the restaurant's menu lists 3 meats, 2 potatoes, 2 salads, and 3 desserts. How many different meals of one meat, potato, salad, and dessert are there?
   - A. 12 meals
   - B. 18 meals
   - C. 36 meals
   - D. 45 meals

16. How many different ways can you arrange the letters in the word MATH?
   - F. 6 ways
   - G. 54 ways
   - H. 24 ways
   - I. 30 ways

17. There are 300 color pegs in a bag. You take out 35 pegs. You find that 15 are white, 6 are green, and the rest are blue. Which is NOT a prediction about the rest of the pegs in the bag?
   - A. The rest of the pegs are white or blue.
   - B. There are about the same number of blue as white pegs.
   - C. There are about half the number of green pegs as blue.
   - D. There are more than twice as many white pegs as green ones.

18. In the equation 0.3y = 51 what is the value of y?
   - F. 0.17
   - G. 1.7
   - H. 17
   - I. 170

Gridded Response
Select the answer choice you would grid.

19. What is $3\frac{1}{3} + \frac{20}{12}$?
   - A. 27/14
   - B. 31/6
   - C. 5.2
   - D. 516

20. You gave the clerk a $20 bill for a $17.85 purchase. How much change should you receive?
   - F. 215
   - G. $2.15
   - H. 2.15
   - I. 2/15

Available in Spanish

Name _____ Class _____ Date _____

Benchmark Test 1

1. What is the value of the digit 2 in the number 4.0725?
   - A. 2 tenths
   - B. 2 hundredths
   - C. 2 thousandths
   - D. 2 ten-thousandths

2. How is the decimal 2.016 expressed in words?
   - A. two and sixteen thousandths
   - B. two and sixteen hundredths
   - C. two and sixteen tenths
   - D. two and sixteenths

3. Quincy ran a lap in seventy-five and thirteen hundredths seconds. How is this time written in standard form?
   - A. 75.013 seconds
   - B. 75.03 seconds
   - C. 75.103 seconds
   - D. 75.13 seconds

4. Which set of decimals is ordered from least to greatest?
   - A. 2.67, 2.71, 2.99, 2.02
   - B. 2.99, 2.67, 2.71, 2.02
   - C. 2.02, 2.67, 2.71, 2.99
   - D. 2.71, 2.02, 2.99, 2.67

5. Which of the following statements is true?
   - A. 1.971 > 1.97
   - B. 2.53 < 2.3
   - C. 4.825 > 4.85
   - D. 6.74 < 6.740

6. The table below shows the surface ocean temperature for five days. On which day was the daily ocean temperature coolest?

   Daily Ocean Temperature

Day	Temperature (°F)
Monday	80.07
Tuesday	81.03
Wednesday	80.90
Thursday	81.50
Friday	81.20

   - A. Monday
   - B. Tuesday
   - C. Wednesday
   - D. Friday

7. Which addition problem is modeled below?

   - A. 8 + 3 = 11
   - B. 0.8 + 3 = 3.8
   - C. 0.8 + 0.3 = 1.1
   - D. 0.08 + 0.3 = 0.38

BENCHMARK TESTS

On PH Website

Test-Taking Strategies: Answering True/False Questions

When you see a True/False question you have to determine if the entire statement is TRUE or if it is FALSE.

For a statement to be true it must be true in all the situations described. If you find only one exception, the statement will be false.

> **HINT:**
>
> Watch for words such as
> ALL, ALWAYS, ANY, NONE, AND NEVER.
>
> When these words are used, the statement may be true for many cases and false for just one.

1. True or False? The square root of any number less than 50 is less than 7.

   For this statement to be true, the square of *each* number less than 50 must be less than 7.

   Try several numbers less than 50: $\sqrt{25} = 5$, $\sqrt{36} = 6$. $\sqrt{49} = 7$. While many numbers less than 50 have square roots less than 7, 49 does not. Therefore, the statement is FALSE.

2. True or False? All whole numbers ending in a zero are divisible by 10.

   For this statement to be true, 10 has to divide into any whole number ending in zero, evenly. Whole numbers ending in zero can be expressed as a product of 10 and another factor. Therefore, each number ending in zero is divisible by 10, and the statement is TRUE.

Name _____ Class _____ Date _____

Chapter 11: Answering True/False Questions
Exercises Sample answers are shown below.

Determine whether each statement is true or false. Explain your reasoning.

1. True or False? If x is divisible by 8, then it is divisible by 6.
   For this statement to be true, every number that is divisible by 8 must also be divisible by 6. Since 16 is divisible by 8 and is *not* divisible by 6, the statement is false.

2. True or False? The sum of two acute angles is always an acute angle.
   For this statement to be true, you cannot have two acute angles whose sum is greater than 90°. But, 60° and 70° are both acute angles and their sum is 130°, which is not an acute angle. Since the statement is not always true, it is false.

3. True or False? If x equals a negative number, then x + 2 is always equal to a negative number.
   Sample answer: This statement is true if every negative number added to 2 results in a sum that is negative. However, when x = −1, x + 2 = 1, which is not negative. Therefore, the statement is false.

4. True or False? If you roll two fair number cubes, the probability of getting a total of 10 is always $\frac{1}{3}$.
   The statement is true since there are three outcomes that total 10: 4, 6; 5, 5; 6, 4, or three outcomes out of 36 possibilities. The probability is $\frac{3}{36}$ or $\frac{1}{12}$.

5. True or False? The probability of events A and B both happening is always the product of the probability of A happening and the probability of B happening.
   The statement is false. If A and B are not independent events, you cannot use the product.

6. True or False? If a number is even, it is divisible by 4.
   The statement is false since 6 is an even number but is not divisible by 4.

---

in math class ...
We have been learning about probability. Here is a list of some of the skills and concepts we have studied.
- Probability
- Making predictions
- Tree diagrams

Home Activities
Here are some activities you can do with your child that use these math skills and concepts.

Select ten cards from a deck of cards that you have in your home. The cards may be picture cards or they may come from a standard deck of cards. All of the cards can be different or you may select combinations of cards. If playing cards are unavailable, use some index cards to make ten cards with numbers or drawings. Show the cards to your child. Discuss the probability of selecting each card. The probability will be $\frac{1}{10}$ for each card if all of the cards are different. If some of the cards are the same, the probabilities will be different. Have your child make a list of the probabilities of each card. Then use the list of probabilities to make a prediction about which card would be drawn for a card selected at random. Finally, mix up the cards and have your child select a card without looking. Discuss how the results compare to the prediction and whether or not you and your child were surprised and why.

Your child can find the probability using the following ratio: number of favorable outcomes/total number of outcomes. For example, if there are 2 kings, 4 queens, 3 jacks, and 1 ace, the probabilities for selecting the cards at random are: P(King) = $\frac{2}{10} = \frac{1}{5}$, P(Queen) = $\frac{4}{10} = \frac{2}{5}$, P(Jack) = $\frac{3}{10}$, and P(Ace) = $\frac{1}{10}$.

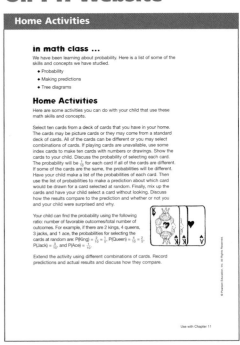

Extend the activity using different combinations of cards. Record predictions and actual results and discuss how they compare.

Available in Spanish;
Web Code: aak-5500

Name _____

Math and Science/Technology

Who Robbed the Pi Bakery?

Use tree diagrams and the counting principle to help determine the identities of a fictitious band of burglars.

The Sweet Tooth Gang was at work again—or so it seemed to Detective Polly Gon at the Math City Police Department. It was a hot summer night when the alarm sounded at police headquarters. There was a burglary in progress at the huge warehouse of the Pi Bakery. Police raced to the scene, but the burglars had made their getaway with 314 Pi pies and a dozen big boxes containing ½-gallon cartons of ice cream.

Police found one eyewitness at the scene, a security guard named Al Gebra, who was left tied up by the burglars. He gave Detective Gon the following description:

The burglars entered the store and overpowered Al at about 1:30 a.m. He saw three burglars, but he couldn't describe them fully. Al said some of the burglars had crew cuts and some had long hair, but he didn't know how many men had hair of each type. He also noticed that one man was tall, one was of medium height, and the other was short.

Al said the burglars spent about 15 minutes carrying boxes of pies and ice cream out of the warehouse and putting them into the back of an old pick-up truck. As the burglars sped off in their truck, Al caught a glimpse of the license plate. He saw an LCM but could not make out the three numbers that followed.

This description is all that you and Detective Polly Gon have to go on. Use the information above and the illustrations below to answer the following questions.

1. The use of scientific evidence to solve a crime is called *forensics*. What kinds of clues left at the scene of a crime might be of use to detectives and forensic scientists?

_____
_____
_____
_____

Use with Chapter 11

Available in Spanish;
Web Code: aak-5500

Name _____

Math and Science/Technology

2. What clues were left behind by the burglars?

3. Police know all six members of the Sweet Tooth Gang. Using Al Gebra's description of the burglars, police also know that two members of the gang were not involved in the burglary. Which two? How did the police know?

4. Al Gebra saw men with crew cuts and long hair. One was tall, one was of medium height, and one was short. How many hair and height combinations are possible for the burglars? Show the possibilities with a tree diagram.

5. Al Gebra remembers that one man was tall and had a crew cut and another was short and had a crew cut. The third man had long hair. With this information Detective Polly Gon now knows the identities of the three burglars. Which ones are they? Explain your answer.

6. At first, Detective Gon knows the three letters of the getaway truck's license plate, but none of the numbers. She figures she will have a lot of license plate numbers to check. How many combinations will she need to check? (Note: there are no zeroes on the plate and there are no repeated numbers.)

7. Al Gebra suddenly remembers that the first two numbers of the license plate were 9 and 2. How many license plates does Detective Gon have to check to find the gang's truck if the final numeral is not a zero or a repeat of any of the other numerals?

_____

8. Detective Polly Gon runs a check of license plates and finds that the missing plate number is a prime number between 6 and 10. That plate is registered to Cal Culus. Detective Gon now has evidence that puts Cal Culus at the scene of the crime. What is Cal Culus' license plate number?

_____
_____
_____
_____

9. Forensic scientists and detectives have many tools to assist them in solving crimes. Do some research to find out about some of them. Pick one and report on how it was used in solving a real-life crime.

_____
_____
_____
_____

Use with Chapter 11

Available in Spanish;
Web Code: aak-5500

Name _____ Class _____ Date _____

What's YOUR Probability?

Puzzle 11

Exploring Probability

Find the probability that each event occurs if you use a fair number cube, a fair coin, and a fair spinner numbered 1, 2, 3, and 4. Starting in the upper left-hand corner, use your answers to move from one square to another in the order of the problems below. You may only move diagonally through the maze.

- The probability of rolling a multiple of 2 with the number cube.
- The probability of landing on a 2 with the spinner.
- The probability of heads with a fair coin.
- The probability of rolling a factor of 24 with the number cube.
- The probability of landing on a multiple of 5 with the spinner.
- The probability of rolling a number greater than 3 with the number cube.
- The probability of landing on 4 with the spinner and rolling a 4 with the number cube.
- The probability of rolling a six with the number cube and landing on a factor of 6 with the spinner.
- The probability of tails with a fair coin and rolling an odd number with the number cube.
- The probability of NOT landing on a 6 with the spinner.

START

$\frac{1}{2}$	$\frac{1}{2}$	1	$\frac{1}{2}$	$\frac{1}{4}$	1	
$\frac{1}{2}$	$\frac{1}{4}$	$\frac{1}{8}$	$\frac{1}{12}$	1	1	**F**
$\frac{1}{2}$	$\frac{1}{4}$	0	$\frac{8}{13}$	$\frac{1}{24}$	1	**I N I S H**
$\frac{1}{2}$	$\frac{5}{6}$	$\frac{1}{3}$	$\frac{1}{2}$	$\frac{1}{6}$	1	

Algebra Readiness Puzzles   11

Web Code: aak-5500

Chapter 11 Overview

In this chapter students explore theoretical and experimental probability, work with tree diagrams and the counting principle, and use permutations. They conclude the chapter by learning how to compute the probability of independent events.

 Reading Math
- Understanding Word Problems, p. 579
- **Vocabulary:** A complete list, plus exercises, in the Chapter Review, p. 586
- **Illustrated Glossary:** Examples for each vocabulary term, plus definitions in English and Spanish, on p. 669

Test-Taking Strategies
Answering True/False Questions, p. 585

Real-World Problem Solving
- **Strategies:** Simulate a Problem, pp. 563–566
- **Real-World Snapshots:** Fair Chance?, pp. 590–591
- **Chapter Project:** Now Playing, p. 641

 www.PHSchool.com
Internet support includes:
- Self-grading Vocabulary and Chapter 11 Tests
- Activity Masters
- Chapter Project support
- Chapter Planner
- Ch. 11 Resources

Plus **iTEXT**

CHAPTER

11

Exploring Probability

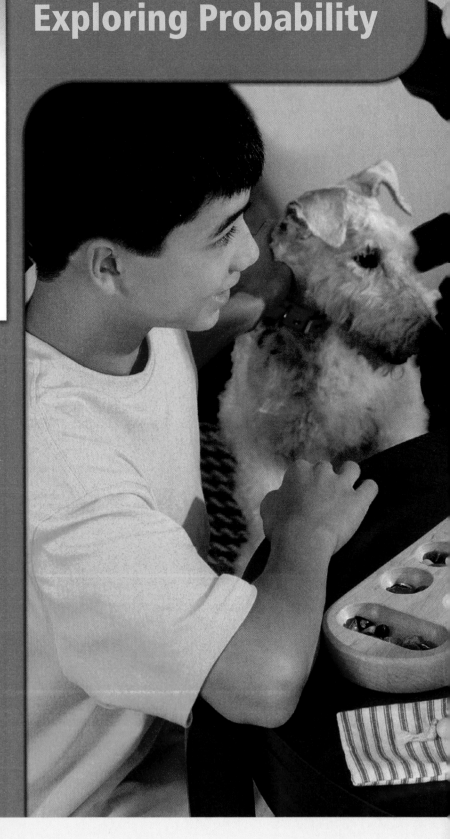

Lessons

11-1 Probability

11-2 Experimental Probability

11-3 Making Predictions From Data

11-4 Problem Solving: Simulate a Problem

11-5 Tree Diagrams and the Counting Principle

11-6 Exploring Permutations

11-7 Independent Events

Key Vocabulary
- compound events (p. 581)
- counting principle (p. 569)
- equally likely outcomes (p. 547)
- event (p. 547)
- experimental probability (p. 553)
- independent events (p. 580)
- permutation (p. 574)
- population (p. 559)
- probability of an event (p. 547)
- sample (p. 559)
- simulation (p. 563)
- tree diagram (p. 568)

544

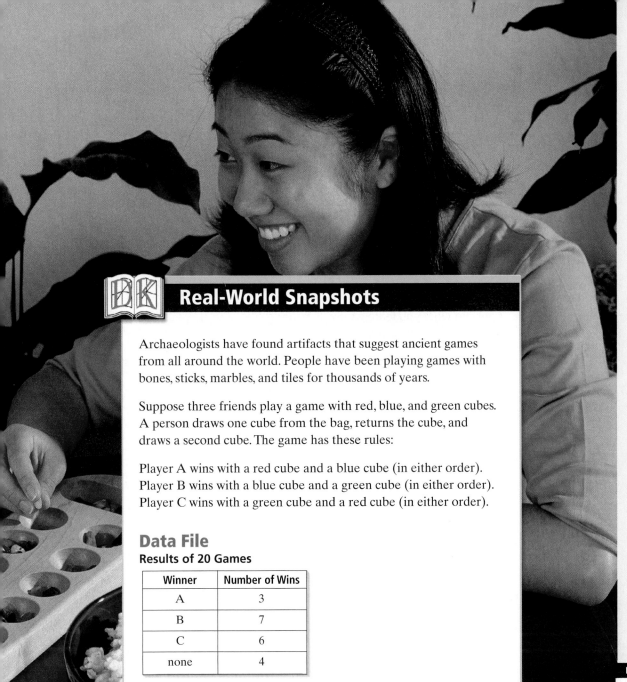

Real-World Snapshots

Archaeologists have found artifacts that suggest ancient games from all around the world. People have been playing games with bones, sticks, marbles, and tiles for thousands of years.

Suppose three friends play a game with red, blue, and green cubes. A person draws one cube from the bag, returns the cube, and draws a second cube. The game has these rules:

Player A wins with a red cube and a blue cube (in either order).
Player B wins with a blue cube and a green cube (in either order).
Player C wins with a green cube and a red cube (in either order).

Data File
Results of 20 Games

Winner	Number of Wins
A	3
B	7
C	6
none	4

You will use the data above in this chapter:

- p. 555 Lesson 11-2
- p. 561 Lesson 11-3
- p. 583 Lesson 11-7

Real-World Snapshots On pages 590 and 591, you will solve problems involving games.

Teaching Notes

Activating Prior Knowledge
In this chapter students build on and extend their knowledge of fractions, decimals and percents to understand the concept of probability and to express probabilities. Also, they use their understanding of solving proportions to find probabilities. Ask questions such as:

- *What is x in $\frac{5}{x} = \frac{15}{24}$?* x = 8
- *What is 80% of 80?* 64
- *What is $\frac{88}{100}$ when simplified?* $\frac{22}{25}$

Real-World Snapshots
The data here will be used throughout the chapter. Have a volunteer read the opening passages that explain the game. Then focus students on the data in the chart and ask:

- *How many games did the players play in all?* 20
- *What fraction expresses the number of games with no winner?* $\frac{4}{20}$ or $\frac{1}{5}$
- *Suppose the players were to play 40 games. How many times might you expect each to win?* Sample:
A, 6; B, 14; C, 12

Reading and Math Literacy

11A: Graphic Organizer   For use before Lesson 11-1

Study Skill: When you review your class notes, use a highlighter to mark important information. Pay special attention to the material you have highlighted when you review for tests.

Write your answers.

1. What is the chapter title? Exploring Probability
2. How many lessons are there in this chapter? 7
3. What is the topic of the Reading Math page? Understanding Word Problems
4. What is the topic of the Test-Taking Strategy page? Answering True/False Questions
5. Look through the chapter and list four real-world connections that are discussed. Answers will vary.

6. Complete the graphic organizer below as you work through the chapter.
   - In the center, write the title of the chapter.
   - When you begin a lesson, write the lesson name in a rectangle.
   - When you complete a lesson, write a skill or key concept in a circle linked to that lesson block.
   - When you complete the chapter, use this graphic organizer to help you review.

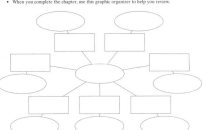

Available in Spanish

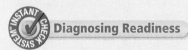 **Diagnosing Readiness**

Students will find answers to these exercises in the back of their textbooks.

Prescribing Intervention
For intervention, direct students to:

Subtracting Decimals
Lesson 1-5: Example 4. Extra Practice, p. 642.

Adding Fractions With Like Denominators
Lesson 4-2: Example 1. Extra Practice, p. 645.

Multiplying Fractions
Lesson 5-1: Example 2. Extra Practice, p. 646.

Writing Equivalent Numerical Expressions
Lesson 6-6: Examples 1–4. Extra Practice, p. 647.

Chapter 11 Preview

Where You've Been

- In Chapters 4 and 5, you learned to write equivalent fractions, and to add, subtract, and multiply fractions.

- In Chapter 6, you learned to convert between decimals, fractions, and percents.

Where You're Going

- In Chapter 11, you will use decimals, fractions, and percents to find probabilities. You will find experimental probabilities and use simulations.

- Applying what you learn, you will make predictions about population.

The world's birthrate decreases every year.

 Instant self-check online and on CD-ROM

Diagnosing Readiness   ? **For help, go to the lesson in green.**

Subtracting Decimals (Lesson 1-5)

Find each difference.

1. $1 - 0.32$ **0.68**   **2.** $1 - 0.08$ **0.92**   **3.** $1 - 0.6$ **0.4**   **4.** $1 - 0.234$ **0.766**

Adding Fractions With Like Denominators (Lesson 4-2)

Find each sum.

5. $\frac{2}{5} + \frac{1}{5}$ $\frac{3}{5}$ **6.** $\frac{3}{6} + \frac{1}{6}$ $\frac{2}{3}$ **7.** $\frac{2}{8} + \frac{5}{8}$ $\frac{7}{8}$ **8.** $\frac{3}{10} + \frac{3}{10}$ $\frac{3}{5}$

Multiplying Fractions (Lesson 5-1)

Find each product.

9. $\frac{1}{2} \times \frac{5}{6}$ $\frac{5}{12}$ **10.** $\frac{3}{4} \times \frac{8}{9}$ $\frac{2}{3}$ **11.** $\frac{7}{10} \times \frac{5}{14}$ $\frac{1}{4}$ **12.** $\frac{2}{3} \times \frac{8}{9}$ $\frac{16}{27}$

Writing Equivalent Numerical Expressions (Lesson 6-6)

Write each fraction as a decimal and then as a percent.

13. $\frac{2}{8}$ **0.25; 25%**   **14.** $\frac{3}{9}$ $0.\overline{3}$; ≈ 33%   **15.** $\frac{4}{5}$ **0.8; 80%**   **16.** $\frac{7}{10}$ **0.7; 70%**

Write each percent as a fraction in simplest form and as a decimal.

 17. 13% $\frac{13}{100}$; 0.13   **18.** 26% $\frac{13}{50}$; 0.26   **19.** 10% $\frac{1}{10}$; 0.10   **20.** 22% $\frac{11}{50}$; 0.22

Probability

What You'll Learn

OBJECTIVE 1
To find the probability of an event

. . . And Why

To find the probability of a winning ticket, as in Example 2

1. Plan

Lesson Preview

✔ **Check Skills You'll Need** PowerPoint

Writing Decimals and Fractions as Percents
Lesson 6-6: Examples 3–4. Extra Practice, p. 647.

Lesson Resources

📁 **Teaching Resources**
Practice, Reteaching, Enrichment

👥 **Reaching All Students**
Practice Workbook 11-1
Spanish Practice Workbook 11-1
Guided Problem Solving 11-1
Hands-On Activities 43, 45

⏱ **Presentation Assistant Plus!**
Transparencies
• Check Skills You'll Need 11-1
• Problem of the Day 11-1
• Additional Examples 11-1
• Student Edition Answers 11-1
• Lesson Quiz 11-1
PH Presentation Pro CD-ROM 11-1

PRENTICE HALL ASSESSMENT SYSTEM

Computer Test Generator CD

💻 **Technology**
Resource Pro® CD-ROM
Computer Test Generator CD
PH Presentation Pro CD-ROM

💻 **www.PHSchool.com**
Student Site
• Teacher Web Code: aak-5500
• Self-grading Lesson Quiz

PH SuccessNet Teacher Center
• Lesson Planner
• Resources

Plus 📘 **iTEXT**

✔ **Check Skills You'll Need**   ❓ For help, go to Lesson 6-6.

Write each number as a percent.

1. 0.32 32%   **2.** $\frac{9}{25}$ 36%   **3.** $\frac{2}{5}$ 40%

4. $\frac{11}{50}$ 22%   **5.** 0.02 2%   **6.** $\frac{17}{20}$ 85%

New Vocabulary   • equally likely outcomes   • event
• probability of an event

OBJECTIVE

1 **Finding Probabilities of Events**

📘 **iTEXT** Interactive lesson includes instant self-check, tutorials, and activities.

If a coin is tossed once, there are two possible outcomes: heads or tails. An *outcome* is the result of an action. Outcomes that have the same chance of occurring are called **equally likely outcomes.**

Suppose you spin the pointer below once. If the arrow is equally likely to land on any of the 10 sections, the spin is random.

The 10 colored sections represent equally likely outcomes.

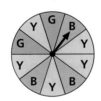

In 3 of the outcomes, the pointer lands on a blue section.

An **event** is an outcome or group of outcomes. The pointer landing on blue is an event.

The **probability of an event** is a number that describes how likely it is that the event will occur. For the spinner, the probability of "blue" is 3 out of 10, or $\frac{3}{10}$. The probability of "not blue" is 7 out of 10, or $\frac{7}{10}$.

> **Key Concepts**   **Probability of an Event**
>
> When outcomes are equally likely,
>
> the probability of an event = $\dfrac{\text{number of favorable outcomes}}{\text{total number of outcomes}}$.

You can write $P(\text{event})$ for the phrase "probability of an event."

✔ **Ongoing Assessment and Intervention**

Before the Lesson
Diagnose prerequisite skills using:
• Check Skills You'll Need

During the Lesson
Monitor progress using:
• Check Understanding
• Additional Examples
• Test Prep

After the Lesson
Assess knowledge using:
• Lesson Quiz
• Computer Test Generator CD

2. Teach

Math Background

An *event* is a collection of possible outcomes or happenings. For example, tossing a coin is an experiment with two *equally likely outcomes*: heads or tails. The *probability* of an event is the likelihood the event will occur. Probability is always a number from 0 (an impossible event) to 1 (a certain event). To find probability, use $P(\text{event}) =$

$$\frac{\text{number of favorable outcomes}}{\text{total number of possible outcomes}}.$$

Teaching Notes

English Learners
Make sure students understand the terms associated with probability: *favorable, outcome, impossible, unlikely, equally likely, likely,* and *certain*.

1 EXAMPLE Tactile Learners

Provide students with number cubes to examine. Ask: *How many numbers are possible when the cube is rolled?* **6 because of the 6 sides**

PowerPoint
Additional Examples

1. A spinner is divided into 8 equal sections numbered 1 through 8. Find each probability for one spin of the spinner.

   a. $P(6)$ $\frac{1}{8}$ **b.** $P(2 \text{ or } 3)$ $\frac{1}{4}$

2. The 6th grade class made 73 of the 100 posters.

   a. Find the probability that a randomly selected poster was made by the 6th grade class. Write your answer as a fraction, a decimal, and a percent. $\frac{73}{100}$, 0.73, 73%

   b. State if the event is *impossible, unlikely, equally likely, likely,* or *certain*. **likely**

Closure

How do you find the probability of an event? **Sample: Divide the number of favorable outcomes by the total number of possible outcomes.**

548

---

1 EXAMPLE Probability of an Event

Each face of a number cube displays one of the numbers 1 through 6. Find the probability of rolling an even number in one roll of a number cube.

There are 3 outcomes for the event "even" out of 6 equally likely outcomes.

$$P(\text{even}) = \frac{3}{6} \quad \leftarrow \text{outcomes with even numbers}$$
$$\phantom{P(\text{even})} \quad \leftarrow \text{total number of outcomes}$$

$$= \frac{1}{2} \quad \leftarrow \text{Simplify.}$$

The probability of rolling an even number on the number cube is $\frac{1}{2}$.

✔ **Check Understanding** ① A number cube is rolled once. Find each probability.

a. $P(\text{odd})$ $\frac{1}{2}$ **b.** $P(5)$ $\frac{1}{6}$ **c.** $P(2 \text{ or } 6)$ $\frac{1}{3}$

d. Reasoning Is $P(3)$ different from $P(4)$? Explain.
Answers may vary. Sample: No; since each event is equally likely, the probabilities are the same.

All probabilities range from 0 to 1. The probability of rolling a 7 on a number cube is 0, which means that this is an *impossible* event. The probability of rolling a positive integer less than 7 is 1, which means this is a *certain* event.

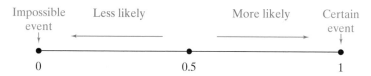

Impossible event	Less likely		More likely	Certain event
0		0.5		1

You can write probabilities as fractions, decimals, or percents.

2 EXAMPLE Real-World 🌐 Problem Solving

Fundraising Every student who participates in a fundraiser is eligible for a prize. Suppose 100 students are eligible, and there are 11 prizes. The name of one student is drawn at random for each prize. What is the probability that you win a prize if you are eligible?

$$P(\text{win a prize}) = \frac{11}{100} \quad \leftarrow \text{number of prizes}$$
$$\phantom{P(\text{win a prize})} \quad \leftarrow \text{total number of eligible students}$$

There is an 11% probability that you win a prize.

✔ **Check Understanding** ② **a. Reasoning** How many prizes would there have to be for each student to have an equal chance to win or not win a prize? **50 prizes**

b. In a bag of mixed nuts, 6 of 10 nuts are pecans. Find the probability of selecting a pecan at random. Write your answer as a fraction, a decimal, and a percent. $\frac{6}{10}$ or $\frac{3}{5}$; 0.6; 60%

548 Chapter 11 Exploring Probability

👥 Reaching All Students

| **Below Level** Have students draw a diagram of the total number of outcomes and color the number of favorable events for both Example 1 and Check Understanding 1a–c. | **Advanced Learners** Have students express the probabilities in Check Understanding 1a–c as fractions, decimals, and percents. **a.** $\frac{1}{2}$, 0.5, 50%; **b.** $\frac{1}{6}$, 0.17, 17%; **c.** $\frac{1}{3}$, 0.33, 33% | **English Learners** See note on page 548. **Tactile Learners** See note on page 548. |

EXERCISES

Ⓐ Practice by Example

Example 1
(page 548)

A jar contains 4 red marbles, 3 yellow marbles, 2 black marbles, and 1 green marble. You select a marble without looking. Find each probability.

1. $P(\text{red})$ $\frac{4}{10}$ or $\frac{2}{5}$

2. $P(\text{yellow})$ $\frac{3}{10}$

3. $P(\text{black})$ $\frac{2}{10}$ or $\frac{1}{5}$

4. $P(\text{green})$ $\frac{1}{10}$

5. $P(\text{black or red})$ $\frac{6}{10}$ or $\frac{3}{5}$

6. $P(\text{yellow or green})$ $\frac{4}{10}$ or $\frac{2}{5}$

7. $P(\text{orange})$ 0

8. $P(\text{yellow, red, or black})$ $\frac{9}{10}$

9. $P(\text{red, blue, green, or black})$ $\frac{7}{10}$

10. $P(\text{red, yellow, black, or green})$ 1

Example 2
(page 548)

Find the probability of each event. Write each probability as a fraction, a decimal, and a percent.

11. A spinner has equal sections of red, blue, pink, green, and yellow. You spin the pointer once and get blue or pink. $\frac{2}{5}$; 0.4; 40%

12. You roll a number cube and get a number greater than 3. $\frac{1}{2}$; 0.5; 50%

13. You write the letters A, B, C, D, E, and F on pieces of paper and select a letter that is a vowel at random. $\frac{1}{3}$; $0.\overline{3}$; $33\frac{1}{3}$%

14. Your name is selected at random from a list of names of 6 students. $\frac{1}{6}$; $0.1\overline{6}$; $16\frac{2}{3}$%

🌐 15. Games A game has a square board divided into 4 equal sections numbered 1 through 4. You win when you toss a chip and it lands on the section numbered 4. What is the probability of winning when a toss lands on the board? $\frac{1}{4}$

Ⓑ Apply Your Skills

Ten cards are numbered 1 through 10. You select a card at random. Find each probability.

16. $P(6)$ $\frac{1}{10}$

17. $P(\text{even number})$ $\frac{5}{10}$ or $\frac{1}{2}$

18. $P(1 \text{ or } 2)$ $\frac{2}{10}$ or $\frac{1}{5}$

19. $P(11)$ 0

20. $P(\text{a number less than 11})$ 1

21. Writing in Math For a game, is the probability of "not winning" always the same as "losing"? Explain. **No; "losing" means not winning and not tying, and "not winning" could be either losing or tying.**

22. Mental Math Is an event with a probability of $\frac{1}{2}$ *more* or *less* likely than an event with a probability of $\frac{2}{3}$? Explain. **less likely; $\frac{1}{2} < \frac{2}{3}$**

23. Open-Ended Give an example of an impossible event and an example of a certain event. **Answers may vary. Sample: An impossible event would be getting a number greater than 6 when rolling a standard number cube. A certain event would be getting either heads or tails when tossing a coin.**

11-1 Probability **549**

Assignment Guide

1 Objective 1
Ⓐ Ⓑ Core 1–35
Ⓒ Extension 36–39

Test Prep 40–45
Mixed Review 46–52

Error Prevention!

Exercises 1–10 Make sure students first find the total number of possible outcomes.

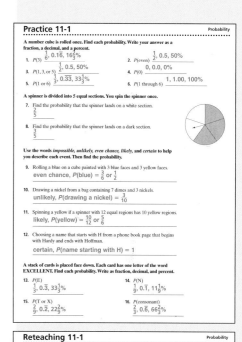

 Use the Guided Problem Solving worksheet with Exercise 24a.

Real-World Connection

The girl chooses her favorite color when she selects the balloon. This is *not* a random event.

24. Party A package of 25 party balloons has 8 red, 6 blue, 6 green, and 5 yellow balloons.

    a. Find the probability of selecting a yellow balloon at random. Write your answer as a fraction, a decimal, and a percent. $\frac{1}{5}$; 0.2; 20%

    b. State whether the event "yellow balloon" is more or less likely than the event "green balloon." **less likely**

Find each probability for one roll of a number cube.

25. P(multiple of 3) $\frac{2}{6}$ or $\frac{1}{3}$

26. P(factor of 8) $\frac{3}{6}$ or $\frac{1}{2}$

27. P(prime number) $\frac{3}{6}$ or $\frac{1}{2}$

28. P(multiple of 4) $\frac{1}{6}$

29. Order the following outcomes from *most* likely to *least* likely. **a, b, d, c**

    a. You flip a coin once and get tails.

    b. You roll a 5 on a number cube.

    c. You roll a 7 on a number cube.

    d. You select a 6 at random from a hat with the numbers 1 through 100 written on pieces of paper.

30. Estimation Suppose you spin the pointer once. Estimate each probability. Give your answer as a percent.

    a. The pointer lands on red. **about 48%**

    b. The pointer lands on green. **about 2%**

    c. The pointer lands on yellow. **about 33%**

For Exercises 31–33, each of the 26 letters in the English alphabet is put on a slip of paper. One slip is selected at random.

31. Find the probability that the letter comes before L in the alphabet. $\frac{11}{26}$

32. Find the probability of selecting one of the letters in MISSISSIPPI. $\frac{2}{13}$

33. Reasoning Which is more likely: selecting a letter from G through O, or from P through Z? Explain. **P through Z; there are more letters in P through Z.**

Reading Math

Icosahedron comes from the Greek words for "twenty" and "bases."

34. Suppose you roll an *icosahedron*, an object with 20 faces. All outcomes are equally likely. Each face is colored red, blue, yellow, or green.

    a. How many faces are colored with each color? **5**

    b. In one roll, what is the probability that a green face will come up? $\frac{1}{4}$

35.

35. Schedules Volunteers use a spinner to determine job assignments at the local park. Each color indicates a different job. Sketch a four-color spinner with the following probabilities: P(Job 1) = 25%, P(Job 2) = 50%, P(Job 3) = 10%, and P(Job 4) = 15%.

550   **Chapter 11** Exploring Probability

Challenge

A bag contains only red, green, and blue marbles. If you select a marble at random, $P(\text{green}) = \frac{1}{3}$ and $P(\text{red}) = \frac{1}{2}$.

36. Find the probability of selecting a blue marble. $\frac{1}{6}$

37. If there are 6 green marbles, how many marbles are there in all?
18 marbles

 38. Twins In the United States, the probability that a child is a twin is about 2.9%. What is the probability that a child is *not* a twin? Write your answer as a fraction, decimal, and percent. $\frac{971}{1,000}$; 0.971; 97.1%

39. Stretch Your Thinking Karol is decorating a cube with seven colors of paint. She paints two dots of each color on each side of the cube. How many dots does she paint on the cube? **84 dots**

 Test Prep

Gridded Response

For Exercises 40–44, a spinner has equal-sized sections numbered 1 through 30. Suppose you spin the pointer once.

40. What is the probability that the pointer lands on 2, 3, or 5? $\frac{1}{10}$

41. What is the probability that the pointer lands on a multiple of 10? $\frac{1}{10}$

Take It to the NET
Online lesson quiz at
www.PHSchool.com
Web Code: aaa-1101

42. What is the probability that the pointer lands on a prime number? $\frac{1}{3}$

43. What is the probability that the pointer lands on an even number? $\frac{1}{2}$

44. What is the probability that the pointer lands on a multiple of 5? $\frac{1}{5}$

45. A bag contains a total of 25 blue and yellow chips. There are 7 more yellow chips than blue chips. What is the probability of selecting a blue chip? $\frac{9}{25}$

Mixed Review

Lesson 10-2   **Find each sum.**

46. $8 + 27$ **35**

47. $-5 + (-13)$ **−18**

48. $10 + (-10)$ **0**

49. $-6 + 4$ **−2**

50. $8 + (-8)$ **0**

51. $-7 + (-3)$ **−10**

52. At 5 A.M., the temperature was $-3°$F. By noon, the temperature had risen $15°$F. What was the temperature at noon? **12°F**

 **Lesson Quiz 11-1**

A box contains 3 red markers, 4 green markers, 2 purple markers, 2 black markers, and 1 blue marker. You pick a marker at random. Find the probability of each event. Write each answer as a fraction, a decimal, and a percent.

1. $P(\text{green})$ $\frac{1}{3}$, 0.33, 33%

2. $P(\text{purple or blue})$ $\frac{1}{4}$, 0.25, 25%

3. $P(\text{pink})$ 0, 0, 0%

4. $P(\text{blue})$ $\frac{1}{12}$, 0.08, 8%

Test Prep

Resources
A sheet of blank grids is available in the *Test-Taking Strategies With Transparencies* booklet. Give copies of this sheet to students so they can practice filling in grids.

For additional practice with a variety of test item formats:
• Test Prep, p. 589
• Test-Taking Strategies, p. 585
• Test-Taking Strategies With Transparencies

Enrichment 11-1   Probability
Critical Thinking

A spinner has four different sections designated by color. The table shows the number of times the spinner landed on a certain color. Create a spinner that best represents the data.

Color	Number of times it landed on color
red	||| ||| ||| |||
green	||| |||
blue	
pink	|||
black	|||
white	

1. How many sections does the spinner have? **4 sections**

2. Do you think *all* of the sections are of equal space? Explain.
Sample answer: No; the spinner landed on some sections more than others. So, it is likely that the sections are not of equal space.

3. Do you think *any* of the sections are of equal space? Explain.
Sample answer: Yes; the spinner landed on the pink and black sections the same number of times. So, it is likely that these sections are of equal space.

4. Classify the event of landing on blue or white as impossible, unlikely, equally likely, likely, or certain. Explain your reasoning.
Impossible; the spinner did not land on either of these two colors. Since the spinner only has four sections and the tally table shows that the spinner landed on four other colors, then the spinner does not have a blue or white section.

5. Use the table to find the probability of the spinner landing on each color.
$P(\text{red})$ $\frac{1}{2}$ $P(\text{green})$ $\frac{1}{4}$ $P(\text{blue})$ 0
$P(\text{pink})$ $\frac{1}{8}$ $P(\text{black})$ $\frac{1}{8}$ $P(\text{white})$ 0

6. Draw a spinner that best represents the data table and your answers to Exercises 1-5.
Sample drawing:

Alternative Assessment

Each student in a pair draws a picture for a situation similar to that used for Exercises 1–10. Partners take turns asking each other questions about the probabilities in their drawings, including questions about events that are unlikely, likely, equally likely, impossible, and certain. Each partner records the probability as it is asked.

551

Extension

Odds

For Use With Lesson 11-1

Odds

This feature extends Lesson 11-1 and introduces students to the concept of odds, which are a way of expressing the chance of success against the chance of failure.

Teaching Notes

Discuss with students that odds are a way of expressing the chance of success against the chance of failure. Elicit from them how the concept of odds differs from the concept of probability. Odds in favor of an event are the ratio of favorable outcomes to *unfavorable* outcomes, while probability is the ratio of favorable outcomes to *possible* outcomes.

Teaching Tip

Students are likely to have heard the term "odds" used, particularly within the realm of sports, without knowing precisely what it means. You may wish to draw upon their prior knowledge by introducing the concept as it applies to sports. For example, explain that if a football team has a record of 10 wins and 2 losses against opponents of similar talent, the odds of winning the next game are 10 to 2, or 5 to 1.

Exercises

Before students begin the exercises, elicit from them that the sum of favorable and unfavorable outcomes is the total number of all outcomes.

Exercise 4 Challenge your more advanced students to come up with a formula to find probability given the odds. For example, ask: *If the odds in favor of A are a to b, find P(A).* $P(A) = \frac{a}{a+b}$

When you roll a number cube, the probability that you will roll a 2 is $\frac{1}{6}$, or 1 out of 6.

You can describe your chances of rolling a 2 using odds.

Odds in favor of an event is the ratio of the number of favorable outcomes to the number of unfavorable outcomes.

Odds against an event is the ratio of the number of unfavorable outcomes to the number of favorable outcomes.

EXAMPLE Odds for an Event

a. In one roll of a number cube, what are the odds in favor of rolling a 2?

There is 1 favorable outcome.
There are 5 unfavorable outcomes.

The odds in favor of rolling a 2 are 1 to 5.

Ways to roll a 2	2
Ways *not* to roll a 2	1 3 4 5 6

b. What are the odds against rolling a 2?

The odds against rolling a 2 are 5 to 1.

EXERCISES

1. You roll a number cube once.
  a. What are the odds in favor of rolling an even number? **3 to 3 or 1 to 1**
  b. What are the odds against rolling an even number? **3 to 3 or 1 to 1**

2. A jar contains 6 marbles: 2 red, 2 blue, 1 yellow, and 1 green. You draw one marble at random.
  a. What are the odds in favor of drawing a blue marble? **2 to 4 or 1 to 2**
  b. What are the odds against drawing a blue marble? **4 to 2 or 2 to 1**

3. A store has a box of 1,000 tennis balls. Suppose the odds in favor of selecting a tennis ball marked "WIN" are 1 to 9. How many tennis balls are winners? **100 balls**

4. (**Algebra**) Suppose the odds in favor of an event are *a* to *b*. What is the probability of the event? (*Hint:* There are *a* favorable outcomes and *b* unfavorable outcomes. What is the total number of outcomes?) $\frac{a}{a+b}$

11-2 Experimental Probability

What You'll Learn

OBJECTIVE 1
To find experimental probabilities

... And Why

To decide whether a game is fair, as in Example 2

 Check Skills You'll Need   **?** For help, go to Lesson 3-4.

Write each fraction in simplest form.

1. $\frac{12}{20}$ $\frac{3}{5}$

2. $\frac{25}{50}$ $\frac{1}{2}$

3. $\frac{8}{30}$ $\frac{4}{15}$

4. $\frac{26}{40}$ $\frac{13}{20}$

5. $\frac{18}{30}$ $\frac{3}{5}$

6. $\frac{17}{51}$ $\frac{1}{3}$

7. $\frac{36}{45}$ $\frac{4}{5}$

8. $\frac{55}{88}$ $\frac{5}{8}$

New Vocabulary   • experimental probability

iTEXT Interactive lesson includes instant self-check, tutorials, and activities.

OBJECTIVE 1
Finding Experimental Probabilities

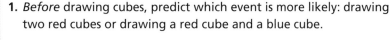

Investigation: Exploring Probabilities

Place 2 red cubes and 2 blue cubes in a bag. Suppose you draw 2 cubes out of the bag without looking. **1–3. Check students' work.**

1. *Before* drawing cubes, predict which event is more likely: drawing two red cubes or drawing a red cube and a blue cube.

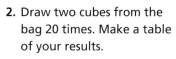

2. Draw two cubes from the bag 20 times. Make a table of your results.

Event	Number of Times Event Occurs	Probability
2 red	■	$\frac{■}{20}$
1 red 1 blue	■	$\frac{■}{20}$

3. a. Based on your results, was your prediction correct?

b. To find the experimental probability of each event, find the ratio of the number of times the event occurs to 20.

Suppose you toss a ball of paper at a trash can. You toss it 12 times, and the ball of paper goes in 5 times. Each toss is a *trial*. To find an experimental probability, which is based on data you collect, use the following ratio.

Key Concepts   **Experimental Probability**

experimental probability: $P(\text{event}) = \dfrac{\text{number of times an event occurs}}{\text{total number of trials}}$

 Ongoing Assessment and Intervention

Before the Lesson	During the Lesson	After the Lesson
Diagnose prerequisite skills using:	**Monitor progress using:**	**Assess knowledge using:**
• Check Skills You'll Need	• Check Understanding • Additional Examples • Test Prep	• Lesson Quiz • Computer Test Generator CD

Lesson Preview

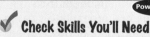

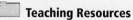 **Check Skills You'll Need**

Writing Fractions in Simplest Form
Lesson 3-4: Example 3. Extra Practice, p. 644.

Lesson Resources

Optional Materials
• 4 cubes or identical objects, 2 each of different colors

📁 **Teaching Resources**
Practice, Reteaching, Enrichment

👥 **Reaching All Students**
Practice Workbook 11-2
Spanish Practice Workbook 11-2
Guided Problem Solving 11-2
Hands-On Activities 45, 46

⏱ **Presentation Assistant Plus!**
Transparencies
• Check Skills You'll Need 11-2
• Problem of the Day 11-2
• Additional Examples 11-2
• Student Edition Answers 11-2
• Lesson Quiz 11-2
PH Presentation Pro CD-ROM 11-2

PRENTICE HALL
ASSESSMENT SYSTEM

Computer Test Generator CD

💻 **Technology**
Resource Pro® CD-ROM
Computer Test Generator CD
PH Presentation Pro CD-ROM

💻 **www.PHSchool.com**
Student Site
• Teacher Web Code: aak-5500
• Self-grading Lesson Quiz

PH SuccessNet Teacher Center
• Lesson Planner
• Resources

Plus **iTEXT**

553

2. Teach

Math Background

The *experimental probability* of an event is the ratio of the number of times the event occurs to the total number of trials. Experimental probability is based on collected data or observations from experiments, so the results often vary from one experiment to the next. A *fair* coin or spinner has equally likely outcomes.

Teaching Notes

Investigation (Optional)
Lead students to the distinctions between theoretical probability and experimental probability:
• Theoretical probability represents what cubes students might *expect* to draw from the bag.
• Experimental probability represents the actual cubes drawn from the bag.

PowerPoint
Additional Examples

1. In 30 times at bat, Jan struck out 14 times. What is the experimental probability that Jan will strike out at her next at-bat? $P(\text{strike-out}) = \frac{7}{15}$

2. You and your friend want to play a game with a spinner. The table below shows the results of 120 spins. Which game seems fair? Explain.

Red	Yellow	Blue
58	23	39

a. You win with yellow and your friend wins with blue. **Not fair, the probabilities of $\frac{23}{120}$ and $\frac{39}{120}$ are not especially close.**

b. You win with red and your friend wins with blue or yellow. **Fair, the probabilities of $\frac{58}{120}$ and $\frac{62}{120}$ are about the same.**

Closure

What is experimental probability? the ratio of the number of times an event occurs to the total number of trials

554

You can find the experimental probability when you compete in sports.

① **EXAMPLE** **Experimental Probability** 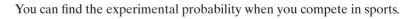 Real World

Tennis In 20 tennis matches against Jennie, Ai-Ling wins 9 times.

a. What is the experimental probability that Ai-Ling wins a match?

$P(\text{Ai-Ling wins}) = \dfrac{9}{20}$ ← number of matches Ai-Ling wins
← total number of matches

The experimental probability that Ai-Ling wins is $\frac{9}{20}$.

b. What is the experimental probability that Jennie wins a match?

$P(\text{Jennie wins}) = \dfrac{11}{20}$ ← number of matches Jennie wins
← total number of matches

The experimental probability that Jennie wins is $\frac{11}{20}$.

✔ **Check Understanding** ① Franklin and Tom play 30 matches. Franklin wins 12 matches. What is the experimental probability that Franklin wins a match? $\frac{2}{5}$

A *fair* coin or number cube generates equally likely outcomes. If coins, cubes, or spinners are unevenly made, they may *not* be fair.

② **EXAMPLE** **Analyzing Experimental Probability** Real World

Fair Games You and your friend want to play a game, but your only number cube is chipped. To make a fair game, you first roll the cube 60 times and record the results. Which of the following games seems fair? Explain.

Outcome	1	2	3	4	5	6
Number of Times Rolled	16	17	12	8	4	3

a. You win with a 6, and your friend wins with a 2.

The experimental probability of rolling a 2 is $\frac{17}{60}$. The experimental probability of rolling a 6 is $\frac{3}{60}$. Since the number cube strongly favors 2, the game seems to be unfair.

b. If the number is even, you win. If it is odd, your friend wins.

$17 + 8 + 3 = 28$ ← Add to find the number of trials for even.

$16 + 12 + 4 = 32$ ← Add to find the number of trials for odd.

So $P(\text{even}) = \frac{28}{60}$ and $P(\text{odd}) = \frac{32}{60}$. Since the probabilities are about the same, the game seems to be fair.

✔ **Check Understanding** ② In Example 2, suppose you win with a 1, 3, or 6, and your friend wins with a 2, 4, or 5. Does this game seem fair? **yes**

👥 Reaching All Students

Below Level Have students make sentences using the words *probability* and *experiment*. Students can compare their sentences with the definition of *experimental probability*.	**Advanced Learners** Have students find the experimental probability of rolling each possible sum when rolling a pair of number cubes. Have students make a line plot of their results.	**Diversity** See note on page 555. **Auditory Learners** See note on page 556.

EXERCISES

 For more practice, see *Extra Practice*.

A Practice by Example

Example 1
(page 554)

The table shows the results of students playing a video game. Find the experimental probability that each person wins.

Game Results

Player	Blake	Troy	Carla	Kate	Sara	Luis
Number of Wins	11	47	63	17	0	14
Number of times game is played	25	80	294	17	15	30

12b. No; since the probability is based on experiments, you expect it to be close, but not exactly the same.

1. Carla $\frac{3}{14}$
2. Luis $\frac{7}{15}$
3. Kate 1

4. Sara 0
5. Troy $\frac{47}{80}$
6. Blake $\frac{11}{25}$

7. You toss a paper cup into the air 48 times. It lands on its side 36 times. Find the experimental probability that it lands on its side. $\frac{3}{4}$

Example 2
(page 554)

Reasoning Suppose Player A and Player B want to play a game with a number cube. The table below shows the results of tossing a number cube 80 times. Tell whether each game seems fair. Explain.

Outcome	1	2	3	4	5	6
Number of Times Rolled	9	12	19	14	25	1

8. No; the experimental probability of rolling an even number is $\frac{27}{80}$.

8. Player A wins if the number is even. Otherwise, Player B wins.

9. Yes; the experimental probability of rolling a 1, 2, or 3 is $\frac{1}{2}$.

9. Player A wins if the number is 1, 2, or 3. Otherwise, Player B wins.

10. Player A wins if the number is 5 or 6. Otherwise, Player B wins.
No; the experimental probability of rolling a 5 or 6 is $\frac{13}{40}$.

B Apply Your Skills

11. **Basketball** A basketball player makes 4 of 12 free throws. Find the experimental probability of the player missing a free throw. $\frac{2}{3}$

GPS

12. **Fair Games** The Mandan people played a game tossing decorated bone disks in a basket. Suppose Player A wins if the side with a decoration lands in the basket and faces up. Otherwise, Player B wins.

a. In 100 trials, $P(\text{A wins}) = \frac{30}{100}$ and $P(\text{B wins}) = \frac{70}{100}$. Does this seem to be a fair game? no

b. **Reasoning** If the two players play the game the next day, will the experimental probabilities of winning be exactly the same? Explain. See above left.

Real-World 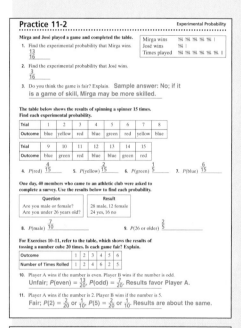 **Connection**

This basket is the type used by the Mandan peoples, who once lived along the banks of the Missouri River.

13. **a.** **Data File, p. 545** Find the experimental probability that Player A wins. $\frac{3}{20}$
b. Find the experimental probability that Player B or Player C wins. $\frac{13}{20}$

11-2 Experimental Probability **555**

GPS Use the Guided Problem Solving worksheet with Exercise 11.

---

3. Practice

Assignment Guide

1 **Objective 1**
A **B** Core 1–30
C Extension 31–33

Test Prep 34–37
Mixed Review 38–46

Diversity
Exercises 1–6 Encourage students to see games as experiments. Take care to avoid references to gambling or risk-taking behaviors.

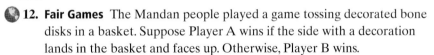

Practice 11-2 — Experimental Probability

Mirga and José played a game and completed the table.
| Mirga wins | | José wins | | Times played | |

1. Find the experimental probability that Mirga wins. $\frac{13}{16}$

2. Find the experimental probability that José wins. $\frac{3}{16}$

3. Do you think the game is fair? Explain. Sample answer: No; if it is a game of skill, Mirga may be more skilled.

The table below shows the results of spinning a spinner 15 times. Find each experimental probability.

Trial	1	2	3	4	5	6	7	8
Outcome	blue	yellow	red	blue	green	red	yellow	blue

Trial	9	10	11	12	13	14	15	
Outcome	blue	green	red	blue	blue	green	red	

4. $P(\text{red})$ $\frac{4}{15}$ 5. $P(\text{yellow})$ $\frac{2}{15}$ 6. $P(\text{green})$ $\frac{3}{15}$ 7. $P(\text{blue})$ $\frac{6}{15}$

One day, 40 members who came to an athletic club were asked to complete a survey. Use the results below to find each probability.

Question	Result
Are you male or female?	28 male, 12 female
Are you under 26 years old?	24 yes, 16 no

8. $P(\text{male})$ $\frac{7}{10}$ 9. $P(26 \text{ or older})$ $\frac{2}{5}$

For Exercises 10–11, refer to the table, which shows the results of tossing a number cube 20 times. Is each game fair? Explain.

Outcome	1	2	3	4	5	6
Number of Times Rolled	1	2	4	6	2	5

10. Player A wins if the number is even. Player B wins if the number is odd. Unfair; $P(\text{even}) = \frac{13}{20}$, $P(\text{odd}) = \frac{7}{20}$. Results favor Player A.

11. Player A wins if the number is 2. Player B wins if the number is 5. Fair; $P(2) = \frac{2}{20}$ or $\frac{1}{10}$, $P(5) = \frac{2}{20}$ or $\frac{1}{10}$. Results are about the same.

Reteaching 11-2 — Experimental Probability

A *fair game* generates equally likely outcomes. To decide whether a game is fair:
① Make a list of all the possible outcomes of the game.
② Determine whether each player has about the same probability of winning.

The Spinner Game
Spin a spinner with equal-size sections numbered 1–8. Player A wins on a multiple of 2 or 3. Player B wins on any other number. Is this game fair?
① Possible outcomes: 1, 2, 3, 4, 5, 6, 7, 8.
② Player A wins with a 2, 3, 4, 6, and 8. Player B wins with a 1, 5, 7.
$P(\text{A winning}) = \frac{5}{8}$, $P(\text{B winning}) = \frac{3}{8}$
The game is not fair.

You can use the results of playing a game to find the *experimental probability* of each player winning.

Example: Two players played a game 25 times. Player A won 15 times and player B won 10 times.

$P(\text{A wins}) = \frac{\text{number of times A won}}{\text{total games played}}$
$= \frac{15}{25}$
$= \frac{3}{5}$

$P(\text{B wins}) = \frac{\text{number of times B won}}{\text{total games played}}$
$= \frac{10}{25}$
$= \frac{2}{5}$

You and your friend play a game. You win if you roll a number cube and it lands on 5. Your friend wins if she rolls a number cube and it lands on a factor of 6.

1. What is the probability that you win? $\frac{1}{6}$

2. What is the probability that your friend wins? $\frac{4}{6}$ or $\frac{2}{3}$

3. Is the game fair? Explain your reasoning. No; the probabilities are not close to being the same.

The line plot shows the results of rolling a number cube 20 times. Find the experimental probability.

4. $P(6)$ $\frac{5}{20}$ or $\frac{1}{4}$

5. $P(\text{less than 4})$ $\frac{9}{20}$

6. $P(\text{greater than 3})$ $\frac{11}{20}$

7. $P(\text{even number})$ $\frac{12}{20}$ or $\frac{3}{5}$

8. $P(\text{prime number})$ $\frac{7}{20}$

Real-World Connection

A good snowboarder knows how to use the snowboard's edges to increase speed.

14. a. **Snowboarding** You and a friend go snowboarding. You make it down the mountain before your friend 13 times out of 20. What is the experimental probability of you getting down the mountain first? $\frac{13}{20}$

   b. What is the experimental probability of your friend being first? $\frac{7}{20}$

15. **Reasoning** From the first 8 weeks of the school year, you find the experimental probability of having pizza on Friday is 100%. Explain what this means. **It seems likely that the school will serve pizza every Friday.**

16. The table shows the results of five groups of students tossing the same coin.

   a. Find the experimental probability of getting heads for each group. **See below left.**

   b. Which group has results that most strongly suggest an unfair coin? **E**

   c. Total the results and find the experimental probability of getting heads. $\frac{12}{25}$

Group	H	T
A	11	9
B	8	12
C	13	7
D	10	10
E	6	14

16a. Group A: $\frac{11}{20}$; Group B: $\frac{2}{5}$; Group C: $\frac{13}{20}$; Group D: $\frac{1}{2}$; Group E: $\frac{3}{10}$

Data Analysis Carlos rolls 2 number cubes and finds the sum. He records the sums in the line plot below. Find each experimental probability.

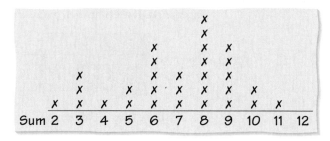

17. $P(\text{sum of }1)$ **0**

18. $P(\text{sum of }3)$ $\frac{3}{30}$ or $\frac{1}{10}$

19. $P(\text{sum of }5)$ $\frac{2}{30}$ or $\frac{1}{15}$

20. $P(\text{sum of }7)$ $\frac{3}{30}$ or $\frac{1}{10}$

21. $P(\text{sum of }8)$ $\frac{7}{30}$

22. $P(\text{sum of }12)$ **0**

23. **Writing in Math** You and your friend want to play a game that uses a spinner with equal sections. Explain how you can use experimental probability to determine if the spinner is fair. **Spin it several times to see if it lands on each section about the same number of times.**

Data Collection Roll a pair of number cubes 50 times. Record your results and find each experimental probability. **24–29. Check students' work.**

24. $P(1 \text{ and } 1)$

25. $P(\text{doubles})$

26. $P(\text{even and even})$

27. $P(\text{odd and odd})$

28. $P(2 \text{ and } 3)$

29. $P(4 \text{ and } 5)$

Game Results	
A wins	⑷⑷ IIII
B wins	⑷⑷ ⑷⑷ I
Times played	⑷⑷ ⑷⑷ ⑷⑷ ⑷⑷

30. The table at the left shows the number of wins for two players after many games. Find the experimental probability of each player winning. **Player A: $\frac{9}{20}$; Player B: $\frac{11}{20}$**

31. Geometry Lisa's dartboard has an area of 40 square inches. In the center is a triangle. In 50 throws that hit the board, Lisa hit the triangle 30 times. Estimate the area of the triangle and explain your answer. See margin.

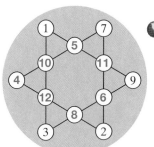

32. Baseball A baseball coach has to decide which player to put in as the designated hitter. Player A has 56 hits in 200 at bats. Player B has 48 hits in 160 at bats. Based on experimental probability, which player is more likely to get a hit? **Player B**

33. Stretch Your Thinking Copy and complete the star at the left. Use each number from 1 through 12 only once. The sum of numbers on the six points of the star, and the sums on each of the six lines, must be 26. **See left.**

Test Prep

Multiple Choice

34. Which of the following probabilities is NOT equal to $\frac{14}{200}$? **D**

A. 7%   **B.** $\frac{7}{100}$ **C.** 0.07   **D.** 14%

35. A coin is tossed 50 times and comes up tails 23 times. What is the experimental probability of getting tails? **H**

F. 23%   **G.** $\frac{23}{100}$ **H.** $\frac{23}{50}$ **I.** 50%

36. A student rolls a number cube 40 times. The number 3 comes up eight times. What is the experimental probability of rolling a 3? **C**

A. 8%   **B.** 12.5%   **C.** 0.20   **D.** $\frac{1}{4}$

Short Response

37. Tristan rolls a number cube 20 times. He rolls four 2's and three 4's. **(a)** What is the experimental probability of rolling a 2? **(b)** A 4? Explain each answer. **See margin.**

Take It to the NET
Online lesson quiz at
www.PHSchool.com
Web Code: aaa-1102

Mixed Review

Lesson 10-3   **Find each difference.**

38. $9 - (-3)$ **12**   **39.** $-9 - 4$ **−13**   **40.** $20 - (-5)$ **25**

41. $-2 - (-12)$ **10**   **42.** $16 - (-21)$ **37**   **43.** $-4 - 17$ **−21**

Lesson 8-7   **Geometry** Tell whether the figures are *congruent* or *similar*.

44.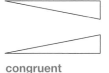

similar

45.

congruent

46.

similar

11-2 Experimental Probability   **557**

PowerPoint Lesson Quiz 11-2

Find the experimental probability that each person makes a foul shot in basketball.

Player	Ayala	Sanjay	Jose
Baskets	0	14	8
Attempts	12	16	12

1. Jose $\frac{2}{3}$ **2.** Ayala 0

3. Sanjay $\frac{7}{8}$

Alternative Assessment

Pairs of students flip two coins twenty times and record the results. Partners find the experimental probability of two heads, two tails, and one head and one tail. Then all pairs combine their results and find the total experimental probabilities.

Test Prep

Resources
For additional practice with a variety of test item formats:
• Test Prep, p. 589
• Test-Taking Strategies, p. 585
• Test-Taking Strategies With Transparencies

Enrichment 11-2   Experimental Probability
Critical Thinking

Hurricane season in the United States is from June 1 to November 30. In an average season, there are ten tropical storms. Six are expected to reach hurricane strength and two of these are likely to strike the U.S. coast. Is the probability that a tropical storm will turn into a hurricane more than 50%?

1. How many tropical storms are there in an average season?
   10 storms

2. How many of the tropical storms are expected to reach hurricane strength in an average season?
   6 storms

3. Describe the ratio you will use to show the probability that a tropical storm will turn into a hurricane.
   number of tropical storms expected to reach hurricane strength:number of tropical storms

4. What is the probability that a tropical storm will turn into a hurricane?
   $\frac{6}{10}$ or $\frac{3}{5}$

5. Write the probability as a percent.
   60%

6. Is the percentage less than, equal to, or greater than 50%?
   greater than

7. What is the probability that a tropical storm will strike the U.S. coast?
   $\frac{2}{10}$ or $\frac{1}{5}$

8. What is the probability that a hurricane will strike the U.S. coast?
   $\frac{2}{6}$ or $\frac{1}{3}$

9. Is the probability that a tropical storm that strikes the U.S. coast will turn into a hurricane less than, equal to, or greater than 50%? Explain.
   $\frac{1}{3} = 33\frac{1}{3}\%$; $33\frac{1}{3}\% < 50\%$.

---

31. Answers may vary. Sample: 24 in.²; the experimental probability of hitting the $\triangle$ is $\frac{3}{5}$, and $\frac{3}{5}$ of the area of the rectangle is $\frac{3}{5} \times 40$, or 24 in.²

37. [2] a. $\frac{1}{5}$; he rolled a 2 four times in twenty rolls, and $\frac{4}{20} = \frac{1}{5}$.

b. $\frac{3}{20}$; he rolled a 4 three times in twenty rolls.

[1] minor error in explanation

557

1. Plan

Lesson Preview

 Check Skills You'll Need

Solving Proportions
Lesson 6-4: Example 2. Extra
Practice, p. 647.

Lesson Resources

Optional Materials
- 10 cubes or identical objects, 8 of one color, two of another color

Teaching Resources
Practice, Reteaching, Enrichment
Checkpoint Quiz 1

Reaching All Students
Practice Workbook 11-3
Spanish Practice Workbook 11-3
Reading and Math Literacy 11B
Spanish Reading and Math
  Literacy 11B
Spanish Checkpoint Quiz 1
Guided Problem Solving 11-3
Hands-On Activities 44, 46

Presentation Assistant Plus!
Transparencies
- Check Skills You'll Need 11-3
- Problem of the Day 11-3
- Additional Examples 11-3
- Student Edition Answers 11-3
- Lesson Quiz 11-3
PH Presentation Pro CD-ROM 11-3

ASSESSMENT SYSTEM

Checkpoint Quiz 1
Computer Test Generator CD

Technology
Resource Pro® CD-ROM
Computer Test Generator CD
PH Presentation Pro CD-ROM

www.PHSchool.com
Student Site
- Teacher Web Code: aak-5500
- Self-grading Lesson Quiz

PH SuccessNet Teacher Center
- Lesson Planner
- Resources

Plus

558

What You'll Learn

OBJECTIVE 1 To make predictions from probabilities

OBJECTIVE 2 To make predictions based on a sample

. . . And Why

To make predictions from a sample, as in Example 2

Check Skills You'll Need

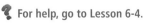 For help, go to Lesson 6-4.

Solve each proportion.

1. $\frac{2}{3} = \frac{4}{x}$ 6

2. $\frac{n}{5} = \frac{10}{25}$ 2

3. $\frac{12}{a} = \frac{6}{7}$ 14

4. In a basket of apples, there are two green apples to every three red apples. If there are six green apples, how many red apples are there?
9 red apples

New Vocabulary • population • sample

 OBJECTIVE 1 Making Predictions From Probabilities

 TEXT Interactive lesson includes instant self-check, tutorials, and activities.

Investigation: Making Predictions

Place 8 blue cubes and 2 green cubes in a bag. Suppose you select one cube at random.

1. What is P(blue)? P(green)? $\frac{4}{5}; \frac{1}{5}$

2. Suppose you draw a cube from the bag and replace it 20 times. How many times do you think you will draw a blue cube? Explain.
Answers may vary. Sample: about 16; $\frac{4}{5} \times 20 = 16$

3. Select a cube and replace it 20 times. Record the color each time.
3–4. Check students' work.

4. Did the number of blue cubes you obtained exactly match your prediction in Exercise 2? Explain why these answers might differ.

Probabilities can help you make predictions about the outcome of an experiment. However, they do not guarantee what will actually occur.

To predict the number of times an event will occur, multiply the probability of the event by the total number of trials.

 Need Help?
For help with multiplying fractions by whole numbers, go to Lesson 5-1.

$$P(\text{event}) \times \boxed{\text{total number of trials}} = \boxed{\text{number of predicted successes}}$$

Suppose you flip a coin 10 times. To predict the number of times you get tails, multiply $\frac{1}{2} \times 10$. You would predict getting 5 tails in 10 trials.

 Ongoing Assessment and Intervention

Before the Lesson	During the Lesson	After the Lesson
Diagnose prerequisite skills using:	Monitor progress using:	Assess knowledge using:
• Check Skills You'll Need	• Check Understanding	• Lesson Quiz
	• Additional Examples	• Computer Test Generator CD
	• Test Prep	• Chapter Checkpoint 1 (p. 562)

 EXAMPLE   **Making a Prediction From a Probability**

In a family with two children, suppose there is a 25% chance that both of the children are boys. Out of 72 families with two children, how many are likely to have two boys?

$P(\text{two boys})$	$\times$	number of families	$=$	number of families with two boys
$\frac{1}{4}$	$\times$	72	$=$	18

← Write 25% as $\frac{1}{4}$. Then multiply.

You can predict about 18 families will have two boys.

✔ **Check Understanding** ① At an arcade, Juanita plays a game 20 times. She has a 30% probability of winning each game. How many times should she expect to win?
6 times

OBJECTIVE

2 **Making Predictions Based on Samples**

A **population** is a group about which you want information. A **sample** is a part of the population. You use a sample and proportions to make predictions about the population.

② **EXAMPLE**   **Real-World** **Problem Solving**

Quality Control A company makes 15,000 toy robots. The company randomly selects a sample of 300 robots for inspection. This sample has 5 faulty robots. Predict how many of the 15,000 robots are faulty.

Words $\dfrac{\text{number of faulty toys in sample}}{\text{total number in sample}} = \dfrac{\text{number of faulty toys in production}}{\text{total number in production}}$

Let n = the number of faulty robots in the population.

Proportion $\dfrac{5}{300} = \dfrac{n}{15,000}$

$\dfrac{5}{300} = \dfrac{n}{15,000}$

$300n = 5 \cdot 15,000$ ← **Write the cross products.**

$300n = 75,000$ ← **Simplify.**

$\dfrac{300n}{300} = \dfrac{75,000}{300}$ ← **Divide each side by 300.**

$n = 250$ ← **Simplify.**

It is likely that about 250 toy robots are faulty.

✔ **Check Understanding** ② Suppose 1,000 toy robots are selected at random from 20,000 robots, and 54 are found faulty. How many of the 20,000 robots are likely to be faulty?
1,080 toy robots

 **Reaching All Students**

Below Level In Check Understanding 1, students can estimate to check for reasonableness. *Is 30% more or less than 50%?* less *Did Juanita win more or less than half her games?* less	**Advanced Learners** Ask students to decide whether the United States census is a sample of the population, then explain their answers. Sample: No, because the entire population is polled.	**English Learners** See note on page 559. **Inclusion** See note on page 561.

---

2. Teach

Math Background

A population is a group that you are interested in. Because it is generally difficult to collect information from every member in a large group, samples are investigated. Using probabilities based on the sample, predictions about the entire population can be made. However, to make accurate predictions, the sample selected must be representative of the population. This often involves randomly selecting the sample so that each member of the population is equally likely to be selected.

Teaching Notes

Investigation (Optional)
Before students conduct trials in Step 3, ask: *Do you think the probability will be the same if you conduct an experiment?* Sample: No, but it should be fairly close.

② **EXAMPLE** English Learners

Help students understand the terms *population* and *sample*. Use plain language to explain that a sample is part of a population, much like a part is part of a whole.

PowerPoint
Additional Examples

① Kiko bought 35 raffle tickets. Each ticket has a 20% probability of winning a prize. How many prizes should he expect to win? **7 prizes**

② A random sample shows that 6 wallets out of 400 are defective. Predict how many wallets out of 15,000 will be defective. **225 wallets**

Closure

- *How can you make predictions using the probability of an event?* multiply the total number of trials by the probability of the event
- *How does a sample relate to its population?* The sample is a part of the population that can be used to make a prediction about the entire population.

559

3. Practice

Assignment Guide

1 Objective 1
Ⓐ Ⓑ Core 1–6, 13–14, 23–25
Ⓒ Extension 27

2 Objective 2
Ⓐ Ⓑ Core 7–12, 15–22
Ⓒ Extension 26

Test Prep 28–31
Mixed Review 32–37

Ⓐ **Practice by Example**

Example 1
(page 559)

The probability of winning a game is 40%. How many times should you expect to win if you play the following number of times?

1. 5 times 2
2. 10 times 4
3. 15 times 6
4. 30 times 12
5. 85 times 34
6. 120 times 48

Example 2
(page 559)

Write and solve a proportion to make each prediction. Exercise 7 has been started for you.

Real-World Connection

Careers At the Kennedy Space Center, engineers show you how to use rocket equipment in space.

200 students

🌐 **7. Tour** On a field trip, a teacher asks 70 students, "Did you see the exhibit on rockets?" Of those questioned, 14 say that they did. If there are 1,000 students on the field trip, how many students saw the exhibit?

saw exhibit in sample → $\dfrac{14}{70} = \dfrac{n}{1{,}000}$ ← total that saw exhibit
total in sample → ← total in school

🌐 **8. Art** The mayor wants the opinions of the city's 18,000 middle grade students about which of two murals to display in city hall. The mayor shows the murals to 120 students, and 22 of them prefer Mural B. Predict how many of the 18,000 students will like Mural B.
3,300 students

Use the following information to make a prediction. A company makes shirts, pants, belts, and T-shirts. It plans to ship 24,000 of each item. Before shipping, a sample of each product is tested. From each given sample, predict the number of items that are likely to have defects.

9. Of 500 shirts, 6 have defects.
288 shirts
10. Of 400 pants, 5 have defects.
300 pants
11. Of 250 belts, 2 have defects.
192 belts
12. Of 160 T-shirts, 3 have defects.
450 T-shirts

Ⓑ **Apply Your Skills**

In a survey, 1,580 parents were asked which trait they think is most desirable in their children. The table shows the results.

Trait	Probability of Response
Honesty	42%
Good judgment	36%
Obeys parents	22%

13. Which trait is considered most desirable? honesty

14. a. How many of the parents surveyed think "good judgment" is the most desirable trait? about 569 parents
b. How many think "honesty" is the most desirable trait? about 664 parents

---

Practice 11-3
Making Predictions from Data

Answer each question in a complete sentence and in your own words.

1. What is a population?
Sample answer: A population is a group of people or other objects about which you want information.

2. What is a sample?
Sample answer: A sample is the part of the population you use to make predictions about the population.

3. How can you predict the number of times an event will occur?
Sample answer: To predict the number of times an event will occur, multiply the total number of trials by the probability of the event.

The probability of an event is 20%. How many times should you expect the event to occur in the given number of trials?

4. 15 trials   3
5. 40 trials   8
6. 75 trials   15
7. 120 trials   24

Write and solve a proportion to make each prediction.

8. In a sample of 400 customers at a fast food restaurant, it was determined that 156 customers ordered a salad. The restaurant typically has 1,200 customers in a day. Predict how many of these customers will order a salad.
468 customers

9. Before a company delivers 600 strings of lights, it tests a sample. A quality inspector examines 75 strings of lights and finds that 3 are defective. Predict how many strings of lights in the delivery are defective.
24 strings of lights

10. A company manufactures egg timers. An inspector finds that there are 22 defective timers in a sample of 500. Predict how many egg timers are defective in a shipment of 4,250 egg timers.
187 egg timers

Reteaching 11-3
Making Predictions From Data

Sometimes you cannot survey an entire *population*. Instead, you survey a *sample*—a part of the population that can be used to make predictions about the entire population.

A city has 5,000 sixth graders. To estimate the number of sixth graders who ride bicycles to school, a random sample was used. Of the 200 sixth graders chosen, 40 said they ride bicycles to school. Predict the number of sixth graders out of 5,000 who ride bicycles to school.

① Write a proportion. $\dfrac{40}{200} = \dfrac{n}{5{,}000}$
② Solve. $200 \times n = 40 \times 5{,}000$
$200n = 200{,}000$
$n = \dfrac{200{,}000}{200}$
$n = 1{,}000$

The sample suggests that 1,000 sixth graders ride bikes to school.

Identify the sample size. Then make a prediction for the population.

1. How many in a class of 100 students prefer banana yogurt to other flavors? Of 10 students asked, 6 prefer banana.
Sample size 10
Prediction for population 60

2. How many of the 1,900 joggers seen at the park like to run at 6 A.M.? Of 190 joggers asked, 35 like to run at 6 A.M.
Sample size 190
Prediction for population 350

3. Of 600 first graders in the school district, 109 are not yet reading. How many first graders out of 180,000 in the entire state are not yet reading?
Sample size 600
Prediction for population 32,700

4. Out of 300 families, 150 read the morning newspaper. There are 2,400 families in town. How many read the morning newspaper?
Sample size 300
Prediction for population 1,200

5. How many in a town of 500 students walk to school? Of 100 students asked, 32 walked to school.
Sample size 100
Prediction for population 160

6. Out of 150 families, 16 drive sport utility vehicles (SUVs). How many of the 4,500 families in the county drive SUVs?
Sample size 150
Prediction for population 480

GPS Use the Guided Problem Solving worksheet with Exercise 22.

15. **Data File, p. 545** Suppose players A, B, and C play the game 30 times.
  a. How many times would you expect Player B to win? *about 11 times*
  b. How many times would you expect Player C to win? *about 9 times*

16. <u>Writing in Math</u> Why would a person take a random sample instead of counting or surveying the whole population? *Answers may vary. Sample: It may not be possible to survey the whole population.*

17. 24 blue; 56 red; 80 orange; 40 yellow

18. 48 blue; 112 red; 160 orange; 80 yellow

19. 30 blue; 70 red; 100 orange; 50 yellow

20. 60 blue; 140 red; 200 orange; 100 yellow

Use the line plot at the right. A box of fruit snacks has many individual pieces. The line plot shows the result when 25 pieces are selected at random. For each box size, predict the number of each color in the box. 17–20. **See left.**

17. 200 pieces   **18.** 400 pieces

19. 250 pieces   **20.** 500 pieces

Fruit Pieces

```
                    X
                    X
                    X
              X     X
              X     X
              X     X     X
              X     X     X
          X   X     X     X
          X   X     X     X
          X   X     X     X
        blue red orange yellow
```

21. **Number Sense** Suppose you take a sample of 15 pieces and a sample of 60 pieces. Which sample is more likely to give you a prediction closer to the actual number of each color? Explain. *60 pieces; experimental probability is more accurate with more trials.*

22. A sample of 100 gadgets is selected from the day's production of 5,000 gadgets. In the sample, 7 are defective. Predict the number of faulty gadgets in the day's production. *350 gadgets*

A computer dart game randomly selects points to represent darts being thrown. The areas of each section are as follows.

- black: 1 in.^{2} • blue: 3 in.^{2}
- yellow: 5 in.^{2} • red: 7 in.^{2}

23. What is the probability that the point is in the yellow section? $\frac{5}{16}$

24. What is the probability that the point is in the red or yellow section? $\frac{12}{16}$ or $\frac{3}{4}$

25. If the computer "throws" 1,000 darts, how many can you expect will "land" in the black area? *about 63 darts*

26a–b. **Check students' work.**

C **Challenge**

26. a. **Data Collection** Ask a sample of students from your school what type of music they listen to. Record your results.
  b. Find the total number of students in your school. Then make a prediction about the music preferences of students in your school.

27. **Stretch Your Thinking** Someone looking at a photo says, "Brothers and sisters have I none, but that man's father is my father's son." Explain how this can be true. *A man is looking at a photo of his son.*

11-3 Making Predictions From Data   **561**

Error Prevention!

Exercises 7–8 Students may not set up the proportions for these problems correctly. Have students set up a general proportion, labeled $\frac{part\ of\ sample}{total\ sample} = \frac{part\ of\ population}{total\ population}$. Students can use this proportion to fill in the given numbers for each exercise.

Inclusion
Exercises 13–14 Point out that surveys predict what a population may think or believe, but they cannot predict what any individual thinks.

 **Lesson Quiz 11-3**

The probability of Derek getting a hit when he comes to bat is 30%. How many hits should he expect to get if he comes to bat the following number of times?

1. 450 times 135

2. 1,200 times 360

3. 700 times 210

 **Chapter Checkpoint**

To check understanding of Lessons 11-1 to 11-3:

Checkpoint Quiz 1 (p. 562)

📁 **Teaching Resources**
Checkpoint Quiz 1 (also in Prentice Hall Assessment System)

👥 **Reaching All Students**
Reading and Math Literacy 11B

Spanish versions available

Exercise 30 Elicit the proportion students should use to solve the problem. $\frac{3}{80} = \frac{n}{20,000}$

Enrichment 11-3   Making Predictions From Data
Decision Making

Sample size may influence the predictions you make.

Suppose your class is asked to choose the type of music to play during the noon hour over the PA system. As leader of the group, you appoint Jeff and Carla to survey students in the middle school to find what type of music they prefer.

- Jeff surveyed 4 students. Of these students, 3 out of 4 students prefer country music and 1 student prefers rock music. So, Jeff reported: P(country music) = $\frac{3}{4}$ and P(rock music) = $\frac{1}{4}$.
- Carla surveyed 35 students. Of these students, 10 students choose country music, 13 choose rock, 9 choose rhythm and blues, and 3 choose jazz. So Carla reported: P(country music) = $\frac{2}{7}$, P(rock music) = $\frac{13}{35}$, P(rhythm and blues) = $\frac{9}{35}$, and P(jazz) = $\frac{3}{35}$. Sample answers are given.

1. Which survey do you think is a more accurate reflection of the preferences of students in your school? Explain.
   Carla's survey; since the sample size is larger,
   its probability is likely to be closer to the actual
   probability.

2. What could you do to ensure a more accurate survey?
   Survey more students; make sure survey
   includes students from different grades, different
   classes, different groups within the school.

3. Which type of music would you recommend be played during the lunch hour? Explain.
   A combination of rock, country, and rhythm and
   blues since Carla's survey indicates a strong
   preference for each of these musical categories.

4. Suppose the principal authorizes you to buy 100 CDs. About how many of each type would you buy based on Carla's survey?
   about 29 country, 37 rock, 26 rhythm and blues,
   and 8 jazz

 Test Prep

Reading Comprehension   Read the passage and answer the questions below.

Moviegoers Flock to See New Summer Blockbuster

Today movie fans got their first look at one of the year's most anticipated films. The movie took more than two years to produce.

We surveyed 40 people who saw a sneak preview and 38 of them said it was excellent. The film will open soon.

28. What is the experimental probability that a viewer thought the movie was excellent? $\frac{19}{20}$

29. If there were 600 people in the theater, how many people are likely to think the movie was excellent? 570

Multiple Choice

 **Take It to the NET**
Online lesson quiz at
www.PHSchool.com
Web Code: aaa-1103

30. A company has 20,000 hats in stock. In a random sample of 80 hats, 3 are defective. How many overall hats are likely to be defective? **D**
   A. 3   **B.** 80   **C.** 667   **D.** 750

31. In a pet store's survey, 45 out of 60 people own at least one cat. How many out of 420 customers are likely to own at least one cat? **H**
   F. 7   **G.** 9   **H.** 315   **I.** 560

◯ **Mixed Review**

Lesson 10-4   **Algebra** Find each product.

32. $10 \times (-8)$ -80 **33.** -6×20 -120 **34.** $16 \times (-1)$ -16

35. $-24 \times (-4)$ 96   **36.** $-7 \times (-12)$ 84   **37.** -15×15 -225

✓ **Checkpoint Quiz 1**   **Lessons 11-1 through 11-3**

 Instant self-check quiz online and on CD-ROM

A number cube is rolled. Find each probability.

1. P(less than 3) $\frac{2}{6}$ or $\frac{1}{3}$ **2.** $P(8)$ 0   **3.** P(5 or 6) $\frac{2}{6}$ or $\frac{1}{3}$

4. A pencil is dropped 20 times. It points left 8 times. Find the experimental probability that it points left. $\frac{2}{5}$

5. In a Patterstown survey, 40 out of 50 people say they eat lunch daily. The town has 35,000 people. Predict the number who eat lunch daily. 28,000 people

562   **Chapter 11**   Exploring Probability

Alternative Assessment

Students in pairs agree on a probability other than 40%. Partners refer to Exercises 1–6 and together find how many times they should expect to win using the new probability.

Test Prep

Resources
For additional practice with a variety of test item formats:
- Test Prep, p. 589
- Test-Taking Strategies, p. 585
- Test-Taking Strategies With Transparencies

Simulate a Problem

What You'll Learn

 OBJECTIVE
1 To solve problems by simulation

. . . And Why

To simulate everyday situations, as in Example 1

 **Check Skills You'll Need**   For help, go to Lesson 11-2.

Find the experimental probability that each person makes a basket during basketball practice.

1. Rachel makes 6 baskets in 22 attempts. $\frac{3}{11}$

2. Liam makes 8 baskets in 30 attempts. $\frac{4}{15}$

New Vocabulary • simulation

OBJECTIVE
1

Solving a Problem by Simulation

iTEXT Interactive lesson includes instant self-check, tutorials, and activities.

When to Use This Strategy Sometimes it is difficult to collect data from an actual situation. Instead, you may be able to use a simulation.

A **simulation** of a real-world situation is a model used to find experimental probabilities. You can use number cubes, spinners, and computers to model real-world situations.

1 EXAMPLE <u>Real-World</u> <u>Problem Solving</u>

Newspaper Delivery Each day, Sue delivers Mrs. Rivers' newspaper sometime between 6:30 A.M. and 7:30 A.M. Mrs. Rivers leaves for work between 7:00 A.M. and 8:00 A.M. What is the probability that Mrs. Rivers will get her paper before she leaves for work?

Read and Understand Sue delivers the paper between 6:30 A.M. and 7:30 A.M. Mrs. Rivers goes to work between 7:00 A.M. and 8:00 A.M. You need to find the probability that Mrs. Rivers will get her paper before she goes to work.

---

1. Plan

Lesson Preview

 Check Skills You'll Need 🔆
Finding Experimental Probability
Lesson 11-2: Example 1. Extra Practice, p. 652.

Lesson Resources

📁 **Teaching Resources**
Practice, Reteaching, Enrichment

👥 **Reaching All Students**
Practice Workbook 11-4
Spanish Practice Workbook 11-4
Guided Problem Solving 11-4
Technology Activities 18

⏱ **Presentation Assistant Plus!**
Transparencies
• Check Skills You'll Need 11-4
• Problem of the Day 11-4
• Additional Examples 11-4
• Student Edition Answers 11-4
• Lesson Quiz 11-4
• Classroom Aid 11, 36
PH Presentation Pro CD-ROM 11-4

PRENTICE HALL
ASSESSMENT *SYSTEM*

Computer Test Generator CD

💻 **Technology**
Resource Pro® CD-ROM
Computer Test Generator CD
PH Presentation Pro CD-ROM

💻 **www.PHSchool.com**
Student Site
• Teacher Web Code: aak-5500
• Self-grading Lesson Quiz

PH SuccessNet Teacher Center
• Lesson Planner
• Resources

Plus

 Ongoing Assessment and Intervention

Before the Lesson	**During the Lesson**	**After the Lesson**
Diagnose prerequisite skills using:	**Monitor progress using:**	**Assess knowledge using:**
• Check Skills You'll Need	• Check Understanding	• Lesson Quiz
	• Additional Examples	• Computer Test Generator CD
	• Test Prep	

2. Teach

Math Background

A *simulation* is a model that is used to find experimental probabilities. Simulations are valuable when it is difficult to directly collect data. A good simulation is simple and easy to use. It must also have the same mathematical characteristics as the original problem situation. You can use coins, number cubes, spinners, and random number tables to model possible outcomes. The more trials that are performed, the more reliable the results of the simulation will be.

Teaching Notes

English Learners
Tell students the term *simulation* means to model a situation. Discuss how many careers such as firefighters, astronauts, and doctors simulate situations as practice and preparation for real situations.

Inclusion
Review *equally likely outcomes* so students understand that a simulation must be fair to make meaningful predictions.

PowerPoint
Additional Examples

1 Yan runs a restaurant. His favorite customer leaves the restaurant each night between 8:00 P.M. and 9:00 P.M. His next best customer comes to the restaurant every night between 8:45 P.M. and 9:45 P.M. What is the probability that these customers will dine in the restaurant at the same time? Use a simulation to solve the problem. **Answers may vary. Sample: $\frac{1}{16}$**

Closure

- *What is a simulation?* a model used to find experimental probabilities
- *When would you use a simulation?* when it is difficult to collect actual data

---

Sue's Delivery Time

6:30
7:30

7:15   6:45

7:00

Time Mrs. Rivers Goes to Work

7:00
8:00

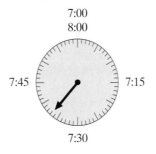

7:45   7:15

7:30

Plan and Solve You can't collect data from Sue and Mrs. Rivers. So, simulate the problem with a model. Assume each time is equally likely.

Use two spinners like the ones at the left. One spinner will simulate a random time from 6:30 A.M. to 7:30 A.M. The other spinner will simulate a random time from 7:00 A.M. to 8:00 A.M.

Spin each spinner once to simulate what may happen on a given day. The table below shows the results for 28 days. For each day, circle the earlier time. If Time 1 is circled, Mrs. Rivers gets her paper.

Time 1 = Sue delivers paper. Time 2 = Mrs. Rivers leaves for work.		
Time 1, Time 2	**Time 1, Time 2**	**Time 1, Time 2**
(7:03), 7:55	(7:14), 7:16	(7:10), 7:18
(6:41), 7:02	(7:08), 7:27	7:21, (7:02)
(6:33), 7:16	(6:41), 7:59	(7:04), 7:46
(6:39), 7:28	(7:00), 7:08	7:09, (7:01)
7:24, (7:06)	(7:22), 7:52	(6:50), 7:28
(6:51), 7:18	(7:05), 7:54	(6:31), 7:52
(7:38), 7:45	(6:36), 7:48	(7:25), 7:27
(6:53), 7:31	(7:04), 7:13	(6:58), 7:34
(6:49), 7:16	(6:59), 7:07	7:23, (7:11)
(6:33), 7:55	(6:52), 7:27	(6:35), 7:57

In the 30 simulations, Mrs. Rivers receives the paper before leaving for work 26 times. So, P(paper before work) $= \frac{26}{30}$, or about 87%.

Look Back and Check The table below summarizes each delivery.

Summary of Delivery Results

Sue Delivers Paper	Mrs. Jones Leaves	Paper Received?
6:30 A.M. to 7:00 A.M.	7:00 A.M. to 7:30 A.M.	Yes
7:00 A.M. to 7:30 A.M.	7:00 A.M. to 7:30 A.M.	Sometimes
6:30 A.M.. to 7:00 A.M.	7:30 A.M. to 8:00 A.M.	Yes
7:00 A.M. to 7:30 A.M.	7:30 A.M. to 8:00 A.M.	Yes

The table shows that it is more likely that she will receive her paper. Since P(paper before work) is $\frac{26}{30}$, or about 87%, the answer is reasonable.

✓ **Check Understanding** 1 The forecast calls for a $\frac{2}{3}$ chance of rain in Detroit and a $\frac{1}{2}$ chance in Tampa. Find the experimental probability that it rains in both cities. Use two number cubes. Let 1, 2, 3, and 4 on one cube represent rain in Detroit. Let 1, 2, and 3 on the other cube represent rain in Tampa. **Check students' wor**

👥 Reaching All Students

Below Level Have students find the following: 45% of 60, 90% of 80, 60% of 160. **27, 72, 96**	**Advanced Learners** Ask: *How do you know what device to use to simulate a problem?* **Pick a device that has the same number (or an easily related number) of outcomes as choices in the situation.**	**English Learners** See note on page 564. **Inclusion** See note on page 564.

Ⓐ Practice by Example

Example 1
(pages 563–564)

Simulate and solve each problem. Show all your work.
1–3. Check students' work.

 1. **Sports** A basketball player makes 75% of her free throws. Find the experimental probability that she will make 2 in a row. Use a spinner with 4 equal sections. Let 3 sections represent a successful free throw.

2. **Quizzes** Use two number cubes to find the experimental probability that both classes have a quiz today. Let 1 and 2 on one cube represent a quiz in science. Let 1, 2, 3, and 4 on the other cube represent a quiz in math.

Probability of a Quiz

Subject	Probability
Math	$\frac{2}{3}$
Science	$\frac{1}{3}$

Need Help?
• Reread the problem.
• Identify the key facts and details.
• Tell the problem in your own words.
• Try a different strategy.
• Check your work.

---

3. **Mail Delivery** Each day, Mr. Hill leaves his house for a walk between 11:00 A.M. and 12:00 P.M. Mr. Hill's mail is delivered between 10:20 A.M. and 11:20 A.M. Find the experimental probability that Mr. Hill will get his mail before he leaves. Use two spinners like those shown below.

6. Answers may vary. Sample: A restaurant chef knows that $\frac{1}{3}$ of the customers order soup with their dinner and $\frac{1}{2}$ order salad. The chef wants to know the probability of a dinner order that includes salad and soup.

Postal Delivery Time
10:20
11:20
11:05
10:35
10:50

Time Mr. Hill Goes for a Walk
11:00
12:00
11:45
11:15
11:30

Ⓑ Apply Your Skills

Strategies

Draw a Diagram
Make a Graph
Make an Organized List
Make a Table and Look for a Pattern
Simulate a Problem
Solve a Simpler Problem
Try, Check, and Revise
Use Logical Reasoning
Work Backward
Write an Equation

Choose a strategy to solve each problem.

4. A family expects to have 4 children. Assume that having a boy and having a girl are equally likely. Answers may vary. Sample: 4 coins
   a. How many coins can you use to simulate this situation?
   b. Find the experimental probability that 3 of the 4 children are girls. Check students' work.

5. Suppose you and a friend make a total of 33 pairs of gloves. Your friend makes twice as many pairs of gloves as you do. How many pairs do you and your friend each make? you: 11 pairs; friend: 22 pairs

6. **Writing in Math** Describe a situation where the strategy *simulate a problem* may be useful. See above left.

7. **Deli** Each time you visit a deli, they stamp a card for you with 1 of 3 kinds of stamps: soup, salad, or sandwich. When your card receives 8 stamps of one kind, they give you that item for free. What is the minimum number of visits you need to get one of each item for free? 24 visits

GPS Use the Guided Problem Solving worksheet with Exercise 8.

Assignment Guide

1 Objective 1
Ⓐ Ⓑ Core 1–7
Ⓒ Extension 8–10

Test Prep 11–15
Mixed Review 16–25

Error Prevention!

Exercise 4 Students may mistakenly look for three flips that represent girls to occur consecutively. Have students list all of the ways a family with four children has three girls. BGGG, GBGG, GGBG, or GGGB

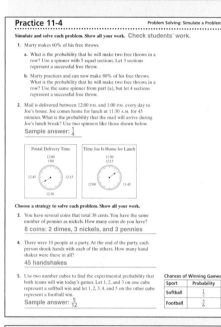

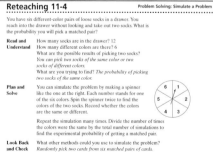

PowerPoint Lesson Quiz 11-4

Simulate and solve the problem. Show all your work.

1. Ms. Martin arrives at work between the hours of 7:15 A.M. and 8:00 A.M. Mrs. Hinkle arrives at work between the hours of 7:30 A.M. and 8:15 A.M. What is the probability that Ms. Martin will arrive at work earlier than Mrs. Hinkle? **Answers may vary. Sample: $\frac{2}{5}$**

Alternative Assessment

Have students work together in pairs to simulate Exercises 1–3. Have partners compare their experimental probabilities with other pairs of students.

Test Prep

Resources

For additional practice with a variety of test item formats:
• Test Prep, p. 589
• Test-Taking Strategies, p. 585
• Test-Taking Strategies With Transparencies

Exercise 14 Before students begin, have them review the order of operations.

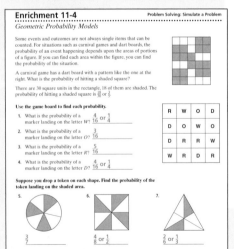

566

C Challenge

8. Collecting Each box of a cereal brand contains one of four prizes. **GPS** A box costs $3.50. You want to collect all four prizes. What is the least amount of money you may need to spend to get all four prizes? **$14**

A jumping spider

9. a. Biology Jumping spiders can jump 40 times their body length. About how far in centimeters can a 15-millimeter spider jump? **60 cm**

   b. Suppose another spider is 3 millimeters longer than the spider in part (a). About how far in centimeters can this spider jump? **72 cm**

10. Stretch Your Thinking How many squares of all sizes fit in a 5-by-5 square grid? Consider only squares that have integer side lengths. **55 squares**

Test Prep

Multiple Choice

11. What is the expression 3.01 + 2.5 in simplest form? **C**
   A. 5.1   **B.** 5.15   **C.** 5.51   **D.** 5.6

12. What is the expression 8.4 − 1.7 in simplest form? **I**
   F. 17.4   **G.** 10.1   **H.** 7.3   **I.** 6.7

13. What is the expression 15 − 2 × 3 + 4 in simplest form? **B**
   A. 5   **B.** 13   **C.** 43   **D.** 91

14. What is the expression 4 + 8 × 6 − 1 in simplest form? **H**
   F. 71   **G.** 60   **H.** 51   **I.** 48

15. What is the expression 20 + 10 ÷ 2 − 4 in simplest form? **C**
   A. 11   **B.** 16   **C.** 21   **D.** 29

Take It to the NET
Online lesson quiz at **www.PHSchool.com**
Web Code: aaa-1104

Mixed Review

Lesson 10-6 **Algebra** Name the point with the given coordinates.

16. $(2, 2)$ *U*   **17.** $(2, -2)$ *R*

18. $(3, -4)$ *W*   **19.** $(-3, -4)$ *S*

20. $(-2, 3)$ *T*   **21.** $(-4, 4)$ *Y*

22. $(-4, 1)$ *P*   **23.** $(4, 3)$ *Q*

Lesson 9-1 Choose an appropriate metric unit for each length or mass.

24. mass of a car **kilogram**   **25.** distance around your waist **centimeter**

Simulations

For Use With Lesson 11-4

You can use a spreadsheet, as shown below, to simulate events. Suppose you want to simulate 25 spins of a spinner with 5 equal parts numbered 1 to 5. You can make rows and columns of random integers from 1 to 5 by entering the following formula in each cell.

$$=\text{RANDBETWEEN}(1,5)$$

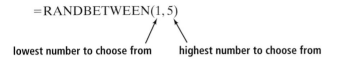

lowest number to choose from   highest number to choose from

You can use formulas to count results automatically. To count all the 3's in the 25 squares shown, enter the following formula.

$$=\text{COUNTIF}(A1{:}E5,3)$$

upper left cell location   number to count

lower right cell location

Random Numbers

	A	B	C	D	E	F
1	3	4	2	1	4	
2	2	4	4	2	4	
3	5	3	5	4	5	
4	4	3	1	4	2	
5	3	1	5	1	5	
6						
7						
8	Number of 3's:					
9	4					

From the results, the experimental probability of spinning a 3 is $\frac{4}{25}$.

EXERCISES

1. Use the random numbers in the spreadsheet above. What is the experimental probability of spinning a 4? $\frac{8}{25}$

2. **Basketball** Michelle plays basketball. Suppose she misses a free throw $\frac{1}{3}$ of the times she attempts one.
   a. To simulate the probability of a successful free throw, let $1 =$ misses, $2 =$ makes, and $3 =$ makes. Write a spreadsheet formula to generate the random numbers for this simulation. **=RANDBETWEEN(1, 3)**
   b. Write a spreadsheet formula to count the 1's in the first 6 rows automatically. **=COUNTIF(A1: E6, 1)**
   c. Out of 30 numbers, how many 1's would you expect? **about 10 ones**
   d. Generate 30 random numbers from 1 to 3. Find the experimental probability that Michelle misses a free throw. **Check students' work.**

3. a. **Writing in Math** Suppose you take a test with three true-false questions. Describe a simulation to find the probability that you guess each answer correctly. **Check students' work.**
   b. Do the simulation you described in part (a). What is the experimental probability that you get all three answers correct? **Check students' work.**

Simulations

This feature is an extension of Lesson 11-4. It introduces students to the use of spreadsheet software, a useful and efficient tool for simulating events.

Optional Material

- spreadsheet software
- Classroom Aid 4

Teaching Notes

Elicit from students some of the advantages of using a computer simulation to do a probability experiment. Guide them to appreciate that spreadsheets can quickly generate a large number of trials using random numbers. Spreadsheets also can keep track of the results.

Error Prevention!

Warn students to be careful of accidentally having the computer recalculate their results before they have completed recording them.

Teaching Tip
Remind students that although they are using a computer to simulate a situation, the simulation is still only a model. The results generated by the spreadsheet are therefore limited to the appropriateness of the model.

After working through the two samples with the whole class, provide time for students, working in pairs, to experiment further, using the formulas and the software.

Exercises
Have partners work together on the exercises. Circulate about the room as they work, checking their formulas. Have pairs share and discuss their results with classmates.

567

11-5 Tree Diagrams and the Counting Principle

Lesson Preview

✓ **Check Skills You'll Need** *PowerPoint*

Finding Probability of an Event
Lesson 11-1: Example 1. Extra
Practice, p. 652.

Lesson Resources

📁 **Teaching Resources**
Practice, Reteaching, Enrichment

👥 **Reaching All Students**
Practice Workbook 11-5
Spanish Practice Workbook 11-5
Guided Problem Solving 11-5

🕐 **Presentation Assistant Plus!**
Transparencies
• Check Skills You'll Need 11-5
• Problem of the Day 11-5
• Additional Examples 11-5
• Student Edition Answers 11-5
• Lesson Quiz 11-5
PH Presentation Pro CD-ROM 11-5

PRENTICE HALL
ASSESSMENT SYSTEM

Computer Test Generator CD

💻 **Technology**
Resource Pro® CD-ROM
Computer Test Generator CD
PH Presentation Pro CD-ROM

💻 **www.PHSchool.com**
Student Site
• Teacher Web Code: aak-5500
• Self-grading Lesson Quiz

PH SuccessNet Teacher Center
• Lesson Planner
• Resources

Plus *iTEXT*

What You'll Learn

 OBJECTIVE 1 To use tree diagrams

 OBJECTIVE 2 To use the counting principle

. . . And Why

To count a number of
options, as in Example 2

✓ **Check Skills You'll Need** ❓ For help, go to Lesson 11-1.

Suppose you roll a number cube once. Find each probability.

1. $P(1)$ $\frac{1}{6}$
2. $P(2 \text{ or } 5)$ $\frac{1}{3}$
3. $P(\text{less than } 7)$ 1
4. $P(\text{prime})$ $\frac{1}{2}$
5. $P(0)$ 0
6. $P(\text{odd})$ $\frac{1}{2}$

New Vocabulary • tree diagram • counting principle

OBJECTIVE
1 **Using Tree Diagrams**

iTEXT Interactive lesson includes instant self-check, tutorials, and activities.

In Lesson 11-1, you found the probability of one event, like tossing a coin.
You can use a **tree diagram** to find the probability of two or more events.

1 EXAMPLE **Probabilities Using Tree Diagrams**

Suppose you roll a number cube
and then toss a coin. What is the
probability that you will get an
even number and tails?

Make a tree diagram to find all
possible outcomes.

The diagram shows 12 equally likely
outcomes. There are 3 outcomes
where an even number is paired
with tails.

So $P(\text{even number, then tails}) = \frac{3}{12}$, or $\frac{1}{4}$.

Number Cube	Coin	Outcome
1	H	1H
	T	1T
2	H	2H
	T	(2T)
3	H	3H
	T	3T
4	H	4H
	T	(4T)
5	H	5H
	T	5T
6	H	6H
	T	(6T)

✓ **Check Understanding** 1 **a.** Find the probability of rolling a 2
and getting heads. $\frac{1}{12}$
b. Number Sense How can you use
your answer from part (a) to find
the probability of rolling a 2 and
getting tails? They have the same number of favorable outcomes (1)
and the same number of possible outcomes (12), so their
probabilities are the same.

568 Chapter 11 Exploring Probability

🔄 Ongoing Assessment and Intervention

Before the Lesson	**During the Lesson**	**After the Lesson**
Diagnose prerequisite skills using:	Monitor progress using:	Assess knowledge using:
• Check Skills You'll Need	• Check Understanding	• Lesson Quiz
	• Additional Examples	• Computer Test Generator CD
	• Test Prep	

Using the Counting Principle

You can use the **counting principle** to find the number of outcomes.

> **Key Concepts** **Counting Principle**
>
> Suppose there are *m* ways of making one choice and *n* ways of making a second choice. Then there are *m* × *n* ways to make the first choice followed by the second choice.

2 **EXAMPLE** Using the Counting Principle Real World

Dessert A restaurant offers a dessert special. You can get one scoop of ice cream, a topping, and a cone for a reduced price. Use the menu at the left. How many different dessert specials can you order?

Use the counting principle to find the total number of specials.

Ice Cream Menu

Flavors	Toppings
Vanilla	Nuts
Chocolate	Sprinkles
Strawberry	Cherries
Banana	**Cones**
Peach	Waffle
	Sugar

Flavors		Toppings		Cones		Dessert specials
↓		↓		↓		↓
5	×	3	×	2	=	30

You can order 30 different dessert specials.

✓ Check Understanding **2** Suppose the restaurant adds Cherry Ripple ice cream and chopped bananas as a topping. Find the new number of different dessert specials.

48 different dessert specials

You can use the counting principle to find probabilities.

3 **EXAMPLE** Finding a Probability Real World

3. On a tree diagram, write M for a male name and F for a female name. Make one column for president and the other for treasurer. Then count the number of the 12 outcomes that are FF.

Club Officers The president and treasurer of a club are randomly chosen from the names shown. What is the probability that both are female?

Find the number of outcomes where both officers are female, and find the total outcomes.

President	Treasurer
Elaine	Pedro
Alan	Dina
Carolyn	Brian
Karen	

President		Treasurer		Pairings	
3	×	1	=	3	← number of all-female outcomes
4	×	3	=	12	← total number of outcomes

$P(\text{both female}) = \frac{3}{12}, \text{or } \frac{1}{4}$

The probability that both officers are female is $\frac{1}{4}$.

✓ Check Understanding **3** **Reasoning** How can you use a tree diagram for Example 3? Explain.
See above left.

11-5 Tree Diagrams and the Counting Principle **569**

👥 Reaching All Students

Below Level Students can make a table in Example 1 to see that the same outcomes can be generated with a familiar listing method. They can then transition to a tree diagram.	**Advanced Learners** Have students write an algebraic formula to represent the counting principle for a three stage probability experiment. *m* · *n* · *o* = total outcomes	**Inclusion** See note on page 570. **Diversity** See note on page 572.

Professional Development

Math Background

A *tree diagram* uses branches for each choice or stage to name all the possible outcomes in an organized fashion. The structure of a tree diagram illustrates the *counting principle* because each decision or stage requires a branch. The counting principle states that the total number of outcomes is the product of the number of outcomes at each stage. Another name for the total collection of outcomes is *sample space*.

Teaching Notes

2 **EXAMPLE** Error Prevention

In Check Understanding 2, students may add 2 + 3 or multiply 2 × 3 instead of multiplying 2 × 2 × 2. Have students make a tree diagram to see the relationship of each of the three stages.

PowerPoint
Additional Examples

1 Suppose you spin a spinner with 5 equal-sized sections numbered 1 through 5. You then toss a coin. What is the probability that you will get an even number and heads? Make a tree diagram to find all possible outcomes. $\frac{1}{5}$

1   2   3   4   5
/\ /\ /\ /\ /\
H T H T H T H T H T
1H 1T 2H 2T 3H 3T 4H 4T 5H 5T

2 Flight attendants can wear one of four shirts, three pants, and two jackets. How many different combinations of uniforms are possible?
24 combinations

3 A clothing manufacturer makes dress shirts in the sizes and colors shown in the table. What is the probability that a randomly selected shirt will be a blue XL? Assume all possibilities are equally likely. $\frac{1}{15}$

Sizes	S, M, L, XL, XXL
Colors	Blue, Green, Tan

569

5. spin 1   spin 2

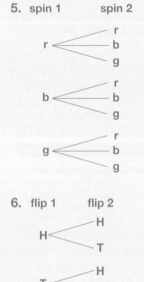

6. flip 1   flip 2

```
        H
   H <
        T
        H
   T <
        T
```

570

More Than One Way

Each lunch for a school field trip will have one sandwich (turkey, roast beef, or bologna), one fruit (orange or apple), and one dessert (cookie or muffin). The same number of each type of lunch will be made. Amanda and Zack would like to know the number of lunch choices.

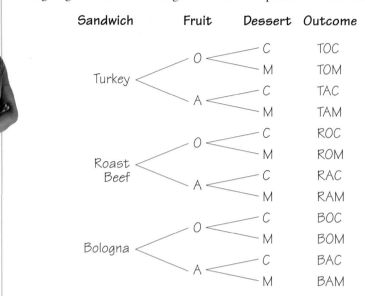

Amanda's Method

I'm going to make a tree diagram to show all possible outcomes.

Sandwich	Fruit	Dessert	Outcome
Turkey	O	C	TOC
		M	TOM
	A	C	TAC
		M	TAM
Roast Beef	O	C	ROC
		M	ROM
	A	C	RAC
		M	RAM
Bologna	O	C	BOC
		M	BOM
	A	C	BAC
		M	BAM

The tree diagram shows 12 outcomes. So, there are 12 lunch choices.

Zack's Method

I'm using the counting principle to find all possible outcomes.

Sandwich	Fruit	Dessert	Lunches
3	$\times$ 2	$\times$ 2	$=$ 12

There are 12 lunch choices.

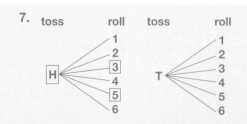

Choose a Method

In the problem above, suppose there is a fourth sandwich choice (peanut butter). How many lunch choices are now available? Describe your method and explain why you chose it.

Answers may vary. Sample: 16; I used the Counting Principle: $4 \times 2 \times 2 = 16$ possible outcomes; it takes less space or I can do it mentally.

7. toss   roll   toss   roll

```
        1                   1
        2                   2
   H <  3              T <  3
        4                   4
        5                   5
        6                   6
```

For more practice, see *Extra Practice*.

3. Practice

Assignment Guide

1 **Objective 1**
  Ⓐ Ⓑ Core 1–7, 16–17
  Ⓒ Extension 20–21

2 **Objective 2**
  Ⓐ Ⓑ Core 8–15, 18–19

Test Prep 22–25
Mixed Review 26–34

Ⓐ **Practice by Example**

Example 1
(page 568)

The tree diagram below shows the possible outcomes for a family having three children. Find the probability of each event.

1. The oldest child is a girl. $\frac{4}{8}$ or $\frac{1}{2}$

2. The two youngest children are boys. $\frac{2}{8}$ or $\frac{1}{4}$

3. All three children are the same gender. $\frac{2}{8}$ or $\frac{1}{4}$

4. Two children are boys and one child is a girl. $\frac{3}{8}$

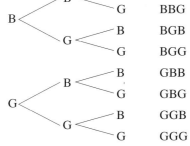

Draw a tree diagram to find each probability. 5–7. See margin for the tree diagrams.

5. A spinner has equal sections of red, blue, and green. You spin the pointer twice. Find the probability of spinning blue and then red. $\frac{1}{9}$

6. You toss a coin two times. Find the probability of getting heads on both tosses. $\frac{1}{4}$

7. You toss a coin and then roll a number cube. Find the probability of getting heads and rolling a 3 or a 5. $\frac{2}{12}$ or $\frac{1}{6}$

Example 2
(page 569)

Use the counting principle to find the total number of outcomes.

8. You toss a coin four times. **16 outcomes**

9. You roll a number cube twice. **36 outcomes**

10. A cafeteria offers 4 soups, 4 salads, 8 main dishes, and 3 desserts. How many meals of soup, salad, main dish, and dessert are there? **384 different meals**

Example 3
(page 569)

Find each probability using the counting principle.

11. You use a spinner like the one shown at the right. You spin the pointer twice. Find the probability of landing on green twice. $\frac{1}{16}$

12. You flip a coin twice. Find the probability of getting two heads. $\frac{1}{4}$

13. You roll a number cube twice. Find the probability of getting an even number followed by an odd number. $\frac{1}{4}$

Auditory Learners
Exercises 5–7 Have students silently "talk themselves through" the listing of outcomes at each stage.

Practice 11-5 — Tree Diagrams and the Counting Principle

Each shape in a set of blocks comes in two sizes (small and large), three colors (yellow, red, and blue), and two thicknesses (thick and thin).

1. Draw a tree diagram to find the total number of outcomes. **Check students' diagrams.**

2. How many outcomes are possible? **12**
3. How many outcomes will be red? **4**
4. How many outcomes will be blue and thin? **2**
5. How many outcomes will be large? **6**
6. Show how you could use the counting principle to find the number of outcomes. **2 · 3 · 2 = 12**
7. Suppose a medium size is also available. How many outcomes are possible now? **18**

Use the counting principle to find the total number of outcomes.

8. You toss a coin 8 times. **256 outcomes**
9. A restaurant offers 12 types of entrees, 6 types of appetizers, and 4 types of rice. How many meals of appetizer, entree, and ice are there? **288 meals**

Find each probability using the counting principle.

10. spinning a 3 each time you spin the spinner 3 times $\frac{1}{512}$
11. spinning a 9 if you spin the spinner 20 times $\frac{0}{512}$ or 0
12. getting two odd numbers in a row if you roll a number cube twice $\frac{9}{36}$ or $\frac{1}{4}$

Reteaching 11-5 — Tree Diagrams and the Counting Principle

Your choices for your new car are an exterior color of white, blue, or black, and an interior of fabric or leather.

A *tree diagram* shows all possible choices. Each branch shows one choice.

You can use the *counting principle* to find the total number of choices.

When there are *m* ways of making one choice and *n* ways of making a second choice, then there are *m × n* ways to make the first choice followed by the second choice.

The tree diagram shows 6 choices. Choosing your car at random, the probability of picking a white car with leather interior is

$P(\text{white, leather}) = \frac{1}{6}$.

Exterior choices		Interior choices		Total
3	×	2	=	6

There are 6 possible choices for your car.

Draw a tree diagram to find each probability. Show your work. **Check students' diagrams.**

1. Marva can have a small, medium, or large salad. She can have Italian, French, or Russian dressing on it. Find the probability that she choses a small salad with French dressing. $\frac{1}{9}$
2. You flip a coin two times. Find the probability of getting tails on both tosses. $\frac{1}{4}$

Use the counting principle to find the total number of outcomes.

3. There are 4 kinds of fruit, 2 kinds of cereal, and 2 kinds of milk. How many ways can a bowl of cereal, fruit, and milk be chosen? **16 ways**
4. There are 4 choices for skis, 2 choices for bindings, and 5 choices for boots. How many ways can skis, bindings, and boots be chosen? **40 ways**
5. There are 3 pairs of jeans, 2 vests, and 5 shirts. How many ways can jeans, a vest, and a shirt be chosen? **30 ways**
6. There are 10 yogurt flavors, 4 syrups, and 5 toppings. How many ways can one flavor, one syrup, and one topping be chosen? **200 ways**

 Use the Guided Problem Solving worksheet with Exercise 14.

20a.

spin 1	spin 2	spin 3

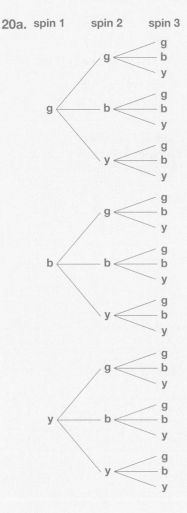

25. [2] a. yogurt   toppings

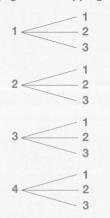

12 outcomes

b. 4 × 3 = 12

[1] minor computational error OR no work shown

---

14. Games To play a game, you spin a spinner and take a card. The spinner has equal sections that tell you to move 1, 2, 3, or 4 spaces. The cards read *Free Turn*, *Lose a Turn*, or *No Change*. Find the probability that you move 3 spaces and lose a turn. $\frac{1}{12}$

15. Baseball A baseball team has starting and relief pitchers shown in the table. Suppose the team's coach selects a starter and a relief pitcher at random. What is the probability of selecting a starter and reliever that are both left-handed? $\frac{2}{15}$

Pitchers on Baseball Team

Pitchers	Number
Left-Handed Starters	1
Right-Handed Starters	4
Left-Handed Relievers	2
Right-Handed Relievers	1

Real-World Connection

Ila Borders is the first woman to start a minor league baseball game.

18. Answers may vary.
Sample: the Counting Principle; 5 × 6 = 30; 30 different cars

Choose a Method Use a tree diagram or the counting principle to find each probability. Explain your choice. **16–17. See margin for explanations.**

16. You roll a number cube three times. Find P(all odd). $\frac{1}{8}$

17. Suppose you select a letter at random from A, B, and C. You replace the letter and select again. Find the probability of selecting an A twice. $\frac{1}{9}$

18. Writing in Math Suppose you have five colors of cars to choose from in six different models. Describe the method you would use to find the number of different cars you can buy. **See left.**

19. Consumer Issues The table below gives some choices available when you buy a computer. You want a monitor larger than 15 inches, but you do not want an adjustable keyboard. How many outcomes are left? **12**

Keyboards	Monitors	Printers
Standard $50	Color 15-in. $369	Inkjet $149
Extended $90	Color 17-in. $699	Color Inkjet $369
Adjustable $130	Color 19-in. $1,399	Laser $819

C Challenge

20d. Answers may vary.
Sample: The probability is $\frac{1}{3} \times \frac{1}{3} \times \frac{1}{3} = \frac{1}{27}$, not just $\frac{1}{3}$.
The student forgot to use the Counting Principle.

20. Suppose you spin the pointer three times. **20a. See margin.**
  a. Draw a tree diagram showing all outcomes.
  b. How many outcomes are there in which each color appears exactly once? **6 outcomes**
  c. Find the probability that exactly two spins are the same color. $\frac{2}{3}$
  d. **Error Analysis** A student says that the probability of spinning yellow all three times is $\frac{1}{3}$. What error did the student make? **See left.**

21. Stretch Your Thinking Find the next four numbers in the pattern.

$$-1, \ 2, \ -2, \ 1, \ -3, \dots \qquad 0, \ -4, \ -1, \ -5$$

16. $\frac{1}{8}$; the total number of favorable outcomes is 3 × 3 × 3, and the total number of possible outcomes is 6 × 6 × 6; $\frac{3 \times 3 \times 3}{6 \times 6 \times 6} = \frac{1}{8}$.

17. $\frac{1}{9}$; the total number of favorable outcomes is 1 × 1, and the total number of possible outcomes is 3 × 3; $\frac{1 \times 1}{3 \times 3} = \frac{1}{9}$.

Test Prep

Multiple Choice

22. You roll a number cube and toss a coin. What is the total number of possible outcomes? **C**

A. 2   **B.** 6   **C.** 12   **D.** 36

Take It to the NET
Online lesson quiz at
www.PHSchool.com
Web Code: aaa-1105

23. A store has 11 kinds of bagels and 5 kinds of spreads. How many different combinations of a bagel with 1 spread can be made? **F**

F. 55   **G.** 16   **H.** 11   **I.** 5

24. Suppose you have more than one kind of shirt and more than one pair of jeans. Which of the following could NOT be the total number of outfits you can make? **A**

A. 3   **B.** 6   **C.** 9   **D.** 12

Short Response

25. A store sells 4 flavors of frozen yogurt and 3 kinds of toppings.
     a. Draw a tree diagram to find the possible outcomes of one flavor of yogurt with one topping.
     b. Justify your answer in part (a) using the counting principle.
25a–b. See margin.

Mixed Review

Lesson 10-7

Read the table to find the profit or loss for each month.

Month	Income	Expenses
March	$8,033	−$10,203
April	$9,625	−$6,731
May	$11,462	−$5,220
June	$6,028	−$7,269

26. March **−$2,170**   **27.** April **$2,894**

28. May **$6,242**   **29.** June **−$1,241**

30. What is the total profit from March through June? **$5,725**

Lesson 9-4

31. Geometry Find the area of the figure below. **12 in.²**

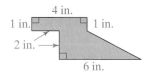

Lesson 8-5

Geometry Write all the possible names for each quadrilateral. Then give the best name. 34. quadrilateral, parallelogram, rhombus; rhombus

32.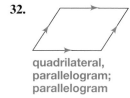
quadrilateral, parallelogram; parallelogram

33.
quadrilateral, trapezoid; trapezoid

34.

11-5   Tree Diagrams and the Counting Principle   **573**

Alternative Assessment

Students work in pairs to complete Exercises 11–13. One partner draws a tree diagram to find the probability while the other uses the counting principle. Partners then compare their answers and trade tasks.

4. Assess

 **Lesson Quiz 11-5**

A new line of mountain bikes has two different models—Eagle and Hawk—and three possible colors—red, blue, and grey.

1. Use a tree diagram to find all possible combinations.
   Er, Eb, Eg, Hr, Hb, Hg

    Eagle   **Hawk**
    / | \   / | \
   red   grey   red   grey
      blue   blue

2. Find the number of choices of bikes if wheels come in two options—aluminum or plastic. **12**

3. What is the probability that a randomly selected bike is red? $\frac{1}{3}$

Test Prep

Resources
For additional practice with a variety of test item formats:
• Test Prep, p. 589
• Test-Taking Strategies, p. 585
• Test-Taking Strategies With Transparencies

Exercise 24 Elicit the fact that the question assumes *at least* 2 shirts and *at least* two pairs of jeans.

Enrichment 11-5   Tree Diagrams and the Counting Principle
Data Patterns

Complete this True-False quiz. Guess if you don't know the answers.

   a. The oboe evolved from an outdoor instrument called the *shawm*.
   b. The bassoon, a member of the oboe family, originally had only two keys.
   c. The English horn, the bass of the oboe family, was once called an *oboe da caccia*.

1. Check your answers with the answer key at the bottom of the page. Record the number of questions answered correctly.
   Check students' answers.

2. What is the probability that you will guess the correct answer to any one item on the quiz? $\frac{1}{2}$

3. How many possible outcomes are there for guessing the correct answer to two questions? To three questions? You can draw a tree diagram on another sheet of paper to help you answer the questions.
   2 questions: 4 outcomes; 3 questions: 8 outcomes

4. What is the probability that you will guess the correct answers to
   a. two questions? $\frac{1}{4}$ **b.** for three questions? $\frac{1}{8}$

5. What pattern do you notice occurring in the probability as you add each additional question to the quiz?
   The denominator doubles, so the probability decreases by one-half.

6. Predict the probability of guessing all the correct answers to a similar quiz that has
   a. five questions? $\frac{1}{32}$ **b.** ten questions? $\frac{1}{1,024}$

7. Try this quiz with sixteen friends. What fraction of them guessed the answers correctly? Is this fraction close to the probability of $\frac{1}{8}$? Explain.
   Sample answer: A larger sample assures a prediction close to $\frac{1}{8}$.

Answer Key: **a.** True. **b.** False, it originally had four keys. **c.** False, the bassoon is the bass member of the family.

573

1. Plan

Lesson Preview

✓ **Check Skills You'll Need**

Multiplying Whole Numbers
Skills Handbook: Multiplying Whole Numbers, p. 658.

Lesson Resources

📁 **Teaching Resources**
Practice, Reteaching, Enrichment
Checkpoint Quiz 2

👥 **Reaching All Students**
Practice Workbook 11-6
Spanish Practice Workbook 11-6
Reading and Math Literacy 11C
Spanish Reading and Math Literacy 11C
Spanish Checkpoint Quiz 2
Guided Problem Solving 11-6
Hands-On Activities 42

⏱ **Presentation Assistant Plus!**
Transparencies
• Check Skills You'll Need 11-6
• Problem of the Day 11-6
• Additional Examples 11-6
• Student Edition Answers 11-6
• Lesson Quiz 11-6
PH Presentation Pro CD-ROM 11-6

(**ASSESSMENT** *SYSTEM*)

Checkpoint Quiz 2
Computer Test Generator CD

💻 **Technology**
Resource Pro® CD-ROM
Computer Test Generator CD
PH Presentation Pro CD-ROM

💻 **www.PHSchool.com**
Student Site
• Teacher Web Code: aak-5500
• Self-grading Lesson Quiz

PH SuccessNet Teacher Center
• Lesson Planner
• Resources

Plus *i*TEXT

What You'll Learn

OBJECTIVE 1 To find permutations

OBJECTIVE 2 To count permutations

... And Why

To find the number of arrangements, as in Example 3

Simplify each expression.

1. 4×3 **12**   2. 10×9 **90**   3. 15×14 **210**
4. 20×19 **380**   5. $4 \times 3 \times 2$ **24**   6. $8 \times 7 \times 6$ **336**

New Vocabulary   • permutation

*i*TEXT Interactive lesson includes instant self-check, tutorials, and activities.

OBJECTIVE 1   Finding Permutations

Investigation: Exploring Order

Suppose a group of three people line up for a photograph.

1. How many arrangements are possible? **6 arrangements**

2. Represent each member of the group with a different letter. Make an organized list of all possible arrangements of the 3 letters. How many arrangements are in your list? **See left.**

2. **ABC BAC CAB
ACB BCA CBA;
6 arrangements**

An arrangement of objects in a particular order is called a **permutation.** For the letters A and M, the permutations AM and MA are different because the orders of the letters are different.

1 EXAMPLE   Using Organized Lists

Find the permutations of the letters in the word FLY.

Make an organized list. Use each letter exactly once.

FLY	LFY	YFL
FYL	LYF	YLF

✓ **Check Understanding** ① Make an organized list to find the permutations for the letters in CAT.
CAT, CTA, ACT, ATC, TCA, TAC

574   **Chapter 11**   Exploring Probability

Ongoing Assessment and Intervention

Before the Lesson
Diagnose prerequisite skills using:
• Check Skills You'll Need

During the Lesson
Monitor progress using:
• Check Understanding
• Additional Examples
• Test Prep

After the Lesson
Assess knowledge using:
• Lesson Quiz
• Computer Test Generator CD
• Chapter Checkpoint 2 (p. 578)

You can also use a tree diagram to find permutations.

② EXAMPLE Using a Tree Diagram

Find the two-digit permutations you can make with the digits 1, 3, 7, and 9.

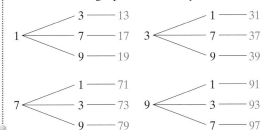

There are 12 permutations.

✔ **Check Understanding** ② Draw a tree diagram to find the 3-letter permutations of the letters in PLAY. Here is how to start. **See back of book for diagram; 24 permutations**

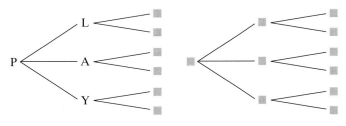

OBJECTIVE

2 **Counting Permutations**

You can think of permutations as selecting objects in some order. First select one object. Then select the second object. Then select the third, and so on. You can use the counting principle to count permutations.

③ EXAMPLE Applying the Counting Principle **Real World**

Track and Field Suppose you are in the 50-meter dash with 4 other students. In how many different ways can the top three runners finish?

Find the product of the number of outcomes for the top three places.

Five choices for first place	Four choices for second place	Three choices for third place	Number of permutations
5	× 4	× 3	= 60

There are 60 different ways for the top three runners to finish.

✔ **Check Understanding** ③ In Example 3, suppose a sixth student enters the 50-meter dash. In how many different orders can all six of you finish? **720 ways**

👥 **Reaching All Students**

Below Level Assign partners. Give each pair of students pattern blocks in different shapes. Students can challenge each other to make permutations of multiple shapes.	**Advanced Learners** Ask students to find the number of permutations of the letters in their first and last names. **Answers will vary.**	**Inclusion** See note on page 576. **Visual Learners** See note on page 575.

 Professional Development

Math Background

A *permutation* is an arrangement of elements where the order of the elements is important. As with sample space, permutations can be found by making an organized list, making a tree diagram, and using the counting principle.

Teaching Notes

Investigation (Optional)
Have students physically arrange themselves in reverse order arrangements, such as ABC and CBA, so that they recognize them as distinct.

① EXAMPLE **Visual Learners**

Call students' attention to the organization of the list with each letter of FLY beginning a column. Then identify the pattern of the second letter in each column. Ask: *Are letters repeated in any of the permutations?* No, each letter is used only once.

PowerPoint
Additional Examples

① Make an organized list to find the permutations of the letters FOUR. **24**

FOUR	OURF	URFO	RFOU
FORU	OUFR	UROF	RFUO
FROU	OFUR	UORF	RUFO
FRUO	OFRU	UOFR	RUOF
FURO	ORUF	UFRO	ROFU
FUOR	ORFU	UFOR	ROUF

② Draw a tree diagram to find the 2-letter permutations of the letters JUMP. **12**

J	U	M	P
/l\	/l\	/l\	/l\
UMP	JMP	JUP	JUM

③ Use the counting principle to find how many different ways you and 5 of your friends can sit on a bench at the bus stop.
$6 \times 5 \times 4 \times 3 \times 2 \times 1 = 720$

Closure

How can you find permutations?
Sample: Make an organized list, make a tree diagram, or use the counting principle.

3. Practice

Assignment Guide

1 Objective 1
- Ⓐ Ⓑ Core 1–7, 11–12, 17–18
- Ⓒ Extension 20

2 Objective 2
- Ⓐ Ⓑ Core 8–10
- Ⓒ Extension 13–16, 19

Test Prep 21–24
Mixed Review 25–32

Inclusion

Exercises 5–7 Each permutation is represented by the path and not the last branch.

Practice 11-6 — Exploring Permutations

1. Make an organized list of how Ali, Ben, and Chou can sit in a row.

Ali	Ali	Ben	Ben	Chou	Chou
Ben	Chou	Ali	Chou	Ali	Ben
Chou	Ben	Chou	Ali	Ben	Ali

2. Make an organized list to find the permutations of the letters in the word BITE. How many of the permutations are English words?

one: bite

BITE	ITEB	TEBI	EBIT
BIET	ITBE	TEIB	EBTI
BTIE	IBTE	TBIE	EITB
BTEI	IBET	TBEI	EIBT
BETI	IETB	TIEB	ETIB
BEIT	IEBT	TIBE	ETBI

3. Draw a tree diagram to find the two-number permutations of the numbers 2, 4, 6, and 8. Use each number exactly once.

2 < 4 – 24 / 6 – 26 / 8 – 28
4 < 2 – 42 / 6 – 46 / 8 – 48
6 < 2 – 62 / 4 – 64 / 8 – 68
8 < 2 – 82 / 4 – 84 / 6 – 86

4. Mrs. Schoup has three errands to do on her way home from work.
   a. Draw a tree diagram to find the permutations of going to the post office, the library, and the gas station. **Check students' diagrams.**

   P < L – G – PLG / G – L – PGL
   L < P – G – LPG / G – P – LGP
   G < P – L – GPL / L – P – GLP

   b. How many different ways can Ms. Schoup organize her errands?
   6 ways

5. Vince has homework in math, science, language, and reading. How many different ways can he do his homework?
24

6. The spring program will feature songs from five grade levels. How many different ways can these grade levels be arranged?
120

7. How many different ways can six posters be displayed side-by-side?
720

8. How many different ways can you scramble the letters in the word CAT?
6

Reteaching 11-6 — Exploring Permutations

An arrangement of items in a particular order is a *permutation*.

Find the number of permutations for lining up Leah, Brian, and Ahmad for a photograph. You can use these different methods.

- Draw a tree diagram.

  Leah < Brian – Ahmad / Ahmad – Brian
  Brian < Leah – Ahmad / Ahmad – Leah
  Ahmad < Leah – Brian / Brian – Leah

- Use the counting principle.

  In how many ways can the first person be chosen? *3 ways*
  In how many ways can the middle person be chosen? *2 ways*
  In how many ways can the remaining person be chosen? *1 way*
  $3 \times 2 \times 1 = 6$

- Make an organized list.
  Leah, Brian, and Ahmad
  Leah, Ahmad, and Brian
  Brian, Leah, and Ahmad
  Brian, Ahmad, and Leah
  Ahmad, Leah, and Brian
  Ahmad, Brian, and Leah

There are 6 permutations of Leah, Brian, and Ahmad.

Make an organized list or a tree diagram to find the permutations of each set of numbers or letters. Use each item exactly once.

1. the letters COW
   COW, OWC, WOC,
   CWO, OCW, WCO
2. the numbers 2, 3, and 8
   238, 328, 823,
   283, 382, 832
3. the letters IF
   IF, FI
4. the numbers 7 and 9
   79, 97

Use a tree diagram, a list, or the counting principle to find the number of permutations of each set.

5. A basketball team has 5 starting players. In how many ways can their names be announced before the game?
   120 ways
6. In how many ways can 8 songs on a CD be played if you use the shuffle feature on your CD player?
   40,320 ways
7. Three students are waiting for the cafeteria to open. In how many ways can they enter the food line?
   6 ways
8. For how many consecutive baseball games can the manager use a different batting order for 9 players?
   362,880 games

576

EXERCISES

? For more practice, see *Extra Practice*.

Ⓐ **Practice by Example**

Example 1 (page 574)

Make an organized list to find the number of permutations of each set of numbers or letters. Use each item exactly once. **1–4. See margin for lists.**

1. the numbers 6, 7, 8, 9
   24 permutations
2. the letters in BOG
   6 permutations
3. the numbers 5 and 6
   2 permutations
4. the letters in WORD
   24 permutations

Example 2 (page 575)

Draw a tree diagram to find the permutations of each set.

5. the two-number permutations of the numbers 1, 2, 3, 4
   12 permutations; see back of book for tree diagram.
6. the three-letter permutations of the letters in BOLT
   24 permutations; see margin for tree diagram.
7. **Movies** Suppose you want to watch two movies. You have a movie with each of the following themes: drama, comedy, action, and sports. In how many orders can you watch two different movies? **12 orders; see back of book for tree diagram.**

Example 3 (page 575)

Use the counting principle to find the number of permutations of each set of letters.

8. the letters in RED **6 permutations**
9. the letters in GAME **24 permutations**

10. **Public Speaking** At a convention, five people will be giving speeches. In how many different orders can the five people give their speeches?
    120 orders

Ⓑ **Apply Your Skills**

For the letters in BEST, find the number of permutations for each exercise. Use the counting principle or a tree diagram.

11. two-letter permutations
    12 permutations
12. three-letter permutations
    24 permutations

13. **Libraries** A library receives a new seven-volume set of nature books.
    a. In how many orders can the books be placed on a shelf? **5,040 orders**
    b. Suppose a new volume is added to the set. In how many orders can the books be placed on a shelf? **40,320 orders**

14. **Fitness** A body builder plans to do four different exercises in his workout. In how many ways can he complete his workout? **24 ways**

15. **Error Analysis** Ann says that the number of permutations of the letters in her name is 6. Explain her error. **See margin.**

16. The expression 4! is read "four factorial." You use factorial notation in math to show the product of all positive integers less than or equal to the given number. For example, $4! = 4 \times 3 \times 2 \times 1$, or 24. Find 5!.
    120

Real-World 🌐 **Connection**
Careers Librarians assist people in finding information.

576 Chapter 11 Exploring Probability

GPS Use the Guided Problem Solving worksheet with Exercise 14.

1. 6789, 6798, 6879, 6897, 6978, 6987, 7689, 7698, 7869, 7896, 7968, 7986, 8679, 8697, 8769, 8796, 8967, 8976, 9678, 9687, 9768, 9786, 9867, 9876

2. BOG, BGO, OBG, OGB, GBO, GOB

3. 56, 65

4. WORD, WODR, WROD, WRDO, WDOR, WDRO, OWRD, OWDR, ORWD, ORDW, ODWR, ODRW, RWOD, RWDO, ROWD, RODW, RDWO, RDOW, DWOR, DWRO, DWRD, DORW, DRWO, DROW

17. <u>**Writing in Math**</u> Write a problem that you can solve by using the tree diagram shown at the right. **See margin.**

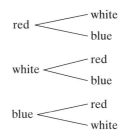

red ⟨ white / blue

white ⟨ red / blue

blue ⟨ red / white

🌐 **18. Olympics** In the bobsled competition of the Olympics, each team takes turns sledding down the track. Draw a tree diagram to show all possible orders in which the teams from Germany, Switzerland, and Italy can compete. **See back of book for diagram; 6 orders.**

Reading Math
For help with Exercise 18, see p. 579.

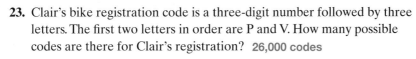

A ⟨ B → AB / C → AC

B ⟨ A → B̶A̶ / C → BC

C ⟨ A → C̶A̶ / B → C̶B̶

Combinations are arrangements in which order does not matter. To find the number of combinations, cross out duplicates in a list of permutations. The tree diagram at the left shows the two-letter combinations of ABC.

Rework each exercise replacing *permutations* with *combinations*.

19. Exercise 11 **6 combinations**   **20.** Exercise 12 **4 combinations**

Decide whether each situation involves a permutation or a combination.

21. choosing 2 pizza toppings from 12 possible toppings **combination**

22. the way 11 people line up to buy movie tickets **permutation**

ⓒ Challenge

23. Clair's bike registration code is a three-digit number followed by three letters. The first two letters in order are P and V. How many possible codes are there for Clair's registration? **26,000 codes**

24. Stretch Your Thinking In a barnyard full of cows and chickens, there are 30 more legs than heads. If the ratio of cows to chickens is 4 to 3, how many cows are in the barnyard? **8 cows**

Test Prep

Multiple Choice

25. What is the expression $4 \times 3 \times 2 \times 1$ in simplest form? **C**
  A. 6   **B.** 12   **C.** 24   **D.** 48

26. What is the expression $5 \times 4 \times 3 \times 2 \times 1$ in simplest form? **G**
  F. 15   **G.** 120   **H.** 720   **I.** 840

Take It to the NET
Online lesson quiz at
www.PHSchool.com
Web Code: aaa-1106

27. How many ways can you arrange 6 video games on a shelf? **D**
  A. 12   **B.** 36   **C.** 120   **D.** 720

Short Response

28. a. What are the permutations of the letters in LIKE?
  b. In part (a), what is the number of permutations? Use the counting principle to justify your answer.
  28a–b. See back of book.

15. Since two of the letters in Ann's name are the same, there are only 3 permutations: ANN, NAN, NNA. She counted each permutation twice, one for each N.

17. Answers may vary. Sample: There are three cars in a race, red, blue, and white. Draw a tree diagram to show the possible orders they can finish the race.

Error Prevention!

Exercise 19 Students may overlook that three of the digits from 3 to 9 are already used in the phone number. Encourage students to write a few sample phone numbers to ensure they understand what numbers can be used for the last four digits.

6.

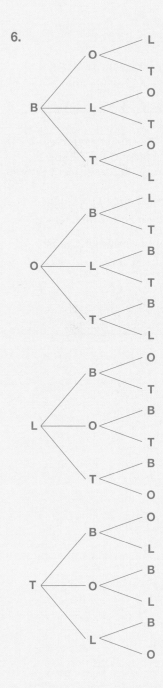

Lesson Quiz 11-6

1. Make an organized list to find the permutations of the letters EAT.

    EAT   ATE   TEA
    ETA   AET   TAE

2. How many ways can 4 people stand in a row? **24**

3. Find the number of permutations of the letters MUSIC. **120**

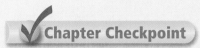

Chapter Checkpoint

To check understanding of Lessons 11-4 to 11-6:

Checkpoint Quiz 2 (p. 578)

📁 **Teaching Resources**
Checkpoint Quiz 2 (also in Prentice Hall Assessment System)

👥 **Reaching All Students**
Reading and Math Literacy 11C

Spanish versions available

 Enrichment 11-6   Exploring Permutations
Decision Making

Suppose you need to wash your car, meet a friend for lunch, and go to the bank between 10:00 A.M. and 2:00 P.M. on Saturday. The bank closes at 11:30 A.M. You need to decide in which order you will perform these tasks.

1. Draw a tree diagram to show the possible orders.

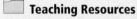

1st Task	2nd Task	3rd Task	Orders
Lunch	Bank	Car	Lunch, bank, car
	Car	Bank	Lunch, car, bank
Car	Lunch	Bank	Car, lunch, bank
	Bank	Lunch	Car, bank, lunch
Bank	Lunch	Car	Bank, lunch, car
	Car	Lunch	Bank, car, lunch

2. In how many different orders can you perform the tree tasks?
   6 orders.

3. Can you eliminate any of the activities as a first choice? Explain.
   Lunch, since 10:00 A.M. is too early to eat lunch.

4. Can you eliminate any of the activities as a last choice? Explain.
   Bank, since it closes at 11:30 A.M.

5. In which order will you perform the tasks on Saturday?
   Sample answer: Go to bank, meet friend for lunch, and wash car.

6. Suppose you also want to go to the library.
   a. How many possible orders are there now?
   24 orders
   b. How will this affect the order in which you perform the tasks? Explain.
   Sample answer: Go to bank first, then to the library either before or after lunch to get the run-around tasks done before doing the messy task of washing the car.

578

Mixed Review

Lesson 10-8   **(Algebra)** Complete each function table. Use the rule.

29. Rule: Add 0.8.

Input	Output	
−0.5	▦	0.3
0.2	▦	1.0
1.2	▦	2.0

30. Rule: Multiply by −5.

Input	Output	
−2	▦	10
0	▦	0
5	▦	−25

Lesson 9-3   Find the area of each square with side *s* or perimeter *P*.

31. $s = 3$ inches $9\ \text{in.}^2$

32. $s = 2$ feet $4\ \text{ft}^2$

33. $s = 3.5$ centimeters $12.25\ \text{cm}^2$

34. $P = 4.4$ meters $1.21\ \text{m}^2$

35. $P = 20$ kilometers $25\ \text{km}^2$

36. $P = 2$ feet $0.25\ \text{ft}^2$

✓ Checkpoint Quiz 2   Lessons 11-4 through 11-6

📱 **TEXT** Instant self-check quiz online and on CD-ROM

Suppose three coins are tossed. Use a tree diagram to find each probability.

1. $P(\text{exactly 1 tail})$ $\frac{3}{8}$ **2.** $P(\text{exactly 2 heads})$ $\frac{3}{8}$ **3.** $P(3\text{ tails})$ $\frac{1}{8}$

4. $P(\text{all the same})$ $\frac{1}{4}$ **5.** $P(1\text{ or more tails})$ $\frac{7}{8}$ **6.** $P(3\text{ heads})$ $\frac{1}{8}$

7. The probabilities of John and Sue winning different games are shown. Find the experimental probability that they both win. Use two number cubes to simulate the problem. Let 1, 2, and 3 on one cube represent "John wins." Let 1 and 2 on the other cube represent "Sue wins."

Game Probabilities   Check students' work.

Name	Game	Probability
John	Game 1	$\frac{1}{2}$
Sue	Game 2	$\frac{1}{3}$

8. Find the permutations of the letters FUN. Use each letter exactly once.
FUN, FNU, UFN, UNF, NFU, NUF

9. Suppose you roll two number cubes once. Use the counting principle to find the probability of rolling a 4 on both cubes. $\frac{1}{36}$

🌐 **10. Hairdos** Alicia is getting her hair braided at a salon. The salon offers four styles of braids, five colors of ribbons to weave into the braids, and three different barrettes. Suppose Alicia picks one ribbon color and one barrette for her braids. How many different hairdos can she get?

60 hairdos

Alternative Assessment

Each student in a pair writes a permutation problem similar to Exercises 1–4. Partners trade papers and solve each other's problem by making an organized list, making a tree diagram, and then using the counting principle.

Test Prep

Resources
For additional practice with a variety of test item formats:
- Test Prep, p. 589
- Test-Taking Strategies, p. 585
- Test-Taking Strategies With Transparencies

Understanding Word Problems

For Use With Exercise 18, Page 577

Read the problem below. Then follow along with what Maya thinks as she solves the problem. Check your understanding by solving the exercises at the bottom of the page.

18. **Olympics** In the bobsled competition, each team takes turns sledding down the track. Draw a tree diagram to show all possible orders in which the teams from Germany, Switzerland, and Italy can compete.

What Maya Thinks

There are three ways to choose the team that will go first.

I see that, for each possible team that can go first, there are two teams left to go second. I will draw lines from the first teams to each of the second teams.

Finally, I see that the only remaining team must go third. I will draw lines from each of the second teams to the third teams.

Now I'll write my answer using the letters G, S, and I.

What Maya Writes

Germany   Switzerland   Italy

Germany ― Switzerland
         ― Italy

Switzerland ― Germany
            ― Italy

Italy ― Germany
      ― Switzerland

Germany ― Switzerland — Italy
        ― Italy ――― Switzerland

Switzerland ― Germany ――― Italy
            ― Italy ――― Germany

Italy ― Germany ――― Switzerland
      ― Switzerland — Germany

GSI, GIS, SGI, SIG, IGS, and ISG.

EXERCISES

1. How many ways can four cars that are red, blue, green, and black be parked in a row?   **24 ways**

2. Dan, Eugene, and Gabi are in line for movie tickets. Draw a tree diagram to show the number of ways they can stand in line. **See margin for diagram; 6 ways**

2.
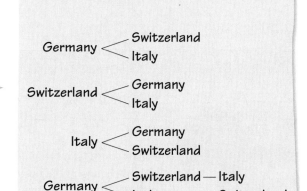

Dan ― Eugene — Gabi
    ― Gabi — Eugene

Eugene ― Dan — Gabi
       ― Gabi — Dan

Gabi ― Dan — Eugene
     ― Eugene — Dan

Understanding Word Problems

Tree diagrams are useful tools for finding all possible outcomes. Students were introduced to tree diagrams in Lesson 11-5. This feature shows how one student uses a tree diagram to solve a word problem about the possible orders in which teams can be entered in a competition.

Teaching Notes

Discuss with students the effectiveness of using a tree diagram to solve problems involving numbers of choices. Elicit from them the advantages of using a tree diagram, rather than using another method, such as making an organized list or using the counting principle.

Teaching Tip
Work through Maya's thinking and writing with the whole class. Point out that students can use abbreviations for each possibility in their tree diagram as a shortcut. For this situation, they might use G, S, and I for each country. When students work Exercise 1, encourage them to choose four cars that begin with different letters, or to simply assign the vehicles letters such as A, B, C, and D.

Exercises
Have students work independently on the Exercises. Ask volunteers to draw their tree diagrams on the board. Have them explain how they made their tree diagrams. Then have students point out the information they provide.

Invite students to formulate their own problems that involve representing possible outcomes. Have them solve the problems first, before giving them to classmates to solve. Students can compare their reasoning and their answers.

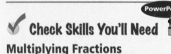

11-7

1. Plan

Lesson Preview

✔ **Check Skills You'll Need** PowerPoint

Multiplying Fractions
Lesson 5-1: Example 2. Extra
Practice, p. 646.

Lesson Resources

📁 **Teaching Resources**
Practice, Reteaching, Enrichment

👥 **Reaching All Students**
Practice Workbook 11-7
Spanish Practice Workbook 11-7
Guided Problem Solving 11-7

⏰ **Presentation Assistant Plus!**
Transparencies
• Check Skills You'll Need 11-7
• Problem of the Day 11-7
• Additional Examples 11-7
• Student Edition Answers 11-7
• Lesson Quiz 11-7
PH Presentation Pro CD-ROM 11-7

 ASSESSMENT SYSTEM

Computer Test Generator CD

💻 **Technology**
Resource Pro® CD-ROM
Computer Test Generator CD
PH Presentation Pro CD-ROM

💻 **www.PHSchool.com**
Student Site
• Teacher Web Code: aak-5500
• Algebra Readiness Puzzles 11
• Self-grading Lesson Quiz

PH SuccessNet Teacher Center
• Lesson Planner
• Resources

Plus 📘**TEXT**

✔ What You'll Learn

OBJECTIVE 1 To identify independent events

OBJECTIVE 2 To find probabilities of compound independent events

. . . And Why

To find the probability of independent events, as in Example 3

✔ Check Skills You'll Need

For help, go to Lesson 5-1.

Find each product.

1. $\frac{3}{4} \times \frac{3}{4}$ $\frac{9}{16}$

2. $\frac{2}{3} \cdot \frac{1}{7}$ $\frac{2}{21}$

3. $\frac{5}{9} \cdot \frac{2}{5}$ $\frac{2}{9}$

4. $\frac{2}{3} \times \frac{1}{9}$ $\frac{2}{27}$

5. $\frac{3}{8} \cdot \frac{2}{15}$ $\frac{1}{20}$

6. $\frac{5}{6} \cdot \frac{1}{2}$ $\frac{5}{12}$

7. $\frac{6}{11} \times \frac{7}{12}$ $\frac{7}{22}$

8. $\frac{5}{6} \times \frac{3}{10}$ $\frac{1}{4}$

9. $\frac{1}{4} \cdot \frac{4}{7}$ $\frac{1}{7}$

New Vocabulary • independent events • compound events

OBJECTIVE 1

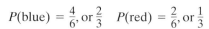

📘**TEXT** Interactive lesson includes instant self-check, tutorials, and activities.

Identifying Independent Events

Suppose you draw a marble from a bag like the one at the left.

$$P(\text{blue}) = \frac{4}{6}, \text{ or } \frac{2}{3} \qquad P(\text{red}) = \frac{2}{6}, \text{ or } \frac{1}{3}$$

When you return or *replace* the marble and draw again, the probabilities do not change. If the occurrence of one event does not affect the probability of another event, the two are **independent events.**

1 EXAMPLE **Identifying Independent Events**

1a. Not independent; after selecting the first card, there is one less card to choose from. The first selection affects the second.

b. Independent; one occurrence has no effect on the other.

Decide whether the given events are independent. Explain.

a. You toss a coin twice. The first toss is heads. The second toss is tails.

   Independent: The first toss has no effect on the second toss.

b. You select a colored pen from a bowl of assorted colored pens. Your brother selects one after you.

   Not independent: After you select one pen, there will be one less pen in the bowl. The first selection affects the second selection.

✔ **Check Understanding** ① Decide whether the events are independent. Explain your answers.
   a. You select a card from eight cards. Without replacing it, you select another card.
   b. You toss a coin and roll a number cube.
   1a–b. See above left.

580 Chapter 11 Exploring Probability

 Ongoing Assessment and Intervention

Before the Lesson	**During the Lesson**	**After the Lesson**
Diagnose prerequisite skills using:	Monitor progress using:	Assess knowledge using:
• Check Skills You'll Need	• Check Understanding	• Lesson Quiz
	• Additional Examples	• Computer Test Generator CD
	• Test Prep	

2. Teach

A **compound event** consists of two or more separate events. When the events are independent, you can use a formula to find the probability.

 Reading Math
Compound means "made by combining parts."

> **Key Concepts** **Probability of Independent Events**
>
> If A and B are independent events, then
> $$P(A, \text{ then } B) = P(A) \times P(B).$$

2 **EXAMPLE** **Probability of Independent Events**

Suppose you have a bag containing three red cubes and two yellow cubes. You draw a cube from the bag and replace it. Then you draw a second cube. Find the probability that both cubes are red.

The events are independent. The probability of drawing a red cube is $\frac{3}{5}$.

$$P(\text{red, then red}) = \frac{3}{5} \times \frac{3}{5} \quad \leftarrow \text{Use the formula.}$$

$$= \frac{9}{25} \quad \leftarrow \text{Multiply.}$$

The probability of drawing two red cubes is $\frac{9}{25}$.

✔ **Check Understanding** **2** For the situation in Example 2, find $P(\text{yellow, then yellow})$. $\frac{4}{25}$

You can multiply to find the probability of more than two events.

3 **EXAMPLE** **Real-World** 🌐 **Problem Solving**

Quiz Show Three questions are asked during a quiz show. Each question has choices A, B, C, and D. Anne guesses each answer at random. What is the probability that she answers all three questions correctly?

For each question, the probability of guessing the answer is $\frac{1}{4}$.

$$P(\text{three correct answers}) = \frac{1}{4} \times \frac{1}{4} \times \frac{1}{4}$$

$$= \frac{1}{64}$$

The probability of Anne answering all three questions correctly is $\frac{1}{64}$.

✔ **Check Understanding** **3** **Reasoning** Suppose the three questions were true-false questions. Would you multiply probabilities to find the probability that Anne answers all three correctly? Explain your reasoning. Then find the probability.
Yes; the three events are independent. $\frac{1}{8}$

Math Background Professional Development

A *compound event* consists of two or more separate events. Two events are *independent* if the outcome of one event has no effect on the probability of the other event. The probabilities of independent events can be multiplied to find the probability of the related compound event.

Teaching Notes

1 **EXAMPLE** **Tactile Learners**

Have students perform each event to see when a change in probabilities occurs.

 **Additional Examples**

1 Decide whether or not the events in each group are independent. Explain.

   a. A card is drawn from a deck and replaced. A second card is then drawn from the deck. Independent; first selection has no effect on the second selection.

   b. A card is drawn from a deck. A second card is then drawn from the deck. Not independent; first selection effects the second because there is one less card.

2 There are six cubes in a bag. Four cubes are red and two cubes are blue. You draw a cube and put it back in the bag. This process is repeated two more times. Find the probability that you draw red cubes all three times.
$\frac{2}{3} \times \frac{2}{3} \times \frac{2}{3} = \frac{8}{27}$

3 Two neighbors have the same alarm system. Each alarm has 600 possible codes. What is the probability that the neighbors have the same code? $\frac{1}{600}$

Closure

• *What are independent events?*
Two events where the occurrence of one event has no effect on the probability of the other event.
• *What are compound events?*
two or more separate events

👥 Reaching All Students

| **Below Level** Let students draw the numbers 1–10 from a bag, trying to draw the number 1. Try once with replacement and once without to demonstrate not independent events. | **Advanced Learners** Have students find the definition of *mutually exclusive*. Ask: *What is the probability that two mutually exclusive events occur simultaneously?* 0 | **Inclusion** See note on page 582. **Tactile Learners** See note on page 581. |

581

3. Practice

Assignment Guide

1 **Objective 1**
- **A B** Core 1–4, 18
- **C** Extension 28

2 **Objective 2**
- **A B** Core 5–17, 19–26
- **C** Extension 27

Test Prep 29–34
Mixed Review 35–38

Inclusion
Exercises 1–4 Students can ask themselves, "Would the second event happen without the first?"

Practice 11-7 — Independent Events

Decide whether or not the events are independent. Explain your answers.

1. You draw a red marble out of a bag. Then you draw a green marble.
no

2. You draw a red marble out of a bag and put it back. Then you draw a green marble.
yes

3. You roll a number cube 3 times.
yes

The spinner at the right is spun twice. Find the probability...

4. both red $\frac{1}{16}$
5. white, then black $\frac{1}{8}$
6. both black $\frac{1}{4}$
7. white, then red $\frac{1}{16}$
8. both white $\frac{1}{16}$
9. black, then red $\frac{1}{8}$

10. Are the spins independent events? Explain
Yes; the second spin does not depend on the first.

A number cube is rolled three times. Find the probability of each sequence of rolls.

11. 2, 3, 6 $\frac{1}{216}$
12. odd, even, odd $\frac{1}{8}$
13. all greater than 1 $\frac{125}{216}$

Suppose each letter of your name is printed on a separate card. Samples for "Linda Carpenter"

14. One card is drawn from a container holding first-name letters. Find P(first letter of your first name). $\frac{1}{5}$

15. One card is drawn from a container holding last-name letters. Find P(first letter of your last name). $\frac{1}{9}$

16. One card is drawn from each container. Find P(your initials). $\frac{1}{45}$

Reteaching 11-7 — Independent Events

Events are *independent* when the occurrence of one event does not affect the other event. If two events are independent, the probability that both will occur is the product of their probabilities.

Example 1: A ball is drawn from the bag, its color noted, and then put back into the bag. Then another ball is drawn. Are the two events independent?

A *compound event* consists of two or more separate events.

Example 2: Find the probability that a red ball is drawn, replaced, and then a blue ball is drawn at random.
- Probability of drawing a red ball is $\frac{2}{5}$.
- Probability of drawing a blue ball is $\frac{1}{5}$.
P(red) × P(blue)
$= \frac{2}{5} \times \frac{1}{5}$
$= \frac{2}{25}$

The events are independent because the color of the first ball drawn does not affect the color of the next ball drawn.

The probability of drawing a red ball, replacing it, and then drawing a blue ball at random is $\frac{2}{25}$.

Decide whether or not the events are independent. Write *yes* or *no*.

1. You pick a green ball from the bag above. You keep the ball out, and pick a red ball. no
2. You toss five coins. yes
3. You get three 4's on three rolls of a number cube. yes
4. You select a colored marker from a package of colored markers. Your teacher selects one after you. no

Find the probability for each situation.

5. A letter is chosen from the words BABY GIRL and then replaced. Find P(Y and R). $\frac{1}{64}$
6. A letter is chosen from the words BABY BOY and then replaced. Find P(B and B). $\frac{9}{49}$

A number cube is rolled and a coin is tossed. Find the probability of each event.

7. the number 6 and tails $\frac{1}{12}$
8. an even number and heads $\frac{1}{4}$
9. a number less than 1 and heads 0
10. an odd number and tails $\frac{1}{4}$
11. A coin is tossed three times. Find the probability that the coin lands on tails, then heads, then tails. $\frac{1}{8}$

582

A Practice by Example

Decide whether the events are independent. Explain your answers.
1–4. See margin for explanations.

Example 1
(page 580)

1. You have nickels and dimes in your pocket. You take out a dime at random and spend it. Then you take out a nickel at random.
not independent

2. You roll five number cubes and the numbers rolled are 1, 2, 3, 4, and 5.
independent

3. At a soccer game, a coin is tossed that comes up heads. At the next game, the same coin is tossed and it comes up heads again.
independent

4. A teacher selects a student to present his report. The teacher then selects another student.
not independent

Example 2
(page 581)

A bag contains 3 red, 5 blue, and 2 green marbles. Marbles are drawn twice, with replacement. Find the probability of each compound event.

5. both red $\frac{9}{100}$
6. both green $\frac{1}{25}$
7. both blue $\frac{1}{4}$

8. red, then blue $\frac{3}{20}$
9. blue, then red $\frac{3}{20}$
10. red, then green $\frac{3}{50}$

 11. **Dining Out** A new gourmet restaurant offers a choice of 4 main courses and 3 desserts. If you randomly choose a main course and a dessert, what is the probability of choosing the chef's favorite main course and dessert? $\frac{1}{12}$

Example 3
(page 581)

A number cube is rolled three times. Find the probability of each sequence of rolls.

12. even, even, odd $\frac{1}{8}$
13. 3, 4, 5 $\frac{1}{216}$
14. all less than 5 $\frac{8}{27}$

B Apply Your Skills

15. **Biology** Assume two parents are equally likely to have a boy or a girl. [GPS] Find the probability that they will have a girl and then have a boy. $\frac{1}{4}$

Suppose you spin the pointer twice.

16. Is the outcome of the second spin independent of the outcome of the first spin? Explain.
See left.

17. **Choose a Method** Use a formula or draw a tree diagram to find the probability that the two spins will each be yellow. $\frac{4}{25}$; check students' methods.

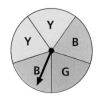

18. **Writing in Math** Give an example of two events that are independent and two events that are not independent. See left.

16. Yes; the first spin has no effect on the second spin.

18. Independent: tossing a coin and then drawing a card from a pile; not independent: drawing one colored marble from a bag and then drawing another one without replacing the first one.

 GPS Use the Guided Problem Solving worksheet with Exercise 15.

1. Not independent; the first pick affects the second because the number of dimes will be 1 less.

2. Independent; none of the rolls has an effect on another.

3. Independent; the first toss does not affect the second toss.

4. Not independent; once the teacher selects a student, there is one less student to choose from.

19. Bells Suppose one of three bells rings first each day. Each day the bells are rung in a random order. What is the probability that the same bell rings first three days in a row? $\frac{1}{27}$

Use the two sets of letters below for Exercises 20–25. One letter is drawn from each set. Find each probability. (*Hint:* Assume Y is a vowel.)

20. P(H and U) $\frac{1}{35}$ **21.** P(Y and S) $\frac{3}{35}$ **22.** P(P and C) $\frac{4}{35}$

23. P(vowel and vowel) **24.** P(consonant and E) **25.** P(A and vowel)
$\frac{4}{35}$ $\frac{3}{35}$ $\frac{2}{35}$

26. Data File, p. 545 Suppose there are equal numbers of red, blue, and green cubes in the bag.
   a. What is the probability of a player winning two games in a row? $\frac{4}{81}$
   b. What is the probability of a player winning three games in a row? $\frac{8}{729}$

 Challenge

27. A bag of five apples contains three ripe apples and two rotten apples.
   a. If a ripe apple is selected first (and eaten), what is the probability that a second apple selected is rotten? $\frac{1}{2}$
   b. If a rotten apple is selected first (and thrown away), what is the probability that a second apple selected is ripe? $\frac{3}{4}$

28. Stretch Your Thinking Suppose n is an integer. When you add -1 to n, the sum is the opposite of the difference when you subtract -5 from n. What is the value of n? -2

Real-World Connection

Bells are used for signaling local events and ringing intervals of time.

Test Prep

Multiple Choice

29. A coin is tossed twice. What is P(heads, then heads)? **B**

   A. 0   **B.** $\frac{1}{4}$ **C.** $\frac{1}{2}$ **D.** 1

30. A number cube is rolled twice. What is P(1, then 1)? **I**

   F. $\frac{1}{2}$ **G.** $\frac{1}{6}$ **H.** $\frac{1}{12}$ **I.** $\frac{1}{36}$

31. A number cube is rolled twice. Which event is *least* likely to happen? **D**
   A. same number   **B.** odd, then even
   C. even, then even   **D.** 3, then even

32. A spinner is divided into three equal sections labeled A, B, and C. What is the probability of spinning an A and then a C? **G**

   F. $\frac{1}{27}$ **G.** $\frac{1}{9}$ **H.** $\frac{1}{3}$ **I.** $\frac{1}{2}$

Take It to the NET
Online lesson quiz at
www.PHSchool.com
Web Code: aaa-1107

A box contains 4 red cubes, 3 blue cubes, 2 green cubes, and 1 yellow cube. You pick two cubes at random, replacing each after you pick. Find the probability of each compound event.

1. both green $\frac{1}{25}$

2. red, then yellow $\frac{1}{25}$

3. both red $\frac{4}{25}$

4. red, then blue $\frac{3}{25}$

Alternative Assessment

Each partner writes two independent events and two events that are not independent similar to those in Exercises 1–4. Partners exchange papers and identify each event as independent or not independent.

Test Prep

Resources

For additional practice with a variety of test item formats:
- Test Prep, p. 589
- Test-Taking Strategies, p. 585
- Test-Taking Strategies With Transparencies

---

33. A spinner is divided into equal sections with letters V, W, X, and Y. You spin the pointer twice. What is P(Y, then Y)? **B**

  A. $\frac{1}{25}$ **B.** $\frac{1}{16}$ **C.** $\frac{1}{4}$ **D.** $\frac{1}{2}$

Extended Response

34. a. A marketer gets three types of answers when she visits a customer to make a sale. They are "yes," "no," and "maybe." Assume each answer is equally likely. Draw a tree diagram to show the possible outcomes when she visits two customers.

    b. Suppose the probability that the marketer makes a sale is $\frac{1}{3}$. What is the probability of the marketer making a sale two times in a row? Justify your answer.

34a–b. See back of book.

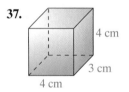 **Mixed Review**

Lesson 11-2   **35.** Pat makes 9 of 15 free throws. Find the experimental probability of Pat making a free throw. $\frac{3}{5}$

    36. Suppose you spin a pointer with four equal sections labeled A, B, C, and D. You spin the pointer nine times and get the letter C twice. What is the experimental probability of getting an A, B, or D? $\frac{7}{9}$

Lesson 9-9   **Find the volume of each rectangular prism.**

37.

4 cm   3 cm   4 cm

48 cm³

38.

2 cm   3 cm   8 cm

48 cm³

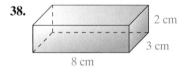 **Math at Work**

Board Game Designer

Board game designer is a career that could be just right for you if you love games. Game design requires an eye for color and a creative mind.

It also calls for mathematical skills. Many games involve the use of spinners or number cubes. That's where probability comes in. Data analysis is used to evaluate marketing information about a game.

Take It to the NET For more information about board game designers, go to **www.PHSchool.com**.
Web Code: aab-2031

Answering True-False Questions

For the answer to a true-false question to be *true*, its statement must be entirely true. Otherwise, the answer is *false*.

 **EXAMPLE**

True or false? When a coin is tossed 21 times and heads comes up 9 times, the experimental probability of getting heads is $\frac{3}{7}$.

For this statement to be true, the ratio $\frac{\text{number of times an event occurs}}{\text{total number of trials}}$ must be equivalent to $\frac{3}{7}$. Since the experimental probability of $\frac{9}{21}$ equals $\frac{3}{7}$, the statement is true.

When a true-false question includes words such as *all, always, none,* or *never,* make sure you consider all possible cases before making a decision.

 **EXAMPLE**

True or false? The equation $|x| = x$ is always true.

This statement is true if x is positive or zero: $|3| = 3$. But it is false whenever x is negative: $|-5| \neq -5$. Since it is not always true, it is false.

EXERCISES

Determine whether each statement is true or false. Explain each answer.

1. When two number cubes are rolled once, P(1, then 2) is the same as P(6, then 6).   True; the probabilities are equal; $\frac{1}{6} \times \frac{1}{6} = \frac{1}{36}$.

2. Joe, Sam, and Nate each toss a coin at the same time. The probability that they all get heads is $\frac{1}{16}$.   False; the probability is $\frac{1}{2} \times \frac{1}{2} \times \frac{1}{2} = \frac{1}{8}$.

Use the letters shown for Exercises 3 and 4. Determine whether each statement is true or false. Explain each answer.

3. Suppose you select a letter at random from the letters at the right, replace it, and select again for a number of trials. You select an M 3 times out of 10. The experimental probability of selecting an M is $\frac{1}{4}$.
   False; the experimental probability is $\frac{3}{10}$.

4. The probability of selecting an A at random is $\frac{1}{4}$.
   True; there are 4 possible outcomes and 1 favorable outcome, so the probability is $\frac{1}{4}$.

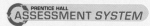
585

Chapter 11 Chapter Review

Vocabulary

compound events (p. 581)	**experimental probability** (p. 553)	**probability of an event** (p. 547)
counting principle (p. 569)		**sample** (p. 559)
equally likely outcomes (p. 547)	**independent events** (p. 580)	**simulation** (p. 563)
event (p. 547)	**permutation** (p. 574)	**tree diagram** (p. 568)
	population (p. 559)	

 Reading Math:
Understanding
Vocabulary

Choose the vocabulary term from the column on the right that best completes each sentence.

1. When tossing a coin, one possible __?__ is "coin shows heads." **D**

2. __?__ have the same chance of occurring. **C**

Take It to the NET
Online vocabulary quiz
at **www.PHSchool.com**
Web Code: aaj-1151

3. The __?__ can be used to find the number of outcomes in a compound event. **B**

4. To make predictions about a population, you can use a(n) __?__ that represents that population. **G**

5. One __?__ of the letters in CAT is TCA. **E**

A. compound event
B. counting principle
C. equally likely outcomes
D. event
E. permutation
F. population
G. sample

Skills and Concepts

11-1 and 11-2
Objectives

▼ To find the probability of an event

▼ To find experimental probabilities

An **event** is an outcome or group of outcomes. The **probability of an event** is the ratio

$$P(\text{event}) = \frac{\text{number of favorable outcomes}}{\text{total number of outcomes}}.$$

You can find probabilities by collecting data. For a series of trials, the **experimental probability** of an event is the ratio

$$P(\text{event}) = \frac{\text{number of times event occurs}}{\text{total number of trials}}.$$

A number cube is rolled once. Find each probability.

6. $P(5)$ $\frac{1}{6}$

7. $P(\text{even})$ $\frac{3}{6}$ or $\frac{1}{2}$

8. $P(4, \text{ or } 6)$ $\frac{2}{6}$ or $\frac{1}{3}$

9. Noel and Kayla play a game 30 times. Noel wins 20 times. What is the experimental probability that Kayla wins? That Noel wins?
   Noel: $\frac{2}{3}$; Kayla: $\frac{1}{3}$

11-3 and 11-4
Objectives

▼ To make predictions from probabilities

▼ To make predictions based on a sample

▼ To solve problems by simulation

You can predict the number of times an event will occur by multiplying the probability of the event by the total number of trials. If you want to make predictions about a **population,** you can use a **sample** to gather the information you need. You can model many situations with a **simulation.**

🌐 **10. Computers** Out of 300 computers, 22 are defective. How many defective computers would you expect in a group of 30,000?
2,200 defective computers

11. The probability of rain in San Francisco on a given day is $\frac{1}{6}$. The probability of rain in Miami is $\frac{5}{6}$. Use two number cubes to find the experimental probability of rain in both cities.
Check students' work.

12. There are 3 kinds of soup and 2 kinds of salad on a menu. Describe how you could do a simulation to find the probability of selecting chicken soup and house salad if both are on the menu. **See margin.**

11-5 and 11-6
Objectives

▼ To use tree diagrams

▼ To use the counting principle

▼ To find permutations

▼ To count permutations

You can make an organized list, draw a tree diagram, or use the **counting principle** to find the number of arrangements, or **permutations,** of objects.

Make an organized list to find the permutations. Use each item once in each permutation.

13. the digits 5, 6, 7, 8
See margin for list; 24 ways

14. the letters in PEN
PEN, PNE, EPN, ENP, NPE, NEP; 6 ways

🌐 **15. Flags** Suppose you want to make a flag with four equal stripes colored red, blue, green, and white. Use the counting principle to find the number of ways you can order the colors. **24 ways**

11-7 Objectives

▼ To identify independent events

▼ To find probabilities of compound events

A **compound event** consists of two or more separate events. If A and B are independent events, you can find the probability of the compound event "A, then B" with the formula

$$P(A, \text{then } B) = P(A) \times P(B).$$

Decide whether the events are independent. Explain your answers.

16. A roll of a number cube is 3. The fourth roll of the number cube is 6.
Independent; the first roll does not affect the second roll.

17. You draw a pink cube from a bag containing pink and yellow cubes. Without replacing the pink cube, you draw a yellow cube.
Not independent; after drawing the first cube, there is one less cube in the bag.

A bag contains two red, four blue, and three green marbles. You draw marbles twice with replacement. Find each probability.

18. both green
$\frac{9}{81}$ or $\frac{1}{9}$

19. green, then red
$\frac{6}{81}$ or $\frac{2}{27}$

20. red, then blue
$\frac{8}{81}$

12. Answers may vary. Sample: Use a set of three cards, numbered 1 through 3 for the different soups. Use a coin for the different salads. Let card number 1 represent chicken soup. Let heads represent house salad. Draw a card and toss the coin once to simulate one choice of soup and salad. Repeat and record your results in a table.

13. 5678, 5687, 5768, 5786, 5867, 5876, 6578, 6587, 6758, 6785, 6857, 6875, 7568, 7586, 7658, 7685, 7856, 7865, 8567, 8576, 8657, 8675, 8756, 8765

Chapter

11 Chapter Test

1. Suppose you read in the newspaper that the probability of rain is 10%. Write this probability as a fraction and as a decimal.
$\frac{1}{10}$, 0.1

2. **Simulation** On any day, suppose there is a probability of $\frac{1}{2}$ that you walk down a certain street to go to school. There is a probability of $\frac{1}{3}$ that a friend walks down the same street.
   a. Describe a simulation to find the experimental probability that both you and your friend walk down the same street today. **See margin.**
   b. Do your simulation to find the probability for part (a). **Check students' work.**

3. The figure at the right has numbered faces from 1 through 12. All outcomes are equally likely. Find each probability for one roll.
   a. P(even number) $\frac{1}{2}$ b. P(prime) $\frac{5}{12}$
   c. P(7 or 8) $\frac{1}{6}$ d. P(13) 0

4. Pam and Tony play a game 18 times. Tony wins 8 times and Pam wins 10 times.
   a. Find the experimental probability that Pam wins. $\frac{10}{18}$ or $\frac{5}{9}$
   b. Find the experimental probability that Tony wins. $\frac{8}{18}$ or $\frac{4}{9}$
   c. **Writing in Math** If Pam and Tony play the game 18 more times, must the experimental probabilities remain the same? Explain. **See margin.**

5. A ranch has 132 cows. You pick 32 of them at random and find that 18 of those cows have spots. Predict the number of cows on the ranch that have spots. **about 74 cows**

6. A bag contains only blue and green chips. The probability of drawing a blue chip is $\frac{5}{12}$. Find P(green). $\frac{7}{12}$

12 permutations; 23, 24, 25, 32, 34, 35, 42, 43, 45, 52, 53, 54

7. Make an organized list to find the two-digit permutations using the digits 2, 3, 4, and 5.

8. Use the counting principle to find the number of permutations of the letters in GLACIER. **5,040 permutations**

A bag contains four red, four blue, and three green cubes. Cubes are drawn twice with replacement. Find each probability.

9. P(blue, then green) $\frac{12}{121}$ 10. P(both red) $\frac{16}{121}$

11. P(both green) $\frac{9}{121}$ 12. P(red, then blue) $\frac{16}{121}$

13. Determine if the events are independent. Explain your answers. **13a–b. See back of book.**
   a. You roll two number cubes. One shows a 3. The other shows a 1.
   b. You draw a red marble from a bag containing red and yellow marbles. You do not put the marble back. You draw another red marble.

Suppose you spin the pointer three times.

14. Make a tree diagram to show all possible outcomes. **See back of book.**

15. Find P(yellow, then red, then yellow). $\frac{1}{8}$

16. Suppose you roll a number cube twice. What is the probability of getting a 2 on the first roll and a 5 on the second roll? $\frac{1}{36}$

2a. Answers may vary. Sample: Roll 2 number cubes at the same time. Let rolling an even number on one cube represent the event that you walk down a street, and let rolling a 1 or 6 represent the event a friend walks down the same street.

4c. No; explanations may vary. Sample: Pam and Tony would have to win the same number of times.

Reading Comprehension Read each passage and answer the questions that follow.

E-commerce In the future, purchasing items online is likely to become more popular than shopping at a store. During a recent year, the most popular items bought online were computer hardware goods.

Online sales for the year were as follows: 24% for computer hardware, 13% for clothing and footwear, 4% for music and videos, and 3% for toys and games.

1. Suppose a website that sells all types of goods receives 200 orders. How many sales would you expect to be for computer hardware goods? **D**
   A. 4   **B.** 13   **C.** 24   **D.** 48

2. What is the probability, given as a fraction, that any computer sale during the year will be for clothing and footwear? **H**
   F. $\frac{1}{24}$ **G.** $\frac{1}{13}$ **H.** $\frac{13}{100}$ **I.** $\frac{6}{25}$

3. What is the percentage of sales that will NOT be any of the items listed in the article? **A**
   A. 56%   **B.** 44%   **C.** 37%   **D.** 7%

4. Suppose an employee of an e-commerce company selects 20 orders at random. Of these, 4 are for clothing and footwear. In this sample, what is the experimental probability of a clothing or footwear order? **H**
   F. 2.6%   **G.** $\frac{13}{100}$ **H.** $\frac{1}{5}$ **I.** $\frac{4}{5}$

Sports Trends Are "ball" sports becoming less popular? From 1993 to 2000, the number of youths who play baseball went down from 23% to 12%. In that same period, the number of youths who play basketball decreased from 58% to 46%.

From 1993 to 2000, in-line skating participation increased from 17% to 30% and snowboarding participation rose by about 8%.

5. In 2000, what is the probability of a youth participating in in-line skating? **C**
   A. 0.58   **B.** 0.46   **C.** 0.30   **D.** 0.17

6. About which sport are you NOT given enough information to find the probability of a youth playing the sport in 1993? **I**
   F. baseball   **G.** basketball
   H. in-line skating   **I.** snowboarding

7. In 1993, suppose 300 youths were asked what sports they played. How many youths were likely to say basketball? **A**
   A. 174   **B.** 138   **C.** 58   **D.** 46

8. Which sport discussed in the article had the greatest percent decrease in participation? **G**
   F. baseball   **G.** basketball
   H. in-line skating   **I.** snowboarding

Test Prep

Students must be able to extract information from reading passages, answer multiple-choice questions, and construct responses in order to be successful in current state and national assessments.

Resources

Teaching Resources
Cumulative Review

Reaching All Students
Spanish Cumulative Review

PRENTICE HALL
ASSESSMENT SYSTEM

Test Preparation
• Ch. 11 standardized test Prep

Assessment Resources
• Cumulative Review

Computer Test Generator CD
• Standardized test prep

www.PHSchool.com
• Standardized test prep
• Resources

Plus **iTEXT**

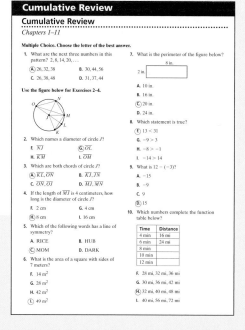

Fair Chance?

Students will use data from these two pages to answer the questions posed here in Put It All Together.

Activating Prior Knowledge

Have students share any experiences they have had playing carnival games, like this one, or others in which they toss to win. Ask them to describe what about each game made it hard to win.

Teaching Notes

Have students examine the information provided. Discuss that the concept of probability is at the heart of all carnival games and games of chance. Elicit from students that games like these can be won, but that the probability of winning will always be less than that of losing. Talk about the difference between fair and unfair games. Provide and discuss examples of each.

Inclusion

As needed, review the distinction between the concepts of favorable and unfavorable outcomes. Use this situation: *You open a 300-page book, hoping to open to a page in the hundreds.*
- *What is an example of a favorable outcome?* any page from 100 through 199
- *An unfavorable outcome?* any page < 100 or > 199

Physical Education Connection

Tell students that some say the hardest thing to do in sports is to hit a pitched baseball successfully. Others counter that it is harder to accurately strike a golf ball! so that it ends up, with as few strokes as possible, in a hole the size of a coffee cup located hundreds of yards away. Then ask students to tell what they think is the hardest thing to do in sports. Have them justify their answers using the concept of probability.

590

Fair Chance?

Applying Probability Toss a ring onto a post, hit a target with a baseball, or pop a balloon with a dart. The real pleasure comes from playing the game, but how likely are you to win? Sometimes you can figure it out by using geometry and probability together.

Horseshoes
The game of horseshoes uses special shoes with a maximum weight of 2 pounds 10 ounces. A shoe must fall within 6 inches of the stake to score.

Heads or Tails?
A coin toss has two possible outcomes: heads or tails.

Milk-bottle array

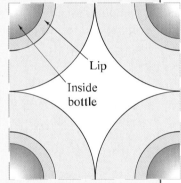

2 inches
Lip
Base
5 inches
Bottle Dimensions

Put It All Together

At the school fair, the student council set up 100 old milk bottles in rows. The challenge is to throw a coin into one of the bottles. The game seems easy because there are so many bottles.

1. The square at the right shows part of the bottle array from above. Copy the diagram. Label as many dimensions as you can.

2. Since a coin can land anywhere within one of these square regions, the diagram shows the possible outcomes of each throw. What is the area of the square?

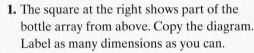

Lip
Inside bottle

Top view of bottles

3. A favorable outcome is when a coin lands inside a bottle.
   a. On your copy of the square, shade the regions in which the coin must pass for a favorable outcome.
   b. **Reasoning** If you made several copies of the square and put the shaded regions together, what shapes would be shaded?
   c. Find the area of the shaded part of your square.

4. a. Calculate the probability of winning the game. Write your answer as a percent.
   b. How many times would you expect to win if you played 100 times?
   c. **Number Sense** It costs $1 for one toss. The student council pays $1.75 for each prize. If 50 people play, how much money can the student council expect to raise with this game? Show your work.

590

---

1. See back of book.

2. 25 in.^{2}

4a. about 12.56%

  b. about 13 times

  c. 50 people pay $50 to play once each.

Expected wins
≈ 0.1256(50) ≈ 6;
6(1.75) = 10.50;
50 − 10.50 = 39.50;
they can expect to raise $39.50.

Carnival Games

Some schools use carnival games as fundraisers.

Take It to the NET For more information about games, go to **www.PHSchool.com**.
Web Code: aae-1153

591

Put It All Together

Have students work in pairs to answer the questions. Begin by having a volunteer read aloud the passage introducing the coin toss game. Ask: *What must be true about the playing space to give the player a better than 50% chance of having success?* Sample: There must be more open bottle space than space outside the openings.

Teaching Tip

Discuss ways to improve or weaken the probability of winning this game. Discuss how to make it a completely fair game. Then ask: *What appeal, if any, is there to playing games that are hard to win because the probabilities are not in the player's favor?* Accept all reasonable responses.

Exercise 4 Ask: *If you use two squares to analyze the milk bottle game, how might your answer compare with the probability you found originally?* Guide students to see that the probability of winning does not change because the area under consideration is double the original area.

3a. Diagrams may vary. Sample:

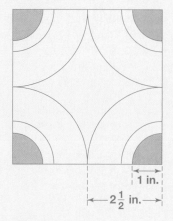

b. circles

c. about 3.14 in.²

Equations and Inequalities

Chapter at a Glance

12-1 Algebra

Solving Two-Step Equations

pp. 595–600

Objectives

▼ Solving Two-Step Equations

New Vocabulary
two-step equations

NCTM Standards
1, 2, 3, 6, 7, 8, 9, 10

Local Standards

12-2 Algebra

Inequalities

pp. 601–605

Objectives

▼ Writing Inequalities

② Identifying Solutions of Inequalities

New Vocabulary
inequality, graph of an inequality, solution of an inequality

NCTM Standards
1, 2, 3, 6, 7, 8, 9, 10

Local Standards

12-3 Algebra

Solving One-Step Inequalities

pp. 606–609

Objectives

▼ Solving Inequalities by Adding or Subtracting

NCTM Standards
1, 2, 6, 7, 8, 9, 10

Local Standards

✔ Checkpoint Quiz 1

12-4 Problem Solving

Comparing Strategies

pp. 611–614

Objectives

▼ Solving a Problem Using Two Different Methods

NCTM Standards
1, 2, 3, 6, 7, 8, 9, 10

Local Standards

12-5

Exploring Square Roots and Rational Numbers pp. 616–620

Objectives

▼ Finding Square Roots

② Classifying Numbers as Rational

New Vocabulary
square root, perfect square, rational number

Optional Materials
geoboard, calculator

NCTM Standards
1, 3, 6, 7, 8, 9, 10

Local Standards

✔ Checkpoint Quiz 2

12-6

Introducing the Pythagorean Theorem

pp. 622–626

Objectives

▼ Using the Pythagorean Theorem

New Vocabulary
legs, hypotenuse, Pythagorean Theorem

Optional Materials
centimeter grid paper, straightedge, scissors

NCTM Standards
1, 2, 3, 4, 6, 7, 8, 9, 10

Local Standards

Reaching All Students

Reading and Math Literacy

Reading Math

Making Sense of Inequalities, p. 610

Reading Math hints, pp. 596, 616

Understanding Vocabulary, p. 628

Writing in Math

Daily Writing Practice, pp. 598, 604, 607, 613, 619, 625, 630

Above Level

C **Challenge exercises**

pp. 599, 605, 608, 614, 619, 625

Hands-On and Technology

Investigations

Exploring Squares, p. 615

Exploring Right Triangles, p. 621

Activities and Projects

Real-World Snapshots

Applying Equations and Inequalities

Chapter Project

Working for a Cause!, p. 641

Test Prep

Daily Test Prep

pp. 600, 605, 608, 614, 620, 626

Test-Taking Strategies

Finding Multiple Correct Answers, p. 627

Test Prep

Cumulative Review (Chapters 1–12), pp.631–633

Chapter Assessment

Checkpoint Quiz

pp. 609, 620

Chapter Review

pp. 628–629

Chapter Test

p. 630

Pacing Options

This chart suggests pacing only for the core lessons and their parts. It is provided as a possible guide. It will help you determine how much time you have in your schedule to cover the additional features and assessment, as described at the left.

Day	Traditional 45-minute class periods	Block 90-minute class periods
1	12-1 ▽	12-1 ▽
		12-2 ▽
2	12-2 ▽	12-2 ▽
		12-3 ▽
3	12-2 ▽	12-4 ▽
		12-5 ▽
4	12-3 ▽	12-5 ▽
		12-6 ▽
5	12-4 ▽	
6	12-5 ▽	
7	12-5 ▽	
8	12-6 ▽	

NCTM STANDARDS 2000

1 Number and Operations
2 Algebra
3 Geometry
4 Measurement
5 Data Analysis and Probability
6 Problem Solving
7 Reasoning and Proof
8 Communication
9 Connections
10 Representation

Math Background

Skills Trace

BEFORE Chapter 12
Grade 5 presented solving of basic equations.

DURING Chapter 12
Course 1 extends the solving of equations to two-step equations and inequalities.

AFTER Chapter 12
Throughout this course students write and solve equations to solve real-world problems.

12-1 Solving Two-Step Equations

Math Understandings
- A two-step equation has two operations, each of which must be undone by using an inverse operation and the properties of equality.
- The usual order for solving a two-step equation is the reverse of the order of operations: first, undo addition or subtraction; then undo multiplication or division. However, it is possible to undo the multiplication or division first if you are careful to multiply or divide each term on each side of the equation.

A **two-step equation,** like $2y + 3 = 11$, is an equation containing two operations. To solve any two-step equation, begin by undoing the addition and subtraction, then undo the multiplication or division.

Example: Solve $2y + 3 = 11$.

$$2y + 3 = 11$$
$$2y + 3 - 3 = 11 - 3 \quad \leftarrow \text{Subtract 3 from each side.}$$
$$2y = 8 \quad \leftarrow \text{Simplify.}$$
$$\frac{2y}{2} = \frac{8}{2} \quad \leftarrow \text{Divide each side by 2.}$$
$$y = 4 \quad \leftarrow \text{Simplify}$$

Check
$$2y + 3 = 11 \quad \leftarrow \text{Check using the original equation.}$$
$$2(4) + 3 = 11 \quad \leftarrow \text{Substitute 4 for } y.$$
$$8 + 3 = 11 \quad \leftarrow \text{Simplify.}$$
$$11 = 11 \quad \leftarrow \text{Simplify.}$$

12-2 Inequalities

Math Understandings
- The solution set for an equation in one variable is most often a single value. The solution set for an inequality in one variable is most often a set of values.
- Graphing the solution set for an inequality on a number line is often the best way to visualize all the solutions.

An **inequality** is a mathematical sentence that contains $<, >, \leq, \geq,$ or $\neq$.

$<$ is less than	$>$ is greater than
$\leq$ is less than or equal to	$\geq$ is greater than or equal to
$\neq$ is not equal to	

The **graph of an inequality** shows all the solutions that satisfy the inequality. An open circle shows that the starting number is *not* included. A closed circle shows that the starting number is included. A **solution of an inequality** is any number that makes the inequality true.

Examples: Graph $x > -3$.

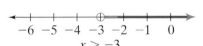
$$x > -3$$

Graph $x \leq 0$.

$$x \leq 0$$

12-3 Solving One-Step Inequalities

Math Understandings
- You can use a similar process to solve an inequality as you use to solve an equation.
- When the only operations you use to solve an inequality are addition and subtraction, the procedure is the same as it is for solving an equation.

To solve an inequality by adding or subtracting, use inverse operations to get the variable alone on one side of the inequality symbol.

Example: Solve $x - 7 > 3$.

$$x - 7 > 3$$
$$x - 7 + 7 > 3 + 7 \quad \leftarrow \text{Add 7 to each side.}$$
$$x > 10 \quad \leftarrow \text{Simplify.}$$

12-4 Comparing Strategies

Math Understandings

- Many problems in mathematic can be solved in more than one way.

You can *draw a diagram* to help you visualize the information given in a problem. To clarify your thinking and generalize the problem, you can *write an equation.*

12-5 Exploring Square Roots and Rational Numbers

Math Understandings

- The inverse of squaring is finding the square root.
- Mathematicians have agreed that the symbol $\sqrt{}$ indicates the nonnegative square root of a number.
- When you find the square root of a number that isn't a perfect square, you can use a calculator.
- A rational number gets the name from the fact that it is the ratio of two integers.

A **square root** of a given number is a number that, when multiplied by itself, is the given number.

Example: Since 3×3 is 9, $\sqrt{9}$ is 3.

A **perfect square** is the square of a whole number.

Examples: 1, 4, 9, 16, 25, 36, 49, 64, 81, and 100 are all perfect squares.

You can also estimate square roots of numbers that are not perfect squares.

Example: Tell which two consecutive whole numbers $\sqrt{5}$ is between.

$4 < 5 < 9$ ← Find the perfect squares close to 5.
$\sqrt{4} < \sqrt{5} < \sqrt{9}$ ← Write the square roots in order.
$2 < \sqrt{5} < 3$ ← Simplify.

A **rational number** is any number that can be written as a quotient of two integers, where the denominator is not 0.

12-6 Introducing the Pythagorean Theorem

Math Understandings

- The Pythagorean Theorem shows how the lengths of the sides in a right triangle are related.
- The labels a, b, and c are commonly used to label the unknown lengths of sides in right triangles (with c most often used for the hypotenuse).

In a right triangle, the two shorter sides are called **legs.** The longest side, which is opposite the right angle, is called the **hypotenuse.** If you know the lengths of any two sides of a right triangle, you can use the Pythagorean Theorem to find the length of the other side.

Pythagorean Theorem

In any right triangle, the sum of the squares of the lengths of the legs (a and b) is equal to the square of the length of the hypotenuse (c).

$a^2 + b^2 = c^2$

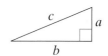

Example: Find the missing side length in a right triangle whose side lengths are 6 and 7.

$a^2 + b^2 = c^2$ ← Write the Pythagorean Theorem.
$6^2 + 7^2 = c^2$ ← Substitute 6 and 7 for a and b.
$36 + 49 = c^2$ ← Square 6 and 7.
$85 = c^2$ ← Add.
$\sqrt{85} = c$ ← Find the square root of each side.
$9.2 \approx c$ ← Simplify.

Additional Professional Development Opportunities

Ongoing Assessment and Intervention

The *Prentice Hall Mathematics* program provides many options for assessment in the Student Edition, Teacher's Edition, and teaching resources. From these options you may choose instructional materials that are appropriate for your students and that support your district's curriculum requirements.

Daily Assessment

 ### Instant Check System™ in Chapter 12

Allows students to check their own learning before, during, and after each lesson.

Diagnosing Readiness before the chapter (p. 594)

Check Skills You'll Need exercises in each lesson (pp. 595, 601, 606, 611, 616, 622)

Check Understanding questions with each Example (pp. 596, 601, 602, 603, 606, 607, 612, 616, 617, 618, 623)

Checkpoint Quiz (pp. 609, 620)

Formal Assessment

Assessment in the Student Text and in Additional Resources

Assess student progress throughout the Course 1 textbook and with blackline masters and CD-ROM.

Student Edition
- Chapter 12 Review, with Vocabulary, Skills, and Concepts Review, pp. 628–629
- Chapter 12 Test, p. 630

Assessment Resources
- Checkpoint Quizzes 1 & 2
- Chapter Test, forms A & B
- Chapter Alternative Assessment

Spanish versions available.

 ### Computer Test Generator CD-ROM
- Instant Chapter Tests™—pre-made tests with items that vary every time you print.
- Online Testing allows you to give tests online and receive progress reports.
- Prepare students by making tests based on standardized test objectives.

Algebra Readiness Tests
- Includes Basic Skills Tests and Concept-Readiness Tests.
- Assess understanding of skills and concepts needed for success in algebra.

Intervention

 ### Skills Intervention Kit

Online Intervention
Integrated within the iText, this online intervention system includes diagnostic tests and prescribed remediation, plus reports to track student mastery.

A *complete* system for the student who is struggling with course-level work

Eight intervention units cover core skills and allow you to:
- **Diagnose** students' gaps in basic skills
- **Prescribe** an individualized course of study
- **Monitor** student progress

Includes print workbooks, tutorial CD-ROM, teacher editions, progress folders, and more. *Available in Spanish.*

How to Use with Chapter 12

12-1	Pre-Algebra Basics, Skill 14
12-5	Pre-Algebra Basics, Skill 19
12-6	Pre-Algebra Basics, Skill 21

Standardized Test Preparation

The *Prentice Hall Mathematics* program integrates preparation for high-stakes standardized tests in every lesson of the Student Edition and continues this support in the Prentice Hall Assessment System.

Test Prep

In Student Text, Chapter 12

Teaches students strategies and gives them practice with all the test item formats they will encounter on high-stakes tests.

Test Prep exercises in each lesson (pp. 600, 605, 608, 614, 620, 626)

Test-Taking Strategies Finding Multiple Correct Answers, p. 627

Test Prep Cumulative Review (Chapters 1–12), pp 631–633

A three-step approach to preparing students for high stakes, national, and state exams.

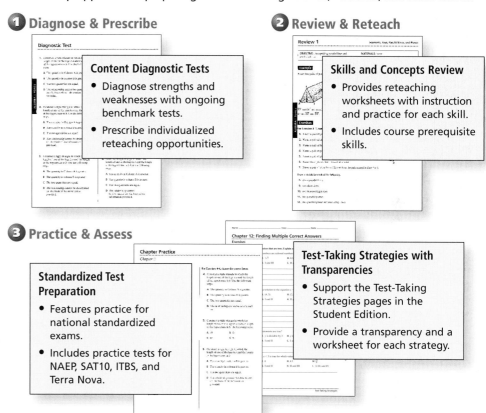

1 Diagnose & Prescribe

Content Diagnostic Tests
- Diagnose strengths and weaknesses with ongoing benchmark tests.
- Prescribe individualized reteaching opportunities.

2 Review & Reteach

Skills and Concepts Review
- Provides reteaching worksheets with instruction and practice for each skill.
- Includes course prerequisite skills.

3 Practice & Assess

Standardized Test Preparation
- Features practice for national standardized exams.
- Includes practice tests for NAEP, SAT10, ITBS, and Terra Nova.

Test-Taking Strategies with Transparencies
- Support the Test-Taking Strategies pages in the Student Edition.
- Provide a transparency and a worksheet for each strategy.

Correlation to Standardized Tests

Lesson		NAEP	Terra Nova			SAT10	Local Test
			CAT6	CTBS	ITBS		
12-1	Solving Two-Step Equations	A4a	■		■		
12-2	Inequalities	A4a	■	■	■		
12-3	Solving One-Step Inequalities	A4a			■		
12-4	Problem Solving: Comparing Strategies						
12-5	Exploring Square Roots and Rational Numbers	N2b, N2d					
12-6	Algebra: Introducing the Pythagorean Theorem	G3d					

NAEP National Assessment of Educational Progress
CAT6/Terra Nova California Achievement Test, 6th Ed.

CTBS/Terra Nova Comprehensive Test of Basic Skills
ITBS Iowa Test of Basic Skills, Form M.

SAT10 Stanford Achievement Test, 10th Ed.

Program Resources

	Resources in Grab & Go™ Files				Resources for Reaching All Students				Spanish Resources			Presentation Assistant Plus! Transparencies					Prentice Hall Presentation Pro CD-ROM
	Practice	Reteach	Enrich	Checkpt Quiz	Reading & Math Literacy	Technology Activities	Hands-On Activities	Guided Problem Solving	Practice	Reading & Math Literacy	Checkpt Quiz	Skills Check	Problem of the Day	Additional Examples	Answers to Exercises	Lesson Quiz	
12-1	■	■	■		■		■	■	■			■	■	■	■	■	■
12-2	■	■	■					■	■			■	■	■	■	■	■
12-3	■	■	■	■	■			■	■	■	■	■	■	■	■	■	■
12-4	■	■	■					■	■			■	■	■	■	■	■
12-5	■	■	■		■			■	■			■	■	■	■	■	■
12-6	■	■	■			■		■	■			■	■	■	■	■	■
For the Chapter	Chapter Projects, Chapter Tests, Alternative Assessment, Cumulative Review, Cumulative Assessment				On web site only: Home Activities, Interdisciplinary Activities, Algebra Readiness Puzzles				Spanish Chapter Tests, Alternative Assessment, Cumulative Review, Cumulative Assessment			Classroom Aid Transparencies					

Also available for use with the chapter:

 *See page 592F.*

- Practice Workbook
- Solution Key
- MathNotes folder

- For teacher support and access to student Web materials, use the Web Code aak-5500.
- For additional online and technology resources, see *below*.

 # Technology

 Online and on CD-ROM

Complete Interactive Student Text online and on CD-ROM—with instant feedback assessment, tutorial help, dynamic activities, instructional and real-world videos, audio, and additional practice.

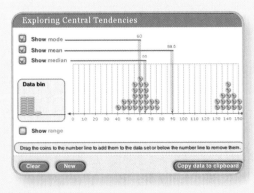

www.PHSchool.com For Students

Use Web codes for easy access to online activities, chapter projects, self-grading lesson quizzes, chapter tests, vocabulary quizzes, updated data sources, graphing calculator procedures, and more.

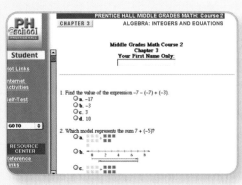

PH SuccessNet For Teachers

Online lesson planning with built-in state correlations, all the teaching resources, complete reference library, your own calendar and Teacher Web page, professional development, and more.

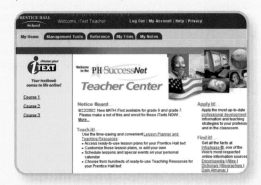

Presentation Assistant Plus!

The *Prentice Hall Presentation Assistant Plus!* provides you with the material you need to teach a lesson from beginning to end. Two easy-to-use formats—Transparencies and PowerPoint®—allow you to present a lesson the way you are most comfortable.

 Transparencies

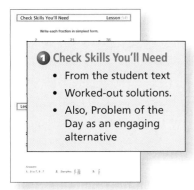
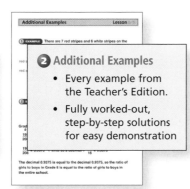

① Check Skills You'll Need
- From the student text
- Worked-out solutions.
- Also, Problem of the Day as an engaging alternative

② Additional Examples
- Every example from the Teacher's Edition.
- Fully worked-out, step-by-step solutions for easy demonstration

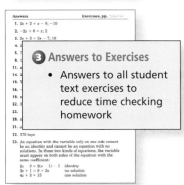
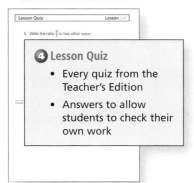

③ Answers to Exercises
- Answers to all student text exercises to reduce time checking homework

④ Lesson Quiz
- Every quiz from the Teacher's Edition
- Answers to allow students to check their own work

PowerPoint Throughout the Teacher's Edition, this symbol indicates material that is available in the Presentation Assistant Plus!

PowerPoint **Prentice Hall Presentation Pro CD-ROM**

- Includes all Transparencies.
- Conveniently organized by lesson so you can easily ① Introduce, ② Teach, ③ Check Homework, and ④ Assess each lesson.
- Animated examples allow step-by-step instruction at your own pace.
- Easy to edit so you can create custom presentations.

Teaching Chapter 12 Using Presentation Assistant Plus!

	① Introduce	**② Teach**	**③ Check Homework**	**④ Assess**
	Check Skills You'll Need	Additional Examples	Student Edition Answers	Lesson Quiz
12-1	p. 102	p. 163	✔	p. 102
12-2	p. 103	pp. 164–165	✔	p. 103
12-3	p. 104	p. 166	✔	p. 104
12-4	p. 105	pp. 167–168	✔	p. 105
12-5	p. 106	pp. 169–170	✔	p. 106
12-6	p. 107	pp. 170–171	✔	p. 107

Prentice Hall Presentation Pro

CD-ROM with dynamic PowerPoint® presentations for every lesson. Helps you introduce and develop concepts, check homework, and assess progress. Part of Presentation Assistant Plus! *(See above.)*

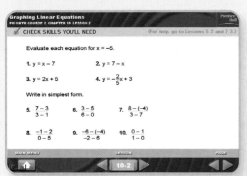

Computer Test Generator

CD-ROM to create practice sheets and tests for course objectives and standardized tests. Includes Instant Chapter Tests™, online testing, and student reports. Part of the PH Assessment System. *(See page 592F.)*

Resource Pro® with Planning Express®

CD-ROM with a lesson planning tool that allows you to import state and local objectives. Includes electronic versions of all the teaching resources.

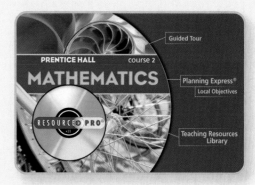

Chapter Resources

Reading and Math Support

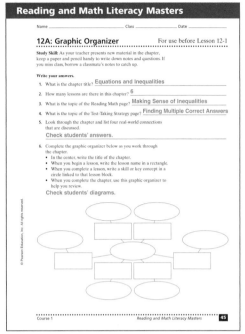

12A: Graphic Organizer — For use before Lesson 12-1

Study Skill: As your teacher presents new material in the chapter, keep a paper and pencil handy to write down notes and questions. If you miss class, borrow a classmate's notes to catch up.

Write your answers.

1. What is the chapter title? **Equations and Inequalities**
2. How many lessons are there in this chapter? **6**
3. What is the topic of the Reading Math page? **Making Sense of Inequalities**
4. What is the topic of the Test-Taking Strategy page? **Finding Multiple Correct Answers**
5. Look through the chapter and list four real-world connections that are discussed.
   Check students' answers.
6. Complete the graphic organizer below as you work through the chapter.
   • In the center, write the title of the chapter.
   • When you begin a lesson, write the lesson name in a rectangle.
   • When you complete a lesson, write a skill or key concept in a circle linked to that lesson block.
   • When you complete the chapter, use this graphic organizer to help you review.
   Check students' diagrams.

Available in Spanish

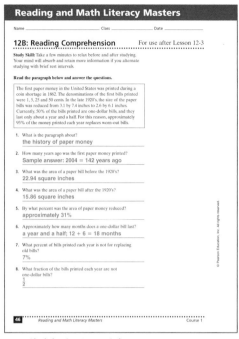

12B: Reading Comprehension — For use after Lesson 12-3

Study Skill: Take a few minutes to relax before and after studying. Your mind will absorb and retain more information if you alternate studying with brief rest intervals.

Read the paragraph below and answer the questions.

The first paper money in the United States was printed during a coin shortage in 1862. The denominations of the first bills printed were 1, 5, 25 and 50 cents. In the late 1920's the size of the paper bills was reduced from 3.1 by 7.4 inches to 2.6 by 6.1 inches. Currently, 50% of the bills printed are one-dollar bills, and they last only about a year and a half. For this reason, approximately 93% of the money printed each year replaces worn-out bills.

1. What is the paragraph about?
   the history of paper money
2. How many years ago was the first paper money printed?
   Sample answer: 2004 = 142 years ago
3. What was the area of a paper bill before the 1920's?
   22.94 square inches
4. What was the area of a paper bill after the 1920's?
   15.86 square inches
5. By what percent was the area of paper money reduced?
   approximately 31%
6. Approximately how many months does a one-dollar bill last?
   a year and a half; 12 ÷ 6 = 18 months
7. What percent of bills printed each year is not for replacing old bills?
   7%
8. What fraction of the bills printed each year are not one-dollar bills?
   $\frac{1}{2}$

Available in Spanish

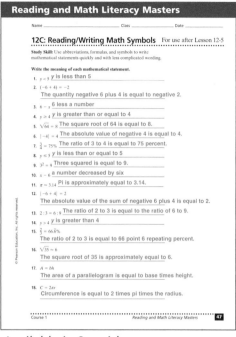

12C: Reading/Writing Math Symbols — For use after Lesson 12-5

Study Skill: Use abbreviations, formulas, and symbols to write mathematical statements quickly and with less complicated wording.

Write the meaning of each mathematical statement.

1. $y < 5$ **y is less than 5**
2. $(-6 + 4) = -2$ **The quantity negative 6 plus 4 is equal to negative 2.**
3. $6 - x$ **6 less a number**
4. $y \geq 4$ **y is greater than or equal to 4**
5. $\sqrt{64} = 8$ **The square root of 64 is equal to 8.**
6. $|-4| = 4$ **The absolute value of negative 4 is equal to 4.**
7. $\frac{3}{4} = 75\%$ **The ratio of 3 to 4 is equal to 75 percent.**
8. $y \leq 5$ **y is less than or equal to 5**
9. $3^2 = 9$ **Three squared is equal to 9.**
10. $x - 6$ **a number decreased by six**
11. $\pi \approx 3.14$ **Pi is approximately equal to 3.14.**
12. $|-6 + 4| = 2$ **The absolute value of the sum of negative 6 plus 4 is equal to 2.**
13. $2 : 3 = 6 : 9$ **The ratio of 2 to 3 is equal to the ratio of 6 to 9.**
14. $y > 4$ **y is greater than 4**
15. $\frac{2}{3} = 66.\overline{6}\%$ **The ratio of 2 to 3 is equal to 66 point 6 repeating percent.**
16. $\sqrt{35} \approx 6$ **The square root of 35 is approximately equal to 6.**
17. $A = bh$ **The area of a parallelogram is equal to base times height.**
18. $C = 2\pi r$ **Circumference is equal to 2 times pi times the radius.**

Available in Spanish

Problem Solving

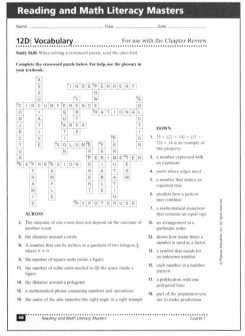

12D: Vocabulary — For use with the Chapter Review

Study Skill: When solving a crossword puzzle, read the clues first.

Complete the crossword puzzle below. For help, use the glossary in your textbook.

ACROSS
2. The outcome of one event does not depend on the outcome of another event.
6. the distance around a circle
8. A number that can be written as a quotient of two integers, $\frac{a}{b}$, where $b \neq 0$.
9. the number of square units inside a figure
11. the number of cubic units needed to fill the space inside a figure
14. the distance around a polygon
16. a mathematical phrase containing numbers and operations
19. the name of the side opposite the right angle in a right triangle

DOWN
1. $15 + (23 + 14) = (15 + 23) + 14$ is an example of this property.
3. a number expressed with an exponent
4. point where edges meet
5. a number that makes an equation true
6. predicts how a pattern may continue
7. a mathematical statement that contains an equal sign
10. an arrangement in a particular order
12. shows how many times a number is used as a factor
13. a symbol that stands for an unknown number
15. each number in a number pattern
17. a polyhedron with one polygonal base
18. part of the population you use to make predictions

Available in Spanish

12-1 • Guided Problem Solving

Student Page 599, Exercise 29:

Commission *Commission* is pay earned as a percent of sales. Suppose a sales representative receives a weekly base salary of $250 plus a commission of 8% of her total weekly sales. At the end of one week, she earns $410. What is her total sales for the week? Use s to represent the total sales. Use the equation $0.08s + 250 = 410$.

Read and Understand
1. What is commission?
   Commission is pay earned as a percent of sales
2. What are you being asked to find?
   the sales total for the week
3. How will you use the given equation to solve the problem?
   Solve the equation for s, the sales total.

Plan and Solve
4. What is the first step in solving the equation?
   Subtract 250 from both sides.
5. Simplify both sides of the equation. **$0.08s = 160$**
6. What is the second step in solving the equation?
   Divide both sides by 0.08.
7. Simplify both sides of the equation. **$s = 2,000$**
8. What is her sales total for the week? **$2,000**

Look Back and Check
9. How can you check your answer?
   Multiply by 0.08 and add $250; $410.

Solve Another Problem
10. During a holiday promotion the sales representative earned $650. What were her sales total for that week?
    $0.08s + 250 = 650$; $5,000; The sales total was $5,000.

12-2 • Guided Problem Solving

Student Page 604, Exercise 22:

Highway Safety Write an inequality for the sign shown at the right.

OVER 3 TONS

Read and Understand
1. What is an *inequality*?
   A mathematical statement that contains inequality symbols.
2. What does the sign say without an inequality?
   No trucks over 3 tons.

Plan and Solve
3. Is a 4-ton truck allowed?
   no
4. Is a 2-ton truck allowed?
   yes
5. A truck has to weigh less than how much?
   3 tons
6. Write an inequality for the sign shown above.
   $w \leq 3$ tons

Look Back and Check
7. What is another way to write this inequality?
   3 tons $\geq w$

Solve Another Problem
8. Write an inequality for the statement, "You must be at least 18 years old to vote."
   $a \geq 18$ years

Name _____ Class _____ Date _____

12-3 • Guided Problem Solving

GPS Student Page 608, Exercise 29:

Budgeting Suppose you want to spend less than $30 total to buy two T-shirts and a pair of shorts. The shorts cost $13. Write and solve an inequality to find how much money you can spend on each T-shirt.

Read and Understand

1. What are you being asked to find?
   the amount of money you can spend on
   each T-shirt

2. Which symbol do you need to use in the inequality, < or >? <

Plan and Solve

3. Given that shorts cost $13, write an expression for the phrase "2 T-shirts and a pair of shorts." Let t represent the cost of one T-shirt.
   $2t + 13$

4. Use the expression in Step 3 to write an inequality for less than 30. $2t + 13 < 30$

5. What do you do first to both sides of the inequality?   Subtract 13.

6. Simplify both sides of the inequality. $2t < 17$

7. What do you do to both sides of the inequality to solve for t?   Divide by 2.

8. What is the solution? $t < 8.5$

9. How much money can you spend on each T-shirt?   less than $8.50

Look Back and Check

10. Can you spend exactly the amount you found in Step 9? Explain.
    No, then you would spend $30. You want to
    spend *less than* $30.

Solve Another Problem

11. Suppose you are able to spend $10 more. How much money can you spend on each T-shirt now?
    $2t + 13 < 40$; $2t < 27$; $t < 13.5$; you can spend
    less than $13.50.

Name _____ Class _____ Date _____

12-4 • Guided Problem Solving

GPS Student Page 613, Exercise 6:

Skyscrapers The John Hancock Center in Chicago has twice as many floors as One Atlantic Center in Atlanta. The Sears Tower in Chicago has 110 floors, which is 40 floors less than the total number of floors in the other two skyscrapers. How many floors are in One Atlantic Center?

Read and Understand

1. What are you being asked to find?
   the number of floors in One Atlantic Center

2. Which strategy would be best suited to solve this problem?
   Work backwards.

Plan and Solve

3. How many floors does the Sears Tower have? 110 floors

4. How many floors does the John Hancock and One Atlantic Center have in total? 110 + 40 or 150 floors

5. What is the relationship between the number of floors at the John Hancock building and the number of floors at One Atlantic Center?
   The John Hancock building has twice as many
   floors as One Atlantic Center.

6. Write an expression for the sum of the heights of the John Hancock Center and the Atlantic Center
   $2h + h = 150$

7. How many floors are in One Atlantic Center?
   $3h = 150$; 50 floors

Look Back and Check

8. How can you check your answer?
   Double the answer and add it to itself.
   Subtract 40. You should get 110.

Solve Another Problem

9. Amanda made some bracelets. She gave half of them to her friends. Then, she gave three to her sister. Her neighbor gave her four bracelets. She then sold half of the bracelets at a yard sale and had three left. How many did Amanda make?
   10 bracelets

Name _____ Class _____ Date _____

12-5 • Guided Problem Solving

GPS Student Page 619, Exercise 40:

Egyptian Pyramids The area of the square base of the Great Pyramid at Giza is 52,900 square meters. What is the length of each side of the square base of the pyramid?

Read and Understand

1. How do you find the area of a square if you are told the length of the side?
   Square the length of the side.

2. What information are you given? What are you being asked to find?
   the area of a square; the length of the side
   of the square

Plan and Solve

3. What is the area of the square?
   $52,900 \text{ m}^2$

4. What is the square root of the answer to Step 3?
   230 m

5. What is the length of each side of the square base?
   230 m

Look Back and Check

6. How can you check your answer?
   Square the answer. It should be equal to
   $52,900 \text{ m}^2$.

Solve Another Problem

7. The area of a square table is $1,296 \text{ in.}^2$. What is the length of each side of the table?
   36 in.

Activities and Projects

Name _____ Class _____ Date _____

12-6 • Guided Problem Solving

GPS Student Page 625, Exercise 18:

Landscaping A landscaper needs to stake the tree at the right. A wire goes from the stake to a spot 40 ft up the trunk, as shown. How long must the wire be?

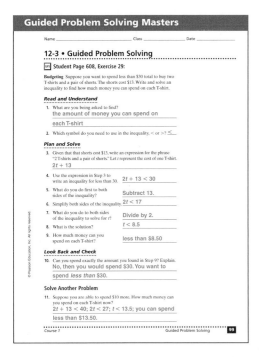

Read and Understand

1. What shape models the picture of the tree and the wire?
   a right triangle

2. What theorem can be used to solve this problem?
   the Pythagorean Theorem

Plan and Solve

3. Label the picture with the labels a, b, and c.

4. Substitute the values for a, b, and c into the formula.
   $9^2 + 40^2 = c^2$

5. Simplify both sides of the formula. $1,681 = c^2$

6. How do you solve for c?
   Take the square root of each side.

7. What is c? 41

8. How long must the wire be? 41 ft

Look Back and Check

9. How can you check your answer?
   Square your answer. Then see if $9^2 + 40^2$
   equals this number.

Solve Another Problem

10. Another tree needs to be staked that is 80 feet tall. The stake will be placed 18 feet from the tree. How long must the wire be for this tree?
    $18^2 + 80^2 = c^2$; $6,724 = c^2$; $82 = c$;
    the wire must be 82 ft.

Name _____ Class _____ Date _____

Activity 47: Two-Step Equation Tiling

Materials needed: algebra tiles

Use algebra tiles to solve these two-step equations. Use the example below as a model.

1. $5x + 9 = 9$
2. $2y - 6 = -2$
3. $12 + p = -4$
4. $10 - 3b = 1$

Example: solve $3a - 2 = 4$

① Model the equation.

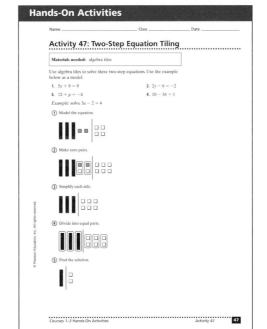

② Make zero pairs.

③ Simplify each side.

④ Divide into equal parts.

⑤ Find the solution.

Name _____ Class _____ Date _____

Activity 48: Circles and the Pythagorean Theorem

Materials needed: compass, protractor, cm ruler

1. Use the compass to draw a circle on a sheet of paper. Label the center point with any letter.

2. Draw and label with different letters a diameter of the circle.
   a. Measure its length with a centimeter ruler.
   b. Write the diameter at the top of the paper.

3. Draw and label a radius that is perpendicular to the diameter.
   a. Name three of the circle's radii on your paper.
   b. What is the length of each radii?

4. Draw a chord from one end of the diameter to the outside point of the perpendicular radius.
   a. What kind of triangle is formed?
   b. Find the length of the third side of the triangle using the Pythagorean theorem. Write it on your paper, too.

5. Draw a different point on the circumference of the circle, such as shown.

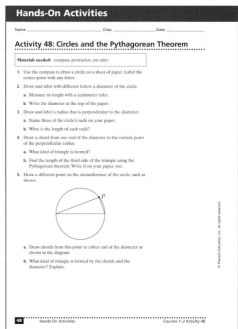

   a. Draw chords from this point to either end of the diameter as shown in the diagram.
   b. What kind of triangle is formed by the chords and the diameter? Explain.

Name _____ Class _____ Date _____

The Pythagorean Theorem   Activity 19

Use your graphing calculator to do this activity.

Example 1: A right triangle has legs that measure 36 cm and 48 cm. Find the length of the hypotenuse.

① You know that the Pythagorean theorem can be represented by the equation $a^2 + b^2 = c^2$, where a and b are the legs, and c is the hypotenuse. To find the length of the hypotenuse, solve the equation for c. The result is $c = \sqrt{a^2 + b^2}$. You can enter this equation into your calculator to find the length of any hypotenuse if you know the lengths of the legs.

② Press [Y=]. Clear any equations entered by pressing [CLEAR].

③ Next to Y₁, enter [2nd] [√] [2nd] [TEST]; then highlight A, press [ENTER] [+]; then highlight B, press [ENTER] [X²]; highlight **Done**, press [ENTER] and press [ENTER].

④ Press [2nd] [QUIT]. Now you are ready to enter the lengths of the legs for the triangle in the problem. Let A = 36 and B = 48.

⑤ Press 36 [STO▸] [2nd] [TEST], highlight **A** and press [ENTER]. Highlight Done and press [ENTER] twice.

⑥ Press 48 [STO▸] [2nd] [TEST], highlight B and press [ENTER]. Highlight **Done** and press [ENTER] twice.

⑦ Now find the value of Y₁ for these values of A and B. Press [2nd] [VARS] 2 1 [ENTER]. The calculator shows 60. The length of the hypotenuse is 60 cm.

Follow similar steps to enter the formula for the length of the leg of a right triangle, $b = \sqrt{c^2 - a^2}$, as Y₂.

Exercises

Use your calculator to find the missing lengths of each right triangle. Round to the nearest tenth.

1. leg = 69 in.   2. leg = ?   3. leg = 102 mm
   leg = 92 in.   leg = 15 m   leg = 135 mm
   hyp = ?   hyp = 26 m   hyp = ?

Name _____ Class _____ Date _____

Chapter 12 Project: Working for a Cause!

Plan a Fundraiser

Beginning the Chapter Project

Have you ever participated in a fundraiser? Schools and sports clubs often use fundraisers as a way to pay for such things as equipment, trips, and camps. You have probably purchased candy bars, magazines, or wrapping paper to help a friend raise money.

In this chapter project, you will plan a fundraiser. You will choose a cause or charity, decide how much money to raise, and determine the type of event to hold or the type of product to sell. As part of your final project, you will present a fundraising plan to your class.

Activities

Activity 1: Investigating Check students' work.

To begin the project, make a list of some of the causes in your school or community for which you might want to raise money. See the table for examples.

Causes
• playground equipment for city park
• new wrestling mats for school's wrestling team
• uniforms for the band

Think about some of these issues during your investigation. What causes interest me? What will the money be used for? Is there interest among the community to help this cause? How much money needs to be raised?

Activity 2: Planning and Researching

After you have established your cause, you need to decide on the type of event to hold or the product to sell to raise money. Brainstorm a list of fundraising ideas, such as a walk-a-thon, a car wash, or a sale of calendars or coupon books.

Research your top three ideas. Create a table showing how much money you can expect to make from each fundraiser. Your table should also have an expense column where you record the amount of expected cost. For instance, if your fundraiser is a car wash, you may need to purchase rags, a bucket, soap, and hoses in order to actually wash the cars.

Name _____ Class _____ Date _____

Chapter 12 Project: Working for a Cause! (continued)

Activity 3: Calculating and Analyzing

Review your table in Activity 2 and the amount of money needed for your fundraiser. Then, write an equation or an inequality for each of the three fundraising ideas. Analyze and solve each equation or inequality to determine which fundraising idea is best suited for your cause.

Finishing the Project

Your final product will be to write a detailed fundraising plan to present to your class. The plan should include the type of fundraiser, the amount of money that needs to be raised, and the reason for donating the money to the cause that you selected. Be sure your work is neat and clear. Write any explanations you think are necessary.

Reflect and Revise

Ask a classmate to review your project with you. Is the type of fundraiser you selected something that will interest your classmates? Is the cost of running the fundraiser reasonable? Are your calculations complete and accurate? Is the information in the letter presented in a clear and appropriate manner? If necessary, make changes to improve your project.

Take It to the NET Visit www.PHSchool.com for information and links you might find helpful as you complete your project.

Name _____ Class _____ Date _____

Chapter Project Manager

Chapter 12: Working for a Cause!

Getting Started

Read about the project. As you work on it, you will need several sheets of paper. If available, a spreadsheet program can be used. Keep all your work for the project in a folder, along with this Project Manager.

Checklist	Suggestions
☐ Activity 1: investigating	☐ Decide if you want to raise money for a community or school cause.
☐ Activity 2: planning and researching	☐ If possible, use a spreadsheet program to create your table.
☐ Activity 3: calculating and analyzing	☐ Review the inequality symbols and the order of operations.
☐ Recommendations	☐ When writing the plan, use proper letter-writing format. Be sure to check your spelling, grammar, and punctuation.

Scoring Rubric

3 Your tables are complete and labeled accurately. Your equations or inequalities are complete and accurate. Your written plan includes all the key elements. It is written neatly and in the proper format. It has no spelling or grammatical errors.

2 Your tables are complete. Your written plan is neat and is in proper form, but does not include all key elements. Almost all of your calculations are accurate.

1 Many of your calculations are inaccurate. Your plan is written in proper form but does not provide accurate information and is missing some key elements.

0 Major elements of the project are incomplete or missing. Your calculations are either inaccurate or disorganized. Your plan is not written or is not in proper form.

Your Evaluation of Project Evaluate your work based on the Scoring Rubric.

Teacher's Evaluation of Project

Name _____ Class _____ Date _____

Chapter Project Teacher Notes

Chapter 12: Working for a Cause!

About the Project

Students will have an opportunity to use their knowledge of equations and inequalities to evaluate and plan a fundraiser.

Introducing the Project

Talk about the kinds of fundraisers that your school has had or that students in your class have participated in. Create a list of the pros and cons of each fundraising idea mentioned. Ask students what type of causes they think are worthy enough to get them to participate in a fundraiser. Talk about where students might get more information about fundraisers, such as the PTO, coaches, advertisements, and the Internet.

Activity 1: Investigating

Have students keep a schedule of when each activity should be completed. This way they are sure to have the project finished on time.

Activity 2: Planning and Researching

Encourage students to use the Internet to search for different types of fundraisers. They can search, for example, the words, *school fundraisers* or *raising money*, and gather the information necessary to analyze various types of fundraisers.

Activity 3: Calculating and Analyzing

Encourage students to use the data in their table to write the necessary equation or inequality.

Finishing the Project

Plan a project day where students share their fundraising plans. Encourage students to vote on who has the most worthy cause.

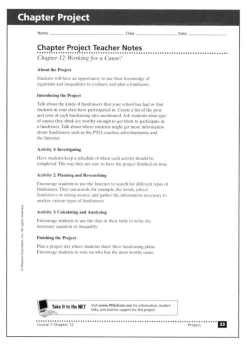

Take It to the NET Visit www.PHSchool.com for information, student links, and teacher support for this project.

Transparencies

Problem of the Day	Lesson 12-1

Find the range, mean, median, and mode for the set of numbers 11, 18, 14, 24, 28.

Answer

range: 17; mean: 19; median: 18; no mode

Problem of the Day	Lesson 12-2

The length of a computer lab is 11 feet more than half its width. What is the perimeter of the lab if it is 18 feet wide?

Answer

76 feet

Problem of the Day	Lesson 12-3

Write $3\frac{1}{7}$ as an improper fraction. Then find the decimal equivalent.

Use a calculator to determine which is larger, $3\frac{1}{7}$ or π.

Answer

$\frac{22}{7}$; 3.1428571; 3.1428571 is larger than π, which is about 3.1415927.

592K

Problem of the Day

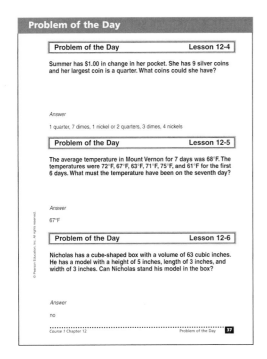

Problem of the Day — **Lesson 12-4**

Summer has $1.00 in change in her pocket. She has 9 silver coins and her largest coin is a quarter. What coins could she have?

Answer

1 quarter, 7 dimes, 1 nickel or 2 quarters, 3 dimes, 4 nickels

Problem of the Day — **Lesson 12-5**

The average temperature in Mount Vernon for 7 days was 68°F. The temperatures were 72°F, 67°F, 63°F, 71°F, 75°F, and 61°F for the first 6 days. What must the temperature have been on the seventh day?

Answer

67°F

Problem of the Day — **Lesson 12-6**

Nicholas has a cube-shaped box with a volume of 63 cubic inches. He has a model with a height of 5 inches, length of 3 inches, and width of 3 inches. Can Nicholas stand his model in the box?

Answer

no

Course 1 Chapter 12 — Problem of the Day — **37**

Check Skills You'll Need

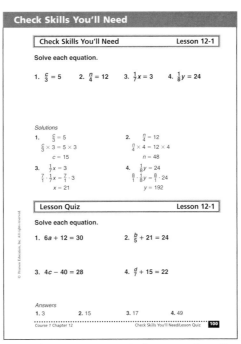

Check Skills You'll Need — **Lesson 12-1**

Solve each equation.

1. $\frac{c}{3} = 5$ 2. $\frac{n}{4} = 12$ 3. $\frac{1}{7}x = 3$ 4. $\frac{1}{8}y = 24$

Solutions

1. $\frac{c}{3} = 5$
$\frac{c}{3} \times 3 = 5 \times 3$
$c = 15$

2. $\frac{n}{4} = 12$
$\frac{n}{4} \times 4 = 12 \times 4$
$n = 48$

3. $\frac{1}{7}x = 3$
$\frac{7}{1} \cdot \frac{1}{7}x = \frac{7}{1} \cdot 3$
$x = 21$

4. $\frac{1}{8}y = 24$
$\frac{8}{1} \cdot \frac{1}{8}y = \frac{8}{1} \cdot 24$
$y = 192$

Lesson Quiz — **Lesson 12-1**

Solve each equation.

1. $6a + 12 = 30$ 2. $\frac{b}{5} + 21 = 24$

3. $4c - 40 = 28$ 4. $\frac{d}{7} + 15 = 22$

Answers

1. 3   2. 15   3. 17   4. 49

Course 1 Chapter 12 — Check Skills You'll Need/Lesson Quiz — **100**

Sample page; see p. H for complete list.

Additional Examples

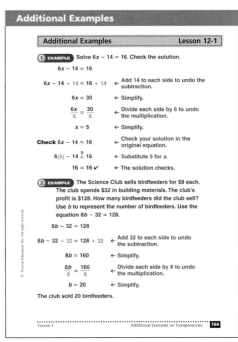

Additional Examples — **Lesson 12-1**

1 EXAMPLE Solve $6x - 14 = 16$. Check the solution.

$6x - 14 = 16$

$6x - 14 + 14 = 16 + 14$ ← Add 14 to each side to undo the subtraction.

$6x = 30$ ← Simplify.

$\frac{6x}{6} = \frac{30}{6}$ ← Divide each side by 6 to undo the multiplication.

$x = 5$ ← Simplify.

Check $6x - 14 = 16$ ← Check your solution in the original equation.

$6(5) - 14 \stackrel{?}{=} 16$ ← Substitute 5 for x.

$16 = 16$ ✓ ← The solution checks.

2 EXAMPLE The Science Club sells birdfeeders for $8 each. The club spends $32 in building materials. The club's profit is $128. How many birdfeeders did the club sell? Use b to represent the number of birdfeeders. Use the equation $8b - 32 = 128$.

$8b - 32 = 128$

$8b - 32 + 32 = 128 + 32$ ← Add 32 to each side to undo the subtraction.

$8b = 160$ ← Simplify.

$\frac{8b}{8} = \frac{160}{8}$ ← Divide each side by 8 to undo the multiplication.

$b = 20$ ← Simplify.

The club sold 20 birdfeeders.

Course 1 — Additional Examples on Transparencies — **164**

Sample page; see p. H for complete list.

Classroom Aid

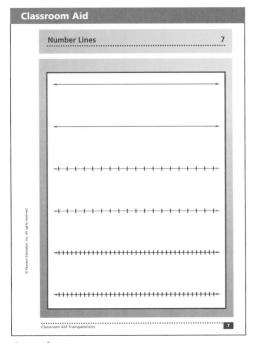

Number Lines   **7**

Classroom Aid Transparencies — **7**

Sample pages.

Classroom Aid

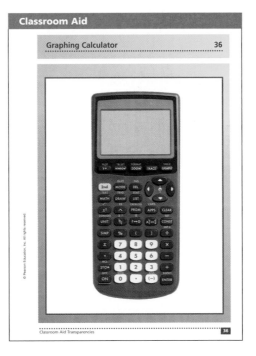

Graphing Calculator   **36**

Classroom Aid Transparencies — **36**

Student Edition Answers

Answers for Lesson *On Your Own* **Exercises**

1. Sample: 1 : 4, 1 to 4, $\frac{1}{4}$
2. Sample: 24 to 25, 24 : 25, $\frac{24}{25}$
3. 12 to 4, $\frac{12}{4}$
4. 8 : 10, $\frac{8}{10}$
5. 5 to 4, 5 : 4
6. 13 to 8, $\frac{13}{8}$
7. 21 to 28, $\frac{21}{28}$
8. 8 to 18, 8 : 18
9. B
10a. 7 : 15, 7 to 15, $\frac{7}{15}$
  b. 7 : 8, 7 to 8, $\frac{7}{8}$
11a. 23 : 19, 23 to 19, $\frac{23}{19}$
  b. 19 : 42, 19 to 42, $\frac{19}{42}$
12. No; the new ratio is 16 : 11.
13. 0.9   14. 3.6   15. 2.7   16. 0.7
17. 0.5   18. 1.0
19a. 225 : 3, 455 : 7
  b. 75, 65
  c. Answers may vary. Sample: Train A travels 75 mi/h while Train B travels 65 mi/h
20a. $\frac{13}{18}$
  b. $\frac{169}{324}$
  c. The ratio of areas is the square of the ratio of sides.
21–26. Answers may vary. Samples are given.
21. 13 : 27, 78 : 162   22. 6 to 22, 3 to 11
23. $\frac{106}{50}, \frac{53}{25}$ 24. $\frac{7}{1}, \frac{14}{2}$ 25. $\frac{9}{18}, \frac{3}{6}$
26. 2 : 12, 3 : 18   27. 5 : 2   28. 1 to 9
29. $\frac{1}{50}$ 30. 4 to 1   31. 1 : 2
32. $\frac{1}{3}$ 33. 25 to 1
34a. 101 and 107
  b. 7 : 12
35a. 8 : 4
  b. 10 qt antifreeze, 5 qt water

Course 2 Chapter 6

Sample page; see p. H for complete list.

Assessment

Check Skills You'll Need — Lesson 12-2

Compare using $<$ or $>$.

1. -3 __ 6 2. 4 __ -9 3. -2 __ -3

4. -94 __ -93 5. 54 __ 47 6. $1{,}001$ __ $1{,}010$

Solutions

1. $-3 < 6$
2. $4 > -9$
3. $-2 > -3$
4. $-94 < -93$
5. $54 > 47$
6. $1{,}001 < 1{,}010$

Lesson Quiz — Lesson 12-2

Use x as the variable. Write an inequality for each graph.

1. (graph)   2. (graph)

3. Graph the inequality $x < 2$ on a number line.

4. Tell which numbers are solutions of $x \geq -4$: $-6, -4, -2, 0, 2$.

Answers

1. $x > -2$ 2. $x \leq 0$ 3. (graph)   4. $-4, -2, 0, 2$

Course 1 Chapter 12 — Check Skills You'll Need/Lesson Quiz — 101

Sample page; see p. H for complete list.

Name _____ Class _____ Date _____

✔ Checkpoint Quiz 1

Use with Lessons 12-1 through 12-3.

Solve each equation. Check the solution.

1. $6a + 7 = 13$ $a = 1$
2. $8j - 4 = 52$ $j = 7$
3. $57 = 9b + 12$ $b = 5$
4. $9x + 21 = 102$ $x = 9$

Write an inequality for each situation.

5. There are fewer than 12 girls in the class. $x < 12$
6. At least 15 people went to the zoo. $x \geq 15$

Solve each inequality. Graph the solution on a number line.

7. $x - 12 \leq 31$ $x \leq 43$
8. $-24 \geq f - (-21)$ $f \leq -45$

9. Eighteen is less than a number added to 35. Write and solve an inequality.
$18 < 35 + n;\ n > -17$

Name _____ Class _____ Date _____

✔ Checkpoint Quiz 2

Use with Lessons 12-4 through 12-5.

Solve each problem by drawing a diagram or writing an equation.

1. A set of holiday lights blinks every 6 seconds. A second set blinks every 8 seconds. The lights blink together when switched on. How many times in a minute do the two sets blink together?
3 times; at 0 s, 24 s, and 48 s

2. A baker is making banana bread. It takes $\frac{1}{4}$ pound of baking soda and other ingredients. If the baker has 5 pounds of baking soda and enough other ingredients, how many loaves can she make?
400 loaves of banana bread

Find each square root.

3. $\sqrt{169}$ 13   4. $\sqrt{81}$ 9   5. $\sqrt{625}$ 25   6. $\sqrt{16}$ 4

Tell whether each number is rational.

7. $\sqrt{37}$ irrational   8. 7.1245 rational   9. $13{,}456.78$ rational   10. $\sqrt{2{,}704}$ rational

24 — Checkpoint Quizzes — Course 1 Chapter 12

Available in Spanish

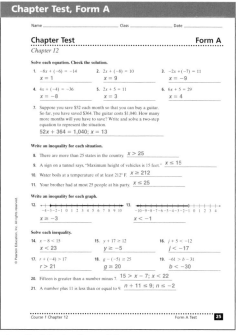

Available in Spanish

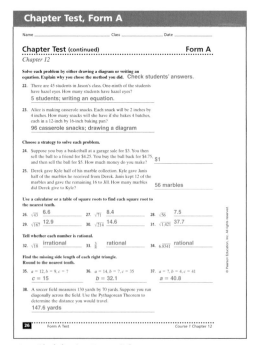

Available in Spanish

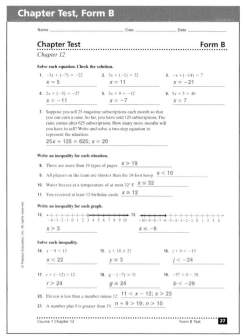

Available in Spanish

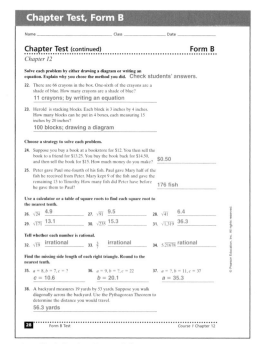

Available in Spanish

Name _____ Class _____ Date _____

Alternative Assessment   Form C
Chapter 12

MOVING DAY

You are helping a friend move. You and your friend want to pack some boxes and then move several boxes that are already packed.

Items to Pack	Weight
50 books	$\frac{1}{2}$ lb per book
4 bookends	3 lb total
miscellaneous	m
CDs, 10 cases	6 lb per case
assorted tapes	x
tape cabinet	24 lb

Suppose you wanted to pack a box with several of the same item. How could you use mathematics to figure out how much the packed box weighs?

Suppose you knew the distance (d) and time (t) it took you to drive from one apartment to another. You want to find out the rate (r) you traveled. By what would you multiply both sides of the equation $d = rt$ to find the rate?

Show all your work on a separate sheet of paper.

1. Suppose you will pack the bookends and the miscellaneous items (m) in one box. Write an expression that tells how much the box will weigh.

2. If you decide to pack the bookends with some books, write an expression that tells how much a box will weigh if you pack the book ends and any number of books (b).

3. You want any packed box to weigh no more than 30 pounds. Use the expression in Exercise 2 to write an inequality for the number of books you could pack in a box with the bookends.

4. The box packed with the books and bookends weighs 24 pounds. How many books are in the box?

Available in Spanish

Name _____ Class _____ Date _____

Alternative Assessment (continued)   Form C
Chapter 12

5. Now you will carry the CD cases (c) and the tape cabinet to the ground floor. You and your friend decide to each carry an equal weight. If your friend carries the cabinet, how many CD cases should you carry? Write and solve an equation.

6. You want to know if the tapes (x) weigh as much as a case of CDs. You know you weigh 118 pounds. When you weigh yourself holding the tapes, you weigh 123 pounds. Do the tapes weigh as much as a case of CDs? Use an equation to explain you answer.

7. The new apartment is 18 miles from the old one. If your average traveling speed is 40 mph, how long will it take you to make a one-way trip? Use the formula $d = rt$.

8. You want to move 48 packed boxes (p) today. You can carry 6 boxes in a hatchback or 8 boxes in a station wagon. You figure a round trip will take about 1 hour. The hatchback gets 25 mpg and the station wagon gets 15 mpg. Write an equation for the number of trips required to move the boxes in each car. Think about the factors involved. Then decide which car to use. Explain your decision.

Excursion

Write about a move you remember, or interview other students or relatives who have moved. Discuss the many ways mathematics could be used to make a move easier and more efficient.

Available in Spanish

Name _____ Class _____ Date _____

Alternative Assessment (continued)
Chapter 12

Scoring Rubric

Exercise	Points	Explanation
1.	1	The expression is $m + 3$
	0	No expression given or expression is incorrect
2.	1	The expression is $\frac{b}{2} + 3$
	0	No expression given or expression is incorrect
3.	2	The inequality is $30 \geq \frac{b}{2} + 3$
	1	Incorrect answer due to one sign error
	0	Expression is not given
4.	2	There are 42 books in the box
	1	Incorrect answer due to one computational error
	0	Incorrect answer
5.	2	$24 = 6c$; 4 cases
	1	Correct answer but no equation given
	0	Incorrect answer and no equation given
6.	2	$118 + x = 123$, $x = 5$; no; the tapes do not weigh as much as a case of CDs
	1	Correct answer but equation or explanation is missing
	0	Incorrect answer and equation. No explanation given
7.	1	0.45 hour, or 27 minutes
	0	Incorrect answer given
8.	2	Station wagon: *8 boxes/trip × n trips = 48 boxes*; Hatchback: *6 boxes/trip × n trips = 48 boxes*; hatchback need $\frac{1}{3}$ more trips (8 to 6), but gets $\frac{2}{3}$ more miles per gallon (25 to 15). A student interested in saving money (cost of gasoline) and who does not care as much about time would choose to use the hatchback. A student interested in saving time and who does not care as much about cost would choose to use the station wagon
	1	Correct response but no explanation given or explanation was not appropriate
	0	Incorrect answer given
Excursion	2	Student clearly stated how mathematics was related to a move of their own or that of a relative
	1	Response given but the information provided was lacking
	0	No response

Available in Spanish

Name _____ Class _____ Date _____

Cumulative Review
Chapters 1–12

Multiple Choice. Choose the letter of the best answer.

1. Find the mode of the data set.

5	3	9	5	6	11	8
3	5	7	9	11	13	15

   A. 5   B. 8
   C. 11   D. no mode

2. Which ordered pair is a solution to the equation $y = 4x - 1$?
   F. (1, 4)   G. (2, 5)
   H. (0, 1)   I. (−1, −5)

3. Multiply. $\frac{5}{8} \cdot \frac{16}{20}$
   A. 10   B. $\frac{25}{32}$
   C. $\frac{1}{2}$ D. 0

4. Identify the transformation shown.

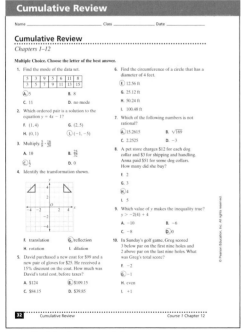

   F. translation   G. reflection
   H. rotation   I. dilation

5. David purchased a new coat for $99 and a new pair of gloves for $25. He received a 15% discount on the coat. How much was David's total cost, before taxes?
   A. $124   B. $109.15
   C. $84.15   D. $39.85

6. Find the circumference of a circle that has a diameter of 4 feet.
   F. 12.56 ft
   G. 25.12 ft
   H. 50.24 ft
   I. 100.48 ft

7. Which of the following numbers is not rational?
   A. 15.2615   B. $\sqrt{169}$
   C. 2.2525   D. −3

8. A pet store charges $12 for each dog collar and $3 for shipping and handling. Anna paid $51 for some dog collars. How many did she buy?
   F. 2
   G. 3
   H. 4
   I. 5

9. Which value of y makes the inequality true? $y > -2(4) + 4$
   A. −10   B. −6
   C. −8   D. 4

10. In Sunday's golf game, Greg scored 3 below par on the first nine holes and 2 above par on the last nine holes. What was Greg's total score?
   F. −2
   G. −1
   H. even
   I. +1

Available in Spanish

Name _____ Class _____ Date _____

Cumulative Review (continued)
Chapters 1–12

11. Sal finds the mean of a data set. He then adds 10 to every number in the data set. How does this affect the mean?
   A. It is multiplied by a factor of 10.
   B. It will be reduced by 10.
   C. The mean will not change.
   D. The mean will increase by 10.

12. The volume of an existing flower box is 35 cubic feet. Evan plans to install a new flower box that measures 4 feet by 5 feet by 3 feet. How much bigger is the new flower box?
   F. 15 feet³
   G. 25 feet³
   H. 60 feet³
   I. 95 feet³

13. Find the median of the data.

5	0 2 6 6
6	1 2 3 3 8 8
7	1 2
8	2 5 8

   A. 56
   B. 62
   C. 63
   D. 88

14. In a football game, Mario gained 5 yards, then lost 12 yards, then gained another 15 yards. What was Mario's total yards gained?
   F. −8 yards
   G. 4 yards
   H. 8 yards
   I. 15 yards

15. What number do you multiply 35 by to get a product of 0?
   A. −35
   B. −1
   C. 0
   D. 1

Extended Response

16. Theo drives at a rate of 45 miles per hour on the turnpike. How long does it take him to travel 337.5 miles if he does not stop? How long does it take him to travel this distance if he stops at a rest area for 45 minutes and then stops again for gasoline for 8 minutes?

   7.5 hours; 8 hours 23 minutes

Gridded Response

17. When adding two fractions, you get the answer $\frac{15}{9}$. Explain how you would show this mixed number on a grid.

   I would enter the numbers and the symbol 15/9 into the grid and color in the bubbles below each number and symbol.

18. Write two ways to mark the answer to the following equation on a grid. $y = -5h$, when $y = -\frac{1}{2}$.

   5/2 or 2.5

Available in Spanish

Name _____ Class _____ Date _____

Benchmark Test 1

1. What is the value of the digit 2 in the number 4.0725?
   A. 2 tenths
   B. 2 hundredths
   C. 2 thousandths
   D. 2 ten-thousandths

2. How is the decimal 2.016 expressed in words?
   A. two and sixteen thousandths
   B. two and sixteen hundredths
   C. two and sixteen tenths
   D. two and sixteenths

3. Quincy ran a lap in seventy-five and thirteen hundredths seconds. How is this time written in standard form?
   A. 75.013 seconds
   B. 75.03 seconds
   C. 75.103 seconds
   D. 75.13 seconds

4. Which set of decimals is ordered from least to greatest?
   A. 2.67, 2.71, 2.99, 2.02
   B. 2.99, 2.67, 2.71, 2.02
   C. 2.02, 2.67, 2.71, 2.99
   D. 2.71, 2.02, 2.99, 2.67

5. Which of the following statements is true?
   A. 1.971 > 1.97
   B. 2.53 < 2.3
   C. 4.825 > 4.85
   D. 6.74 < 6.740

6. The table below shows the surface ocean temperature for five days. On which day was the daily ocean temperature coolest?

   Daily Ocean Temperature

Day	Temperature (°F)
Monday	80.07
Tuesday	81.03
Wednesday	80.90
Thursday	81.50
Friday	81.20

   A. Monday
   B. Tuesday
   C. Wednesday
   D. Friday

7. Which addition problem is modeled below?

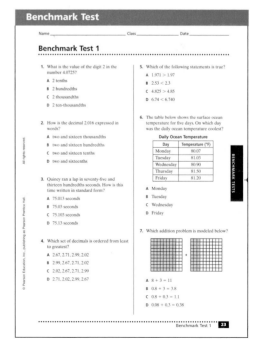

   A. 8 + 3 = 11
   B. 0.8 + 3 = 3.8
   C. 0.8 + 0.3 = 1.1
   D. 0.08 + 0.3 = 0.38

Test-Taking Strategies transparency

Test-Taking Strategies: Finding Multiple Correct Answers

In multiple correct answer questions, you have to determine whether each option provided is true or false.

As you test each statement, mark it as true or false. Then choose the answer choice that lists the true options.

EXAMPLE
Which of the following numbers are divisible by 3, 6, and 9?
  I. 18   II. 27   III. 108   IV. 162

A. I only   B. I and II   C. II and IV   D. I, III, and IV

First check which numbers are divisible by 3, 6, and 9.
  I. 18 is divisible by 3, 6, and 9: TRUE
  II. 27 is *not* divisible by 3, 6, and 9: FALSE
  III. 108 is divisible by 3, 6, and 9: TRUE
  IV. 162 is divisible by 3, 6, and 9: TRUE

Choices I, III, and IV are all divisible by 3, 6, and 9. So, the correct answer choice is D.

1. If $y = 10 - x$, which of the statements are true?
  I. $y = 7$ when $x = 3$
  II. The equation is linear.
  III. y is always odd when x is an even number.

A. I only   B. I and II   C. I and III   D. I, II, and III

2. Which ordered pair can be found on the line $y = 2x - 2$?
  I. (4, 6)   II. (2, 0)   III. (−4, −10)   IV. (0.5, −1)

F. I only   G. I and II   H. II and III   I. I, III, and IV

Transparency 13

Test-Taking Strategies worksheet

Name _____ Class _____ Date _____

Chapter 12: Finding Multiple Correct Answers
Exercises

Choose the option with all choices that are true. Explain your answers.

1. Which of the following numbers are rational numbers?
  I. −14   II. $\sqrt{7}$ III. 0.3   IV. $\sqrt{49}$

  A. I only   B. I and III   C. II and IV   D. I, III, and IV

Since −14 is an integer, it is also a rational number. $\sqrt{7}$ cannot be written as an integer or as a fraction. 0.3 can be written as $\frac{3}{10}$, so it is a rational number. $\sqrt{49}$ is 7, which is an integer, so it is a rational number. Choices I, III, and IV are all rational numbers, so, the answer is D.

2. Which of these points is a solution to the equation $y = 2x − 5$?
  I. (0, −5)   II. (4,3)   III. (2, 1)

  F. I only   G. I and II   H. II and III   I. I, II, and III

Substitute each x and y value into the equation.
  I. $−5 = 2(0) − 5; −5 = 0 − 5$ is true.
  II. $3 = 2(4) − 5; 3 = 8 − 5$ is true.
  III. $1 = 2(2) − 5; 1 = 4 − 5$ is not true since $4 − 5 = −1$.

Only I and II result in a true statement, so the answer is G.

3. If $y = 13$, which of the statements are true?
  I. y is prime   II. y is divisible by 3   III. y is odd

  A. I only   B. I and II   C. I and III   D. I, II, and III

y is a prime number, an odd number, and it is not divisible by 3. Only I and III are true statements, so the answer is C.

4. The statement $x > 3$ and $x < 5$ is true for which values of x?
  I. 4   II. 6   III. 4.5   IV. $\frac{25}{6}$

  F. I only   G. I and II   H. II and III   I. I, III, and IV

Choices I, III, and IV all lie between 3 and 5, so the answer is I.

12   Course 1   Test-Taking Strategies

Home Activities

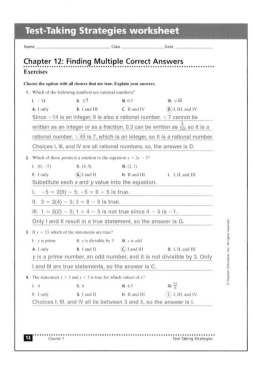

in math class ...
We have been learning about equations and graphs. Here is a list of some of the skills and concepts we have studied.

  ◆ Understanding and writing equations
  ◆ Relating equations and inequalities
  ◆ Solving two-step equations

Home Activities
Try to speak to your child with phrases that can be interpreted as inequalities. For example, if your child asks how much longer it will be until dinner is ready, you can say, "Fewer than 10 minutes" or "More than 10 minutes." Ask your child to write an inequality, using a variable, such as m, for the number of minutes until dinner ($m < 10$ or $m > 10$). If you are going somewhere in the car, and your child asks how long it will take to get there, you can say, "At least 15 minutes." Have your child interpret your answer (15 minutes or more; $m \geq 15$).

Use number lines to show stories.

A story for the number line above might be:
A football team gained 30 yards. Then it fumbled the ball, and the other team ran it back 50 yards. The football is at −20 yards:
$30 − 50 = −20$

Use with Chapter 12

Available in Spanish;
Web Code: aak-5500

Interdisciplinary Activities

Name _____   *Math and Science/Technology*

It Looks Like Rain

Solve integer equations using weather data.

If you have ever watched a weather report on television, you've probably seen a meteorologist at work. Meteorologists are scientists who analyze and forecast the weather. One of the important tools they use is radar, which stands for radio detection and ranging.

Radar works like this. An instrument sends out waves of energy from an antenna in much the same way as a radio station's tower broadcasts radio signals. The big difference between the two is that radar sends out a short burst of energy, called a pulse, rather than continuous energy signals. If the pulse hits an area of moist air, such as that of a thunderstorm, it bounces back to the radar dish, which is a receiver inside the tower. The more intense the storm, the stronger the signal that is reflected back to the dish.

The radar system's computer changes the reflected signals into different colors or shades to form a "picture" of a storm on a weather map. Meteorologists observe such pictures as time passes. The more often the meteorologists trace the path and intensity of a storm. Much of the work is done by the radar's computer, which calculates the speed and direction of the storm. The computer will follow or "track" the storm, analyzing its speed, direction, and the amount of moisture or precipitation it is producing. Using this information, a meteorologist can predict where a storm will be in the next few hours. So, when you hear a television meteorologist predict "thunderstorms are headed our way and should arrive by midnight" it is likely that radar has provided the data behind the prediction.

Shadings, or different colors, on a televised weather map indicate variations in precipitation. This simulation shows heavy rain (darkest area) in eastern Pennsylvania.

1. What do the different colors, or shades of colors, on a radar picture of a rainstorm indicate?

2. To make a complete weather picture, the radar pulses move through the sky at different heights. As they do so, they provide images of different levels of the sky. In calm weather, the radar produces 5 of these images every 10 minutes, which provide a complete picture of the sky.

   a. How many minutes, m, does it take to make one image during calm weather? How many images, p, does it produce in one hour?

Use with Chapter 12

Available in Spanish;
Web Code: aak-5500

Interdisciplinary Activities

Name _____   *Math and Science/Technology*

  b. When there is more precipitation in the forecast area, the radar speeds up. It produces 9 images in just 6 minutes. How many seconds, s, does it take to produce each image?

Temperature (°F)	Ratio of Snow to Rain (in.)
30 – 32	5:1
20 – 29	10:1
10 – 19	15:1
0 – 9	20:1
below 0	25:1

3. A radar map shows the location of a storm. Twenty minutes later, the storm has moved about 10 miles in a northeasterly direction. At what rate in miles per hour (r) is the storm traveling?

  a. What is the relationship between temperature and the ratio of volumes of snow to rain?

4. Coastal flooding is very common along the south shore of Long Island, New York. The land is very flat and is constantly hit with storms from the Atlantic Ocean. If flood conditions occur when 2.25 inches of rain have fallen, how many hours, h, will it take to reach flood stage if the rain keeps up at a pace of 0.5 inch per hour?

  b. A winter storm drops 1.24 inches of rain in 2 hours on the coast of New Jersey, where the temperature is 33°F. The rainstorm moves inland over an area whose temperature is 25°F. If the rate of precipitation remains unchanged, how much snow accumulation can be expected in the inland area if the storm lasts 3 hours?

5. A radar signal is reflected by liquid in clouds. When the temperature is above freezing, this usually means that rain will fall. But if the temperature is below freezing, snow falls. If you've ever tried melting snow to get water, you probably know that snow takes up much more space than the equivalent volume of liquid water. In fact, when temperatures are around 25°F, 10 potfuls of snow will melt into 1 potful of water. Examine the chart and answer the questions that follow.

6. Watch a television weather report when there is a storm near your area. Pay special attention to the radar weather map. Take notes about the location of the storm, its direction, and the amount of precipitation it is causing. Watch the same broadcast over the next day or two. Compare the meteorologist's prediction with the actual weather that followed. Make temperature and precipitation charts to show the contrasts between the predicted and actual weather.

Use with Chapter 12

Available in Spanish;
Web Code: aak-5500

Algebra Readiness Puzzles

Name _____   Class _____   Date _____

Mr. E. Quation's Combination   Puzzle 12

Equations and Inequalities

Solve the following inequalities. In order to find the combination to Mr. E. Quation's safe, find the whole number value that will satisfy both inequalities for each numbered problem.

1. $x + 8 < 14$ $6x \geq 30$

2. $22 + x > 24$ $9x < 36$

3. $75 + x > 85$ $\frac{x}{2} < 6$

4. $x − 6 \geq 0$ $40x \leq 240$

The combination to Mr. E. Quation's safe is

_____

12   Algebra Readiness Puzzles   © Pearson Education, Inc.

Web Code: aak-5500

Name _____ Class _____ Date _____

Equations That Balance   Puzzle 80

Find the missing weights by writing and solving an
equation for each problem.

Example:

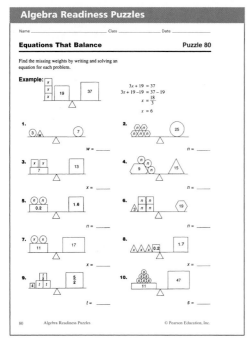

$$3x + 19 = 37$$
$$3x + 19 - 19 = 37 - 19$$
$$x = \frac{18}{3}$$
$$x = 6$$

1.

w = _____

2.

n = _____

3.

x = _____

4.

n = _____

5.

n = _____

6.

n = _____

7.

x = _____

8.

x = _____

9.

t = _____

10.

s = _____

80   Algebra Readiness Puzzles   © Pearson Education, Inc.

Web Code: aak-5500

Name _____ Class _____ Date _____

A Reading Assignment   Puzzle 87

An eighth-grade student noticed that during the school
year she had read books of certain lengths. She drew
graphs describing the number of pages in each book.

Read each description. Then write the letter of the
appropriate graph next to its description.

1. A book with more than or fewer than 150 pages _____

2. A book with more than 150 pages _____

3. A book with fewer than 150 pages _____

4. A book with either 150 pages or more than 150 pages _____

5. A book with either 150 pages or fewer than 150 pages _____

6. A book with 150 pages _____

7. A book with fewer than 150 pages but more than 130 pages _____

8. A book with more than 150 pages but fewer than 170 pages _____

A 130 140 150 160 170   B 130 140 150 160 170

C 130 140 150 160 170   D 130 140 150 160 170

E 130 140 150 160 170   F 130 140 150 160 170

G 130 140 150 160 170   H 130 140 150 160 170

© Pearson Education, Inc.   Algebra Readiness Puzzles   87

Web Code: aak-5500

Name _____ Class _____ Date _____

Which Strategy?   Puzzle 113

Name the strategy, or strategies, that you
would use to solve each problem. Then
write the answer.

> **Problem-Solving Strategies**
> • Try, Test, Revise.   • Draw a picture
> • Choose an operation.   or diagram.
> • Make an organized list.   • Make a table.
> • Act it out.   • Use objects.
> • Find a pattern.   • Work backward.
> • Write an equation.   • Solve a simpler
> • Use logical reasoning.   problem.

1. What are the next three letters?
a, d, g, j, m, p, ___ , ___ , ___

Strategy _____

Answer _____

2. The sum of two numbers is 80. The difference between the
numbers is 14. Find the numbers.

Strategy _____

Answer _____

3. Sue, Julie, Caroline, Nan, Fred, Juan, and Ken are in the same dance
class. How many possible dance pairs are there? (Girls must dance
with boys.)

Strategy _____

Answer _____

4. George walked 2 blocks north. Then he walked 3 blocks east, 1 block
south, and 3 blocks west. How far was he from where he started?

Strategy _____

Answer _____

5. Kieron bought 4 shirts that were the same price. He paid $38, which
included $2 tax. How much money did each shirt cost?

Strategy _____

Answer _____

6. Work in a small group. Write four problems that you could solve using
more than one strategy. Trade problems with another group. Solve the
new problems. Try several strategies.

© Pearson Education, Inc.   Algebra Readiness Puzzles   113

Web Code: aak-5500

Equations and Inequalities

Chapter 12 Overview

In this chapter students continue their work with equations and algebraic concepts by exploring inequalities and solving inequalities, by exploring square roots and rational numbers, and by working with the Pythagorean Theorem.

 Reading Math
- Making Sense of Inequalities, p. 610
- **Vocabulary:** A complete list, plus exercises, in the Chapter Review, p. 628
- **Illustrated Glossary:** Examples for each vocabulary term, plus definitions in English and Spanish, on p. 669

 Test-Taking Strategies
Finding Multiple Correct Answers, p. 627

 Real-World Problem Solving
- **Strategies:** Comparing Strategies, pp. 611–614
- **Real-World Snapshots:** A Bright Idea, pp. 634–635
- **Chapter Project:** Working for a Cause!, p. 641

www.PHSchool.com
Internet support includes:
- Self-grading Vocabulary and Chapter 12 Tests
- Activity Masters
- Chapter Project support
- Chapter Planner
- Ch. 12 Resources

Plus *i*TEXT

Algebra

Equations and Inequalities

Lessons

Key Vocabulary

- graph of an inequality (p. 602)
- hypotenuse (p. 622)
- inequality (p. 601)
- legs (p. 622)
- perfect square (p. 616)
- Pythagorean Theorem (p. 622)
- rational number (p. 617)
- solution of an inequality (p. 602)
- square root (p. 616)
- two-step equation (p. 596)

Real-World Snapshots

At night, human-made lights highlight the heavily populated and developed areas on Earth's surface. Lights consume energy in the form of electricity. Appliances in your home also consume energy. Some appliances consume more energy than others.

Data File
Energy Used by Appliances

Appliance	Average Monthly Energy Use (kilowatt-hours)
Dishwasher (air dry)	20
Dishwasher (cycle dry)	80
Dryer	100
Hair dryer	5
Microwave oven	25
TV (27-inch color)	110
VCR	4
Washer	10
Water heater	600

SOURCE: Boone REMC Electricity Utility Cooperative

You will use the data above in this chapter:
- p. 605   Lesson 12-2
- p. 613   Lesson 12-4

 Real-World Snapshots On pages 634 and 635, you will solve problems involving electricity costs and light bulbs.

Teaching Notes

Activating Prior Knowledge
In this chapter students build on and extend their knowledge of algebraic concepts, integers, and their writing and solving of equations to solve inequalities. They draw upon their understanding of integers and fractions when they work with rational numbers. They apply their knowledge of the properties of triangles when they learn about and apply the Pythagorean Theorem. Ask questions such as:
- *Write these numbers in order from greatest to least:* $-6, 2, 2\frac{3}{4}, -1, \frac{1}{2}$. $2\frac{3}{4}, 2, \frac{1}{2}, -1, -6$
- *How many right angles does a right triangle have? Explain.* Sample: 1; triangles have 180°, two right angles would add to 180° by themselves.
- *What is x in* $4x = 30$? $x = 7.5$

 **Real-World Snapshots**
The data here about energy used by household appliances will be used throughout the chapter. Have a volunteer read the opening passage and the title of the chart. Discuss that a kilowatt-hour is a unit of energy. Focus students on the data in the chart and ask:
- *Which appliance uses the most energy?* water heater
- *How many kilowatt-hours would a microwave use in three average months of use?* 75

Reading and Math Literacy

12A: Graphic Organizer   For use before Lesson 12-1

Study Skill: As your teacher presents new material in the chapter, keep a paper and pencil handy to write down notes and questions. If you miss class, borrow a classmate's notes to catch up.

Write your answers.
1. What is the chapter title? Equations and Inequalities
2. How many lessons are there in this chapter? 6
3. What is the topic of the Reading Math page? Making Sense of Inequalities
4. What is the topic of the Test-Taking Strategy page? Finding Multiple Correct Answers
5. Look through the chapter and list four real-world connections that are discussed.
Answers will vary.

6. Complete the graphic organizer below as you work through the chapter.
- In the center, write the title of the chapter.
- When you begin a lesson, write the lesson name in a rectangle.
- When you complete a lesson, write a skill or key concept in a circle linked to that lesson block.
- When you complete the chapter, use this graphic organizer to help you review.

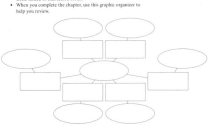

Available in Spanish

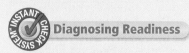

Students will find answers to these exercises in the back of their textbooks.

Prescribing Intervention
For intervention, direct students to:

Solving Equations by Subtracting or Adding
Lesson 2-6: Examples 1, 3. Extra Practice, p. 643.

Solving Equations by Dividing or Multiplying
Lesson 2-7: Examples 1, 3. Extra Practice, p. 643.

Writing Exponents
Lesson 2-8: Example 1. Extra Practice, p. 643.

Comparing Integers
Lesson 10-1: Example 4. Extra Practice, p. 651.

Chapter 12 Preview

Where You've Been

- In Chapter 2, you solved one-step equations. In Chapter 10, you added, subtracted, multiplied, and divided integers.

Where You're Going

- In Chapter 12, you will solve two-step equations and inequalities. You will also learn about square roots, rational numbers, and the Pythagorean Theorem.

- Applying what you learn, you will use inequalities to represent the training goals of a marathoner.

Edith Hunkeler won the Boston Marathon women's wheelchair division in 2002 with a time of 1:45:57.

 Instant self-check online and on CD-ROM

Diagnosing Readiness

For help, go to the lesson in green.

Algebra **Solving Equations by Subtracting or Adding** (Lesson 2-6)

Solve each equation.

1. $c + 9 = 34$ **25**   **2.** $a + 5 = -8$ **−13**   **3.** $x - 2 = 6$ **8**

4. $y - 15 = 28$ **43**   **5.** $b - 21 = -11$ **10**   **6.** $p + 35 = 17$ **−18**

Algebra **Solving Equations by Dividing or Multiplying** (Lesson 2-7)

Solve each equation.

7. $9x = 117$ **13**   **8.** $5r = 35$ **7**   **9.** $14z = 266$ **19**

10. $m \div 4 = 16$ **64**   **11.** $s \div 9 = 7$ **63**   **12.** $y \div 25 = 5$ **125**

Writing Exponents (Lesson 2-8)

Write each expression using an exponent. Name the base and the exponent.

13. $4 \times 4 \times 4$ 4^3; **4; 3**   **14.** 2×2 2^2; **2; 2**   **15.** $1 \times 1 \times 1 \times 1$ 1^4; **1; 4**

16. $12 \times 12 \times 12 \times 12 \times 12 \times 12$ 12^6; **12; 6**   **17.** $8 \times 8 \times 8 \times 8 \times 8 \times 8 \times 8$ 8^7; **8; 7**

Comparing Integers (Lesson 10-1)

Compare using $<$ or $>$.

18. $4 \blacksquare 8$ $<$ **19.** $-2 \blacksquare -1$ $<$ **20.** $-100 \blacksquare -101$ $>$

12-1 Solving Two-Step Equations

What You'll Learn

OBJECTIVE 1 To solve two-step equations

. . . And Why

To find the cost of items bought, as in Example 2

 Check Skills You'll Need

 For help, go to Lesson 5-5.

Solve each equation.

1. $\dfrac{c}{3} = 5$ 15

2. $\dfrac{n}{4} = 12$ 48

3. $\dfrac{1}{7}x = 3$ 21

4. $\dfrac{1}{8}y = 24$ 192

New Vocabulary

• two-step equation

Lesson Preview

PowerPoint

 Check Skills You'll Need
Solving Fraction Equations
Lesson 5-5: Examples 1–2. Extra Practice p. 646.

Lesson Resources

 Teaching Resources
Practice, Reteaching, Enrichment

Reaching All Students
Practice Workbook 12-1
Spanish practice Workbook 12-1
Guided Problem Solving 12-1
Hands-On Activities 47

 Presentation Assistant Plus!
Transparencies
• Check Skills You'll Need 12-1
• Problem of the Day 12-1
• Additional Examples 12-1
• Student Edition Answers 12-1
• Lesson Quiz 12-1
• Classroom Aid 8, 37
PH Presentation Pro CD-ROM 12-1

PRENTICE HALL
ASSESSMENT SYSTEM

Computer Test Generator CD

 Technology
Resource Pro® CD-ROM
Computer Test Generator CD
PH Presentation Pro CD-ROM

 www.PHSchool.com
Student Site
• Teacher Web Code: aak-5500
• Algebra Readiness Puzzles 80
• Self-grading Lesson Quiz

PH SuccessNet Teacher Center
• Lesson Planner
• Resources

Plus i TEXT

OBJECTIVE

1 **Solving Two-Step Equations**

i TEXT Interactive lesson includes instant self-check, tutorials, and activities.

Suppose your dog has a litter of 3 puppies. To weigh the puppies, you put them together in a basket.

The empty basket weighs 2 pounds. The basket and puppies together weigh 14 pounds. You can solve the equation $3x + 2 = 14$ to find the average weight of each puppy. Algebra tiles can help you understand the solution.

$3x + 2 = 14$    ← Model the equation.

$3x + 2 - 2 = 14 - 2$    ← Remove 2 tiles from each side.

$3x = 12$    ← Simplify.

$\dfrac{3x}{3} = \dfrac{12}{3}$    ← Divide each side into three equal groups.

$x = 4$ ← Simplify.

12-1 Solving Two-Step Equations   **595**

Ongoing Assessment and Intervention

Before the Lesson
Diagnose prerequisite skills using:
• Check Skills You'll Need

During the Lesson
Monitor progress using:
• Check Understanding
• Additional Examples
• Test Prep

After the Lesson
Assess knowledge using:
• Lesson Quiz
• Computer Test Generator CD

Math Background

Professional Development

Two-step equations involve two distinct operations—either addition or subtraction for one step and multiplication or division for the other step. The goal in solving two-step equations is the same as solving any equation: To get the variable alone on one side of the equation by using inverse operations.

Teaching Notes

1 EXAMPLE Teaching Tip

Emphasize that it is often easier to solve a two-step equation if students add or subtract before they multiply or divide. Solve Check Understanding 1b both ways to illustrate the point.

Add first, then divide:

$$3x - 4 = 23$$
$$3x - 4 + 4 = 23 + 4$$
$$3x = 27$$
$$3x \div 3 = 27 \div 3$$
$$x = 9$$

Divide first, then add:

$$3x - 4 = 23$$
$$(3x - 4) \div 3 = 23 \div 3$$
$$x - \frac{4}{3} = \frac{23}{3}$$
$$x - \frac{4}{3} + \frac{4}{3} = \frac{23}{3} + \frac{4}{3}$$
$$x = \frac{27}{3}$$
$$x = 9$$

2 EXAMPLE Inclusion

Have students draw a picture of the problem situation. It should include the key information: Each watermelon costs $8, the cost for paper goods was split 3 ways, and each person spends $20.

Error Prevention!

Help students rewrite $\frac{p}{3} + 8 = 20$ in Example 2 as $\frac{1}{3}p + 8 = 20$. In this form, students may better understand that they need to multiply by the reciprocal of $\frac{1}{3}$, or 3.

A **two-step equation,** like $3x + 2 = 14$, is an equation containing two operations. To solve any two-step equation, begin by undoing the addition or subtraction, then undo the multiplication or division.

1 EXAMPLE   Solving a Two-Step Equation

Solve $2y + 3 = 11$.

$$2y + 3 = 11$$
$$2y + 3 - 3 = 11 - 3 \quad \leftarrow \text{Subtract 3 from each side to undo the addition.}$$
$$2y = 8 \quad \leftarrow \text{Simplify.}$$
$$\frac{2y}{2} = \frac{8}{2} \quad \leftarrow \text{Divide each side by 2 to undo the multiplication.}$$
$$y = 4 \quad \leftarrow \text{Simplify.}$$

Check $2y + 3 = 11 \quad \leftarrow$ Check your solution in the original equation.
$2(4) + 3 = 11 \quad \leftarrow$ Substitute 4 for y.
$11 = 11$ ✓ $\quad \leftarrow$ The solution checks.

Reading Math

$2y \div 2$ and $\frac{2y}{2}$ are each read "$2y$ divided by 2." Both simplify to y.

✓ **Check Understanding** 1 Solve each equation. Check the solution.
 a. $5x + 3 = 18$ **3** **b.** $3x - 4 = 23$ **9**
 c. Mental Math What is the solution to $2a - 1 = 11$? **6**

2 EXAMPLE   Real-World  Problem Solving

Block Party Three neighbors are hosting a block party. They each purchase an $8 carved watermelon and they split the cost for paper goods. If each person spends $20, what was the total cost for the paper goods? Use p to represent the cost of the paper goods. Use the equation $\frac{p}{3} + 8 = 20$.

$$\frac{p}{3} + 8 = 20$$
$$\frac{p}{3} + 8 - 8 = 20 - 8 \quad \leftarrow \text{Subtract 8 from each side to undo the addition.}$$
$$\frac{p}{3} = 12 \quad \leftarrow \text{Simplify.}$$
$$3 \cdot \frac{p}{3} = 12 \cdot 3 \quad \leftarrow \text{Multiply each side by 3 to undo the division.}$$
$$p = 36 \quad \leftarrow \text{Simplify.}$$

The paper goods cost $36.

Real-World  **Connection**

Watermelon carving is an artistic way to display food.

✓ **Check Understanding** 2 Jim and Scott agree to split the cost to rent a moped. Scott pays the entire bill, considers the $9 that he owes Jim, and tells Jim he now owes $12. How much was the total bill? Use m to represent the cost to rent the moped. Use the equation $\frac{m}{2} - 9 = 12$. **$42**

596   Chapter 12   Equations and Inequalities

👥 Reaching All Students

| **Below Level** Give students two-step expressions to evaluate for $x = 6$. Have students show their work.

$3x - 4$ $3(6) - 4 = 18 - 4 = 14$
$5x + 1$ $5(6) + 1 = 30 + 1 = 31$
$\frac{x}{2} + 7$ $\frac{6}{2} + 7 = 3 + 7 = 10$ | **Advanced Learners** Explain that $7x - 2x = 5x$ and $7y + 2y = 9y$. Then have students solve these equations:

$7x - 4 = 2x + 6$ **2**
$7y + 3 = 30 - 2y$ **3** | **Inclusion**
See note on page 596.
Diversity
See note on page 599. |

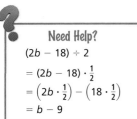

More Than One Way

Solve $2b - 18 = 34$.

Michael's Method

First I'll add. Then I'll divide.

$$2b - 18 = 34$$
$$2b - 18 + 18 = 34 + 18 \quad \leftarrow \text{Add 18 to each side.}$$
$$2b = 52 \quad \leftarrow \text{Simplify.}$$
$$\frac{2b}{2} = \frac{52}{2} \quad \leftarrow \text{Divide each side by 2.}$$
$$b = 26 \quad \leftarrow \text{Simplify.}$$

Lauren's Method

Since each number in the equation is an even number, I'll begin by dividing each side of the equation by 2.

$$2b - 18 = 34$$
$$(2b - 18) \div 2 = 34 \div 2 \quad \leftarrow \text{Divide each side by 2.}$$
$$b - 9 = 17 \quad \leftarrow \text{Divide } 2b, 18, \text{ and 34 by 2.}$$
$$b - 9 + 9 = 17 + 9 \quad \leftarrow \text{Add 9 to each side.}$$
$$b = 26 \quad \leftarrow \text{Simplify.}$$

Need Help?

$(2b - 18) \div 2$

$= (2b - 18) \cdot \frac{1}{2}$

$= \left(2b \cdot \frac{1}{2}\right) - \left(18 \cdot \frac{1}{2}\right)$

$= b - 9$

Choose a Method

Solve $5p + 75 = 245$. Describe your method and explain why you chose it. **Answers may vary. Sample: 34; first I subtracted 75 from each side of the equation. Then I divided each side by 5. I chose this method so that I would have to do only one division.**

EXERCISES

? For more practice, see *Extra Practice*.

A Practice by Example

Example 1
(page 596)

Solve each equation. Exercises 1–3 have been started for you.

1. $2b + 4 = 12$ **4**

$2b + 4 - 4 = 12 - 4$

2. $3j - 6 = 12$ **6**

$3j - 6 + 6 = 12 + 6$

3. $\frac{a}{3} + 2 = 8$ **18**

$\frac{a}{3} + 2 - 2 = 8 - 2$

4. $2y + 5 = 9$ **2**

5. $2p + 13 = 3$ **−5**

6. $5x + 7 = 22$ **3**

7. $\frac{a}{2} + 4 = 8$ **8**

8. $\frac{x}{3} + 2 = 5$ **9**

9. $\frac{n}{6} - 1 = 3$ **24**

Tactile Learners

Allow students to use algebra tiles to physically work through Check Understanding 2. This may help them more fully describe the operations involved.

Error Prevention!

Help students recognize that when they divide both sides of an equation, they need to make sure they divide each entire side. In the *More Than One Way* feature, Lauren divided the entire left side of the equation when she divided both sides by 2. To do this, she used the Distributive Property, $(2b - 18) \div 2 = (2b \div 2) - (18 \div 2)$, or $b - 9$. Stress that Lauren could not just divide $2b$ by 2 and ignore the -18.

Additional Examples

1 Solve $6x - 14 = 16$. Check the solution. **5**

2 The Science Club sells birdfeeders for $8 each. The club spends $32 in building materials. The club's profit is $128. How many birdfeeders did the club sell? Use b to represent the number of birdfeeders. Use the equation $8b - 32 = 128$. **20 birdfeeders**

Closure

• *What is a two-step equation?* an equation that contains two operations

• *How do you solve a two-step equation?* Sample: Use inverse operations to get the variable alone on one side of the equation.

• *How can you check your solution?* Sample: Substitute the solution for the variable in the original equation and simplify. You should get the same value on both sides.

Assignment Guide

1 Objective 1
Ⓐ Ⓑ Core 1–34
Ⓒ Extension 35–39

Test Prep 40–44
Mixed Review 45–49

Teaching Tip
Exercises 1–9 Have volunteers read each equation aloud and say the two inverse operations that will solve it. You might remind students that it is usually easier to first undo the addition or subtraction.

Practice 12-1 .... Solving Two-Step Equations

Explain what was done to the first equation to get the second equation.

1. $\frac{x}{5} - 3 = 12 \rightarrow x = 75$
   Add 3 to both sides, then multiply both sides by 5.

2. $6x + 7 = 31 \rightarrow x = 4$
   Subtract 7 from both sides, then divide both sides by 6.

3. $\frac{x}{3} + 2 = 4 \rightarrow x = 6$
   Subtract 2 from both sides, then multiply both sides by 3.

Solve each equation. Check the solution.

4. $3x + 7 = 37$	5. $31 = 7x - 11$	6. $11k - 84 = 92$
$x = $ 10	$x = $ 6	$k = $ 16
7. $4r + 13 = 57$	8. $\frac{z}{2} + 16 = 21$	9. $7 = \frac{t}{6} - 3$
$r = $ 11	$z = $ 20	$t = $ 60
10. $6q - 18 = 30$	11. $\frac{w}{15} + 26 = 42$	12. $15u + 18 = 18$
$q = $ 8	$w = $ 240	$u = $ 0
13. $9 = 7b - 12$	14. $\frac{x}{11} + 21 = 35$	15. $\frac{s}{7} - 11 = 17$
$b = $ 3	$x = $ 154	$s = $ 196

16. Hideki baked 41 cookies. He gave the same number of cookies to each of 5 friends, saving 11 cookies for himself. How many cookies did each friend receive?
6 cookies

17. Estelle is buying dresses by mail. She pays $65 for each dress, plus a shipping and handling charge of $8 for the entire order. If her order costs $268, how many dresses did she buy?
4 dresses

18. Ms. Juarez planted a 7-foot-tall tree. The height (h) of the tree, in feet, after n years is given by the equation $h = 4n + 7$. In how many years will the height be 39 feet?
8 years

Reteaching 12-1 .... Solving Two-Step Equations

Some equations contain two operations. To solve them, use inverse operations to get the variable alone on one side of the equation. Begin by undoing addition or subtraction. Then undo multiplication or division.

Example: Solve $2d + 1 = 9$.

$2d + 1 = 9$

$2d + 1 - 1 = 9 - 1$ Subtract 1 from each side to undo the addition.
$\frac{2d}{2} = \frac{8}{2}$ Divide each side by 2 to undo the multiplication.
$d = 4$ Simplify.

   Check your work by substituting 4 for d in the equation and solving.
$2 \cdot 4 + 1 \stackrel{?}{=} 9$
$9 = 9$ Since 9 = 9, the solution is correct.

1. Solve $7x - 5 = 16$.
   a. What must you first do to both sides? Add 5.
   b. What must you next do to both sides? Divide by 7.
   c. What is the solution? $x = 3$

2. Solve $12 = \frac{t}{5} + 8$.
   a. What must you first do to both sides? Subtract 8.
   b. What must you next do to both sides? Multiply by 5.
   c. What is the solution? $t = 20$

Solve each equation. Check the solution.

3. $7y - 6 = 8$ 4. $81 = 3x - 6$
   $y = 2$ $x = 29$
5. $\frac{c}{8} + 10 = 15$ 6. $2f - 6 = 4$
   $c = 40$ $f = 5$
7. $4k + 20 = 24$ 8. $\frac{e}{5} + 100 = 120$
   $k = 1$ $e = 100$

Example 2 **10. Shopping** You want to buy a pair of pants and three shirts. You can
(page 596)   spend $90 on the items and still have enough money to pay the sales tax.
If the pants you choose cost $24, how much can you spend on each shirt?
Use s to represent the cost of a shirt. Use the equation $24 + 3s = 90$.
$22

11. Brendan orders a telephone for $34 and some pens at $2 each. Not including shipping or tax, his order totals $46. How many pens did he order? Use p to represent the number of pens he ordered. Use the equation $34 + 2p = 46$. **6 pens**

Ⓑ **Apply Your Skills**

Mental Math Solve each equation.

| 12. $2y + 1 = 11$ **5** | 13. $5c + 15 = 30$ **3** | 14. $4d - 12 = 8$ **5** |
| 15. $3n - 1 = 17$ **6** | 16. $\frac{w}{2} - 6 = 4$ **20** | 17. $\frac{a}{5} + 7 = 12$ **25** |

Choose the correct equation for each problem. Then use the equation to solve the problem.

18. Exercise It costs $75 to join a health club, plus a monthly fee. Your uncle spends $495 for his first year in the club. What is the monthly fee? Use m for the monthly fee. **A; $35**
A. $75 + 12m = 495$ **B.** $75 + 495 = 12m$

19. Donations Mr. Lewis has $200 to donate to his favorite causes. He wants to give $35 to the local animal shelter and then make $15 donations to a variety of other causes. How many other causes can he support? Use c for the number of other causes. **B; 11 causes**
A. $35c + 15 = 200$ **B.** $35 + 15c = 200$

20. Your brother buys 4 games. Each game costs the same amount. He uses a coupon for $5 off the total purchase price, and owes the cashier $30.80. How much does each game cost? Use c for the cost of one game.
A. $4c + 5 = 30.8$ **B.** $4c - 5 = 30.8$ **B; $8.95**

21. Reading Beth is reading a 160-page book. She has already read 100 pages. If she reads 15 pages each day, how many days will it take her to finish the book? Use d for the number of days to finish. **B; 4 days**
A. $15d = 160$ **B.** $100 + 15d = 160$

Real-World Connection

Instead of money, you can donate your home as a foster home for an animal.

Solve each equation. Check the solution.

| 22. $9e + 5 = -4$ **−1** | 23. $7h + 12 = -9$ **−3** | 24. $3a + 8 = 2$ **−2** |
| 25. $2y - 3 = -11$ **−4** | 26. $-6 = 4b - 10$ **1** | 27. $1 + \frac{g}{2} = -5$ **−12** |

28. 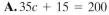 **Writing in Math** How is solving $16e - 32 = 176$ different from solving $16e = 176$? Answers may vary. Sample: To solve $16e - 32 = 176$, first add 32 to each side and then divide each side by 16. To solve $16e = 176$, simply divide each side by 16.

GPS Use the Guided Problem Solving worksheet with Exercise 29.

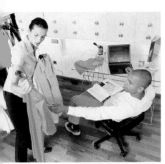

Real-World 🌐 **Connection**

Careers A sales representative for a clothing manufacturer sells the latest fashions to retail stores.

29. **Commission** *Commission* is pay earned as a percent of sales. Suppose [GPS] a sales representative receives a weekly base salary of $250 plus a commission of 8% of her total weekly sales. At the end of one week, she earns $410. What is her sales total for the week? Use s to represent the total sales. Use the equation $0.08s + 250 = 410$. **$2,000**

30. Suppose you save $26 each week so you can buy a camcorder for $260. So far, you have saved $182. In how many more weeks will you have saved $260? Use w to represent the number of weeks. Use the equation $26w + 182 = 260$. **3 weeks**

Complete each function table given the rule.

31. Rule: Multiply by 2, then add 3.

Input	1	10	12
Output	▦5	▦	▦

23   27

32. Rule: Divide by 3, then add 1.

Input	3	9	15
Output	▦2	▦4	▦6

Write a rule for each function using two operations. Then complete the function table. (*Hint:* Multiply or divide first.)

33.

Input	Output
2	7
4	11
7	17
8	▦ 19
15	▦ 33

Rule: Multiply by 2, then add 3.

34.

Input	Output
6	−6
9	−5
15	−3
30	▦ 2
63	▦ 13

Rule: Divide by 3, then subtract 8.

○C Challenge

35. After subtracting 4 from each side, the student should have multiplied each side by 5 instead of dividing by 5.

35. **Error Analysis** A student solves the equation $4 + \frac{m}{5} = 19$. Look at the solution at the right. What error does the student make? **See left.**

$$4 + \frac{m}{5} = 19$$

$$\frac{m}{5} = 15$$

$$m = 3 \ ✗$$

Solve each equation.

36. $3x - \frac{5}{2} = \frac{7}{2}$ **2**

37. $\frac{a}{2} + \frac{2}{3} = 5\frac{1}{3}$ **$9\frac{1}{3}$**

38. $8.25y + 3.5 = 36.5$ **4**

39. **Stretch Your Thinking** The perimeter of the figure below is 30.75 inches. Write an equation to represent the perimeter of the figure. Solve for x. (*Note:* The figure is not drawn to scale.) **$5x - 18 = 30.75$; 9.75**

$x - 3$ $x - 4$ $x - 6$ $x - 5$ x

Visual Learners
Exercises 10–11 Suggest that students make a drawing for the problem situation that includes the given information and the equation. Have students add their answer to their diagrams.

Diversity
Exercise 18 Some students may be unfamiliar with health clubs. Ask volunteers to describe what a health club is and the forms of exercise commonly available.

PowerPoint Lesson Quiz 12-1

Solve each equation.

1. $6a + 12 = 30$ 3

2. $\frac{b}{5} + 21 = 24$ 15

3. $4c - 40 = 28$ 17

4. $\frac{d}{7} + 15 = 22$ 49

Alternative Assessment

Provide algebra tiles to pairs of students. Partners use the tiles to model and solve exercises such as Exercises 1–9. Partners take turns recording each step of the solution process.

Test Prep

Resources

A sheet of blank grids is available in the *Test-Taking Strategies With Transparencies* booklet. Give copies of this sheet to students so they can practice filling in grids.

For additional practice with a variety of test item formats:
- Test-Prep, pp. 631–633
- Test-Taking Strategies, p. 627
- Test-Taking Strategies With Transparencies

 Test Prep

Gridded Response   What is the solution of each equation?

40. $7x - 4 = 10$ 2

41. $3x + 5 = 11$ 2

42. $\frac{x}{4} + 2 = 10$ 32

43. $\frac{x}{2} - 5 = 1$ 12

 **Take It to the NET**
Online lesson quiz at
www.PHSchool.com
Web Code: aaa-1201

44. Your sister buys 3 headbands. Each headband costs the same amount. She uses a $2-off coupon and pays $7 to the cashier. How much money, in dollars, does each headband cost? Use h to represent the cost of each headband. Use the equation $3h - 2 = 7$.   3

Mixed Review

Lesson 11-1   **A bag contains 3 red marbles, 2 green marbles, and 2 blue marbles. You pick one marble from the bag. Find the probability for each selection.**

45. $P(\text{red})$ $\frac{3}{7}$

46. $P(\text{blue})$ $\frac{2}{7}$

47. $P(\text{yellow})$ 0

Lesson 9-5   **Find the unknown length for a circle with the given dimension.**

48. $r = 12$ inches, $d = \blacksquare$ 24 in.

49. $d = 0.36$ meter, $r = \blacksquare$ 0.18 m

Practice Game   What's My Rule?

How to Play

- Player A writes a rule for a two-step equation using only integers. The first step should use multiplication or division, and the second step should use addition or subtraction. Sample: To get y, multiply x by 5, and then subtract 3.
- Player B must figure out the rule. So Player B tells Player A a value for x. Player A responds with the correct y-value based on the rule. Player B records the x- and y- values in a function table like the one at the right.
- If Player B provides an incorrect rule, the round ends. If Player B gives the correct rule, then Player B gets 1 point.
- Players take turns writing and determining the rules.
- The player with the most points wins.

x	y
2	7
-2	-13
0	-3

Enrichment 12-1   Solving Two-Step Equations
Problem Solving

Solve the equation $6x - 2 = 16$.

- Emma solved the equation by using inverse operations.

  $6x - 2 = 16$
  $6x - 2 + 2 = 16 + 2$
  $6x = 18$
  $\frac{6x}{6} = \frac{18}{6}$
  $x = \frac{18}{6}$
  $x = 3$

- Evan solved the equation by first dividing all terms by 6, the coefficient of x.

  $6x - 2 = 16$
  $\frac{6x}{6} - \frac{2}{6} = \frac{16}{6}$
  $x - \frac{2}{6} = \frac{16}{6}$
  $x - \frac{2}{6} + \frac{2}{6} = \frac{16}{6} + \frac{2}{6}$
  $x = \frac{18}{6}$
  $x = 3$

1. Did both students arrive at the same solution? yes

2. Compare the two approaches. Which one was easier? Explain.
   Sample answer: Emma's; using the inverse operations involved fewer steps.

3. Use Emma's method to solve the equation.
   $6x - 18 = 48$
   $x = 11$

4. Use Evan's method to solve the equation.
   $6x - 18 = 48$
   $x = 11$

5. Use Emma's method to solve the equation.
   $10x + 50 = 70$
   $x = 2$

6. Use Evan's method to solve the equation.
   $10x + 50 = 70$
   $x = 2$

7. When does dividing first work best?
   Sample answer: when each of the numbers in the equation is divisible by the whole number coefficient of x

600   Chapter 12   Equations and Inequalities

12-2 Inequalities

What You'll Learn

OBJECTIVE 1 To write inequalities

OBJECTIVE 2 To identify solutions of inequalities

. . . And Why

To tell who can ride a roller coaster, as in Example 4

✔ Check Skills You'll Need   ❓ For help, go to Lesson 10-1.

Compare using < or >.

1. $-3 \ \blacksquare \ 6$ <
2. $4 \ \blacksquare \ -9$ >
3. $-2 \ \blacksquare \ -3$ >
4. $-94 \ \blacksquare \ -93$ <
5. $54 \ \blacksquare \ 47$ >
6. $1{,}001 \ \blacksquare \ 1{,}010$ <

New Vocabulary
- inequality
- graph of an inequality
- solution of an inequality

Lesson Preview

✔ Check Skills You'll Need   PowerPoint
Comparing Integers
Lesson 10-1: Example 4. Extra Practice p. 651.

Lesson Resources

📁 **Teaching Resources**
Practice, Reteaching, Enrichment

👥 **Reaching All Students**
Practice Workbook 12-2
Spanish Practice Workbook 12-2
Guided Problem Solving 12-2

🕐 **Presentation Assistant Plus!**
Transparencies
- Check Skills You'll Need 12-2
- Problem of the Day 12-2
- Additional Examples 12-2
- Student Edition Answers 12-2
- Lesson Quiz 12-2
- Classroom Aid 7
PH Presentation Pro CD-ROM 12-2

PRENTICE HALL ASSESSMENT SYSTEM

Computer Test Generator CD

💻 **Technology**
Resource Pro® CD-ROM
Computer Test Generator CD
PH Presentation Pro CD-ROM

💻 **www.PHSchool.com**
Student Site
- Teacher Web Code: aak-5500
- Algebra Readiness Puzzles 87
- Self-grading Lesson Quiz

PH SuccessNet Teacher Center
- Lesson Planner
- Resources

Plus **iTEXT**

OBJECTIVE

1 Writing Inequalities

 **iTEXT** Interactive lesson includes instant self-check, tutorials, and activities.

Recall that an equation contains an equal sign, $=$. An **inequality** is a mathematical sentence that contains $<$, $>$, $\leq$, $\geq$, or $\neq$.

Symbol	Meaning
$<$	is less than
$>$	is greater than
$\leq$	is less than or equal to
$\geq$	is greater than or equal to
$\neq$	is not equal to

Some inequalities like $a < 8$ contain a variable. Real-world problems can sometimes be represented by inequalities.

1 EXAMPLE   Writing an Inequality

Bison You must take less than 10 seconds to cross the field shown at the left. Otherwise, the bison may catch you! Write an inequality to express the time in which you must cross the field.

Words	time for you to cross field	is less than	time for bison to cross field

Let t = your time to cross the field.

Inequality	t	$<$	10

The inequality is $t < 10$.

✔ Check Understanding **1** Most skydivers jump from an altitude of 14,500 feet or less. Write an inequality to express the altitude from which most skydivers jump.
Let a represent the altitude from which most skydivers jump. $a \leq 14{,}500$

DONT CROSS THIS FIELD UNLESS YOU CAN DO IT IN 99 SECONDS. THE BULL CAN DO IT IN 10

12-2 Inequalities   **601**

 Ongoing Assessment and Intervention

Before the Lesson
Diagnose prerequisite skills using:
- Check Skills You'll Need

During the Lesson
Monitor progress using:
- Check Understanding
- Additional Examples
- Test Prep

After the Lesson
Assess knowledge using:
- Lesson Quiz
- Computer Test Generator CD

601

2. Teach

Math Background

An equation is a mathematical sentence with an equal sign, =. An *inequality* is a mathematical sentence that contains one of the following five symbols: < (less than), > (greater than), ≤ (less than or equal to), ≥ (greater than or equal to), or ≠ (not equal to).

The *solution of an inequality* is any number that makes the inequality true. An inequality may have many possible solutions. You can graph an inequality on a number line to visualize all the solutions. An open circle indicates the endpoint is not included, and is used with the symbols < or >. A closed circle indicates the endpoint is included, and is used with ≤ or ≥.

Teaching Notes

English Learners

Help students recognize the prefix *in-* in the term *inequality*. Explain that the prefix means "not." Have students help generate a list of other English words that begin with the prefix *in-*. For instance: *invisible, inactive, incorrect, inexpensive,* and *insincere.* Point out that some words, such as *insect* and *ink,* begin with the letters *in,* but not the prefix *in-.*

① EXAMPLE Error Prevention

For Check Understanding 1, discuss *14,500 or less* to make sure that students understand what *or* means mathematically. Ask:
- *Does 14,500 make the sentence true?* yes
- *Does 14,000 make the sentence true?* yes
- *Does 15,000 make the sentence true?* no *Explain.* Sample: The number has to be equal to or less than 14,500.

③ EXAMPLE Teaching Tip

Point out that an open circle is used for inequalities that contain > or <. The open circle signifies that the beginning value is *not* included. A closed circle shows the beginning value *is* included and describes inequalities with either ≤ or ≥.

602

The **graph of an inequality** shows all the solutions that satisfy the inequality. An open circle shows that the starting number is *not* included. A closed circle shows that the starting number *is* included.

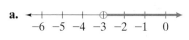 **② EXAMPLE** **Writing Inequalities From Number Lines**

Write an inequality for each graph.

a.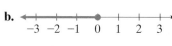

Since the circle is open, use < or >.
← Since the graph shows values greater than −3, use >.

$x > -3$

b.

Since the circle is closed, use ≤ or ≥.
← Since the graph shows values less than or equal to 0, use ≤.

$x \le 0$

✓ **Check Understanding ②** Write an inequality for each graph.

a.

$x < -1$

b.

$x \ge 4$

 **OBJECTIVE 2** **Identifying Solutions of Inequalities**

A **solution of an inequality** is any number that makes the inequality true. An inequality may have many possible solutions. Graphing an inequality on a number line can help you visualize all the solutions.

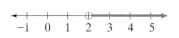 **③ EXAMPLE** **Graphing Inequalities**

Write an inequality to represent each situation. Then graph the inequality.

a. Karen rode her scooter more than 2 miles.

If k = Karen's distance, $k > 2$.

Use an open circle to show that the
← distance cannot include 2 miles.
Include all the numbers greater than 2.

b. The temperature was 3 degrees or less.

If t = the temperature, $t \le 3$.

Use a closed circle to show that the
← temperature can include 3 degrees.
Include all the numbers less than 3.

✓ **Check Understanding ③** Write an inequality to represent the situation. Then graph the inequality.

Linda spent at least 2 hours studying. $\ell \ge 2$; see above left for graph.

602 Chapter 12 Equations and Inequalities

🧑‍🤝‍🧑 Reaching All Students

Below Level Help students interpret the graph below. Ask: *Can x be 0?* yes *Can x be 1?* no *How can you tell?* There is an open circle at 1.	Advanced Learners Solve each inequality.	English Learners See note on page 602.
	$x + 2 > x + 1$ all numbers	Inclusion See note on page 603.
	$x + 2 < x + 1$ no solution	
	$x - 2 > x - 1$ no solution	
	$x - 2 < x - 1$ all numbers	

You can use an inequality to determine if someone or something meets a requirement.

4 EXAMPLE Identifying Solutions of an Inequality

Roller Coasters A person must be at least 48 inches to ride a certain roller coaster. Write an inequality to represent this requirement. Who of the following people can ride the roller coaster: Sally ($48\frac{1}{2}$ inches tall), Dean (48 inches tall), Kelsey ($46\frac{3}{4}$ inches tall)?

| Words | person's height | is at least | 48 inches |

Let h = a person's height.

| Inequality | h | $\geq$ | 48 | ← "At least" means $\geq$. |

To determine who can ride the roller coaster, find which heights are solutions of $h \geq 48$. Replace h with the height of each person. Then decide whether the inequality is true or false.

Sally	$48\frac{1}{2} \geq 48$	true
Dean	$48 \geq 48$	true
Kelsey	$46\frac{3}{4} \geq 48$	false

● Sally and Dean are tall enough to ride the roller coaster.

✓ **Check Understanding** 4 a. To be allowed into a certain jumping tent, you must be younger than 8 years old. Who of the following people can enter the jumping tent:
Marissa; Teagan Marissa (7 years, 11 months), Teagan (5 years), Ian (8 years, 3 months)?
  b. **Reasoning** Are the solutions to $x < 3$ and $x \leq 3$ the same? Explain.
     No; 3 is a solution to $x \leq 3$ but not to $x < 3$.

EXERCISES

For more practice, see *Extra Practice*.

Ⓐ **Practice by Example**

Example 1
(page 601)

Write an inequality for each situation.

1. There are more than 14 girls in the class. $g > 14$

2. No more than 45 students participated in the car-wash fundraiser.
   $s \leq 45$

3. Your sister had at least 15 people at her birthday party. $p \geq 15$

4. There were more than 15 ladybugs on the windowsill. $\ell > 15$

5. A sign on a bridge reads, "Maximum height of vehicles is 12 feet."
   $h \leq 12$

6. Cooking food at 165°F or higher will kill most bacteria. $f \geq 165$

Some students may mix up which way an inequality symbol is facing or should face. Remind them that the sharp point of the arrow points to the smaller value. Students can place their index finger on the point of the inequality symbol to verify that their finger is next to the smaller value in the inequality.

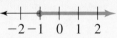
Additional Examples

1 Write an inequality to express the situation. *Maria threw the softball more than 90 feet.*
  $m > 90$

2 Write an inequality for the graph. $x \geq -1$

$$\leftarrow\!\!+\!\!\!\bullet\!\!\!+\!\!\!+\!\!\!+\!\!\to$$
$$-2 -1 \quad 0 \quad 1 \quad 2$$

3 Write an inequality to represent the situation. Then graph the inequality. *Everyone in our class is 10 years old or older.* $a \geq 10$

$$\leftarrow\!\!+\!\!\!+\!\!\!\bullet\!\!\!+\!\!\!+\!\!\to$$
$$0 \quad 5 \quad 10 \; 15 \; 20$$

4 Every student who brings 3.5 pounds or more of recyclable aluminum gets into the Environment Dance free. Who of the following students can attend free: Ben (3.35 lb), Rinaldo (2.75 lb), Juanita (3.75 lb)? Juanita

Closure

• *When do you graph an open circle on a number line?*
  Sample: when you are showing less than or greater than and you don't want to include the number at that point

• *How do you test to see if a number is a solution to an inequality?* Sample: Replace the variable with the number and simplify. If the inequality statement is true, the number is a solution to the inequality.

Assignment Guide

1 Objective 1
Ⓐ Ⓑ Core 1–10, 22, 25

2 Objective 2
Ⓐ Ⓑ Core 11–21, 23–24, 26
Ⓒ Extension 27–28

Test Prep 29–32
Mixed Review 33–35

Error Prevention!

Exercises 11–14 Have students verbalize "open circle" or "closed circle" before they graph.

Practice 12-2 — Inequalities

Reteaching 12-2 — Inequalities

Example 2
(page 602)

Write an inequality for each graph.

7.
$x < 2$

8.
$x > 4$

9.
$x \le -3$

10.
$x \ge 7$

Example 3
(page 602)

11.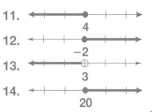
4

12.
−2

13.
3

14.
20

Write an inequality to represent each situation. Then graph the inequality.
See left for graphs.

11. Four people or fewer are allowed on the ride at once. $p \le 4$

12. The temperature never went below −2 degrees. $t \ge -2$

13. Kristen has less than three days to write her paper. $k < 3$

14. You must deposit at least \$20 to open a bank account. $d \ge \$20$

Example 4
(page 603)

15. **DVDs** To buy a certain DVD, you must be at least 13 years old. Who of the following people can buy the DVD: Carl (12 years, 9 months), Cara (15 years, 4 days), Molly (13 years), Peter (8 years, 11 months)?
Cara, Molly

16. **Playgrounds** To ride on the playground animals, you must be under 50 pounds. Who of the following children can ride the animals: Hugh (50 pounds), Paul (45 pounds), Andrea (25 pounds), Michelle (53 pounds), Tim (49 pounds)? **Paul, Andrea, Tim**

Ⓑ **Apply Your Skills**

Tell whether each inequality is true or false.

17. $6 \le 6$
true

18. $|-5| < 5$
false

19. $-4^2 < (-4)^2$
true

20. $0.05 > 0.5$
false

21. **Football** You must weigh 120 pounds or less to play in a junior football league. The table shows the weights of boys who would like to play. Which of the boys qualify to play? **Aaron, Steve, James**

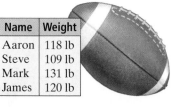

Name	Weight
Aaron	118 lb
Steve	109 lb
Mark	131 lb
James	120 lb

22. **Highway Safety** Write an inequality for the sign shown at the left.
$w \le 3$

23. **Writing in Math** Describe how to graph the inequality $x < -20$.
See margin.

24. Replace ▓ with $<$, $=$, or $>$ to make each statement true.
a. If $50 > b$, then b ▓ 50. $<$
b. If $a = b$ and $b < 50$, then a ▓ 50. $<$

25. **Driving** The minimum speed limit on an interstate is 50 miles per hour. The maximum speed limit is 65 miles per hour.
a. Write an inequality to describe a car that is going too slow. $s < 50$
b. Write an inequality to describe a car that is going too fast. $s > 65$

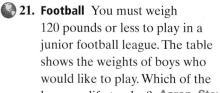

OVER 3 TONS

Exercise 22

GPS Use the Guided Problem Solving worksheet with Exercise 22.

23. Answers may vary. Sample: Use an open circle to exclude −20, and shade to the left of the open circle to show numbers less than 20.

26. **Data File, p. 593** Write an inequality for an average monthly energy usage greater than 80 kWh. Which appliances have an average monthly energy usage greater than 80 kWh? *a* > 80; dryer, TV, water heater

 Challenge

27. **Number Sense** Graph the following inequality on a number line: *x* ≠ 4.

28. **Stretch Your Thinking** Solve and graph |*x*| < 2.
    −2 < *x* < 2

 Test Prep

Reading Comprehension   Read the passage and answer the questions below.

A Career in Law Enforcement

The work of police officers, detectives, and FBI agents seems exciting to many people. Individuals seeking a career in law enforcement must be citizens of the United States and must be at least 20 years of age at the time of appointment. Those seeking careers in federal law enforcement agencies, such as the FBI, must be at least 21 years of age, but less than 37.

29. Write an inequality showing the general age requirement for law-enforcement candidates. *a* ≥ 20

 **Take It to the NET**
Online lesson quiz at
www.PHSchool.com
Web Code: aaa-1202

30. Write an inequality showing the minimum age requirement for federal law-enforcement candidates. *a* ≥ 21

31. Write an inequality showing the maximum age requirement for federal law-enforcement candidates. *a* < 37

Multiple Choice

32. Which inequality does NOT have −2 as a solution? C
    A. *x* ≥ −2   **B.** *x* < −1   **C.** *x* > −1   **D.** *x* < 2

 Mixed Review

Lesson 11-2   **Find the experimental probability that each person wins.**

33. Tom won a game 84 times and lost 24 times. $\frac{7}{9}$

34. Rhonda played a game 222 times and won 88 times. $\frac{44}{111}$

Lesson 9-10   35. You multiply a number by 6 and then subtract 4. The result is 38. Work backward to find the number. 7

 **Lesson Quiz 12-2**

Use *x* as the variable. Write an inequality for each graph.

1.
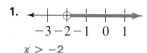
   x > −2

2.

   x ≤ 0

3. Graph the inequality *x* < 2 on a number line.

4. Tell which numbers are solutions of *x* ≥ −4: −6, −4, −2, 0, 2. −4, −2, 0, 2

Alternative Assessment

Each partner writes an inequality such as *x* > −8 or *n* ≥ 7. Partners exchange papers, graph the inequality, and check each other's graphs.

Test Prep

Resources
For additional practice with a variety of test item formats:
• Test-Prep, pp. 631–633
• Test-Taking Strategies, p. 627
• Test-Taking Strategies With Transparencies

Enrichment 12-2   Inequalities
Decision Making

"Hey, Coach, who's up first?"

Can you help the coach make a batting order? In the table below are player statistics. Answer the questions to determine who should bat in which position. Then fill in the last column of the table.

Player	Runs	Hits	Doubles	Triples	Homeruns	Batting Average	Batting Order
Allie	79	137	40	1	20	0.268	6
Anna	59	109	21	0	14	0.240	8
Bobbie	56	92	15	0	15	0.243	7
Jason	128	209	51	2	39	0.300	2
Jessie	124	191	26	0	18	0.297	1
Kelly	120	176	34	1	41	0.314	3
Tommy	102	204	37	2	19	0.333	4
Zach	39	121	35	3	20	0.245	9
Tony	68	115	17	0	27	0.247	5

1. The first hitter has at least as many hits as Kelly, but less than Tommy.
2. The second hitter has at least as many doubles as Tommy and a batting average less than Kelly.
3. Batter three has fewer triples than Zach, a lower batting average than Tommy, but a better average than Jason.
4. Batter four has the same or fewer homeruns than Allie, but more doubles than Zach.
5. The fifth batter has no triples, but has a batting average greater than Zach.
6. Batter six has fewer hits than Kelly and more triples than Tony.
7. Batter seven has fewer doubles than Tony, but fewer triples than Zach.
8. Batter eight has as many or more triples than Jessie, more doubles than Tony, but fewer homeruns than Bobbie.

12-3 Solving One-Step Inequalities

1. Plan

Lesson Preview

✓ **Check Skills You'll Need**

Solving Equations by Adding or Subtracting
Lesson 2-6: Examples 1, 3. Extra Practice p. 643.

Lesson Resources

📁 **Teaching Resources**
Practice, Reteaching, Enrichment
Checkpoint Quiz 1

👥 **Reaching All Students**
Practice Workbook 12-3
Spanish Practice Workbook 12-3
Reading and Math Literacy 12B
Spanish Reading and Math
  Literacy 12B
Spanish Checkpoint Quiz 1
Guided Problem Solving 12-3

⏰ **Presentation Assistant Plus!**
Transparencies
• Check Skills You'll Need 12-3
• Problem of the Day 12-3
• Additional Examples 12-3
• Student Edition Answers 12-3
• Lesson Quiz 12-3
PH Presentation Pro CD-ROM 12-3

ASSESSMENT SYSTEM

Checkpoint Quiz 1
Computer Test Generator CD

💻 **Technology**
Resource Pro® CD-ROM
Computer Test Generator CD
PH Presentation Pro CD-ROM

💻 **www.PHSchool.com**
Student Site
• Teacher Web Code: aak-5500
• Algebra Readiness Puzzles 12
• Self-grading Lesson Quiz

PH SuccessNet Teacher Center
• Lesson Planner
• Resources

Plus

What You'll Learn

OBJECTIVE 1 To solve inequalities by adding or subtracting

. . . And Why

To determine how close you are to meeting a goal, as in Example 2

✓ Check Skills You'll Need

🔎 For help, go to Lesson 2-6.

Solve each equation.

1. $y + 4 = -5$ -9
2. $x + 6 = 9$ 3
3. $b - 18 = 35$ 53
4. $c - 5 = 16$ 21
5. $3 + m = 10$ 7
6. $-8 + c = 11$ 19

OBJECTIVE 1

 Interactive lesson includes instant self-check, tutorials, and activities.

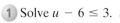 **Solving Inequalities by Adding or Subtracting**

To solve an inequality, use inverse operations to get the variable alone.

1 EXAMPLE Solving an Inequality by Adding

Solve $s - 7 < 3$.

$$s - 7 < 3$$
$$s - 7 + 7 < 3 + 7 \quad \leftarrow \text{Add 7 to each side to undo the subtraction.}$$
$$s < 10 \quad \leftarrow \text{Simplify.}$$

✓ **Check Understanding** ① Solve $u - 6 \le 3$. $u \le 9$

2 EXAMPLE Solving an Inequality by Subtracting 🌐 Real World

Real-World 🌐 Connection
Khalid Khannouchi set this world record for marathon running in 1999. He then beat it in 2002 with a time of 2.05.38.

Running Suppose a marathon runner plans to run at least 55 miles this week. He has already run 42 miles. Write and solve an inequality to find how many more miles he needs to run in order to meet his goal.

Words	miles run	+	miles to run	is at least	55 miles

Let m = the number of miles he still needs to run.

Inequality	42	+	m	$\ge$	55

$$42 + m \ge 55$$
$$42 + m - 42 \ge 55 - 42 \quad \leftarrow \text{Subtract 42 from each side.}$$
$$m \ge 13 \quad \leftarrow \text{Simplify.}$$

The marathon runner needs to run at least 13 more miles this week.

Ongoing Assessment and Intervention

Before the Lesson
Diagnose prerequisite skills using:
• Check Skills You'll Need

During the Lesson
Monitor progress using:
• Check Understanding
• Additional Examples
• Test Prep

After the Lesson
Assess knowledge using:
• Lesson Quiz
• Computer Test Generator CD
• Chapter Checkpoint 1 (p. 609)

✓ **Check Understanding** ② A restaurant can serve a maximum of 115 people. There are already 97 people dining in the restaurant. Write and solve an inequality to find how many more people the restaurant can serve. **Let p = the number of additional people the restaurant can serve; $p + 97 \leq 115$; $p \leq 18$; the restaurant can serve at most 18 more people.**

EXERCISES

🔍 For more practice, see *Extra Practice*.

Ⓐ **Practice by Example**

Solve each inequality.

Example 1
(page 606)

1. $x - 2 \geq 5$ $x \geq 7$ **2.** $z - 5 < 0$ $z < 5$ **3.** $k - 21 > 1$ $k > 22$

4. $j - 2 > -9$ $j > -7$ **5.** $n - 96 < -58$ $n < 38$ **6.** $s - 4 \leq 8$ $s \leq 12$

Example 2
(page 606)

7. $r + 5 \geq 7$ $r \geq 2$ **8.** $y + 12 \leq 11$ $y \leq -1$ **9.** $w + 2 > -7$
                                                                    $w > -9$

10. $14 + d \leq 24$ $d \leq 10$ **11.** $13 + f > 7$ $f > -6$ **12.** $5 + g \leq 62$ $g \leq 57$

🌐 **13. Banks** To avoid fees, you must have a minimum of $250 in your bank account. You currently have $143 in your account. Write and solve an inequality to find how much money you must deposit to avoid fees.
$d + 143 \geq 250$; $107

14. To get an A on a four-part test, Dana must score a minimum of 270 points. She scored 240 points on the first 3 parts of the test. What does she need to earn on the fourth part in order to receive an A?
$p + 240 \geq 270$; 30 points

Ⓑ **Apply Your Skills**

For Exercises 15–19, write an inequality for each sentence or problem. Then solve the inequality.

15. Nine is less than or equal to a number n added to seven. $9 \leq n + 7$; $n \geq 2$

16. The sum of a number x and 5 is greater than 25. $x + 5 > 25$; $x > 20$

17. The difference of a number a and 8 is less than 7. $a - 8 < 7$; $a < 15$

18. 12 is greater than or equal to a number c minus 10. $12 \geq c - 10$; $c \leq 22$

🌐 **19. Souvenirs** Suppose you have $15 to spend on souvenirs. You already bought the visor at the right. How much more money can you spend?
$7.01

20. **Writing in Math** Without computing, how can you tell that $3n > 3n$ has no solutions?
Answers may vary. Sample: No algebraic expression can be greater than itself.

👥 **Reaching All Students**

| **Below Level** Write inequalities like the following. Have students write the inverse operation on each side.

$t + 3 < 10$ $t + 3 - 3 < 10 - 3$
$x - 7 \leq 9$ $x - 7 + 7 \leq 9 + 7$ | **Advanced Learners** Find possible integer values for a and b in the inequality $n \div a \leq b$ that would yield a solution of $n \leq -8$. **Samples:**
$a = 1, b = -8$; $a = 2, b = -4$;
$a = 4, b = -2$; $a = 8, b = -1$ | **Inclusion**
See note on page 607.
Alternative Method
See note on page 607. |

---

2. Teach

Math Background

Solving an inequality involves the same basic goal as solving an equation: isolating the variable. You get the variable alone on one side of the equation by using inverse operations. Addition undoes subtraction and subtraction undoes addition.

Teaching Notes

① EXAMPLE **Alternative Method**

Some students better understand the process when it is shown vertically.

$$\begin{array}{rcl} s - 7 &<& 3 \\ + 7 &=& + 7 \\ \hline s &<& 10 \end{array}$$

A similar procedure can be used for Example 2.

② EXAMPLE **Inclusion**

Some students prefer to solve the related equation. First write the related equation.

$$42 + m \geq 55 \rightarrow 42 + m = 55$$

Then solve the related equation.

$$42 + m = 55$$
$$42 + m - 42 = 55 - 42$$
$$m = 13$$

Finally, substitute the inequality symbol for the equality.

$$m = 13 \rightarrow m \geq 13$$

Teaching Tip
Ask: *What does it mean if you at least 10 years old?* **Sample: You are 10 years old or older.**

🖥 **PowerPoint**

Additional Examples

① Solve $f - 4 \geq 8$. $f \geq 12$

② Missy wants to save at least $150 this month. She has saved $112 so far. Write and solve an inequality to find how much more money she would like to save this month.
$d + 112 \geq 150$; $d \geq $38

Closure

How do you solve a one-step inequality? **Sample: Use inverse operations to get the variable alone on one side of the inequality.**

607

3. Practice

Assignment Guide

1 **Objective 1**
Ⓐ Ⓑ Core 1–29
Ⓒ Extension 30–32

Test Prep 33–36

Mixed Review 37–42

Error Prevention!

Exercises 1–12 Students often copy the symbol incorrectly. Have them read each symbol aloud as they write it.

---

21. Flying Mary is flying her plane at an altitude lower than its upper safety limit of 32,000 feet. To avoid a storm, she rises 2,500 feet without going above 32,000 feet. Write an inequality, and then use the inequality to find the maximum original altitude of the plane.
$a + 2{,}500 \le 32{,}000$; 29,500 ft

Mental Math Solve each inequality.

22. $c + 9 < 15$ $c < 6$ **23.** $t - 6 > 24$ $t > 30$ **24.** $q + 8 \le 14$ $q \le 6$

25. $b - 3 > 12$ $b > 15$ **26.** $c - 2 \le 8$ $c \le 10$ **27.** $d + 4 \ge 12$ $d \ge 8$

28. Reasoning What number is a solution to $y + 2 \ge 10$ but not to $y + 2 > 10$? **8**

29. Budgeting Suppose you want to spend less than \$30 total to buy two T-shirts and a pair of shorts. The shorts cost \$13. Write and solve an inequality to find how much money you can spend on each T-shirt.
$2t + 13 < 30$; \$8.49

Ⓒ **Challenge**   **Solve each inequality.**

30. $3d > 36$ $d > 12$ **31.** $4p < 20$ $p < 5$

32. Stretch Your Thinking A jar balances with a bottle on a scale. The same jar also balances with a mug and a plate. Three of these plates balance with two bottles identical to the first bottle. How many mugs identical to the first mug will balance the jar? **3 mugs**

Test Prep

Multiple Choice

33. Which of the following operations would you use to get the variable in $x + 14 \le 23$ alone on one side of the inequality? **B**
   A. Add 14 to each side.   **B.** Subtract 14 from each side.
   C. Add 23 to each side.   **D.** Subtract 23 from each side.

34. What is the solution of $y - 6 \ge -3$? **G**
   F. $y > -9$ **G.** $y \ge 3$ **H.** $y \le -9$ **I.** $y \le 3$

35. What is the solution of $z + 3 > 4$? **C**
   A. $z > 7$ **B.** $z < 17$ **C.** $z > 1$ **D.** $z < 1$

Short Response

36. Fifteen is subtracted from a number. The result is greater than 8.
   a. Write an inequality to describe the situation.
   b. What is the smallest integer value that is a solution for the inequality? Explain. [2] a. $n - 15 > 8$
   b. $n - 15 + 15 > 8 + 15$; $n > 23$;
   Since n must be greater than 23, the smallest integer n can be is 24.
   [1] minor computational error OR correct answer with no work shown

Use the Guided Problem Solving worksheet with Exercise 29.

41.

Practice 12-3   Solving One-Step Inequalities

Solve each inequality.

1. $x - 5 < 15$	2. $m + 7 \ge 12$	3. $k + 5 < -10$	4. $15 + w \ge 4$
$x < 20$	$m \ge 5$	$k < -15$	$w \ge -11$
5. $g - (-4) \ge 0$	6. $-6 > b - 24$	7. $f - 6 < 12$	8. $d + 8 \ge 2$
$g \ge -4$	$b < 18$	$f < 18$	$d \ge -6$
9. $q + 9 < 60$	10. $h + (-1) > -1$	11. $42 + p \ge 7$	12. $-27 > a - 5$
$q < 51$	$h > 0$	$p \ge -35$	$a < -22$

Write an inequality for each sentence. Then solve the inequality.

13. Five is greater than a number minus 2. $5 > x - 2$; $x < 7$

14. Twenty is less than or equal to a number plus 4. $20 \le x + 4$; $x \ge 16$

15. A number minus 5 is greater than 25. $n - 5 > 25$; $n > 30$

16. A number plus 18 is less than or equal to 20. $n + 18 \le 20$; $n \le 2$

Write an inequality for each problem. Then solve the inequality.

17. You and the chess teacher have been playing chess for 18 minutes. To make the chess club, you must win the game in less than 45 minutes. How much time do you have to win the chess game?
$x + 18 < 45$; 27 more minutes

18. Your phone card allows you to talk long distance for up to 120 minutes. You have been on a long distance call for 72 minutes. How much longer do you have to talk before your phone card expires?
$x + 72 \le 120$; 48 more minutes

Solve each inequality mentally.

19. $9x < 108$	20. $s - 18 \ge 12$	21. $t + 5 < -15$
$x < 12$	$s \ge 30$	$t < -20$
22. $\frac{1}{6}g > 20$	23. $k + 4 \ge 25$	24. $24 > b + 16$
$g > 120$	$k \ge 100$	$b < 8$

Reteaching 12-3   Solving One-Step Inequalities

You can solve an inequality by using inverse operations to get the variable alone.

Example 1: Solve $x - 7 \le 2$. Then check the solution.

   $x - 7 \le 2$
   $x - 7 + 7 \le 2 + 7$ Add 7 to both sides.
   $x \le 9$

Check. Test a number greater than 9 and another number less than 9.

Try 11. $11 - 7 \le 2$ Try 5. $5 - 7 \le 2$
          $4 \le 2$ false $-2 \le 2$ true

Example 2: Solve $a + 15 > 10$. Then check the solution.

   $a + 15 > 10$
   $a + 15 - 15 > 10 - 15$ Subtract 15 from both sides.
   $a > -5$

Test a number greater than −5 and another number less than −5.

Try 0. $0 + 15 > 10$ Try −6. $-6 + 15 > 10$
          $15 > 10$ true $9 > 10$ false

Solve each inequality.

1. $x + 8 < 15$	2. $y + 2 > 8$
$x < 7$	$y > 6$
3. $a - 5 \ge -1$	4. $x - 10 \le -11$
$a \ge 4$	$x \le -1$
5. $y - 7 \ge 2$	6. $d - 18 \ge 2$
$y \ge 9$	$d \ge 20$
7. $13 + c \le 33$	8. $-12 + b \ge 4$
$c \le 20$	$b \ge 16$
9. $4 + w \ge 18$	10. $x + 15 < -9$
$w \ge 14$	$x < -24$

Lesson 11-4 **37.** A quiz consists of four true-false questions. Use a simulation to find the experimental probability of guessing correctly on every question. Use four coins to model this situation. Let heads represent true and tails represent false. **Check students' work.**

Lesson 9-7 **Name each figure.**

38.

pentagonal pyramid

39.

rectangular prism

40.

hexagonal prism

Lesson 8-9 **Copy each diagram on graph paper and draw its reflection of the shape over the given line of reflection.** **See margin.**

41.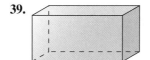

42.

Checkpoint Quiz 1 **Lessons 12-1 through 12-3**

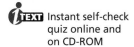 Instant self-check quiz online and on CD-ROM

Solve each equation.

1. $4t + 5 = 37$ **8** **2.** $\frac{r}{2} - 8 = -4$ **8** **3.** $5m - 8 = 57$ **13**

4. Tell whether each number is a solution to $x \le -5$.
a. -8 **yes** **b.** -4 **no** **c.** 3 **no** **d.** 7 **no**

Graph the solution to each inequality on a number line.

5. $c > -2$

6. $d \le 4$

7. $e < -4$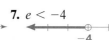

Solve each inequality.

8. $p + 8 < 3$ **$p < -5$** **9.** $n - 5 \ge 14$ **$n \ge 19$**

10. Miguel sells coupon books. He earns $30 a day plus $2 for each book sold. Miguel would like to make a minimum of $65 each day. How many coupon books must he sell per day to earn the minimum?
18 coupon books

12-3 Solving One-Step Inequalities **609**

42.

Alternative Assessment

Each student in a pair writes two one-step inequalities: one with addition and one with subtraction. Partners exchange papers and solve each other's inequalities.

PowerPoint **Lesson Quiz 12-3**

Solve each inequality.

1. $q - 5 \ge 8$ **$q \ge 13$**

2. $r + 10 < 4$ **$r < -6$**

3. $6 + x \le 21$ **$x \le 15$**

4. $m - 9 > 7$ **$m > 16$**

✔ **Chapter Checkpoint**

To check understanding of Lessons 12-1 to 12-3:

Checkpoint Quiz 1 (p. 609)

📁 **Teaching Resources**
Checkpoint Quiz 1 (also in Prentice Hall Assessment System)

👥 **Reaching All Students**
Reading and Math Literacy 12B

Spanish versions available

Test Prep

Resources
For additional practice with a variety of test item formats:
• Test-Prep, pp. 631–633
• Test-Taking Strategies, p. 627
• Test-Taking Strategies With Transparencies

Enrichment 12-3 Solving One-Step Inequalities

Patterns in Numbers

With any exercise program—losing weight, getting in shape, or training—you should be aware of your target heart rate. Target heart rates are recommended rates established by the medical community in order to maintain a healthy body.

• *Healthy Heart Zone* (Warm up): 50-60% of maximum heart rate: For warming up or for people just starting a fitness program.

• *Fitness Zone* (Fat Burning): 60-70% of maximum heart rate: This zone burns more total calories than the healthy heart zone.

• *Aerobic Zone* (Endurance Training): 70-80% of maximum heart rate: The aerobic zone will improve your cardiovascular and respiratory system. This is the recommended zone if you are training for an endurance event.

You can use the formula below to find the range for your target heart rate. Let a = age, h = heart rate, and t = target heart rate. Subtract your age from 220 to calculate your maximum heart rate.

(minimum zone%)(220 − a) ≤ t (maximum zone%)(220 − a) ≤ t

1. Complete the table to find the target heart rates for people at these ages for the healthy heart zone. Round your answer to the nearest whole number.

Age	Minimum Rate	Maximum Rate
12	50%(220 − 12) = 104	60%(220 − 12) = 125
18	101	121
24	98	118
30	95	114

2. Complete the table to find the target heart rates for people at these ages for the fitness zone. Round your answer to the nearest whole number.

Age	Minimum Rate	Maximum Rate
12	125	146
18	121	141
24	118	137
30	114	133

3. Complete the table to find the target heart rates for people at these ages for the aerobic zone. Round your answer to the nearest whole number.

Age	Minimum Rate	Maximum Rate
12	146	166
18	141	162
24	137	157
30	133	152

4. Describe any patterns you notice.
The target heart rate decreases as you age.

Making Sense of Inequalities

This page presents three forms in which inequalities can be expressed. That they can be expressed coherently in these different forms underscores the idea that reading mathematics presents unique challenges for students.

Teaching Notes

Visual Learners
Review the difference in meaning between open and closed circles in the graph of an inequality. Emphasize the importance of including the arrowhead in the graph to show that all points in the direction of that line satisfy the inequality.

Inclusion
When you review the inequality symbols, remind students that the pointed end is always directed at the lesser number and that the wider side is directed at the greater number.

Teaching Tip
When you review how inequalities can be expressed in paragraph form, guide students to look for words and groups of words that generally indicate inequality, such as "greater than," "less than," "at least as much as," and so on. Write these and other expressions students suggest on the board.

Exercises
As needed, alert students that each row has enough information for them to know what symbol to use, what graph to make, or what word problem to write. Circulate as students work, to check their efforts. Expect that some will need guidance translating into symbols and graphs the inequalities that appear in the word problems.

Reading Math

Making Sense of Inequalities

For Use With Lesson 12-3

Inequalities can be expressed in three forms.

- as a word problem
- as a graph
- with symbols

Word Problem	Symbols	Graph
Sam ran less than 10 miles last week. How many miles could Sam have run?	$m < 10$	←———⊕——→ 10
Jennifer has $28. She buys a shirt for $18. How much more can she spend without going over $28?	$m + 18 \leq 28$	←———●——→ 10
To win a contest, the band has to wash at least 50 cars. Students have already washed 30 cars. How many more cars must they wash to win the contest?	$c + 30 \geq 50$	←———●——→ 20

When you are working with inequalities, you can interchange the different forms shown above to help you understand and solve problems.

Sometimes, you will need to think of a situation that lends itself to a certain graph or set of symbols.

EXERCISES

Write entries that could appear in each row of the table below.

Answers may vary. Samples are given.

	Word Problem	Symbols	Graph
1.	Celia has $20 in her savings account. How much does she need to deposit to have more than $100 in the account?	? $m + 20 > 100$	? ←——⊕—→ 80
2.	A pair of jeans costs more than $15. How much could the jeans cost?	$j > 15$?	? ←—⊕——→ 15
3.	You can invite less than 10 people to a party. How many ? people can you invite?	$x < 10$	? ←——⊕—→ 10
4.	You want to exercise at least 30 minutes. How long ? can you exercise?	$e \geq 30$?	←—●——→ 30

Comparing Strategies

What You'll Learn

OBJECTIVE 1 To solve a problem using two different methods

. . . And Why

To compare strategies in problem solving, as in Example 1

 **Check Skills You'll Need**

For help, go to Lesson 2-7.

Solve each equation. Then check the solution.

1. $x \div 5 = 19$ **95**

2. $6y = 144$ **24**

3. $13b = 143$ **11**

4. $a \div 12 = 40$ **480**

5. $m \div 23 = 6$ **138**

6. $18p = 324$ **18**

Lesson Preview

 PowerPoint

Check Skills You'll Need

Solving Equations by Multiplying or Dividing
Lesson 2-7: Examples 1, 3. Extra Practice p. 643.

Lesson Resources

Teaching Resources
Practice, Reteaching, Enrichment

Reaching All Students
Practice Workbook 12-4
Spanish Practice Workbook 12-4
Guided Problem Solving 12-4

Presentation Assistant Plus!
Transparencies
• Check Skills You'll Need 12-4
• Problem of the Day 12-4
• Additional Examples 12-4
• Student Edition Answers 12-4
• Lesson Quiz 12-4
• Classroom Aid 2
PH Presentation Pro CD-ROM 12-4

ASSESSMENT SYSTEM

Computer Test Generator CD

Technology
Resource Pro® CD-ROM
Computer Test Generator CD
PH Presentation Pro CD-ROM

www.PHSchool.com
Student Site
• Teacher Web Code: aak-5500
• Algebra Readiness Puzzles 12, 113
• Self-grading Lesson Quiz

PH SuccessNet Teacher Center
• Lesson Planner
• Resources

Plus

 TEXT Interactive lesson includes instant self-check, tutorials, and activities.

OBJECTIVE

1 Solving a Problem Using Two Different Methods

When to Use These Strategies You can **draw a diagram** to help you visualize the information given in a problem. This may help you understand and solve a problem. To clarify your thinking and provide a model of a problem, you can **write an equation.**

You may use either of these strategies to solve the following problem.

1 EXAMPLE Using Two Different Methods

 Real World

Gardening A class is planning to plant a garden. The rectangular plot for the garden is 6 meters by 9 meters. The class wants to use 4 square meters of garden for each type of vegetable they plant. How many different vegetables can they plant?

Read and Understand The dimensions of the rectangular plot are 6 meters by 9 meters. Each vegetable will use 4 square meters of space. The goal is to find how many types of vegetables they can plant.

Plan and Solve

Real-World Connection

City land is sometimes available to neighborhoods for community gardening.

Method 1
Draw a diagram of the plot. Then divide the diagram into sections that are 4 square meters in size.

Thirteen sections of 4 square meters will fit in the plot. So, the class can plant 13 vegetables.

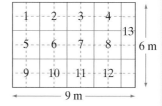

Ongoing Assessment and Intervention

Before the Lesson
Diagnose prerequisite skills using:
• Check Skills You'll Need

During the Lesson
Monitor progress using:
• Check Understanding
• Additional Examples
• Test Prep

After the Lesson
Assess knowledge using:
• Lesson Quiz
• Computer Test Generator CD

Math Background

Some students naturally favor one problem-solving strategy over another. You can compare the strategies of *draw a diagram* and *write an equation* by using them to solve the same problem. Such experiences help sharpen students' problem-solving skills.

Teaching Notes

1 EXAMPLE **English Learners**

Students may misinterpret information about square meters within a word problem and assume the shape must be a square. Point out that *square meters* is used to express an area.

Error Prevention!

Remind students that once they solve an equation, they still need to interpret their answer. For instance, in Method 2 the result is $v = 13.5$. But an answer of 13.5 vegetables would not make sense in the context of the problem.

Inclusion

Guide students in Check Understanding 1b to recognize that the equation $\ell + \ell + 14 = 54$ can be written as $2\ell + 14 = 54$.

PowerPoint

Additional Examples

1. Marcus is building a fenced rectangular enclosure for his turtles. He has 42 feet of fencing. Each short side will be 8 feet long. How long will each long side be? **13 feet**

Closure

- *How does drawing a diagram help you solve a problem?* Sample: Drawing a diagram makes relationships between key information visible.

- *How do you solve a problem by writing an equation?* Sample: Define the variable and write an expression that relates the known and unknown quantities; solve for the variable; check that the answer is reasonable.

612

Method 2
Write and solve an equation.

Words	space for each vegetable	times	number of vegetables	equals	space available in garden

Let v = the number of vegetables the class can plant.

Equation $\quad\quad 4 \quad\quad \cdot \quad\quad v \quad\quad = \quad\quad 54$

$$4v = 54$$

$$\frac{4v}{4} = \frac{54}{4} \quad \leftarrow \text{Divide each side by 4.}$$

$$v = 13.5 \quad \leftarrow \text{Simplify.}$$

Since $v = 13.5$, the rectangular plot can be divided into 13.5 sections of 4 square meters. The half section only represents 2 square meters. The class can plant 13 different vegetables in the garden.

Look Back and Check There are 13 sections in the plot, and each section is 4 square meters. The total area used by the vegetables is 13×4, or 52 square meters. Since 52 square meters is only 2 square meters less than the size of the garden, the answer checks.

✓ **Check Understanding** 1 **a. Reasoning** Look back at the two methods used to solve the example. Which method would you use? Why? **See margin.**

b. The length of a board is 54 inches. You cut the board into two pieces. One piece is 14 inches longer than the other. How long is each piece? **20 in., 34 in.**

EXERCISES

? For more practice, see *Extra Practice*.

A **Practice by Example**

Solve each problem by either drawing a diagram or writing an equation. Explain why you chose the method you did. **1–2. See margin.**

Example 1 (page 611)

1. Baking Tim is making granola bars. The top of each granola bar will be 2 inches by 3 inches. How many bars will he have if he bakes 3 batches, each in a 10-inch by 12-inch baking pan?

Need Help?
- Reread the problem.
- Identify the key facts and details.
- Tell the problem in your own words.
- Try a different strategy.
- Check your work.

 2. Carpet A rectangular carpet is three times as long as it is wide. If the carpet was 3 meters shorter and 3 meters wider, it would be square. What are the dimensions of the rectangular carpet?

3. Biking Suppose you bike along a 250-mile trail. You bike 40% of the distance the first day and 25% of the distance the second day. How many miles do you have to bike the third day to complete the trail? Explanations may vary. Sample: 87.5 mi; a diagram would have been difficult to draw accurately.

Reaching All Students

Below Level Review diagrams in a simpler context: Have students draw and label a 6-by-6 square. Students divide the square into 2-by-4 rectangles. How many rectangles fit? **4.5 rectangles**	**Advanced Learners** Write a problem and draw a diagram for $3x - 2 = 10$. Sample: On stilts Megan is 10 ft tall. She is 2 ft shorter than the sum of the height of her 3 equal-height friends. How tall is each friend?	**English Learners** See note on page 612. **Inclusion** See note on page 612.

B Apply Your Skills **Choose a strategy to solve each problem.**

3. Practice

Strategies

Draw a Diagram
Make a Graph
Make an Organized List
Make a Table and
   Look for a Pattern
Simulate a Problem
Solve a Simpler Problem
Try, Check, and Revise
Use Logical Reasoning
Work Backward
Write an Equation

4. A pizza costs $8.00. Each additional topping costs 75¢. If the total cost of the pizza is $11.75, how many additional toppings are on the pizza?
5 toppings

5. Trisha buys 30 calendars for $4 each. She then sells each calendar individually for a higher price. She earns $165 in profit from selling all the calendars. What did she charge for each calendar? **$9.50**

6. Skyscrapers The John Hancock Center in Chicago has twice as many floors as One Atlantic Center in Atlanta. The Sears Tower in Chicago has 110 floors, which is 40 floors less than the total number of floors in the other two skyscrapers. How many floors are in One Atlantic Center? **50 floors**

7. Dora and Kevin are making propellers for their model helicopters. Dora puts a number on her propeller. She notices that when she turns the propeller, she has the same number. Kevin would like to do the same thing to his propeller. What is the next greatest number that has this property?
6,009

8. Data File, p. 593 Your neighbors use a water heater, microwave oven, TV, VCR, and hair dryer. Suppose they use the hair dryer four times as much as the average household, but they use the TV only half as much. What is the average monthly energy use for your neighbor's home?
704 Kilowatt-hours

9. One set of holiday lights blinks every 5 seconds. A second set of holiday lights blinks every 8 seconds. Assume the lights blink together when you first turn them on. How many times in one minute do the two sets of lights blink together? **2 times**

10. The two sets of lights would blink together three times at 0; 24; and 48 s.

10. Writing in Math Refer to Exercise 9. Suppose the first set of lights blinks every 6 seconds. Explain how this would change the answer.
See left.

11. Yard Sale Suppose you purchase a soccer ball at a yard sale for $2. You then sell the ball to a friend for $2.50. You buy the ball back for $2.75 and then sell the ball for $3.25. How much money do you make?
$1.00

12-4 Comparing Strategies **613**

Assignment Guide

1 **Objective 1**
   Ⓐ Ⓑ Core 1–11
   Ⓒ Extension 12–13

Test Prep 14–18
Mixed Review 19–27

Auditory Learners
Exercises 1–3 Have volunteers read problems aloud to allow students to picture the scene as they listen. The students can then reread the problems on their own for details.

Practice 12-4 — Problem Solving: Comparing Strategies

Solve each problem by either drawing a diagram or writing an equation. Explain why you chose the method you did.

1. Derrick is thinking of a negative integer. When he multiplies the integer by itself and then adds three times the integer to the product, he gets 180. What is Derrick's integer?
   −15

2. During a pancake making contest, Team A made 8 more pancakes than Team B. Team C made twice as many pancakes as Team B. Together, the three teams made a total of 72 pancakes. How many pancakes did Team A make?
   24

3. The area of a rectangle is 18 square inches. How many rectangles whose sides are measured in whole numbers can be drawn having this area?
   1 by 18; 2 by 9; 3 by 6; 3

Choose a strategy to solve each problem.

4. Howard plans to drive from Seattle, Washington, to Portland, Oregon, a road distance of 172 miles. He needs to be in Portland by 11:45 A.M. If he drives at a rate of 60 miles per hour, what is the latest time he can leave Seattle?
   8:53 A.M.

5. Heather and Denise are running laps. They start together at the same starting point. Heather completes a lap every 120 seconds, and Denise completes a lap every 96 seconds. In how many seconds will they again meet at the starting point?
   after 480 seconds

6. A triangle has angles D, E, and F. The complement of ∠D is 42°, and the supplement of ∠E is 54°. What is the measure of ∠F?
   6°

7. Ernesto, Michelina, and Kale volunteer at the zoo. Ernesto works every 5 days, Michelina works every 6 days, Kale works every 15 days. They work together today. How many days will it be until the next time they work together?
   30 days

8. Cassie is lining up 45 students in the chorus. She wants each row to have the same number of students. She also wants the number of students in each row to be a prime number. What are her options?
   15 rows of 3 students or 9 rows of 5 students

Reteaching 12-4 — Problem Solving: Comparing Strategies

You can sometimes draw a diagram or write an equation to solve a problem.

Example Kristin staked out a rectangular garden that has one side measuring 6 ft. If the area of the garden is 48 ft, what are the dimensions of the garden?

Read and Understand

The area of a rectangular garden is 48 ft². One side is 6 ft long.

Plan and Solve

Method 1: Draw a diagram.

Draw a row of 6 equal squares to represent one side of the garden.

Add rows to the diagram until you have 48 total squares.

The rectangle is 6 squares long and 8 squares wide, so the garden is 6 ft × 8 ft.

Method 2: Write and solve an equation.

Use the formula for the area of a rectangle.

$l \cdot w = A$
$6 \cdot w = 48$
$w = 8$

The garden is 6 ft × 8 ft.

Look Back and Check

The length times the width of the garden must equal the area of the garden.

$6 \cdot 8 \stackrel{?}{=} 48$
$48 = 48$ The answer checks.

Choose a strategy and solve each problem.

1. Carlos is packing mugs in a box with a bottom that is 56 centimeters by 72 centimeters. In order to prevent his mugs from breaking, Carlos needs a square with area 64 centimeters² for each mug. Assuming he doesn't stack the mugs, how many mugs can he fit in the box?
   63 mugs

2. Agatha is hiking along a 150-mile trail. She hikes 10% of the trail the first day and 15% of the trail the second day. How many miles of the trail are left?
   112.5 miles

3. Beth uses one-foot wide square tiles to cover a rectangular area. The rectangle has 16 tiles on one side, and she uses 192 tiles to cover the area. What are the dimensions of the rectangle?
   16 ft × 12 ft

4. Todd is stacking boxes against a wall that is 12 m high. If he has stacked 3 boxes and the pile reaches halfway to the ceiling, what is the height of each box?
   2 m

Check Understanding

1a. Answers may vary. Sample: I would use Method 2, because I have to spend less time thinking about possible sizes and shapes for the small sections for each vegetable.

Exercises

1–2. Explanations may vary. Samples are given:

1. 60 bars; drawing a diagram helps you decide how to fit the bars in the pan.

 GPS Use the Guided Problem Solving worksheet with Exercise 6.

2. 3 m by 9 m; 3x − 3 = x + 3 so x = 3, a diagram would have been difficult to draw accurately.

1. Hector is cutting small cards from construction paper. Each sheet of construction paper is 12 in. wide and 14 in. long. Each card is 2 in. by 3 in. At most, how many cards can he cut from 2 sheets of construction paper? **56 cards**

Alternative Assessment

Each student in a pair writes a problem that can be solved by either drawing a diagram or writing an equation. Then partners exchange problems and solve each other's problem.

Test Prep

For additional practice with a variety of test item formats:
• Test-Prep, pp. 631–633
• Test-Taking Strategies, p. 627
• Test-Taking Strategies With Transparencies

Enrichment 12-4   Comparing Strategies
Problem Solving

The perimeter of a rectangular bookstore is 220 feet and its length is 50 feet. What is the annual rent for the bookstore if the rent is $20 per square foot each year? Explain.

1. Circle the perimeter, length, and annual rent of the bookstore.

2. The rent is per square foot. How do you find the number of square feet in a rectangular figure?
Find length × width.

3. You are given the length of one side of the bookstore. What is the length of the opposite side of the bookstore?
50 feet

4. Given the perimeter, how can you use the length of two opposite sides to find the width of the other two sides in a rectangle?
Subtract twice the length from the perimeter.
Divide the difference by 2.

5. What is the width of the bookstore?
60 feet

6. What operation will you use to find the annual rent?
multiplication

7. Write a number sentence to find the number of square feet.
50 × 60 = 3,000

8. Find the annual rent for the bookstore.
$60,000

9. Explain why it was necessary to follow the steps above to find the width of the store, its area, and its rent.

10. Explain how drawing a diagram helps solve this problem.
Sample answer: It is easier to visualize the dimensions.

11. The perimeter of a rectangular bookstore is 180 feet, and its length is 50 feet. What is the annual rent for the bookstore if the rent is $25 per square foot each year? Explain.
Width is 40 feet, area is 2,000 feet²;
2,000 × 25 = $50,000.

C Challenge **12. Packaging** A book publisher ships its books packed in boxes. Each box is 12 inches long, 9 inches wide, and 8 inches high. If each book is 9 inches long, $7\frac{1}{4}$ inches wide, and $\frac{1}{2}$ inch thick, what is the maximum number of books the publisher can pack into each box? **25 books**

13. **Stretch Your Thinking** An unknown number is divisible by 23 and 3. The two-digit number in the thousands and hundreds place is one less than the two-digit number in the tens and ones place. The unknown number is greater than 2,000, but less than 4,000. What is the unknown number?
2,829

Test Prep

Multiple Choice

14. Which is a solution for $x \geq 7$? **D**
   A. −1   **B.** 5   **C.** 6   **D.** 7

15. The solution to which sentence is graphed at the right? **H**

$$\begin{array}{c} \leftarrow\!+\!+\!+\!+\!\bullet\!+\!+\!+\!\rightarrow \\ -4 \ -3 \ -2 \ -1 \ \ 0 \ \ 1 \ \ 2 \end{array}$$

   F. $x > -1$ **G.** $x < -1$ **H.** $x \geq -1$ **I.** $x \leq -1$

16. What is the solution of $6x + 9 = 81$? **A**
   A. 12   **B.** 13.5   **C.** 66   **D.** 72

17. What is the solution of $3x + 26 = -34$? **F**
   F. −20   **G.** $-2\frac{2}{3}$ **H.** $2\frac{2}{3}$ **I.** 20

Take It to the NET
Online lesson quiz at
www.PHSchool.com
Web Code: aaa-1204

Short Response

18. Chuck buys 6 herbs. He also buys a planting pot for $7. The total cost of the herbs and pot is $14.50. **See margin.**
   a. Write an equation to determine how much each herb costs.
   b. Solve your equation.

Mixed Review

Lesson 11-3   **The probability of winning a game is 60%. How many times should you expect to win if you play each of the following number of times?**

19. 5 times 3   20. 20 times 12   21. 75 times 45   22. 150 times 90

Lesson 9-6   **Find the area of each circle to the nearest tenth. Use 3.14 for π.**

23. $r = 2$ in.   24. $d = 4$ ft   25. $r = 6$ m   26. $d = 15$ km
   12.6 in.²   12.6 ft²   113.0 m²   176.6 km²

Lesson 9-2   27. **Cars** A car is travelling at 40 kilometers per hour. How many meters per hour is this? **40,000 meters per hour**

614   **Chapter 12**   Equations and Inequalities

18. [2] a. $6h + 7 = 14.5$
   b. $6h + 7 - 7 = 14.5 - 7$
     $6h = 7.5$
     $\frac{6h}{6} = \frac{7.5}{6}$
     $h = 1.25$

[1] minor computational error OR no work shown

2a. Answers may vary.
Sample: The numbers in both columns increase from top to bottom. Each number in the left column is the square of the corresponding number in the right column.

Investigation

Exploring Squares

For Use With Lesson 12-5

You will need a geoboard and rubber bands.

Look at the geoboard at the right. Each side of the square is 1 unit long. The area is 1 square unit.

Activity

1a. Check students' work.

1. **a.** Use your geoboard to make squares with areas of 4, 9, and 16 square units.
   b. Copy the table at the right. Enter the length of a side for each square you made in part (a).

Area of Square (units²)	Length of Side (units)
1	1
4	2
9	3
16	4

2. **a.** Look at your table. What pattern(s) do you notice?
   b. Continue the table for squares with areas of 25, 36, and 49 square units.
   2a–b. Answers may vary. See margin for sample.

3. Make the figure shown at the right using your geoboard. The figure is a square with an area of 2 square units.
   a. Use your table to estimate the length of a side of this square. **See margin.**
   b. Recall that the formula for the area of a square is $A = s^2$. Use a calculator and the *Try, Check, and Revise* strategy. To the nearest hundredth, find the length of a side of a square with an area of 2 square units. **1.41 units**

4. **a.** Use your calculator and the *Try, Check, and Revise* strategy. To the nearest hundredth, find the length of a side of a square with an area of 8 square units. **2.83 units**
   b. How does the side length you found in Step 3(b) compare with your answer to Step 4(a)? **about half as much**

5. Use your geoboard to make a square with an area of 8 square units.
   Check students' work.

6. **Stretch Your Thinking** Use your geoboard to make a square with an area of 5 square units. **Check students' work.**

Investigation   Exploring Squares   **615**

b.

Area of Square (sq units)	Length of Side (units)
25	5
36	6
49	7

3a. Answers may vary.
Sample: $1\frac{1}{2}$ units;
I knew the length had to be more than 1 but less than 2.

Investigation

Exploring Squares

In this activity, students use a geoboard to model squares with different areas in order to investigate patterns involving the areas of squares and the lengths of their sides.

Optional Materials

- geoboard
- rubber bands
- calculator
- Classroom Aid 6, 11

Resources

Student Manipulatives Kit

Teaching Notes

Teaching Tip
Have students examine the numbers in the first column. Ask:
- *What can you say about each of these numbers?* **Each is a square number.**
- *If you continue the pattern, what are the next three numbers?* **25, 36, 49**

Have students work in pairs to form the different squares. As needed, discuss that the squares they make may appear in a different orientation than what they customarily see in texts. Circulate as partners make the different-size squares. Invite pairs to share their results and conclusions with others.

Technology Tip
Ask a volunteer to explain the calculator steps he or she used in Question 3b to find the length of a side of a square with an area of 2 square units.

Alternative Method
Instead of using geoboards, students can construct the squares on graph paper or dot paper. If they do, guide them to use a straightedge to make the drawings.

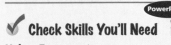

1. Plan

Lesson Preview

PowerPoint

Using Exponents
Lesson 2-8: Example 1. Extra
Practice p. 643.

Lesson Resources

📁 **Teaching Resources**
Practice, Reteaching, Enrichment
Checkpoint Quiz 2

👥 **Reaching All Students**
Practice Workbook 12-5
Spanish Practice Workbook 12-5
Reading and Math Literacy 12C
Spanish Reading and Math
  Literacy 12C
Spanish Checkpoint Quiz 2
Guided Problem Solving 12-5

⏰ **Presentation Assistant Plus!**
Transparencies
• Check Skills You'll Need 12-5
• Problem of the Day 12-5
• Additional Examples 12-5
• Student Edition Answers 12-5
• Lesson Quiz 12-5
• Classroom Aid 6, 11
PH Presentation Pro CD-ROM 12-5

PRENTICE HALL
ASSESSMENT SYSTEM

Checkpoint Quiz 2
Computer Test Generator CD

💻 **Technology**
Resource Pro® CD-ROM
Computer Test Generator CD
PH Presentation Pro CD-ROM

💻 **www.PHSchool.com**
Student Site
• Teacher Web Code: aak-5500
• Self-grading Lesson Quiz

PH SuccessNet Teacher Center
• Lesson Planner
• Resources

Plus 🅸TEXT

616

12-5 Exploring Square Roots and Rational Numbers

What You'll Learn

OBJECTIVE 1 To find square roots

OBJECTIVE 2 To classify numbers as rational

. . . And Why

To find the dimensions of a square, as in Example 3

✔ **Check Skills You'll Need**   🔍 For help, go to Lesson 2-8.

Write each expression using an exponent. Name the base and the exponent.

1. 5×5 5^2; 5, 2
2. $6 \times 6 \times 6$ 6^3; 6, 3
3. $4 \times 4 \times 4 \times 4 \times 4$ 4^5; 4, 5
4. $999 \times 999 \times 999$ 999^3; 999, 3
5. 72 72^1; 72, 1
6. 3.6×3.6 3.6^2; 3.6, 2

New Vocabulary
• square root • perfect square • rational number

OBJECTIVE 1

🅸TEXT Interactive lesson includes instant self-check, tutorials, and activities.

Finding Square Roots

📖 **Reading Math**
The expression $\sqrt{9}$ is read "the square root of 9."

The *square* of 3 is 3^2, or 9. The inverse of squaring is finding the square root. A **square root** of a given number is a number that, when multiplied by itself, is the given number. The square root of 9 is 3. In symbols, $\sqrt{9} = 3$. You will only find positive square roots in this course.

$3 \times 3 = 9$

① EXAMPLE Finding Square Roots

a. Find $\sqrt{64}$.
Since $8 \times 8 = 64$, $\sqrt{64} = 8$.

b. Find $\sqrt{49}$.
Since $7 \times 7 = 49$, $\sqrt{49} = 7$.

✔ **Check Understanding** ① Find each square root.   **a.** $\sqrt{4}$ 2   **b.** $\sqrt{100}$ 10

A **perfect square** is the square of a whole number. The number 64 is a perfect square because $64 = 8^2$. When finding the square root of a number that isn't a perfect square, you can use a calculator.

② EXAMPLE Using a Calculator to Find a Square Root

Calculator Find $\sqrt{50}$ to the nearest tenth.

$\sqrt{50} \approx 7.071067812$ ← On a calculator, press [2nd] [x²] 50 [=].

≈ 7.1 ← Round to the nearest tenth.

✔ **Check Understanding** ② Find each square root to the nearest tenth.
a. $\sqrt{7}$ 2.6   **b.** $\sqrt{10}$ 3.2   **c.** $\sqrt{24}$ 4.9   **d.** $\sqrt{86}$ 9.3

✔ **Ongoing Assessment and Intervention**

Before the Lesson	**During the Lesson**	**After the Lesson**
Diagnose prerequisite skills using:	Monitor progress using:	Assess knowledge using:
• Check Skills You'll Need	• Check Understanding • Additional Examples • Test Prep	• Lesson Quiz • Computer Test Generator CD • Chapter Checkpoint 2 (p. 620)

③ EXAMPLE Real-World  Problem Solving

Board Games The square board has an area of 121 square inches. How long is each side of the game board?

The area of a square is found by squaring a side. So, find the square root of 121. Look for a number that is equal to 121 when it is squared.

Since $11^2 = 121$, $\sqrt{121} = 11$.

○ Each side of the game board is 11 inches long.

✓**Check Understanding** ③ How long is each side of a game board with an area of 81 square inches? **9 in.**

You can also estimate square roots of numbers that are not perfect squares. For example, notice that $\sqrt{3}$ is between $\sqrt{1}$ and $\sqrt{4}$.

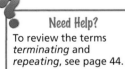

Thus, $\sqrt{3}$ is between 1 and 2.

④ EXAMPLE Approximating a Square Root

4a. Answers may vary. Sample: Closer to 2; $2^2 = 4$ and $3^2 = 9$; 5 is closer to 4 than to 9, so the square root of 5 is closer to 2 than to 3.

Tell which two consecutive whole numbers $\sqrt{5}$ is between.

$4 < 5 < 9$ ← Find the perfect squares close to 5.

$\sqrt{4} < \sqrt{5} < \sqrt{9}$ ← Write the square roots in order.

$2 < \sqrt{5} < 3$ ← Simplify.

○ $\sqrt{5}$ is between 2 and 3.

✓**Check Understanding** ④ **a. Number Sense** Is $\sqrt{5}$ closer to 2 or to 3? Explain. **See above left.**
b. Tell which two consecutive numbers $\sqrt{8}$ is between. **between 2 and 3**

OBJECTIVE

2 Classifying Numbers as Rational

Need Help?
To review the terms *terminating* and *repeating*, see page 44.

A **rational number** is any number that can be written as a quotient of two integers, where the denominator is not 0. You can write any integer as a quotient with a denominator of 1, so all integers are rational numbers. Examples of rational numbers are $2\left(\text{or } \frac{2}{1}\right), \frac{4}{5}, 0.38\left(\text{or } \frac{38}{100}\right), -8\left(\text{or } \frac{-8}{1}\right)$.

Rational numbers in decimal form either terminate or repeat.

12-5 Exploring Square Roots and Rational Numbers   **617**

👥 Reaching All Students

Below Level Below Level Have students copy and continue this pattern to find the perfect squares from 1 to 100: 1, 4, 9, . . . , 100.
$1 \times 1 = 1$ $\sqrt{1} = 1$ $2 \times 2 = 4$ $\sqrt{4} = 2$
$3 \times 3 = 9$ $\sqrt{9} = 3$ $4 \times 4 = 16$ $\sqrt{16} = 4$

Advanced Learners Solve each mystery digit problem.
$\sqrt{AB} = B$ A = 2, B = 5 or A = 3, B = 6
$\sqrt{ZZY} = XY$ Z = 2, Y = 5, X = 1 or Z = 4, Y = 1, X = 2

Inclusion
See note on page 617.
Alternative Method
See note on page 617.

2. Teach

Professional Development

Math Background

The *square* of a number is the number multiplied by itself, such as $3 \cdot 3$, or 3^2, which is 9. A *square root* is a number that when multiplied by itself is equal to the given number. For example, the square root of 144, or $\sqrt{144}$, is 12 because $12 \cdot 12 = 144$. A *perfect square* is the square of a whole number. So, square roots of perfect squares are also whole numbers.

A *rational number* can be expressed as a ratio of two integers $\frac{a}{b}$ where *b* is nonzero. A rational number can also be expressed as a terminating or a repeating decimal such as 2.5 or $2.\overline{3}$ or 2.333333 . . . . One can approximate or use a calculator to find square roots for numbers that are not perfect squares, such as $\sqrt{15}$. Such numbers are called *irrational* because they neither terminate nor repeat when written as a decimal.

Teaching Notes

② EXAMPLE Error Prevention

Make sure students round correctly in Check Understanding 2a–d. To round to the nearest tenth, students must examine the number in the hundredths' place.

Inclusion
Have students find the square of 7.1. $7.1^2 = 50.41$ This helps to show them why the answer to Example 2 is written with the approximately equal sign. So, $\sqrt{50} \approx 7.1$, and *not* $\sqrt{50} = 7.1$.

④ EXAMPLE Alternative Method

In Check Understanding 4, choose a number that is not a perfect square, such as 45. Tell students to ask themselves these questions: *What perfect squares are closest to this number?* **36 and 49** *What are their square roots?* **6 and 7** Rewrite the numbers with a square root symbol in numerical order: $\sqrt{36}$ $\sqrt{45}$ $\sqrt{49}$. Point out that on a number line 45 is closer to 49 than it is to 36. Thus, $\sqrt{45}$ is between 6 and 7, but closer to 7; 6.7 is a good approximation.

617

 EXAMPLE Teaching Tip

In Check Understanding 6a–d, have students check their answers by using a calculator.

Number Sense

In addition to the basic squares from 1–10, help students recognize these square roots:

$\sqrt{121} = 11$ $\sqrt{144} = 12$
$\sqrt{169} = 13$ $\sqrt{196} = 14$
$\sqrt{225} = 15$ $\sqrt{256} = 16$

PowerPoint

Additional Examples

1. Find $\sqrt{25}$. **5**

2. Use a calculator to find $\sqrt{20}$ to the nearest tenth. **4.5**

3. A store is advertising its new square beach towels with an area of 64 square feet each. How long is each side of the towel? **8 feet**

4. Tell which two consecutive whole numbers $\sqrt{90}$ is between. **9 and 10**

5. Tell whether each number is rational.
   a. 1.5 **rational**
   b. $\frac{3}{4}$ **rational**
   c. 1.42443444 . . . **not rational**

6. Tell whether each number is rational.
   a. $\sqrt{8}$ **not rational**
   b. $\sqrt{169}$ **rational**
   c. $\sqrt{900}$ **rational**

Closure

- *What is a square root? Give an example.* Sample: A number that, when multiplied by itself, is equal to the given number. $\sqrt{9}$ is 3.

- *How can you tell if a number is a rational number?* Sample: A rational number can be expressed as a decimal that terminates or has a repeating pattern. The square root of a number is rational if the number is a perfect square.

---

5 EXAMPLE   Identifying Rational Numbers

Tell whether each number is rational.

a. 6.7   6.7 is a terminating decimal. It is rational.

b. $8.\overline{9}$ $8.\overline{9}$ is a repeating decimal. It is rational.

c. $\frac{1}{5}$ $\frac{1}{5}$ is a quotient of integers. It is rational.

d. 3.262272228 . . .   This decimal does not repeat or terminate. It is not rational.

e. −10   −10 is an integer. It is rational.

✔ **Check Understanding** 5 Tell whether each number is rational.

a. 0.232323   b. $\frac{3}{8}$ c. 1.112111211112 . . .
    rational   rational   not rational

The square root of a whole number is rational only when the whole number is a perfect square.

6 EXAMPLE   Classifying Square Roots of Whole Numbers

Tell whether each number is rational.

a. $\sqrt{16}$ 16 is a perfect square. $\sqrt{16}$ is rational.

b. $\sqrt{26}$ $\sqrt{26}$ is between 5 and 6. $\sqrt{26}$ is not rational.

✔ **Check Understanding** 6 Tell whether each number is rational.

a. $\sqrt{7}$ b. $\sqrt{36}$ c. $\sqrt{53}$ d. $\sqrt{121}$
not rational   rational   not rational   rational

EXERCISES

? For more practice, see *Extra Practice*.

A Practice by Example   **Find each square root.**

Example 1 (page 616)

1. $\sqrt{1}$ 1   2. $\sqrt{25}$ 5   3. $\sqrt{81}$ 9   4. $\sqrt{9}$ 3

5. $\sqrt{16}$ 4   6. $\sqrt{36}$ 6   7. $\sqrt{100}$ 10   8. $\sqrt{144}$ 12

Example 2 (page 616)

Calculator   **Find each square root to the nearest tenth.**

9. $\sqrt{21}$ 4.6   10. $\sqrt{33}$ 5.7   11. $\sqrt{50}$ 7.1   12. $\sqrt{75}$ 8.7

618   Chapter 12   Equations and Inequalities

39. Yes; no; explanations may vary. Sample: Since $\sqrt{1} = 1$, $\sqrt{2}$ must be greater than 1. Since $\sqrt{4} = 2$, $\sqrt{2}$ must be less than 2.

Example 3
(page 617)

13. Patios A square patio has an area of 169 square feet. How long is each side of the patio? **13 ft**

14. Quilts The area of a quilt is 36 square feet. How long is each side? **6 ft**

Example 4
(page 617)

Tell which two consecutive whole numbers the square root is between.

15. $\sqrt{2}$ 1, 2   **16.** $\sqrt{6}$ 2, 3   **17.** $\sqrt{28}$ 5, 6   **18.** $\sqrt{18}$ 4, 5

19. $\sqrt{23}$ 4, 5   **20.** $\sqrt{73}$ 8, 9   **21.** $\sqrt{90}$ 9, 10   **22.** $\sqrt{55}$ 7, 8

Examples 5, 6
(page 618)

Tell whether each number is rational.

23. $6.\overline{8}$ rational   **24.** $\frac{9}{11}$ rational   **25.** $0.10010001\ldots$ not rational   **26.** $-2\frac{1}{2}$ rational

29. rational

27. $\frac{7}{9}$ rational   **28.** 15 rational   **29.** 6.2319743   **30.** $3\frac{1}{3}$ rational

34. not rational

31. $\sqrt{4}$ rational   **32.** $\sqrt{9}$ rational   **33.** $\sqrt{49}$ rational   **34.** $\sqrt{18}$

35. $\sqrt{1}$ rational   **36.** $\sqrt{11}$ not rational   **37.** $\sqrt{42}$ not rational   **38.** $\sqrt{100}$ rational

B **Apply Your Skills**

Real-World **Connection**

The Great Pyramid at Giza is the largest Egyptian pyramid.

39. Reasoning Is $\sqrt{2}$ greater than 1? Is $\sqrt{2}$ greater than 2? Explain. **See margin.**

40. Egyptian Pyramids The area of the square base of the Great Pyramid at Giza is 52,900 square meters. What is the length of each side of the square base of the pyramid? **230 m**

Estimation Estimate to the nearest whole number.

41. $\sqrt{6}$ 2   **42.** $\sqrt{7}$ 3   **43.** $\sqrt{11}$ 3   **44.** $\sqrt{26}$ 5   **45.** $\sqrt{58}$ 8

46. Calculator Use a calculator to evaluate each expression: $\sqrt{27}$, $\sqrt{9} \times \sqrt{3}$, and $3 \times \sqrt{3}$. What do you notice? **See margin.**

47. Writing in Math Find two consecutive whole numbers that have $\sqrt{29}$ between them. Explain how you chose the numbers.
Answers may vary. See margin for sample.

C **Challenge**

48. Number Sense Find two perfect squares that have a sum of 100. **36 and 64**

49. Simplify each expression.
   a. $(\sqrt{2})^2$ 2   **b.** $(\sqrt{3})^2$ 3   **c.** $(\sqrt{8})^2$ 8   **d.** $(\sqrt{16})^2$ 16
   e. Number Sense What do you get when you square the square root of a number? **You get the original number.**

50. Stretch Your Thinking Arrange the digits 1 through 9 in the bubbles in the triangle so the sum of the numbers along each side is 17. **See left.**

50.
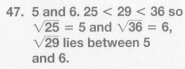

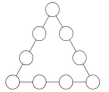

12-5 Exploring Square Roots and Rational Numbers **619**

46. The expressions are all equal.

47. 5 and 6. 25 < 29 < 36 so $\sqrt{25}$ = 5 and $\sqrt{36}$ = 6, $\sqrt{29}$ lies between 5 and 6.

 GPS Use the Guided Problem Solving worksheet with Exercise 40.

4. Assess

PowerPoint Lesson Quiz 12-5

Find each square root.

1. $\sqrt{49}$ 7   **2.** $\sqrt{81}$ 9

3. Tell which two consecutive whole numbers $\sqrt{14}$ is between. 3 and 4

Tell whether each number is rational.

4. $\sqrt{27}$ not rational

5. $3.\overline{45}$ rational

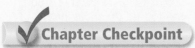

Chapter Checkpoint

To check understanding of Lessons 12-4 to 12-5:

Checkpoint Quiz 2 (p. 620)

📁 **Teaching Resources**
Checkpoint Quiz 2 (also in Prentice Hall Assessment System)

👥 **Reaching All Students**
Reading and Math Literacy 12C

Spanish versions available

Test Prep

Multiple Choice

51. What is $\sqrt{196}$? C
A. 12   **B.** 13   **C.** 14   **D.** 15

52. Between which consecutive whole numbers does $\sqrt{290}$ lie? H
F. 7 and 8   **G.** 8 and 9   **H.** 17 and 18   **I.** 18 and 19

💻 **Take It to the NET**
Online lesson quiz at
www.PHSchool.com
Web Code: aaa-1205

53. A square afghan has an area of 3,600 square inches. How long is each side of the afghan? B
A. 6 inches   **B.** 5 feet
C. 60 square inches   **D.** 50 feet

Short Response

54. The ceiling of a square room has an area of 256 square feet. What is the perimeter of the room? Justify your answer. See margin.

Mixed Review

Lesson 11-6   **Find the number of possible permutations of each set of items.**

55. the numbers 5, 6, and 7 6   **56.** the letters R, E, A, D 24

Lesson 9-10   **Work backward to solve each problem.**

57. If you multiply a number by 9, and then subtract 16, the result is 56. What is the number? 8

58. Kayla gives Mike one-third of her pretzels. Mike gives Ronnie half of the pretzels he received from Kayla. Ronnie keeps 6 of the pretzels and gives 12 to Jeff. How many pretzels did Kayla give Mike? 36 pretzels

---

Checkpoint Quiz 2   Lessons 12-4 through 12-5

ITEXT Instant self-check quiz online and on CD-ROM

1. A ribbon is 29 inches long. You cut the ribbon into two pieces so that one piece is 7.8 inches longer than the other. How long is each piece? Solve by either drawing a diagram or writing an equation. Explain why you chose the method you did. 10.6 in. and 18.4 in.; explanations may vary. Sample: I drew a diagram so I could see what it looked like.

Find each square root.

2. $\sqrt{121}$ 11   **3.** $\sqrt{36}$ 6

Tell whether each number is rational.

4. $\frac{1}{12}$ rational   **5.** $\sqrt{169}$ rational

Alternative Assessment

Students work in pairs to make a table of the perfect squares for 1–100. Partners turn their table facedown. They then take turns naming the two consecutive whole numbers that each square root in Exercises 15–22 comes between. Partners must agree on responses. They can use their table to check responses.

Test Prep

Resources
For additional practice with a variety of test item formats:
• Test-Prep, pp. 631–633
• Test-Taking Strategies, p. 627
• Test-Taking Strategies With Transparencies

Exploring Right Triangles

For Use With Lesson 12-6

Investigation

Exploring Right Triangles

Recall that a right triangle is a triangle with a right angle.

Activity

Step 1 Use centimeter grid paper to draw a right triangle. The right angle should be included between sides that are 3 centimeters and 4 centimeters long.

Step 2 Draw a 3-by-3 square along the side that is 3 centimeters long. Label the square A. Draw a 4-by-4 square along the side that is 4 centimeters long. Label the square B.

Step 3 Use another piece of the grid paper to make a square on the side opposite the right angle. Label the square C.

Step 1	Step 2	Step 3
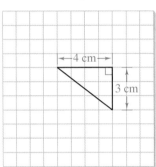	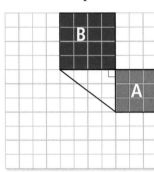	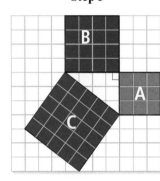

In this activity, students explore the relationship between the lengths of the sides of a right triangle. They investigate the areas of squares formed from the legs and the hypotenuse of the triangle. Working through this feature prepares students for exploring and using the Pythagorean Theorem in Lesson 12-6.

Materials

- centimeter grid paper
- straightedge
- scissors

Teaching Notes

Teaching Tip
Elicit from students the characteristics that a right triangle shares with all triangles, **3 sides, 3 angles that equal 180°** and the way in which it differs from them. **one 90° angle** Review the meanings of *leg* and *hypotenuse*.

Have students work in pairs to make the drawings. Circulate to check students' work.

Exercise 2 Ask: *How can you use the drawings you have made to physically show the relationship between the areas of the two smaller squares and that of the third square?* **Sample: Trace and cut out the squares to show that the combined areas of the two smaller squares will equal (cover exactly) the area of the largest one. Make additional cuts, as needed, to show this relationship.**

EXERCISES

1. Repeat the activity for the triangles shown in the table below. Copy and complete the table.

Sides of Triangle	Area of Square A	Area of Square B	Area of Square C
3, 4, 5	9	16	25
5, 12, ■13	■ 25	■ 144	■ 169
6, 8, ■10	■ 36	■ 64	■ 100
9, 12, ■15	■ 81	■ 144	■ 225

2. **Reasoning** Look at your table. What is the relationship between the areas of the two smaller squares (A and B) and the area of the largest square (C)? **See margin.**

54. **[2] Explanations may vary. Sample: 64 feet. Each side of the room has a length of √(256); or 16 feet. Perimeter is 16 + 16 + 16 + 16 = 64 ft.**

[1] correct answer but no explanation given

Investigation

2. **The sum of the areas of the two smaller squares (A and B) is equal to the area of the largest square (C).**

Lesson Preview

 **Check Skills You'll Need**

Finding Square Roots
Lesson 12-5: Example 1. Extra
Practice p. 653.

Lesson Resources

 Teaching Resources
Practice, Reteaching, Enrichment

Reaching All Students
Practice Workbook 12-6
Spanish Practice Workbook 12-6
Guided Problem Solving 12-6
Technology Activities 19
Hands-On Activities 48

Presentation Assistant Plus!
Transparencies
• Check Skills You'll Need 12-6
• Problem of the Day 12-6
• Additional Examples 12-6
• Student Edition Answers 12-6
• Lesson Quiz 12-6
• Classroom Aid 2, 11
PH Presentation Pro CD-ROM 12-6

ASSESSMENT SYSTEM

Computer Test Generator CD

Technology
Resource Pro® CD-ROM
Computer Test Generator CD
PH Presentation Pro CD-ROM

www.PHSchool.com
Student Site
• Teacher Web Code: aak-5500
• Self-grading Lesson Quiz

PH SuccessNet Teacher Center
• Lesson Planner
• Resources

 Plus **iTEXT**

12-6 Introducing the Pythagorean Theorem

What You'll Learn

OBJECTIVE 1 To use the Pythagorean Theorem

...And Why

To find the height of a ramp, as in Example 2

Find each square root.

1. $\sqrt{9}$ 3
2. $\sqrt{64}$ 8
3. $\sqrt{25}$ 5
4. $\sqrt{36}$ 6
5. $\sqrt{121}$ 11
6. $\sqrt{625}$ 25

New Vocabulary
• legs • hypotenuse • Pythagorean Theorem

OBJECTIVE 1   **Using the Pythagorean Theorem**

iTEXT Interactive lesson includes instant self-check, tutorials, and activities.

Recall that a right triangle contains an angle measuring 90°. In a right triangle, the two shorter sides are called **legs.** The longest side, which is opposite the right angle, is called the **hypotenuse.**

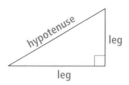

Remember that the symbol ⌐ in an angle indicates that the angle is a right angle.

The Pythagorean Theorem shows how the lengths of sides in a right triangle are related. The labels *a*, *b*, and *c* are commonly used to label the unknown lengths of sides in right triangles, but any labels can be used.

Key Concepts   **Pythagorean Theorem**

In any right triangle, the sum of the squares of the lengths of the legs (*a* and *b*) is equal to the square of the length of the hypotenuse (*c*).

Arithmetic   **Algebra**

$$3^2 + 4^2 = 5^2 \qquad\qquad a^2 + b^2 = c^2$$

---

622   **Chapter 12**   Equations and Inequalities

Ongoing Assessment and Intervention

Before the Lesson	During the Lesson	After the Lesson
Diagnose prerequisite skills using:	**Monitor progress using:**	**Assess knowledge using:**
• Check Skills You'll Need	• Check Understanding • Additional Examples • Test Prep	• Lesson Quiz • Computer Test Generator CD

If you know the lengths of any two sides of a right triangle, you can use the Pythagorean Theorem to find the length of the other side.

1 EXAMPLE Finding the Length of a Hypotenuse

Find the length of the hypotenuse of the triangle.

$a^2 + b^2 = c^2$ ← **Write the Pythagorean Theorem.**

$9^2 + 12^2 = c^2$ ← **Substitute 9 for a and 12 for b.**

$81 + 144 = c^2$ ← **Square 9 and 12.**

$225 = c^2$ ← **Add.**

$\sqrt{225} = \sqrt{c^2}$ ← **Find the square root of each side.**

$15 = c$ ← **Simplify.**

The length of the hypotenuse is 15 units.

✓ Check Understanding **1** **a.** Find the length of the hypotenuse of a triangle with legs of 12 inches and 16 inches. **20 in.**

   b. Reasoning If both legs of a triangle are less than 12 inches, will its hypotenuse always be less than your answer to part (a)? **yes**

2 EXAMPLE Finding the Length of a Leg 🌐 Real World

Ramps A ramp forms part of the right triangle below. How high is the top of the ramp? Round to the nearest tenth.

One leg has length 13 feet. The hypotenuse has length 14 feet.

$a^2 + b^2 = c^2$ ← **Write the Pythagorean Theorem.**

$a^2 + 13^2 = 14^2$ ← **Substitute 13 for b and 14 for c.**

$a^2 + 169 = 196$ ← **Square 13 and 14.**

$a^2 + 169 - 169 = 196 - 169$ ← **Subtract 169 from each side.**

$a^2 = 27$ ← **Simplify.**

$\sqrt{a^2} = \sqrt{27}$ ← **Find the square root of each side.**

$a \approx 5.196152423$ ← **Simplify**

Real-World 🌐 Connection
Ramps help people in wheelchairs get into buildings.

The top of the ramp is about 5.2 feet high.

✓ Check Understanding **2** A ramp is attached to a rental truck forming a right triangle. The base of the triangle is 10 feet and the hypotenuse is 11 feet. How high is the top of the ramp? Round to the nearest tenth. **4.6 ft**

12-6 Introducing the Pythagorean Theorem **623**

🎓 Reaching All Students

Below Level Draw several right triangles of different sizes and orientations. Help students identify the hypotenuse as the longest side and opposite the right angle. Have students label the sides a, b, and c, respectively.	**Advanced Learners** Have students explain whether the equation $(a + b)^2 = c^2$ is the same as $a^2 + b^2 = c^2$. **Sample:** No; exponents cannot be distributed over addition	**Inclusion** See note on page 623. **Visual Learners** See note on page 625.

623

3. Practice

Assignment Guide

1 Objective 1

Ⓐ Ⓑ Core 1–24

Ⓒ Extension 25–27

Test Prep 28–31
Mixed Review 32–43

Teaching Tip

Exercises 1–17 Encourage students to write $a^2 + b^2 = c^2$ as the first step. This reduces errors when substituting lengths.

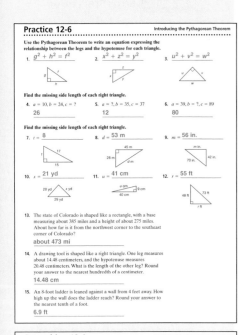

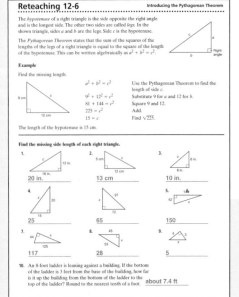

EXERCISES

? For more practice, see *Extra Practice*.

Ⓐ **Practice by Example**

Find the missing side length of each right triangle. Exercise 1 has been started for you. If necessary, round to the nearest tenth.

Example 1
(page 623)

1.

$$a^2 + b^2 = c^2$$
$$7^2 + 24^2 = c^2$$
$$49 + 576 = c^2$$

2.

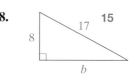

3. $a = 4, b = 3, c = \blacksquare$ 5

4. $a = 10, b = 24, c = \blacksquare$ 26

5. $a = 6, b = 8, c = \blacksquare$ 10

6. $a = 21, b = 20, c = \blacksquare$ 29

Example 2
(page 623)

7.

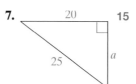

8.

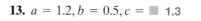

9. $a = \blacksquare, b = 7, c = 9$ 5.7

10. $a = 2, b = \blacksquare, c = 5$ 4.6

11. A 10-foot ladder leans against a building. The base of the ladder is 6 feet from the building. How high is the point where the ladder touches the building? **8 ft**

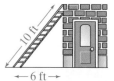

← 6 ft →

🌐 **12. Flags** Suppose you are sewing a Jamaican flag (like the one shown) that is 4 feet by 6 feet. How long will the yellow strip of fabric be? Round to the nearest tenth.
7.2 ft

Ⓑ **Apply Your Skills**

Find the missing side length of each right triangle. The hypotenuse in each triangle is named *c*. Round to the nearest tenth.

13. $a = 1.2, b = 0.5, c = \blacksquare$ 1.3

14. $a = 6, b = 3, c = \blacksquare$ 6.7

15. $a = 3, b = \blacksquare, c = 17$ 16.7

16. $a = \blacksquare, b = 9, c = 12$ 7.9

17. The broken pole at the left forms a right triangle with the ground. How tall was the pole before it was broken? **75 ft**

24 ft

← 45 ft →

624 Chapter 12 Equations and Inequalities

GPS Use the Guided Problem Solving worksheet with Exercise 18.

23. No; the sum of the squares of the lengths of the legs in a right triangle is equal to the square of the length of the hypotenuse. The square of the length of the hypotenuse is greater than the square of the length of either leg, so the hypotenuse is longer than either leg.

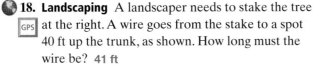

18. **Landscaping** A landscaper needs to stake the tree at the right. A wire goes from the stake to a spot 40 ft up the trunk, as shown. How long must the wire be? **41 ft**

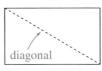

19. **Number Sense** A set of three whole numbers that are the lengths of the sides of a right triangle is called a Pythagorean triple. Tell whether each of the following is a Pythagorean triple.
   a. $a = 9, b = 12, c = 15$ **yes**
   b. $a = 1, b = 2, c = 4$ **no**
   c. $a = 5, b = 6, c = 11$ **no**
   d. $a = 45, b = 24, c = 51$ **yes**

In Exercises 20–22 you will be asked about diagonals. A *diagonal* of a rectangle connects opposite vertices, as shown at the right.

diagonal

20. **Framing** Corey is constructing a picture frame. The length of the frame is 24 inches and the width is 10 inches. To make sure the frame has square corners, Corey measures the diagonal. What should be the length of the diagonal? **26 in.**

21. **Television** The size of a television set is based on the size of the diagonal of the screen. Suppose you see an advertisement for a 27-inch television set. The screen has a height of 15 inches. What is the width of the screen, to the nearest inch? **22 in.**

22. **Quilting** The diagonals for a quilting frame must be the same length to ensure the frame is rectangular. To the nearest tenth, what should be the lengths of the diagonals be for a quilting frame 86 inches by 100 inches? Round to the nearest tenth of an inch. **131.9 in.**

23. **Writing in Math** Can a leg of a right triangle ever be longer than the hypotenuse? Explain. **See above left.**

24. **Algebra** Use the Pythagorean Theorem to write an equation that expresses the relationship between the legs and the hypotenuse for the triangle at the right. $r^2 + s^2 = t^2$

C Challenge

25.
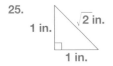
√2 in.
1 in.
1 in.

25. Draw a triangle with a hypotenuse that is $\sqrt{2}$ inches long. **See below left.**

26. **Number Sense** What is the length of the hypotenuse of a triangle whose legs are $\sqrt{9}$ and $\sqrt{16}$ inches long? **5 in.**

27. **Stretch Your Thinking** A door is 6 feet 8 inches tall and 3 feet wide. Suppose you need to fit a board that is 7 feet 3 inches wide through the doorway. Will it fit? **yes**

12-6 Introducing the Pythagorean Theorem **625**

4. Assess

PowerPoint Lesson Quiz 12-6

Find the missing side length of each right triangle.

1. $a = \blacksquare$, $b = 24$, $c = 30$ 18

2. $a = 8$, $b = \blacksquare$, $c = 10$ 6

3. $a = 5$, $b = 3$, $c = \blacksquare$ 5.8

Alternative Assessment

Students in pairs take turns naming two out of three lengths in a right triangle. The partner finds the missing length. Together they verify the results by showing that $a^2 + b^2 = c^2$.

Test Prep

Resources
For additional practice with a variety of test item formats:
• Test-Prep, pp. 631–633
• Test-Taking Strategies, p. 627
• Test-Taking Strategies With Transparencies

Multiple Choice

28. A right triangle has a leg measuring 9 feet and a hypotenuse measuring 15 feet. What is the length of the other leg in feet? **A**

A. 12 **B.** 81 **C.** 144 **D.** 225

29. A rectangular park is 120 meters long and 40 meters wide. If a walk is built along a diagonal of the park, about how many meters long will the walk be? **F**

F. 126 **G.** 400 **H.** 1,600 **I.** 14,400

30. Two girls walked along a 17-mile trail in a forest. They headed 5 miles due east and then 12 miles due north. If they were to make their own trail directly back to where they started, how long would the trail be? **B**

A. 11 miles **B.** 13 miles **C.** 17 miles **D.** 34 miles

Extended Response

31. A surveyor needs to find the distance from point A to point B across the pond shown at the right. The surveyor sets a stake at point C so that $\angle B$ is a right angle. He measures the distance from point B to point C as 40 meters. The distance from point A to point C is 50 meters. **31a–b. See margin.**

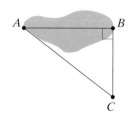

a. Write an equation relating the lengths of the triangle.

b. Explain in words how to solve the equation for the missing length. Then solve the equation.

Take It to the NET
Online lesson quiz at
www.PHSchool.com
Web Code: aaa-1206

Mixed Review

Lesson 11-7

A bag contains 3 red, 2 blue, and 1 green marble. Marbles are drawn twice with replacement. Find the probability of each compound event.

32. both blue $\frac{1}{9}$

33. both red $\frac{1}{4}$

34. blue, then green $\frac{1}{18}$

35. red, then *not* red $\frac{1}{4}$

Lesson 10-1

Find each value.

36. $|0|$ 0 **37.** $|-3|$ 3 **38.** $|85|$ 85 **39.** $|-84|$ 84

Compare using $<$ or $>$.

40. $9 \;{\overset{>}{\blacksquare}}\; 4$ **41.** $5 \;{\overset{>}{\blacksquare}}\; -5$ **42.** $-8 \;{\overset{<}{\blacksquare}}\; 43$ **43.** $1 \;{\overset{>}{\blacksquare}}\; -6$

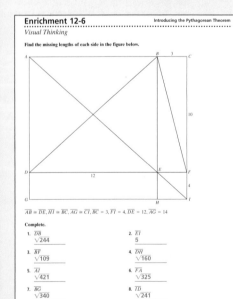

Enrichment 12-6
Visual Thinking   Introducing the Pythagorean Theorem

Find the missing lengths of each side in the figure below.

$\overline{AB} \cong \overline{DE}$, $\overline{HI} \cong \overline{BC}$, $\overline{AG} \cong \overline{CI}$, $\overline{BC} = 3$, $\overline{FI} = 4$, $\overline{DE} = 12$, $\overline{AG} = 14$

Complete.

1. $\overline{DB}$ $\sqrt{244}$	2. $\overline{EI}$ 5
3. $\overline{BF}$ $\sqrt{109}$	4. $\overline{DH}$ $\sqrt{160}$
5. $\overline{AI}$ $\sqrt{421}$	6. $\overline{FA}$ $\sqrt{325}$
7. $\overline{BG}$ $\sqrt{340}$	8. $\overline{ID}$ $\sqrt{241}$

31. **[4] a.** $a^2 + 40^2 = 50^2$

b. Square 40 and 50. Subtract $2,500 - 1,600$ (40^2 from 50^2). Find the square root of the difference, 900.

The distance from A to B is 30 m.

[3] appropriate methods; with one computational error

[2] incorrect methods, but solved correctly

[1] correct answer but no work shown

In questions with multiple correct answers, determine whether each option is true or false. Then choose the answer with options that are all true.

○ EXAMPLE

Fewer than 35 students are at a birthday party. Let s be the number of students at the birthday party. Which numbers are reasonable values for s?

    I. 24

    II. 33.5

    III. 35

A. I only   **B.** I and II   **C.** I and III   **D.** II and III

Begin by drawing a graph.

$$\overset{\oplus}{\underset{32\quad33\quad34\quad35\quad36\quad37\quad38}{\longleftarrow\!+\!\!+\!\!+\!\!+\!\!+\!\!+\!\!+\!\longrightarrow}}$$

Test each option.

    I. 24   True; 24 is on the graph.

    II. 33.5   False; you cannot have 33.5 people.

    III. 35   False; 35 is not on the graph.

○ Since I is the only option that is true, the answer is A.

EXERCISES

1. Which numbers are solutions of $x \le 0$? **C**

    I. -1

    II. 0

    III. 1

    A. I only   **B.** II only   **C.** I and II   **D.** I, II, and III

2. Which numbers are NOT solutions of $d \ge 2$? **F**

    I. 1

    II. 2.5

    III. 3

    F. I only   **G.** III only   **H.** I and II   **I.** I, II, and III

3. There are fewer than 4 boxes of cereal in the pantry. Let b be the number of cereal boxes in the pantry. Which numbers are reasonable values for b? **B**

    I. -4

    II. 0

    III. 4

    A. I only   **B.** II only   **C.** I and II   **D.** I, II, and III

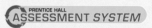
Test-Taking Strategies

Finding Multiple Correct Answers

On some multiple-choice tests, students need to determine whether answers that have more than one part are fully correct. This feature provides a strategy for distinguishing between multiple answers that are true and those that are false or only partially true.

Resources

PRENTICE HALL
ASSESSMENT SYSTEM

Test-Taking Strategies With Transparencies
• Transparency 13
• Practice master, p. 12

Teaching Notes

Exercises
Have students work in pairs to complete the exercises.

Error Prevention!

You may need to review how to read inequality symbols. In addition, remind all students to very carefully read all choices presented on multiple-correct answer questions before making their decision.

Test-Taking Strategies With Transparencies

Chapter 12: Finding Multiple Correct Answers

Exercises

Choose the option with all choices that are true. Explain your answers.

1. Which of the following numbers are rational numbers?

  I. -14 II. $\sqrt{7}$ III. 0.3   IV. $\sqrt{49}$

  A. I only   B. I and III   C. II and IV   ⓓ I, III, and IV

Since -14 is an integer, it is also a rational number. $\sqrt{7}$ cannot be written as an integer or as a fraction. 0.3 can be written as $\frac{3}{10}$, so it is a rational number. $\sqrt{49}$ is 7, which is an integer, so it is a rational number. Choices I, III, and IV are all rational numbers, so, the answer is D.

2. Which of these points is a solution to the equation $y = 2x - 5$?

  I. $(0, -5)$ II. $(4, 3)$ III. $(2, 1)$

  F. I only   ⓖ I and II   H. II and III   I. I, II, III

Substitute each x and y value into the equation.

I. $-5 = 2(0) - 5$; $-5 = 0 - 5$ is true.

II. $3 = 2(4) - 5$; $3 = 8 - 5$ is true.

III. $1 = 2(2) - 5$; $1 = 4 - 5$ is not true since $4 - 5$ is -1.

Only I and II result in a true statement, so the answer is G.

3. If $y = 13$, which of the statements are true?

  I. y is prime   II. y is divisible by 3   III. y is odd

  A. I only   B. I and II   ⓒ I and III   D. I, II, and III

y is a prime number, an odd number, and it is not divisible by 3. Only I and III are true statements, so the answer is C.

4. The statement $x > 3$ and $x < 5$ is true for which values of x?

  I. 4   II. 6   III. 4.5   IV. $\frac{25}{6}$

  F. I only   G. I and II   H. II and III   ⓘ I, III, and IV

Choices I, III, and IV all lie between 3 and 5, so the answer is I.

627

Chapter
12 **Chapter Review**

Resources

Student Edition
Extra Practice, Ch. 12, p. 653
English/Spanish Glossary, p. 669
Table of Symbols, p. 666

 Reaching All Students
Reading and Math Literacy 12D
Spanish Reading and Math
Literacy 12D

 PRENTICE HALL
ASSESSMENT SYSTEM

Test Preparation
• Chapter 12 practice in test
formats

 www.PHSchool.com
Student Site
• Self-grading vocabulary test

PH SuccessNet Teacher Center
• Resources

Plus

Vocabulary

graph of an inequality (p. 602)	**perfect square** (p. 616)	**solution of an inequality** (p. 602)
hypotenuse (p. 622)	**Pythagorean Theorem** (p. 622)	**square root** (p. 616)
inequality (p. 601)	**rational number** (p. 617)	**two-step equation** (p. 596)
legs (p. 622)		

 Reading Math:
Understanding
Vocabulary

Choose the vocabulary term from the column on the right that best completes each sentence. Not all choices will be used.

1. A(n) _?_ in decimal form terminates or repeats. **E**

2. A(n) _?_ is the square of a whole number. **D**

3. A(n) _?_ is a mathematical sentence using the symbol $<$, $>$, $\leq$, $\geq$, or $\neq$. **B**

Take It to the NET
Online vocabulary quiz
at **www.PHSchool.com**
Web Code: aaj-1251

4. The inverse of squaring a number is finding the _?_. **F**

5. The longest side of a right triangle is called the _?_. **A**

A. hypotenuse
B. inequality
C. leg
D. perfect square
E. rational number
F. square root

Skills and Concepts

12-1 Objective
▼ To solve two-step equations

A **two-step equation** is an equation containing two operations. To solve a two-step equation, undo the addition or subtraction, then undo the multiplication or division.

Solve each equation. Check the solution.

6. $3h + 6 = 15$ **3**

7. $2j - 4 = -2$ **1**

8. $\frac{f}{5} + 4 = 29$ **125**

12-2 Objectives
▼ To write inequalities
▼ To identify solutions of inequalities

An **inequality** compares expressions that are not equal. A **solution of an inequality** is any number that makes the inequality true.

State whether the given number is a solution of $x \leq -4$.

9. 4 **no**

10. -4 **yes**

11. -2 **no**

12. -6 **yes**

Graph each inequality. 13–16. See margin.

13. $p > -4$

14. $h < 8$

15. $k \geq -5$

16. $g \leq 3$

Spanish Reading and Math Literacy

Reading and Math Literacy

12D: Vocabulary   For use with the Chapter Review

Study Skill: When solving a crossword puzzle, read the clues first.

Complete the crossword puzzle below. For help, use the glossary in your textbook.

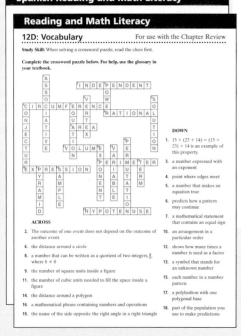

628 Chapter 12 Chapter Review

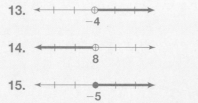

12-3 Objectives

▼ To solve inequalities by adding or subtracting

To solve an inequality, get the variable alone on one side of the inequality.

Solve each inequality.

17. $q + 6 < 9$ **18.** $t - 7 < -2$ **19.** $v - 4 > 12$ **20.** $y + 9 \geq -11$
$q < 3$ $t < 5$ $v > 16$ $y \geq -20$

12-4 Objective

▼ To solve a problem using two different methods

You can solve a problem using different strategies.

Solve each problem by either drawing a diagram or writing an equation. Explain why you chose the method you did. 21–22. See margin.

21. There are 35 people at a banquet. Three-fifths of the people are wearing black pants. How many people are wearing black pants?

22. A student cuts strips from a sheet that measures 60 inches by 80 inches Each strip is 2 inches by 13 inches. How many strips can the student cut?

12-5 Objectives

▼ To find square roots
▼ To classify numbers as rational

A **square root** of a number is a number that, when multiplied by itself, is the given number. A **perfect square** is the square of a whole number.

A **rational number** is a number that can be written as a quotient of two integers, where the divisor is not 0.

Find each square root. Round to the nearest tenth, if necessary.

23. $\sqrt{81}$ 9   **24.** $\sqrt{24}$ 4.9   **25.** $\sqrt{30}$ 5.5   **26.** $\sqrt{144}$ 12

Tell which two consecutive whole numbers each square root is between.

27. $\sqrt{6}$ 2, 3   **28.** $\sqrt{12}$ 3, 4   **29.** $\sqrt{21}$ 4, 5   **30.** $\sqrt{31}$ 5, 6

Tell whether each number is rational.

31. $0.\overline{3}$ rational   **32.** $\sqrt{18}$ not rational   **33.** 0.123 rational   **34.** $\sqrt{64}$ rational

12-6 Objective

▼ To use the Pythagorean Theorem

The **Pythagorean Theorem** states that, given the triangle at the right, $a^2 + b^2 = c^2$.

Find the missing side length of each right triangle. Round to the nearest tenth, if necessary.

35. $a = 6, b = 8, c = \blacksquare$ 10   **36.** $a = 15, b = \blacksquare, c = 17$ 8

37. $a = 1, b = 2, c = \blacksquare$ 2.2   **38.** $a = \blacksquare, b = 6, c = 8$ 5.3

21. 21 people; drawing a diagram would be tedious.

22. 184 strips; there are too many strips to include in a diagram.

630

Chapter
12 **Chapter Test**

Take It to the NET
Online chapter test at
www.PHSchool.com
Web Code: aaa-1252

Chapter Test

Solve each equation. Check the solution.

1. $4u + 7 = 35$ 7   2. $6r - 4 = 20$ 4

3. $\frac{f}{3} + 5 = 20$ 45   4. $\frac{n}{8} - 2 = -1$ 8

5. An eraser and five pencils cost $1.20. If the
   eraser costs $.45, how much is each pencil?
   $.15

6. Write an inequality for each situation. $h < 6$
   a. There are less than 6 hamsters in the cage.
   b. Fifty or more people are at the county fair.
   $p \ge 50$

7. Write an inequality for the graph below.

$$\leftarrow \!\!-\!\!+\!\!-\!\!+\!\!-\!\!+\!\!-\!\!\bullet\!\!-\!\!+\!\!-\!\!+\!\!-\!\!+\!\!-\!\!+\!\!\rightarrow$$
   $-9\ -8\ -7\ -6\ -5\ -4\ -3$

   $x \le -6$

8. Tell whether each number is a solution of
   $c \le -8$.
   a. 8 no   b. −7 no   c. −8 yes   d. −10 yes

Graph each inequality on a number line.
9–12. See margin.

9. $w > -5$ 10. $x \le 4$

11. $y < 7$ 12. $z \ge -12$

13. **Writing in Math** Is −9 a solution of the
    inequality $d \le -9$? Explain. See margin.

Solve each inequality.

14. $j + 4 \ge 9$ $j \ge 5$ 15. $k - 6 < 2$ $k < 8$

16. $s - 6 < 42$ $s < 48$ 17. $f + 2 \ge -1$ $f \ge -3$

 18. **Bank Fees** You have $159 in a bank account.
    You need at least $200 to avoid bank fees.
    Write and solve an inequality to find how
    much more money you should deposit.
    $m + 159 \ge 200$; at least $41

**Solve the problem by either drawing a diagram or
writing an equation.**

19. **Jogging** A person jogs 520 feet per minute.
    If the person continues to jog at the same rate,
    how far will the person jog in 30 minutes?
    15,600 ft
20. Your friend bought cream cheese for $2.10
    and bagels for $.50 each. She spent a total of
    $6.60. How many bagels did your friend buy?
    9 bagels

**Find the square root. Round to the nearest tenth,
if necessary.**

21. $\sqrt{25}$ 5   22. $\sqrt{49}$ 7   23. $\sqrt{60}$ 7.7

**Tell which two consecutive whole numbers each
square root is between.**

24. $\sqrt{5}$ 25. $\sqrt{14}$ 26. $\sqrt{97}$
    2, 3   3, 4   9, 10

Tell whether each number is rational.

27. $\sqrt{14}$ 28. $5.\overline{5}$ 29. $\frac{1}{13}$
    not rational   rational   rational

Find the missing side length.

30.   12   15   31.   45
                              b 51
       c 9
                                    24

32. The solution to which inequality is
    represented by the graph below? C

$$\leftarrow \!\!+\!\!-\!\!+\!\!-\!\!+\!\!-\!\!\oplus\!\!-\!\!+\!\!-\!\!+\!\!-\!\!+\!\!-\!\!\rightarrow$$
    $-8\ -7\ -6\ -5\ -4\ -3\ -2$

    A. $25 > y + 20$ **B.** $y - 5 < -10$
    C. $y - 15 > -20$ **D.** $y + 10 \ge -15$

9. $\leftarrow \!\!+\!\!-\!\!+\!\!\oplus\!\!-\!\!+\!\!-\!\!+\!\!-\!\!+\!\!\rightarrow$
      -5

10. $\leftarrow \!\!+\!\!-\!\!+\!\!-\!\!+\!\!\bullet\!\!-\!\!+\!\!-\!\!+\!\!\rightarrow$
      4

11. $\leftarrow \!\!+\!\!-\!\!\oplus\!\!-\!\!+\!\!-\!\!+\!\!\rightarrow$
      7

12. $\leftarrow \!\!+\!\!-\!\!\bullet\!\!-\!\!+\!\!-\!\!+\!\!-\!\!+\!\!\rightarrow$
       -12

13. Yes; answers may vary.
    Sample: The inequality
    includes the equal sign,
    so −9 is a solution.

Test Prep

CUMULATIVE REVIEW
CHAPTERS 1–12

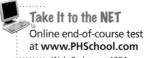
Take It to the NET
Online end-of-course test
at **www.PHSchool.com**
Web Code: aaa-1254

Multiple Choice

Choose the correct letter.

1. What operation would you perform first in the expression $3.9 + 4.1 \times 16 - 6 \div 4.8$? **B**
  A. Add 3.9 and 4.1.
  B. Multiply 4.1 and 16.
  C. Subtract 6 from 16.
  D. Divide 10 by 4.8.

2. Four servers at a restaurant equally share $87.44 in tips. How much does each server receive? **H**
  F. $20.68   **G.** $20.86
  H. $21.86   **I.** $22.86

3. Find the next two terms in the pattern: 2, 6, 12, 20, . . . **C**
  A. 24, 32   **B.** 28, 36
  C. 30, 42   **D.** 32, 44

4. Solve the equation $0.2x = 46$. **I**
  F. 2.3   **G.** 9.2   **H.** 23   **I.** 230

5. Find the quotient $0.317 \div 0.08$. **B**
  A. 0.039625   **B.** 3.9625
  C. 39.625   **D.** 396.25

6. Simplify the expression **F**
  $4 + 6 \times (-3) - (-10) \div (-2)$.
  F. -19 **G.** -10 **H.** 10   **I.** 19

7. Solve the equation $c + 3\frac{2}{3} = 7\frac{4}{5}$. **C**
  A. $3\frac{2}{15}$ **B.** $3\frac{7}{15}$ **C.** $4\frac{2}{15}$ **D.** $4\frac{7}{15}$

8. Estimate the product $7\frac{3}{8} \times 5\frac{3}{4}$. **H**
  F. 35   **G.** 40   **H.** 42   **I.** 48

9. Find the reciprocal of $4\frac{2}{5}$. **A**
  A. $\frac{5}{22}$ **B.** $\frac{1}{4}$ **C.** $\frac{5}{2}$ **D.** $2\frac{4}{5}$

10. What is the ordered pair for P? **I**
  F. (3, 2)
  G. (−2, −3)
  H. (2, −2)
  I. (−3, 2)

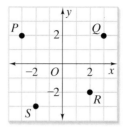

11. Estimate the 8% sales tax for a sweater that costs $29.99. **A**
  A. $2.40   **B.** $20.40
  C. $24.00   **D.** $240.00

12. Which of the following is NOT equivalent to 48%? **H**
  F. $\frac{48}{100}$ **G.** $\frac{24}{50}$ **H.** 0.048   **I.** 0.48

13. Which of the following is the most appropriate choice to display your height for each year since your birth. **C**
  A. circle graph   **B.** line plot
  C. bar graph   **D.** frequency table

14. What is the value of cell D3 in the spreadsheet below? **F**

	A	B	C	D
1	Test A	Test B	Test C	Mean
2	92	86	80	
3	79	82	82	
4	95	95	95	

  F. 81   **G.** 86   **H.** 243   **I.** 285

15. Find the LCM of 20, 35, and 100. **D**
  A. 5   **B.** 10   **C.** 100   **D.** 700

16. You buy tape and seven boxes for $18.55. If the tape costs $2.10, how much is each box?
  F. $.70   **G.** $2.35
  H. $2.65   **I.** $2.95   **G**

Item	1	2	3	4	5	6	7	8	9	10	11	12	13	14	15	16
Lesson	1-10	1-9	2-1	2-7	1-9	10-5	4-6	5-2	5-3	10-6	6-7	6-6	7-4	7-6	3-6	2-7

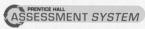

35. [2] a. $s \le 12$

b.

12

[1] incorrect inequality OR incorrect graph

36. [2] 4.358898944…; $\sqrt{19}$ is not a rational number because 19 is not a perfect square. (OR some equivalent explanation)

[1] correct response with incorrect explanation

37. [2] 10 miles; by the Pythagorean Theorem: $8^2 + 6^2 = c^2$, $64 + 36 = c^2$, $100 = c^2$, $\sqrt{100} = \sqrt{c^2}$, $10 = c$

[1] appropriate method, but with one computational error OR correct answer with no work shown

38. [2] two correct congruences given from possible $\overline{RS} \cong \overline{WU}$; $\overline{RT} \cong \overline{WV}$; $\overline{ST} \cong \overline{UV}$; $\angle SRT \cong \angle UWV$; $\angle RTS \cong \angle WVU$; $\angle RST \cong \angle WUV$

[1] one incorrect congruence

39. [2] 37.41; $x = 0.43 \times 87$, $x = 37.41$ (OR equivalent equation)

[1] appropriate method, but with one computational error OR correct answer with no work shown

40. [2] 4 h 15 min; 7 h 45 min − 3 h 15 min = 4 h 30 min, 4 h 30 min − 15 min = 4 h 15 min

[1] appropriate method but with one computational error OR correct answer with no work shown

632

---

17. Solve the proportion $\frac{2m}{21} = \frac{8}{35}$. B

A. $1\frac{3}{5}$ B. $2\frac{2}{5}$ C. 7   D. 12

18. Which drawing shows a rotation of the face below? G

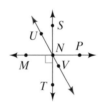

F. G.

H. I.

19. Which decimal is equivalent to $\frac{3}{8}$? B

A. 0.037   B. 0.375   C. 0.38   D. 3.75

20. Solve $-9 + w < 12$. H

F. $w < -21$ G. $w > -21$

H. $w < 21$ I. $w > 21$

21. What is 4.3 in words? D

A. four and thirteen hundredths

B. four hundred and three

C. forty-three

D. four and three tenths

22. Which of the following is NOT true about the diagram below? H

F. $\angle TNV$ is congruent to $\angle SNU$.

G. $\angle SNP$ is a right angle.

H. $\angle UNS$ is congruent to $\angle PNV$.

I. $\overleftrightarrow{ST}$ is perpendicular to $\overleftrightarrow{NP}$.

23. Which set of numbers is ordered from least to greatest? B

A. $\frac{1}{2}, \frac{3}{4}, \frac{2}{3}, \frac{4}{5}, \frac{9}{10}$ B. $\frac{1}{2}, \frac{2}{3}, \frac{3}{4}, \frac{4}{5}, \frac{9}{10}$

C. $\frac{1}{3}, \frac{1}{2}, \frac{2}{3}, \frac{9}{10}, \frac{4}{5}$ D. $\frac{1}{4}, \frac{3}{10}, \frac{8}{5}, \frac{1}{2}, \frac{2}{3}$

Item	17	18	19	20	21	22	23
Lesson	6-4	8-9	6-6	12-3	1-2	8-3	3-7

Item	24	25	26	27	28	29	30	31	32	33	34
Lesson	11-7	11-3	9-8	11-3	12-1	11-6	2-8	2-9	2-2	1-10	8-3

Gridded Response

24. A bag contains 1 red marble, 1 yellow marble, and 1 green marble. Your friend choses the yellow marble. Your turn is next. If the yellow marble is NOT replaced in the bag, find the probability that you will choose the red marble. $\frac{1}{2}$

25. Out of a sample of 125 CDs, 9 were found to have scratches. In a shipment of 5,000 CDs, how many would you predict will have scratches? 360

26. Find the surface area in square feet of the figure below. 108

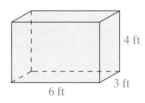

27. The probability of losing a particular game is 55%. Suppose you play this game 20 times. How many times would you expect to win the game? 9

28. Solve the equation $4j - 8 = 12$ for j. 5

29. Find the number of permutations of the letters in the word WYOMING. 5040

30. Write 5.6×10^3 in standard form. 5600

31. Simplify the expression 16.1 $(16 - 8) \times 2 + (10 \div 100)$.

32. Evaluate the expression $j \div 10 + 8.3$ for $j = 11$. 9.4

33. Simplify the expression $3 \times 8 - 4 + 5$. 25

34. Find the measure in degrees of $\angle KLM$. 120

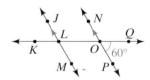

46. [4] a. $t + 7 > 20$ (OR an equivalent inequality);

b. $t + 7 - 7 > 20 - 7$, $t > 13$

c.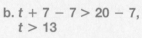
13

Short Response

Show your work. 35–44. See margin.

35. No more than 12 students volunteered to work at the local food pantry.
    a. Write an inequality for this situation.
    b. Graph the solution on a number line.

36. a. Find $\sqrt{19}$.
    b. Is $\sqrt{19}$ a rational number?

37. You and a friend walk along a 14-mile trail in a park. You head 8 miles due west and then 6 miles due south. If you make your own trail directly back to where you started, how long would the trail be?

38. The triangles below are congruent. Write two congruences involving corresponding parts of the triangles.

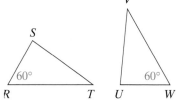

39. Write and then use an equation to find 43% of 87.

40. Sam works at a book store. When he punched in, the time clock read 3:15 P.M. When he punched out, the time clock read 7:45 P.M. He took a 15-minute break. How long did he work?

41. Solve $\frac{b}{2} + 5 = 4$.

42. Solve $n + 9 \geq 17$.

43. Find the prime factorization of 98 by using a factor tree.

44. A map with the scale 5 inches : 325 miles shows two landmarks that are 2 inches apart. How many miles apart are the landmarks?

Extended Response 45–46. See margin.

45. Find the mean, median, and mode of the data in the line plot.

Number of Students Absent

```
X
X                   X
X           X   X
X   X   X   X   X
M   T   W   Th  F
        Day
```

46. The sum of a number t and 7 is greater than 20.
    a. Write an inequality for this situation.
    b. Solve the inequality.
    c. Graph the solution on a number line.

47–50. See back of book.

47. A rectangle measures 5 inches by 7 inches.
    a. What is the area of the rectangle?
    b. A 1-inch by 1-inch square is cut from each corner of the rectangle. What is the area of the new figure? Explain.

48. An open box is made by folding the sides of the net below.

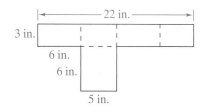

    a. Find the surface area of the open box.
    b. Now find the volume of the box.

49. The cost of your dinner is $18.64. You want to leave a 15% tip for the server.
    a. How much is the tip?
    b. What is the total cost of dinner, excluding any tax?

50. A store sells socks in two colors (gray or white), three sizes (small, medium, or large), and two fabrics (cotton or wool).
    a. Make a tree diagram to find the number of sock choices.
    b. If the store has one of every type of sock, what is the probability you will choose a wool sock at random?

Item	35	36	37	38	39	40	41	42	43	44	45	46	47	48	49	50
Lesson	12-2	12-5	12-6	8-7	6-7	4-7	12-1	12-3	3-2	6-5	7-1 & 7-2	12-3	9-3	9-8 & 9-9	6-7	11-5

[3] appropriate methods but with one computational error

[2] incorrect inequality solved and graphed correctly

[1] correct inequality OR solution OR graph, without work shown

47–50. See back of book.

41. [2] -2; $\frac{b}{2} + 5 = 4$,
    $\frac{b}{2} + 5 - 5 = 4 - 5$,
    $\frac{b}{2} = -1$,
    $\frac{b}{2} \times (2) = (-1) \times (2)$,
    $b = -2$

    [1] appropriate method but with one computational error OR correct answer with no work shown

42. [2] $n + 9 - 9 \geq 17 - 9$,
    $n \geq 8$

    [1] appropriate method but with one computational error OR correct answer with no work shown

43. $2 \times 7 \times 7$;

    ```
          98
         /  \
       (2)   49
            /  \
          (7)  (7)
    ```

    [1] correct prime factorization but no factor tree shown

44. [2] 130 mi; by an appropriate method such as cross multiplication:
    $\frac{5}{325} = \frac{2}{x}$, $5x = 2 \times 325$,
    $5x = 650$, $x = 130$

    [1] incorrect method OR incorrect solution

45. [4] mean = 2.2,
    $\frac{4 + 1 + 1 + 2 + 3}{5} =$
    $\frac{11}{5} = 2.2$; median = 2, order data from least to greatest: 1, 1, 2, 3, 4; identify middle value: 2; mode = 1, identify the number of absences that appears most often: 1

    [3] appropriate methods but with one computational error

    [2] correct mean, median, and mode, without work shown OR 2 out of the 3 correct with correct work

    [1] mean OR median OR mode is correct

633

A Bright Idea

Students will use data from these two pages to answer the questions posed here in Put It All Together.

Activating Prior Knowledge

Have students share what they know about different kinds of lighting, including the nature of the light each emits, how long each lasts, and how much each costs. Ask students to tell which kind of lighting they prefer.

Teaching Notes

Have volunteers read aloud the data about light and light bulbs. Discuss that we measure the power of light in watts. Then talk about the typical wattage listed on incandescent bulbs.

History Connection

Tell students that the first lamps appeared at least 50,000 years ago. These were hollow rocks or shells filled with moss or similar materials soaked in animal fat. Then tell them that the fluorescent lamp made its appearance in 1867 (although not perfected until the 1930s), while the first incandescent lamps appeared a few years later. Have students research the history of lamps (from the Greek word *lampas*, meaning "torch.") from these earliest ones, to oil and gas lamps, to the different kinds of electric lamps we have today.

Science Connection

Many students are likely to be familiar with another kind of electric light—a halogen light. Ask students to find out how a halogen bulb differs from both fluorescent and incandescent bulbs. In addition, challenge students to find out what an "electric flowerpot" is and what we call it today. It was a light for plants invented in the 1890s; now we call it a flashlight.

A Bright Idea

Applying Equations Suppose you are changing the light bulbs in your bedroom. Regular (incandescent) light bulbs provide light, but they also get warm. Fluorescent light bulbs stay cool because they convert more energy into light. They cost more than regular bulbs, but they're cheaper to run. Should you replace your regular bulbs with fluorescent bulbs?

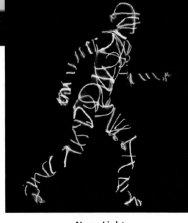

Neon Light

Colored glass tubes filled with neon gas glow when an electrical charge moves through the gas.

Fireflies

Fireflies, or lightning bugs, make light inside their bodies. The light can be any color from pale yellow to reddish green.

634

1. $14.00

2a. incandescent light bulb: 1,000 watts
    fluorescent light bulb: 320 watts

b. incandescent light bulb: 1 kilowatt-hour
   fluorescent light bulb: 0.32 kilowatt-hour

c. $.15/$.05

3a. incandescent light bulb life: 1,000 hours;
    $365 \times 10 = 3{,}650$ hours/year
    $3{,}650 \div 1{,}000 = 3.65$. You will use about 4 light bulbs.
    fluorescent light bulb life: 10,000 hours;
    $365 \times 10 = 3{,}650$ hours/year $3{,}650 < 10{,}000$. You will need only one light bulb.

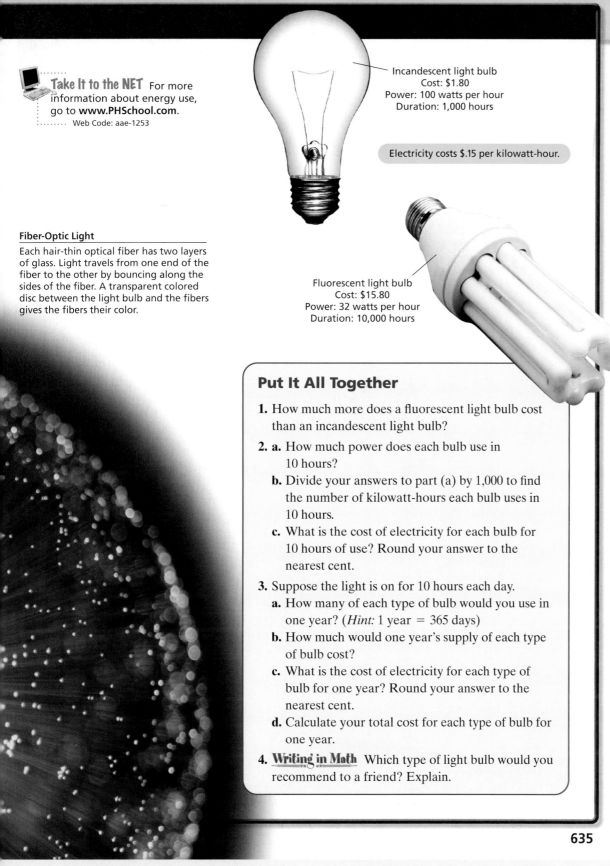

Take It to the NET For more information about energy use, go to **www.PHSchool.com**.
Web Code: aae-1253

Fiber-Optic Light

Each hair-thin optical fiber has two layers of glass. Light travels from one end of the fiber to the other by bouncing along the sides of the fiber. A transparent colored disc between the light bulb and the fibers gives the fibers their color.

Incandescent light bulb
Cost: $1.80
Power: 100 watts per hour
Duration: 1,000 hours

Electricity costs $.15 per kilowatt-hour.

Fluorescent light bulb
Cost: $15.80
Power: 32 watts per hour
Duration: 10,000 hours

Put It All Together

1. How much more does a fluorescent light bulb cost than an incandescent light bulb?

2. **a.** How much power does each bulb use in 10 hours?

   b. Divide your answers to part (a) by 1,000 to find the number of kilowatt-hours each bulb uses in 10 hours.

   c. What is the cost of electricity for each bulb for 10 hours of use? Round your answer to the nearest cent.

3. Suppose the light is on for 10 hours each day.

   a. How many of each type of bulb would you use in one year? (*Hint:* 1 year = 365 days)

   b. How much would one year's supply of each type of bulb cost?

   c. What is the cost of electricity for each type of bulb for one year? Round your answer to the nearest cent.

   d. Calculate your total cost for each type of bulb for one year.

4. **Writing in Math** Which type of light bulb would you recommend to a friend? Explain.

635

Put It All Together

Have students work in pairs to answer the questions.

English Learners
Help students distinguish between some of the terms that appear in the activity: *fluorescent* and *incandescent*; *light* and *bulb*; *watt* and *kilowatt*.

Exercise 1 Students may think the fluorescent bulb gives less light than the incandescent bulb based on its wattage, only 32 watts compared to 100 watts. Inform students that watts measure electrical power going into the bulb, whereas the brightness of the light produced by a lamp is measured in *lumens*. Guide students to see that although it may appear otherwise, the two lights are comparable in the amount of light they provide.

Exercise 4 Ask students to tell whether limited use of the bulb, say only 5 hours per day, would affect their recommendation. Have them explain their reasoning.

b. incandescent light bulb: 4 × $1.80 = $7.20 fluorescent light bulb: 1 × $15.80 = $15.80

c. incandescent light bulb: $.15 × 365 = $54.75; fluorescent light bulb: $.05 × 365 = $18.25

d. incandescent light bulb: $7.20 + $54.75 = $61.95; fluorescent light bulb: $15.80 + $18.25 = $34.05

4. Check students' work.

Chapter Projects

Chapter Projects

Celebration

Students apply their number sense and common sense to plan a celebration.

Resources

📁 **Teaching Resources**
Chapter 1 Project Support with Project Manager, Student Activities, Teacher Notes

Teaching Notes

Activating Prior Knowledge
Have students share experiences planning parties. Then ask:
• *What things will you consider to help you plan your celebration?* Sample: how many guests; what foods, entertainment, and decorations to have; what these things cost; how many people will share the costs

Careers
Event planning and fundraising are careers that might interest students. Discuss what skills these careers require.

Stepping Stones

Students apply their knowledge of geometrical patterns to construct a model of a fort.

Resources

📁 **Teaching Resources**
Chapter 2 Project Support with Project Manager, Student Activities, Teacher Notes

Teaching Notes

Activating Prior Knowledge
Discuss the kinds of patterns that might emerge when students build their forts. Ask:
• *How will you record the patterns?* Sample: using tables

Social Studies Connection
Invite volunteers to research the architecture of the Maya and compare Mayan structures with those of the Egyptians or Greeks.

CELEBRATION

Chapter 1 Decimals

Suppose your class is planning to honor someone special in the community or to congratulate a winning team. You need to decide when and where you will hold the event, how you will decorate, and what entertainment and refreshments you will provide. You may also need to decide how to raise funds for the celebration.

Plan a Celebration Your chapter project is to plan a celebration. You must decide how much it will cost and how much money each member of the class must raise. Your plan should include a list of supplies for the event and their costs.

💻 **Take It to the NET** Go to **www.PHSchool.com** for information to help you complete your project.
Web Code: aad-0161

STEPPING STONES

Chapter 2 Patterns and Variables

Think about a historic building, such as one of the ancient pyramids or the Eiffel Tower. How many pieces of stone do you think were needed for the bottom of a pyramid compared to a layer near the top? Many buildings use mathematical patterns in their designs.

Building a Fort For this project, you will build a model of a simple fort. You will record the amounts of materials needed for each layer. You will look for patterns and write equations to describe the patterns.

💻 **Take It to the NET** Go to **www.PHSchool.com** for information to help you complete your project.
Web Code: aad-0261

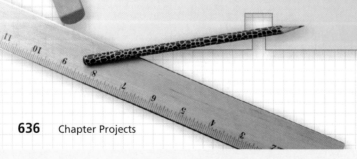

636 Chapter Projects

In Malcolm's daydream, he floats in the air on the way to a slam dunk. In reality, he tosses pieces of paper into a wastebasket. He makes some shots, and he misses others.

Chapter 3 *Number Theory and Fractions*

Compare Basketball Statistics Your project will be to record and compare baskets attempted and baskets made by the players on your own imaginary basketball team. You can shoot baskets with a real basketball on a real court, or you can toss pieces of paper into a wastebasket.

 Take It to the NET Go to **www.PHSchool.com** for information to help you complete your project.
Web Code: aad-0361

Have you ever conducted a science experiment? Scientists perform experiments to prove if an idea is correct or incorrect. You can prove if something is correct or not in math class, too.

Chapter 4 *Adding and Subtracting Fractions*

Design a Demonstration You will learn ways to add fractions and mixed numbers with unlike denominators, but can you prove these techniques really work? Your goal is to prove that they do by giving several demonstrations.

 Take It to the NET Go to **www.PHSchool.com** for information to help you complete your project.
Web Code: aad-0461

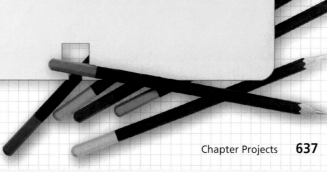

Chapter Projects **637**

Chapter Projects

Home Court Advantage

Students apply their knowledge of comparing fractions to making a basket in basketball.

Resources

📁 **Teaching Resources**
Chapter 3 Project Support with Project Manager, Student Activities, Teacher Notes

Teaching Notes

Activating Prior Knowledge
Initiate a discussion on free-throw statistics. Ask:
• *How can you tell if your "shooting" improves over time?* Sample: Shoot in regular sets of 5 or 10; record your results as fractions and compare them.

Physical Education Connection
Have students discuss free-throw statistics for both men and women pro players.

Seeing is Believing

Students apply their knowledge of adding fractions to prove that an adding technique works.

Resources

📁 **Teaching Resources**
Chapter 4 Project Support with Project Manager, Student Activities, Teacher Notes

Teaching Notes

Activating Prior Knowledge
Discuss the idea of carefully designing an experiment and recording the results. Then ask:
• *How can you use models to add fractions with different denominators?* Sample: use fraction models that demonstrate renaming

Inclusion
Discuss and demonstrate that "renaming" a fraction as an equivalent fraction with a different denominator does not change the value of that fraction.

T637

Crack It and Cook It

Students apply their knowledge of multiplying fractions and mixed numbers to adjust a recipe.

Resources

📁 **Teaching Resources**
Chapter 5 Project Support with Project Manager, Student Activities, Teacher Notes

Teaching Notes

Activating Prior Knowledge
Discuss how cooks adjust the amounts of ingredients in recipes to make enough of the dish to feed different numbers of diners. Ask:
- *How would you have to adjust the amounts of the ingredients of a dish that serves 4 in order to serve 12?* multiply the quantity of each ingredient by 3

Careers
Discuss mathematical skills that a chef might need. For example, estimating cooking time, amounts of ingredients; working with money amounts, percents, and so on.

Planet of the Stars

Students apply their knowledge of ratios to make scale models of two planets.

Resources

📁 **Teaching Resources**
Chapter 6 Project Support with Project Manager, Student Activities, Teacher Notes

Teaching Notes

Activating Prior Knowledge
Talk about models of the solar system that students have seen in planetariums or museums. Ask:
- *How do you think the builders of these models chose the scale to use?* Sample: the size of the space available or the size they want the models to be.

CRACK IT and Cook It!

Chapter 5 *Multiplying and Dividing Fractions*

Eating a hearty breakfast is a great way to start any day! You are probably familiar with pouring a bowl of cereal, making toast, or maybe even scrambling eggs. But have you ever made an omelet? An omelet recipe can be pretty simple—eggs, water, and maybe some salt or pepper. However, you can add other ingredients to this basic recipe to suit your taste. A cheese omelet is delicious. So is a bacon-and-tomato omelet. You might also add mushrooms, onions, and peppers.

Create a Recipe Put on your chef's hat. In this chapter project, you will write and name your own recipe for an omelet. Your final project will be a recipe that can feed everyone in your class.

💻 **Take It to the NET** Go to **www.PHSchool.com** for information to help you complete your project.
Web Code: aad-0561

Planet of the Stars

Chapter 6 *Ratios, Proportions, and Percents*

When you look up at the stars in the sky, you may not think about how far away they are. Stars appear a lot closer than they really are. The same is true of planets. The huge distances between planets make it impossible for books to show how vast our solar system really is.

Make a Scale Model In this chapter project, you will make scale models of two planets. You will compare their sizes and distances from the sun and calculate the ratios involved in your scale model.

💻 **Take It to the NET** Go to **www.PHSchool.com** for information to help you complete your project.
Web Code: aad-0661

ON YOUR OWN TIME

Chapter 7 *Data and Graphs*

RING!!! The last bell of the day has rung. You and your classmates will soon head in different directions. Some of your classmates are on the same team or in the same club as you. Some of them are not. Do you know how much time your classmates spend on their favorite activities? You could guess the answers to the last question, but a more accurate method of finding the answers would be to collect real data.

Conduct a Survey For this chapter project, you will survey 25 of your friends and classmates. You can choose the survey subject, such as how much time your classmates spend on sports. You will organize and graph the data. Then you will present your findings to your class.

 **Take It to the NET** Go to **www.PHSchool.com** for information to help you complete your project.
Web Code: aad-0761

Puzzling Pictures

Chapter 8 *Tools of Geometry*

Do you remember putting together simple puzzles when you were younger? Puzzles designed for young children are often made of wood and have large pieces. The pieces have straight sides so that the child can put the puzzle together easily.

Create a Puzzle Think about one of your favorite pictures. How would it look as a puzzle? Your project is to make an attractive but challenging puzzle for your classmates. Include as many geometric shapes as you can.

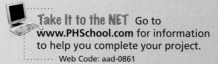 **Take It to the NET** Go to **www.PHSchool.com** for information to help you complete your project.
Web Code: aad-0861

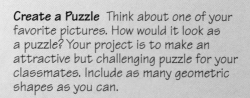

Chapter Projects **639**

Chapter Projects

On Your Own Time

Students apply their knowledge of data collection and graphing to conduct a survey and present their results.

Resources

📁 **Teaching Resources**
Chapter 7 Project Support with Project Manager, Student Activities, Teacher Notes

Teaching Notes

Activating Prior Knowledge
Discuss the different graphs and the kinds of data each displays. Then ask:
• *Which graph would be appropriate to show students' findings?* Sample: bar graphs

Careers
Have students brainstorm a list of jobs in which gathering, organizing, displaying, and interpreting data play a key role. Sample: marketing director, baseball manager

Puzzling Pictures

Students apply their knowledge of geometric shapes to make a puzzle.

Resources

📁 **Teaching Resources**
Chapter 8 Project Support with Project Manager, Student Activities, Teacher Notes

Teaching Notes

Activating Prior Knowledge
Discuss how solving jigsaw puzzles can help make one. Ask:
• *What math concepts can help you make your puzzle?*
Sample: congruent and similar figures, slides, flips, turns, tessellations

Inclusion
Have students begin by dividing their puzzle into rectangles. They can then sub-divide the rectangles into other, smaller shapes.

T639

Go Fish

Students apply their knowledge of geometry and measurement to design a class aquarium.

Resources

 Teaching Resources
Chapter 9 Project Support with Project Manager, Student Activities, Teacher Notes

Teaching Notes

Activating Prior Knowledge

Invite students to share their experiences setting up and caring for a fish tank. Ask:

- *What considerations must you keep in mind when planning your proposed aquarium?* Sample: number of fish desired, what plants and objects you want

Science Connection

Have students visit a pet store to learn more about aquariums and differences types of fish.

The Time of Your Life

Students apply their knowledge of measurement to create time lines that show key events in their lives.

Resources

 Teaching Resources
Chapter 10 Project Support with Project Manager, Student Activities, Teacher Notes

Teaching Notes

Activating Prior Knowledge

Have students discuss what kinds of events belong on a time line of their lives. Then ask:

- *What might be your first step in setting up a time line of your life?* Sample: choose time intervals

Diversity

Have students who are not comfortable displaying personal data make a time line for a day in a pet's life.

T640

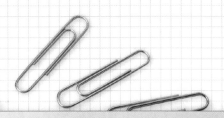

Go Fish

Have you ever spent time gazing into an aquarium full of fish? You can get lost in thought as you look through the glass watching the fish. Many people enjoy having an aquarium because they feel peaceful while observing nature in this miniature form.

Design an Aquarium In this chapter project, you will design an aquarium for your classroom. You should consider how many fish you want in the aquarium. Also consider the size of each type of fish that you plan to place in the aquarium. As part of your final project, you will create a drawing of your proposed aquarium.

 Take It to the NET Go to **www.PHSchool.com** for information to help you complete your project.
Web Code: aad-0961

The TIME of your life

Do you know an older person who has lived an interesting life? That person could probably tell you a lot of stories about his or her life. You can tell stories about your life, too. You may not have lived as long, but there have been important events in your past, and there will be others in your future.

Draw a Time Line Your project will be to build a time line of your life—past, present, and future. Think about the time lines you have seen in your social studies classes. You will have a chance to apply math skills such as ratios, measurements, scale drawings, and integers.

Take It to the NET Go to **www.PHSchool.com** for information to help you complete your project.
Web Code: aad-1061

Chapter 11 *Exploring Probability*

Suppose you and a friend have to choose among three movies, and you can't make up your mind. Should you flip a coin? You'd probably agree that assigning "heads" to one movie, "tails" to the second, and "lands on edge" to the third would not give the third movie much of a chance. What should you do?

Design a Three-Choice System Your project will be to design a device or system that is equally fair to three different outcomes. You will test your system to make sure each outcome can be expected one third of the time over a large number of trials.

Take It to the NET Go to **www.PHSchool.com** for information to help you complete your project.
Web Code: aad-1161

WORKING for a Cause

Have you ever participated in a fundraiser? Schools and sports clubs often use fundraisers as a way to pay for such things as equipment, trips, and camps. You have probably purchased candy bars, magazines, or wrapping paper to help a friend raise money.

Chapter 12 *Equations and Inequalities*

Plan a Fundraiser In this chapter project, you will plan a fundraiser. You will choose a cause or charity, decide how much money you would like to raise, and determine the type of event to hold or the type of product to sell. As part of your final project, you will present a fundraising plan to your class.

Take It to the NET Go to **www.PHSchool.com** for information to help you complete your project.
Web Code: aad-1261

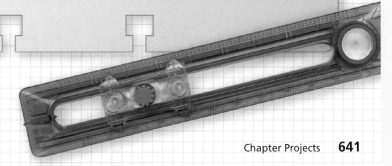

Now Playing

Students apply their understanding of probability to design a fair way to choose among three movies.

Resources

📁 **Teaching Resources**
Chapter 11 Project Support with Project Manager, Student Activities, Teacher Notes

Teaching Notes

Activating Prior Knowledge
Discuss the idea of equally likely outcomes with students. Ask:
- *How could you use a six-sided number cube to give each of the three movies the same chance of being chosen?* Sample: Assign 1–2 for one movie, 3–4 for another, and 5–6 for the third.

Physical Education Connection
Have students talk about how the idea of equal outcomes applies in the sports world.

Working for a Cause

Students apply their knowledge of operations with money to come up with a fundraising plan.

Resources

📁 **Teaching Resources**
Chapter 12 Project Support with Project Manager, Student Activities, Teacher Notes

Teaching Notes

Activating Prior Knowledge
Discuss fundraising by focusing on who does it and how they do it. Invite students to share their experiences raising money. Ask:
- *What must you consider when you plan how to raise money for a charity?* Sample: how much money is needed, where to find interested contributors, how to motivate them to contribute, how to keep track of and safeguard the money

T641

1. eight hundred fifty-four

2. ten thousand, fifty-nine

3. seven thousand, three hundred two

4. one million, two hundred five thousand, eight hundred seven

5. twenty-six hundredths

6. three thousand four hundred eighty-one ten thousandths

7. seventy-two and fifty-three thousandths

8. six hundred ninety-one and four tenths

Chapter 1

Extra Practice

● **Lesson 1-1 and Lesson 1-2** **Write each number in words.** 1–8. See margin.

1. 854   **2.** 10,059   **3.** 7,302   **4.** 1,205,807

5. 0.26   **6.** 0.3481   **7.** 72.053   **8.** 691.4

Write each number in standard form.

9. two hundred sixteen   216   **10.** two hundred twenty-two thousandths   0.222

● **Lesson 1-3** **Order each set of decimals from least to greatest.**

11. 0.2, 0.4, 0.7   **12.** 0.2, 0.02, 0.202, 0.002   **13.** 6.25, 6.05, 6.2, 6.025
    0.2, 0.4, 0.7   0.002, 0.02, 0.2, 0.202   6.025, 6.05, 6.2, 6.25

● **Lesson 1-4** **Use rounding, front-end estimation, or compatible numbers to estimate.**

14. 5.32×2.01 **15.** $15.348 - 7.92$ **16.** $22.961 \div 3.6$ **17.** $728.6 + 36.09$
    about 10   about 7   about 6   about 770

● **Lesson 1-5** **First estimate and then find each sum or difference.**

18. $1.14 + 9.3$ 10; 10.44   **19.** $3.541 + 1.333$ 5; 4.874   **20.** $5.45 - 2.8$ 2; 2.65   **21.** $4.11 - 2.621$ 1; 1.489

● **Lesson 1-6** **Use a Problem-Solving Plan to solve the problem.**

22. A bag of popcorn costs $2.35. A coupon will save you $2.00 on 4 bags. How much will 5 bags cost before tax if you use the coupon? $9.75

● **Lesson 1-7** **Find each product.**

23. 1.8×4.302 7.7436   **24.** $0.29(0.43)$ 0.1247   **25.** $7.4(930)$ 6,882   **26.** $0.617 \cdot 0.09$ 0.05553

● **Lesson 1-8** **Use mental math to find each product or quotient.**

27. $3.85 \times 1,000$ 3,850   **28.** $100 \cdot 2.7$ 270   **29.** $93.1 \div 10$ 9.31   **30.** $105 \div 1,000$ 0.105

● **Lesson 1-9** **Find each quotient. Identify each as a terminating or repeating decimal.**

31. $8 \div 9$ **32.** $23 \div 25$ **33.** $348 \div 60$ **34.** $11 \div 16$
    $0.\overline{8}$; repeating   0.92; terminating   5.8; terminating   0.6875; terminating

● **Lesson 1-10** **Find the value of each expression.**

35. $2 + 6 \times 3 + 1$ 21   **36.** $(14 + 44) \div 2$ 29   **37.** $3 + 64 \div 4 - 10$ 9   **38.** $144 + 56 \div 4$ 158

Chapter 2 Extra Practice

Lesson 2-1 Write the next three terms and write a rule for each number pattern. **1–4.** See margin.

1. $1, 4, 16, 64, \ldots$ **2.** $2, 6, 18, 54, \ldots$ **3.** $7, 11, 15, 19, \ldots$ **4.** $80, 74, 68, 62, \ldots$

Lesson 2-2 Evaluate each expression for $n = 9$.

5. $n - 7$ 2   **6.** $3n - 5$ 22   **7.** $22 - 2n$ 4   **8.** $4n \div 6$ 6

Lesson 2-3 Write an expression for each word phrase.

9. 1 less than b $b - 1$ **10.** p times 2 $2p$ **11.** 4 more than b $b + 4$ **12.** n divided by 2 $n \div 2$

Lesson 2-4 Use the strategy *Make a Table and Look for a Pattern.*

13. For $3.00, Audrey buys a sandwich and milk for lunch. Suppose the amount she spends for lunch increases $.10 each day. What will Audrey pay for lunch on the sixth day? $3.50

Lesson 2-5 Tell whether each equation is true or false.

14. $65 = 10 + 85$ false   **15.** $8 \times 6 = 48$ true   **16.** $1 \times 9.8 = 9.8$ true   **17.** $9 = 24 \div 3$ false

Use mental math to solve each equation.

18. $20 = y + 1$ 19   **19.** $t - 10 = 24$ 34   **20.** $a \div 3 = 3$ 9   **21.** $178 = 10b$ 17.8

Lessons 2-6 and 2-7 Solve each equation. Then check the solution.

22. $b + 4 = 7.7$ 3.7   **23.** $c + 3.5 = 7.5$ 4   **24.** $n - 1.7 = 8$ 9.7   **25.** $8.4 = s - 0.2$ 8.6

26. $15t = 600$ 40   **27.** $62 = 2b$ 31   **28.** $x \div 5 = 2.5$ 12.5   **29.** $a \div 0.05 = 140$ 7

Lesson 2-8 Write each number in expanded form using powers of 10. **30–33.** See margin.

30. $9,450$ **31.** $72,003$ **32.** $300,026$ **33.** $8,120,432$

Simplify each expression.

34. $7 + 5^2$ 32   **35.** $(6 - 2)^3 \times 3$ 192   **36.** 8^3 512   **37.** $9^2 + 2^2$ 85

Lesson 2-9 Use the Distributive Property to simplify each expression.

38. 7×78 546   **39.** 3×19 57   **40.** 6×66 396   **41.** 4×47 188

Margin

1. 256; 1,024; 4,096; the first term is 1. Multiply each term by 4.

2. 162; 486; 1,458; the first term is 2. Multiply each term by 3.

3. 23, 27, 31; the first term is 7. Add 4 to each term.

4. 56, 50, 44; the first term is 80. Subtract 6 from each term.

30. $9 \times 10^3 + 4 \times 10^2 + 5 \times 10^1 + 0 \times 1$

31. $7 \times 10^4 + 2 \times 10^3 + 0 \times 10^2 + 0 \times 10^1 + 3 \times 1$

32. $3 \times 10^5 + 0 \times 10^4 + 0 \times 10^3 + 0 \times 10^2 + 2 \times 10^1 + 6 \times 1$

33. $8 \times 10^6 + 1 \times 10^5 + 2 \times 10^4 + 0 \times 10^3 + 4 \times 10^2 + 3 \times 10^1 + 2 \times 1$

● **Lesson 3-1** Test each number for divisibility by 2, 3, 5, 9, or 10.

1. 324 2, 3, 9 **2.** 2,685 3, 5 **3.** 540 **4.** 114 2, 3 **5.** 31 none **6.** 981 3, 9
2, 3, 5, 9, 10

● **Lesson 3-2** Tell whether each number is prime or composite.

7. 24 **8.** 49 **9.** 7 **10.** 81 **11.** 37 **12.** 29
composite composite prime composite prime prime

● **Lesson 3-3** Find the GCF of each set of numbers.

13. 10, 30 10 **14.** 15, 18 3 **15.** 25, 35 5 **16.** 28, 36 4 **17.** 45, 72 9 **18.** 8, 12, 20 4

● **Lesson 3-4** Write each fraction in simplest form.

19. $\frac{6}{60}$ $\frac{1}{10}$ **20.** $\frac{3}{5}$ $\frac{3}{5}$ **21.** $\frac{27}{36}$ $\frac{3}{4}$ **22.** $\frac{40}{50}$ $\frac{4}{5}$ **23.** $\frac{3}{4}$ $\frac{3}{4}$ **24.** $\frac{42}{70}$ $\frac{3}{5}$

● **Lesson 3-5** Write each mixed number as an improper fraction. Write each improper fraction as a mixed number in simplest form.

25. $1\frac{7}{8}$ $\frac{15}{8}$ **26.** $2\frac{3}{5}$ $\frac{13}{5}$ **27.** $11\frac{1}{9}$ $\frac{100}{9}$ **28.** $\frac{25}{7}$ $3\frac{4}{7}$ **29.** $\frac{39}{12}$ $3\frac{1}{4}$ **30.** $\frac{12}{5}$ $2\frac{2}{5}$

● **Lesson 3-6** Find the LCM of each set of numbers.

31. 4, 8 8 **32.** 6, 14 42 **33.** 15, 25 75 **34.** 20, 36 180 **35.** 3, 4, 12 12 **36.** 8, 10, 15
120

● **Lesson 3-7** Order each set of numbers from least to greatest.

37. $\frac{4}{7}, \frac{4}{5}, \frac{4}{9}$ **38.** $\frac{6}{16}, \frac{7}{16}, \frac{5}{16}$ **39.** $\frac{2}{3}, \frac{5}{6}, \frac{7}{12}$ **40.** $\frac{3}{4}, \frac{4}{6}, \frac{7}{9}$ **41.** $2\frac{3}{4}, 2\frac{1}{8}, 2\frac{1}{2}$ **42.** $\frac{5}{8}, \frac{3}{5}, \frac{9}{20}$
$\frac{4}{9}, \frac{4}{7}, \frac{4}{5}$ $\frac{5}{16}, \frac{6}{16}, \frac{7}{16}$ $\frac{7}{12}, \frac{2}{3}, \frac{5}{6}$ $\frac{4}{6}, \frac{3}{4}, \frac{7}{9}$ $2\frac{1}{8}, 2\frac{1}{2}, 2\frac{3}{4}$ $\frac{9}{20}, \frac{3}{5}, \frac{5}{8}$

● **Lesson 3-8** Write each decimal as a fraction or mixed number in simplest form.

43. 1.25 $1\frac{1}{4}$ **44.** 0.02 $\frac{1}{50}$ **45.** 0.32 $\frac{8}{25}$ **46.** 3.45 $3\frac{9}{20}$ **47.** 0.175 $\frac{7}{40}$ **48.** 2.16 $2\frac{4}{25}$

Write each fraction or mixed number as a decimal. Use a bar to indicate repeating digits.

49. $\frac{2}{3}$ $0.\overline{6}$ **50.** $\frac{2}{5}$ 0.4 **51.** $\frac{1}{4}$ 0.25 **52.** $7\frac{5}{12}$ $7.41\overline{6}$ **53.** $4\frac{2}{3}$ $4.\overline{6}$ **54.** $\frac{13}{8}$ 1.625

● **Lesson 3-9** Use the strategy *Try, Check, and Revise* to solve the problem.

55. Reed pays $.40 for tolls twice a day. He must use exact change. How many quarters, nickels, and dimes does he need for five days?
Answers may vary. Sample: 10 quarters, 10 nickels, and 10 dimes

Chapter 4

Extra Practice

● **Lesson 4-1** Estimate each sum or difference. Use the benchmarks 0, $\frac{1}{2}$, or 1.

1. $\frac{2}{3} + \frac{1}{8}$ about $\frac{1}{2}$ **2.** $\frac{3}{5} + \frac{4}{7}$ about 1 **3.** $\frac{5}{6} - \frac{3}{8}$ about $\frac{1}{2}$ **4.** $\frac{3}{8} - \frac{5}{12}$ about 0

Estimate each sum or difference.

5. $12\frac{3}{4} - 7\frac{4}{9}$ about 6 **6.** $5\frac{7}{9} + 9\frac{3}{5}$ about 16 **7.** $2\frac{1}{3} - 1\frac{6}{7}$ about 0 **8.** $6\frac{3}{10} + 4\frac{5}{8}$ about 11

● **Lessons 4-2 and 4-3** Find each sum or difference.

9. $\frac{5}{8} + \frac{1}{8}$ $\frac{3}{4}$ **10.** $\frac{4}{5} - \frac{2}{5}$ $\frac{2}{5}$ **11.** $\frac{11}{12} + \frac{5}{12}$ $1\frac{1}{3}$ **12.** $\frac{7}{8} - \frac{3}{8}$ $\frac{1}{2}$

13. $\frac{5}{6} + \frac{2}{3}$ $1\frac{1}{2}$ **14.** $\frac{7}{8} - \frac{3}{4}$ $\frac{1}{8}$ **15.** $\frac{3}{5} + \frac{5}{8}$ $1\frac{9}{40}$ **16.** $\frac{3}{8} - \frac{1}{12}$ $\frac{7}{24}$

● **Lesson 4-4** Find each sum.

17. $6\frac{2}{3} + 1\frac{1}{2}$ $8\frac{1}{6}$ **18.** $5\frac{7}{8} + 1\frac{3}{4}$ $7\frac{5}{8}$ **19.** $8\frac{1}{4} + 3\frac{1}{3}$ $11\frac{7}{12}$ **20.** $7\frac{3}{10} + 3\frac{1}{4}$ $10\frac{11}{20}$

● **Lesson 4-5** Find each difference.

21. $7\frac{3}{8} - 1\frac{2}{3}$ $5\frac{17}{24}$ **22.** $11\frac{1}{6} - 2\frac{3}{4}$ $8\frac{5}{12}$ **23.** $7\frac{5}{6} - 2\frac{1}{10}$ $5\frac{11}{15}$ **24.** $6\frac{1}{3} - 2\frac{1}{4}$ $4\frac{1}{12}$

● **Lesson 4-6** Solve each equation.

25. $x + 6\frac{4}{9} = 8\frac{1}{9}$ $1\frac{2}{3}$ **26.** $y + 2\frac{3}{8} = 8\frac{1}{5}$ $5\frac{33}{40}$ **27.** $a + 9 = 12\frac{7}{9}$ $3\frac{7}{9}$ **28.** $4\frac{5}{7} = b - 3\frac{1}{2}$ $8\frac{3}{14}$

29. $c - 11\frac{2}{3} = 15$ $26\frac{2}{3}$ **30.** $n + 4\frac{1}{2} = 5$ $\frac{1}{2}$ **31.** $m - 5\frac{3}{4} = 10\frac{1}{2}$ $16\frac{1}{4}$ **32.** $p - 8\frac{1}{3} = 9\frac{1}{4}$ $17\frac{7}{12}$

● **Lesson 4-7** Find the elapsed time between each pair of times.

33. from 3:45 P.M. to 5:15 P.M.   1 h 30 min   **34.** from 8:10 P.M. to 11:55 P.M.   3 h 45 min

35. from 11:45 A.M. to 6:23 P.M.   6 h 38 min   **35.** from 4:05 A.M. to 4:10 P.M.   12 h 5 min

37. from 3:25 P.M. to 5:02 P.M.   1 h 37 min   **38.** from 8:10 A.M. to 11:55 A.M.   3 h 45 min

● **Lesson 4-8** Use the strategy *Draw a Diagram* to solve the problem.

39. All pies at a bakery are the same size. Apple pies are cut into eight equal pieces. Custard pies are cut into six equal pieces. Two slices of apple pie and three slices of custard pie are placed in a pie tin for a carry-out order. What fraction of the pie tin is filled? $\frac{3}{4}$ of the tin

Chapter 5 Extra Practice

● **Lesson 5-1 Find each product.**

1. $\frac{1}{2}$ of $\frac{2}{3}$ $\frac{1}{3}$ **2.** $\frac{1}{3}$ of $\frac{1}{5}$ $\frac{1}{15}$ **3.** $\frac{7}{8} \times \frac{3}{4}$ $\frac{21}{32}$ **4.** $\frac{7}{6} \times 42$ 49

● **Lesson 5-2 Find each product.**

5. $7\frac{1}{2} \times 2\frac{2}{3}$ 20   **6.** $6\frac{2}{3} \times 7\frac{1}{5}$ 48   **7.** $5\frac{5}{8} \times 2\frac{1}{3}$ $13\frac{1}{8}$ **8.** $12\frac{1}{4} \times 6\frac{2}{7}$ 77

● **Lesson 5-3 Find each quotient.**

9. $2 \div \frac{4}{5}$ $2\frac{1}{2}$ **10.** $\frac{2}{3} \div \frac{2}{5}$ $1\frac{2}{3}$ **11.** $\frac{1}{4} \div \frac{1}{5}$ $1\frac{1}{4}$ **12.** $\frac{4}{11} \div 8$ $\frac{1}{22}$

● **Lesson 5-4 Estimate each quotient.**

13. $12 \div 3\frac{1}{5}$ 4   **14.** $7\frac{3}{7} \div 1\frac{2}{5}$ 7   **15.** $41\frac{8}{10} \div 6\frac{1}{3}$ 7   **16.** $36\frac{2}{7} \div 4\frac{3}{9}$ 9

Find each quotient.

17. $2\frac{1}{4} \div \frac{2}{3}$ $3\frac{3}{8}$ **18.** $4\frac{1}{2} \div 3\frac{1}{3}$ $1\frac{7}{20}$ **19.** $2\frac{2}{5} \div \frac{2}{25}$ 30   **20.** $5\frac{2}{3} \div 1\frac{1}{2}$ $3\frac{7}{9}$

● **Lesson 5-5 Solve each equation. Check the solution.**

21. $\frac{x}{4} = 8$ 32   **22.** $\frac{a}{3} = 9$ 27   **23.** $\frac{c}{7} = 24$ 168   **24.** $\frac{m}{2} = 14$ 28

25. $\frac{r}{4} = 3.5$ 14   **26.** $\frac{t}{12} = 3$ 36   **27.** $\frac{1}{3}y = 15$ 45   **28.** $\frac{3}{4}w = 12$ 16

● **Lesson 5-6 Use the strategy *Solve a Simpler Problem* to solve the problem.**

29. You want to make a quilt that is 75 inches long and 50 inches wide. How many $6\frac{1}{4}$-inch squares do you need? **96 squares**

● **Lesson 5-7 Choose an appropriate unit for each measurement.**

30. capacity of a bathtub gallons   **31.** weight of a school bus tons

32. width of a computer monitor inches   **33.** weight of a pair of jeans ounces

34. your height feet   **35.** capacity of a water pitcher quarts

● **Lesson 5-8 Complete each statement.**

36. 4 ft = ▦ yd $1\frac{1}{3}$ **37.** 48 oz = ▦ lb 3   **38.** 32 qt = ▦ gal 8   **39.** 8,000 lb = ▦ t 4

40. 10 lb = ▦ oz 160   **41.** ▦ ft = 60 in. 5   **42.** 64 c = ▦ pt 32   **43.** 9 mi = ▦ ft 47,520

Extra Practice

● **Lesson 6-1** Write two different ratios equal to each ratio.   1-5. Answers may vary.

1. $\frac{30}{60}$ $\frac{1}{2}, \frac{4}{8}$

2. $5:15$ $1:3, 10:30$

3. 13 to 52
1 to 4, 26 to 104

4. $7:77$
$1:11, 14:154$

5. 18 to 72
1 to 4, 9 to 36

● **Lesson 6-2** Find each unit price. Round to the nearest cent. Then determine the better buy.

6. cereal: 12 ounces for $2.99
16 ounces for $3.59
$.25 per ounce; $.22 per ounce; 16 ounces for $3.59

7. rice: 8 ounces for $1.95
12 ounces for $2.99
$.24 per ounce; $.25 per ounce; 8 ounces for $1.95

● **Lesson 6-3** Do the ratios in each pair form a proportion?

8. $\frac{6}{30}, \frac{3}{15}$ yes

9. $\frac{9}{12}, \frac{12}{9}$ no

10. $\frac{13}{3}, \frac{26}{6}$ yes

11. $\frac{5}{225}, \frac{2}{95}$ no

12. $\frac{64}{130}, \frac{5}{10}$ no

● **Lesson 6-4** Solve each proportion.

13. $\frac{a}{50} = \frac{3}{75}$ 2

14. $\frac{18}{b} = \frac{3}{10}$ 60

15. $\frac{51}{17} = \frac{c}{3}$ 9

16. $\frac{2}{16} = \frac{d}{24}$ 3

17. $\frac{3}{45} = \frac{4}{g}$ 60

● **Lesson 6-5** Find each actual distance. Use a map scale of 1 centimeter : 100 kilometers.

18. 3.5 cm 350 km

19. 1.3 cm 130 km

20. 0.7 cm 70 km

21. 5 cm 500 km

● **Lesson 6-6** Write each percent as a decimal and as a fraction in simplest form.

22. 42%
0.42; $\frac{21}{50}$

23. 96%
0.96; $\frac{24}{25}$

24. 80%
0.8; $\frac{4}{5}$

25. 1%
0.01; $\frac{1}{100}$

26. 87%
0.87; $\frac{87}{100}$

27. 88%
0.88; $\frac{22}{25}$

Write each decimal or fraction as a percent.

28. 0.18 18%

29. 0.32 32%

30. 0.05 5%

31. $\frac{1}{4}$ 25%

32. $\frac{3}{4}$ 75%

33. $\frac{5}{8}$ 62.5%

● **Lesson 6-7** Find each answer.

34. 20% of 80 16

35. 15% of 22.5 3.375

36. 50% of 86 43

37. 90% of 100 90

● **Lesson 6-8** Estimate a 15% tip for each bill amount.   38–43. Answers may vary. Samples are given.

38. $34.90
about $5.25

39. $9.54
about $1.50

40. $17.50
about $2.70

41. $24.80
about $3.75

42. $15.21
about $2.25

43. $42.36
about $6.30

● **Lesson 6-9** Use the strategy *Write an Equation* to solve the problem.

44. Kennedy Middle School has 550 students. If the number of students increases by 8 percent, how many students will there be? 594 students

1. mean: 21.875
median: 22.5
mode: 22

2. mean: 12.483
median: 12.5
mode: none

3. mean: 44.875
median: 43.5
mode: 29

4.

Books Read	Tally	Frequency
1					3
2				3
3				2
4						4

```
                X
    X    X      X
    X    X   X  X
    X    X   X  X
  ─────────────────
    1    2   3  4
```

5.

wpm	Tally	Frequency
35						4
40					3
45		0
50		0
55				2
60		0
65				2
70			1

```
  X
  X   X
  X   X          X        X
  X   X          X     X  X
  X   X          X     X  X  X
  ──────────────────────────────
  35  40  45  50  55  60  65  70
```

7. hours of reading per year per person; type of reading material

11b. The United States received 25 silver medals during the 2000 Summer Olympics.

13.
```
6 | 9
7 | 2 4 7 8
8 | 5 6 9
9 | 1
```

Key: 6 | 9 means 69

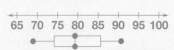
```
 ├─┼──┼──┼──┼──┼──┼──┤
 65 70 75 80 85 90 95 100
```

T648

● **Lesson 7-1** **Find the mean, median, and mode of each data set.** 1–3. See margin.

   1. 23, 26, 22, 25, 22, 28, 22, 10   **2.** 14.2, 11.3, 12.0, 11.1, 13.0, 13.3   **3.** 36, 42, 58, 29, 45, 63, 57, 29

● **Lesson 7-2** **Make a frequency table and a line plot for each set of data.** 4–5. See margin.

   4. books read each month:
3, 1, 4, 2, 4, 1, 3, 2, 4, 4, 2, 1

   5. words typed per minute:
65, 35, 40, 65, 40, 40, 55, 35, 35, 70, 35, 55

● **Lesson 7-3** **Use the strategy** *Make an Organized List* **to solve the problem.**

   6. How many ways can you make $1 using any combination of quarters, nickels, and dimes? **29 ways**

● **Lesson 7-4** **Use the bar graph for Exercises 7–8.**

   7. What information is given on each axis? **See margin.**

   8. What is the average yearly reading time for books?
about 100 hours

Average Yearly Reading by Americans

Hours per Person: 0, 50, 100, 150, 200 — Magazines, Newspapers, Books — Print

● **Lesson 7-5** **Use the circle graph for Exercises 9–10.**

   9. What item accounts for the most money in Malinda's budget? **rent**

   10. About what percent of her budget does Malinda use for rent? **25%**

Malinda's Budget

Clothes, Food, Rent, Savings, Charity, Insurance, Other

● **Lesson 7-6** **The spreadsheet below shows the number of medals the United States won during the 2000 Summer Olympics.**

   11. a. What is the value in C2? **25**
      b. What does this number mean?
      See margin.
   12. Write the formula for cell E2.
      = B2 + C2 + D2

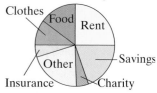

	A	B	C	D	E
1	Country	Gold	Silver	Bronze	Total
2	United States	39	25	33	■

● **Lesson 7-7** **Make a stem-and-leaf plot and a box-and-whisker plot for the set of data below.**

   13. test scores (percents): 86, 74, 72, 89, 69, 85, 78, 91, 77
      See margin.

● **Lesson 7-8** **Use the line graph at the right.**

   14. Explain why the graph is misleading.
      The intervals on the vertical scale are not the same.
   15. Use the data to draw a graph that is not misleading. **See margin.**

Daily Total Sales

Amount: $143, $147, $155, $169 — Mon. Tue. Wed. Thu. Fri. — Day

15.

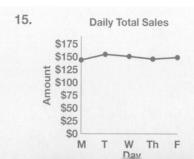

Daily Total Sales

Amount: $0, $25, $50, $75, $100, $125, $150, $175 — M T W Th F — Day

25.
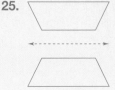

● **Lessons 8-1 and 8-2** Use the diagram at the right for Exercises 1–8.
Name each of the following. 1–2. Answers may vary.

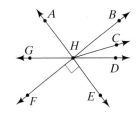

1. three collinear points
   Sample: *G, H, D.*

2. six rays
   Sample: $\overrightarrow{HA}$, $\overrightarrow{HB}$,
   $\overrightarrow{HC}$, $\overrightarrow{HD}$, $\overrightarrow{HE}$, $\overrightarrow{HF}$

3. two perpendicular lines
   Sample: $\overleftrightarrow{AE}$ and $\overleftrightarrow{FB}$

Use a protractor to measure each angle. Classify each angle as *acute*, *right*,
obtuse, or *straight*.

4. $\angle BHF$ straight 5. $\angle FHC$ obtuse 6. $\angle FHA$ right 7. $\angle CHD$ acute 8. $\angle AHC$ obtuse

● **Lesson 8-3** Find the complement and the supplement of each angle measure.

9. 28° 10. 13.5° 11. 56.3° 12. 79° 13. 85°
complement: 62° complement: 76.5° complement: 33.7° complement: 11° complement: 5°
supplement: 152° supplement: 166.5° supplement: 123.7° supplement: 101° supplement: 95°

● **Lesson 8-4** Classify each triangle with the given side lengths by its sides.

14. 7 inches, 9 inches, 7 inches 15. 3 feet, 3 feet, 3 feet 16. 18 yards, 16 yards, 5 yards
isosceles equilateral scalene

● **Lesson 8-5** Classify each statement as *true* or *false*.

17. All octagons have eight sides. 18. All rhombuses are squares. 19. All squares are rectangles.
true false true

● **Lesson 8-6** Use the strategy of *Use Logical Reasoning* to solve the problem.

20. You have four pairs of pants, six T-shirts, and five vests. How many
different outfits of pants, T-shirt, and vest can you wear? **120 outfits**

● **Lesson 8-7** Each pair of figures appears to be *similar*. Confirm your answer
by finding whether corresponding sides are proportional.

21.
similar

22.
similar

23.
not similar

● **Lesson 8-8** Trace the figure at the right.

24. Draw all lines of symmetry in the figure.

● **Lesson 8-9** Copy the figure at the right on graph paper.

25. Draw its reflection over the given line of reflection.
See margin.

T649

● **Lesson 9-1** **Choose an appropriate metric unit of measure.**

1. capacity of a shampoo bottle mL **2.** mass of a television kg **3.** length of your shoe cm

● **Lesson 9-2** **Complete each statement.**

4. 35 mm = ▨ cm **5.** 10.8 km = ▨ m **6.** ▨ L = 2,400 mL **7.** 1,008 g = ▨ kg
    3.5   10,800   2.4   1.008

● **Lesson 9-3** **Estimate the area of each figure. Each square represents 1 square centimeter.**

8. about 16 cm² **9.** about 18 cm² **10.** about 16 cm²

● **Lessons 9-3 and 9-4** **Find the area of each figure.**

11.  5.5 ft 52.25 ft² **12.** 12 m² **13.** 144 cm² 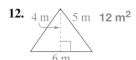 18 cm
       9.5 ft   6 m   10 cm   8 cm

● **Lessons 9-5 and 9-6** **Find the circumference and the area of a circle with the given diameter _d_ or radius _r_. Use 3.14 for _π_ and round to the nearest whole number.**

14. $d = 26$ yards **15.** $d = 10.6$ feet **16.** $r = 30$ inches **17.** $r = 11$ miles **18.** $d = 8.5$ meters

    82 yd; 531 yd²   33 ft; 88 ft²   188 in.; 2,826 in.²   69 mi; 380 mi²   27 m; 57 m²

● **Lesson 9-7** **Name each figure.**

19.   **20.**   **21.**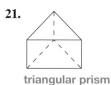

    rectangular pyramid   pentagonal prism   triangular prism

● **Lessons 9-8 and 9-9** **Find the surface area and the volume of each rectangular prism with the given dimensions.**

22. $\ell = 10$ ft, $w = 5$ ft, $h = 8$ ft   **23.** $\ell = 12$ m, $w = 16$ m, $h = 12$ m
    340 ft²; 400 ft³   1,056 m²; 2,304 m³

● **Lesson 9-10** **Use the strategy _Work Backward_ to solve this problem.**

24. If you multiply a number by 6 and then subtract 5, the result is 13. What is the number? 3

● **Lesson 10-1** Order from least to greatest.

1. 3, −1, 0, −2
−2, −1, 0, 3

2. 4, −8, −5, 2
−8, −5, 2, 4

3. −6, 8, 7, −8
−8, −6, 7, 8

4. −1, −8, 0, 1
−8, −1, 0, 1

● **Lesson 10-2** Find each sum.

5. −3 + (−1) −4
6. −14 + 28 14
7. −72 + (−53)
−125
8. −101 + 121 20
9. 65 + (−5) 60

● **Lesson 10-3** Find each difference.

10. −3 − 1 −4
11. 4 − 8 −4
12. 31 − (−52) 83
13. −27 − (−27) 0
14. 19 − (−18) 37

● **Lessons 10-4 and 10-5** Find each product or quotient.

15. −8 × 5 −40
16. −4 × (−9) 36
17. 1 × (−12) −12
18. 93 ÷ (−3) −31

19. −68 ÷ 4 −17
20. −5 ÷ (−2) 2.5
21. 154 ÷ (−11) −14
22. −54 ÷ 9 −6

● **Lesson 10-6** Use the coordinate grid at the right for Exercises 23–30.
Find the coordinates of each point.

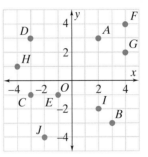

23. A (2, 3)
24. B (3, −3)
25. C (−3, −1)
26. D (−3, 3)

Name the point with the given coordinates.

27. (4, 2) G
28. (2, −2) I
29. (−4, 1) H
30. (−2, −4) J

● **Lesson 10-7** Look at the data for Snazzy Stuff. Find the profit or loss for each month.

31. January $5,002
32. March $1,263
33. May −$86

34. Draw a line graph based on the profits and losses for Snazzy Stuff.
See margin.

Snazzy Stuff

Month	Income	Expenses
Jan.	$9,002	−$4,000
Feb.	$8,410	−$5,113
Mar.	$7,596	−$6,333
Apr.	$7,523	−$7,641
May	$7,941	−$8,027
June	$8,569	−$6,299

● **Lesson 10-8** Make a table and graph each function.

35. Kilometers are a function of meters. See margin.

36. Yards are a function of feet. See margin.

● **Lesson 10-9** Use the strategy *Make a Graph* to solve this problem.

37. A health bar charges $1.76 for a 16-ounce shake and $2.20 for a 20-ounce shake. What should the health bar charge for a 24-ounce shake?
Answers may vary. $2.64

34.

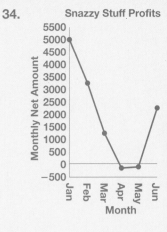

Snazzy Stuff Profits

35.

m	1,000	1,500	2,000	2,500
km	1	1.5	2	2.5

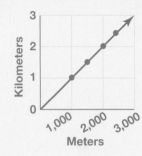

36.

Ft	3	6	9	12
Yd	1	2	3	4

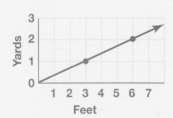

T651

17.

18.

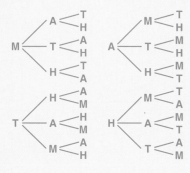

● **Lesson 11-1** **A jar contains 2 red, 4 yellow, 3 green, and 5 blue marbles. You select a marble without looking. Find each probability.**

1. P(yellow) $\frac{2}{7}$ **2.** P(green) $\frac{3}{14}$ **3.** P(red or blue) $\frac{1}{2}$ **4.** P(red, green, or blue) $\frac{5}{7}$

● **Lesson 11-2** **Find the experimental probability that each person wins.**

5. Yelena won 168 of 196 games. $\frac{6}{7}$

6. Chang played a game 43 times and did not lose a game. 100%

● **Lesson 11-3** **The probability of winning a game is 80%. How many times should you expect to win if you play the following number of times?**

7. 4 3   **8.** 10 8   **9.** 30 24   **10.** 55 44   **11.** 125 100   **12.** 520 416

Write and solve a proportion to make the prediction.

13. In a school of 2,037 students, 500 were asked to name their favorite fruit. Apples were named by 325 students. Predict how many of the 2,037 students would name apples as their favorite fruit. 1,324 students

● **Lesson 11-4** **Use the strategy *Simulate a Problem* to solve the problem.**

14. The forecast calls for a $\frac{2}{3}$ chance of rain for each of the next three days. Find the experimental probability that it rains on two of the three days. Use three number cubes. Let 1, 2, 3, and 4 represent rain. Check students' work.

● **Lesson 11-5** **Use the counting principle.**

15. You flip a coin six times. Find P(three tails). $\frac{1}{8}$

16. You roll a number cube two times. Find P(two odds). $\frac{1}{4}$

● **Lesson 11-6** **Draw a tree diagram to find the permutations. Use each item exactly once.**   17–18. See margins for diagrams.

17. the numbers 6, 7, 8 6   **18.** the letters M, A, T, H 24

● **Lesson 11-7** **A bag contains 2 red, 6 blue, and 2 green marbles. Marbles are drawn twice with replacement. Find the probability of each compound event.**

19. blue, then red $\frac{3}{25}$ **20.** both blue $\frac{9}{25}$ **21.** both not green $\frac{16}{25}$

● **Lesson 12-1** Solve each equation.

1. $2a + 8 = 26$ 9

2. $3c + 2.5 = 29.5$ 9

3. $5b - 13 = 17$ 6

4. $7.5d - 7 = 53$ 8

5. $4e - 1 = -93$ −23

6. $\frac{f}{8} + 6 = 8$ 16

7. $2 + 8g = 34$ 4

8. $-4 + \frac{h}{4} = 4$ 32

● **Lesson 12-2** Write an inequality for each graph.

9.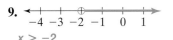
$x > -2$

10.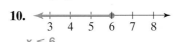
$x \leq 6$

11.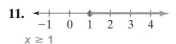
$x \geq 1$

Write an inequality to represent each situation. Then graph the inequality. 12–14. See margin for graphs.

12. The temperature stayed below 0°. $d < 0$

13. You must bring at least $5 to cover the cost of lunch. $c \geq 5$

14. The paintings for display can be a maximum of 12 inches wide. $p \leq 12$

● **Lesson 12-3** Solve each inequality.

15. $m + 8 < 14$
$m < 6$

16. $n - 16 \geq 3$
$n \geq 19$

17. $p + 9 \leq -5$
$p \leq -14$

18. $q - 8 > 7$
$q > 15$

● **Lesson 12-4** Use the strategy *Draw a Diagram* or *Write an Equation* to solve each problem. Explain why you chose the method you did.

19. There are 120 bicycles in a parade. Thirty-five percent of them have streamers. How many bicycles have streamers? 42; check students' explanations.

20. Your fabric is 10 feet by 8 feet. You want small strips that are 6 inches long and 4 inches wide. How many strips can you cut from the fabric?
480; check students' explanations.

● **Lesson 12-5** Find each square root.

21. $\sqrt{49}$ 7

22. $\sqrt{81}$ 9

23. $\sqrt{169}$ 13

24. $\sqrt{484}$ 22

25. $\sqrt{625}$ 25

26. $\sqrt{900}$ 30

Tell which two consecutive whole numbers the square root is between.

27. $\sqrt{3}$
1, 2

28. $\sqrt{11}$
3, 4

29. $\sqrt{17}$
4, 5

30. $\sqrt{29}$
5, 6

31. $\sqrt{51}$
7, 8

32. $\sqrt{92}$
9, 10

● **Lesson 12-6** Find the missing side length of each right triangle.

33. $a = 16, b = 30, c = \blacksquare$
34

34. $a = 21, b = \blacksquare, c = 35$
28

35. $a = \blacksquare, b = 9, c = 15$
12

12.
$d < 0$

14.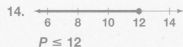
$P \leq 12$

13.
$c \geq 5$

Skills Handbook

Place Value of Whole Numbers

The digits in a whole number are grouped into periods. A period has three digits, and each period has a name. Each digit in a whole number has both a place and a value.

Billions Period			Millions Period			Thousands Period			Ones Period		
Hundred billions	Ten billions	Billions	Hundred millions	Ten millions	Millions	Hundred thousands	Ten thousands	Thousands	Hundreds	Tens	Ones
9	5	1	6	3	7	0	4	1	1	8	2

The digit 5 is in the ten billions place. So, its value is 5 ten billions, or 50 billion.

 EXAMPLE

a. In what place is the digit 7?

millions

b. What is the value of the digit 7?

7 million

EXERCISES

Use the chart above. Write the place of each digit.

1. the digit 3   ten millions
2. the digit 4   ten thousands
3. the digit 6   hundred millions
4. the digit 8   tens
5. the digit 9   hundred billions
6. the digit 0   hundred thousands

Use the chart above. Write the value of each digit.

7. the digit 3   3 ten million
8. the digit 4   4 ten thousand
9. the digit 6   6 hundred million
10. the digit 8   8 ten
11. the digit 9   9 hundred billion
12. the digit 0   0 hundred thousand

Write the value of the digit 6 in each number.

13. 633
6 hundred
14. 761,523
6 ten thousand
15. 163,500,000
6 ten million
16. 165,417
6 ten thousand

17. 265
6 ten
18. 4,396
6 one
19. 618,920
6 hundred thousand
20. 204,602
6 hundred

21. 162,450,000,000
6 ten billion
22. 7,682
6 hundred
23. 358,026,113
6 thousand
24. 76,030,100
6 million

25. 642,379
6 hundred thousand
26. 16,403
6 thousand
27. 45,060
6 ten
28. 401,601,001
6 hundred thousand

Rounding Whole Numbers

Number lines can help you round numbers. On a number line, 5 is halfway between 0 and 10, 50 is halfway between 0 and 100, and 500 is halfway between 1 and 1,000. The accepted method of rounding is to round 5 up to 10, 50 up to 100, and 500 up to 1,000.

 **1 EXAMPLE**

Round 2,462 to the nearest ten.

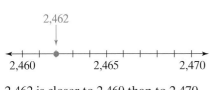

2,462 is closer to 2,460 than to 2,470.

2,462 rounded to the nearest ten is 2,460.

2 EXAMPLE

Round 247,451 to the nearest hundred.

247,451 is closer to 247,500 than to 247,400.

247,451 rounded to the nearest hundred is 247,500.

EXERCISES

Round each number to the nearest ten.

1. 65 70   **2.** 832 830   **3.** 4,437 4,440   **4.** 21,024 21,020   **5.** 3,545 3,550

Round each number to the nearest hundred.

6. 889 900   **7.** 344 300   **8.** 2,861 2,900   **9.** 1,138 1,100   **10.** 50,549 50,500

11. 6,411 6,400   **12.** 88,894 88,900   **13.** 13,735 13,700   **14.** 17,459 17,500   **15.** 6,059 6,100

Round each number to the nearest thousand.

16. 2,400 2,000   **17.** 16,218 16,000   **18.** 7,430 7,000   **19.** 89,375 89,000   **20.** 9,821 10,000

21. 15,631 16,000   **22.** 76,900 77,000   **23.** 163,875 164,000   **24.** 38,295 38,000   **25.** 102,359 102,000

26. Describe a situation in which it is helpful to round data. Check students' work.

27. Explain how to round number 17 in the exercises above to the nearest ten thousand.   Check students' work.

28. Suppose you round 31 to the nearest hundred. Is 0 a reasonable response? Explain your answer.   Answers may vary. Sample: Yes; 31 is closer to 0 than it is to 100.

Adding Whole Numbers

When you add, line up the digits in the correct columns. Begin by adding the ones. You may need to regroup from one column to the next.

1 EXAMPLE

Add 463 + 58.

Step 1	Step 2	Step 3
1	11	11
463	463	463
+ 58	+ 58	+ 58
1	21	521

2 EXAMPLE

Find each sum.

a. 962 + 120

962
+ 120
1,082

b. 25 + 9 + 143

1
25
9
+ 143
177

c. 3,887 + 1,201

1
3,887
+ 1,201
5,088

EXERCISES

Find each sum.

1. 45 + 31 = 76

2. 56 + 80 = 136

3. 25 + 16 = 41

4. 43 + 29 = 72

5. 66 + 78 = 144

6. 87 + 35 = 122

7. 81 + 312 = 393

8. 406 + 123 = 529

9. 207 + 72 = 279

10. 480 + 365 = 845

11. 217 + 347 = 564

12. 675 + 329 = 1,004

13. 2,051 + 843 = 2,894

14. 786 + 4,109 = 4,895

15. 5,227 + 1,527 = 6,754

16. 3,104 + 2,698 = 5,802

17. 5,337 + 1,812 = 7,149

18. 4,282 + 7,518 = 11,800

19. 78 + 56 = 134

20. 35 + 96 = 131

21. 105 + 71 = 176

22. 29 + 342 = 371

23. 654 + 103 = 757

24. 286 + 42 = 328

25. 55 + 77 = 132

26. 242 + 83 = 325

27. 32 + 68 = 100

28. 108 + 13 = 121

29. 589 + 318 = 907

30. 642 + 975 = 1,617

31. 2,308 + 451 = 2,759

32. 976 + 4,035 = 5,011

33. 8,228 + 1,024 = 9,252

34. 5,417 + 2,391 = 7,808

35. 6,470 + 9,828 = 16,298

36. 7,121 + 5,359 = 12,480

Subtracting Whole Numbers

When you subtract, line up the digits in the correct columns. Begin by subtracting the ones. Rename if the bottom digit is greater than the top digit. You may need to rename more than once.

① EXAMPLE

Subtract 725 − 86.

Step 1

$$
\begin{array}{r}
{\scriptstyle 1\,1\,5} \\
725 \\
-\ 86 \\
\hline
9
\end{array}
$$

Step 2

$$
\begin{array}{r}
{\scriptstyle 1\,1} \\
{\scriptstyle 6\,\,15} \\
725 \\
-\ 86 \\
\hline
39
\end{array}
$$

Step 3

$$
\begin{array}{r}
{\scriptstyle 1\,1} \\
{\scriptstyle 6\,\,15} \\
725 \\
-\ 86 \\
\hline
639
\end{array}
$$

② EXAMPLE

Find each difference.

a. 602 − 174

$$
\begin{array}{r}
{\scriptstyle 9} \\
{\scriptstyle 5\,10\,12} \\
602 \\
-\ 174 \\
\hline
428
\end{array}
$$

b. 625 − 273

$$
\begin{array}{r}
{\scriptstyle 5\,12} \\
625 \\
-\ 273 \\
\hline
352
\end{array}
$$

c. 5,002 − 1,247

$$
\begin{array}{r}
{\scriptstyle 9\ \ 9} \\
{\scriptstyle 4\,10\,10\,12} \\
5,002 \\
-\ 1,247 \\
\hline
3,755
\end{array}
$$

EXERCISES

Find each difference.

1. 81 − 37 = 44	**2.** 59 − 23 = 36	**3.** 41 − 19 = 22	**4.** 83 − 25 = 58	**5.** 99 − 78 = 21	**6.** 87 − 31 = 56
7. 707 − 361 = 346	**8.** 680 − 47 = 633	**9.** 240 − 63 = 177	**10.** 881 − 391 = 490	**11.** 517 − 287 = 230	**12.** 973 − 529 = 444
13. 7,411 − 583 = 6,828	**14.** 3,789 − 809 = 2,980	**15.** 6,508 − 2,147 = 4,361	**16.** 8,000 − 5,274 = 2,726	**17.** 3,003 − 1,998 = 1,005	**18.** 8,282 − 4,118 = 4,164

19. 78 − 19 59 **20.** 231 − 99 132 **21.** 901 − 65 836 **22.** 629 − 382 247 **23.** 918 − 133 785

24. 800 − 435 365 **25.** 403 − 122 281 **26.** 973 − 228 745 **27.** 721 − 119 602 **28.** 522 − 146 376

29. 642 − 223 419 **30.** 427 − 193 234 **31.** 444 − 345 99 **32.** 988 − 489 499 **33.** 601 − 425 176

Multiplying Whole Numbers

When you multiply by a one-digit number, multiply the one-digit number by each digit in the other number.

 EXAMPLE

Multiply 294 × 7.

Step 1 Multiply 7 by the ones digit.

$$\begin{array}{r} \overset{2}{294} \\ \times\quad 7 \\ \hline 8 \end{array}$$

Step 2 Multiply 7 by the tens digit.

$$\begin{array}{r} \overset{62}{294} \\ \times\quad 7 \\ \hline 58 \end{array}$$

Step 3 Multiply 7 by the hundreds digit.

$$\begin{array}{r} \overset{62}{294} \\ \times\quad 7 \\ \hline 2{,}058 \end{array}$$

When you multiply by a two-digit number, first multiply by the ones. Then multiply by the tens. Add the products. Remember, 0 times any number is equal to 0.

2 EXAMPLE

Multiply 48 × 327.

Step 1 Multiply the ones.

$$\begin{array}{r} \overset{25}{327} \\ \times\quad 48 \\ \hline 2{,}616 \end{array}$$

Step 2 Multiply the tens.

$$\begin{array}{r} \overset{12}{327} \\ \times\quad 48 \\ \hline 2616 \\ +\ 1308 \\ \hline \end{array}$$

Step 3 Add the products.

$$\begin{array}{r} 327 \\ \times\quad 48 \\ \hline 2616 \\ +\ 1308 \\ \hline 15{,}696 \end{array}$$

EXERCISES

Find each product.

1. $\begin{array}{r} 81 \\ \times\ 3 \\ \hline 243 \end{array}$

2. $\begin{array}{r} 47 \\ \times\ 2 \\ \hline 94 \end{array}$

3. $\begin{array}{r} 58 \\ \times\ 6 \\ \hline 348 \end{array}$

4. $\begin{array}{r} 678 \\ \times\ 5 \\ \hline 3{,}390 \end{array}$

5. $\begin{array}{r} 412 \\ \times\ 7 \\ \hline 2{,}884 \end{array}$

6. $\begin{array}{r} 326 \\ \times\ 4 \\ \hline 1{,}304 \end{array}$

7. 7 × 45 **315**
8. 62 × 3 **186**
9. 213 × 4 **852**
10. 8 × 177 **1,416**
11. 673 × 9 **6,057**

12. 5 × 41 **205**
13. 3 × 82 **246**
14. 94 × 6 **564**
15. 63 × 4 **252**
16. 58 × 3 **174**

17. $\begin{array}{r} 25 \\ \times\ 46 \\ \hline 1{,}150 \end{array}$

18. $\begin{array}{r} 62 \\ \times\ 88 \\ \hline 5{,}456 \end{array}$

19. $\begin{array}{r} 808 \\ \times\ 60 \\ \hline 48{,}480 \end{array}$

20. $\begin{array}{r} 409 \\ \times\ 70 \\ \hline 28{,}630 \end{array}$

21. $\begin{array}{r} 915 \\ \times\ 27 \\ \hline 24{,}705 \end{array}$

22. $\begin{array}{r} 312 \\ \times\ 53 \\ \hline 16{,}536 \end{array}$

23. 415 × 76 **31,540**
24. 500 × 80 **40,000**
25. 320 × 47 **15,040**
26. 562 × 18 **10,116**
27. 946 × 37 **35,002**

28. 76 × 103 **7,828**
29. 32 × 558 **17,856**
30. 371 × 84 **31,164**
31. 505 × 40 **20,200**
32. 620 × 19 **11,780**

658 Skills Handbook

Multiplying and Dividing Whole Numbers by 10, 100, and 1,000

Basic facts and patterns can help you when multiplying and dividing whole numbers by 10, 100, and 1,000.

$8 \times 1 = 8$	$5,000 \div 1 = 5,000$
$8 \times 10 = 80$	$5,000 \div 10 = 500$
$8 \times 100 = 800$	$5,000 \div 100 = 50$
$8 \times 1,000 = 8,000$	$5,000 \div 1,000 = 5$

Count the number of ending zeros.

The product will have this many zeros.

Count the zeros in the divisor.

If possible, remove this many zeros from the dividend. This number will be the quotient.

 EXAMPLE

Multiply or divide.

a. $77 \times 1,000$

77,000   ← Insert three zeros.

b. $430 \div 10$

43   ← Remove one zero.

EXERCISES

Multiply.

1. 85×10
850
2. 85×100
8,500
3. $85 \times 1,000$
85,000
4. $420 \times 1,000$
420,000
5. 420×100
42,000
6. 420×10
4,200
7. 603×100
60,300
8. 97×10
970
9. 31×100
3,100
10. 10×17
170
11. 100×56
5,600
12. $1,000 \times 4$
4,000
13. 13×10
130
14. 68×100
6,800
15. $19 \times 1,000$
19,000

Divide.

16. $3,200 \div 10$
320
17. $3,200 \div 100$
32
18. $32,000 \div 1,000$
32
19. $8,000 \div 100$
80
20. $8,000 \div 10$
800
21. $170 \div 10$
17
22. $45,000 \div 1,000$
45
23. $9,300 \div 10$
930
24. $90 \div 10$
9
25. $6,100 \div 100$
61
26. $7,900 \div 100$
79
27. $2,400 \div 10$
240
28. $240 \div 10$
24
29. $78,000 \div 1,000$
78
30. $9,900 \div 10$
990

Multiply or divide.

31. 76×100
7,600
32. $52 \times 1,000$
52,000
33. $370 \div 10$
37
34. 505×10
5,050
35. $6,200 \div 100$
62
36. $340 \div 10$
34
37. $14,000 \div 1,000$
14
38. 253×100
25,300
39. $3,700 \div 10$
370
40. 418×10
4,180

Dividing Whole Numbers

Division is the opposite of multiplication. So, you multiply the divisor by your estimate for each digit in the quotient. Then subtract. You repeat this step until you have a remainder that is less than the divisor.

 **EXAMPLE**

Divide 23)1,178.

Step 1 Estimate the quotient.

$1,178 \div 23$ ← The dividend is 1,178. The divisor is 23.

$\downarrow \quad \downarrow$

$1,200 \div 20 = 60$ ← Round 1,178 to the nearest hundred. Round 23 to the nearest ten.

Step 2

```
      6     ← Try 6 tens.
23)1178
  − 138    ← 6 × 23 = 138
           You cannot
           subtract, so
           6 tens is
           too much.
```

Step 3

```
      5     ← Try 5 tens.
23)1178
  − 115    ← 5 × 23 = 115
      2     ← Subtract.
```

Step 4

```
      51 R5
23)1178
  − 115↓
      28   ← Bring down 8.
    − 23   ← 1 × 23 = 23
       5   ← Subtract. The
             remainder is 5.
```

Step 5 Check your answer.

First compare your answer to the estimate. Since 51 R5 is close to 60, the answer is reasonable.

Then find $51 \times 23 + 5$.

EXERCISES

Find each quotient. Check your answer.

1. $9)659$ 73 R2
2. $9)376$ 41 R7
3. $3)280$ 93 R1
4. $8)541$ 67 R5
5. $8)232$ 29

6. $1,058 \div 5$ 211 R3
7. $3,591 \div 3$ 1,197
8. $5,072 \div 7$ 724 R4
9. $1,718 \div 4$ 429 R2
10. $3,767 \div 6$ 627 R5

11. $3,872 \div 17$ 227 R13
12. $19)1,373$ 72 R5
13. $27)1,853$ 68 R17
14. $4,195 \div 59$ 71 R6
15. $41)4,038$ 98 R20

16. $2,612 \div 31$ 84 R8
17. $34)1,609$ 47 R11
18. $1,937 \div 40$ 48 R17
19. $54)1,350$ 25
20. $1,824 \div 32$ 57

21. **Writing in Math** Describe how to estimate a quotient. Use the words *dividend* and *divisor* in your description. **Check students' work.**

Zeros in Quotients

When you divide, after you bring down a digit you must write a digit in the quotient. In this example, the second digit in the quotient is 0.

EXAMPLE

Find $19\overline{)5{,}823}$.

Step 1

Estimate the quotient.

$5{,}823 \div 19$

↓ ↓

$5{,}800 \div 20 = 290$

Step 2

$$\begin{array}{r} 3 \\ 19\overline{)5{,}823} \\ -\,57 \\ \hline 1 \end{array}$$

Step 3

$$\begin{array}{r} 30 \\ 19\overline{)5{,}823} \\ -\,57 \\ \hline 12 \\ -\,0 \\ \hline 12 \end{array}$$

Step 4

$$\begin{array}{r} 306\ R9 \\ 19\overline{)5{,}823} \\ -\,57 \\ \hline 12 \\ -\,0 \\ \hline 123 \\ -\,114 \\ \hline 9 \end{array}$$

Step 5

Check your answer.
Since 306 is close to 290,
the answer is reasonable.
Find $306 \times 19 + 9$.

EXERCISES

Find each quotient.

1. $7\overline{)212}$ 30 R2

2. $9\overline{)367}$ 40 R7

3. $3\overline{)271}$ 90 R1

4. $8\overline{)485}$ 60 R5

5. $6\overline{)483}$ 80 R3

6. $34\overline{)1{,}371}$
40 R11

7. $19\overline{)1{,}335}$
70 R5

8. $62\overline{)1{,}881}$
30 R21

9. $54\overline{)1{,}094}$
20 R14

10. $41\overline{)3{,}710}$
90 R20

11. $282 \div 4$ 70 R2

12. $143 \div 7$ 20 R3

13. $181 \div 3$ 60 R1

14. $400 \div 8$ 50

15. $365 \div 9$ 40 R5

16. $1{,}008 \div 5$
201 R3

17. $3{,}018 \div 6$
503

18. $4{,}939 \div 7$
705 R4

19. $1{,}682 \div 4$
420 R2

20. $3{,}647 \div 6$
607 R5

21. $2{,}488 \div 31$
80 R8

22. $3{,}372 \div 67$
50 R22

23. $1{,}937 \div 48$
40 R17

24. $4{,}165 \div 59$
70 R35

25. $1{,}686 \div 82$
20 R46

Reading Thermometer Scales

The thermometer at the right shows temperature in degrees Celsius (°C) and degrees Fahrenheit (°F).

1 EXAMPLE

How do you read point *A* on the Celsius thermometer below?

Each 1-degree interval is divided into 10 smaller intervals of 0.1 degree each. The reading at point *A* is 36.2°C.

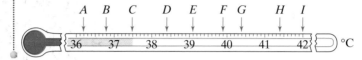

2 EXAMPLE

How do you read point *V* on the Fahrenheit thermometer below?

Each 1-degree interval is divided into 5 smaller intervals. Since 10 ÷ 5 = 2, each smaller interval represents 0.2 degree. Count by 0.2, beginning with 98.0. The reading at point *V* is 98.6°F.

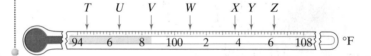

EXERCISES

Use the thermometers above to write the temperature reading for each point. Tell whether the reading is in degrees Celsius (°C) or degrees Fahrenheit (°F).

1. *B* 36.8°C   **2.** *C* 37.5°C   **3.** *D* 38.4°C   **4.** *T* 94.6°F   **5.** *U* 96.6°F   **6.** *Z* 106.2°F

Use the thermometers above to name the point that relates to each temperature reading.

7. 40.4°C *G*   **8.** 42.0°C *I*   **9.** 39.9°C *F*   **10.** 104.8°F *Y*   **11.** 101°F *W*   **12.** 103.8°F *X*

Degrees Celsius — Degrees Fahrenheit

- 120 / 250
- 110 / 230
- Boiling point of water — 100 / 210
- 90 / 190
- 80 / 170
- 70 / 150
- 60 / 130
- Normal body temp. — 50 / 110
- 40
- Hot day — 30 / 90
- Room temp. — 20 / 70
- 10 / 50
- Freezing point of water — 0 / 30
- −10 / 10
- Cold day — −20 / 0

Roman Numerals

The ancient Romans used letters to represent numerals. The table below shows the value of each Roman numeral.

I	V	X	L	C	D	M
1	5	10	50	100	500	1,000

Here are the Roman numerals from 1 to 10.

1	2	3	4	5	6	7	8	9	10
I	II	III	IV	V	VI	VII	VIII	IX	X

Roman numerals are read in groups from left to right.

If the value of the second numeral is the same as or less than the first numeral, add the values. The Roman numerals II, III, VI, VII, and VIII are examples in which you use addition.

If the value of the second numeral is greater than the first numeral, subtract the values. The Roman numerals IV and IX are examples in which you use subtraction.

Find the value of each Roman numeral.

a. CD

500 − 100

400

b. MXXVI

1,000 + 10 + 10 + 5 + 1

1,026

c. XCIV

(100 − 10) + (5 − 1)

90 + 4 = 94

EXERCISES

Find the value of each Roman numeral.

1. XI 11

2. DIII 503

3. XCV 95

4. CMX 910

5. XXIX 29

6. DLIX 559

7. MLVI 1,056

8. LX 60

9. CDIV 404

10. DCV 605

Write each number as a Roman numeral.

11. 15
XV

12. 35
XXXV

13. 1,632
MDCXXXII

14. 222
CCXXII

15. 159
CLIX

16. 67
LXVII

17. 92
XCII

18. 403
CDIII

19. 1,990
MCMXC

20. 64
LXIV

Estimating Lengths Using Nonstandard Units

Jan wanted to find a way to estimate lengths when she did not have any measuring tools. She measured her hand in several ways, the length of her foot and the length of her walking stride. Then she used these "natural units" as measuring tools.

Span

Finger width

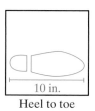
Hand

Heel to toe

Stride

EXAMPLE

Jan used strides to measure the length of her room. She counted about 5 strides. What is the approximate length of the room?

1 stride ≈ 32 in.	← **Write the relationship between strides and inches.**
5 × 1 stride ≈ 5 × 32 in.	← **Multiply both sides by 5.**
5 strides ≈ 160 in.	← **Change strides to inches.**
160 in. ≈ (160 ÷ 12) ft	← **Change inches to feet.**
160 in. ≈ 13 ft	

The approximate length of the room is 13 feet.

EXERCISES

Measure your "finger width," "hand," "span," and "heel to toe." Use these natural units to find the indicated measure for each object. Then give the approximate measure in inches, feet, or yards. 1–9. Answers may vary.

1. thickness of a math book
2. height of a chair
3. height of a door
4. length of an eraser
5. height of your desk
6. length of a new pencil
7. distance across a room
8. thickness of a door
9. length of a chalkboard

10. **Open-Ended** Measure your stride. Then measure something such as a hallway in strides, and approximate the length in feet or yards. Tell what distance you measured. Check students' work.

Tables

Table 1 Measures

Metric	United States Customary
Length	**Length**
10 millimeters (mm) = 1 centimeter (cm)	12 inches (in.) = 1 foot (ft)
100 cm = 1 meter (m)	36 in. = 1 yard (yd)
1,000 mm = 1 meter	3 ft = 1 yard
1,000 m = 1 kilometer (km)	5,280 ft = 1 mile (mi)
	1,760 yd = 1 mile
Area	**Area**
100 square millimeters (mm²) =	144 square inches (in.²) =
1 square centimeter (cm²)	1 square foot (ft²)
10,000 cm² = 1 square meter (m²)	9 ft² = 1 square yard (yd²)
	4,840 yd² = 1 acre
Volume	**Volume**
1,000 cubic millimeters (mm³) =	1,728 cubic inches (in.³) =
1 cubic centimeter (cm³)	1 cubic foot (ft³)
1,000,000 cm³ = 1 cubic meter (m³)	27 ft³ = 1 cubic yard (yd³)
Mass	**Mass**
1,000 milligrams (mg) = 1 gram (g)	16 ounces (oz) = 1 pound (lb)
1,000 g = 1 kilogram (kg)	2,000 lb = 1 ton (t)
Liquid Capacity	**Liquid Capacity**
1,000 milliliters (mL) = 1 liter (L)	8 fluid ounces (fl oz) = 1 cup (c)
1,000 L = 1 kiloliter (kL)	2 c = 1 pint (pt)
	2 pt = 1 quart (qt)
	4 qt = 1 gallon (gal)

Time

60 seconds (s) = 1 minute (min)
60 min = 1 hour (h)
24 h = 1 day
7 days = 1 week (wk)
365 days ≈ 52 wk ≈ 1 year (yr)

Table 2 Reading Math Symbols

+	plus (addition)	p. 5
=	is equal to	p. 6
>	is greater than	p. 6
<	is less than	p. 6
−	minus (subtraction)	p. 17
×, ·	times (multiplication)	p. 19
≈	is approximately equal to	p. 19
÷, $\sqrt{}$	divide (division)	p. 20
( )	parentheses for grouping	p. 25
. . .	and so on	p. 44
°	degree(s)	p. 79
≠	is not equal to	p. 84
$\stackrel{?}{=}$	Is the statement true?	p. 84
3^4	3 to the power 4	p. 99
$\frac{1}{4}$	reciprocal of 4	p. 230
3 : 5	ratio of 3 to 5	p. 269
%	percent	p. 293
*	multiply (in a spreadsheet formula)	p. 348
$\overline{AB}$	segment AB	p. 373
$\overrightarrow{AB}$	ray AB	p. 373
$\overleftrightarrow{AB}$	line AB	p. 373
∠ABC	angle with sides BA and BC	p. 379
∠A	angle with vertex A	p. 379
∟	right angle (90°)	p. 380

P	perimeter	p. 441
ℓ	length	p. 441
w	width	p. 441
A	area	p. 441
s	side	p. 442
b	base	p. 446
h	height	p. 446
C	circumference	p. 453
d	diameter	p. 453
π	pi; ≈ 3.14	p. 453
r	radius	p. 453
S.A.	surface area	p. 469
V	volume	p. 472
B	area of base	p. 472
−6	opposite of 6	p. 491
|5|	absolute value of 5	p. 492
(2, 3)	ordered pair with x-coordinate 2 and y-coordinate 3	p. 518
P(event)	probability of the event	p. 548
!	factorial	p. 576
≥	is greater than or equal to	p. 601
≤	is less than or equal to	p. 601
$\sqrt{9}$	square root of 9	p. 616

Formulas and Properties

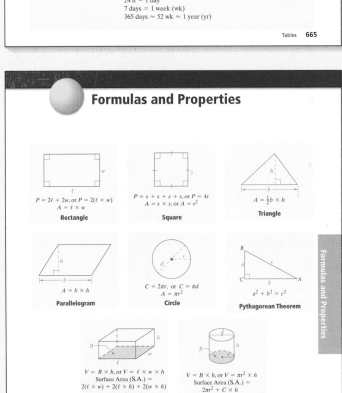

$P = 2\ell + 2w,$ or $P = 2(\ell + w)$
$A = \ell \times w$
Rectangle

$P = s + s + s + s,$ or $P = 4s$
$A = s \times s,$ or $A = s^2$
Square

$A = \frac{1}{2}b \times h$
Triangle

$A = b \times h$
Parallelogram

$C = 2\pi r,$ or $C = \pi d$
$A = \pi r^2$
Circle

$a^2 + b^2 = c^2$
Pythagorean Theorem

$V = B \times h,$ or $V = \ell \times w \times h$
Surface Area (S.A.) =
$2(\ell \times w) + 2(\ell \times h) + 2(w \times h)$
Rectangular Prism

$V = B \times h,$ or $V = \pi r^2 \times h$
Surface Area (S.A.) =
$2\pi r^2 + C \times h$
Cylinder

Properties of Numbers

Unless otherwise stated, the variables $a, b, c,$ and d used in these properties can be replaced with any number represented on a number line.

Associative Properties
Addition $(a + b) + c = a + (b + c)$
Multiplication $(a \cdot b) \cdot c = a \cdot (b \cdot c)$

Commutative Properties
Addition $a + b = b + a$
Multiplication $a \cdot b = b \cdot a$

Identity Properties
Addition $a + 0 = a$ and $0 + a = a$
Multiplication $a \cdot 1 = a$ and $1 \cdot a = a$

Inverse Properties
Addition
$a + (-a) = 0$ and $-a + a = 0$
Multiplication
$a \cdot \frac{1}{a} = 1$ and $\frac{1}{a} \cdot a = 1$ $(a \neq 0)$

Distributive Properties
$a(b + c) = ab + ac$
$a(b - c) = ab - ac$

Cross Products Property
If $\frac{a}{c} = \frac{b}{d}$, then $ad = bc$ $(c \neq 0, d \neq 0)$.

Zero-Product Property
If $ab = 0$, then $a = 0$ or $b = 0$.

Properties of Equality
Addition   If $a = b$, then $a + c = b + c$.
Subtraction   If $a = b$, then $a - c = b - c$.
Multiplication   If $a = b$, then $a \cdot c = b \cdot c$.
Division   If $a = b$, and $c \neq 0$, then $\frac{a}{c} = \frac{b}{c}$.
Substitution   If $a = b$, then b can replace a in any expression.

Reflexive $a = a$
Symmetric   If $a = b$, then $b = a$.
Transitive   If $a = b$ and $b = c$, then $a = c$.

Properties of Inequality
Addition   If $a > b$, then $a + c > b + c$.
     If $a < b$, then $a + c < b + c$.
Subtraction   If $a > b$, then $a - c > b - c$.
     If $a < b$, then $a - c < b - c$.

Multiplication
If $a > b$ and c is positive, then $ac > bc$.
If $a < b$ and c is positive, then $ac < bc$.
Division
If $a > b$ and c is positive, then $\frac{a}{c} > \frac{b}{c}$.
If $a < b$ and c is positive, then $\frac{a}{c} < \frac{b}{c}$.

Note: The Properties of Inequality apply also to ≤ and ≥.

English/Spanish Illustrated Glossary

A

Absolute value (p. 492) The absolute value of a number is its distance from 0 on a number line.

Valor absoluto (p. 492) El valor absoluto de un número es su distancia del 0 en una recta numérica.

-7 is 7 units from 0, so $|-7| = 7$.

Acute angle (p. 380) An acute angle is an angle with a measure between 0° and 90°.

Ángulo agudo (p. 380) Un ángulo agudo es un ángulo que mide entre 0° y 90°.

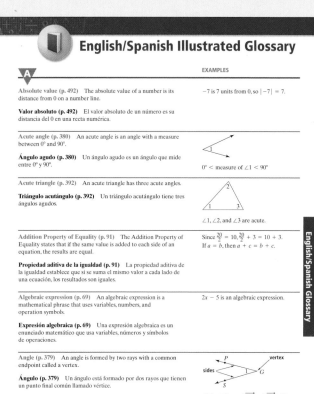

$0° <$ measure of $\angle 1 < 90°$

Acute triangle (p. 392) An acute triangle has three acute angles.

Triángulo acutángulo (p. 392) Un triángulo acutángulo tiene tres ángulos agudos.

$\angle 1$, $\angle 2$, and $\angle 3$ are acute.

Addition Property of Equality (p. 91) The Addition Property of Equality states that if the same value is added to each side of an equation, the results are equal.

Propiedad aditiva de la igualdad (p. 91) La propiedad aditiva de la igualdad establece que si se suma el mismo valor a cada lado de una ecuación, los resultados son iguales.

Since $\frac{20}{2} = 10$, $\frac{20}{2} + 3 = 10 + 3$.
If $a = b$, then $a + c = b + c$.

Algebraic expression (p. 69) An algebraic expression is a mathematical phrase that uses variables, numbers, and operation symbols.

Expresión algebraica (p. 69) Una expresión algebraica es un enunciado matemático que usa variables, números y símbolos de operaciones.

$2x - 5$ is an algebraic expression.

Angle (p. 379) An angle is formed by two rays with a common endpoint called a vertex.

Ángulo (p. 379) Un ángulo está formado por dos rayos que tienen un punto final común llamado vértice.

$\angle 1$ is made up of $\overrightarrow{GP}$ and $\overrightarrow{GS}$ with common endpoint G.

Angle bisector (p. 385) An angle bisector is a ray that divides an angle into angles of equal measure.

Bisectriz de un ángulo (p. 385) La bisectriz de un ángulo es un rayo que divide un ángulo en ángulos de igual medida.

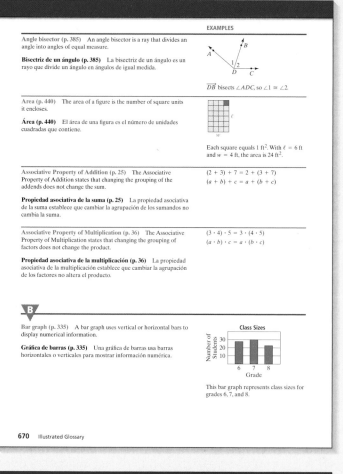

$\overrightarrow{DB}$ bisects $\angle ADC$, so $\angle 1 \cong \angle 2$.

Area (p. 440) The area of a figure is the number of square units it encloses.

Área (p. 440) El área de una figura es el número de unidades cuadradas que contiene.

Each square equals 1 ft². With $\ell = 6$ ft and $w = 4$ ft, the area is 24 ft².

Associative Property of Addition (p. 25) The Associative Property of Addition states that changing the grouping of the addends does not change the sum.

Propiedad asociativa de la suma (p. 25) La propiedad asociativa de la suma establece que cambiar la agrupación de los sumandos no cambia la suma.

$(2 + 3) + 7 = 2 + (3 + 7)$
$(a + b) + c = a + (b + c)$

Associative Property of Multiplication (p. 36) The Associative Property of Multiplication states that changing the grouping of factors does not change the product.

Propiedad asociativa de la multiplicación (p. 36) La propiedad asociativa de la multiplicación establece que cambiar la agrupación de los factores no altera el producto.

$(3 \cdot 4) \cdot 5 = 3 \cdot (4 \cdot 5)$
$(a \cdot b) \cdot c = a \cdot (b \cdot c)$

B

Bar graph (p. 335) A bar graph uses vertical or horizontal bars to display numerical information.

Gráfica de barras (p. 335) Una gráfica de barras usa barras horizontales o verticales para mostrar información numérica.

This bar graph represents class sizes for grades 6, 7, and 8.

Base (p. 99) When a number is written in exponential form, the number that is used as a factor is the base.

Base (p. 99) Cuando un número se escribe en forma exponencial, el número que se usa como factor es la base.

$5^4 = 5 \times 5 \times 5 \times 5$
$\quad\; \llcorner$ base

Bases of two-dimensional figures (pp. 446, 447) See *Parallelogram*, *Triangle*, and *Trapezoid*.

Bases de figuras bidimensionales (pp. 446, 447) Ver *Parallelogram*, *Triangle* y *Trapezoid*.

Benchmark (p. 171) A benchmark is a convenient number used to replace fractions that are less than 1.

Punto de referencia (p. 171) Un punto de referencia es un número conveniente que se usa para reemplazar fracciones menores que 1.

Using benchmarks, you would estimate $\frac{5}{6} + \frac{4}{9}$ as $1 + \frac{1}{2}$.

Box-and-whisker plot (p. 356) A box-and-whisker plot is a graph that summarizes a data set using five key values. There is a box in the middle and "whiskers" at either side. The quartile values show how each fourth of the data is distributed.

Gráfica de caja y brazos (p. 356) Una gráfica de caja y brazos es un diagrama que resume un conjunto de datos usando cinco valores clave. Hay una caja en el centro y extensiones a cada lado. Los valores cuartiles muestran cómo se distribuye cada cuarto de los datos.

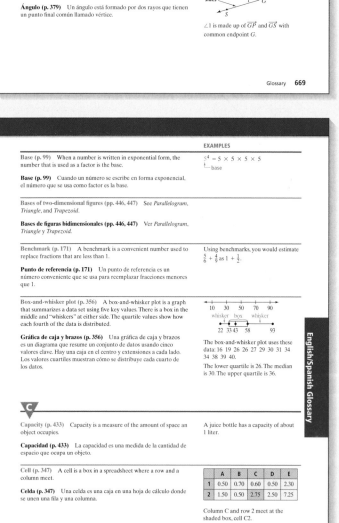

The box-and-whisker plot uses these data: 16 19 26 26 27 29 30 31 34 34 38 39 40.
The lower quartile is 26. The median is 30. The upper quartile is 36.

C

Capacity (p. 433) Capacity is a measure of the amount of space an object occupies.

Capacidad (p. 433) La capacidad es una medida de la cantidad de espacio que ocupa un objeto.

A juice bottle has a capacity of about 1 liter.

Cell (p. 347) A cell is a box in a spreadsheet where a row and a column meet.

Celda (p. 347) Una celda es una caja en una hoja de cálculo donde se unen una fila y una columna.

	A	B	C	D	E
1	0.50	0.70	0.60	0.50	2.30
2	1.50	0.50	2.75	2.50	7.25

Column C and row 2 meet at the shaded box, cell C2.

Center of a circle (p. 452) A circle is named by its center.

Centro de un círculo (p. 452) Un círculo es denominado por su centro.

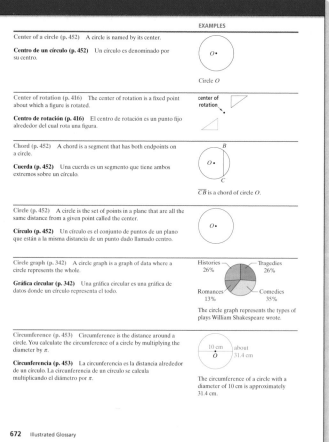

Circle O

Center of rotation (p. 416) The center of rotation is a fixed point about which a figure is rotated.

Centro de rotación (p. 416) El centro de rotación es un punto fijo alrededor del cual rota una figura.

center of rotation

Chord (p. 452) A chord is a segment that has both endpoints on a circle.

Cuerda (p. 452) Una cuerda es un segmento que tiene ambos extremos sobre un círculo.

$\overline{CB}$ is a chord of circle O.

Circle (p. 452) A circle is the set of points in a plane that are all the same distance from a given point called the center.

Círculo (p. 452) Un círculo es el conjunto de puntos de un plano que están a la misma distancia de un punto dado llamado centro.

Circle graph (p. 342) A circle graph is a graph of data where a circle represents the whole.

Gráfica circular (p. 342) Una gráfica circular es una gráfica de datos donde un círculo representa el todo.

Histories 26%   Tragedies 26%
Romances 13%   Comedies 35%

The circle graph represents the types of plays William Shakespeare wrote.

Circumference (p. 453) Circumference is the distance around a circle. You calculate the circumference of a circle by multiplying the diameter by π.

Circunferencia (p. 453) La circunferencia es la distancia alrededor de un círculo. La circunferencia de un círculo se calcula multiplicando el diámetro por π.

10 cm, about 31.4 cm

The circumference of a circle with a diameter of 10 cm is approximately 31.4 cm.

Collinear (p. 374)   Points on the same line are collinear.

Colineal (p. 374)   Los puntos que están en la misma recta son colineales.

Points B, C, R, and S are collinear.

Common factor (p. 128)   A factor that two or more numbers share is a common factor.

Factor común (p. 128)   Un número que es factor de dos o más números, es un factor común.

4 is a common factor of 8 and 20.

Common multiple (p. 143)   A multiple shared by two or more numbers is a common multiple.

Múltiplo común (p. 143)   Un número que es múltiplo de dos o más números, es un múltiplo común.

12 is a common multiple of 4 and 6.

Commutative Property of Addition (p. 25)   The Commutative Property of Addition states that changing the order of the addends does not change the sum.

Propiedad conmutativa de la suma (p. 25)   La propiedad conmutativa de la suma establece que al cambiar el orden de los sumandos no se altera la suma.

$3 + 1 = 1 + 3$
$a + b = b + a$

Commutative Property of Multiplication (p. 36)   The Commutative Property of Multiplication states that changing the order of the factors does not change the product.

Propiedad conmutativa de la multiplicación (p. 36)   La propiedad conmutativa de la multiplicación establece que al cambiar el orden de los factores no se altera el producto.

$6 \cdot 3 = 3 \cdot 6$
$a \cdot b = b \cdot a$

Compass (p. 384)   A compass is a geometric tool used to draw circles or arcs.

Compás (p. 384)   Un compás es una herramienta que se usa en geometría para dibujar círculos o arcos.

Compatible numbers (p. 20)   Compatible numbers are numbers that are easy to compute mentally.

Números compatibles (p. 20)   Los números compatibles son números con los que se puede calcular mentalmente con facilidad.

Estimate $151 \div 14.6$.
$151 \approx 150, 14.6 \approx 15$
$150 \div 15 = 10$
$151 \div 14.6 \approx 10$

Complementary (p. 386)   Two angles are complementary if the sum of their measures is 90°.

Complementario (p. 386)   Dos ángulos son complementarios si la suma de sus medidas es 90°.

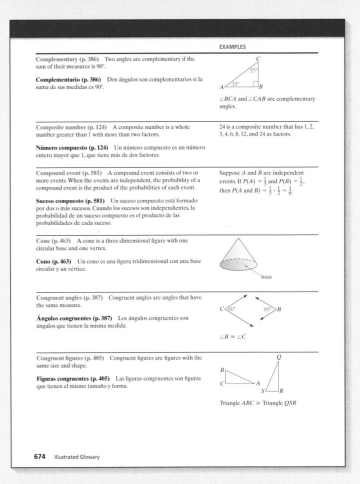

∠BCA and ∠CAB are complementary angles.

Composite number (p. 124)   A composite number is a whole number greater than 1 with more than two factors.

Número compuesto (p. 124)   Un número compuesto es un número entero mayor que 1, que tiene más de dos factores.

24 is a composite number that has 1, 2, 3, 4, 6, 8, 12, and 24 as factors.

Compound event (p. 581)   A compound event consists of two or more events. When the events are independent, the probability of a compound event is the product of the probabilities of each event.

Suceso compuesto (p. 581)   Un suceso compuesto está formado por dos o más sucesos. Cuando los sucesos son independientes, la probabilidad de un suceso compuesto es el producto de las probabilidades de cada suceso.

Suppose A and B are independent events. If $P(A) = \frac{1}{3}$ and $P(B) = \frac{1}{2}$, then $P(A \text{ and } B) = \frac{1}{3} \cdot \frac{1}{2} = \frac{1}{6}$.

Cone (p. 463)   A cone is a three-dimensional figure with one circular base and one vertex.

Cono (p. 463)   Un cono es una figura tridimensional con una base circular y un vértice.

base

Congruent angles (p. 387)   Congruent angles are angles that have the same measure.

Ángulos congruentes (p. 387)   Los ángulos congruentes son ángulos que tienen la misma medida.

∠B ≅ ∠C

Congruent figures (p. 405)   Congruent figures are figures with the same size and shape.

Figuras congruentes (p. 405)   Las figuras congruentes son figuras que tienen el mismo tamaño y forma.

Triangle ABC ≅ Triangle QSR

Congruent segments (p. 393)   Segments that have the same length are congruent segments.

Segmentos congruentes (p. 393)   Los segmentos que tienen la misma longitud son segmentos congruentes.

$\overline{AB}$ is congruent to $\overline{WX}$.

Conjecture (p. 64)   A conjecture is a prediction that suggests what can be expected to happen.

Conjetura (p. 64)   Una conjetura es una predicción que sugiere lo que se puede esperar que ocurra.

Every clover has three leaves.

Coordinate plane (p. 518)   A coordinate plane is formed by a horizontal number line called the x-axis and a vertical number line called the y-axis.

Plano de coordenadas (p. 518)   Un plano de coordenadas está formado por una recta numérica horizontal llamada eje de x y por una recta numérica vertical llamada eje de y.

Corresponding parts (p. 405)   The matching parts of similar figures are called corresponding parts.

Partes correspondientes (p. 405)   Las partes que coinciden de figuras semejantes se llaman partes correspondientes.

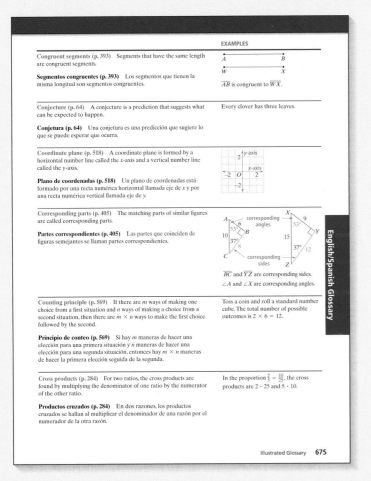

$\overline{BC}$ and $\overline{YZ}$ are corresponding sides.
∠A and ∠X are corresponding angles.

Counting principle (p. 569)   If there are m ways of making one choice from a first situation and n ways of making a choice from a second situation, then there are m × n ways to make the first choice followed by the second.

Principio de conteo (p. 569)   Si hay m maneras de hacer una elección para una primera situación y n maneras de hacer una elección para una segunda situación, entonces hay m × n maneras de hacer la primera elección seguida de la segunda.

Toss a coin and roll a standard number cube. The total number of possible outcomes is $2 \times 6 = 12$.

Cross products (p. 284)   For two ratios, the cross products are found by multiplying the denominator of one ratio by the numerator of the other ratio.

Productos cruzados (p. 284)   En dos razones, los productos cruzados se hallan al multiplicar el denominador de una razón por el numerador de la otra razón.

In the proportion $\frac{2}{5} = \frac{10}{25}$, the cross products are $2 \cdot 25$ and $5 \cdot 10$.

Cube (p. 462)   A cube is a rectangular prism whose faces are all squares.

Cubo (p. 462)   Un cubo es un prisma rectangular cuyas caras son todas cuadradas.

Cubic unit (p. 472)   A cubic unit is a cube whose edges are one unit long.

Unidad cúbica (p. 472)   Una unidad cúbica es un cubo cuyos lados tienen una unidad de longitud.

1 cm

Cylinder (p. 463)   A cylinder is a three-dimensional figure with two congruent parallel bases that are circles.

Cilindro (p. 463)   Un cilindro es una figura tridimensional con dos bases congruentes paralelas que son círculos.

base
height
base

D

Decagon (p. 397)   A decagon is a polygon with 10 sides.

Decágono (p. 397)   Un decágono es un polígono que tiene 10 lados.

Degrees (p. 379)   Angles are measured in units called degrees.

Grados (p. 379)   Los ángulos se miden en unidades llamadas grados.

The measure of ∠A is 45°.

Diameter (p. 452)   A diameter is a segment that passes through the center of a circle and has both endpoints on the circle.

Diámetro (p. 452)   Un diámetro es un segmento que pasa por el centro de un círculo y que tiene ambos extremos sobre el círculo.

$\overline{RS}$ is a diameter of circle O.

Distributive Property (p. 105)   The Distributive Property shows how multiplication affects an addition or subtraction:
$a(b + c) = ab + ac.$

Propiedad distributiva (p. 105)   La propiedad distributiva muestra cómo la multiplicación afecta a una suma o a una resta:
$a(b + c) = ab + ac.$

$2\left(3 + \frac{1}{2}\right) = 2 \cdot 3 + 2 \cdot \frac{1}{2}$
$8(5 - 3) = 8 \cdot 5 - 8 \cdot 3$

T667

Divisible (p. 119) A whole number is divisible by a second whole number if the first number can be divided by the second number with a remainder of 0.

Divisible (p. 119) Un número entero es divisible por un segundo número entero si el primer número se puede dividir por el segundo número y el residuo es 0.

16 is divisible by 1, 2, 4, 8, and 16.

Division Property of Equality (p. 95) The Division Property of Equality states that if both sides of an equation are divided by the same nonzero number, the results are equal.

Propiedad de división de la igualdad (p. 95) La propiedad de división de la igualdad establece que si ambos lados de una ecuación se dividen por el mismo número distinto de cero, los resultados son iguales.

Since $3(2) = 6, 3(2) \div 2 = 6 \div 2$.
If $a = b$ and $c \neq 0$, then $\frac{a}{c} = \frac{b}{c}$.

Double bar graph (p. 340) A double bar graph is a graph that uses bars to compare two sets of data.

Gráfica de doble barra (p. 340) Una gráfica de doble barra es una gráfica que usa barras para comparar dos conjuntos de datos.

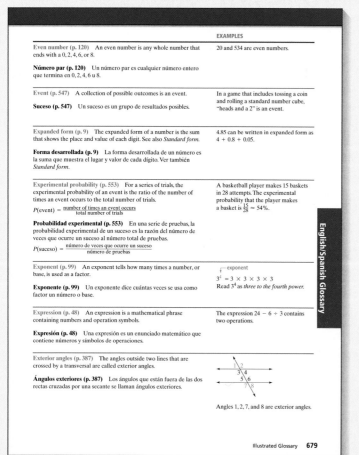

This double bar graph shows class size for grades 6, 7, and 8 for boys and girls.

Double line graph (p. 340) A double line graph is a graph that compares changes over time for two sets of data.

Gráfica de doble línea (p. 340) Una gráfica de doble línea es una gráfica que compara los cambios de dos conjuntos de datos a través del tiempo.

This double line graph represents seasonal air conditioner and snowblower sales for a large department store chain.

E

Edge (p. 462) An edge is a segment formed by the intersection of two faces of a three-dimensional figure.

Arista (p. 462) Una arista es un segmento formado por la intersección de dos caras de una figura tridimensional.

edge

Elapsed time (p. 202) The time between two events is elapsed time.

Tiempo transcurrido (p. 202) El tiempo que hay entre dos sucesos es el tiempo transcurrido.

The elapsed time between 8:10 A.M. and 8:45 A.M. is 35 minutes.

Equal ratios (p. 270) Equal ratios name the same number. Equal ratios written as fractions are equivalent fractions.

Razones iguales (p. 270) Las razones iguales indican el mismo número. Las razones iguales escritas como fracciones son fracciones equivalentes.

The ratios $\frac{4}{7}$ and $\frac{8}{14}$ are equal.

Equally likely outcomes (p. 547) Equally likely outcomes are outcomes that have the same chance of occurring.

Resultados igualmente probables (p. 547) Los resultados igualmente probables son resultados que tienen la misma posibilidad de ocurrir.

When a number cube is rolled once, the outcomes 1, 2, 3, 4, 5, and 6 are all equally likely outcomes.

Equation (p. 84) An equation is a mathematical sentence with an equal sign.

Ecuación (p. 84) Una ecuación es una oración matemática con un signo igual.

$27 \div 9 = 3$ and $x + 10 = 8$ are examples of equations.

Equilateral triangle (p. 393) An equilateral triangle is a triangle with three congruent sides.

Triángulo equilátero (p. 393) Un triángulo equilátero es un triángulo que tiene tres lados congruentes.

$\overline{SL} \cong \overline{LW} \cong \overline{WS}$

Equivalent fractions (p. 134) Equivalent fractions are fractions that name the same amount.

Fracciones equivalentes (p. 134) Las fracciones equivalentes son fracciones que indican la misma cantidad.

$\frac{1}{2}$ and $\frac{25}{50}$ are equivalent fractions.

Evaluating algebraic expressions (p. 69) To evaluate an algebraic expression, replace each variable with a number. Then follow the order of operations.

Evaluación de una expresión algebraica (p. 69) Para evaluar una expresión algebraica se reemplaza cada variable con un número. Luego se sigue el orden de las operaciones.

To evaluate the expression $3x + 2$ for $x = 4$, substitute 4 for x.
$3x + 2 = 3(4) + 2 = 14$

Even number (p. 120) An even number is any whole number that ends with a 0, 2, 4, 6, or 8.

Número par (p. 120) Un número par es cualquier número entero que termina en 0, 2, 4, 6 u 8.

20 and 534 are even numbers.

Event (p. 547) A collection of possible outcomes is an event.

Suceso (p. 547) Un suceso es un grupo de resultados posibles.

In a game that includes tossing a coin and rolling a standard number cube, "heads and a 2" is an event.

Expanded form (p. 9) The expanded form of a number is the sum that shows the place and value of each digit. See also *Standard form*.

Forma desarrollada (p. 9) La forma desarrollada de un número es la suma que muestra el lugar y valor de cada dígito. Ver también *Standard form*.

4.85 can be written in expanded form as $4 + 0.8 + 0.05$.

Experimental probability (p. 553) For a series of trials, the experimental probability of an event is the ratio of the number of times an event occurs to the total number of trials.

$P(\text{event}) = \frac{\text{number of times an event occurs}}{\text{total number of trials}}$

Probabilidad experimental (p. 553) En una serie de pruebas, la probabilidad experimental de un suceso es la razón del número de veces que ocurre un suceso al número total de pruebas.

$P(\text{suceso}) = \frac{\text{número de veces que ocurre un suceso}}{\text{número de pruebas}}$

A basketball player makes 15 baskets in 28 attempts. The experimental probability that the player makes a basket is $\frac{15}{28} \approx 54\%$.

Exponent (p. 99) An exponent tells how many times a number, or base, is used as a factor.

Exponente (p. 99) Un exponente dice cuántas veces se usa como factor un número o base.

exponent
$3^4 = 3 \times 3 \times 3 \times 3$
Read 3^4 as *three to the fourth power*.

Expression (p. 48) An expression is a mathematical phrase containing numbers and operation symbols.

Expresión (p. 48) Una expresión es un enunciado matemático que contiene números y símbolos de operaciones.

The expression $24 - 6 \div 3$ contains two operations.

Exterior angles (p. 387) The angles outside two lines that are crossed by a transversal are called exterior angles.

Ángulos exteriores (p. 387) Los ángulos que están fuera de las dos rectas cruzadas por una secante se llaman ángulos exteriores.

Angles 1, 2, 7, and 8 are exterior angles.

F

Face (p. 462) A face is a flat, polygon-shaped surface of a three-dimensional figure.

Cara (p. 462) Una cara es una superficie plana de una figura tridimensional que tiene la forma de un polígono.

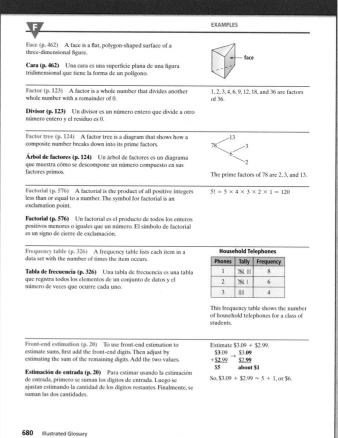

face

Factor (p. 123) A factor is a whole number that divides another whole number with a remainder of 0.

Divisor (p. 123) Un divisor es un número entero que divide a otro número entero y el residuo es 0.

1, 2, 3, 4, 6, 9, 12, 18, and 36 are factors of 36.

Factor tree (p. 124) A factor tree is a diagram that shows how a composite number breaks down into its prime factors.

Árbol de factores (p. 124) Un árbol de factores es un diagrama que muestra cómo se descompone un número compuesto en sus factores primos.

The prime factors of 78 are 2, 3, and 13.

Factorial (p. 576) A factorial is the product of all positive integers less than or equal to a number. The symbol for factorial is an exclamation point.

Factorial (p. 576) Un factorial es el producto de todos los enteros positivos menores o iguales que un número. El símbolo de factorial es un signo de cierre de exclamación.

$5! = 5 \times 4 \times 3 \times 2 \times 1 = 120$

Frequency table (p. 326) A frequency table lists each item in a data set with the number of times the item occurs.

Tabla de frecuencia (p. 326) Una tabla de frecuencia es una tabla que registra todos los elementos de un conjunto de datos y el número de veces que ocurre cada uno.

Household Telephones

Phones	Tally	Frequency
1	𝍢 |||	8
2	𝍢		6
3						4

This frequency table shows the number of household telephones for a class of students.

Front-end estimation (p. 20) To use front-end estimation to estimate sums, first add the front-end digits. Then adjust by estimating the sum of the remaining digits. Add the two values.

Estimación de entrada (p. 20) Para estimar usando la estimación de entrada, primero se suman los dígitos de entrada. Luego se ajustan estimando la cantidad de los dígitos restantes. Finalmente, se suman las dos cantidades.

Estimate $\$3.09 + \$2.99$.
$\$3.09$ → $\$3.09$
$+\$2.99$ → $\$2.99$
$\$5$ → about $\$1$
So, $\$3.09 + \$2.99 \approx 5 + 1$, or $\$6$.

Function (p. 527) A function is a relationship that assigns exactly one output value for each input value.

Función (p. 527) Una función es una relación que asigna exactamente un valor resultante a cada valor inicial.

Earned income *i* is a function of the number of hours worked *h*. If you earn $6 per hour, then your income can be expressed by the function $i = 6h$.

G

Gram (p. 432) The standard unit of mass in the metric system is the gram.

Gramo (p. 432) La unidad de masa estándar en el sistema métrico es el gramo.

A paper clip has the mass of about 1 gram.

Graph of a function (p. 528) The graph of a function is the graph of all the points whose coordinates are solutions of the equation.

Gráfica de una función (p. 528) La gráfica de una función es la gráfica de todos los puntos cuyas coordenadas son soluciones a la ecuación.

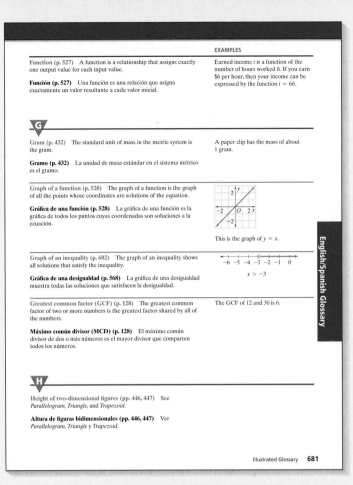

This is the graph of $y = x$.

Graph of an inequality (p. 602) The graph of an inequality shows all solutions that satisfy the inequality.

Gráfica de una desigualdad (p. 568) La gráfica de una desigualdad muestra todas las soluciones que satisfacen la desigualdad.

$$x > -3$$

Greatest common factor (GCF) (p. 128) The greatest common factor of two or more numbers is the greatest factor shared by all of the numbers.

Máximo común divisor (MCD) (p. 128) El máximo común divisor de dos o más números es el mayor divisor que comparten todos los números.

The GCF of 12 and 30 is 6.

H

Height of two-dimensional figures (pp. 446, 447) See *Parallelogram, Triangle,* and *Trapezoid.*

Altura de figuras bidimensionales (pp. 446, 447) Ver *Parallelogram, Triangle* y *Trapezoid.*

Hexagon (p. 397) A hexagon is a polygon with six sides.

Hexágono (p. 397) Un hexágono es un polígono que tiene seis lados.

Histogram (p. 336) A histogram is a bar graph with no spaces between the bars. The height of each bar shows the frequency of data within that interval.

Histograma (p. 336) Un histograma es una gráfica de barras sin espacio entre las barras. La altura de cada barra muestra la frecuencia de los datos dentro del intervalo.

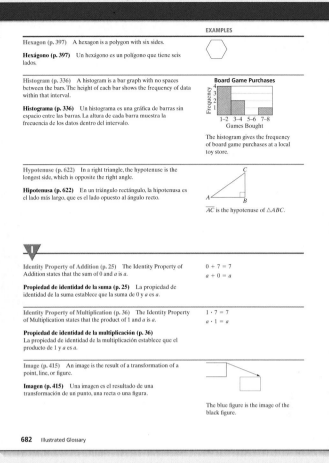

The histogram gives the frequency of board game purchases at a local toy store.

Hypotenuse (p. 622) In a right triangle, the hypotenuse is the longest side, which is opposite the right angle.

Hipotenusa (p. 622) En un triángulo rectángulo, la hipotenusa es el lado más largo, que es el lado opuesto al ángulo recto.

$\overline{AC}$ is the hypotenuse of $\triangle ABC$.

I

Identity Property of Addition (p. 25) The Identity Property of Addition states that the sum of 0 and *a* is *a*.

Propiedad de identidad de la suma (p. 25) La propiedad de identidad de la suma establece que la suma de 0 y *a* es *a*.

$$0 + 7 = 7$$
$$a + 0 = a$$

Identity Property of Multiplication (p. 36) The Identity Property of Multiplication states that the product of 1 and *a* is *a*.

Propiedad de identidad de la multiplicación (p. 36) La propiedad de identidad de la multiplicación establece que el producto de 1 y *a* es *a*.

$$1 \cdot 7 = 7$$
$$a \cdot 1 = a$$

Image (p. 415) An image is the result of a transformation of a point, line, or figure.

Imagen (p. 415) Una imagen es el resultado de una transformación de un punto, una recta o una figura.

The blue figure is the image of the black figure.

Improper fraction (p. 139) An improper fraction has a numerator that is greater than or equal to its denominator.

Fracción impropia (p. 139) Una fracción impropia tiene un numerador mayor o igual que su denominador.

$\frac{24}{15}$ and $\frac{16}{16}$ are improper fractions.

Independent events (p. 580) Two events are independent events if the occurrence of one event does not affect the probability of the occurrence of the other.

Sucesos independientes (p. 580) Dos sucesos son independientes si el acontecimiento de uno no afecta la probabilidad de que el otro suceso ocurra.

Suppose you draw two marbles, one after the other, from a bag. If you replace the first marble before drawing the second marble, the events are independent.

Inequality (p. 601) An inequality is a mathematical sentence that contains $<$, $>$, $\leq$, $\geq$, or $\neq$.

Desigualdad (p. 601) Una desigualdad es una oración matemática que contiene los signos $<$, $>$, $\leq$, $\geq$ o $\neq$.

$$x < -5$$
$$x > 8$$
$$x \leq 1$$
$$x \geq -11$$
$$x \neq 3$$

Integers (p. 491) Integers are the set of positive whole numbers, their opposites, and 0.

Enteros (p. 491) Los enteros son el conjunto de números enteros positivos, sus opuestos y el 0.

$$\ldots -3, -2, -1, 0, 1, 2, 3, \ldots$$

Interior angles (p. 387) The angles between two lines that are crossed by a transversal are called interior angles.

Ángulos interiores (p. 387) Los ángulos que están entre dos rectas, cruzadas por una secante se llaman ángulos interiores.

Angles 3, 4, 5, and 6 are interior angles.

Intersecting lines (p. 374) Intersecting lines lie in the same plane and have exactly one point in common.

Rectas que se intersectan (p. 374) Las rectas que se intersectan están en el mismo plano y tienen exactamente un punto en común.

Inverse operations (p. 90) Inverse operations are operations that undo each other.

Operaciones inversas (p. 90) Las operaciones inversas son las operaciones que se anulan entre ellas.

Addition and subtraction are inverse operations.

Isosceles triangle (p. 393) An isosceles triangle is a triangle with at least two congruent sides.

Triángulo isósceles (p. 393) Un triángulo isósceles es un triángulo que tiene al menos dos lados congruentes.

$\overline{LM} \cong \overline{LB}$

L

Least common denominator (LCD) (p. 148) The least common denominator of two or more fractions is the least common multiple (LCM) of their denominators.

Mínimo común denominador (mcd) (p. 148) El mínimo común denominador de dos o más fracciones es el mínimo común múltiplo (mcm) de sus denominadores.

The LCD of the fractions $\frac{3}{8}$ and $\frac{7}{10}$ is 40.

Least common multiple (LCM) (p. 143) The least common multiple of two numbers is the smallest number that is a multiple of both numbers.

Mínimo común múltiplo (mcm) (p. 143) El mínimo común múltiplo de dos números es el menor número que es múltiplo de ambos números.

The LCM of 15 and 6 is 30.

Legs of a right triangle (p. 622) The legs of a right triangle are the two shorter sides of the triangle.

Catetos de un triángulo rectángulo (p. 622) Los catetos de un triángulo rectángulo son los dos lados más cortos del triángulo.

$\overline{AB}$ and $\overline{BC}$ are the legs of triangle ABC.

Line (p. 373) A line is a series of points that extends in two opposite directions without end.

Recta (p. 373) Una recta es una serie de puntos que se extiende indefinidamente en dos direcciones opuestas.

$\overrightarrow{CG}$ is shown.

Line graph (p. 336) A line graph is a graph that uses a series of line segments to show changes in data. Typically, a line graph shows changes over time.

Gráfica lineal (p. 336) Una gráfica lineal es una gráfica que usa una serie de segmentos de recta para mostrar cambios en los datos. Típicamente, una gráfica lineal muestra cambios a través del tiempo.

Line of reflection (p. 416) A line of reflection is a line over which a figure is reflected.

Eje de reflexión (p. 416) Un eje de reflexión es una recta sobre la cual se refleja una figura.

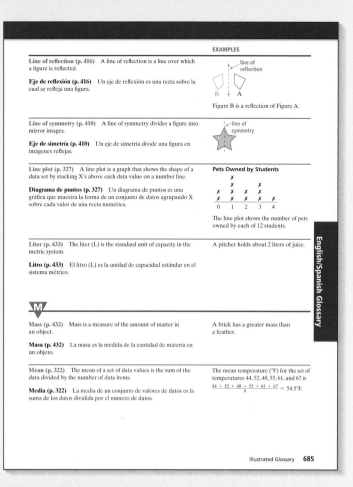

line of reflection

Figure B is a reflection of Figure A.

Line of symmetry (p. 410) A line of symmetry divides a figure into mirror images.

Eje de simetría (p. 410) Un eje de simetría divide una figura en imágenes reflejas.

line of symmetry

Line plot (p. 327) A line plot is a graph that shows the shape of a data set by stacking X's above each data value on a number line.

Diagrama de puntos (p. 327) Un diagrama de puntos es una gráfica que muestra la forma de un conjunto de datos agrupando X sobre cada valor de una recta numérica.

Pets Owned by Students

```
        X
    X   X       X
X   X   X   X   X
0   1   2   3   4
```

The line plot shows the number of pets owned by each of 12 students.

Liter (p. 433) The liter (L) is the standard unit of capacity in the metric system.

Litro (p. 433) El litro (L) es la unidad de capacidad estándar en el sistema métrico.

A pitcher holds about 2 liters of juice.

M

Mass (p. 432) Mass is a measure of the amount of matter in an object.

Masa (p. 432) La masa es la medida de la cantidad de materia en un objeto.

A brick has a greater mass than a feather.

Mean (p. 322) The mean of a set of data values is the sum of the data divided by the number of data items.

Media (p. 322) La media de un conjunto de valores de datos es la suma de los datos dividida por el número de datos.

The mean temperature (°F) for the set of temperatures 44, 52, 48, 55, 61, and 67 is $\frac{44 + 52 + 48 + 55 + 61 + 67}{6} = 54.5°F$.

Median (p. 323) The median of a data set is the middle value when the data are arranged in numerical order. When there is an even number of data values, the median is the mean of the two middle values.

Mediana (p. 323) La mediana de un conjunto de datos es el valor del medio cuando los datos están organizados en orden numérico. Cuando hay un número par de valores de datos, la mediana es la media de los dos valores del medio.

A set of temperatures (°F) arranged in order are 44, 48, 52, 55, and 58. The median temperature is 52°F because it is the middle number in the set of data.

Meter (p. 431) The meter (m) is the standard unit of length in the metric system.

Metro (p. 431) El metro (m) es la unidad de longitud estándar en el sistema métrico.

A doorknob is about 1 meter from the floor.

Metric system (p. 431) The metric system of measurement is a decimal system. Prefixes indicate the relative size of units.

Sistema métrico (p. 431) El sistema métrico de medidas es un sistema decimal. Los prefijos indican el tamaño relativo de las unidades.

1 kilogram = 1,000 grams

1 centimeter = $\frac{1}{100}$ meter

1 milliliter = $\frac{1}{1,000}$ liter

Midpoint (p. 384) The midpoint of a segment is the point that divides the segment into two segments of equal length.

Punto medio (p. 384) El punto medio de un segmento es el punto que divide el segmento en dos segmentos de igual longitud.

$XM = YM$. M is the midpoint of $\overline{XY}$.

Mixed number (p. 139) A mixed number is the sum of a whole number and a fraction.

Número mixto (p. 139) Un número mixto es la suma de un número entero y una fracción.

$3\frac{11}{16}$ is a mixed number. $3\frac{11}{16} = 3 + \frac{11}{16}$.

Mode (p. 323) The mode of a data set is the item that occurs with the greatest frequency.

Moda (p. 323) La moda de un conjunto de datos es el dato que sucede con mayor frecuencia.

The mode of the set of prices $2.50, $2.75, $3.60, $2.75, and $3.70 is $2.75.

Multiple (p. 143) A multiple of a number is the product of the number and any nonzero whole number.

Múltiplo (p. 143) Un múltiplo de un número es el producto de ese número y cualquier número entero diferente de cero.

The number 39 is a multiple of 13.

Multiplication Property of Equality (p. 96) The Multiplication Property of Equality states that if each side of an equation is multiplied by the same number, the results are equal.

Propiedad multiplicativa de la igualdad (p. 96) La propiedad multiplicativa de la igualdad establece que si cada lado de una ecuación se multiplica por el mismo número, los resultados son iguales.

Since $\frac{12}{2} = 6$, $\frac{12}{2} \cdot 2 = 6 \cdot 2$.
If $a = b$, then $a \cdot c = b \cdot c$.

N

Net (p. 464) A net is a two-dimensional pattern that can be folded to form a three-dimensional figure.

Plantilla (p. 464) Una plantilla es un patrón bidimensional que se puede doblar para formar una figura tridimensional.

These are nets for a cube.

Numerical expression (p. 68) A numerical expression is an expression with only numbers and operation symbols.

Expresión numérica (p. 68) Una expresión numérica es una expresión que tiene sólo números y símbolos de operaciones.

$2(5 + 7) - 14$ is a numerical expression.

O

Obtuse angle (p. 380) An obtuse angle is an angle with a measure greater than 90° and less than 180°.

Ángulo obtuso (p. 380) Un ángulo obtuso es un ángulo que mide más de 90° y menos de 180°.

Obtuse triangle (p. 392) An obtuse triangle is a triangle with one obtuse angle.

Triángulo obtusángulo (p. 392) Un triángulo obtusángulo es un triángulo que tiene un ángulo obtuso.

N
J X

The measure of $\angle J$ is between 90° and 180°. Triangle NJX is an obtuse triangle.

Octagon (p. 397) An octagon is a polygon with eight sides.

Octágono (p. 397) Un octágono es un polígono que tiene ocho lados.

Odd number (p. 120) An odd number is a whole number that ends with a 1, 3, 5, 7, or 9.

Número impar (p. 120) Un número impar es un número entero que termina en 1, 3, 5, 7 ó 9.

43 and 687 are odd numbers.

Odds (p. 552) When outcomes are equally likely, odds are expressed as the following ratios.
odds *in favor* of an event = number of favorable outcomes : number of unfavorable outcomes
odds *against* an event = number of unfavorable outcomes : number of favorable outcomes

Posibilidades (p. 552) Cuando los resultados son igualmente posibles, las posibilidades se expresan como las siguientes razones.
posibilidades *en favor* de un suceso = número de resultados favorables : número de resultados desfavorables
posibilidades *en contra* de un suceso = número de resultados desfavorables : número de resultados favorables

You roll a standard number cube. The odds in favor of getting a 4 are $\frac{1}{5}$. The odds against getting a 4 are $\frac{5}{1}$.

Open sentence (p. 85) An open sentence is an equation with one or more variables.

Proposición abierta (p. 85) Una proposición abierta es una ecuación con una o más variables.

$b - 7 = 12$

Opposites (p. 491) Opposites are two numbers that are the same distance from 0 on a number line, but in opposite directions.

Opuestos (p. 491) Opuestos son dos números que están a la misma distancia del 0 en una recta numérica, pero en direcciones opuestas.

17 and −17 are opposites.

Ordered pair (p. 518) An ordered pair identifies the location of a point. The x-coordinate shows a point's position left or right of the y-axis. The y-coordinate shows a point's position up or down from the x-axis.

Par ordenado (p. 518) Un par ordenado identifica la ubicación de un punto. La coordenada x muestra la posición de un punto a la izquierda o derecha del eje de y. La coordenada y muestra la posición de un punto arriba o abajo del eje de x.

The x-coordinate of the point (−2, 1) is −2, and the y-coordinate is 1.

Order of operations (pp. 48, 100)
1. Work inside grouping symbols.
2. Do all work with exponents.
3. Multiply and divide in order from left to right.
4. Add and subtract in order from left to right.

$2^3(7 - 4) = 2^3 \cdot 3 = 8 \cdot 3 = 24$

Orden de las operaciones (pp. 48, 100)
1. Trabaja dentro de los signos de agrupación.
2. Trabaja con los exponentes.
3. Multiplica y divide en orden de izquierda a derecha.
4. Suma y resta en orden de izquierda a derecha.

Origin (p. 518) The origin is the point of intersection of the x- and y-axes on a coordinate plane.

Origen (p. 518) El origen es el punto de intersección de los ejes de x y de y en un plano de coordenadas.

The ordered pair that describes the origin is $(0, 0)$.

Outcome (p. 547) An outcome is any of the possible results that can occur in an experiment.

Resultado (p. 547) Un resultado es cualquiera de los posibles desenlaces que pueden ocurrir en un experimento.

The outcomes of rolling a standard number cube are 1, 2, 3, 4, 5, and 6.

Outlier (p. 322) An outlier is a data item that is much greater or less than the other items in a data set.

Valor extremo (p. 322) Un valor extremo es un dato que es mucho más alto o más bajo que los demás datos de un conjunto de datos.

An outlier in the data set 6, 7, 9, 10, 11, 12, 14, and 52 is 52.

P

Parallel lines (p. 374) Parallel lines are lines in the same plane that never intersect.

Rectas paralelas (p. 378) Las rectas paralelas son rectas en el mismo plano que nunca se intersectan.

$\overleftrightarrow{EF}$ is parallel to $\overleftrightarrow{HI}$.

Parallelogram (p. 398) A parallelogram is a quadrilateral with both pairs of opposite sides parallel.

Paralelogramo (p. 398) Un paralelogramo es un cuadrilátero cuyos pares de lados opuestos son paralelos.

$\overline{KV}$ is parallel to $\overline{AD}$ and $\overline{AK}$ is parallel to $\overline{DV}$, so $KVDA$ is a parallelogram.

Pentagon (p. 397) A pentagon is a polygon with five sides.

Pentágono (p. 397) Un pentágono es un polígono que tiene cinco lados.

Percent (p. 294) A percent is a ratio that compares a number to 100.

Porcentaje (p. 294) Un porcentaje es una razón que compara un número con 100.

$\frac{25}{100} = 25\%$

Perfect square (p. 616) A perfect square is a number that is the square of an integer.

Cuadrado perfecto (p. 616) Un cuadrado perfecto es un número que es el cuadrado de un entero.

Since $25 = 5^2$, 25 is a perfect square.

Perimeter (p. 441) The perimeter of a figure is the distance around the figure.

Perímetro (p. 441) El perímetro de una figura es la distancia alrededor de la figura.

The perimeter of rectangle $ABCD$ is 12 ft.

Permutation (p. 574) A permutation is an arrangement of objects in a particular order.

Permutación (p. 574) Una permutación es un arreglo de objetos en un orden particular.

The permutations of the letters W, A, and X are WAX, WXA, AXW, AWX, XWA, and XAW.

Perpendicular bisector (p. 384) A perpendicular bisector is a line that is perpendicular to a segment and passes through that segment's midpoint.

Mediatriz (p. 384) Una mediatriz es una recta que es perpendicular a un segmento y que pasa pol el punto medio del segmento.

$\overleftrightarrow{MK} \perp \overline{AB}$, $AM = MB$. $\overleftrightarrow{MK}$ is the perpendicular bisector of $\overline{AB}$.

Perpendicular lines (p. 380) Perpendicular lines intersect to form right angles.

Rectas perpendiculares (p. 380) Las rectas perpendiculares se intersectan para formar ángulos rectos.

$\overleftrightarrow{RS}$ is perpendicular to $\overleftrightarrow{DE}$.

Pi (p. 453) Pi (π) is the ratio of the circumference C of any circle to its diameter d.

Pi (p. 453) Pi (π) es la razón de la circunferencia C de cualquier círculo a su diámetro d.

$\pi = \frac{C}{d}$

Place value (p. 5) The place value tells you the value of a digit based on its place in a particular number.

Valor posicional (p. 5) El valor posicional indica el valor de un dígito, basándose en el lugar que ocupa en un número en particular.

In 26, the 6 represents 6 ones, or 6.
In 604, The 6 represents 6 hundreds, or 600.

Plane (p. 374) A plane is a flat surface with no thickness that extends without end in all directions on the surface.

Plano (p. 374) Un plano es una superficie plana que no tiene grosor, que se extiende indefinidamente en todas las direcciones sobre la superficie.

$DEFG$ is a plane.

Point (p. 373) A point is a location that has no size.

Punto (p. 373) Un punto es una ubicación que no tiene tamaño.

A is a point.

Polygon (p. 397) A polygon is a closed figure formed by three or more line segments that do not cross.

Polígono (p. 397) Un polígono es una figura cerrada que está formada por tres o más segmentos de recta que no se cruzan.

Population (p. 559) A population is a group of objects or people about which information is wanted.

Población (p. 559) Una población es un grupo de objetos o personas sobre el que se busca información.

In a survey regarding the hobbies of teenagers, the population would be all people ages 13 through 19.

Power (p. 100) A power is a number that can be expressed using an exponent.

Potencia (p. 100) Una potencia es un número que se puede expresar usando un exponente.

3^4, 5^2, and 2^{10} are powers.

Prime factorization (p. 124) Writing a composite number as the product of prime numbers is the prime factorization of the number.

Factorización en primos (p. 124) Escribir un número compuesto como el producto de sus factores primos es la factorización en primos del número.

The prime factorization of 12 is $2 \cdot 2 \cdot 3$, or $2^2 \cdot 3$.

Prime number (p. 124) A prime number is a whole number with exactly two factors, 1 and the number itself.

Número primo (p. 124) Un número primo es un entero que tiene exactamente dos factores, 1 y el mismo número.

13 is a prime number because its only factors are 1 and 13.

Prism (p. 462) A prism is a three-dimensional figure with two parallel and congruent faces that are polygons. These faces are called bases. A prism is named for the shape of its base.

Prisma (p. 462) Un prisma es una figura tridimensional que tiene dos caras paralelas y congruentes que son polígonos. Estas caras se llaman bases. Un prisma recibe su nombre por la forma de su base.

Rectangular Prism   Triangular Prism

Probability of an event (p. 547) When outcomes are equally likely, the probability of an event is given by this formula:

$P(\text{event}) = \frac{\text{number of favorable outcomes}}{\text{total number of possible outcomes}}$

See *Experimental probability*.

Probabilidad de un suceso (p. 547) Cuando los resultados son igualmente posibles, la probabilidad de un suceso se da por esta fórmula:

$P(\text{suceso}) = \frac{\text{número favorable de resultados}}{\text{número total de resultados posibles}}$

Ver *Probabilidad experimental*.

Proper fraction (p. 139) A proper fraction has a numerator that is less than its denominator.

Fracción propia (p. 139) Una fracción propia tiene un numerador que es menos que su denominador.

$\frac{3}{8}$ and $\frac{11}{12}$ are proper fractions.

Proportion (p. 278) A proportion is an equation stating that two ratios are equal.

Proporción (p. 278) Una proporción es una ecuación que establece que dos razones son iguales.

$\frac{3}{12} = \frac{9}{36}$ is a proportion.

Pyramid (p. 463)   A pyramid is a three-dimensional figure with triangular faces that meet at a vertex. Its base is a polygon. A pyramid is named for the shape of its base.

Pirámide (p. 463)   Una pirámide es una figura tridimensional que tiene caras triangulares que coinciden en un vértice. Su base es un polígono. Una pirámide recibe su nombre por la forma de su base.

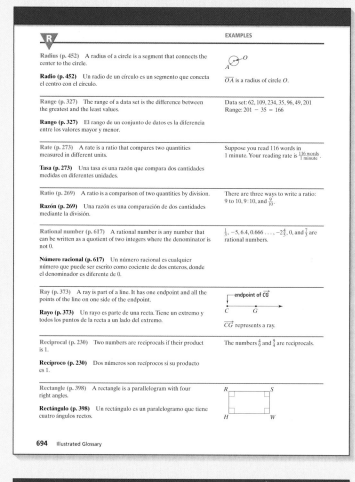

Triangular Pyramid   Rectangular Pyramid

Pythagorean Theorem (p. 622)   In any right triangle, the sum of the squares of the lengths of the legs (a and b) is equal to the square of the length of the hypotenuse (c): $a^2 + b^2 = c^2$.

Teorema de Pitágoras (p. 622)   En cualquier triángulo rectángulo, la suma del cuadrado de la longitud de los catetos (a y b) es igual al cuadrado de la longitud de la hipotenusa (c): $a^2 + b^2 = c^2$.

The right triangle has leg lengths 3 and 4 and hypotenuse length 5.

$$3^2 + 4^2 = 5^2.$$

Q

Quadrants (p. 518)   The x- and y-axes divide the coordinate plane into four regions called quadrants.

Cuadrantes (p. 518)   Los ejes de x y de y dividen el plano de coordenadas en cuatro regiones llamadas cuadrantes.

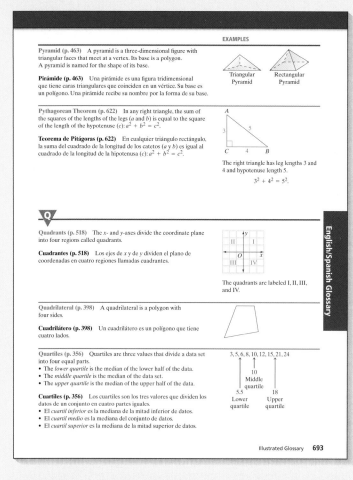

The quadrants are labeled I, II, III, and IV.

Quadrilateral (p. 398)   A quadrilateral is a polygon with four sides.

Cuadrilátero (p. 398)   Un cuadrilátero es un polígono que tiene cuatro lados.

Quartiles (p. 356)   Quartiles are three values that divide a data set into four equal parts.
- The *lower quartile* is the median of the lower half of the data.
- The *middle quartile* is the median of the data set.
- The *upper quartile* is the median of the upper half of the data.

Cuartiles (p. 356)   Los cuartiles son los tres valores que dividen los datos de un conjunto en cuatro partes iguales.
- El *cuartil inferior* es la mediana de la mitad inferior de datos.
- El *cuartil medio* es la mediana del conjunto de datos.
- El *cuartil superior* es la mediana de la mitad superior de datos.

3, 5, 6, 8, 10, 12, 15, 21, 24

10
Middle
quartile

5.5   18
Lower   Upper
quartile   quartile

Radius (p. 452)   A radius of a circle is a segment that connects the center to the circle.

Radio (p. 452)   Un radio de un círculo es un segmento que conecta el centro con el círculo.

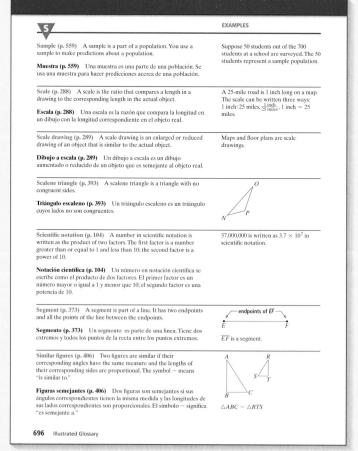

$\overline{OA}$ is a radius of circle O.

Range (p. 327)   The range of a data set is the difference between the greatest and the least values.

Rango (p. 327)   El rango de un conjunto de datos es la diferencia entre los valores mayor y menor.

Data set: 62, 109, 234, 35, 96, 49, 201
Range: $201 - 35 = 166$

Rate (p. 273)   A rate is a ratio that compares two quantities measured in different units.

Tasa (p. 273)   Una tasa es una razón que compara dos cantidades medidas en diferentes unidades.

Suppose you read 116 words in 1 minute. Your reading rate is $\frac{116 \text{ words}}{1 \text{ minute}}$.

Ratio (p. 269)   A ratio is a comparison of two quantities by division.

Razón (p. 269)   Una razón es una comparación de dos cantidades mediante la división.

There are three ways to write a ratio: 9 to 10, 9 : 10, and $\frac{9}{10}$.

Rational number (p. 617)   A rational number is any number that can be written as a quotient of two integers where the denominator is not 0.

Número racional (p. 617)   Un número racional es cualquier número que puede ser escrito como cociente de dos enteros, donde el denominador es diferente de 0.

$\frac{1}{3}, -5, 6.4, 0.666\ldots, -2\frac{4}{5}, 0,$ and $\frac{7}{3}$ are rational numbers.

Ray (p. 373)   A ray is part of a line. It has one endpoint and all the points of the line on one side of the endpoint.

Rayo (p. 373)   Un rayo es parte de una recta. Tiene un extremo y todos los puntos de la recta a un lado del extremo.

endpoint of $\overrightarrow{CG}$

$\overrightarrow{CG}$ represents a ray.

Reciprocal (p. 230)   Two numbers are reciprocals if their product is 1.

Recíproco (p. 230)   Dos números son recíprocos si su producto es 1.

The numbers $\frac{4}{9}$ and $\frac{9}{4}$ are reciprocals.

Rectangle (p. 398)   A rectangle is a parallelogram with four right angles.

Rectángulo (p. 398)   Un rectángulo es un paralelogramo que tiene cuatro ángulos rectos.

Reflection (p. 416)   A reflection, or flip, is a transformation that flips a figure over a line of reflection.

Reflexión (p. 416)   Una reflexión es una transformación que voltea una figura sobre un eje de reflexión.

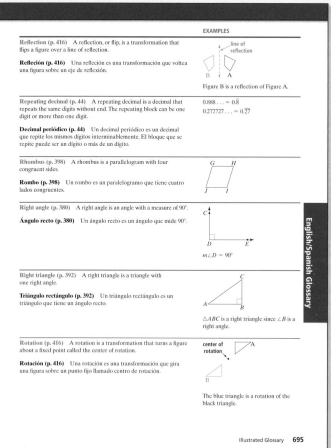

line of reflection

Figure B is a reflection of Figure A.

Repeating decimal (p. 44)   A repeating decimal is a decimal that repeats the same digits without end. The repeating block can be one digit or more than one digit.

Decimal periódico (p. 44)   Un decimal periódico es un decimal que repite los mismos dígitos interminablemente. El bloque que se repite puede ser un dígito o más de un dígito.

$0.888\ldots = 0.\overline{8}$
$0.272727\ldots = 0.\overline{27}$

Rhombus (p. 398)   A rhombus is a parallelogram with four congruent sides.

Rombo (p. 398)   Un rombo es un paralelogramo que tiene cuatro lados congruentes.

Right angle (p. 380)   A right angle is an angle with a measure of 90°.

Ángulo recto (p. 380)   Un ángulo recto es un ángulo que mide 90°.

$m\angle D = 90°$

Right triangle (p. 392)   A right triangle is a triangle with one right angle.

Triángulo rectángulo (p. 392)   Un triángulo rectángulo es un triángulo que tiene un ángulo recto.

$\triangle ABC$ is a right triangle since $\angle B$ is a right angle.

Rotation (p. 416)   A rotation is a transformation that turns a figure about a fixed point called the center of rotation.

Rotación (p. 416)   Una rotación es una transformación que gira una figura sobre un punto fijo llamado centro de rotación.

center of rotation

The blue triangle is a rotation of the black triangle.

Sample (p. 559)   A sample is a part of a population. You use a sample to make predictions about a population.

Muestra (p. 559)   Una muestra es una parte de una población. Se usa una muestra para hacer predicciones acerca de una población.

Suppose 50 students out of the 700 students at a school are surveyed. The 50 students represent a sample population.

Scale (p. 288)   A scale is the ratio that compares a length in a drawing to the corresponding length in the actual object.

Escala (p. 288)   Una escala es la razón que compara la longitud en un dibujo con la longitud correspondiente en el objeto real.

A 25-mile road is 1 inch long on a map. The scale can be written three ways: 1 inch : 25 miles, $\frac{1 \text{ inch}}{25 \text{ miles}}$, 1 inch = 25 miles.

Scale drawing (p. 289)   A scale drawing is an enlarged or reduced drawing of an object that is similar to the actual object.

Dibujo a escala (p. 289)   Un dibujo a escala es un dibujo aumentado o reducido de un objeto que es semejante al objeto real.

Maps and floor plans are scale drawings.

Scalene triangle (p. 393)   A scalene triangle is a triangle with no congruent sides.

Triángulo escaleno (p. 393)   Un triángulo escaleno es un triángulo cuyos lados no son congruentes.

Scientific notation (p. 104)   A number in scientific notation is written as the product of two factors. The first factor is a number greater than or equal to 1 and less than 10; the second factor is a power of 10.

Notación científica (p. 104)   Un número en notación científica se escribe como el producto de dos factores. El primer factor es un número mayor o igual a 1 y menor que 10; el segundo factor es una potencia de 10.

37,000,000 is written as 3.7×10^7 in scientific notation.

Segment (p. 373)   A segment is part of a line. It has two endpoints and all the points of the line between the endpoints.

Segmento (p. 373)   Un segmento es parte de una línea. Tiene dos extremos y todos los puntos de la recta entre los puntos extremos.

endpoints of $\overline{EF}$

$\overline{EF}$ is a segment.

Similar figures (p. 406)   Two figures are similar if their corresponding angles have the same measure and the lengths of their corresponding sides are proportional. The symbol ~ means "is similar to."

Figuras semejantes (p. 406)   Dos figuras son semejantes si sus ángulos correspondientes tienen la misma medida y las longitudes de sus lados correspondientes son proporcionales. El símbolo ~ significa "es semejante a."

$\triangle ABC \sim \triangle RTS$

Simplest form (p. 135) A fraction is in simplest form when the numerator and denominator have no common factors other than 1.

Mínima expresión (p. 135) Una fracción está en su mínima expresión cuando el numerador y el denominador no tienen otro factor común más que el uno.

The simplest form of $\frac{3}{9}$ is $\frac{1}{3}$.

Simulation (p. 563) A simulation of a real-world situation is a model used to find experimental probabilities.

Simulación (p. 563) Una simulación de una situación real es un modelo que se usa para hallar probabilidades experimentales.

A baseball team has equal chances of winning or losing the next game. You can use a coin to simulate the outcome.

Skew lines (p. 374) Skew lines are neither parallel nor intersecting. They lie in different planes.

Rectas cruzadas (p. 374) Las rectas cruzadas no son paralelas ni se intersecan. Están en planos diferentes.

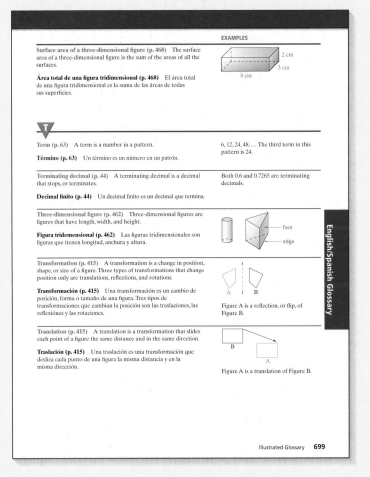

$\overleftrightarrow{MT}$ and $\overleftrightarrow{QR}$ are skew lines.

Solution (pp. 85, 602) A solution is any value or values that makes an equation or inequality true.

Solución (pp. 85, 602) Una solución es cualquier valor o valores que hacen que una ecuación o una desigualdad sea verdadera.

4 is the solution of $x + 5 = 9$.

7 is a solution of $x < 15$.

Sphere (p. 463) A sphere is the set of all points in space that are the same distance from a center point.

Esfera (p. 463) Una esfera es el conjunto de todos los puntos en el espacio que están a la misma distancia de un punto central.

Spreadsheet (p. 347) A spreadsheet is a tool used for organizing and analyzing data. Spreadsheets are arranged in numbered rows and lettered columns.

Hoja de cálculo (p. 347) Una hoja de cálculo es una herramienta que se usa para organizar y analizar datos. Las hojas de cálculo se organizan en filas numeradas y columnas en orden alfabético.

	A	B	C	D	E
1	0.50	0.70	0.60	0.50	2.30
2	1.50	0.50	2.75	2.50	7.25

Column C and row 2 meet at cell C2.

Square (p. 398) A square is a parallelogram with four right angles and four congruent sides.

Cuadrado (p. 398) Una cuadrado es un paralelógramo que tiene cuatro ángulos rectos y cuatro lados congruentes.

$QRST$ is a square. $\angle Q$, $\angle R$, $\angle S$, and $\angle T$ are right angles, and $\overline{QR} \cong \overline{RS} \cong \overline{ST} \cong \overline{QT}$.

Square root (p. 616) Finding the square root of a number is the inverse of squaring a number.

Raíz cuadrada (p. 616) Hallar la raíz cuadrada de un número es el inverso de elevar un número al cuadrado.

$\sqrt{9} = 3$ because $3^2 = 9$.

Standard form (p. 9) A number written using digits and place value is in standard form. See also *Expanded form*.

Forma normal (p. 9) Un número escrito usando dígitos y valor posicional está escrito en forma normal. Ver también *Expanded form*.

2,174 is in standard form.

Stem-and-leaf plot (p. 352) A stem-and-leaf plot is a graph that uses the digits of each number to show the shape of the data. Each data value is broken into a "stem" (digit or digits on the left) and a "leaf" (digit or digits on the right).

Diagrama de tallo y hojas (p. 352) Un diagrama de tallo y hojas es una gráfica en la que se usan los dígitos de cada número para mostrar la forma de los datos. Cada valor de los datos se divide en "tallo" (dígito o dígitos a la izquierda) y "hojas" (dígito o dígitos a la derecha).

stem	leaves
27	7
28	5 6 8
29	6 9
30	8

Key: 27 | 7 means 27.7

This stem-and-leaf plot displays recorded times in a race. The stems represent whole numbers of seconds. The leaves represent tenths of a second.

Straight angle (p. 380) A straight angle is an angle with a measure of 180°.

Ángulo llano (p. 380) Un ángulo llano es un ángulo que mide 180°.

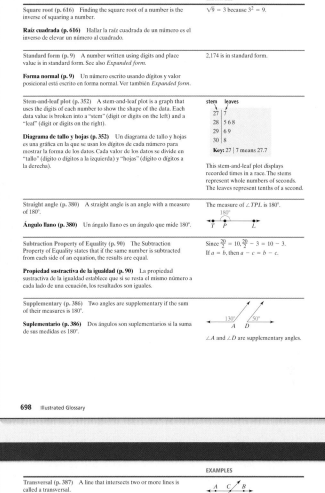

The measure of $\angle TPL$ is 180°.

Subtraction Property of Equality (p. 90) The Subtraction Property of Equality states that if the same number is subtracted from each side of an equation, the results are equal.

Propiedad sustractiva de la igualdad (p. 90) La propiedad sustractiva de la igualdad establece que si se resta el mismo número a cada lado de una ecuación, los resultados son iguales.

Since $\frac{20}{2} = 10$, $\frac{20}{2} - 3 = 10 - 3$.
If $a = b$, then $a - c = b - c$.

Supplementary (p. 386) Two angles are supplementary if the sum of their measures is 180°.

Suplementario (p. 386) Dos ángulos son suplementarios si la suma de sus medidas es 180°.

$\angle A$ and $\angle D$ are supplementary angles.

Surface area of a three-dimensional figure (p. 468) The surface area of a three-dimensional figure is the sum of the areas of all the surfaces.

Área total de una figura tridimensional (p. 468) El área total de una figura tridimensional es la suma de las áreas de todas sus superficies.

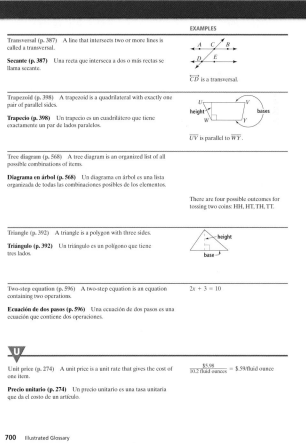

T

Term (p. 63) A term is a number in a pattern.

Término (p. 63) Un término es un número en un patrón.

6, 12, 24, 48, … The third term in this pattern is 24.

Terminating decimal (p. 44) A terminating decimal is a decimal that stops, or terminates.

Decimal finito (p. 44) Un decimal finito es un decimal que termina.

Both 0.6 and 0.7265 are terminating decimals.

Three-dimensional figure (p. 462) Three-dimensional figures are figures that have length, width, and height.

Figura tridimensional (p. 462) Las figuras tridimensionales son figuras que tienen longitud, anchura y altura.

face
edge

Transformation (p. 415) A transformation is a change in position, shape, or size of a figure. Three types of transformations that change position only are translations, reflections, and rotations.

Transformación (p. 415) Una transformación es un cambio de posición, forma o tamaño de una figura. Tres tipos de transformaciones que cambian la posición son las traslaciones, las reflexiones y las rotaciones.

Figure A is a reflection, or flip, of Figure B.

Translation (p. 415) A translation is a transformation that slides each point of a figure the same distance and in the same direction.

Traslación (p. 415) Una traslación es una transformación que desliza cada punto de una figura la misma distancia y en la misma dirección.

Figure A is a translation of Figure B.

Transversal (p. 387) A line that intersects two or more lines is called a transversal.

Secante (p. 387) Una recta que interseca a dos o más rectas se llama secante.

$\overleftrightarrow{CD}$ is a transversal.

Trapezoid (p. 398) A trapezoid is a quadrilateral with exactly one pair of parallel sides.

Trapecio (p. 398) Un trapecio es un cuadrilátero que tiene exactamente un par de lados paralelos.

$\overline{UV}$ is parallel to $\overline{WY}$.

Tree diagram (p. 568) A tree diagram is an organized list of all possible combinations of items.

Diagrama en árbol (p. 568) Un diagrama en árbol es una lista organizada de todas las combinaciones posibles de los elementos.

There are four possible outcomes for tossing two coins: HH, HT, TH, TT.

Triangle (p. 392) A triangle is a polygon with three sides.

Triángulo (p. 392) Un triángulo es un polígono que tiene tres lados.

Two-step equation (p. 596) A two-step equation is an equation containing two operations.

Ecuación de dos pasos (p. 596) Una ecuación de dos pasos es una ecuación que contiene dos operaciones.

$2x + 3 = 10$

U

Unit price (p. 274) A unit price is a unit rate that gives the cost of one item.

Precio unitario (p. 274) Un precio unitario es una tasa unitaria que da el costo de un artículo.

$\frac{\$5.98}{10.2 \text{ fluid ounces}} = \$.59/\text{fluid ounce}$

English/Spanish Glossary

Unit rate (p. 273) The rate for one unit of a given quantity is called the unit rate.

Tasa unitaria (p. 273) La tasa para una unidad de una cantidad dada se llama tasa unitaria.

If you drive 130 miles in 2 hours, your unit rate is $\frac{65 \text{ miles}}{1 \text{ hour}}$ or 65 mi/h.

Variable (p. 69) A variable is a letter that stands for a number. The value of an algebraic expression varies, or changes, depending upon the value given to the variable.

Variable (p. 69) Una variable es una letra que representa un número. El valor de una expresión algebraica varía, o cambia, dependiendo del valor que se le dé a la variable.

x is a variable in the equation $9 + x = 7$.

Vertex of an angle (p. 379) The vertex of an angle is the point of intersection of two sides of an angle or figure.

Vértice de un ángulo (p. 379) El vértice de un ángulo es el punto de intersección de dos lados de un ángulo o figura.

vertex

Vertical angles (p. 387) Vertical angles are formed by two intersecting lines. Vertical angles have equal measures.

Ángulos verticales (p. 387) Los ángulos verticales están formados por dos rectas que se intersecan. Los ángulos verticales tienen la misma medida.

$\angle 1$ and $\angle 2$ are vertical angles, as are $\angle 3$ and $\angle 4$.

Volume (p. 472) The volume of a three-dimensional figure is the number of cubic units needed to fill the space inside the figure.

Volumen (p. 472) El volumen de una figura tridimensional es el número de unidades cúbicas que se necesitan para llenar el espacio dentro de la figura.

each cube = 1 in.³

The volume of the rectangular prism is 36 in.³.

x-axis (p. 518) The x-axis is the horizontal number line that, together with the y-axis, forms the coordinate plane.

Eje de x (p. 518) El eje de x es la recta numérica horizontal que, junto con el eje de y, forma el plano de coordenadas.

---

x-coordinate (p. 518) The x-coordinate is the first number in an ordered pair. It tells the number of horizontal units a point is from 0.

Coordenada x (p. 518) La coordenada x es el primer número en un par ordenado. Indica el número de unidades horizontales a las que un punto está del cero.

The x-coordinate is −2 for the ordered pair $(-2, 1)$. The x-coordinate is 2 units to the left of the y-axis.

y-axis (p. 518) The y-axis is the vertical number line that, together with the x-axis, forms the coordinate plane.

Eje de y (p. 518) El eje de y es la recta numérica vertical que, junto con el eje de x, forma el plano de coordenadas.

y-coordinate (p. 518) The y-coordinate is the second number in an ordered pair. It tells the number of vertical units a point is from 0.

Coordenada y (p. 518) La coordenada y es el segundo número en un par ordenado. Indica el número de unidades verticales a las que un punto está del cero.

The y-coordinate is 1 for the ordered pair $(-2, 1)$. The y-coordinate is 1 unit up from the x-axis.

Zero pair (p. 496) The pairing of one "+" chip with one "−" chip is called a zero pair.

Par cero (p. 496) El emparejamiento de una ficha "+" con una ficha "−" se llama par cero.

$\oplus \ominus$ ← a zero pair

Answers to Instant Check System™

Chapter 1

Diagnosing Readiness   p. 4

1. 310 **2.** 7,530 **3.** 40 **4.** 60 **5.** 700 **6.** 1,990 **7.** 175 **8.** 145 **9.** 14,192 **10.** 3,027 **11.** 10,000 **12.** 1,392 **13.** 747 **14.** 4,544 **15.** 43,700 **16.** 25,000 **17.** 462 **18.** 1,856 **19.** 5 **20.** 17 **21.** 72 **22.** 32 **23.** 13 **24.** 73

Lesson 1-1   pp. 5–6

Check Skills You'll Need 1. 2 tens **2.** 2 ones **3.** 2 thousand **4.** 2 hundred million

Check Understanding 1. twenty-six billion, two hundred thirty-six million, eight hundred forty-six thousand eighty dollars **2a.** < **b.** 9,789; 9,897; 9,987

Lesson 1-2   pp. 9–10

Check Skills You'll Need 1. twenty-eight **2.** eight thousand, six hundred seventy-two **3.** six hundred twelve thousand, nine hundred eighty **4.** fifty-eight million, twenty-six thousand, one hundred thirteen

Check Understanding 1a. 3 + 0.1 + 0.04 + 0.001 + 0.0006 **b.** 0.8 + 0.06 + 0.005 **c.** 30 + 7 + 0.5 **d.** No; the zero in 6.207 is covered when you write "+ 0.007." **2a.** sixteen thousand, seven hundred two and three tenths **b.** one thousand six hundred seventy and two hundred thirty-four thousandths **c.** one and sixty-seven thousand twenty-three hundred-thousandths **3a.** 9.587 **b.** the 5, since 0.5 > 0.007

Lesson 1-3   pp. 13–17

Check Skills You'll Need 1. > **2.** > **3.** > **4.** > **5.** digits on the left

Check Understanding

1.

0.59   0.6
0.6 is greater.

2.

3a. < **b.** > **c.** = **d.** Answers may vary. Sample: Compare the digits starting with the highest place values. The ones and tenths digits are the same. The hundredths digit in 1.697 is greater than the hundredths digit in 1.679. So, 1.697 > 1.679. **4a.** 2.076, 2.6, 2.76 **b.** 3.059, 3.46, 3.64

Checkpoint Quiz 1 1. six trillion, eighty billion, four hundred five and thirty-one hundredths **2.** 10 + 2 + 0.03 + 0.005 **3.** 400.7 **4.** < **5.** 8.0, 8.05, 8.7, 9, 9.31

Lesson 1-4   pp. 19–21

Check Skills You'll Need 1. 50 **2.** 65,330 **3.** 132,800 **4.** 30,910,000 **5.** 6,000 **6.** 15,345,000

Check Understanding 1a. about 32 **b.** about 3 **c.** about 112 **2a.** because 28 is divisible by 4 **b.** about 250 **3a.** about $22 **b.** About $6; front-end estimation always includes the cents, so the estimates are higher and less likely to leave you short of money.

Lesson 1-5   pp. 25–27

Check Skills You'll Need 1. 9 **2.** 10 **3.** 5 **4.** 1 **5.** 3 **6.** 3

Check Understanding 1a. about 6; 6.16 **2a.** 13.9 **b.** 94 **c.** 9.4 **3a.** about 2; 1.8 **b.** about 8; 7.53 **c.** about 0.3; 0.27 **d.** Answers may vary. Sample: Aligning the decimal points aligns all the places correctly. **4a.** about 91; 91.2 **b.** about 32; 31.68 **c.** about 77; 77.084

Lesson 1-6   pp. 30–31

Check Skills You'll Need 1. 62 **2.** 57 **3.** 24 **4.** 82 **5.** 77 **6.** 3,815

Check Understanding 1. 0.16 s

Lesson 1-7   pp. 35–39

Check Skills You'll Need 1. 147 **2.** 816 **3.** 21,607 **4.** 42,340

Check Understanding 1a. 0.78 **b.** 21.85 **2a.** 0.06 **b.** 0.126 **c.** It is less than either factor. **3a.** 7.464 **b.** 57.984 **4a.** 23 **b.** 310 **c.** 333

Checkpoint Quiz 2

1–4. Answers may vary. Samples are given. **1.** 29 **2.** 60 **3.** 15 **4.** 8 **5.** 7.32 **6.** 8.26 **7.** 32.76 **8.** 1.42 **9.** 1.65 lb **10.** Answers may vary. Sample: 8 · 13.1 · 0.5 = 8 · 0.5 · 13.1 Comm. Prop. of Add. = (8 · 0.5) · 13.1 Assoc. Prop. of Add. = 4 · 13.1 = 52.4 Assoc. Prop. of Add.; 8(0.5) = 4 and 4(13.1) = 52.4

Lesson 1-8   pp. 40–41

Check Skills You'll Need 1. 360 **2.** 3,600 **3.** 36,000 **4.** 470 **5.** 47 **6.** 4.7

Check Understanding 1a. 342 **b.** 2.35 **c.** 55,200 **2a.** 5.342 **b.** 0.0235 **c.** 0.0552 **d.** Sample: To divide by 10,000, move the decimal point in the dividend four places to the left; 0.00073.

Lesson 1-9   pp. 43–45

Check Skills You'll Need 1. 5 **2.** 32 **3.** 101 **4.** 27 **5.** yes **6.** no **7.** yes **8.** yes

Check Understanding 1a. 1.52 **b.** 48.2 **c.** 0.144 **2a.** 0.6; repeating **b.** 0.25; terminating **c.** $0.\overline{18}$; repeating **3a.**

0.8
0.4
b.
0.6
0.2
c.
0.9
0.15
2
3
6

d. the number of groups **4a.** 6.2 **b.** 108 **c.** 30.5

Lesson 1-10   pp. 48–49

Check Skills You'll Need 1. = **2.** > **3.** > **4.** > **5.** < **6.** <

Check Understanding 1a. 8 **b.** 11.7 **c.** 16 **d.** I would add before multiplying if the addition of two numbers is done within parentheses and the multiplication is done outside of the parentheses. **2.** $46.85

Chapter 2

Diagnosing Readiness   p. 62

1. about 50 **2.** about 7 **3.** about 52 **4.** about 42; 42.15 **5.** about 9; 9.5 **6.** about 5; 5.1 **7.** 379 **8.** 3,040 **9.** 1.57 **10.** 26.5 **11.** 39 **12.** 17.2

Lesson 2-1   pp. 63–65

Check Skills You'll Need 1. 0.0105, 0.105, 10.5 **2.** 3.1, 3.31, 3.331 **3.** 9.06, 9.09, 9.6 **4.** 0.602, 20.06, 26.0 **5.** 100.01, 100.1, 101.0 **6.** 0.35, 0.4, 0.99

Check Understanding 1a. 41, 51 **b.** 24, 16 **c.** 57, 64 **d.** 22 tiles **2a.** 90, 75, 60, 45, 30, 15 **b.** 1, 3, 9, 27, 81, 243 **c.** 17, 36, 55, 74, 93, 112 **3a.** 2,401, 16,807, 117,649; the first term is 1; multiply each term by 7 to get the next term. **b.** 6.4, 5.2, 4; the first term is 10.0; subtract 1.2 from a term to get the next term. **c.** 32, 16, 8; the first term is 256; divide each term by 2 to get the next term.

Lesson 2-2   pp. 68–70

Check Skills You'll Need 1. 32 **2.** 19 **3.** 44.1 **4.** 4

Check Understanding 1a.

b.   **c.**

2a. 36 **b.** 5 **c.** 28 **d.** x was replaced by 7; 7 was multiplied by 4; 28 was subtracted from 56. **3.** $255

Lesson 2-3   pp. 74–78

Check Skills You'll Need 1. 10 **2.** 1 **3.** 15 **4.** 30 **5.** 48 **6.** 11

Check Understanding 1a. 5 ÷ y **b.** 6z **c.** m + 3.4 **2.** h + 2 **3.** Answers may vary. Samples are given. **a.** n ÷ 2 **b.** n + 4 **4a.** b + 28 **b.** 41

Checkpoint Quiz 1 1. 1,296; 7,776; 46,656; the first term is 1; multiply a term by 6 to get the next term. **2.** 225, 210, 195; the first term is 285; subtract 15 from a term to get the next term. **3.** 0.005, 0.0005, 0.00005; the first term is 50; divide a term by 10 to get the next term. **4.** 56 **5.** 9 **6.** 10.5 **7.** 17 − d **8.** ae **9.** 14 ÷ q **10a.** 5q + 3 **b.** 63

Answers to Instant Check System™

Chapter 1

Diagnosing Readiness p. 4

1. 310 **2.** 7,530 **3.** 40 **4.** 60 **5.** 700 **6.** 1,990 **7.** 175 **8.** 145 **9.** 14,192 **10.** 3,027 **11.** 10,000 **12.** 1,392 **13.** 747 **14.** 4,544 **15.** 43,700 **16.** 25,000 **17.** 462 **18.** 1,856 **19.** 5 **20.** 17 **21.** 72 **22.** 32 **23.** 13 **24.** 73

Lesson 1-1 pp. 5–6

Check Skills You'll Need **1.** 2 tens **2.** 2 ones **3.** 2 thousand **4.** 2 hundred million

Check Understanding **1.** twenty-six billion, two hundred thirty-six million, eight hundred forty-six thousand eighty dollars **2a.** < **b.** 9,789; 9,897; 9,987

Lesson 1-2 pp. 9–10

Check Skills You'll Need **1.** twenty-eight **2.** eight thousand, six hundred seventy-two **3.** six hundred twelve thousand, nine hundred eighty **4.** fifty-eight million, twenty-six thousand, one hundred thirteen

Check Understanding **1a.** 3 + 0.1 + 0.04 + 0.001 + 0.0006 **b.** 0.8 + 0.06 + 0.005 **c.** 30 + 7 + 0.5 **d.** No; the zero in 6.207 is covered when you write "+ 0.007." **2a.** sixteen thousand, seven hundred two and three tenths **b.** one thousand six hundred seventy and two hundred thirty-four thousandths **c.** one and sixty-seven thousand twenty-three hundred-thousandths **3a.** 9.587 **b.** the 5, since 0.5 > 0.007

Lesson 1-3 pp. 13–17

Check Skills You'll Need **1.** > **2.** > **3.** > **4.** > **5.** digits on the left

Check Understanding

1.

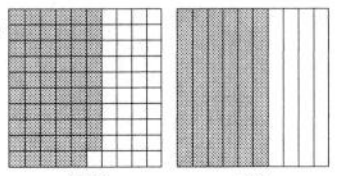

0.6 is greater.

2.

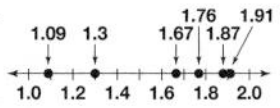

3a. < **b.** > **c.** = **d.** Answers may vary. Sample: Compare the digits starting with the highest place values. The ones and tenths digits are the same. The hundredths digit in 1.697 is greater than the hundredths digit in 1.679. So, 1.697 > 1.679. **4a.** 2.076, 2.6, 2.76 **b.** 3.059, 3.46, 3.64

Checkpoint Quiz 1 **1.** six trillion, eighty billion, four hundred five and thirty-one hundredths **2.** 10 + 2 + 0.03 + 0.005 **3.** 400.7 **4.** < **5.** 8.0, 8.05, 8.7, 9, 9.31

Lesson 1-4 pp. 19–21

Check Skills You'll Need **1.** 50 **2.** 65,330 **3.** 132,800 **4.** 30,910,000 **5.** 6,000 **6.** 15,345,000

Check Understanding **1a.** about 32 **b.** about 3 **c.** about 112 **2a.** because 28 is divisible by 4 **b.** about 250 **3a.** about $22 **b.** About $6; front-end estimation always includes the cents, so the estimates are higher and less likely to leave you short of money.

Lesson 1-5 pp. 25–27

Check Skills You'll Need **1.** 9 **2.** 10 **3.** 5 **4.** 1 **5.** 3 **6.** 3

Check Understanding **1.** about 6; 6.16 **2a.** 13.9 **b.** 94 **c.** 9.4 **3a.** about 2; 1.8 **b.** about 8; 7.53 **c.** about 0.3; 0.27 **d.** Answers may vary. Sample: Aligning the decimal points aligns all the places correctly. **4a.** about 91; 91.2 **b.** about 32; 31.68 **c.** about 77; 77.084

Lesson 1-6 pp. 30–31

Check Skills You'll Need **1.** 62 **2.** 57 **3.** 24 **4.** 82 **5.** 77 **6.** 3,815

Check Understanding **1.** 0.16 s

Lesson 1-7 pp. 35–39

Check Skills You'll Need **1.** 147 **2.** 816 **3.** 21,607 **4.** 42,340

Check Understanding **1a.** 0.78 **b.** 21.85 **2a.** 0.06 **b.** 0.126 **c.** It is less than either factor. **3a.** 7.464 **b.** 57.984 **4a.** 23 **b.** 310 **c.** 333

Checkpoint Quiz 2

1–4. Answers may vary. Samples are given. **1.** 29 **2.** 60 **3.** 15 **4.** 8 **5.** 7.32 **6.** 8.26 **7.** 32.76 **8.** 1.42 **9.** 1.65 lb **10.** Answers may vary. Sample: 8 · 13.1 · 0.5 = 8 · 0.5 · 13.1 Comm. Prop. of Add. = (8 · 0.5) · 13.1 Assoc. Prop. of Add. = 4 · 13.1 = 52.4 Assoc. Prop. of Add.; 8(0.5) = 4 and 4(13.1) = 52.4

Lesson 1-8 pp. 40–41

Check Skills You'll Need **1.** 360 **2.** 3,600 **3.** 36,000 **4.** 470 **5.** 47 **6.** 4.7

Check Understanding **1a.** 342 **b.** 2.35 **c.** 55,200 **2a.** 5.342 **b.** 0.0235 **c.** 0.0552 **d.** Sample: To divide by 10,000, move the decimal point in the dividend four places to the left; 0.00073.

Lesson 1-9 pp. 43–45

Check Skills You'll Need **1.** 5 **2.** 32 **3.** 101 **4.** 27 **5.** yes **6.** no **7.** yes **8.** yes

Check Understanding **1a.** 1.52 **b.** 48.2 **c.** 0.144 **2a.** $0.\overline{6}$; repeating **b.** 0.25; terminating **c.** $0.\overline{18}$; repeating **3a.**

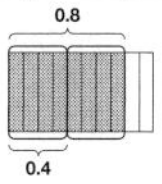

2

b.

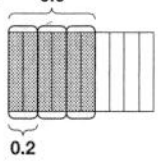

3

c.

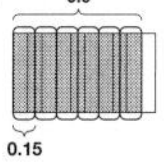

6

d. the number of groups **4a.** 6.2 **b.** 108 **c.** 30.5

Lesson 1-10 pp. 48–49

Check Skills You'll Need **1.** = **2.** > **3.** > **4.** > **5.** < **6.** <

Check Understanding **1a.** 8 **b.** 11.7 **c.** 16 **d.** I would add before multiplying if the addition of two numbers is done within parentheses and the multiplication is done outside of the parentheses. **2.** $46.85

Chapter 2

Diagnosing Readiness p. 62

1. about 50 **2.** about 7 **3.** about 52 **4.** about 42; 42.15 **5.** about 9; 9.5 **6.** about 5; 5.1 **7.** 379 **8.** 3,040 **9.** 1.57 **10.** 26.5 **11.** 39 **12.** 17.2

Lesson 2-1 pp. 63–65

Check Skills You'll Need **1.** 0.0105, 0.105, 10.5 **2.** 3.1, 3.31, 3.331 **3.** 9.06, 9.09, 9.6 **4.** 0.602, 20.06, 26.0 **5.** 100.01, 100.1, 101.0 **6.** 0.35, 0.4, 0.99

Check Understanding **1a.** 41, 51 **b.** 24, 16 **c.** 57, 64 **d.** 22 tiles **2a.** 90, 75, 60, 45, 30, 15 **b.** 1, 3, 9, 27, 81, 243 **c.** 17, 36, 55, 74, 93, 112 **3a.** 2,401, 16,807, 117,649; the first term is 1; multiply each term by 7 to get the next term. **b.** 6.4, 5.2, 4; the first term is 10.0; subtract 1.2 from a term to get the next term. **c.** 32, 16, 8; the first term is 256; divide each term by 2 to get the next term.

Lesson 2-2 pp. 68–70

Check Skills You'll Need **1.** 32 **2.** 19 **3.** 44.1 **4.** 4

Check Understanding **1a.**

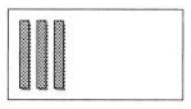

b.

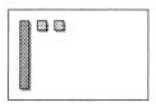

c.

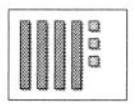

2a. 36 **b.** 5 **c.** 28 **d.** x was replaced by 7; 7 was multiplied by 4; 28 was subtracted from 56. **3.** $255

Lesson 2-3 pp. 74–78

Check Skills You'll Need **1.** 10 **2.** 1 **3.** 15 **4.** 30 **5.** 48 **6.** 11

Check Understanding **1a.** $5 \div y$ **b.** $6z$ **c.** $m + 3.4$ **2.** $h + 2$ **3.** Answers may vary. Samples are given. **a.** $n \div 2$ **b.** $n + 4$ **4a.** $b + 28$ **b.** 41

Checkpoint Quiz 1 **1.** 1,296; 7,776; 46,656; the first term is 1; multiply a term by 6 to get the next term. **2.** 225, 210, 195; the first term is 285; subtract 15 from a term to get the next term. **3.** 0.005, 0.0005, 0.00005; the first term is 50; divide a term by 10 to get the next term. **4.** 56 **5.** 9 **6.** 10.5 **7.** $17 - d$ **8.** ae **9.** $14 \div q$ **10a.** $5q + 3$ **b.** 63

Lesson 2-4 p. 80

Check Skills You'll Need **1.** 256; 1,024; 4,096 **2.** 35, 42, 49 **3.** 112, 224, 448 **4.** 52, 43, 34 **5.** 6.1, 7.2, 8.3 **6.** 5; 2.5; 1.25

Check Understanding **1.** No; for 10 tables, there are 64 seats, but for 20 tables there are 124 seats (not 128).

Lesson 2-5 pp. 84–86

Check Skills You'll Need **1.** about 6 **2.** about 4 **3.** about 2 **4.** about 16 **5.** about 24 **6.** about 5

Check Understanding **1a.** true **b.** false **c.** false **2a.** 9 **b.** 80 **c.** 1.2 **3a–d.** Answers may vary. Samples are given. **3a.** about 29 **b.** about 6 **c.** about 18

Lesson 2-6 pp. 90–92

Check Skills You'll Need **1.** 9 **2.** 1 **3.** 70 **4.** 2 **5.** 9 **6.** 3

Check Understanding **1.** 4.8 **2.** 9.8 lb **3a.** 81 **b.** 55 **c.** 6.4 **4.** t = temperature at 7:00 P.M., $t - 9 = 54$; 63°F

Lesson 2-7 pp. 95–98

Check Skills You'll Need **1–6.** Answers may vary. Samples are given. **1.** 7 **2.** 6 **3.** 16 **4.** 3 **5.** 8 **6.** 32

Check Understanding **1a.** 4 **b.** 2.7 **c.** 40 **2.** Equations may vary. Sample: $.35c = 302.75$; 865 cards **3a.** 200 **b.** 15 **c.** 1.58

Checkpoint Quiz 2 **1.** 13 **2.** 18.2 **3.** 2.2 **4.** 14.4 **5.** 10.8 **6.** 20 **7.** 8.4 **8.** 7 **9.** 5 **10.** x = change received; $x + 5.73 = 10.00$; $4.27

Lesson 2-8 pp. 99–101

Check Skills You'll Need **1.** 25 **2.** 0 **3.** 19.2 **4.** 10,000 **5.** 1 **6.** 2

Check Understanding **1a.** 3.94^2; 3.94; 2 **b.** 7^4; 7; 4 **c.** x^3; x; 3 **d.** No; 5^4 means $5 \times 5 \times 5 \times 5$, which is 625. 5×4 is 20. **2a.** $5 \times 10^4 + 5 \times 10^3 + 6 \times 10^2 + 0 \times 10^1 + 7 \times 1$ **b.** $3 \times 10^5 + 8 \times 10^4 + 0 \times 10^3 + 2 \times 10^2 + 5 \times 10^1 + 4 \times 1$ **3a.** 100,000 **b.** 19,683 **c.** 1.331 **d.** No; 2^5 means $2 \times 2 \times 2 \times 2 \times 2$, which is 32; 5^2 means 5×5, which is 25. **4a.** 6 **b.** 112 **c.** 14

Lesson 2-9 pp. 105–106

Check Skills You'll Need **1.** 13.4 **2.** 17.3 **3.** 23.3 **4.** 16.5

Check Understanding **1a.** $3 \times (40 + 2) = (3 \times 40) + (3 \times 2) = 120 + 6 = 126$ **1b.** $5 \times (70 - 2) = (5 \times 70) - (5 \times 2) = 350 - 10 = 340$ **2.** $14

Chapter 3

Diagnosing Readiness p. 118

1. four tenths **2.** thirty-seven hundredths **3.** one and eight tenths **4.** two hundred five thousandths **5.** twenty and eighty-eight hundredths **6.** one hundred fifty thousandths **7.** 4.02, 4.2, 4.21 **8.** 0.033, 0.3, 0.33 **9.** 6.032, 6.203, 6.302 **10.** 0.8 **11.** 0.55 **12.** 19 **13.** 36.3 **14.** 132 **15.** 53 **16.** 3^3 **17.** 5^2 **18.** 2^6

Lesson 3-1 pp. 119–120

Check Skills You'll Need **1.** 49 **2.** 41 **3.** 41.5 **4.** 145 **5.** 41 **6.** 50

Check Understanding **1a.** no **b.** yes **c.** $54 = 9 \times 6 = 9 \times (2 \times 3)$ **2a.** 2, 5, and 10 **b.** 5 **c.** none **d.** 2 **3a.** no **b.** yes **c.** yes **4a.** yes **b.** no **c.** yes **d.** If the sum of the digits is divisible by 9, the sum is divisible by 3, since 9 is divisible by 3.

Lesson 3-2 pp. 123–124

Check Skills You'll Need **1.** 2, 3, 5, 9, and 10 **2.** none **3.** 5 **4.** 2, 5, and 10 **5.** 2, 5, and 10 **6.** 2

Check Understanding **1.** 1, 2, 3, 6, 7, 14, 21, 42 **2a.** composite; $39 = 3 \times 13$ **b.** Prime; it has only two factors, 1 and 47. **c.** composite; $63 = 3 \times 21$ or $63 = 7 \times 9$ **3a.** $2^2 \times 3^2$ **b.** 5^3

Lesson 3-3 pp. 128–131

Check Skills You'll Need **1.** $3^2 \times 5$ **2.** 3×7 **3.** $3^2 \times 11$ **4.** 3×31 **5.** 3×13 **6.** 2^7 **7.** 21 is not prime.

Check Understanding **1a.** factors of 6: 1, 2, 3, 6; factors of 21: 1, 3, 7, 21; GCF of 6 and 21: 3 **b.** factors of 18: 1, 2, 3, 6, 9, 18; factors of 49: 1, 7, 49; GCF of 18; and 49: 1 **c.** factors of 14: 1, 2, 7, 14; factors of 28: 1, 2, 4, 7, 14, 28; GCF of 14 and 28: 14 **d.** three from the set of 18 and five from the set of 30

2a.

```
2)24  54     GCF = 6
3)12  27
   4   9
```

b.

```
3)18  27  36     GCF = 9
3) 6   9  12
   2   3   4
```


3a.

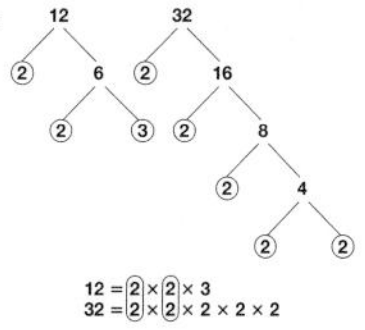

GCF = 4

b.

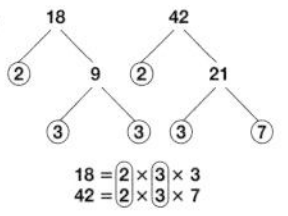

GCF = 6

Checkpoint Quiz 1 **1.** 3, 5 **2.** 2 **3.** 2, 3, 5, 10 **4.** $2^4 \times 3$ **5.** $2^4 \times 5$ **6.** $2^3 \times 5^3$ **7.** 5 **8.** 24 **9.** 3 **10.** 1, 2, 3, 6

Lesson 3-4 pp. 134–135

Check Skills You'll Need **1.** 4 **2.** 5 **3.** 6 **4.** 1 **5.** 4 **6.** 7

Check Understanding **1a–c.** Answers may vary. Samples are given. **1a.** $\frac{2}{5}, \frac{8}{20}, \frac{12}{30}$ **b.** $\frac{10}{16}, \frac{15}{24}, \frac{25}{40}$ **c.** $\frac{1}{3}, \frac{4}{12}, \frac{6}{18}$ **2a.** $\frac{3}{4}$ **b.** $\frac{2}{7}$ **c.** $\frac{1}{5}$ **3a.** $\frac{7}{20}$ **b.** dog food and bird food; $42 + 18 = 60$, and $\frac{60}{120} = \frac{1}{2}$

Lesson 3-5 pp. 139–140

Check Skills You'll Need **1.** $\frac{1}{3}$ **2.** $\frac{2}{3}$ **3.** $\frac{5}{16}$ **4.** $\frac{1}{17}$ **5.** $\frac{9}{10}$ **6.** There are 60 minutes in an hour, so compare 35 to 60 by using the fraction $\frac{35}{60}$. In simplest form, $\frac{35}{60}$ is $\frac{7}{12}$.

Check Understanding **1.** $\frac{25}{7}$ **2.** whole units **3a.** $4\frac{4}{9}$ **b.** $5\frac{1}{3}$ **c.** $5\frac{3}{4}$ **d.** $1\frac{2}{3}$

Lesson 3-6 pp. 143–144

Check Skills You'll Need **1.** $2^4 \times 5$ **2.** 2^5 **3.** 5×19 **4.** $2^2 \times 5^3$ **5.** $2^4 \times 13$ **6.** 5^4

Check Understanding **1a.** 60 **b.** 12, 24, 36, 48, 60 **2.** 350

Lesson 3-7 pp. 148–152

Check Skills You'll Need **1–9.** Answers may vary. Samples are given. **1.** $\frac{6}{14}, \frac{15}{35}$ **2.** $\frac{1}{3}, \frac{21}{63}$ **3.** $\frac{1}{5}, \frac{2}{10}$ **4.** $\frac{4}{6}, \frac{20}{30}$ **5.** $\frac{5}{6}, \frac{20}{24}$ **6.** $\frac{1}{6}, \frac{5}{30}$ **7.** $\frac{3}{4}, \frac{12}{16}$ **8.** $\frac{4}{10}, \frac{120}{300}$ **9.** $\frac{16}{10}, \frac{24}{15}$

Check Understanding **1a.** < **b.** = **c.** > **d.** 40 min, 36 min; $\frac{2}{3}$ **2a.** < **b.** > **c.** = **d.** Yes; $\frac{7}{8} = \frac{28}{32}$ and $\frac{28}{32} > \frac{27}{32}$. So $6\frac{7}{8} > 6\frac{27}{32}$. **3.** $2\frac{2}{3}, 2\frac{4}{5}, 2\frac{5}{6}$

Checkpoint Quiz 2 **1.** $\frac{2}{3}$ **2.** $\frac{3}{4}$ **3.** $\frac{1}{4}$ **4.** $\frac{16}{5}$ **5.** $1\frac{5}{8}$ **6.** 60 **7.** $\frac{1}{8}, \frac{3}{16}, \frac{1}{3}$ **8.** < **9.** > **10.** >

Lesson 3-8 pp. 153–154

Check Skills You'll Need **1.** 1.5; terminating **2.** $0.\overline{6}$; repeating **3.** 1.6; terminating **4.** 0.375; terminating **5.** 0.3; terminating **6.** 0.24; terminating **7.** 0.24; terminating **8.** 0.2; terminating **9.** 3.2; terminating

Check Understanding **1a.** $\frac{3}{5}$ **b.** $\frac{7}{20}$ **c.** $5\frac{2}{25}$ **d.** $7\frac{81}{200}$ **e.** Using the digits to the right of the decimal point, the number you say first tells you the numerator, and the number that is read with "-th" at the end tells you the denominator. **2a.** 0.45 **b.** The mixed number $2\frac{3}{4}$ is equal to the whole number 2 plus the decimal equivalent of $\frac{3}{4}$. To find the decimal equivalent of $\frac{3}{4}$, divide the numerator 3 by the denominator 4. Add the quotient 0.75 to the whole number 2 to get 2.75. **3a.** $0.\overline{6}$ **b.** $0.1\overline{6}$ **c.** $0.\overline{5}$ **d.** $1.\overline{3}$ **e.** when the numerator is not divisible by 3

Lesson 3-9 pp. 157–158

Check Skills You'll Need **1.** 10, 12, 14 **2.** 32, 64, 128 **3.** 54, 162, 486 **4.** 85, 80, 75 **5.** 21, 26, 31 **6.** 9, 11, 13

Check Understanding **1.** 20 adult tickets

Chapter 4

Diagnosing Readiness p.170

1. 2.59 **2.** 1.99 **3.** 6.22 **4.** $\frac{1}{2}$ **5.** $\frac{2}{5}$ **6.** $\frac{3}{4}$ **7.** $9\frac{2}{3}$ **8.** $5\frac{1}{4}$ **9.** $7\frac{1}{2}$ **10.** $\frac{26}{3}$ **11.** $\frac{23}{3}$ **12.** $\frac{151}{9}$ **13.** 72 **14.** 80 **15.** 210

Lesson 4-1 pp. 171–172

Check Skills You'll Need **1.** > **2.** < **3.** = **4.** < **5.** > **6.** <

Check Understanding **1a.** $1\frac{1}{2}$ **b.** 1 **2.** 5 hours

Lesson 4-2 pp. 175–176

Check Skills You'll Need **1.** $\frac{1}{4}$ **2.** $\frac{1}{3}$ **3.** $\frac{4}{5}$ **4.** $\frac{4}{5}$ **5.** $\frac{2}{3}$ **6.** $\frac{3}{4}$ **7.** $\frac{5}{6}$ **8.** $\frac{3}{7}$ **9.** $\frac{3}{7}$

Check Understanding **1a.** $\frac{5}{6}$ **b.** $\frac{3}{5}$ **2a.** $1\frac{1}{8}$ **b.** $1\frac{2}{5}$ **c.** Answers may vary. Sample: If the numerator and denominator have a common factor, the answer is not in simplest form. **3a.** $\frac{1}{5}$ **b.** $\frac{1}{2}$ **c.** $\frac{1}{3}$ yard

Lesson 4-3 pp. 180–184

Check Skills You'll Need **1.** 18 **2.** 36 **3.** 120 **4.** 240 **5.** 150 **6.** 60 **7.** 24. Explanations may vary. Sample: List multiples of 8: 8; 16; 24. List multiples of 12: 12; 24. The LCM is 24.

Check Understanding **1.** $\frac{7}{10}$ **2.** $1\frac{5}{12}$ h **3.** $\frac{1}{8}$ **4.** $\frac{1}{10}$ yd

Checkpoint Quiz 1 **1.** $1\frac{1}{2}$ **2.** 1 **3.** $1\frac{1}{5}$ **4.** $\frac{1}{2}$ **5.** $1\frac{1}{4}$ **6.** $\frac{17}{30}$ **7.** $\frac{1}{2}$ **8.** $\frac{7}{10}$ **9.** $\frac{11}{18}$ of the class **10.** $1\frac{1}{6}$ c

Lesson 4-4 pp. 185–187

Check Skills You'll Need **1.** $4\frac{1}{2}$ **2.** $3\frac{1}{3}$ **3.** $1\frac{1}{3}$ **4.** $2\frac{1}{2}$ **5.** $1\frac{3}{4}$ **6.** $2\frac{1}{2}$ **7.** $2\frac{2}{5}$. Explanations may vary. Sample: Divide 36 by 15. The quotient 2 is the integer of the mixed number. The remainder 6 is the numerator, and 15 is the denominator: $2\frac{6}{15}$. Reduce to $2\frac{2}{5}$.

Check Understanding **1.** Answers may vary. Sample: It doesn't matter because addition is commutative. **2a.** $5\frac{7}{12}$ h **b.** $2\frac{1}{3} + 3\frac{1}{4} \approx 2 + 3$, or 5 **3a.** $9\frac{3}{4}$ **b.** $19\frac{1}{8}$ **c.** $21\frac{4}{15}$ **4.** No; you need $3\frac{1}{4}$ c of milk, but you have only 3 c.

Lesson 4-5 pp. 190–192

Check Skills You'll Need **1.** $1\frac{1}{2}$ **2.** $2\frac{2}{3}$ **3.** $4\frac{3}{5}$ **4.** $2\frac{1}{2}$ **5.** $2\frac{1}{2}$ **6.** $2\frac{2}{5}$ **7.** Divide 24 by 10. The quotient 2 is the integer of the mixed number. The remainder 4 is the numerator, and 10 is the denominator: $2\frac{4}{10}$. Reduce to $2\frac{2}{5}$.

Check Understanding **1a.** $\frac{11}{16}$ in. **b.** Yes; answers may vary. Sample: 32 is a common multiple of 8 and 4, so it is also a common denominator. **2a.** $1\frac{1}{3}$ **b.** $5\frac{3}{4}$ **3.** Answers may vary. Sample: If the benchmark of the first fraction is less than the benchmark of the second fraction, then rename before subtracting.

Lesson 4-6 pp. 196–197

Check Skills You'll Need **1.** 26 **2.** 268 **3.** 3.8 **4.** 18.9 **5.** 0 **6.** 14.2

Check Understanding **1a.** $3\frac{2}{3}$ **b.** $11\frac{1}{4}$ **c.** $2\frac{3}{4}$ **2a.** $\frac{7}{12}$ **b.** $\frac{1}{4}$ **3.** $1\frac{3}{4}$ in.

Lesson 4-7 pp. 201–205

Check Skills You'll Need **1.** $\frac{16}{60}$ **2.** $\frac{15}{60}$ **3.** $\frac{12}{60}$ **4.** $\frac{20}{60}$ **5.** $\frac{40}{60}$ **6.** $\frac{35}{60}$

Check Understanding **1.** 31 days **2.** 47 min **3a.** 9 h 15 min **b.** Answers may vary. Sample: Adding 12 hours makes both times the hours elapsed since midnight, so they can be subtracted. **4.** 5:20 P.M.

Checkpoint Quiz 2 **1.** $5\frac{5}{8}$ **2.** $4\frac{3}{4}$ **3.** $14\frac{5}{6}$ **4.** $5\frac{8}{9}$ **5.** $\frac{1}{2}$ **6.** $1\frac{2}{9}$ **7.** $\frac{3}{10}$ **8.** $\frac{2}{15}$ **9.** 6 h 47 min **10.** 9 h 43 min

Lesson 4-8 pp. 206–207

Check Skills You'll Need **1–6.** Answers may vary. Samples are given. **1.** 6 **2.** 10 **3.** 11 **4.** 2 **5.** 19 **6.** 2

Check Understanding **1.** 35 mats

Chapter 5

Diagnosing Readiness p. 218

1. 4 **2.** 5 **3.** 12 **4.** 112 **5.** 100 **6.** 5 **7.** 54 **8.** 0.6 **9.** 3 **10.** 12 **11.** 7 **12.** 3 **13.** 20 **14.** 6 **15.** 21 **16.** $\frac{3}{7}$ **17.** $\frac{2}{3}$ **18.** $\frac{1}{3}$ **19.** $\frac{3}{8}$ **20.** $\frac{1}{4}$ **21.** $\frac{3}{7}$ **22.** $\frac{2}{3}$ **23.** $\frac{7}{8}$ **24.** $\frac{3}{7}$

Lesson 5-1 pp. 219–221

Check Skills You'll Need **1.** $\frac{1}{2}$ **2.** $\frac{3}{5}$ **3.** $\frac{2}{3}$ **4.** $\frac{9}{10}$ **5.** $\frac{3}{4}$ **6.** $\frac{3}{4}$ **7.** Answers may vary. Sample: Yes; the GCF of 9 and 16 is 1.

Check Understanding **1.** 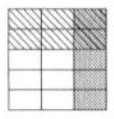 $\frac{2}{15}$ **2a.** $\frac{3}{20}$ **b.** $\frac{10}{63}$

Instant Check System™ Answers

c. When you add $\frac{3}{8}$ and $\frac{5}{8}$ you add numerators and keep the same denominator. When you multiply the fractions, you multiply numerators and multiply denominators. **3a.** $\frac{28}{5} = 5\frac{3}{5}$ **b.** $\frac{40}{3} = 13\frac{1}{3}$ **4.** $4\frac{1}{2}$ mi

Lesson 5-2 pp. 224–226

Check Skills You'll Need **1.** 2 **2.** 13 **3.** 30 **4.** 8 **5.** 6 **6.** 6

Check Understanding **1a.** 36 **b.** 56 **c.** 143 **d.** The actual product is greater than $80 \cdot \frac{1}{8}$, since $82\frac{5}{7} >$ 80. So the actual product is greater than 10. $83 \cdot 0$ would give an estimate of 0, which is not realistic. **2a.** $3\frac{7}{16}$ **b.** $27\frac{1}{2}$ **c.** 18 **3.** $2\frac{5}{8}$ mi

Lesson 5-3 pp. 230–232

Check Skills You'll Need **1.** 6 **2.** 4 **3.** $\frac{1}{5}$ **4.** 1 **5.** $\frac{1}{7}$ **6.** $\frac{4}{11}$

Check Understanding **1a.** $\frac{4}{3}$ or $1\frac{1}{3}$ **b.** $\frac{1}{7}$ **c.** $\frac{7}{8}$ **2a.** $10\frac{2}{3}$ **b.** $31\frac{1}{2}$ **c.** $10\frac{1}{2}$ **3a.** $\frac{3}{4}$ **b.** $\frac{3}{4}$ **c.** $\frac{4}{5}$ **d.** Answers may vary. Sample: $\frac{2}{3}$ is between $\frac{1}{2}$ and 1. There are 2 fourths in $\frac{1}{2}$, and 4 fourths in 1. So there must be between 2 and 4 fourths in $\frac{2}{3}$. **4a.** $\frac{1}{32}$ **b.** $\frac{1}{150}$ **c.** Answers may vary. Sample: $\frac{1}{5}$ of the original piece, or $\frac{1}{6}$ yd.

Lesson 5-4 pp. 236–240

Check Skills You'll Need **1.** 28 **2.** $23\frac{1}{3}$ **3.** $\frac{7}{24}$ **4.** $\frac{1}{6}$ **5.** $\frac{15}{16}$ **6.** $2\frac{8}{11}$ **7.** When you divide by a fraction, find its reciprocal and multiply by it.

Check Understanding **1a.** about 7 **b.** about 5 **c.** about 10 **d.** Answers may vary. Sample: about 10 **2.** $1\frac{1}{4}$ c **3a.** 6 **b.** $2\frac{1}{20}$ **c.** $3\frac{1}{2}$ **d.** When you divide a number by a greater number, the quotient is less than 1.

Checkpoint Quiz 1 **1.** 15 **2.** $23\frac{5}{8}$ **3.** 64 **4.** $\frac{1}{6}$ **5.** $1\frac{11}{21}$ **6.** $\frac{3}{5}$ **7.** $16\frac{1}{3}$ **8.** $2\frac{7}{30}$ **9.** 39 ft **10.** 24 cookies

Lesson 5-5 pp. 242–243

Check Skills You'll Need **1.** $\frac{7}{30}$ **2.** $\frac{3}{11}$ **3.** $\frac{2}{5}$

Check Understanding **1a.** 30 **b.** 72 **2a.** 20 **b.** 25 **c.** 48 **3.** 10 boards

Lesson 5-6 pp. 246–247

Check Skills You'll Need **1.** $1\frac{1}{2}$ **2.** $\frac{10}{27}$ **3.** 10 **4.** $\frac{25}{36}$ **5.** $6\frac{2}{5}$ **6.** $\frac{11}{12}$

Check Understanding **1.** 408 cards

Lesson 5-7 pp. 250–253

Check Skills You'll Need **1.** > **2.** > **3.** > **4.** > **5.** < **6.** =

Check Understanding

1–3. Answers may vary. Samples are given. **1a.** Inches; pencils are shorter than a foot. **b.** Feet or yards; adult whales are longer than humans. **c.** Inches are a short unit of measure. Inches are too small to measure a walking distance. **2a.** Pounds; a refrigerator weighs less than a grand piano. **b.** Ounces; an ice cube weighs about the same as a slice of bread. **3a.** Gallons; a tanker truck holds more gasoline than can fit in a small bucket. **b.** Fluid ounces or cups; a serving of yogurt is less than a pint. **c.** Gallons; a bathtub can hold a few small buckets of water. **d.** Fluid ounces; a bottle of cough syrup holds less than a pint.

Checkpoint Quiz 2 **1.** $10\frac{1}{2}$ **2.** $\frac{2}{5}$ **3.** mile **4.** pound **5.** 51 markers

Lesson 5-8 pp. 254–255

Check Skills You'll Need **1.** $25\frac{1}{2}$ **2.** $10\frac{1}{2}$ **3.** 24 **4.** $\frac{55}{78}$ **5.** $\frac{3}{8}$ **6.** $\frac{20}{27}$ **7.**

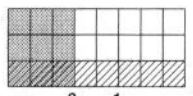

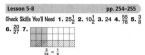

$\frac{3}{24} = \frac{1}{8}$

Check Understanding **1a.** $3\frac{3}{4}$ **b.** $4\frac{25}{36}$ **c.** $2\frac{1}{2}$ yd **2a.** $6\frac{1}{2}$ **b.** 4,500 **3.** 8 lb 1 oz

Chapter 6

Diagnosing Readiness p. 268

1. 18 **2.** 7 **3.** 48 **4.** 132 **5.** 24 **6.** 42 **7.** 9 **8.** 16 **9.** $\frac{2}{5}$ **10.** $\frac{5}{11}$ **11.** $\frac{2}{3}$ **12.** $\frac{1}{3}$ **13.** > **14.** > **15.** < **16.** = **17.** $\frac{8}{21}$ **18.** $\frac{1}{2}$ **19.** $3\frac{8}{9}$ **20.** $4\frac{1}{8}$

Lesson 6-1 pp. 269–270

Check Skills You'll Need **1.** $\frac{1}{3}$ **2.** $\frac{2}{3}$ **3.** $\frac{2}{9}$ **4.** $\frac{1}{16}$

Check Understanding **1a.** 2 to 4, 2 : 4, $\frac{2}{4}$ **b.** 2 to 6, 2 : 6, $\frac{2}{6}$ **2a–c.** Answers may vary. Samples are given. **2a.** $\frac{2}{7}$, $\frac{4}{14}$ **b.** 4 : 1, 8 : 2 **c.** 4 to 11, 12 to 33 **d.** 9 to 5 is a comparison of two numbers by division. $1\frac{4}{5}$ is not a comparison of two numbers.

3a. 1 : 5 **b.** 10 to 9 **c.** $\frac{13}{1}$ **d.** 1 to 8

Lesson 6-2 pp. 273–274

Check Skills You'll Need **1.** $\frac{4}{1}$ **2.** $\frac{4}{1}$ **3.** $\frac{5}{1}$ **4.** $\frac{6}{1}$ **5.** $\frac{25}{1}$ **6.** $\frac{13}{1}$

Check Understanding **1a.** 33 pages per hour **b.** \$.79 per pound **c.** $\frac{12 \text{ inches}}{1 \text{ foot}}$; it is the number of inches in 1 foot. **2a.** $\frac{\$5.25}{1 \text{ hour}} = \frac{\$26.25}{5 \text{ hours}}$ **b.** $\frac{25 \text{ words}}{1 \text{ minute}} = \frac{250 \text{ words}}{10 \text{ minutes}}$ **3a.** \$.11 per ounce; \$.09 per ounce; the 32-ounce container **b.** \$.14 per minute; \$.09 per minute; the 15 minutes for \$1.35 **c.** Answers may vary. Sample: It helps find the less expensive item.

Lesson 6-3 pp. 278–280

Check Skills You'll Need **1.** < **2.** = **3.** < **4.** < **5.** > **6.** =

Check Understanding **1a.** yes **b.** no **c.** no **2a.** 15 **b.** 6

Lesson 6-4 pp. 283–285

Check Skills You'll Need **1.** 10 **2.** 6 **3.** 7 **4.** 12 **5.** 108 **6.** 56

Check Understanding **1.** Yes; the cross products are equal. **2a.** 15 **b.** 4 **c.** 5 **3a.** \$4.50 **b.** about \$3.20

Lesson 6-5 pp. 288–292

Check Skills You'll Need **1.** 20 **2.** 25 **3.** 6 **4.** 2 **5.** 1 **6.** 105

Check Understanding **1.** 1 in. : 14 in. **2.** about 100 mi **3.** 17 in.

Checkpoint Quiz 1 **1.** 18 to 40, $\frac{18}{40}$ **2.** \$2.85 **3.** \$17.50 **4.** no **5.** no **6.** yes **7.** 12 **8.** 78 **9.** \$16.20 **10.** 1 in. : 3 ft

Lesson 6-6 pp. 294–296

Check Skills You'll Need **1.** $\frac{6}{25}$ **2.** $\frac{2}{5}$ **3.** $\frac{3}{4}$ **4.** $\frac{1}{3}$ **5.** $\frac{79}{100}$

Check Understanding 1a. 0.18 **b.** 0.02 **c.** 0.25 2a. $\frac{1}{25}$ **b.** $\frac{11}{20}$ **c.** $\frac{3}{4}$ **d.** $\frac{1}{5}$ 3a. 52% **b.** 5% **c.** 50% **d.** Move the decimal point two places to the left. **4a.** 5% **b.** 1, 2, 4, 5, 10, 20, 25, 50, 100 **5.** about 7%

Lesson 6-7 pp. 299–300

Check Skills You'll Need **1.** 18 **2.** 8 **3.** 15 **4.** 78 **5.** 85 **6.** 230 **7.** Answers may vary. Sample: Use cross products. $39 \times 40 = 100 \times x$; $1{,}560 = 100x$. Divide both sides by 100. The solution is 15.6.

Check Understanding **1.** 48 **2a.** 10.92 **b.** 21.78 **3a.** 5.6 **b.** 9 **c.** 18

Lesson 6-8 pp. 303–306

Check Skills You'll Need **1.** 30 **2.** 120 **3.** 2,000 **4.** 400

Check Understanding **1a.** about \$10.50 **b.** Answers may vary. Sample: High estimate; I may estimate too low and not have enough money. **2.** about \$6 **3a.** about \$24 **b.** High estimate; the original price was rounded up but the percent was kept at 40%.

Checkpoint Quiz 2 **1.** 0.74, $\frac{37}{50}$ **2.** 84% **3.** tax: \$0.75; \$15.75 **4.** 110 **5.** 18

Lesson 6-9 p. 307

Check Skills You'll Need **1.** 5 **2.** 90 **3.** 4.5 **4.** 58 **5.** 22 **6.** 200

Check Understanding **1.** \$39.96

Chapter 7

Diagnosing Readiness p. 320

1. 0.12, 0.13, 0.21, 0.35, 0.45 **2.** 44, 45.01, 45.1, 46.01 **3.** 99.9, 100.80, 102, 124.32, 133 **4.** 0.22, 0.99, 2.5, 4.9, 7.04 **5.** 63.1 **6.** 423.9 **7.** 105.82 **8.** 25.87 **9.** 20.21 **10.** 1.06 **11.** 1.8 **12.** 14.203 **13.** 22.6 **14.** 4.03

Lesson 7-1 pp. 322–323

Check Skills You'll Need **1.** 27.5 **2.** 42.58 **3.** 59.35 **4.** 5.9 **5.** 8.55 **6.** 3.09

Check Understanding **1a.** 3.5 **b.** 22.4 **c.** 20 **d.** 57 **e.** 45; the new mean is much less. **2a.** 88 **b.** 27.5 **3.** apple

Lesson 7-2 pp. 326–327

Check Skills You'll Need **1.** blue and green **2.** 5.2; 5; 4 **3.** 2; 1.25; 0

Instant Check System™ Answers

Check Understanding **1a.**

Initial	Tally	Frequency
A	I	1
B	I	1
C	I	1
D	II	2
J	I	1
K	II	2
L	III	3
P	I	1
S	I	1
T	I	1
V	I	1

mode: L

b. The data items are letters, not numbers.

2. Number of Phone Calls

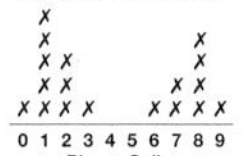
0 1 2 3 4 5 6 7 8 9
Phone Calls

3a. 32 **b.** 0.17 **c.** No; explanations may vary. Sample: Add 10 to all data in the first set. The range stays the same, but the median increases by 10.

Lesson 7-3 pp. 331–333

Check Skills You'll Need **1.** 35, 42, 49 **2.** 13, 16, 19 **3.** 52, 43, 34 **4.** 324, 972, 2,916

Check Understanding **1.** day 8

Checkpoint Quiz 1 **1.** 30; 30; 30; 26 **2.** 21 **3.** 21

4.

Grams of Fat	Tally	Frequency
0	~~IIII~~ III	8
1	~~IIII~~ IIII	9
2	~~IIII~~	5
3	III	3

5. 10 ways

Lesson 7-4 pp. 335–337

Check Skills You'll Need

1. 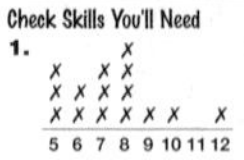
5 6 7 8 9 10 11 12

2. 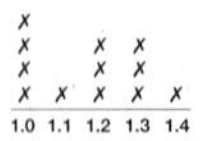
1.0 1.1 1.2 1.3 1.4

3. 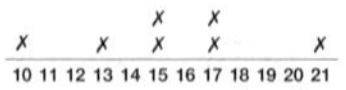
10 11 12 13 14 15 16 17 18 19 20 21

Check Understanding **1.**

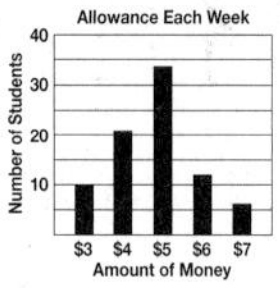
Allowance Each Week
Number of Students
40
30
20
10
$3 $4 $5 $6 $7
Amount of Money

2. 12–15 hours **3.**

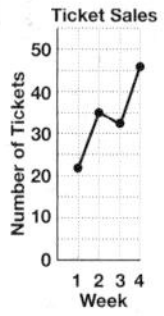
Ticket Sales
Number of Tickets
50
40
30
20
10
0
1 2 3 4
Week

Lesson 7-5 pp. 341–343

Check Skills You'll Need **1.** 98 **2.** 104 **3.** 96 **4.** 88 **5.** 615 **6.** 136

Check Understanding **1a.** 39% are processed **b.** 87%

2. Lunches of 50 Students

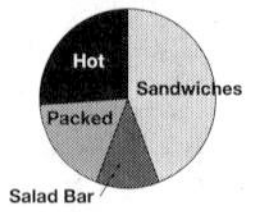
Hot
Sandwiches
Packed
Salad Bar

Lesson 7-6 pp. 347–350

Check Skills You'll Need **1.** $5x$ **2.** $b - 7$ **3.** $52 - x$ **4.** $\frac{a}{9}$ **5.** xy **6.** $\frac{a}{b}$

Check Understanding **1a.** 30; the third country CD is 30 min long. **b.** A2, B2, C2, D2; the length (in minutes) of each of the three rock/pop CDs **2a.** =B2+B3+B4 **b.** =D2+D3+D4

Checkpoint Quiz 2 **1.** =B2+B3+B4+B5 **2.** \$800

3. Money Raised By Fundraisers

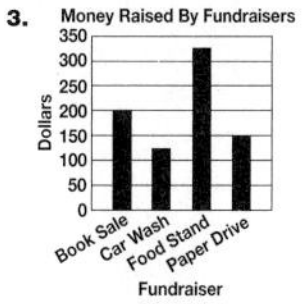

4. Money Raised by Fundraisers

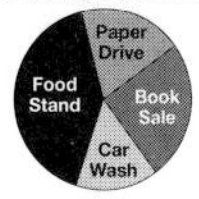

5.

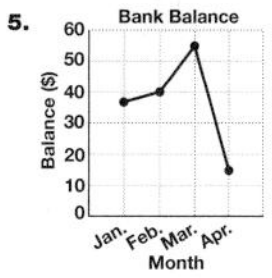

Lesson 7-7 pp. 352–353

Check Skills You'll Need **1.** 32 **2.** 15 **3.** 212 **4.** 5.2

Check Understanding **1a.** 3 **b.** 35

c. Answers may vary. Sample: A stem-and-leaf plot groups the data so that it is easier to find the median and mode.

2.

12	1 3 4 5 5 6 7
13	0 2 3 6 7 8 8
14	0 1 4 5
15	0 5
16	
17	
18	1

Key: 12|3 means 123

Lesson 7-8 pp. 358–359

Check Skills You'll Need **1.** 55.5 **2.** 13.5 **3.** 131 **4.** 63.7 **5.** The data set in Exercise 4, which has outliers.

Check Understanding **1.**

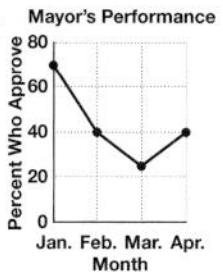

2a. two times taller **b.** 3 cars

c.

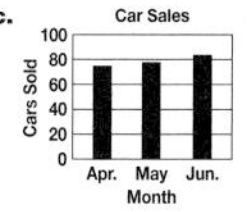

3a. $950,000

b. Median; the mode is the least data value. It occurs only twice, so its value is really too low to give a good idea of what a typical data value is.

Chapter 8

Diagnosing Readiness p. 372

1. 9 **2.** 9 **3.** 4 **4.** 10 **5.** 1.27 **6.** 59.5 **7.** 27.1 **8.** 17.5 **9.** 33.3 **10.** 12.07 **11.** Yes **12.** No **13.** No **14.** Yes **15.** No **16.** Yes

Lesson 8-1 pp. 373–375

Check Skills You'll Need **1.** $2\frac{13}{16}$ in. **2.** 2 in. **3.** $3\frac{3}{8}$ in. or $3\frac{6}{16}$ in.

Check Understanding **1a.** Answers may vary. Sample: $\overleftrightarrow{VP}$, $\overleftrightarrow{MV}$ **b.** $\overline{VM}$, $\overline{VP}$, $\overline{MP}$ **c.** Answers may vary. Samples are given. $\overrightarrow{VM}$ is a ray that has vertex *V* and contains *M*. $\overrightarrow{MV}$ is a ray that has vertex *M* and contains *V*. **2.** Answers may vary. Samples are given. **a.** *Q*, *T*, and *M* **b.** *N*, *Q*, and *M* **3.** Answers may vary. Samples are given. **a.** NE 3rd St. and NE 2nd St. **b.** NE 4th St. and N Miami Ave. **c.** No; all lines on the map represent streets in the same plane.

Lesson 8-2 pp. 379–381

Check Skills You'll Need **1.** Answers may vary. Samples are given. $\overleftrightarrow{AC}$, $\overleftrightarrow{BE}$, $\overleftrightarrow{DB}$ **2.** No; they do not lie on the same line.

Instant Check System™ Answers

Check Understanding **1a.** 125° **b.** greater **2a.** Answers may vary. Sample: 60° **b.** acute

Lesson 8-3 pp. 386–390

Check Skills You'll Need **1–4.** Check students' work.

Check Understanding **1.** 37° **2.** 35° **3a.** ∠3 and ∠6 **b.** Answers may vary. Sample: ∠6 and ∠5

Checkpoint Quiz 1 **1–10.** Answers may vary. Samples are given. **1.** $\overleftrightarrow{LM}$ and $\overleftrightarrow{KN}$ **2.** $\overrightarrow{JP}$ and $\overrightarrow{NK}$ **3.** ∠*PJM* **4.** ∠*PJK* **5.** ∠*PJN* **6.** ∠*LJM* **7.** ∠*KJL* and ∠*MJN* **8.** ∠*KJL* **9.** ∠*PJK* and ∠*KJL* **10.** ∠*LJN* and ∠*NJM*

Lesson 8-4 pp. 392–394

Check Skills You'll Need **1.** acute **2.** obtuse **3.** acute **4.** obtuse **5.** right **6.** acute **7.** obtuse **8.** straight

Check Understanding **1a.** right triangle **b.** acute triangle **2.** 50° 3a. isosceles **b.** scalene **4.** isoceles right triangle

Lesson 8-5 pp. 397–398

Check Skills You'll Need **1–3.** Answers may vary. Samples are given. **1.** $\overline{DC}$ and $\overline{FG}$ **2.** $\overline{CB}$ and $\overline{GH}$ **3.** $\overline{FG}$ and $\overline{BC}$

Check Understanding **1a.** quadrilateral **b.** hexagon **c.** octagon **2a.** parallelogram, rectangle **b.** Rectangle; answers may vary. Sample: A rectangle has four right angles and two pairs of parallel lines. **c.** Yes; every square has 4 congruent sides.

Lesson 8-6 pp. 401–402

Check Skills You'll Need **1.**

0	1	2	3	4
|||	|||	|||	|||	|

2.

75	|
80	|||
82	|
85	||
90	|||
100	||

3.

80	||
82	||
85	|
87	||
88	||
89	|

Check Understanding **1.**

	a.	b.	c.	d.
a.	T	H	A	T
b.	H	E	X	A
c.	A	X	E	S
d.	T	A	S	K

2. Janna was born in Jamaica. Georgine was born in France. Tanika was born in Peru.

Lesson 8-7 pp. 405–407

Check Skills You'll Need **1.** scalene **2.** isosceles **3.** scalene

Check Understanding **1a.** no **b.** yes **2a.** yes **b.** no **3.** Congruent and similar; all of their sides and angles are congruent.

Lesson 8-8 pp. 410–414

Check Skills You'll Need **1.** yes **2.** yes

Check Understanding **1.** No; if you fold the figure along the line, the two parts do not match.

2a. 1

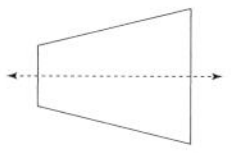

b. 4

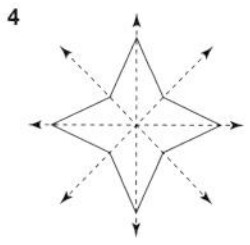

c. Infinitely many; any line that goes through the center of a circle is a line of symmetry.

Checkpoint Quiz 2 **1.** obtuse **2.** right **3.** acute **4.** isosceles **5.** scalene **6.** equilateral **7.** 4 m **8.** Fred is the teacher. Matt is the writer. Alison is the artist. **9.** B, D, and E **10.** B and E

Lesson 8-9 pp. 415–417

Check Skills You'll Need **1.**

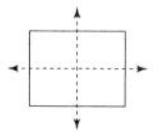

2.

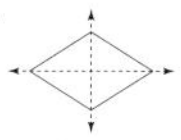

3.

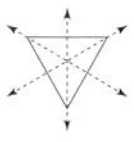

Check Understanding **1.** no

2a.

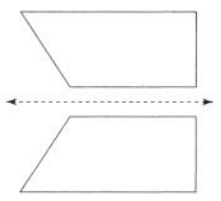

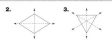

b.

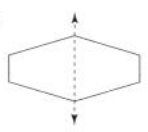

3a. no **b.** yes **c.** no

Chapter 9

Diagnosing Readiness p. 430

1. pounds **2.** gallons **3.** miles **4.** inches **5.** 144 **6.** $3\frac{5}{6}$ **7.** $3\frac{5}{8}$ **8.** $2\frac{1}{4}$ **9.** 26 **10.** $1\frac{1}{2}$ **11.** > **12.** < **13.** > **14.** < **15.** < **16.** = **17.** rhombus **18.** isosceles triangle **19.** trapezoid

Lesson 9-1 pp. 431–433

Check Skills You'll Need **1.** ounces **2.** pounds **3.** Feet; yards would also be appropriate. **4.** Pints; cups or fluid ounces would also be appropriate.

Check Understanding **1.** meter **2a.** 20 mm or 2 cm **b.** 36 mm or 3.6 cm **c.** 79 mm or 7.9 cm **3a.** kilograms **b.** kilograms **c.** grams **d.** milligrams **4a.** liters **b.** kiloliters **c.** milliliters

Lesson 9-2 pp. 436–437

Check Skills You'll Need **1.** 3,900 **2.** 53 **3.** 574 **4.** 0.07 **5.** 1.43 **6.** 980

Check Understanding **1a.** 150 mm **b.** 837,000 m **c.** 5 m is greater; 1 m = 1,000 mm, but 5 m = 5,000 mm. **2a.** 0.005 m **b.** 7.5 cm **c.** 60 km **3a.** 0.015 **b.** 0.386 **c.** 0.082

Lesson 9-3 pp. 440–443

Check Skills You'll Need **1.** 16 **2.** 36 **3.** 81 **4.** 29.16 **5.** 2.56 **6.** 100

Check Understanding **1.** Answers may vary. Sample: about 144 square miles **2.** $P = 26$ ft, $A = 40$ ft^2 **3a.** 49 in.^{2} **b.** 36 ft^2

Lesson 9-4 pp. 446–448

Check Skills You'll Need **1.** quadrilateral, trapezoid; trapezoid **2.** quadrilateral, parallelogram; parallelogram **3.** quadrilateral, rectangle, rhombus, square; square

Check Understanding **1a.** 70 m^2 **b.** 519 ft^2 **2a.** 259.5 m^2 **b.** The area would double. **3a.** 16m^2 **b.** Answers may vary. Sample:

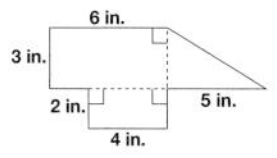

Checkpoint Quiz 1 **1.** 0.062 L **2.** 4,300 g **3.** 1.78 m **4.** 72.25 cm^2 **5.** 18 mi^2

Lesson 9-5 pp. 452–453

Check Skills You'll Need **1.** 6.28 **2.** 25.12 **3.** 157 **4.** 219.8 **5.** 37.68 **6.** 62.8

Check Understanding **1.** $\overline{AC}$, $\overline{BD}$ **2a.** 4 cm **b.** 20 in. **3.** 18 cm

Lesson 9-6 pp. 456–457

Check Skills You'll Need **1.** 49 **2.** 25 **3.** 16 **4.** 100 **5.** 18 **6.** 144

Check Understanding **1a.** 452.16 km^2 **b.** 28.26 in.^{2} **c.** 50.24 yd^2 **2a.** 1,386 m^2 **b.** 616 cm^2 **c.** 38.5 mi^2 **d.** 154 in.^{2}

Lesson 9-7 pp. 462–464

Check Skills You'll Need **1.** hexagon **2.** quadrilateral **3.** triangle

Check Understanding **1a.** pentagonal prism **b.** rectangular prism **c.** triangular prism **d.** rectangle **2a.** rectangular prism **b.** Answers may vary. Sample: They both have a circle as a base. But a cylinder has two bases, a cone has one.

Lesson 9-8 pp. 467–469

Check Skills You'll Need **1.** 200.96 m^2 **2.** 12.56 yd^2 **3.** 5,024 mm^2

Check Understanding **1.** Answers may vary. Sample:

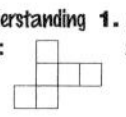

2a. 1,728 m^2 **b.** 336 in.^{2}

Instant Check System™ Answers

3a. The areas of the top and bottom of the can are πr^2. The area around the can is the product of the height of the can and the distance around the can. The distance around the can is the circumference of the can, so the area around the can is *Ch*. **b.** 96.6 in.^{2}

Lesson 9-9 pp. 472–476

Check Skills You'll Need **1.** 8 yd^2 **2.** 500 km^2

Check Understanding **1a.** 12 units^3 **b.** 36 units^3 **c.** The volume would double. **2.** 560 m^3 **3.** 452 in.^{3}

Checkpoint Quiz 2 **1.** triangular pyramid **2.** cone **3.** pentagonal pyramid **4.** hexagonal prism **5.** 62 cm^2 **6.** 30 cm^3 **7.** 31.4 m **8.** 78.5 m^2 **9.** 314.0 m^2 **10.** 392.5 m^3

Lesson 9-10 pp. 477–478

Check Skills You'll Need **1.** 36 **2.** 7 **3.** 9 **4.** 68 **5.** 105 **6.** 14

Check Understanding **1.** 21 pencils

Chapter 10

Diagnosing Readiness p. 490

1. 39 **2.** 31 **3.** 100 **4.** 79 **5.** 31 **6.** 118 **7.** 6 **8.** 66 **9.** 4 **10.** 72 **11.** 15 **12.** 252 **13.** < **14.** > **15.** = **16.** $\frac{1}{12}, \frac{1}{8}, \frac{1}{3}$ **17.** $\frac{4}{9}, \frac{7}{12}, \frac{5}{6}$ **18.** $\frac{1}{4}, \frac{1}{2}, \frac{6}{7}$

Lesson 10-1 pp. 491–493

Check Skills You'll Need **1.** > **2.** = **3.** > **4.** $\frac{4}{3}, \frac{14}{9}, \frac{8}{5}$ **5.** $\frac{1}{4}, \frac{2}{5}, \frac{3}{6}$ **6.** $\frac{3}{8}, \frac{6}{15}, \frac{4}{5}$

Check Understanding **1.** −8 **2.** 5 **3a.** 1 **b.** 7 **c.** 9 **4a.** > **b.** < **5.** −50 , −25 , 75, 100

Lesson 10-2 pp. 497–499

Check Skills You'll Need **1.** 15 **2.** 12 **3.** 8 **4.** 8 **5.** Answers may vary. Sample: No; absolute value is the distance the number is from zero on a number line.

Check Understanding **1a.** −4 **b.** 12 **c.** −9 **d.** negative **2a.** 16 **b.** −21 **3a.** 3 **b.** 3 **4a.** −3 **b.** −7 **c.** 9 **d.** If the integer with the greatest absolute value is negative, then the sum will be negative. **5.** 2 ft

Lesson 10-3 pp. 503–505

Check Skills You'll Need **1.** 17 **2.** 31 **3.** 7 **4.** 0 **5.** 158 **6.** 180 **7.** about 38

Check Understanding **1a.** 3 **b.** 5 **c.** 8 **d.** It is the same as adding the opposite. **2a.** 12 **b.** −4 **c.** −8 **d.** If the first number is larger than the second number, the difference will be positive; the difference will be negative if either the second number is larger OR they are both negative and the second number has a smaller absolute value. **3.** 622 ft **4a.** −6 **b.** 10

Lesson 10-4 pp. 509–511

Check Skills You'll Need **1.** −8 **2.** 64 **3.** −28 **4.** −90 **5.** 162 **6.** −46

Check Understanding **1a.** −12 **b.** 12 **c.** −12 **2a.** −42 **b.** 27 **c.** −15 **3.** −20

Lesson 10-5 pp. 513–516

Check Skills You'll Need **1.** 576 **2.** 8 **3.** 252 **4.** 6 **5.** 540 **6.** 3

Check Understanding **1a.** −4 **b.** 18 **2a.** $z = -6$ **b.** $u = -28$ **3.** −4

Checkpoint Quiz 1 **1.** −3 **2.** −2 **3.** −12 **4.** −6 **5.** −12 **6.** −36 **7.** −16 **8.** −7 **9.** 7 **10.** −20

Lesson 10-6 pp. 518–519

Check Skills You'll Need **1.**

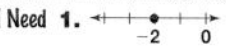

2.

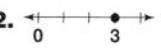

3.

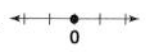

4.

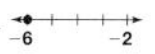

5.

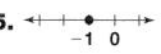

6.

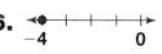

Check Understanding **1a.** *C*(1, 3) **b.** *D*(−2, −3) **c.** *E*(2, −2) **2a–c.**

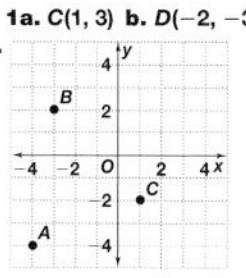

3a. City Hall **b.** (3, −1)

Lesson 10-7 pp. 523–524

Check Skills You'll Need **1.** 38 **2.** 9 **3.** −13 **4.** −28 **5.** −14 **6.** −6 **7.** −31 **8.** −59 **9.** 26

Check Understanding **1a.** −$2,886 **b.** $821 **c.** −$1,529 **d.** −$337 **2.** March, April, June, July, August, November, December

Instant Check System™ Answers

Lesson 10-8   pp. 527–532

Check Skills You'll Need 1. 11 2. 12 3. 6 4. 18 5. 14 6. 50 7. 76 8. 33

Check Understanding

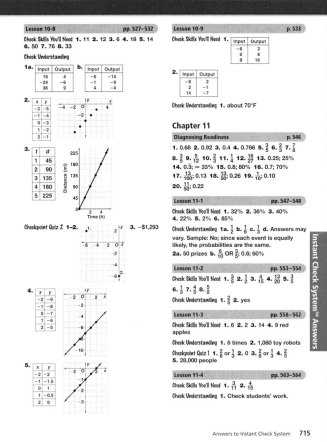

1a.

Input	Output
16	4
−24	−6
36	9

b.

Input	Output
−6	−14
−1	−9
4	−4

2.

x	y
−2	−5
−1	−4
0	−3
1	−2
2	−1

3.

t	d
1	45
2	90
3	135
4	180
5	225

Checkpoint Quiz 1 1–2. (graph)   3. −$1,293

4.

x	y
−2	−9
−1	−8
0	−7
1	−6
2	−5

5.

x	y
−2	−2
−1	−1.5
0	1
1	−0.5
2	0

Lesson 10-9   p. 533

Check Skills You'll Need 1.

Input	Output
−6	2
0	8
8	16

2.

Input	Output
−8	2
2	−1
14	−7

Check Understanding 1. about 70°F

Chapter 11

Diagnosing Readiness   p. 546

1. 0.68 2. 0.92 3. 0.4 4. 0.766 5. $\frac{3}{5}$ 6. $\frac{2}{3}$ 7. $\frac{7}{8}$ 8. $\frac{3}{5}$ 9. $\frac{5}{12}$ 10. $\frac{2}{3}$ 11. $\frac{1}{4}$ 12. $\frac{16}{27}$ 13. 0.25; 25% 14. $0.\overline{3}$; ≈ 33% 15. 0.8; 80% 16. 0.7; 70% 17. $\frac{13}{100}$; 0.13 18. $\frac{13}{50}$; 0.26 19. $\frac{1}{10}$; 0.10 20. $\frac{11}{50}$; 0.22

Lesson 11-1   pp. 547–548

Check Skills You'll Need 1. 32% 2. 36% 3. 40% 4. 22% 5. 2% 6. 85%

Check Understanding 1a. $\frac{1}{2}$ b. $\frac{1}{6}$ c. $\frac{1}{3}$ d. Answers may vary. Sample: No; since each event is equally likely, the probabilities are the same. 2a. 50 prizes b. $\frac{6}{10}$ OR $\frac{3}{5}$; 0.6; 60%

Lesson 11-2   pp. 553–554

Check Skills You'll Need 1. $\frac{3}{5}$ 2. $\frac{1}{2}$ 3. $\frac{4}{15}$ 4. $\frac{13}{20}$ 5. $\frac{3}{5}$ 6. $\frac{1}{3}$ 7. $\frac{4}{5}$ 8. $\frac{5}{8}$

Check Understanding 1. $\frac{2}{5}$ 2. yes

Lesson 11-3   pp. 558–562

Check Skills You'll Need 1. 6 2. 3 3. 14 4. 9 red apples

Check Understanding 1. 6 times 2. 1,080 toy robots

Checkpoint Quiz 1 1. $\frac{2}{6}$ or $\frac{1}{3}$ 2. 0 3. $\frac{2}{6}$ or $\frac{1}{3}$ 4. $\frac{4}{5}$ 5. 28,000 people

Lesson 11-4   pp. 563–564

Check Skills You'll Need 1. $\frac{3}{11}$ 2. $\frac{4}{15}$

Check Understanding 1. Check students' work.

Lesson 11-5   pp. 568–570

Check Skills You'll Need 1. $\frac{1}{6}$ 2. $\frac{1}{3}$ 3. 1 4. $\frac{1}{2}$ 5. 0 6. $\frac{1}{2}$

Check Understanding 1a. $\frac{1}{12}$ b. They have the same number of favorable outcomes (1) and the same number of possible outcomes (12), so their probabilities are the same. 2. 48 different dessert specials 3. On a tree diagram, write M for a male name and F for a female name. Make one column for president and the other for treasurer. Then count the number of the 12 outcomes that are FF.

Lesson 11-6   pp. 574–578

Check Skills You'll Need 1. 12 2. 90 3. 210 4. 380 5. 24 6. 336

Check Understanding 1. CAT, CTA, ACT, ATC, TCA, TAC

2.

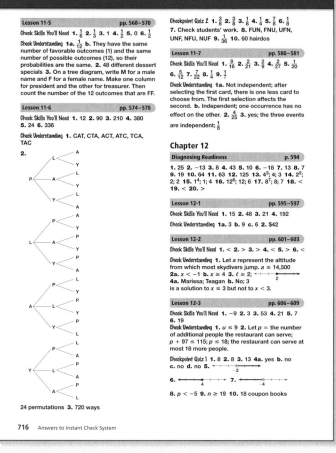

24 permutations 3. 720 ways

Checkpoint Quiz 1 1. $\frac{3}{8}$ 2. $\frac{3}{8}$ 3. $\frac{1}{4}$ 4. $\frac{5}{8}$ 5. $\frac{7}{8}$ 6. $\frac{1}{8}$ 7. Check students' work. 8. FUN, FNU, UFN, UNF, NFU, NUF 9. $\frac{1}{36}$ 10. 60 hairdos

Lesson 11-7   pp. 580–581

Check Skills You'll Need 1. $\frac{9}{16}$ 2. $\frac{2}{21}$ 3. $\frac{2}{9}$ 4. $\frac{2}{27}$ 5. $\frac{1}{20}$ 6. $\frac{5}{12}$ 7. $\frac{1}{22}$ 8. $\frac{1}{4}$ 9. $\frac{1}{7}$

Check Understanding 1a. Not independent; after selecting the first card, there is one less card to choose from. The first selection affects the second. b. Independent; one occurrence has no effect on the other. 2. $\frac{4}{25}$ 3. yes; the three events are independent; $\frac{1}{8}$

Chapter 12

Diagnosing Readiness   p. 594

1. 25 2. −13 3. 8 4. 43 5. 10 6. −18 7. 13 8. 7 9. 19 10. 64 11. 63 12. 125 13. 4^3; 4; 3 14. 2^2; 2; 2 15. 1^4; 1; 4 16. 12^6; 12; 6 17. 8^7; 8; 7 18. < 19. < 20. >

Lesson 12-1   pp. 595–597

Check Skills You'll Need 1. 15 2. 48 3. 21 4. 192

Check Understanding 1a. 3 b. 9 c. 6 2. $42

Lesson 12-2   pp. 601–603

Check Skills You'll Need 1. < 2. > 3. > 4. < 5. > 6. <

Check Understanding 1. Let a represent the altitude from which most skydivers jump. $a \le 14{,}500$ 2a. $x < -1$ b. $x \ge 4$ 3. $\ell \ge 2$; (number line) 4a. Marissa; Teagan b. No; 3 is a solution to $x \le 3$ but not to $x < 3$.

Lesson 12-3   pp. 606–609

Check Skills You'll Need 1. −9 2. 3 3. 53 4. 21 5. 7 6. 19

Check Understanding 1. $u \le 9$ 2. Let $p =$ the number of additional people the restaurant can serve; $p + 97 \le 115$; $p \le 18$; the restaurant can serve at most 18 more people.

Checkpoint Quiz 1 1. 8 2. 8 3. 13 4a. yes b. no c. no d. no 5. (number line) 6. (number line) 7. (number line) 8. $p < -5$ 9. $n \ge 19$ 10. 18 coupon books

---

Lesson 12-4   pp. 611–612

Check Skills You'll Need 1. 95 2. 24 3. 11 4. 480 5. 138 6. 18

Check Understanding 1a. Answers may vary. Sample: I would use Method 2, because I have to spend less time thinking about possible sizes and shapes for the small sections for each vegetable. b. 20 in., 34 in.

Lesson 12-5   pp. 616–620

Check Skills You'll Need 1. 5^2; 5, 2 2. 6^3; 6, 3 3. 4^5; 4, 5 4. 999^3; 999, 3 5. 72^1; 72, 1 6. 3.6^2; 3.6, 2

Check Understanding 1a. 2 b. 10 2a. 2.6 b. 3.2 c. 4.9 d. 9.3 3. 9 in. 4a. Answers may vary. Sample: Closer to 2; $2^2 = 4$ and $3^2 = 9$; 5 is closer to 4 than to 9, so the square root of 5 is closer to 2 than to 3. b. between 2 and 3 5a. rational b. rational c. not rational 6a. not rational b. rational c. not rational d. rational

Checkpoint Quiz 1 1. 10.6 in. and 18.4 in.; explanations may vary. Sample: I drew a diagram so I could see what it looked like. 2. 11 3. 6 4. rational 5. rational

Lesson 12-6   pp. 622–623

Check Skills You'll Need 1. 3 2. 8 3. 5 4. 6 5. 11 6. 25

Check Understanding 1a. 20 in. b. yes 2. 4.6 ft

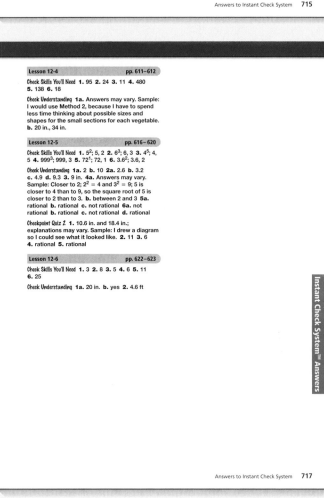

Selected Answers

Chapter 1

Lesson 1-1 pp. 6–7

EXERCISES **1.** 25; twenty-five **3.** 508,310; five hundred eight thousand, three hundred ten **7.** < **9.** > **13.** 51,472; 51,572; 54,172; 57,142 **15.** 17,414; 17,444; 17,671; 18,242 **17.** 4 ten thousands or 40,000 **19.** 4 thousands or 4,000 **25.**

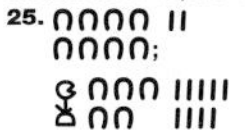

27. Braeburn, Empire, Idared, York, McIntosh **29.** >, > **31.** <, < **37.** 390 **39.** 2,129

Lesson 1-2 pp. 10–12

EXERCISES **1.** 500 + 30 + 0.3 + 0.04 **3.** 0.2 + 0.03 **9.** two and three tenths **11.** nine and five tenths **17.** 40.009 **19.** 0.0012 **21.** 8 + 0.2; eight and two tenths **23.** 90 + 1 + 0.09 + 0.001; ninety-one and ninety-one thousandths **25.** 0.20 **27.** 0.25 **29.** The value of each 2 is 10 times greater than the value of the 2 to its right. **31.** 4 tenths, or 0.4 **33.** 4 ten-thousandths, or 0.0004 **35.** $.006 **37.** $.053 **39.** 0.618 **47.** <

Lesson 1-3 pp. 16–17

EXERCISES **1.**

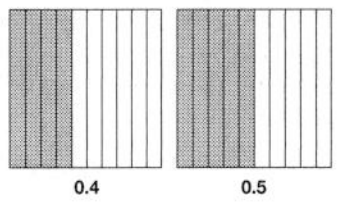

0.4
0.5

0.53 is greater.

3.

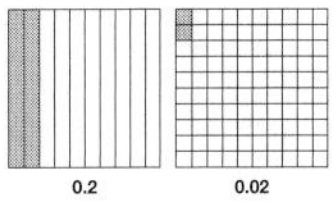

0.2
0.02

0.2 is greater.

5.

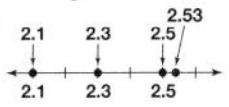

2.1
2.3
2.5
2.53
2.1
2.3
2.5

7.

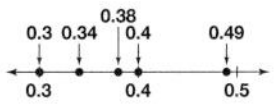

0.38
0.3 0.34
0.4
0.49
0.3
0.4
0.5

9. > **11.** > **15.** 13.7, 17.1, 17.7 **17.** 9.02, 9.024, 9.2, 9.209 **23.** 0.6595, 0.6095, 0.62 **25.** Alia; 11.88 < 11.9 **33.** 125 **35.** 10,136

Lesson 1-4 pp. 21–23

EXERCISES **1.** about 37 **3.** about 34 **9.** about 600 **11.** about 270 **17.** about $15 **19.** about $48 **21.** about 9 **23.** about 3.1 oz **25.** about 1.9 oz **27.** 70 **29.** 2.320 **41a.** about $9 **b.** Compatible numbers make the division easy to compute mentally. **43.** about 24 **45.** about 15 **53.** < **55.** > **57.** 0.23 **59.** 0.0038

Lesson 1-5 pp. 27–29

EXERCISES **1.** about 4; 4 **3.** about 9; 8.771 **7.** 9.7 **9.** 12.37 **13.** about 18; 17.9 **15.** about 5; 5.69 **21.** 2.72 m **23.** $270.15 **27.** > **29.** = **31.** 0; Ident. Prop. of Add. **33.** 7.5; Comm. Prop. of Add.
41a. No; the value of the number he drew is 32,009. **b.**

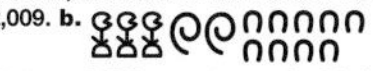

37. 1; total U.S. energy supply **39.** hydroelectric **51.** 21,000 **53.** 0.1

Lesson 1-6 pp. 32–33

EXERCISES **1.** $26 **3.** 6:25 **5.** 16 min **7.** 12 teams **9a.** 6 cuts **b.** 27 pieces **c.** 2 pieces; there is one side of the wooden block initially without paint. 8 pieces of that side have painted sides; 1 does not. There is also a piece in the center that doesn't get painted. **17.** 1.76 **19.** 1.71 **21.** tens **23.** hundreds

Lesson 1-7 pp. 37–39

EXERCISES **1.** 0.072 **3.** 173.6 **9.** 0.14 **11.** 0.15 **17.** 1,035 **19.** 14.4 **25.** $3.55 **27.** 2.8 **29.** 190 **35.** $50.00 **37.** 68.28 **39.** 56.414 **45.** 58.5 mi **47.** 483.48 million mi **49.** Incorrect; the decimal point should move left one place. **51.** Incorrect; addition was used instead of multiplication. **59.** < **61.** >

Lesson 1-8 pp. 41–42

EXERCISES **1.** 62 **3.** 92.5 **7.** 12.29 **9.** 1.617 **13.** < **15.** < **17.** about 2.75 mi/h **19.** False; 300 ÷ 100 ≠ 300 × 0.1. **21.** true

Lesson 1-9 pp. 45–47

EXERCISES **1.** 25.25 **3.** 7.2 **9.** $3.18 **11.** $0.\overline{54}$; repeating **13.** 0.76; terminating
19.

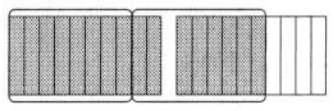

21.

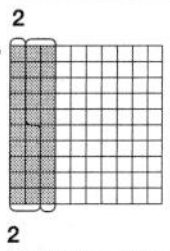

2
2

23. 73.75 **25.** 3.31 **29.** 0.8 **31.** 0.05 **33.** 20.30 **35.** 8.12 **37.** $4.95 **39.** 5; terminating **41.** 0.2; terminating **45.** 29.4 mi/gal **53.** 0.22675 **55.** 46.48

Lesson 1-10 pp. 49–51

EXERCISES **1.** 12 **3.** 60 **7.** 28.6 **9.** 7.7 **11a.** 1 × $.45 + 3 × $.95 + 2 × $.65 **b.** $4.60 **13.** 10 × 3 **15.** 9 ÷ 3 **17.** 2 **19.** 0 **21.** = **23.** > **27.** C **29.** (11 − 7) ÷ 2 = 2 **31.** (7 − 2) × 2 − 1 = 9 **45.** 280 **47.** 0.00462

Chapter Review pp. 54–55

1. Ident. Prop. of Add. **2.** expression **3.** standard form **4.** repeating decimal **5.** Assoc. Prop. of Add. **6.** 6,004,030 **7.** 6.043 **8.** five hundred twenty-five and five tenths; 500 + 20 + 5 + 0.5 **9.** five million, twenty-five; 5,000,000 + 20 + 5 **10.** five thousand, two hundred fifty-five ten-thousandths; 0.5 + 0.02 + 0.005 + 0.0005 **11.** five and twenty-five thousandths; 5 + 0.02 + 0.005 **12.** > **13.** < **14.** < **15.** > **16.** 0.06; 0.14; 0.4; 0.52 **17.** 23; 23.03; 23.2; 23.25 **18.** 9.04; 9.2; 9.24; 9.4

19–22. Answers may vary. Samples are given. **19.** about 357 **20.** about 1 **21.** about 3 **22.** about 6 **23.** 3.4 **24.** 0.17 **25.** 3.867 **26.** 7.4 **27.** $.48 **28.** 35.4 **29.** 2.02 **30.** 480 **31.** 9.18 **32.** 3.4 **33.** 0.9 **34.** 0.98127 **35.** 37 **36.** 0 **37.** 44.4

Chapter 2

Lesson 2-1 pp. 65–67

EXERCISES **1.** 18, 22 **3.** 81, 243 **5.** 7, 11, 15, 19, 23, 27, . . . **7.** 625; 3,125; 15,625; the first term is 1; multiply a term by 5 to get the next term. **9.** 6,000; 600, 60; the first term is 6,000,000, divide a term by 10 to get the next term. **11a.** 4:51, 5:51 **b.** 3:17, 4:02, 4:47, 5:32 **13.** 6 **15.** 1,200 **19.** 189 **21.** 216 **29.**

37. about 3; 3.2 **39.** about 49; 49.21

Lesson 2-2 pp. 71–72

EXERCISES **1.**

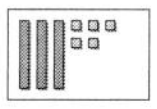

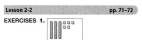

3.

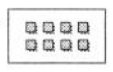

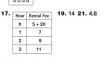

9. 20 **11.** 13

17.

Hour	Rental Fee
h	$5 + 2h$
1	7
2	9
3	11

19. 14 **21.** 4.8

29. 2006 + 12x **31.**

x	$x + 6$
1	7
4	10
7	13

33.

x	$100 - x$
20	80
35	65
50	50

45. 9, 3 **47.** 29.16 **49.** 0.0374

Lesson 2-3 pp. 76–78

EXERCISES **1.** $k - 34$ **3.** $50 + d$ **7.** $10 + 8h$ **9.** $n - 3$ **11.** $n + 2$ **13a.** $y - 20$ **b.** 7 years **15.** $11n$ **17a.** $10w$ **b.** 70 feet **19.** $3j + 12$ **29.** 5.441 **31.** 3.149 **33.** about 380

Lesson 2-4 pp. 81–82

EXERCISES **1.** 62 seats **3a.** 11 fence posts **b.** 10 fence posts **5.** 35 cars **7.** 9 pairs **9.** 132 in. **17.** $12c$ **19.** $4.5 + n$ **23.** 3 **25.** 32

Lesson 2-5 pp. 86–88

EXERCISES **1.** false **3.** false **7.** 2 **9.** 0 **15.** 15 straps **23.** true **25.** yes **29.** 20 lb **31.** False; 1 more than a number can never be equal to the number. **33.** True; (100 − 2) simplifies to 98. $98n = 98n$ **35.** 100 **37.** 500 **39.** No; $2x = 3x$ is true if $x = 0$. **55.** 324, 972, 2,916 **57.** 60 **59.** 16

Lesson 2-6 pp. 92–94

EXERCISES **1.** 26 **3.** 52 **11.** s = sale price of the jeans; $s + 4.99 = 29.97$; $s = \$24.98$ **13.** 11.4 **15.** 48 **21.** m = height of male giraffe; $m - 3.2 = 14.1$; 17.3 feet **23.** 8.2 **25.** 1.5 **29.** No; using estimation, about 60 + about 30 = about 90, and 90 is not at all close to 31.8. **31.** Let c = approximate area of Cape Cod National Seashore; $c + 14{,}101 = 57{,}627$; 43,526 acres **41.** 37; 40; 43; 46; 49 **43.** 0 **45.** 24

Lesson 2-7 pp. 97–98

EXERCISES **1.** 20 **3.** 1.7 **11.** 32,000,000 square miles **13.** 441 **15.** 51,772 **21.** $2.99 per video **23.** 0.4096 **25.** 900 **29.** The teammate could not have scored half the goals because half of 41 is 20.5. It is impossible to score half of a goal. **41.** = **43.** 0.18

Lesson 2-8 pp. 101–103

EXERCISES **1.** 3^2; 3; 2 **3.** 9^3; 9; 3 **11.** $8 \times 10^4 + 3 \times 10^3 + 7 \times 10^2 + 9 \times 10^1 + 2 \times 1$ **13.** $6 \times 10^4 + 0 \times 10^3 + 2 \times 10^2 + 5 \times 10^1 + 1 \times 1$ **17.** 64 **19.** 15,625 **29.** 54,872 **31.** 60 **35.** 3 **37.** 3 **39a.** 10,000; 10^5; 100,000 **b.** The exponent tells the number of 0's in standard form. **c.** 10^7; 10,000,000; 10^8; 100,000,000 **41.** $3 \times 10^7 + 5 \times 10^6$ **43.** 27; 64; 125; 216 **45.** 2^7 **47.** 10^5 **49.** 80 **51.** 12 **61.** 1,123 **63.** 880 **67.** < **69.** =

Lesson 2-9 pp. 107–108

EXERCISES **1.** (4 × 10) + (4 × 8) = 40 + 32 = 72 **3.** 8(20 + 8) = 8 × 20 + 8 × 8 = 160 + 64 = 224 **7.** $27.00 **9.** 8.7 **11.** 9.5 **15.** 265 mi **17.** One way to find the total area is to find the area of each rectangle and then add the areas: (6.8 × 2.5) + (2 × 2.5). Another way to find the total area is to multiply the total length of the rectangle by its width: (6.8 + 2) × 2.5. **25.** false **27.** 32, 64

Chapter Review pp. 110–111

1. term **2.** algebraic expression OR equation **3.** base **4.** variable **5.** exponent **6.** 162; 486; 1,458; the first term is 2; multiply a term by 3 to get the next term. **7.** 55, 67, 79; the first term is 7; add 12 to a term to get the next term. **8.** 112, 224, 448; the first term is 7; multiply a term by 2 to get the next term. **9.** 8 **10.** 49 **11.** 42 **12.** $x \div 12$ **13.** $2b$ **14.** $h + k$ **15.** 28 laps **16.** false **17.** true **18.** false **19.** 5 **20.** 8 **21.** 8 **22.** 5,640 **23.** 7 **24.** 1,010 **25.** 56 **26.** 128 **27.** 6.06 **28.** 1.4 **29.** 0.9 **30.** 60.8 **31.** 128 **32.** 40 **33.** 17 **34.** 15 **35.** 7(20 + 8) = 140 + 56 = 196 **36.** 5(3 + 0.4) = 15 + 2.0 = 17 **37.** (10 + 1)57 = 570 + 57 = 627 **38.** $19.00

Chapter 3

Lesson 3-1 pp. 121–122

EXERCISES **1.** yes **3.** yes **7.** 2, 5, and 10 **9.** 2 **13.** yes **15.** yes **19.** no **21.** yes **25.** Yes; since 1 + 1 + 4 = 6 and 6 is divisible by 3, 114 is divisible by 3. **27.** 3 and 9 **29.** 2 **35.** 4 **37.** 4 **39.** 2, 3, 4, 5, 6, and 10 **41a.** 30, 36, 42, 48 **b.** All are divisible by 2 and 3. **c.** Any number that is divisible by both 2 and 3 is also divisible by 6. **49.** 45 **51.** 16.2 **55.** 1 **57.** 11.5

Lesson 3-2 pp. 125–126

EXERCISES **1.** 1, 2, 4, 8 **3.** 1, 2, 3, 6, 9, 18 **9.** composite; 55 = 5 × 11 **11.** Prime; the only factors are 1 and 83. **17.** 2^5 **19.** $5^2 \times 3$ **25.** 1,001 **27.** 1 × 36; 2 × 18; 3 × 12; 4 × 9; 6 × 6 **29.** composite; $3^3 \times 5$ **31.** composite; 2 × 3 × 5 × 7 **45.** 50 **47.** > **49.** <

Lesson 3-3 pp. 129–131

EXERCISES **1.** factors of 14: 1, 2, 7, 14; factors of 35: 1, 5, 7, 35; GCF of 14 and 35: 7 **3.** factors of 26: 1, 2, 13, 26; factors of 34: 1, 2, 17, 34; GCF of 26 and 34: 2 **7.** 2) 10 18 GCF = 2
5 9

9. GCF = 1

13.

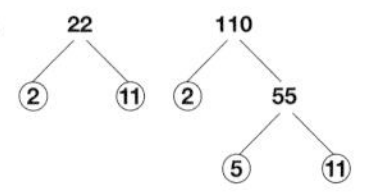

22
110
2
11
2
55
5
11

22 = 2 × 11 × 3
110 = 2 × 5 × 11

GCF = 22

15.

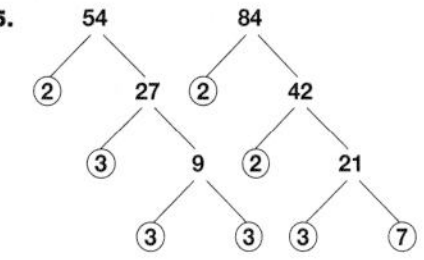

54
84
2
27
2
42
3
9
2
21
3
3
3
7

54 = 2 × 3 × 3 × 3
84 = 2 × 2 × 3 × 7

GCF = 6 **21.** 140 **23.** 25 **27.** Brand B with 12 cards and Brand C with 15 cards because 12 and 15 are divisible by 3. **29.** 4 **31.** 10 **33.** 48; 1, 2, 3, 4, 6, 8, 12, 16, 24, 48 **39a.** 3 × $1.25 + $1.50 **b.** $5.25 **41.** nine tenths **43.** eighty hundredths

Lesson 3-4 pp. 136–137

EXERCISES **9.** $\frac{2}{3}$ **11.** $\frac{1}{2}$ **17.** $\frac{3}{5}$ **19.** no; $\frac{1}{2}$ **21.** no; $\frac{5}{6}$ **31.** The first engineer is recording time in minutes. The second engineer is recording fractions of an hour. **33.** Divide the numerator and the denominator by their GCF. **35.** $\frac{8}{12}, \frac{3}{5}$; no **37.** $\frac{1}{2}$ **47.** 3 **49.** 150 **51.** 0.9 **53.** 20

Lesson 3-5 pp. 141–142

EXERCISES **1.** $\frac{23}{6}$ **3.** $\frac{23}{5}$ **13.** $3\frac{2}{5}$ **15.** $2\frac{1}{4}$ **21.** $\frac{33}{7}$ **23.** $21\frac{1}{5}$ **29.** $1\frac{13}{16}$ in.; $1\frac{3}{4}$ in. **31.** $\frac{33}{2}$; $16\frac{1}{2}$ **33.** $\frac{106}{4}$; $26\frac{1}{2}$ **37.** $8\frac{1}{3}$ melons; 9 melons **45.** false **47.** 26 **49.** 6

Lesson 3-6 pp. 145–146

EXERCISES **1.** 36 **3.** 60 **9.** 48 **11.** 72 **17.** 120th customer **19.** 84 **21.** 315 **29a.** 15 days **b.** If Monday is day 1, then the first time both items are picked up on a Sunday will be on day 91. **31a.** 2, 4, 5 **b.** 40 **33.** $2x$ **45.** 0.3, 0.37, 0.49, 0.51, 0.6 **47.** 5^3; 5, 3 **49.** 7^3; 7, 3

Lesson 3-7 pp. 150–152

EXERCISES **1.** < **3.** > **11.** = **13.** > **17.** $\frac{2}{3}, \frac{3}{4}, \frac{5}{6}$ **19.** $\frac{1}{8}, \frac{7}{40}, \frac{3}{10}$ **23.** the cherry-flavored drink **25a.** $\frac{1}{2}, \frac{1}{4}, \frac{1}{8}, \frac{1}{16}$ **b.**

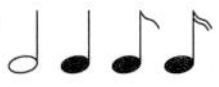

c. Yes; the note symbol that is "open" has the greatest value, and for the other symbols, the more flags there are, the less the value of the note. **27.** <; the numerators are equal, so the fraction with the lesser denominator is greater. **29.** > **31.** > **33.** true **35.** true **37.** In fractions with the same numerators, the fraction with the greater denominator is the lesser fraction. **47.** $\frac{17}{3}$ **49.** $\frac{36}{21}$, or $\frac{12}{7}$ **51.** $\frac{3}{7}$ **53.** $\frac{3}{11}$

Lesson 3-8 pp. 155–156

EXERCISES **1.** $\frac{3}{10}$ **3.** $\frac{3}{4}$ **13.** 0.4 **15.** 0.375 **25.** 1.25 **27.** Write 0.125 as $\frac{125}{1{,}000}$. Divide numerator and denominator by 125 to express the fraction in simplest form as $\frac{1}{8}$. **29.** greater than **31.** equal to **33.** $4\frac{3}{4}$ lb, 4.75 lb **35.** 0.8, 0.87, $\frac{7}{8}$ **37.** $6.625, $8.50 **49.** 126 **51.** $20.\overline{3}$ **53.** 180 miles

Lesson 3-9 pp. 158–160

EXERCISES **1.** 48 juices **3.** 11 years old and 16 years old **5.**

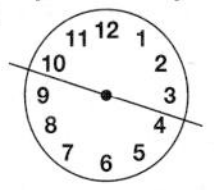

12
1
2
3
4
5
6
7
8
9
10
11

7. 12:20 P.M. **9.** 24 sweatshirts **19.** = **21.** = **25.** 0.32 **27.** 10.5 **31.** $p - 3$

Chapter Review pp. 162–163

1. B **2.** D **3.** A **4.** C **5.** E **6.** 3 and 9 **7.** 3, 5, and 9 **8.** 2, 3, and 9 **9.** 2, 3, 5, 9, and 10 **10.** $2^2 \times 7$ **11.** 51 = 3 × 17 **12.** $2^2 \times 5^2$ **13.** 2×5^3 **14.** 2 **15.** 2 **16.** 5 **17.** 8 **18.** no; $\frac{1}{4}$; $\frac{2}{8}, \frac{3}{12}$ **19.** no; $\frac{2}{3}; \frac{8}{12}, \frac{20}{30}$ **20.** yes; $\frac{2}{6}, \frac{6}{18}$ **21.** yes; $\frac{4}{18}, \frac{6}{27}$ **22.** $\frac{14}{3}$ **23.** $\frac{41}{5}$ **24.** $4\frac{1}{3}$ **25.** $9\frac{2}{3}$ **26.** 10 **27.** 18 **28.** 132 **29.** 140 **30.** $\frac{1}{6}, \frac{1}{4}, \frac{1}{2}$ **31.** $2\frac{4}{15}, 2\frac{1}{3}, 2\frac{2}{5}$ **32.** $\frac{5}{16}, \frac{7}{20}, \frac{17}{40}$ **33.** 0.1875 **34.** $6.208\overline{3}$ **35.** $\frac{3}{50}$ **36.** $4\frac{13}{25}$ **37.** 76 chicken dinners **38.** two 36-exposure rolls, five 24-exposure rolls

Chapter 4

Lesson 4-1 pp. 173–174

EXERCISES **1.** $\frac{1}{2}$ **3.** $1\frac{1}{2}$ **7.** 10 **9.** 5 **13.** about 4 ft **15.** $\frac{1}{2}$ **17.** $\frac{1}{2}$ **23.** about $3\frac{1}{2}$ in. **33.** 0.047 **35.** 0.006 **39.** $20h$ **41.** $s + 12$

Lesson 4-2 pp. 177–178

EXERCISES **1.** $\frac{1}{2}$ **3.** $\frac{2}{3}$ **9.** $\frac{2}{3}$ **11.** $\frac{1}{5}$ **17.** $\frac{1}{2}$ in. **19.** $\frac{2}{6}+\frac{3}{6}=\frac{5}{6}$ **21.** $\frac{1}{10}$ **23.** $\frac{9}{20}$ **25.** $\frac{4}{5}$ **43.** 5

Lesson 4-3 pp. 182–184

EXERCISES **1.** $\frac{9}{10}$ **3.** $\frac{1}{2}$ **7.** $1\frac{23}{40}$ mi **9.** $\frac{1}{4}$ **11.** $\frac{9}{16}$ **15.** $\frac{5}{12}$ c **17.** $\frac{11}{15}$ **19.** $\frac{3}{10}$ **25a.** $1\frac{1}{2}$ in. **b.** $1\frac{7}{40}$ in. **27.** $\frac{9}{20}$ mi per min **29.** $\frac{1}{8}$ **43.** 11 **45.** 30 **47.** 16 **49.** 49 **51.** 720

Lesson 4-4 pp. 187–189

EXERCISES **1.** $3\frac{1}{6}$ **3.** $4\frac{6}{7}$ **5.** $4\frac{1}{4}$ lb **7.** $11\frac{1}{6}$ **9.** $4\frac{3}{8}$ **13.** $21\frac{1}{8}$ min **15.** > **17.** < **21.** $4\frac{1}{8}$ in. **23.** $10\frac{23}{24}$ **25.** 13 yd **31.** C **33.** B

Lesson 4-5 pp. 192–194

EXERCISES **1.** $2\frac{3}{8}$ **3.** $1\frac{3}{8}$ **9.** $1\frac{1}{6}$ h **11.** $3\frac{3}{8}$ **13.** $6\frac{7}{10}$ **17.** $1\frac{15}{16}$ in. **19.** $\frac{5}{6}$ **21.** $2\frac{1}{2}$ **29.** 6 in. **31.** 1 ft $5\frac{1}{2}$ in. **41.** $1\frac{1}{2}$ **43.** $\frac{4}{5}$ **47.** $\frac{2}{7}$ **49.** 2

Lesson 4-6 pp. 198–199

EXERCISES **1.** $3\frac{2}{5}$ **3.** $7\frac{1}{5}$ **7.** $1\frac{5}{42}$ **9.** $1\frac{17}{24}$ **13.** Sample: Let b = amount of book read; $b=\frac{1}{3}+\frac{1}{4}$; $\frac{7}{12}$ of the book. **15.** $\frac{1}{4}$ **17.** $3\frac{17}{25}$ **21.** $g=\frac{3}{10}+\frac{1}{2}$; $g=\frac{4}{5}$ mi **23.** $r=1-\frac{2}{5}-\frac{1}{3}$; $r=\frac{4}{15}$ **33.** $\frac{1}{4}$ **35.** $\frac{11}{12}$ **37.** $\frac{3}{10}, \frac{1}{2}, \frac{4}{7}, \frac{2}{3}$ **39.** $\frac{0}{5}, \frac{2}{11}, \frac{5}{9}, \frac{8}{7}$

Lesson 4-7 pp. 203–205

EXERCISES **1.** 90 min **3.** 482 min **7.** 1 h 10 min **9.** 5 h 46 min **13.** 9 h 47 min **15.** 29 min **17.** 1:00 P.M. **19.** 11:00 A.M. **31.** 36 **33.** 3.8

Lesson 4-8 pp. 207–208

EXERCISES **5.** 18 lights **9.** 80 gifts **17.** $3\frac{1}{2}$ **19.** $13\frac{15}{16}$ **21.** $7\frac{7}{10}$

Chapter Review pp. 210–211

1. benchmark **2.** elapsed time **3–10.** Answers may vary. Samples are given. **3.** $1\frac{1}{2}$ **4.** 0 **5.** 1 **6.** 0 **7.** 14 **8.** 10 **9.** 15 **10.** 6 **11.** about 6 c **12.** $1\frac{2}{5}$ **13.** $\frac{1}{2}$ **14.** $\frac{3}{5}$ **15.** $\frac{5}{9}$ **16.** $\frac{7}{8}$ **17.** $\frac{1}{2}$ **18.** $\frac{1}{8}$ **19.** $1\frac{7}{30}$ **20.** $\frac{13}{15}$ mi **21.** $7\frac{1}{8}$ **22.** $17\frac{1}{3}$ **23.** $6\frac{1}{2}$ **24.** about $59\frac{7}{12}$ in. **25.** $\frac{3}{7}$ **26.** $\frac{1}{8}$ **27.** $1\frac{1}{9}$

28. $3\frac{1}{3}$ **29.** $11\frac{1}{18}$ **30.** $6\frac{2}{5}$ **31.** 3 h 41 min **32.** 8 h 48 min **33.** 8:10 P.M. **34.** 180 cards **35.** 24 plants

Chapter 5

Lesson 5-1 pp. 222–223

EXERCISES

1. 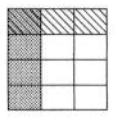 $\frac{1}{12}$

3. 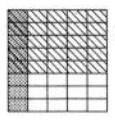 $\frac{5}{40}=\frac{1}{8}$

5. $\frac{3}{16}$ **7.** $\frac{11}{16}$ **15.** 22 **17.** $16\frac{1}{3}$ **21.** 11 **23.** 5 **29.** In the first and third fractions, divide the denominator and numerator by the common factor 3. In the second and third fractions, divide numerator and denominator by the common factor 4. You get $\frac{2}{{}_{1}3}\cdot\frac{4^{1}}{5}\cdot\frac{3^{1}}{4_{1}}$ or $\frac{2}{1}\cdot\frac{1}{5}\cdot\frac{1}{1}$. **31.** 10 **33.** $\frac{3}{5}$ **35.** $\frac{3}{10}$ **43.** $1\frac{1}{6}$ **45.** $\frac{8}{45}$ **51.** composite **53.** prime

Lesson 5-2 pp. 226–228

EXERCISES **1.** 4 **3.** 60 **7.** 65 **9.** $10\frac{1}{2}$ **17.** 5 in. by 5 in. **19.** 48 **21.** 18 **23.** No; the carpenter needs $6\times3\frac{1}{2}=21$ ft of wood and two 10-ft boards are only 20 ft. **25.** 6 in. **27.** $104\frac{13}{15}$ **29.** $49\frac{5}{6}$ **39.** $7\frac{3}{5}$ **41.** $7\frac{5}{8}$ **45.** 30 **47.** 100

Lesson 5-3 pp. 232–234

EXERCISES **1.** $\frac{5}{2}$, or $2\frac{1}{2}$ **3.** $\frac{1}{11}$ **7.** $6\frac{2}{3}$ **9.** $11\frac{2}{3}$ **13.** $2\frac{2}{3}$ **15.** $7\frac{1}{3}$ **21.** $\frac{1}{4}$ **23.** $\frac{11}{12}$ **25.** $\frac{3}{16}$ t **27.** $\frac{10}{11}$ **29.** $\frac{11}{27}$ **35.** about $4\frac{1}{2}$ times more **37.** 36 **39.** $\frac{5}{12}$ **45.** 64 pieces **47.** 3 **49.** 2 **61.** 20 **63.** 15 **65.** 2, 3 **67.** 5

Lesson 5-4 pp. 238–240

EXERCISES **1.** 10 **3.** 11 **7.** 9 points **9.** $\frac{19}{20}$ **11.** $\frac{13}{16}$ ft **13.** 4 **15.** $2\frac{2}{9}$ **19.** $\frac{5}{14}$ **21.** $\frac{2}{9}$ **29.** about 24 strips **31.** 70 **33.** 5 **35.** 30 books **37.** $\frac{4}{11}$ **39.** $\frac{5}{18}$ **41.** $1\frac{1}{15}$ **43.** $2\frac{7}{9}$ **45a.** 80; 800; 80,000

b. As a gets larger, $8\div\frac{1}{a}$ also gets larger. **47.** $1\frac{1}{25}$ **49.** $\frac{7}{8}$ **61.** 9 **63.** 20 **65.** $2^4\times3^2$ **67.** $2^2\times3\times23$

Lesson 5-5 pp. 244–245

EXERCISES **1.** 36 **3.** 324 **11.** 15 **13.** 24 **17.** $7\frac{1}{2}\times p=3$; $\frac{2}{5}$ lb **19.** 20 **21.** $\frac{4}{7}$ **27.** k is greater than 11, because if it were 11 or less, multiplying it by $\frac{3}{5}$ would give a product less than 11. **29.** $\frac{8}{5}k=12$; $7\frac{1}{2}$ mi **31.** about 300 mi **41.** $2\frac{1}{4}$ **43.** $21\frac{8}{9}$ **45.** $\frac{9}{100}$

Lesson 5-6 pp. 247–249

EXERCISES **1.** 7 classes **3.** 18 cuts **5.** 48 brownies **7a.** 1 in. **b.** 70 in. **11.** $79.20 **21.** $2\frac{1}{2}$ **23.** $\frac{20}{21}$ **27.** 6 **29.** 4

Lesson 5-7 pp. 252–253

EXERCISES **1–12.** Answers may vary. Samples are given. **1.** Feet; lots are usually measured in feet. **3.** Inches; a license plate is a little longer than a foot-ruler. **5.** Pounds; one orange weighs less than a pound, so a bag of oranges would weigh more. **7.** Pounds; a bowling ball weighs more than a loaf of bread. **9.** Fluid ounces; a sample-size bottle of shampoo holds less than a cup. **11.** Gallon; lawnmowers usually hold about 1 gallon of gas. **13.** > **15.** < **17.** about $13\frac{1}{3}$ times as heavy **27.** $1\frac{1}{3}$ **29.** 1 h 59 min

Lesson 5-8 pp. 256–257

EXERCISES **1.** 96 **3.** 66 **7.** about $\frac{1}{2}$ t **9.** 6 ft 7 in. **11.** 1 lb 1 oz **13.** = **15.** < **21.** 15 **23.** 68 **27.** $1\frac{8}{9}$, or about 2 yd **35.** $5\frac{3}{14}$ **37.** $1\frac{7}{18}$ **39.** $5\frac{2}{3}$ **41.** $12\frac{3}{4}$

Chapter Review pp. 260–261

1. 12 **2.** 12 **3.** 80 **4.** 84 **5.** $\frac{3}{10}$ **6.** $\frac{2}{39}$ **7.** $\frac{2}{5}$ **8.** 15 **9.** $17\frac{1}{2}$ **10.** $3\frac{7}{8}$ **11.** $6\frac{14}{15}$ **12.** $20\frac{15}{22}$ **13.** $\frac{1}{3}$ c **14.** 1 **15.** 3 **16.** 3 **17.** 2 **18.** 16 **19.** $5\frac{2}{3}$ **20.** $\frac{5}{11}$ **21.** $\frac{8}{9}$ **22.** $1\frac{3}{7}$ **23.** $\frac{2}{25}$ **24.** $2\frac{1}{112}$ **25.** $3\frac{3}{28}$ **26.** 96 **27.** 25 **28.** 2 **29.** $\frac{3}{4}$ **30.** 4 **31.** 2 **32.** $7\frac{1}{5}$ **33.** $\frac{13}{50}$ **34.** 79 s **35.** tons **36.** fluid ounces **37.** $73\frac{1}{3}$ **38.** 40 **39.** 6 **40.** = **41.** > **42.** >

Chapter 6

Lesson 6-1 pp. 271–272

EXERCISES **1.** 35 to 24, 35 : 24, $\frac{35}{24}$ **3.** 11 to 70, 11 : 70, $\frac{11}{70}$ **9.** 4 : 3 **11.** $\frac{1}{3}$ **17.** 700. **19.** 45 **25.** Divide the terms of the original ratio by their GCF, 8. **27.** 5 : 7 **29.** 4 : 2, $\frac{4}{2}$, 4 to 2 **31.** 2 : 3, $\frac{2}{3}$, 2 to 3 **45.** $\frac{15}{32}$ **47.** $\frac{1}{7}$

Lesson 6-2 pp. 275–276

EXERCISES **1.** 70 heartbeats per minute **3.** $6.50 per T-shirt **7.** $\frac{3\text{ feet}}{1\text{ yard}}=\frac{45\text{ feet}}{15\text{ yards}}$ **9.** $\frac{45\text{ students}}{1\text{ bus}}=\frac{225\text{ students}}{5\text{ buses}}$ **11.** $.95 per bagel; $.80 per bagel; 5 for $4.00 **13.** $.63 per lb; $.79 per lb; 3 lb for $1.89 **15.** 99 pages in 3 hours **17.** 33 mi in 3 hours **19a.** 85 jumps per min **b.** 288 jumps per min **c.** 203 times **31.** $1\frac{1}{5}$ **33.** $2\frac{1}{20}$ **37.** $\frac{1}{14}$ **39.** $\frac{25}{33}$

Lesson 6-3 pp. 280–282

EXERCISES **1.** yes **3.** no **9.** 105 **11.** 114 **17.** 30 in. **19.** yes **21.** yes **23.** 14 in. **25.** 144 mi **27.** 60 **29.** 168 **39.** 5 **41.** 6 **43.** $1\frac{8}{9}$ **45.** $4\frac{1}{2}$

Lesson 6-4 pp. 285–287

EXERCISES **1.** yes **3.** yes **7.** 63 **9.** 6.75 **15.** 28.8 oz **17.** no **19.** 1 **21.** 45 **25a.** about 16.7 ft **b.** No; the ratios need only to have the same units in corresponding places in the proportion. **27.** 16 teachers **29.** 32,815.41 ft **31.** 8,760 h **35.** No; the unit rates are different. **45.** $\frac{1}{5}$ **47.** $\frac{4}{25}$

Lesson 6-5 pp. 290–292

EXERCISES **1.** 1 : 25 **3.** 1 : 20 **9.** 4 in. **11.** $1\frac{1}{3}$ in. **13.** 1.25 cm **15.** 40 cm **19a.** Reduce; the map is 4 cm wide and 3 cm high. For each centimeter on the map, I would draw 0.5 centimeter on my drawing. My drawing would measure 2 cm wide and 1.5 cm high. **b.** 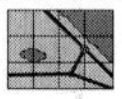 **21.** 5 in. **31.** 2 **33.** 2 **35.** 10 **37.** $49\frac{1}{2}$

Lesson 6-6 pp. 296–298

EXERCISES **1.** 0.15 **3.** 0.82 **11.** $\frac{7}{10}$ **13.** $\frac{1}{20}$

Selected Answers

21. 17% **23.** 98% **31.** 60% **33.** about 27% **35.** about 63% **37.** about 7% **45.** 0.7, 70% **47.** about 83% **49.** 45% **57.** 72.5% **69.** 18 **71.** 20

Lesson 6-7 pp. 301–302

EXERCISES **1.** 7.2 **3.** 16.8 **9.** 30.6 **11.** 26.23 **15.** 32 **17.** 12.5 **21.** 152 **23.** 14 **27.** $10 **29.** $89.50 **41.** 2 : 5 **43.** $\frac{2}{3}$ **49.** $2\frac{1}{2}$ **51.** $8\frac{2}{5}$

Lesson 6-8 pp. 305–306

EXERCISES **1.** $1.96, $29.96 **3.** $1.05, $16.05 **5.** $6.30 **7.** $12 **9.** $24 **11.** $5.10 **13.** Florida: $4.80, $84.80; Georgia: $3.20, $83.20; Massachusetts: $4.00, $84.00; Tennessee: $5.60, $85.60 **15.** Florida: $.05, $.85; Georgia: $.03, $.83; Massachusetts: $.04, $.84; Tennessee: $.06, $.86 **19.** 45 **21.** 90 **25.** I could round to $4.50 and multiply by 4; I could round to $4.50 and multiply by 3. **33.** 1,488 times **35.** 130 min **37.** 380 min **39.** 180 **41.** 360

Lesson 6-9 pp. 308–309

EXERCISES **1.** 6,000,000 subscribers **3.** $79.90 **5.** $15.93 **7.** $15 **9.** $13.25 **13.** 9,200,000 **15.** 1,250 t **23.** yes **25.** 44 **27.** 20

Chapter Review pp. 312–313

1. E **2.** B **3.** D **4.** C **5.** A **6.** 15 to 23, 15 : 23, $\frac{15}{23}$ **7.** 15 to 8, 15 : 8, $\frac{15}{8}$ **8.** 23 to 8, 23 : 8, $\frac{23}{8}$ **9.** 15 to 46, 15 : 46, $\frac{15}{46}$ **10.** 1 to 4 **11.** $\frac{3}{5}$ **12.** 3 ft : 1 yd **13.** $\frac{5}{6}$ **14.** 40 min **15.** $12.50 **16.** $1.40 for 24 oz **17.** no **18.** yes **19.** yes **20.** no **21.** 354 **22.** 99 ft **23.** 148.5 in. **24.** 11 ft or 132 in. **25.** $\frac{3}{10}$, 0.3 **26.** $\frac{1}{4}$, 0.25 **27.** $\frac{14}{25}$; 0.56 **28.** $\frac{3}{25}$; 0.12 **29.** 60 **30.** 60% **31–34.** Answers may vary. Samples are given. **31.** 10 **32.** $1.20 **33.** $6 **34.** $21.40 **35.** 3 weeks **36.** $2.75

Chapter 7

Lesson 7-1 pp. 324–325

EXERCISES **1.** 10 **3.** 2 **7.** 0.5 **9.** 20.7 **11.** 8 **13.** 94 **15.** $2.09 **17.** 13; 13; no mode **19.** Increase; decrease; stay the same; explanations may vary. Sample: If a new value is added to a data set, and if the value is greater than/less than/equal to the mean of the original data set, the new mean will increase/decrease/stay the same. **21.** 240 **27.** 0.55; 55% **29.** 0.02; 2% **31.** 160 **33.** 30

Lesson 7-2 pp. 328–330

EXERCISES **1.**

Number of Days	Tally	Frequency
28	|	1
30	||||	4
31	𝍸 ||	7

3. 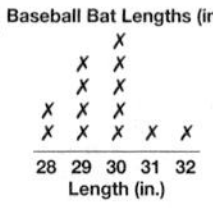
Baseball Bat Lengths (in.)
28 29 30 31 32
Length (in.)

5. 43,612 square miles **7.** 1.7 m

9a.

Letter	Tally	Frequency
a	|||	3
b	|	1
c	||	2
d	|	1
e	|	1
f	|	1
g	𝍸 ||	7
h	||	2
i	|||	3
l	𝍸 𝍸 |	11
n	||||	4
o	𝍸 |	6
p	|	1
r	||||	4
s	|	1
t	|	1
w	||||	4
y	𝍸	5

b. Use the mode, L; the data are not numbers, therefore the mode is the best way to represent the data. **11.** frequency of letter grades in science **13.** 11 students

15. 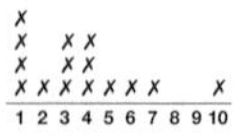
1 2 3 4 5 6 7 8 9 10

17a. 1, 1 **b.** Answers may vary. Sample: No; the mean is not a whole number. **c.** 27 siblings **19.** 6,622 meters **27.** 500 km **29.** 830 km **31.** $\frac{3}{10}$ **33.** $\frac{2}{9}$

Lesson 7-3 pp. 332–333

EXERCISES **1.** 12 ways **3.** 43 **5a.** $1, $3, $7, $15, $31, $63 **b.** Answers may vary. Sample: The total saved will be $1 less than twice the amount saved that week. **13.** 1 lb **15.** 8 oz **17.** $\frac{1}{16}$ **19.** $\frac{4}{5}$

Lesson 7-4 pp. 337–339

EXERCISES **1.** 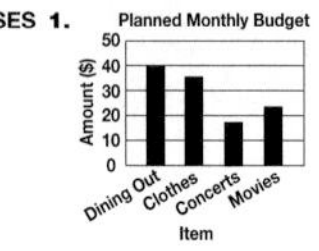
Planned Monthly Budget
Amount ($)
0
10
20
30
40
50
Dining Out
Clothes
Concerts
Movies
Item

3. 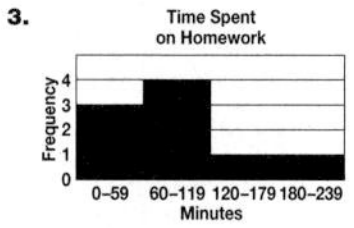
Time Spent on Homework
Frequency
0
1
2
3
4
0–59
60–119
120–179
180–239
Minutes

5. 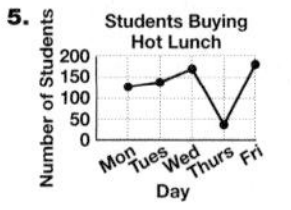
Students Buying Hot Lunch
Number of Students
0
50
100
150
200
Mon
Tues
Wed
Thurs
Fri
Day

7a. 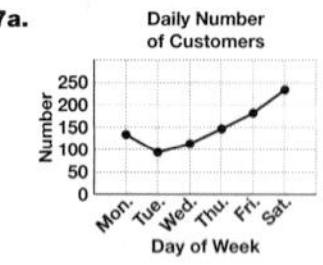
Daily Number of Customers
Number
0
50
100
150
200
250
Mon.
Tue.
Wed.
Thu.
Fri.
Sat.
Day of Week

b. The daily number of customers increases, starting on Wednesday.

9a. 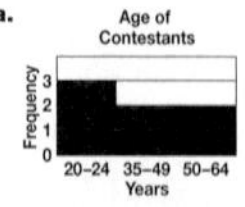
Age of Contestants
Frequency
0
1
2
3
20–24
35–49
50–64
Years

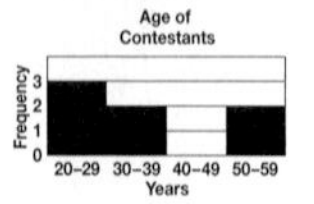
Age of Contestants
Frequency
0
1
2
3
20–29
30–39
40–49
50–59
Years

b. 4 intervals; the second histogram shows that there are no contestants in the interval 40–49.

Lesson 7-5 pp. 343–345

EXERCISES **1.** tennis **3.** tennis, volleyball, basketball, baseball, soccer

5. 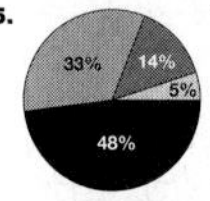
33%
14%
5%
48%

7. 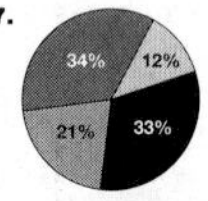
34%
12%
21%
33%

11. 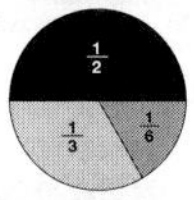
1/2
1/3
1/6

13. 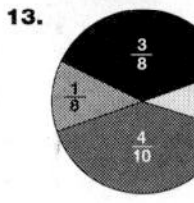
3/8
1/8
1/10
4/10

15a. 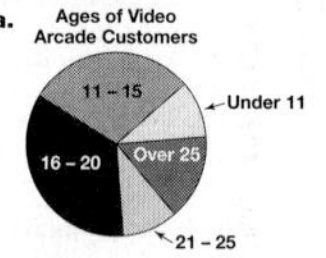
Ages of Video Arcade Customers
11 – 15
Under 11
16 – 20
Over 25
21 – 25

b. 60% **c.** No; explanations may vary. Sample: You can find only the percent of customers 11 to 15 years old. **17.** 24% **23.** 12 **25.** 164 **27.** 30 **29.** 5

Lesson 7-6 pp. 348–350

EXERCISES **1.** C2, C3, C4, C5 **3.** B5, C5, D5, E5, F5 **5.** 100 **7.** 95 **9.** =B4+C4+D4 **11.** =C2−B2; 5 **13.** =D5*7 or =E2+E3+E4 **21.** 4.5 **23.** $\frac{5}{6}$ c; equations may vary. Sample: $\frac{2}{3}+w=1\frac{1}{2}$

Lesson 7-7 pp. 353–355

EXERCISES **1.** 8 seconds **3.** none

5. Heights of Tomato Plants (inches)

Stem	Leaf
2	6 7 9
3	0 1 3 3 5 6 6
4	0 1

Key: 2|6 means 26 in.

Selected Answers

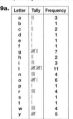

7. Number of Jelly Beans in a Scoop

```
2 | 7 8
3 | 2 4 5 5 8
4 | 3 5 7 7
5 | 3 8
6 |
7 | 6
```
Key: 2|7 means 27 jelly beans

11a. Ages of People
```
0 | 9
1 | 1 2 2 2 2 3 5 5 5 9
2 | 0 1 3 4
3 | 5
4 | 0
```
Key: 1|1 means 11

b. Ages of Eighteen People
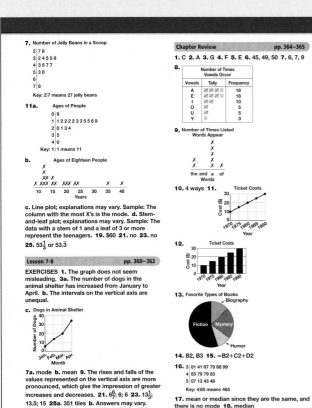

c. Line plot; explanations may vary. Sample: The column with the most X's is the mode. **d.** Stem-and-leaf plot; explanations may vary. Sample: The data with a stem of 1 and a leaf of 3 or more represent the teenagers. **19.** $60 **21.** no **23.** no **25.** $53\frac{1}{3}$ or $53.\overline{3}$

Lesson 7-8 pp. 360–362
EXERCISES **1.** The graph does not seem misleading. **3a.** The number of dogs in the animal shelter has increased from January to April. **b.** The intervals on the vertical axis are unequal.
c. Dogs in Animal Shelter
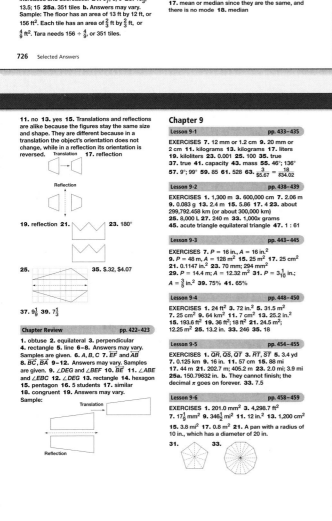

7a. mode **b.** mean **9.** The rises and falls of the values represented on the vertical axis are more pronounced, which give the impression of greater increases and decreases. **21.** $6\frac{6}{7}$; 6 **23.** $13\frac{1}{3}$; 13.5; 15 **25a.** 351 tiles **b.** Answers may vary. Sample: The floor has an area of 13 ft by 12 ft, or 156 ft². Each tile has an area of $\frac{2}{3}$ ft by $\frac{2}{3}$ ft, or $\frac{4}{9}$ ft². Tara needs $156 \div \frac{4}{9}$, or 351 tiles.

Chapter Review pp. 364–365
1. C **2.** A **3.** G **4.** F **5.** E **6.** 45, 49, 50 **7.** 6, 7, 9
8.

Number of Times Vowels Occur

Vowels	Tally	Frequency
A	𝍷𝍷𝍷	18
E	𝍷𝍷𝍷	18
I	𝍷𝍷	10
O	𝍷	5
U	𝍷	5
Y		3

9. Number of Times Listed Words Appear
```
          X
          X
    X     X
    X     X
    X X   X   X
the and a of
   Words
```
10. 4 ways **11.** Ticket Costs
12. Ticket Costs
13. Favorite Types of Books — Biography, Mystery, Fiction, Humor
14. B2, B3 **15.** =B2+C2+D2
16.
```
3 | 01 41 67 79 88 99
4 | 65 79 79 83
5 | 07 12 43 48
```
Key: 4|65 means 465
17. mean or median since they are the same, and there is no mode **18.** median

Chapter 8

Lesson 8-1 pp. 375–377
EXERCISES **1.** B **3.** D **5.** $\overline{HJ}$ **7.** $\overline{XY}$ **13.** A, B, and C **22.** sometimes **25.** never **41.** 520 **43.** 145 **45.** $\frac{11}{20}$ **47.** $\frac{1}{20}$

Lesson 8-2 pp. 381–383
EXERCISES **1.** 120° **3.** 90° **7.** acute **9.** acute **11.** [fig] **13.** [fig]
17. No; the measure of an angle is not related to the length of the rays that form the angle. **19.** Fold the piece of paper lengthwise. Without unfolding, fold it widthwise. **21.** ∠AGE, ∠BGE, ∠BGF, ∠CGF **23.** ∠AGF **39.** 8; red, crew; red, v-neck; black, crew; black, v-neck; white, crew; white, v-neck; green, crew; green, v-neck **41.** inches **43.** inches

Lesson 8-3 pp. 388–390
EXERCISES **1.** 78°; 168° **3.** 7°; 97° **7.** 64° **9.** $\overline{CE}$ **13.** sometimes **15.** never **17.** 50° **19.** 20° **21.** 85°; 95° **23.** An obtuse angle does not have a complement. **31.** 5 **33.** 9.6

Lesson 8-4 pp. 394–396
EXERCISES **1.** right **3.** obtuse **5.** 90° **7.** 25° **11.** isosceles **13.** isosceles **17.** isosceles, obtuse **19a.** sides $\frac{7}{8}$ in., $1\frac{1}{2}$ in., $1\frac{3}{4}$ in.; angles: 30°; 60°; 90°; sides: $1\frac{1}{16}$ in., $1\frac{1}{16}$ in., $1\frac{1}{2}$ in.; angles: 45°, 45°, 90° **b.** right; right scalene; isosceles **23.** right scalene **25.** obtuse scalene **39.** 66 mi **41.** 15 mi

Lesson 8-5 pp. 399–400
EXERCISES **1.** pentagon **3.** quadrilateral **5.** parallelogram, rectangle; quadrilateral, rectangle **13.** [fig] **15.** No **17.** All **25.** C3 **27.** 36%

Lesson 8-6 pp. 402–404
EXERCISES **1.**

	a.	b.	c.	d.
a.	S	U	M	S
b.	U	N	I	T
c.	M	I	L	E
d.	S	T	E	M

3. Amy has a green bike. Bill has a red bike. Chuck has a blue bike. **5.** Sue **7.** 49 cards **9.** 68, 60. Start with 65. Subtract 2 for next term. Add the next consecutive number from what you subtracted. Subtract the next consecutive number. Continue alternately adding and subtracting consecutive numbers. **11a.** 360° **b.** 540°; 720° **c.** 900°; 1,080° **d.** yes
17.
```
1 | 4, 6, 6, 6      19. 4, 2
2 | 3, 5, 8
3 | 3, 7
4 | 2, 5
```
Key: 1|4 means 14

Lesson 8-7 pp. 407–409
EXERCISES **1.** yes **3.** yes **7.** no **9.** yes **11.** similar **13.** Congruent; the window must be exactly the same size. **15.** C **17.** A and E, H and J **21.** 8 **29.** 75% **31.** 40%

Lesson 8-8 pp. 412–414
EXERCISES **1.** No; if you fold the figure along the line, the two parts do not match. **3.** Yes; if you fold the figure along the line, the two parts match.
7. 2 [fig] **9.** 1 [fig] **11.** yes
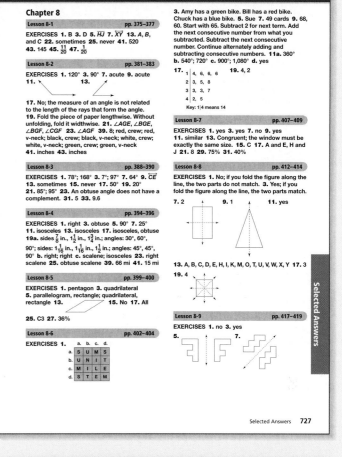
13. A, B, C, D, E, H, I, K, M, O, T, U, V, W, X, Y **17.** 3 **19.** 4 [fig]

Lesson 8-9 pp. 417–419
EXERCISES **1.** no **3.** yes
5. [fig] **7.** [fig]

11. no **13.** yes **15.** Translations and reflections are alike because the figures stay the same size and shape. They are different because in a translation the object's orientation does not change, while in a reflection its orientation is reversed. **17.** reflection
Translation [fig]
Reflection [fig]
19. reflection **21.** [fig] **23.** 180°
25. [fig] **35.** $.32, $4.07
37. $9\frac{1}{9}$ **39.** $7\frac{1}{3}$

Chapter Review pp. 422–423
1. obtuse **2.** equilateral **3.** perpendicular **4.** rectangle **5.** line **6–8.** Answers may vary. Samples are given. **6.** A, B, C **7.** $\overline{EF}$ and $\overline{AB}$ **8.** $\overline{BC}, \overline{BA}$ **9–12.** Answers may vary. Samples are given. **9.** ∠DEG and ∠BEF **10.** $\overline{BE}$ **11.** ∠ABE and ∠EBC **12.** ∠DEG **13.** rectangle **14.** hexagon **15.** pentagon **16.** 5 students **17.** similar **18.** congruent **19.** Answers may vary. Sample:
Translation [fig]
Reflection [fig]

Chapter 9

Lesson 9-1 pp. 433–435
EXERCISES **7.** 12 mm or 1.2 cm **9.** 20 mm or 2 cm **11.** kilograms **13.** kilograms **17.** liters **19.** kiloliters **23.** 0.001 **25.** 100 **35.** true **37.** true **41.** capacity **43.** mass **55.** 46°; 136° **57.** 9°; 99° **59.** 85 **61.** 528 **63.** $\frac{3}{\$5.67} = \frac{18}{\$34.02}$

Lesson 9-2 pp. 438–439
EXERCISES **1.** 1,300 m **3.** 600,000 cm **7.** 2.06 m **9.** 0.083 g **13.** 2.4 m **15.** 5.86 **17.** 4 **23.** about 299,792.458 km (or about 300,000 km) **25.** 8,000 L **27.** 240 m **33.** 1,000x grams **45.** acute triangle equilateral triangle **47.** 1 : 61

Lesson 9-3 pp. 443–445
EXERCISES **7.** P = 16 in., A = 16 in.² **9.** P = 48 m, A = 128 m² **15.** 25 m² **17.** 25 cm² **21.** 0.1147 in.² **23.** 70 mm; 294 mm² **29.** P = 14.4 m; A = 12.32 m² **31.** $P = 3\frac{1}{10}$ in.; $A = \frac{8}{9}$ in.² **39.** 75% **41.** 65%

Lesson 9-4 pp. 448–450
EXERCISES **1.** 24 ft² **3.** 72 in.² **5.** 31.5 m² **7.** 25 cm² **9.** 64 km² **11.** 7 cm² **13.** 25.2 in.² **15.** 193.6 ft² **19.** 36 ft²; 18 ft² **21.** 24.5 m²; 12.25 m² **25.** 13.2 in. **33.** 246 **35.** 18

Lesson 9-5 pp. 454–455
EXERCISES **1.** $\overline{QR}, \overline{QS}, \overline{QT}$ **3.** $\overline{RT}, \overline{ST}$ **5.** 3.4 yd **7.** 0.125 km **9.** 16 in. **11.** 57 cm **15.** 88 mi **17.** 44 m **21.** 202.7 m; 405.2 m **23.** 2.0 mi; 3.9 mi **25a.** 150.79632 in. **b.** They cannot finish; the decimal π goes on forever. **33.** 7.5

Lesson 9-6 pp. 458–459
EXERCISES **1.** 201.0 mm² **3.** 4,298.7 ft² **7.** $17\frac{1}{3}$ mm² **9.** $346\frac{1}{2}$ mi² **11.** 12 in.² **13.** 1,200 cm² **15.** 3.8 mi² **17.** 0.8 m² **21.** A pan with a radius of 10 in., which has a diameter of 20 in.
31. [fig] **33.** [fig]

Lesson 9-7 pp. 464–466
EXERCISES **1.** triangular prism **3.** rectangular prism **7.** cylinder **9.** cone **13.** sphere **15.** rectangular prism **17.** [fig]
19. [fig]
35. [fig] **37.** $.96
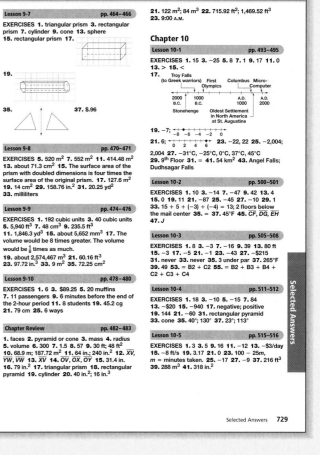

Lesson 9-8 pp. 470–471
EXERCISES **5.** 520 m² **7.** 552 m² **11.** 414.48 m² **13.** about 71.3 cm² **15.** The surface area of the prism with doubled dimensions is four times the surface area of the original prism. **17.** 127.6 m² **19.** 14 cm² **29.** 158.76 m² **31.** 20.25 yd² **33.** milliliters

Lesson 9-9 pp. 474–476
EXERCISES **1.** 192 cubic units **3.** 40 cubic units **5.** 5,940 ft³ **7.** 48 cm³ **9.** 235.5 ft³ **11.** 1,846.3 yd³ **15.** about 5,652 mm³ **17.** The volume would be 8 times greater. The volume would be 8 times as much. **19.** about 2,574,467 m³ **21.** 60.16 ft³ **23.** 97.72 in.³ **33.** 9 m² **35.** 72.25 cm²

Lesson 9-10 pp. 478–480
EXERCISES **1.** 6 **3.** $89.25 **5.** 20 muffins **7.** 11 passengers **9.** 6 minutes before the end of the 2-hour period **11.** 8 students **19.** 45.2 cg **21.** 79 cm **26.** 6 ways

Chapter Review pp. 482–483
1. faces **2.** pyramid or cone **3.** mass **4.** radius **5.** volume **6.** 300 **7.** 1.5 **8.** 57 **9.** 30 ft; 48 ft² **10.** 68.9 m; 187.72 m² **11.** 64 in.; 240 in.² **12.** $\overline{XV}, \overline{YW}, \overline{VW}$ **13.** $\overline{XV}$ **14.** $\overline{OV}, \overline{OX}, \overline{OY}$ **15.** 31.4 in. **16.** 79 in.² **17.** triangular prism **18.** rectangular pyramid **19.** cylinder **20.** 40 in.²; 16 in.³

21. 122 m²; 84 m³ **22.** 715.92 ft²; 1,469.52 ft³ **23.** 9:00 A.M.

Chapter 10

Lesson 10-1 pp. 493–495
EXERCISES **1.** 15 **3.** -25 **5.** 8 **7.** 1 **9.** 17 **11.** 0 **13.** > **15.** <
17.
Troy Falls (to Greek warriors) 2000 B.C. / Stonehenge; First Olympics 1000 B.C.; Oldest Settlement in North America at St. Augustine; Columbus A.D.; Micro-Computer A.D. 2000
19. -7 [number line]
21. 6 [number line] **23.** -22, 22 **25.** -2,004; 2,004 **27.** -31°C, -25°C, 0°C, 37°C, 45°C **29.** 9th Floor **31.** = **41.** 54 km² **43.** Angel Falls; Dudhsagar Falls

Lesson 10-2 pp. 500–501
EXERCISES **1.** 10 **3.** -14 **7.** -47 **9.** 42 **13.** 4 **15.** 0 **19.** 11 **21.** -87 **25.** -45 **27.** -10 **29.** 1 **33.** 15 + 5 + (-3) + (-4) = 13; 2 floors below the mail center **35.** = **37.** 45°F **45.** $\overline{CF}, \overline{DG}, \overline{EH}$ **47.** J

Lesson 10-3 pp. 505–508
EXERCISES **1.** 8 **3.** -7 **5.** -16 **9.** 39 **13.** 80 ft **15.** -3 **17.** -521 **21.** -1 **23.** -43 **27.** -$215 **31.** never **33.** never **35.** 3 under par **37.** 265°F **39.** 49 **53.** = B2 + C2 **55.** = B2 + B3 + B4 + C2 + C3 + C4

Lesson 10-4 pp. 511–512
EXERCISES **1.** 18 **3.** -10 **5.** -15 **7.** 84 **13.** -$20 **15.** -940 **17.** negative; positive **19.** 144 **21.** -60 **31.** rectangular pyramid **33.** cone **35.** 40°; 130° **37.** 23°; 113°

Lesson 10-5 pp. 515–516
EXERCISES **1.** 3 **3.** 5 **9.** 16 **11.** -12 **13.** -$3/day **15.** -8 ft/s **19.** 3.17 **21.** 0 **23.** 100 - 25m, m = minutes taken. **25.** -17 **27.** -9 **37.** 216 ft³ **39.** 288 m³ **41.** 318 in.³

Lesson 10-6 — pp. 520–521

EXERCISES 1. (−3, 1) 3. (3, 2) 5. A 7. J
15. grocery store 21. (−8, −3) 25. (0, 2), (1, 2), (1, 4), (0, 4), (2, 6), (2, 5), (4, 5), (4, 6), (6, 4), (5, 4), (5, 2), (6, 2), (4, 0), (4, 1), (2, 1), (2, 0) 27. Yes; answers may vary. Sample: The first coordinate tells you how far to move along the x-axis and the second coordinate tells you where to move along the y-axis. 35. The statistic is misleading because four of the five distances are less than 25 feet.

Lesson 10-7 — pp. 524–526

EXERCISES 1. −$2,256 3. $194 5a. Monday: $9; Tuesday: $18; Wednesday: −$9; Thursday: $17; Friday: −$12; Saturday: −$1

b.

c. Tuesday; Friday 7. 15 9. 23 13. Miami; Rochester 15. A company has made a profit if its total expenses are less than its total income. 23. acute 25. acute 31. 14

Lesson 10-8 — pp. 530–532

EXERCISES

1.

Input	Output
−5	−1
8	12
31	35

3.

Input	Output
−3	24
4	−32
9	−72

5.

x	y
−2	−4
−1	−3
0	−2
1	−1
2	0

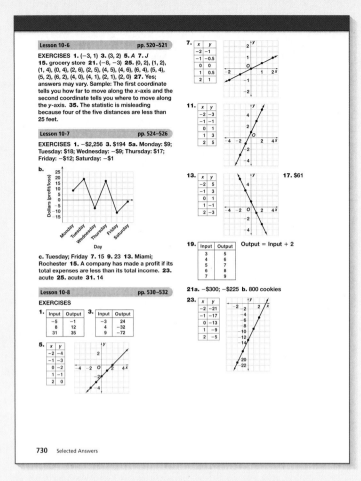

7.

x	y
−2	−1
−1	−0.5
0	0
1	0.5
2	1

11.

x	y
−2	−3
−1	−1
0	1
1	3
2	5

13.

x	y
−2	5
−1	3
0	1
1	−1
2	−3

17. $61

19.

Input	Output
3	5
4	6
5	7
6	8
7	9

Output = Input + 2

21a. −$300; −$225 b. 800 cookies

23.

x	y
−2	−21
−1	−17
0	−13
1	−9
2	−5

25.

x	y
−2	−12
−1	−9
0	−6
1	−3
2	0

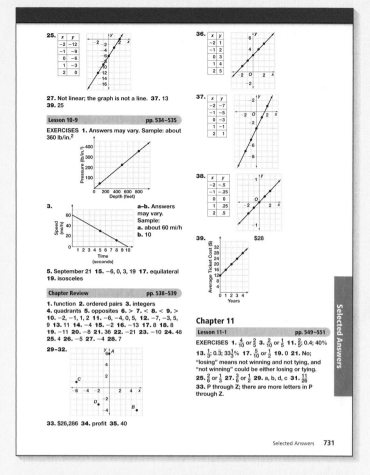

27. Not linear; the graph is not a line. 37. 13 39. 25

Lesson 10-9 — pp. 534–535

EXERCISES 1. Answers may vary. Sample: about 360 lb/in.²

3. a–b. Answers may vary. Sample: a. about 60 mi/h b. 10
5. September 21 15. −6, 0, 3, 19 17. equilateral 19. isosceles

Chapter Review — pp. 538–539

1. function 2. ordered pairs 3. integers 4. quadrants 5. opposites 6. > 7. < 8. < 9. > 10. −2, −1, 1, 2 11. −6, −4, 0, 5 12. −7, −3, 5, 9 13. 11 14. −4 15. −2 16. −13 17. 8 18. 8 19. −11 20. −8 21. 36 22. −21 23. −10 24. 48 25. 4 26. −5 27. −4 28. 7

29–32.

33. $26,286 34. profit 35. 40

36.

x	y
−2	1
−1	2
0	3
1	4
2	5

37.

x	y
−2	−7
−1	−5
0	−3
1	−1
2	1

38.

x	y
−2	−.5
−1	−.25
0	0
1	.25
2	.5

39. $28

Chapter 11

Lesson 11-1 — pp. 549–551

EXERCISES 1. $\frac{4}{10}$ or $\frac{2}{5}$ 3. $\frac{2}{10}$ or $\frac{1}{5}$ 11. $\frac{5}{5}$; 0.4; 40%
13. $\frac{1}{3}$; $0.\overline{3}$; $33\frac{1}{3}\%$ 17. $\frac{5}{10}$ or $\frac{1}{2}$ 19. 0 21. No; "losing" means not winning and not tying, and "not winning" could be either losing or tying.
25. $\frac{2}{6}$ or $\frac{1}{3}$ 27. $\frac{3}{6}$ or $\frac{1}{2}$ 29. a, b, c 31. $\frac{11}{26}$
33. P through Z; there are more letters in P through Z.

---

35. 47. −18 49. −2

Lesson 11-2 — pp. 555–557

EXERCISES 1. $\frac{3}{14}$ 3. 1 7. $\frac{3}{4}$ 9. Yes; the experimental probability of rolling a 1, 2, or 3 is $\frac{1}{2}$.
11. $\frac{2}{3}$ 13a. $\frac{3}{20}$ b. $\frac{13}{20}$ 15. It seems likely that the school will serve pizza every Friday. 17. 0 19. $\frac{9}{30}$ or $\frac{3}{10}$ 23. Spin it several times to see if it lands on each section about the same number of times. 39. −13 41. 10 45. congruent

Lesson 11-3 — pp. 560–562

EXERCISES 1. 2 3. 6 7. 200 students 9. 288 shirts 11. 192 belts 13. honesty 15a. about 11 times b. about 9 times 17. 24 blue; 56 red; 80 orange; 40 yellow 19. 30 blue; 70 red; 100 orange; 50 yellow 21. 60 pieces; experimental probability is usually more accurate with more trials. 23. $\frac{5}{16}$ 25. about 63 darts 33. −120 35. 96

Lesson 11-4 — pp. 565–566

EXERCISES 5. you: 11 pairs; friend: 22 pairs 7. 24 visits 17. R 19. S 25. centimeter

Lesson 11-5 — pp. 571–573

EXERCISES 1. $\frac{4}{8}$ or $\frac{1}{2}$ 3. $\frac{2}{8}$ or $\frac{1}{4}$

5. spin 1   spin 2

$\frac{1}{9}$

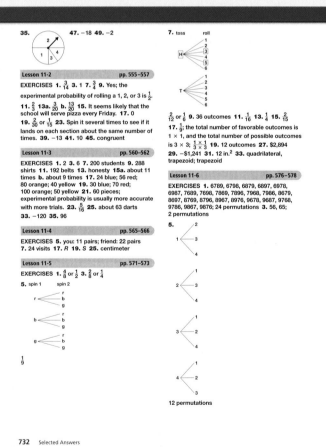

7. toss   roll

$\frac{2}{12}$ or $\frac{1}{6}$ 9. 36 outcomes 11. $\frac{1}{16}$ 13. $\frac{1}{4}$ 15. $\frac{2}{15}$
17. $\frac{1}{9}$; the total number of favorable outcomes is 1×1, and the total number of possible outcomes is 3×3; $\frac{1}{3} \times \frac{1}{3}$ 19. 12 outcomes 27. $2,894
29. −$1,241 31. 12 in.² 33. quadrilateral, trapezoid; trapezoid

Lesson 11-6 — pp. 576–578

EXERCISES 1. 6789, 6798, 6879, 6897, 6978, 6987, 7689, 7698, 7869, 7896, 7968, 7986, 8679, 8697, 8769, 8796, 8967, 8976, 9678, 9687, 9768, 9786, 9867, 9876; 24 permutations 3. 56, 65; 2 permutations

5.

12 permutations

7.

12 orders

9. 24 permutations 11. 12 permutations 13a. 5,040 ways b. 40,320 ways 15. Since two of the letters in Ann's name are the same, there are only 3 permutations: ANN, NAN, NNA. She counted each permutation twice, one for each N. 25. 0.3, 1.0, 2.0 27. 9 in.² 29. 12.25 cm²

Lesson 11-7 — pp. 582–584

EXERCISES 1. Not independent; the first pick affects the second because the number of dimes will be 1 less. 3. Independent; the first toss does not affect the second. 5. $\frac{9}{100}$ 7. $\frac{1}{4}$ 11. $\frac{1}{12}$
13. $\frac{1}{216}$ 15. $\frac{1}{4}$ 17. $\frac{4}{25}$; check students' methods.
19. $\frac{3}{35}$ 21. $\frac{3}{35}$ 23. $\frac{4}{35}$ 35. $\frac{3}{9}$ 37. 48 cm³

Chapter Review — pp. 586–587

1. D 2. C 3. B 4. G 5. E 6. $\frac{1}{6}$ 7. $\frac{3}{6}$ or $\frac{1}{2}$ 8. $\frac{2}{6}$ or $\frac{1}{3}$
9. Noel: $\frac{2}{3}$; Kayla: $\frac{1}{3}$ 10. 2,200 defective computers 11. Check students' work. 12. Answers may vary. Sample: Use a set of three cards, numbered 1 through 3 for the different soups. Use a coin for the different salads. Let card number 1 represent chicken soup. Let heads represent house salad. Draw a card and toss the coin once to simulate one choice of soup and salad. Repeat and record your results in a table. 13. 5678, 5687, 5768, 5786, 5867, 5876, 6578, 6587, 6758, 6785, 6857, 6875, 7568, 7586, 7658, 7685, 7856, 7865, 8567, 8576, 8657, 8675, 8756, 8765; 24 ways 14. PEN, PNE, EPN, ENP, NPE, NEP; 6 ways 15. 24 ways 16. Independent; the first roll does not affect the second roll. 17. Not independent; after drawing the first cube, there is one less cube in the bag.
18. $\frac{9}{81}$ or $\frac{1}{9}$ 19. $\frac{6}{81}$ or $\frac{2}{27}$ 20. $\frac{8}{81}$

Chapter 12

Lesson 12-1 — pp. 597–600

EXERCISES 1. 4 3. 18 11. 6 pens 13. 3 15. 6
19. B; 11 causes 21. B; 4 days 23. −3 25. −4
29. $2,000 31. 5; 23; 27 33. Rule: Multiply by 2, then add 3. 19; 33 45. $\frac{4}{7}$ 47. 0 49. 0.18 m

Lesson 12-2 — pp. 603–605

EXERCISES 1. $g > 14$ 3. $p \geq 15$ 7. $x < 2$
9. $x \leq -3$ 11. $p \leq 4$;

13. $k < 3$;

15. Cara, Molly 17. true 19. true 21. Aaron, Steve, James 25a. $s < 50$ b. $s > 65$ 33. $\frac{7}{9}$ 35. 7

Lesson 12-3 — pp. 607–609

EXERCISES 1. $x \geq 7$ 3. $k > 22$ 7. $r \geq 2$
9. $w > -9$ 13. $d + 143 \geq 250$; $107
15. $9 \leq n + 7$; $n \geq 2$ 17. $a - 3 < 7$; $a < 15$
19. $7.01 21. $a + 2,500 \leq 32,000$; 29,500 ft
23. $t > 30$ 25. $b > 15$ 29. $2t + 13 < 30$; $8.49
39. rectangular prism

41.

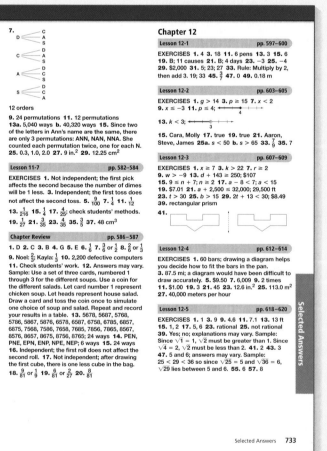

Lesson 12-4 — pp. 612–614

EXERCISES 1. 60 bars; drawing a diagram helps you decide how to fit the bars in the pan.
3. 87.5 mi; a diagram would have been difficult to draw accurately. 5. $9.50 7. 6,009 9. 2 times
11. $1.00 19. 3 21. 45 23. 12.6 in.² 25. 113.0 m² 27. 40,000 meters per hour

Lesson 12-5 — pp. 618–620

EXERCISES 1. 3 9. 9 4. 6 11. 7.1 13. 13 ft
15. 1, 2 17. 5, 6 23. rational 25. not rational
39. Yes; no; explanations may vary. Sample: Since $\sqrt{1} = 1$, $\sqrt{2}$ must be greater than 1. Since $\sqrt{4} = 2$, $\sqrt{2}$ must be less than 2. 41. 2 43. 3
47. 5 and 6; answers may vary. Sample: $25 < 29 < 36$ so since $\sqrt{25} = 5$ and $\sqrt{36} = 6$, $\sqrt{29}$ lies between 5 and 6. 55. 6 57. 8

Selected Answers

Lesson 12-6   pp. 624–626

EXERCISES 1. 25 **3.** 5 **5.** 7 **7.** 15 **9.** 5.7 **11.** 8 ft
13. 1.3 **15.** 16.7 **17.** 75 ft **19a.** yes **b.** no **c.** no
d. yes **21.** 22 in. **23.** No; the sum of the squares
of the lengths of the legs in a right triangle is
equal to the square of the length of the
hypotenuse. The square of the length of the
hypotenuse is greater than the square of either
leg, so the hypotenuse is longer than either leg.
33. $\frac{1}{25}$ **35.** $\frac{1}{4}$ **37.** 3 **39.** 84 **41.** > **43.** >

Chapter Review   pp. 628–629

1. E **2.** D **3.** B **4.** F **5.** A **6.** 3 **7.** 1 **8.** 125 **9.** no
10. yes **11.** no **12.** yes **13.**

14.   **15.**

16.   **17.** $q < 3$ **18.** $t < 5$

19. $v > 16$ **20.** $y \geq -20$ **21–22.** Explanations
may vary. Samples are given. **21.** 21 people;
drawing a diagram would be tedious.
22. 184 strips; there are too many strips to
include in a diagram. **23.** 9 **24.** 4.9 **25.** 5.5
26. 12 **27.** between 2 and 3 **28.** between 3 and
4 **29.** between 4 and 5 **30.** between 5 and 6
31. rational **32.** not rational **33.** rational
34. rational **35.** 10 **36.** 8 **37.** 2.2 **38.** 5.3

Extra Practice

Chapter 1   p. 642

1. eight hundred fifty-four **3.** seven thousand
three hundred two **9.** 216 **11.** 0.2, 0.4, 0.7
13. 6.025, 6.05, 6.2, 6.25 **15.** about 7 **17.** about
770 **19.** 5; 4.874 **21.** 1; 1.489 **23.** 7.7436
25. 6.882 **27.** 3,850 **29.** 9.31 **31.** 0.8; repeating
33. 5.8; terminating **35.** 21 **37.** 9

Chapter 2   p. 643

1. 256; 1,024; 4,096; start with 1 and multiply by 4
repeatedly. **3.** 23, 27, 31; start with 7 and add 4
repeatedly. **5.** 2 **7.** 4 **9.** $b - 1$ **11.** $b + 4$
13. \$3.50 **15.** true **17.** false **19.** 34 **21.** 17.8
23. 4 **25.** 8.6 **31.** $7 \times 10^4 + 2 \times 10^3 + 0 \times 10^2$
$+ 0 \times 10^1 + 3 \times 1$ **33.** $8 \times 10^6 + 1 \times 10^5 + 2 \times$
$10^4 + 0 \times 10^3 + 4 \times 10^2 + 3 \times 10^1 + 2 \times 1$
35. 192 **37.** 85 **39.** 57 **41.** 188

Chapter 3   p. 644

1. 2, 3, 9 **3.** 2, 3, 5, 9, 10 **7.** composite **9.** prime
13. 10 **15.** 5 **19.** $\frac{1}{10}$ **21.** $\frac{3}{4}$ **25.** $\frac{15}{8}$ **27.** $\frac{100}{9}$ **31.** 8
33. 75 **37.** $\frac{4}{9}, \frac{4}{7}, \frac{4}{5}$ **39.** $\frac{7}{12}, \frac{2}{3}, \frac{5}{6}$ **43.** $1\frac{1}{4}$ **45.** $\frac{8}{25}$
49. $0.\overline{6}$ **51.** 0.25

Chapter 4   p. 645

9. $\frac{3}{4}$ **11.** $1\frac{1}{3}$ **17.** $8\frac{1}{6}$ **19.** $11\frac{7}{12}$ **21.** $5\frac{17}{24}$ **23.** $5\frac{11}{15}$
25. $1\frac{2}{3}$ **27.** $7\frac{7}{9}$ **33.** 1 h 30 min **35.** 6 h 38 min **39.** $\frac{3}{4}$
of the tin

Chapter 5   p. 646

1. $\frac{1}{3}$ **3.** $\frac{21}{32}$ **5.** 20 **7.** $13\frac{1}{9}$ **9.** $2\frac{1}{2}$ **11.** $1\frac{1}{4}$ **13.** 4 **15.** 7
17. $3\frac{3}{8}$ **19.** 30 **21.** 32 **23.** 168 **29.** 96 squares
31. tons **33.** pounds **37.** 3 **39.** 4

Chapter 6   p. 647

7. \$.24 per ounce; \$.25 per ounce; 8 ounces for
\$2.99 **9.** no **11.** no **13.** 2 **15.** 9 **19.** 130 km
21. 500 km **23.** 0.96; $\frac{24}{25}$ **25.** 0.01; $\frac{1}{100}$ **29.** 32%
31. 25% **35.** 3.375 **37.** 90

Chapter 7   p. 648

1. mean: 22.25; median: 22.5; mode: 22 **3.** mean:
44.875; median: 43.5; mode: 29

5.

wpm	Tally	Frequency
35	IIII	4
40	III	3
45		0
50		0
55	II	2
60		0
65	II	2
70	I	1

```
 x
 x                        x
 x          x       x     x
 x   x      x       x     x   x
35  40  45  50  55  60  65  70
```

7. vertical axis: hours of reading per year per
person; horizontal axis: different forms of print
material **9.** rent **11a.** 25 **b.** The United States

---

won 25 silver medals during the 2000 Summer
Olympics. **13.**

```
6 | 9
7 | 2 4 7 8
8 | 5 6 9
9 | 1
Key: 6 | 9 means 69
```

```
+----+---+------+----+
65  70  75  80  85  90  95  100
```

15. Graphs may vary. Sample:

Daily Total Sales

Amount	\$175 \$150 \$125 \$100 \$75 \$50 \$25

M T W Th F
Days

Chapter 8   p. 649

3. $\overline{AE}$ and $\overline{FB}$ **5.** obtuse **9.** complement: 62°;
supplement: 152° **11.** complement: 33.7°;
supplement: 123.7° **15.** equilateral **17.** true
19. true **21.** similar **23.** not similar

25.

Chapter 9   p. 650

1. mL **3.** cm **5.** 10,800 **7.** 1.008 **9.** about 18 cm^2
11. 52.25 ft^2 **13.** 144 cm^2 **15.** 33 ft; 88 ft^2
17. 69 mi; 380 mi^2 **19.** rectangular pyramid
21. triangular prism **23.** 1,056 m^2; 2,304 m^3

Chapter 10   p. 651

1. −2, −1, 0, 3 **3.** −8, 6, 7, 8 **5.** −4 **7.** −125
11. −4 **13.** 0 **15.** −40 **17.** −12 **23.** (2, 3)
25. (−3, −1) **27.** G **29.** H **31.** \$5,002 **33.** −\$86

35.

m	1,000	1,500	2,000	2,500
km	1	1.5	2	2.5

Kilometers / Meters

37. \$2.64

Chapter 11   p. 652

1. $\frac{2}{7}$ **3.** $\frac{1}{2}$ **5.** $\frac{6}{7}$ **7.** 3 **9.** 24 **13.** 1,324 students **15.** $\frac{1}{8}$

17. $6 < \frac{7}{8}$ **19.** $\frac{3}{25}$ **21.** $\frac{16}{25}$
$\quad\quad 7 < \frac{6}{8}$
$\quad\quad 8 < \frac{7}{6}$

Chapter 12   p. 653

1. 9 **3.** 6 **9.** $x > -2$ **11.** $x \geq 1$
13. $c \geq 5$
```
-10  -5   0   5   10  15
```
15. $m < 6$
17. $p \leq -14$ **21.** 7 **23.** 13 **27.** 1 and 2 **29.** 4 and
5 **33.** 34 **35.** 12

Skills Handbook

Place Value of Whole Numbers   p. 654

1. ten millions **3.** hundred millions
7. 3 ten million **9.** 6 hundred million
13. 6 hundred **15.** 6 ten million

Rounding Whole Numbers   p. 655

1. 70 **3.** 4,440 **7.** 300 **9.** 1,100 **17.** 16,218 is
closer to 16,000 than to 17,000; 16,218 rounded to
the nearest ten thousand is 16,000. **19.** 89,000

Adding Whole Numbers   p. 656

1. 76 **3.** 41 **7.** 393 **9.** 279 **13.** 2,894 **15.** 6,754

Subtracting Whole Numbers   p. 657

1. 44 **3.** 22 **7.** 346 **9.** 177 **13.** 6,828 **15.** 4,361

Multiplying Whole Numbers   p. 658

1. 243 **3.** 348 **9.** 852 **11.** 6,057 **17.** 1,150
19. 48,480

Multiplying and Dividing Whole Numbers by 10, 100, and 1,000   p. 659

1. 850 **3.** 85,000 **17.** 32 **19.** 80 **31.** 7,600 **33.** 37

Dividing Whole Numbers   p. 660

1. 73 R2 **3.** 93 R1 **11.** 227 R13 **13.** 68 R17

Zeros in Quotients   p. 661

1. 30 R2 **3.** 90 R1 **7.** 70 R5 **9.** 20 R14 **17.** 503
19. 420 R2

Reading Thermometer Scales   p. 662

1. 36.8°C **3.** 38.4°C **7.** G **9.** F

Roman Numerals   p. 663

1. 11 **3.** 95 **11.** XV **13.** MDCXXXII

Additional Answers

CHAPTER 7

pages 326–327   Check Understanding

1a.

Initial	Tally	Frequency
A	|	1
B	|	1
C	|	1
D	||	2
J	|	1
K	||	2
L	|||	3
P	|	1
S	|	1
T	|	1
V	|	1

The mode is L.

page 335   Check Skills You'll Need

1.

```
            X
  X     X   X
  X  X  X   X
  X  X  X X X X    X
  5  6  7 8 9 10 11 12
```

2.

```
  X
  X        X     X
  X        X     X
  X   X    X  X  X
  1.0 1.1 1.2 1.3 1.4
```

3.

```
                  X      X
    X      X   X  X              X
  10 11 12 13 14 15 16 17 18 19 20 21
```

pages 335–336   Check Understanding

1.

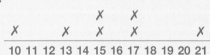

Allowance Each Week

3.

Ticket Sales

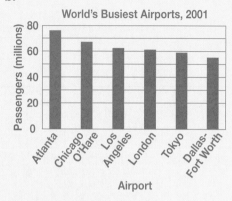

pages 337–338   Exercises

5.

Students Buying Hot Lunch

9a.

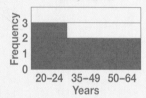

Age of Contestants

Age of Contestants

b. 4 intervals; the second histogram shows that there are no contestants in the interval 40–49.

10a. bar graph; a bar graph is better for comparing amounts.

b.

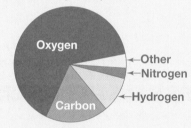

World's Busiest Airports, 2001

pages 344–345   Exercises

8. Human Body Composition

Oxygen → Other → Nitrogen → Hydrogen Carbon

10. What Part of the U.S. Price of Gasoline Goes for Tax

Tax / Price Minus Tax

What Part of the U.K. Price of Gasoline Goes for Tax

Price Minus Tax / Tax

12.

$\frac{3}{4}$ $\frac{1}{20}$ $\frac{1}{10}$ $\frac{1}{10}$

13.

15a. Ages of Video Arcade Customers

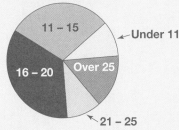

b. 60%

c. No; explanations may vary. Sample: You can find only the percent of customers 11 to 15 years old.

page 345

22. [2] No; explanations may vary. Sample: The 5 portion is less than half of the circle graph.

[1] incorrect answer OR correct answer without explanation

page 350   Exercises

19. [2] (36 × 13) + (105 × 18.5) + (10 × 26.5) = 468 + 1,942.5 + 265 = 2,675.5; $2,675.50 Explanations may vary. Sample: First calculate the total for each type of seat, then add the totals together.

[1] correct answer without explanation

page 350   Checkpoint Quiz 2

3. Money Raised By Fundraisers

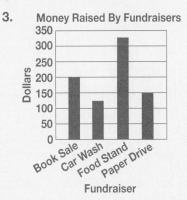

4. Money Raised by Fundraisers

page 351   Technology

2. Graphs may vary. Sample:
How Theo Spends his Weekly Allowance

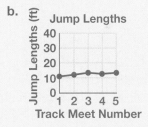

pages 354–355   Exercises

11a. Ages of People

```
0 | 9
1 | 1 2 2 2 2 3 3 5 5 6 9
2 | 0 1 3 4
3 | 5
4 | 0
```

Key: 1|1 means 11

b. Ages of Eighteen People

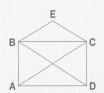

14.

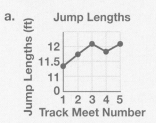

Routes may vary. Samples:
A B C A D B E C D or A B E C D B C A D

18. [2] Range; the stem-and-leaf plot sorts the data, so the high and low data are easy to find. Then compute range = high − low (OR equivalent explanation).

[1] correct answer without explanation

page 361   Exercises

10–11. Graphs may vary. Samples are given.

10. Money Pledged to Public Radio Station

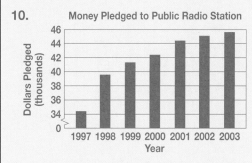

11. Money Pledged to Public Radio Station

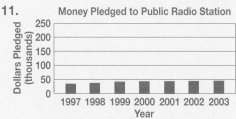

13. Graphs may vary. Samples are given.

a. Jump Lengths

b. Jump Lengths

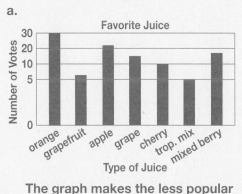

14. Answers may vary. Sample:

a. Favorite Juice

The graph makes the less popular juices appear to be quite popular.

b.

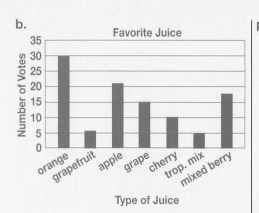

Favorite Juice

page 366　Chapter Test

4. State Fair Pumpkin Weights (lb)

```
20 | 3 7
21 | 0 2 2 8
22 | 6
23 | 3
24 | 7
25 |
26 | 2 9
27 | 1
28 | 8
```

Key: 27|1 means 271 lb

CHAPTER 8

pages 374–375　Check Understanding

1c. Answers may vary. Samples are given. $\overrightarrow{VM}$ is a ray that has vertex V and contains M. $\overrightarrow{MV}$ is a ray that has vertex M and contains V.

page 395　Exercises

27.

28.

29.

page 401　Check Skills You'll Need

2.

75	I
80	III
82	I
85	II
90	III
100	II

3.

80	II
82	II
85	I
87	II
88	II
89	I

page 416　Check Understanding

2a.

b.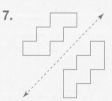

pages 417–418　Exercises

7.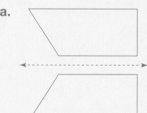

8.

9.

24.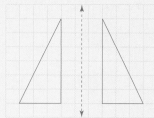

25.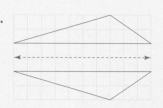

page 425　Test Prep

12. [2] a. $\frac{6.00}{12} = \frac{x}{5}$

$12x = 30.00$

$x = \frac{30.00}{12} = 2.50$

5 bagles cost $2.50.

b. $\frac{6.00}{12} = 0.50$

The unit cost is $.50/bagel.

[1] one part correct

CHAPTER 9

pages 434–435　Exercises

46. Sample: a piece of paper or the length of your arm

47. Sample: a person or a bowling ball

54. [2] No; two 650-mL bottles is equal to 1,300 mL or 1.3L, which would not all fit in a 1-Liter container

[1] answer is correct but explanation is missing

page 445　Exercises

38. [2] 2. Let w = width

$\frac{16}{1} = \frac{576}{w}$

$16w = 576$

$w = \frac{576}{16} = 36$

[1] one part correct

page 446　Check Skills You'll Need

1. quadrilateral, trapezoid; trapezoid

2. quadrilateral, parallelogram; parallelogram

3. quadrilateral, rectangle, rhombus, square; square

page 460 Reading Math

1.

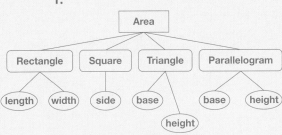

2. Answers may vary. Sample:

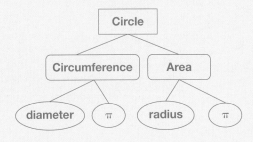

page 461 Investigation

2.

 front

 right

 top

3.

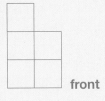 front

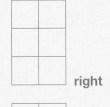 right

 top

page 463 Check Understanding

2b. Answers may vary. Sample: They both have a circle as a base. But a cylinder has two bases, a cone has one.

page 470 Exercises

3. Answers may vary. Sample:

page 476 Exercises

31. [4] a. 1 cm by 1 cm by 18 cm,
1 cm by 2 cm by 9 cm,
1 cm by 3 cm by 6 cm
2 cm by 3 cm by 3 cm

b. 1 cm by 1 cm by 18 cm

[3] Answer to part (b) and partial answer to part (a).

[2] Answer to part (a) only.

[1] Answer to part (b) only.

page 479 Exercises

13. 1) Cut and remove one link from length 1. Attach lengths 2 and 3 to this open link and rejoin, forming a 7-link length.

2) Cut and remove another link from length 1. Attach length 4 and the 7-link length and rejoin, forming an 11-link length.

3) Cut the remaining link from length 1. Attach both ends of the 11-link length and rejoin, forming the circular chain.

CHAPTER 10

page 518 Check Skills You'll Need

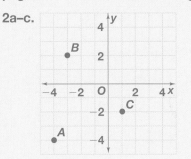

page 519 Check Understanding

2a–c.

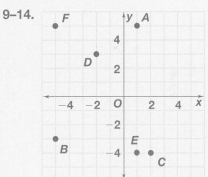

page 520 Exercises

9–14.

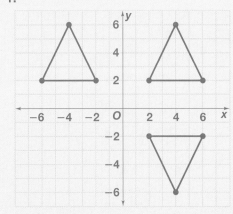

page 522 Extension

1.

2.

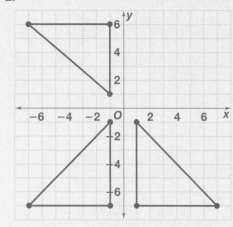

4.

x	y
−2	0
−1	1
0	2
1	3
2	4

9.

x	y
−2	1
−1	0.5
0	0
1	−0.5
2	−1

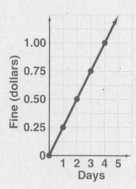

3.

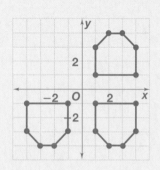

5.

x	y
−2	−4
−1	−3
0	−2
1	−1
2	0

10.

x	y
0	0
1	0.25
2	0.50
3	0.75
4	1.00

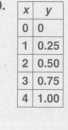

page 526   Exercises

17.

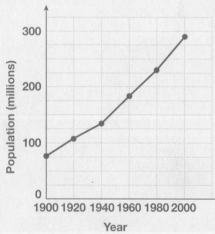

6.

x	y
−2	−4
−1	−2
0	0
1	2
2	4

11.

x	y
−2	−3
−1	−1
0	1
1	3
2	5

7.

x	y
−2	−1
−1	−0.5
0	0
1	0.5
2	1

12.

x	y
−2	−5
−1	−3
0	−1
1	1
2	3

page 528   Check Understanding

3.

t	d
1	45
2	90
3	135
4	180
5	225

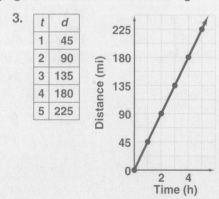

8.

x	y
−2	0
−1	0.5
0	1
1	1.5
2	2

13.

x	y
−2	5
−1	3
0	1
1	−1
2	−3

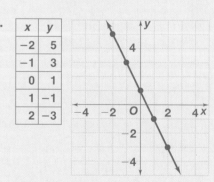

14.

x	y
−2	3
−1	1
0	−1
1	−3
2	−5

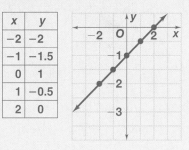

15.

x	y
−2	−2
−1	1
0	4
1	7
2	10

16.

x	y
−2	11
−1	7
0	3
1	−1
2	−5

22.

x	y
−2	−16
−1	−14
0	−12
1	−10
2	−8

23.

x	y
−2	−21
−1	−17
0	−13
1	−9
2	−5

24.

x	y
−2	0
−1	0.5
0	1
1	1.5
2	2

25.

x	y
−2	−12
−1	−9
0	−6
1	−3
2	0

35. [2] Explanations may vary. Sample: No; for each value of x, the point on the graph of y = x − 2 is 4 units below the corresponding point on the graph of y = x + 2; the graphs are parallel.

[1] correct answer without explanation

page 532   Checkpoint Quiz 2

1–2.

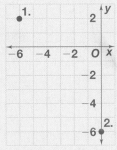

4.

x	y
−2	−9
−1	−8
0	−7
1	−6
2	−5

5.

x	y
−2	−2
−1	−1.5
0	1
1	−0.5
2	0

page 534   Exercises

1. Answers may vary. About 360 lb/in².

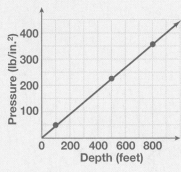

2.

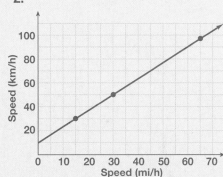

Estimates may vary. Sample: about 95 km/h

3.

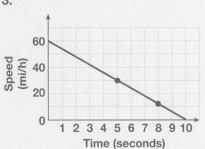

a–b. Answers may vary. Sample:

a. about 60 mi/h

b. 10

4. Nate: drum,
   Nina: violin,
   Nancy: clarinet,
   Ned: trumpet;
   check students' work.

page 534   Lesson Quiz

1.

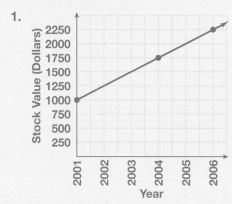

page 539   Chapter Review

29–32.

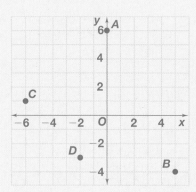

page 540   Chapter Test

26. a–c.

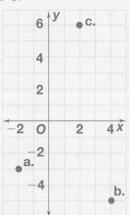

27a. Jan.: $486,
     Feb.: $2,000,
     Mar.: −$266,
     Apr.: $673

b.

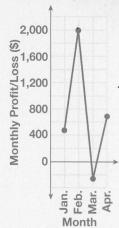

page 541   Test Prep

14. [2] Check students' work; 25 ft.

    [1] correct length without sketch
    OR correct length with
    incorrect sketch OR incorrect
    length with correct sketch

15. [2] −3

    [1] incorrect integer OR incorrect
    number line

page 575   Check Understanding

2.

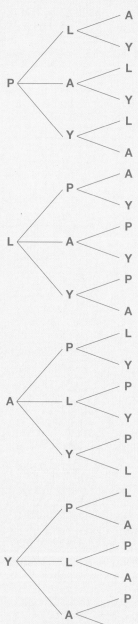

pages 576–577 Exercises

5.

7.

```
    C
D   A
    S

    D
C   A
    S

    D
A   C
    S

    D
S   C
    A
```

18.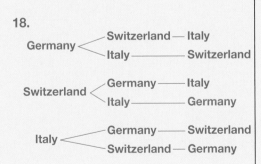

```
Germany ──┬── Switzerland ── Italy
          └── Italy ──────── Switzerland

Switzerland ──┬── Germany ── Italy
              └── Italy ──── Germany

Italy ──┬── Germany ────── Switzerland
        └── Switzerland ── Germany
```

28. [2] a.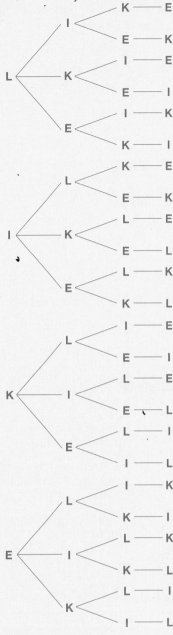

b. 4 × 3 × 2 × 1 = 24 permutations

[1] minor error in part (a) OR incorrect number of permutations OR correct answer with no work shown

page 584 Exercises

34. [4] a.

b. Since $P(A \text{ and } B) = P(A) \times P(B)$, $P(\text{Sale then Sale}) = P(\text{Sale}) \times P(\text{Sale}) = \frac{1}{3} \times \frac{1}{3} = \frac{1}{9}$.

[3] omits 1 part of explanation

[2] omits 2 parts of explanation

[1] very little explanation OR correct answer with no explanation

page 588

13a. Independent; one roll does not affect the other.

b. Not independent; after you remove the first marble, there is one less marble in the bag.

14.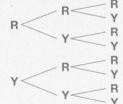

1. **Diagrams may vary. Sample:**

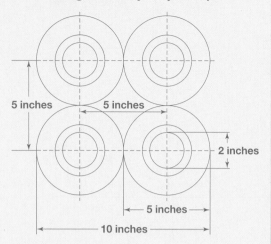

5 inches   5 inches

2 inches

5 inches

10 inches

CHAPTER 12

page 633   Test Prep

47. [4] a. 35 in.^{2}; $5 \times 7 = 35$

b. 31 in.^{2}; the area of each square cut from the rectangle is $1 \times 1 = 1$, or 1 in.^{2}. The total area being cut is $1 + 1 + 1 + 1 = 4$, or 4 in.^{2}. Subtract this from the total area: $35 - 4 = 31$, or 31 in.^{2}.

[3] correct methods, but one computational error

[2] incorrect rectangular area OR incorrect area of 2nd figure

[1] one correct solution without explanation given

48. [4] a. 96 in.^{2}; by an appropriate method such as: $(3 \times 22) + (6 \times 5) = 66 + 30 = 96$

b. 90 in.^{3}; $3 \times 6 \times 5 = 90$

[3] appropriate methods but with one computational error

[2] surface area correct OR volume correct

[1] correct surface area OR volume, without work shown

49. [4] a. $2.80; $18.64 \times 0.15 = 2.796 \approx 2.80$

b. $21.44; $18.64 + 2.80 = 21.44$

[3] correct methods but with one computational error

[2] 2 out of 3 correct OR correct tax, tip, and total without work shown

[1] correct tax OR tip OR total, without work shown

50. [4] a. 12 choices

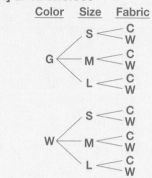

Color   Size   Fabric

G — S — C, W; M — C, W; L — C, W

W — S — C, W; M — C, W; L — C, W

b. $\frac{1}{2}$

[3] correct tree diagram, but incorrect part b

[2] incorrect tree diagram, but correct probability according to tree

[1] correct probability with no tree diagram

Index

Index

Mathematical techniques. *See* Estimation; Mental Math; Number Sense; Problem Solving

Math in the Media, 455

Mean
    defined, 322, 364
    exploring, 321
    finding, 322, 324–325, 326, 362, 364, 521

Measurement
    of angles, 379–380, 381–383, 393
    customary system of. *See* Customary system of measurement
    of elapsed time, 253
    exercises that use, 98, 109, 173, 252–253, 256–257, 381–382, 430, 433–435, 438–439
    in metric units. *See* Metric units
    in Real-World Applications, 172, 173, 221
    units of. *See* Unit of measurement

Measures of central tendency
    mean, 321, 322, 324–325, 326, 362, 364, 521
    median, 323, 324–325, 326, 352, 362, 364, 377, 455
    mode, 323, 324–325, 326, 362, 364

Median
    defined, 323, 364
    finding, 323, 324–325, 326, 362, 364, 377, 455

Mental Math
    addition using, 26, 105, 183, 185, 187, 188, 196, 199
    comparing fractions with, 151, 196
    with decimals, 26, 37, 40, 51, 62, 184, 436
    divisibility and, 119–120, 121–122
    division using, 41, 42, 51, 55, 62, 436
    exercises that use, 26, 27, 37, 38, 40, 41, 51, 62, 86, 90, 130, 150, 183, 184, 185, 187, 188, 198, 199, 222, 295, 300, 301, 436, 458, 549, 596, 598, 608
    finding greatest common factor, 130
    finding percent using, 295, 300, 301
    with fractions, 183, 187, 222, 242, 295
    with mixed numbers, 185, 188, 196, 199

multiplication using, 37, 40, 51, 62, 184, 222, 436
solving equations using, 84–85, 86, 90, 196, 198, 242, 596, 598
subtraction using, 26

Meter (m), 431, 482

Metric System, 431, 482

Metric units
    of capacity, 433, 434–435, 437, 438–439
    choosing, 431–433, 434–435, 566
    converting, 436–437, 438–439
    of length, 431–432, 434–435, 436–437, 438–439
    of mass, 432, 434–435, 437, 438–439

Middle quartile, 356

Midpoint, 384

Mile, 240

Milligram, 432

Millimeter, 431

Misleading graphs, 358–359, 360–362

Misleading statistics, 358–359, 360–362

Mixed numbers
    adding, 185–189, 206, 224, 228
    comparing, 149, 150–152, 160, 491
    defined, 139, 163
    dividing, 236–237, 238–240, 246, 260, 276
    estimating products of, 224, 225, 226, 260, 298
    estimating quotients of, 236, 238, 260
    estimating with, 240
    multiplying, 225, 227–228, 234, 260, 298
    ordering, 491
    Real-World Snapshots, 169, 214–215, 217, 264–265
    subtracting, 190–192, 193–194, 206, 224, 245, 257, 282
    writing as improper fractions, 140, 141–142, 152, 170
    writing improper fractions as, 140, 141–142, 170, 185, 190, 257, 302
    See also Fraction(s)

Mixed Reviews, 7, 12, 17, 23, 29, 33, 39, 42, 47, 67, 72, 78, 82, 88, 94, 98, 103, 108, 122, 126, 131, 137, 142, 146, 152, 156, 160, 174, 178, 184, 189, 194, 199, 205, 208, 223, 228, 234, 240, 245, 249, 253, 257, 272, 276, 282, 287, 292, 298, 302, 306, 309, 325, 330, 333, 339, 345, 350, 355, 362, 377, 383, 390, 396, 400, 404, 409, 414, 419, 435, 439, 445, 450, 455, 459, 466, 471, 476, 480, 495, 501, 508, 512, 516, 521, 526, 532, 535, 551, 557, 566, 573, 578, 584, 600, 605, 609, 614, 620, 626

Mode
    defined, 323, 364
    finding, 323, 324–325, 326, 362, 364

Modeling
    addition, 24, 496
    algebra tiles for, 69, 71
    decimals, 8, 13, 16, 24, 34, 35, 46, 53
    divisibility, 123
    division, 44, 46, 229
    equivalent fractions, 134
    exercises that use, 16, 24, 34, 46, 89, 132, 136, 177, 179, 182, 183, 222, 293, 294, 502
    expressions, 69, 71, 89
    fractions, 132–133, 139, 148, 175, 177, 179, 180, 181, 182, 183, 219, 220, 229, 254, 294

integers, 491, 496–498, 502–503
    multiplication, 34, 35, 219, 220, 254
    numerators and denominators, 139
    percent, 293, 310, 400
    for solving equations, 89
    subtraction, 24, 89, 179, 181, 502
    unlike denominators, 179

Money
    Chinese kwan note, 22
    profit and loss, 523, 524–526, 539, 573
    Real-World Applications of, 11, 22, 38, 56, 107, 122, 274, 275–276, 301, 304, 305–306, 312, 339, 478, 479

More Than One Way, 15, 70, 144, 192, 226, 280, 343, 380–381, 442–443, 529, 570, 597

Multicultural. See Diversity

Multiple, 297. *See also* Least common multiple

Multiplication,
    Associative Property of, 36, 37, 54, 55, 86–88
    Commutative Property of, 36, 37, 54, 55, 86–88
    of decimals, 35–37, 38–39, 40–42, 53, 55, 72, 78, 452
    using Distributive Property, 105–106, 107–108, 111, 156
    of fractions, 219, 220, 221–223, 230, 242, 254, 257, 260, 268, 272, 276, 292, 330, 546, 580
    Identity Property of, 36–37, 38, 86–88
    of integers, 509–510, 511–512, 539, 562
    Mental Math for, 37, 40, 51, 62, 184, 222, 436
    of mixed numbers, 225, 227–228, 234, 260, 298
    modeling, 34, 35, 219, 220, 254
    solving equations by, 96, 97–98, 126, 218, 268, 325, 490, 513, 594, 595, 611
    of whole numbers, 4, 658, 659

Multiplication Property of Equality, 96, 97–98, 111, 283

N

Need Help?, 6, 19, 23, 25, 32, 69, 81, 119, 123, 154, 158, 176, 191, 207, 220, 237, 247, 270, 283, 308, 333, 348, 406, 456, 469, 478, 499, 504, 534, 565, 597, 612, 617

Negative integers, 491, 492

Net
    defined, 467
    drawing, 467, 470
    finding surface areas using, 468–471

Noncollinear points, 374, 376, 414, 508

Notation
    scientific, 104
    standard. *See* Standard form

Number(s)
    classifying, 617, 618, 619, 629
    compatible, 20, 21–23, 55, 85, 95
    composite, 124, 162, 223
    even, 120
    in expanded form, 5, 9–11, 100–101
    finding percent of, 299–300, 301–302, 345, 350, 390, 450

Index

fractions, 117, 166–167
geometry, 371, 426–427
integers, 489, 542–543
mixed numbers, 169, 214–215, 217, 264–265
patterns, 61, 114–115
probability, 545, 590–591
proportions, 267, 316–317
volume, 429, 486–487

Reasonableness of solutions, 25, 26, 27, 36, 43, 80, 158, 182, 186, 190, 191, 206, 225, 237, 247, 322, 332, 457, 533, 564

Reasoning
exercises that use, 9, 20, 22, 26, 39, 42, 44, 47, 49, 50, 64, 69, 87, 100, 120, 127, 135, 140, 153, 154, 185, 202, 220, 224, 239, 273, 274, 286, 295, 303, 322, 326, 327, 329, 344, 352, 354, 359, 361, 374, 375, 379, 382, 389, 398, 411, 413, 435, 445, 448, 455, 463, 469, 471, 475, 495, 499, 507, 512, 516, 521, 548, 550, 555, 556, 569, 581, 603, 608, 612, 619, 621
logical, 401–404
making conjectures, 64
proportional, 278
spatial, 462–463, 464–466
validating conclusions. *See* Justification
See also Error Analysis; Justification; Problem-Solving Strategies

Reciprocal
defined, 230, 260
finding, 230
using to divide by a fraction, 231–234, 260

Rectangle
area of, 441, 444–445
defined, 398, 399, 423
perimeter of, 441, 444–445

Rectangular prism, 468, 470, 472–473, 474–476

Reflection
defined, 416
drawing, 416, 417–419, 466
graphing, 522
line of, 416, 418, 609

Repeating decimal, 44

Representation. *See* Modeling

Reteaching, 2G, 60G, 116G, 168G, 216G, 266G, 318G, 370G, 428G, 488G, 544G, 592G

Review. *See* Assessment; Extra Practice; Mixed Review; Need Help?; Skills Handbook

Rhombus, 398, 399–400, 423

Right angle, 380, 389, 423, 622

Right triangle
defined, 392, 423
exploring, 621
finding length of hypotenuse of, 623
finding length of legs of, 623
Pythagorean Theorem and, 621–626, 629

Roman numerals, 663

Root. *See* Square root

Rotation (turn), 415, 416, 417–419, 423

Rounding
decimals, 19, 21–23
estimating by, 19, 21–23, 25, 55, 84, 170, 190, 655
percents, 297
whole numbers, 4, 19, 655

Rule(s)
for divisibility, 119–122
function, 527–529
writing number patterns from, 64, 65

S

Sale price, 304, 305–306, 339

Sales tax, 305, 419

Sample(s)
defined, 559, 587
making predictions from, 559, 560–562

Scale
defined, 288, 313
finding, 289, 290–292, 313
finding actual dimensions, 289, 290–292
of maps, 289, 290–291, 330, 396, 445
thermometer, 662
writing as ratio, 289, 290

Scale drawings, 289, 290–292

Scalene triangle, 393, 423

Scientific calculator, 52. *See also* Calculator

Scientific notation, 104

Segment, 373, 374, 375–377, 379, 422, 508

Selected Answers, 718

Semi-circle, 498

Sentence, open, 84, 85, 110, 111

Side(s)
classifying triangles by, 393, 394–395
congruent, 405, 407–409

Sieve of Eratosthenes, 127

Similar figures
defined, 406, 423
identifying, 406, 407–409

Simpler problem, solving, 246–249, 306, 362

Simplest form
defined, 135
of fractions, 135, 139, 152, 163
of powers, 100, 101–103
of ratios, 270–272

Simulate a Problem **Problem-Solving Strategy,** 563–566

Simulation, 563–564, 565–566, 567, 609

Skew line, 374, 375–377, 397, 422

Skills Check. See Check Skills You'll Need

Skills Handbook, 654–664
adding whole numbers, 656
dividing whole numbers, 660
estimating lengths using nonstandard units, 664
multiplying whole numbers, 658
multiplying and dividing whole numbers by 10, 659
place value of whole numbers, 654
reading thermometer scales, 662
Roman numerals, 663
rounding whole numbers, 655
subtracting whole numbers, 657
zeros in quotients, 661

Slide. *See* Translation

Solid figures. *See* Three-dimensional figures

Solution
defined, 85
to equations, 85, 86–88, 90–94, 95–98

estimating, 85, 86–88
of inequalities, 603, 604–605

Solve a Simpler **Problem Problem-Solving Strategy,** 246–249, 306, 362

Solving equations
by adding, 91–94, 122, 249, 372, 490, 594, 606
with algebra tiles, 69, 71
by dividing, 95–96, 97–98, 119, 137, 218, 268, 490, 513, 594, 595, 611
with fractions, 172–174, 175–178, 180–184
with integers, 505, 514, 526
inverse operations and, 90, 95, 505, 514, 596–597
with Mental Math, 84–85, 86, 90, 196, 198, 242, 596, 598
with mixed numbers, 196–197, 198–199, 243, 244–245
by modeling, 89, 595
by multiplying, 96–98, 126, 218, 268, 325, 490, 513, 594, 595, 606, 611
Number Sense for, 80, 84–88, 99, 102
one-step equations, 307, 309
by subtracting, 90–91, 92–94, 160, 249, 372, 490, 594, 606
two-step equations, 596–597, 598–600
using reciprocals for, 243–245

Spanish Support, 2G, 60G, 116G, 168G, 216G, 266G, 318G, 370G, 428G, 488G, 544G, 592G

Spatial reasoning, 462–463, 464–466

Spatial visualization
drawing a diagram, 421
drawing nets, 467, 470
drawing tessellations, 420
See also Manipulatives; Modeling

Sphere, 463

Spinner, 547–551

Spreadsheet
cell in, 347, 365
defined, 347
exercises that use, 348–350, 400
formulas in, 348, 349–350, 508
making a graph from, 351
organizing data in, 347, 348–350, 365
using, 347–348, 349–350

Square
area of, 442, 444–445, 476, 578
defined, 398, 399–400, 423
perfect, 616, 629
perimeter of, 442, 444–445

Square numbers, 616

Square root
approximating, 617
classifying, 618, 619
defined, 616, 629
finding, 616–617, 618–620, 622
symbol for, 616

Standard form
defined, 5
writing decimals in, 9–12, 23
writing numbers in, 5, 9–12, 23

Standardized Test Preparation. *See* Assessment

Statistics
box-and-whisker plot, 356–357
histogram, 336, 337–338

Index

Acknowledgments

Staff Credits

The people who made up the *Prentice Hall Mathematics Courses 1, 2, and 3* team—representing design services, editorial, editorial services, market research, educational technology, production services, product services, project office, and publishing processes—are listed below. Bold type denotes the core team members.

Amy Acer, Leora Adler, Scott Andrews, Carolyn Artin, Barbara Bertell, Suzanne Biron, Stephanie Bradley, **Judith Buice,** Christine Cannon, Ronit Carter, Justin Collins, Bob Cornell, Patricia Crotty, Patrick Culleton, Carol Dance, Sheila DeFazio, Marian DeLollis, Jo DiGiustini, Delphine Dupee, Emily Ellen, **Janet Fauser,** Debby Faust, Suzanne Feliciello, Steve Fenton, Michael Ferrio, Jonathan Fisher, Barbara Hardt, Richard Heater, Kerri Hoar, Jayne Holman, Karen Holtzman, Kate House, Alan Hull, **Nancy Jones,** Judie Jozokos, Melissa Kent, Russ Lappa, Lisa LaVallee, Christine Lee, Carolyn Lock, Rebecca Loveys, Catherine Maglio, **Cheryl Mahan,** Barry Maloney, Chris Maniatis, **Tim McDonald**, Autumn Mellor, Eve Melnechuk, Terri Mitchell, Janet Morris, Sandra Morris, Kyai Mullei, **Cindy Noftle,** Marsha Novak, Greg Oles, Marie Opera, Jill Ort, Michael Oster, Christopher Ott, Steve Ouellette, Joan Paley, Dorothy Preston, Roberto Portocarrero, John Reece, Sandy Roedel-Baker, Rashid Ross, Irene Rubin, Alan Ruffin, Donna Russo, John Saxe, JoAnne Sgroi, Vicky Shen, Dennis Slattery, Lisa Smith-Ruvalcaba, **Nancy Smith,** Emily Soltanoff, Debby Sommer, David Spangler, Cynthia Speranza, Karen Swanson, Mark Tricca, Michael Vogel, Nate Walker, Lisa Walston, Roberta Warshaw, Matthew Wilson, Helen Young, **Carol Zacny**

Cover Design

Peter Brooks, Brainworx Studios

Cover Photos

t, PhotoDisc, Inc./Getty Images, Inc.; b, Wolfgang Kaehler/Corbis

Technical Illustration

New England Typographic Services

Photo Research

Sharon Donahue, Sue McDermott, Kathy Beaura Ringrose

Illustration

Brucie Rosch: 20, 90, 580
Daniel Collins: 527
Joel Dubin: 158, 160, 201, 226, 269, 289, 321, 326, 440, 468, 470, 473, 520, 534
John Edwards: 22, 29, 65, 151, 204, 270, 298, 398, 468, 478, 479, 525, 569, 604
Kenneth Batelman: 133, 141, 225, 235, 257, 309, 432, 473, 613
Precision Graphics: 77
Roberta Warshaw: 7, 17, 27, 49, 132, 178, 228
Trevor Johnston: 28, 94, 103, 132, 204, 223, 342, 345, 351
Wilkinson Studios: 251, 257
XNR Productions: 204, 233, 245, 289, 290, 440, 521

Photography

Front Matter: Pages vii, L. Clarke/Corbis; **viii,** Jerry Lodriguss/Photo Researchers, Inc.; **ix,** Bill Miles/Corbis; **x,** Tony Freeman/PhotoEdit; **xi,** Alan Linda Detrick/Grant Heilman Photography, Inc.; **xii,** AP Photo/The Grand Rapids Press, Lance Wynn; **xiii,** Gary Braasch/Getty Images, Inc.; **xiv,** Barros & Barros/Getty Images, Inc.; **xv,** Tim Thompson/Getty Images, Inc.; **xvi,** Myrleen Gerguson Cate/Photo Edit; **xvii,** Layne Kennedy/Corbis; **xviii,** Pete Saloutos/Corbis

Chapter 1: Pages 2–3, Andrew Leyerle/Dorling Kindersley; **4,** D. Young-Wolff/PhotoEdit; **5,** Joseph Nettis/Photo Researchers, Inc.; **7,** Frank Siteman/Rainbow; **10,** AP Photo/Tom Gannam; **11,** Royalty-Free/Getty Images, Inc.; **12,** David Young-Wolff/PhotoEdit; **14,** Carl Purcell/Photo Researchers, Inc.; **15 both,** Richard Haynes; **16,** Getty Images, Inc.; **18,** Robert Burke/Getty Images, Inc.; **21,** Lisette Le Bon/Superstock, Inc.; **22 l,** Tom Stack & Associates, Inc.; **22 r,** U.S. Bureau of Engraving and Printing; **26,** Bob Daemmrich/The Image Works; **28,** Spencer Grant/PhotoEdit; **31,** Reuters NewMedia Inc./Corbis; **32 t,** Russ Lappa; **32 b,** Syracuse Newspapers/The Image Works; **34,** Tony Freeman/PhotoEdit; **36,** L. Clarke/Corbis; **37,** www.SellPhotos.CA; **38,** Russ Lappa; **41,** James Watt/Animals Animals/Earth Scenes; **43,** Chad Slattery/Getty Images, Inc.; **45,** John Moore; **46,** Liaison/Getty Images, Inc.; **48,** Lori Adamski Peek/Getty Images, Inc.; **50 t,** John Moore; **50 b,** Mitch Kezar/Getty Images, Inc.; **53,** Jeff Affleck/SuperStock, Inc.; **58 t,** The British Museum/Dorling Kindersley; **58 bl,** The Science Museum/Dorling Kindersley; **58 br,** Russ Lappa; **59 tl,** The Science Museum/Dorling Kindersley; **59 tr,** Steve Gorton/Dorling Kindersley; **59 b,** Alistair Duncan/Dorling Kindersley

Chapter 2: Pages 60–61, Vanessa Vick/Photo Researchers, Inc.; **62,** Bryn Colton/Corbis; **64,** Michael Rosenfeld/Getty Images, Inc.; **66,** Jerry Lodriguss/Photo Researchers, Inc.; **67,** Phil Degginger/Color-Pics, Inc.; **69,** Benelux Press/Index Stock Imagery, Inc.; **70 both,** Richard Haynes; **72,** Tom Prettyman/PhotoEdit; **75,** Alan Thornton/Getty Images, Inc.; **77,** David Young-Wolff/PhotoEdit; **81,** Michael S. Yamashita/Corbis; **82,** Eyewire/Getty Images, Inc.; **85,** Russ Lappa; **87,** Grant Heilman Inc.; **91,** Image Source/SuperStock, Inc.; **93,** Russ Lappa; **93 b,** Marc Muench/Corbis; **93 t,** Getty Images, Inc.; **97,** Dianna Blell/Peter Arnold, Inc.; **100 both,** Russ Lappa; **107,** Chris Salvo/Getty Images, Inc.; **108,** Mark Richards/PhotoEdit; **109,** Mark Thayer; **114 l,** R. P. Meleski; **114 tr,** Baum/Dorling Kindersley; **114–115 b,** Carlyn Iverson/Absolute Science; **114–115,** Denis Scott/Stock Boston; **115 t,** Grace Davies/Omni-Photo Communications, Inc.

Chapter 3: Pages 116–117, Blair Seitz/Photo Researchers, Inc.; **117,** C Squared Studios/Getty Images, Inc.; **118,** Dennis MacDonald/PhotoEdit; **120,** Wally McNamee/Corbis; **122,** Mark Richards/PhotoEdit; **125,** Joanna McCarthy/SuperStock, Inc.; **126 both,** Richard Haynes; **128,** Österreichische Post AG; **130,** Jeff Greenberg/PhotoEdit; **133 l,** Russ Lappa; **133 ml,** Russ Lappa; **133 mr,** Russ Lappa; **133 r,** Russ Lappa; **133 tl,** Art Wolfe/Getty Images, Inc.; **133 tr,** Davies + Starr/Getty Images, Inc.; **135,** TSI Pictures/Getty Images, Inc.; **136,** Bettman/Corbis; **137,** David Young-Wolff/PhotoEdit; **139,** Mark Burnett/Stock Boston; **140,** Russ Lappa; **142,** Steve Cohen/Getty Images, Inc.; **143,** Tom Stewart/Corbis; **144,** Pictor/Uniphoto; **144 l,** Richard Haynes; **144 r,** Richard Haynes; **146,** Tony Freeman/PhotoEdit; **149,** Bill Miles/Corbis; **151,** Tim Ridley/Dorling Kindersley; **155 br,** Alan Schein Photography/Corbis; **155 l,** AP/Wide World Photos; **155 t,** Alan Schein Photography/Corbis; **157,** Bob Daemmrich/Stock Boston; **159,** Mary Kate Denny/PhotoEdit; **166 b,** S. Wanke/Getty Images, Inc.; **166 t,** Geoff Brightling/Dorling Kindersley; **167 bl,** Andy Crawford/Dorling Kindersley; **167 br,** Richard Megna/Fundamental Photographs; **167 ml,** Dave King/Dorling Kindersley; **167 t,** Dorling Kindersley; **167 tl,** Andy Crawford/Dorling Kindersley

Chapter 4: Pages 168–169, Mark C. Burnett/Photo Researchers, Inc.; **170,** Terry Cosgrove/Getty Images, Inc.; **172,** David Young-Wolff/PhotoEdit; **173,** Russ Lappa; **176,** Superstock, Inc.; **177,** NIBSC/Photo Researchers, Inc.; **178 t,** C Squared Studios/Getty Images, Inc.; **178 bl,** John A. Rizzo/Getty Images, Inc.; **178 br,** David Toase/Getty Images, Inc.; **180,** Russ Lappa; **181,** Bob Daemmrich/Stock Boston; **183,** Faidley/Agliolol/International Stock; **185,** Russ Lappa; **186,** Ronn Maratea/Image State; **188 t,** Tony Freeman/PhotoEdit; **188 b,** John Moore; **190,** Renee Lynn/Corbis; **192 both,** Richard Haynes; **193,** Tony Freeman/PhotoEdit; **198 t,** Adam Smith/Getty Images, Inc.; **198 b,** Frozen Images/The Image Works; **204,** Vicki Silbert/PhotoEdit; **206,** Photo Edit; **207 l,** Pictor Uniphoto; **207 r,** Yuman/

The Image Works; **208,** Strauss/Curtis/Corbis; **214 t,** AP/Wide World Photos; **214 l,** AFP/Corbis; **214 r,** Russ Lappa; **215 t,** Robert Laberge/Getty Images, Inc.; **215 b,** AP/Wide World Photos

Chapter 5: Pages 216–217, The Image Works; **218,** Tom Stewart/Corbis Stock Market; **219,** John Moore; **221,** Silver Burdett Ginn; **222,** Brian Parker/Tom Stack & Associates, Inc.; **224,** Guinness World Records, Ltd.; **226,** Richard Haynes; **227,** John Moore; **228 both,** Richard Haynes; **229,** John Moore; **232,** Alan Linda Detrick/Grant Heilman Photography, Inc.; **233 b,** John Moore; **233 t,** Silver Burdett Ginn; **236,** Dan McCoy/Rainbow; **237,** Russ Lappa; **239,** Ariel Skelley/Corbis Stock Market; **240,** Alan Oddie/PhotoEdit; **243,** John Moore; **243,** Syracuse Newspapers/The Image Works; **246,** Owaki-Kulla/Corbis; **248 l,** Photodisc, Inc./Getty Images, Inc.; **248 ml,** Photodisc, Inc./Getty Images, Inc.; **248 mr,** Photodisc, Inc./Getty Images, Inc.; **248 r,** Photodisc, Inc./Getty Images, Inc.; **249,** John Moore; **250,** G. Biss/Masterfile Corporation; **252,** Past /Project Exploration; **255,** Bettmann/Corbis; **256,** AP/Wide World Photos; **259,** David Young-Wolff/PhotoEdit; **260,** 1995. Drabble by Kevin Fagan/United Feature Syndicate, Inc.; **264 b,** Annabelle Halls/Dorling Kindersley; **264 t,** James Muldowney/Getty Images, Inc.; **264–265,** Mike Powell/Getty Images, Inc.; **265 all,** James Jackson/Dorling Kindersley, Ltd.

Chapter 6: Pages 266–267, Tom Bean; **268,** Carl & Ann Purcell/Corbis; **271,** Russ Lappa; **272,** Frederick M. Brown/Getty Images, Inc.; **274,** Russ Lappa; **275,** AP Photo/The Grand Rapids Press, Lance Wynn; **278,** SW Production/Index Stock Imagery, Inc.; **279,** American Honda Motor Co., Inc.; **280,** Richard Haynes; **281 t,** OMNI-Photo Communication Inc.; **281 b,** Tony Latham/Getty Images, Inc.; **282,** SuperStock, Inc.; **285,** Ken O'Donoghue; **286,** AP/Wide World Photos; **290,** Pictor Uniphoto; **295,** David Hanover/Getty Images, Inc.; **297,** The Academy of Natural Science/Corbis; **299,** Dennis MacDonald/PhotoEdit; **303,** Russ Lappa; **304,** Russ Lappa; **307,** Michael Spingler/AP/Wide World Photos; **308,** Russ Lappa; **309,** Russ Lappa; **310,** Russ Lappa; **316 t,** Royal Tyrrell Museum/Alberta Community Development/Dorling Kindersley; **316–317 m,** Jim Channell/Dorling Kindersley; **317 tl,** Jeffrey Sylvester/Getty Images, Inc.; **317 tr,** Andy Crawford/Dorling Kindersley; **317 m,** John Paul Endress; **317 br,** Brady

Chapter 7: Pages 318–319, Mack Henley/Visuals Unlimited; **320,** International Stock/ImageState; **323,** Dick Blume/Syracuse Newspaper/Image Works; **325,** Gary Braasch/Getty Images, Inc.; **327,** Craig Lovell/Corbis; **329,** Nancy Sheehan/PhotoEdit; **330,** Jane Burton/Dorling Kindersley; **331,** Ryan McVay/Getty Images, Inc.; **337,** Lon C. Diehl/PhotoEdit; **338 l,** AP/Wide World Photos; **338 ml,** Eddie Adams/Getty Images, Inc.; **338 mr,** Homer Sykes/Woodfin Camp & Associates; **338 r,** Pascal Volery Reuters/Getty Images, Inc.; **343 both,** Richard Haynes; **344,** Bill Bachmann/Image Works; **347,** Spencer Grant/PhotoEdit; **349,** Bob Daemmrich/Stock Boston; **352,** Merritt Vincent/PhotoEdit; **354,** Richard Cummins/Corbis; **359,** Stone/Getty Images, Inc.; **360,** Royalty-Free/Corbis; **369,** David Robbins/Getty Images, Inc.

Chapter 8: Pages 370–371, Joseph Nettis/Photo Researchers, Inc.; **372,** Ronny Jaques/Photo Researchers, Inc.; **373,** Dennis Di Cicco/Peter Arnold, Inc.; **375,** Barros & Barros/Getty Images, Inc.; **376,** Russ Lappa; **377,** William H. Mullins/Photo Researchers, Inc.; **379,** David Brooks/Corbis; **380,** Richard Haynes; **381,** Richard Haynes; **382,** Howie Garber/Animals Animals/Earth Scenes; **387,** George Shelley/Corbis; **388,** Peter Menzel/Stock Boston; **389 l,** Corbis; **389 r,** Russ Lappa; **394 both,** Russ Lappa; **395,** Russ Lappa; **395,** Rob Crandall/Stock Boston; **397 l,** S. Wanke/PhotoDisc/Getty Images, Inc.; **397 m,** Ryan McVay/Getty Images, Inc.; **397 r,** Russel Illig/Getty Images, Inc.; **399,** Raphael Gaillarde/Gamma Liaison/Getty Images, Inc.; **400,** AP/Wide World Photos; **403 l,** C Squared Studios/Getty Images, Inc.; **403 ml,** Siede Preis/Getty Images, Inc.; **403 mr,** Siede Preis/Getty Images, Inc.; **403 r,** Siede Preis/Getty Images, Inc.; **403 b,** Tony Freeman/PhotoEdit; **405,** W. Cody/Corbis; **407,** AP/Wide World Photos; **410,** Corel; **413 l,** Andrew J. Martinez/Photo Researchers, Inc.; **413 r,** Rod Planck/Photo Researchers, Inc.; **415,** Corbis; **416,** Suzanne & Nick Geary/Getty Images, Inc.; **418,** Dallas & John Heaton/Stock Boston; **420,** M.C. Escher © 2003 Cordon Art B.V.-Baarn-Holland; **420 t,** Russ Lappa; **426 b,** Paul Barton/Corbis; **426 t,** Tony Freeman/PhotoEdit; **426–427 m,** David Jeffrey/Getty Images, Inc.; **427 b,** PhotoEdit; **427 t,** Jim Hiss/Hispanic Business Inc.

Chapter 9: Pages 428–429, Jeff Greenberg/Peter Arnold, Inc.; **430,** Corbis; **431,** Ken O'Donoghue; **432,** Russ Lappa; **433,** Russ Lappa; **434,** Topham/The Image Works; **437,** NASA/Goddard Flight Center; **438,** Warren Bolster/Getty Images, Inc.; **441,** AP Photo/Elise Amendola; **442,** Richard Haynes; **443,** Richard Haynes; **444,** George McLean/Cardinal Spellman Philatelic Museum; **447,** Tim Thompson/Getty Images, Inc.; **449,** Tony Hopewell/Getty Images, Inc.; **453,** Tony Freeman/PhotoEdit; **454,** Digital Vision/Getty Images, Inc.; **455,** Bill Amend/Universal Press Syndicate; **457,** Russ Lappa; **459,** Photo Researchers, Inc.; **463,** Bob Krist/Corbis; **465 bl,** Tony Freeman/PhotoEdit; **465 br,** John Elk III/Stock Boston; **465 tl,** Tony Freeman/PhotoEdit; **465 tr,** R.M. Arakaki/International Stock; **468,** Alan Klehr/Getty Images, Inc.; **475,** Robin Weiner/WIREPIX/The Image Works; **477,** Russell Illig/Getty Images, Inc.; **480,** Stephen Simpson/Getty Images, Inc.; **486 m,** Photo Courtesy of Northland College, Ashland, Wisconsin; **486 t,** Kim Sayer/Dorling Kindersley; **486–487 b,** Elfi Kluck/Index Stock Imagery, Inc.; **487 t,** Neil Setchfield/Dorling Kindersley

Chapter 10: Pages 488–489, Science VU/Visuals Unlimited; **491,** Neal Preston/Corbis; **493,** Tom Carter/PhotoEdit; **494,** Corbis; **499,** AP/Wide World Photo; **500,** Walter Bibikow/Index Stock Imagery/PictureQuest; **504,** Rid Catanach/Woods Hole Oceanographic Institution; **506,** Judith Canty/Stock Boston; **508,** John Moore; **509,** Tom Sanders/Corbis; **511,** Bob Daemmrich Photo, Inc.; **514 both,** Michael Schwartz/The Image Works; **517,** Spencer Grant/PhotoEdit; **520,** Myrleen Ferguson Cate/Photo Edit; **523,** Susan Van Etten/PhotoEdit; **524,** Tom Stewart/Corbis; **528,** Cary Wollinsky/Stock Boston; **529 both,** Richard Haynes; **531,** Sally & Derk Kuper; **533,** Yvette Californiardozo/Index Stock Imagery/PictureQuest; **534 l,** Siede Preis/Getty Images, Inc.; **534 ml,** C Squared Studios/Getty Images, Inc.; **534 mr,** C Squared Studios/Getty Images, Inc.; **534 r,** C Squared Studios/Getty Images, Inc.; **537,** Marc Romanelli/Getty Images, Inc.; **542 b,** Harald Sund/Getty Images, Inc.; **542 t,** Art Wolfe, Inc.; **542–543,** Planetary Visions, Ltd.; **543 bl,** David Muench/Getty Images, Inc.; **543 br,** Harvery Lloyd/Getty Images, Inc.; **543 ml,** Jeff Greenberg/Omni-Photo Communications, Inc.; **543 mr,** Getty Images/Eyewire, Inc.; **543 t,** Gery Randall/Getty Images, Inc.; **543 tr,** Peter Gridley/Getty Images, Inc.

Chapter 11: Pages 544–545, Richard Haynes; **546,** Anthea Sieveking/Petit Format/Photo Researchers, Inc.; **547,** Russ Lappa; **548 t,** Russ Lappa; **548 b,** David Young-Wolff/PhotoEdit; **550,** Elyse Lewin/Getty Images, Inc.; **553,** Russ Lappa; **554,** Tony Di Zinno/See Jane Run; **556,** Corbis; **559,** Paul Barton/Corbis; **560,** NASA/Dorling Kindersley Picture Library; **563,** Mark Burnett/Stock Boston; **566,** Joe McDonald/Corbis; **570 both,** Richard Haynes; **572,** Layne Kennedy/Corbis; **574,** Getty Images, Inc.; **575,** Rudi Von Briel/PhotoEdit; **576,** EyeWire/Getty Images, Inc.; **577,** United Media/United Feature Syndicate, Inc.; **581,** Syracuse Newpaper/The Image Works; **583 l,** Ken Ross/Getty Images, Inc.; **583 r,** Russ Lappa; **584,** Courtesy of Milton Bradley Co.; **585,** Russ Lappa; **590 t,** C Squared Studios/Getty Images, Inc.; **590 b,** Al Francekevich/Corbis; **591,** MMI Flash! Light/Stock Boston

Chapter 12: Pages 592–593, Ron Brown/Superstock, Inc.; **594,** AFP Photo/Don Emmert/Corbis; **595,** Pete Saloutos/Corbis; **595,** Ron Brown/Superstock, Inc.; **596,** Gary Conner/PhotoEdit; **597 both,** Richard Haynes; **598,** Tom & Dee Ann McCarthy/Corbis; **599,** (ZF) T. Knsselmann/Masterfile; **600,** Richard Haynes; **601,** 1986 James Mayo/Chicago Tribune; **603,** Tony Freeman/PhotoEdit; **604,** SuperStock, Inc.; **605,** Spokane Police Department; **606,** AP/Wide World Photos; **607,** Russ Lappa; **608,** Tim Thompson/Corbis; **611,** Bohemian Nomad Picturemakers/Corbis; **613,** David Young-Wolff/PhotoEdit; **616,** Ron Brown/Superstock, Inc.; **617,** Cynthia Hart Designer/Corbis; **619,** Roger Wood/Corbis; **623,** Zigy Kaluzny/Getty Images, Inc.; **625,** Jon Chomitz; **632 l,** Chris Bjornberg/Photo Researchers, Inc.; **632 t,** Tim Flach/Getty Images, Inc.; **632–633 b,** Amanda Friedman/Getty Images, Inc.; **633 b,** General Electric Lighting; **633 t,** Davies & Starr/Getty Images, Inc.

Teacher's Edition

Editorial and Production Services: The GTS Companies
Design Coordination: Susan Gerould/Perspectives